FROG LANE COL_____
Sixty Years On

**Commemorating the closure of Frog Lane Colliery
– the last deep pit in the Bristol Coalfield**

Produced by
The South Gloucestershire Mines Research Group and The Yate and
District Heritage Centre

with support from South Gloucestershire Council

British Library Cataloguing-in-Publication Data. A catalogue record for this book is available from the British Library
ISBN 9781899889334

Designed by Ian Pope

Published on behalf of the SGMRG by
Lightmoor Press
Unit 144b, Lydney Industrial Estate, Harbour Road, Lydney, GL15 4EJ
www.lightmoor.co.uk
Printed by England by Information Press, Eynsham, Oxford
www.informationpress.com

Colliers at the coal face in 1906 taken by J. C. Burrow. *J. C. Burrow, courtesy Anne Matson*

Front cover: A rare postcard view of Frog Lane taken from the tip circa 1900. *courtesy Andrew Williams*

CONTENTS

Introduction..5

Coal Mining Before Frog Lane...7

A Brief History of Frog Land Colliery 13

Frog Lane Colliery Surface..25

Working Underground 43

The Frog Lane Colliery Railway 69

Mining Miscellany 83

Living in a Mining Community: Family Life 87

                                      Religion, Sport & Leisure 91

Coalpit Heath since 1949 99

Information & Sources..104

Taken circa 1906, this image of a miner with 'guss and crook' hauling a box loaded with coal, probably to transfer into the waiting dram. This photograph had been previously thought to have been taken at Easton Colliery, Bristol. Its position in an album of Frog Lane only pictures by Burrows gives us confidence that it was taken at Frog Lane where the use of 'guss and crook' for underground haulage has not been previously documented.

J. C. Burrow courtesy Anne Matson

THE LAST OF COALPIT HEATH

By "TILMANSTONE"

The recent closing of Coalpit Heath Colliery marks the end of the Bristol Coalfield whose recorded history goes back for 750 years.

Photographs by H. A. Summers

COALPIT HEATH COLLIERY FROM THE RAILWAY SIDING

O UR coalfields in the West Country—Somerset, Dean, and South Gloucestershire, are alike in the rural nature of their setting; the mines are too few or too small to give the impression of overwhelming industrial dominance. As we steam north from Mangotsfield, on the first stretch of the old Midland line that runs up from Bristol to Cheltenham and beyond, we soon notice, away to the left and over a prospect of country pastureland, the unobtrusive buildings, chimney, and winding wheel of a colliery. That colliery is Coalpit Heath. It has never been one of England's greater pits, but now by a strange chance of fortune it marks a notable, if sad event in Gloucestershire history, one indeed that is by no means without its meaning for England as a whole. For its recent closing marks the end, temporary maybe but none the less definite for the present, of the historic Bristol coalfield whose recorded history goes back for 750 years.

The Bristol field must of course be distinguished from that further south in Somerset and centred round Radstock. But the seams near Bristol itself run under the Avon, and the coalfield has seen some of its activity on the Somerset side of the city—at Brislington in the eighteenth century, and on a larger scale in modern times at Ashton Vale and South Liberty and among the very houses of Bedminster. Yet for the most part it lay in Gloucestershire, and the famous associations are with the northern side. The earliest, most notable scene of Bristol coal-mining was the ancient Royal Forest of Kingswood.

Perhaps the first record of coal-getting in Kingswood is one of the year 1200, but in those early days the coalpits were not the main feature of the Forest. Though kings themselves no longer hunted there it was still a source of supply of jealously preserved bucks for the Royal table, and in the Forest glades there had long been the "pannage of hogs" that comes as so frequent an entry in the pages of Domesday. But even in early Elizabethan times the digging was on a small scale; it was not till industrial Bristol came more fully into its own that the coal-

BASE OF CORNISH BEAM ENGINE IN BUILDING ON LEFT OF SHAFT SEEN IN PICTURE ABOVE

This brief outline, written just after Frog Lane's closure, is thought to come from a local magazine. We only have the first page but thought it worthy of inclusion.

Ian Pope collection

INTRODUCTION

This booklet is dedicated to our oral history interviewees, all of whom have given freely of their time, knowledge and materials to give us a colourful view of their lives and memories. John Mills, one of our first interviewees, passed away early in 2009. Before he died John gave his approval for us to use the image of him with hat and lamp that appears in the logo for 'Frog Lane 2009'.

My interest in local Coal Mining history goes back to the 1980s when I started looking at overgrown walls and features in out of the way corners of South Gloucestershire and so in many ways it is inevitable that sooner or later I would commit myself to print! This booklet started life in mid 2008 at one of the committee meetings of the South Gloucestershire Mines Research Group (SGMRG) when we realised that 2009 was the 60th anniversary of Frog Lane Colliery's closure. We also realised that many of the surviving miners would not be with us indefinitely and so we should speed up the mining oral history project that we had been working on with David Hardill and the Yate & District Heritage Centre (Y&DHC).

Whilst the history of Frog Lane Colliery has been briefly covered in other books, we felt the 60th anniversary of closure was an opportunity to deal with this in more detail and include a description of life in the mining community. We thought that the personal quotes from the oral history interviews were the best way to bring all of this to life.

So in short that's why you have this booklet which is being produced for the start of the 'Frog Lane 2009' programme of exhibitions and talks commencing in May. As with all publications, we have tried to strike a balance between excessive detail and simplistic explanations and between personal memories and lengthy monologues. We have had great pleasure and learned a lot from going through the individual stories, researching the community and colliery details and trying to turn them into an interesting account for a broad audience.

We have been particularly fortunate to have a large body of men able to recall working at Frog Lane Pit as well as the sons and daughters of miners who are no longer with us. Combined with the recollections of some of the areas senior residents, we hope we have provided an interesting series of accounts that will enable the reader to glimpse mining and community life 60 years ago in Coalpit Heath.

Due to publishing deadlines we have not been able to complete all the scheduled interviews and transcriptions and when this book is published the work will still be continuing. So please accept our apologies for the stories and materials that we have not been able to include.

There will inevitably be both errors and omissions and I accept full responsibility for these. If sufficient new material becomes available an updated or revised publication may be possible. So please do contact me if you have any additional materials or artefacts or would like to suggest some corrections.

This is very much a team effort and could not have been produced by one person, I would particularly like to thank:

- David Hardill of the Y&DHC who led the oral history work, fortunately for us all David has previously organised and managed a mining oral history project in Warwickshire. David has also contributed some of the sections of the book.
- Sarah Morris and Kathryn Sherrington who have contributed large sections of the book and who have worked enthusiastically and with real skill on a subject that is new to them.
- Jan Hazelby the unsung heroine of the Y&HDC who has transcribed all the mini discs of interview recordings containing strange terms and local accents into hundreds of pages of Oral History transcripts.

Everyone in SGMRG has been very supportive and I would particularly like to thank:

- Chris Wilmore, our secretary, for keeping me focussed and on track.
- Roger Gosling, our treasurer, for organising the finances and providing calm and sound counsel.
- Andy Brander, our webmaster, for helping structure the materials, proof reading and undertaking a number of interviews
- David Hardwick, my predecessor as Chairman for his wide ranging inputs.
- Jenni Humpris and Jackie Ashman for helping with some of the early interviews.
- Stuart Latham for locating and copying the 1947 Frog Lane Inventory from the Kew Public Records Office

Information and assistance has come from a wide range of sources and I would also like to thank:

- Trevor and Maureen Thomson and Ian Haddrell of the Frampton Cotterell Local History Society (FC&DLHS) for allowing us to use their photographic materials and providing feedback on contents.
- The staff at the Bristol Records Office for being unfailingly helpful and tolerant of my requests for information and for willingly giving permission to reproduce images of them.
- Staff at the Gloucestershire Archives and the National Monuments Record in Swindon for help and permission to use their materials.
- John Scantlebury for sacnning the Hewitt collection.
- Our book designer, Ian Pope of Black Dwarf Lightmoor Publications Ltd, who has struggled manfully to turn my poor attempts at format and structure into an attractive product and has also contributed materials.

Lastly and very importantly I would particularly like to thank:

- My wife Diane and family for putting up with even greater neglect than usual whilst I worked on the materials for this book.
- My parents Jean and Peter Grudgings for being perpetually enthusiastic about what I do and for feeding me when I visit.
- Anne Matson and Family for loaning us the 'Hewitt Collection' of photographs, many of which are reproduced here.

Steve Grudgings,
31 Laverstoke Lane
Laverstoke, Whitchurch
Hants, RG28 7NY

This group of ten nicely posed, moustachioed miners, taken around 1906, is one of the best know of J. C. Burrow's Frog Lane pictures. The detail is excellent and clearly shows the well constructed wall, solid sandstone roof, the peg and ball oil lamps used, the miners tin flasks and hob nail boots. They are obviously keeping very still for the camera. The names of some of the men are know too, far left is Joseph Fletcher who lived on Badminton Road and is reported to have had 13 children. His step son Tom Fletcher is bottom right and next to him is Frank Britton, both of whom lived near the Swan at Nibley where they are alleged to have spent most of their free time!

J. C. Burrow courtesy Ann Matson

COAL MINING BEFORE FROG LANE

Mining in the area around Coalpit Heath has been documented as far back as the early fourteenth century.[1] By the 1700s, the industry is understood to have been well organised and for both this and the following century, reference materials are extensive,[2] deserving their own book. The Bristol Records Office (BRO) holds written 'perambulations' by the local worthies who in 1691 and 1696 walked around Westerleigh Parish noting the location, depth, seams worked and ownership of each pit.[3]

The perambulation documents a number of pits in the Parish of Westerleigh and we know there were others operating on the Serridge estate (which was not perambulated). Andrew Ravensdale used the records of parish maps and field boundaries to enable some of these early pits to be located precisely in his excellent 1988 article *The perambulations of coal in the parish of Westerleigh 1691 and 1696.*[4]

Ravensdale's article give a good picture of the activities of the early owner/operators prior to the concentration of the industry in the hands of the predecessors of the Coalpit Heath Colliery Company (CPHCC). These owner/operators are understood to to have been local farmers or landowners, able to determine the location of the seams from the pattern of the outcrops.

At this time coal working concentrated on the shallow and

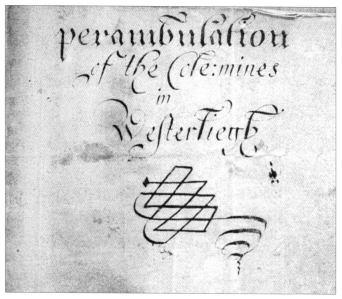

Front cover of the 1691 perambulation, *courtesy BRO*

This picture was taken some time ago and based on current knowledge, is understood to be where a later drainage level joins Samuel Astry's 'Great Levelle' of around 1700. This series of levels still drain a wide area of Coalpit Heath apart from where they have been damaged or blocked. Note the good roof and carefully constructed stone walls, probably in a section of loose ground. This is understood to be around 12 yards below the surface.

easily workable deposits where the coal seams appeared at the surface (known as the outcrop). Often started as simple opencast or quarry type workings, they became quickly exhausted and early shallow mine shafts were sunk (often called bell pits because of the bell shape of the pit cross section). As the accessible coal was exhausted so these workings became deeper, requiring better drainage and ventilation and this is the state of the industry up to about 1700 when few pits exceeded 100ft in depth.

Shaft sinking would have been undertaken by specialist teams of local workmen – one look at all the shafts on the local geological map will highlight the pattern of their labours! As early as 1690, it appears that black powder was in use for penetrating the very hard local pennant sandstone.[5]

Much of the driving force behind development of local mining came from Samuel Astry, Lord of the Manor of Westerleigh. He is understood to have commissioned the driving of the 'Great Levelle' an underground drainage tunnel to lower the local water table, reported to run from Damsons bridge on the Frome up to Trinham, a field opposite Frog lane.

The other major mine owners in the area were the Dennys family, on the Serridge Estate and the Player family who held the Manor of Frampton Cotterell. After Astry died in 1704, the Lordship of The Manor of Westerleigh passed, via the hands in marriage of his three daughters, to Jarret Smith, Alexander Colston and Lord Middleton (Thomas Willoughby). This succession and the relationships are complex and beyond the scope of this book. Suffice it to say that Jarret Smith, who was understood to have already been working the coal under his own land at Mayshill, appears to have led the efforts to develop coal mining locally and to consolidate the hold of the Lordship of The Manor of Westerleigh on them. They acquired the mineral rights in 1746 for the Serridge Estate, purchasing it outright in 1786. The Ashton Court papers also contain many references to their purchase of other local land under which coal was thought to exist.[6]

The steam era from 1750

The first Newcomen 'Atmospheric' steam pumping engine was installed in the Black Country in 1712 and over the following decades its application spread across all major mining areas.It enabled mine operators to lower the water table and thus access coal seams that were previously unworkable. These engines were expensive and the technology was not reliable until the late eighteenth century. The first installation around Coalpit Heath was not by the Lord of The Manor of Westerleigh but by Bragge (who had succeeded the Player Family as Lord of the Manor of Frampton Cotterell) at Nibley in 1750.[7]

Jarret Smith appears to be the driving force behind the installation of the first and second Coalpit Heath engines in 1751 and 1763 the sites of both, between Henfield Lane and Badminton Road,having disappeared beneath the main railway line when it was constructed in 1903. Two more engines are known to have been commissioned, one at Ram Engine around 1773 and the fourth at Serridge beside Henfield Lane in 1790. These four engines were not all working concurrently (the commissioning of the Serridge Engine in 1790 is thought to have enabled one of the earlier ones to be decommissioned[8]).

These engines enabled the local coal seams down to about 350 feet to be reached, and so this period saw a major expansion of coal mining in the area. The engines were only used for pumping, winding of coal and men was still done by horse gin (short for 'engine') or by 'reel and stander' (the same principle as drawing water from a well).

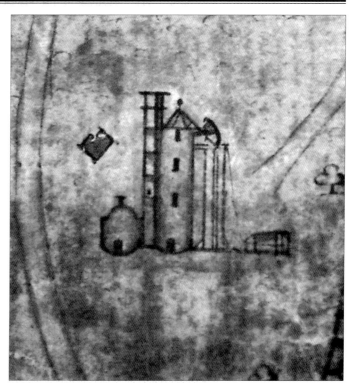

This superb hand drawn image of what is understood to be the first Newcomen engine commissioned at Coalpit Heath in 1751 appears on the 1772 Map of the Parish of Westerleigh held by the BRO under reference AC/PL 89/1. Note the external boiler on the left of the house and the beam end and pump rods to the right. Most unusually, the engine house appears to be round rather than the normal square form. A full set of the contractors bills exist for this engine and this will form the basis of a separate study .   *courtesy BRO*

Another image from the 1772 Map of the Parish of Westerleigh, showing what is understood to be the second Newcomen Engine commissioned at Coalpit Heath in 1763 around 200 yards from the 1751 Engine.
                                                                    courtesy BRO

The shaft top of what is understood to be the Coalpit Heath's third Newcomen Engine commissioned at Ram Engine Pit around 1773. This shaft was reportedly filled with the spoil from the demolition of one of the local chapels in the last century. *courtesy Mr and Mrs Pugh*

What we understand to be the basement of the fourth Newcomen Engine, installed at Serridge in 1790. SGMRG members have surveyed, conserved and stabilised this chamber. *courtesy Mr and Mrs Tooze*

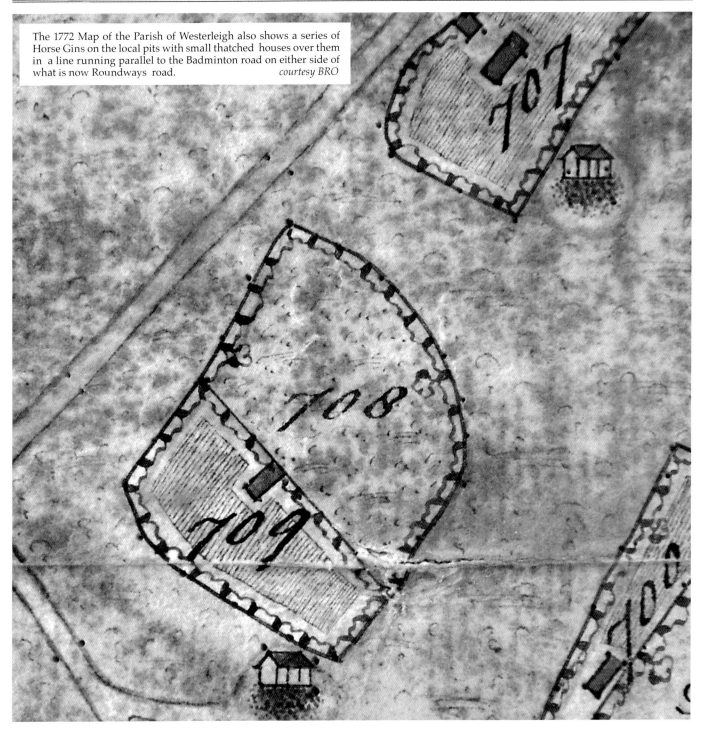

The 1772 Map of the Parish of Westerleigh also shows a series of Horse Gins on the local pits with small thatched houses over them in a line running parallel to the Badminton road on either side of what is now Roundways road. *courtesy BRO*

Horse gins were a well established technology and, whilst they had their limitations, they were portable and cheap and easy to commission and operate, and it is understood that they were used until well into the nineteenth century. The Horse Gin Houses are easily recognised on old maps by their distinctive keyhole shape. The local Horse Gin remains that we are aware of at New Engine and Ram Hill date from the 1820s.

The 1772[9] Westerleigh Parish Map show a clear pattern to the pit locations, the most obvious ones the lines of pits east of and parallel to the Badminton Road. Horse Gin Houses on the pits are shown on the 1772 map as being contained in thatched housings. A number of these pits

have been uncovered and filled in during the recent housing developments in this part of Coalpit Heath. The other recognisable pattern is the curved line of pits to the south of Serridge Farm. The reason for these patterns is that the coal seams are roughly at the same depth (ie the maximum for the available technology) and the pits simply follow the lines of the seam.

The existing pits were productive into the early 1800s but by that time the CPHCC must have been concerned that its known reserves were nearing the end of their life, they had after all been worked for 150 years by this time. The area immediately to the North and East of Coalpit Heath was largely untouched as the seams were much deeper here due

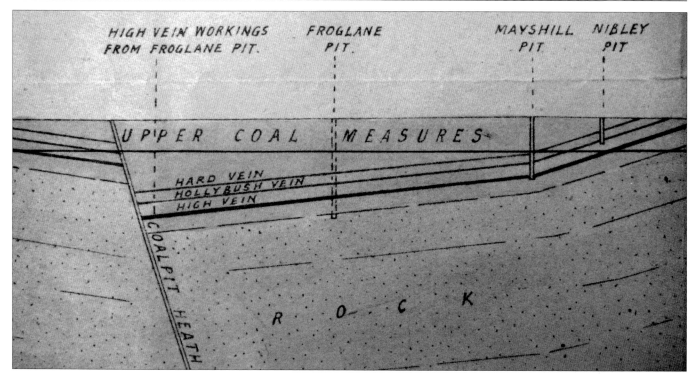

This cross section across the three pits clearly illustrates the angle of the seams and also why Frog Lane miners always referred to 'walking up to Mayshill Pit'. This is an extract of the cross section held by the BRO under reference AC/PL 150.

courtesy BRO

to a fault. There was, however, no certainty that they could be reached nor what their quality would be, a major investment would be needed for the new sinking to reach them.

The CPHCC were also well aware of the large fault running through New Engine Pit, continuing to pass to the east of their Ox Bridge Pit. This fault caused the seams to drop deeper, but by how much was not clear (around 400 feet as it turned out) They also knew that the three seams came to the surface around Nibley and dipped steeply from here southwards. From their work at the Dudley pits near Parkfield they would also have known that the three seams held up well to that point. This knowledge of the coal measures surrounding what would become Frog Lane Colliery, probably coupled with some trial bores would have given the company the confidence to embark on sinking the new pit in the early 1850s.

The situation here was mirrored at Parkfield where the extensive older shallower workings had limited reserves and the deeper measures were unproved, Parkfield sinking also commenced in the early 1850s.

References

1. Images of England - Frampton Cotterell and Coalpit Heath page 8.
2. The Ashton Court Papers (Ref AC/AS) in the Bristol Records Office (BRO) and the Middleton Papers at the Nottingham University Archive are the most comprehensive sources we are aware of. Additional information is contained in the Gloucestershire Archive and the Wiltshire Records Office.
3. BRO AC/AS 73/3.
4. 'The perambulations of coal in Westerleigh in 1691 and 1696', Andrew Ravensdale, *Bristol and Avon Archaeology 7*, 1988.
5. See above page 30.
6. BRO AC/AS 98 Letter of 25th October 1786 from Middleton to Smythe about 'Vowles Farm Purchase'.
7. *The Newcomen Engine in the West of England* by K. H. Rogers 1976, page 30.
8. Letter from Thomas Smythe to Middleton on 11/2/1790 about 'keeping 2 engines going'.
9. 1772 Westerleigh Parish Map AC PL 89/1

This view of the pit head at Frog Lane is believed to date from around 1870. On the left are likely to be the boilers under the pantiled roof next to the engine house containing the beam pumping engine. This is the only known image showing the original vertical winding engine house which on the right. The railway wagons on the right are possibly some of those supplied by the Midland Waggon Co. of Birmingham and appear to be of four-plank construction and have dumb buffers. Unfortunately no lettering can be made out on their sides but they do seem to be painted a light colour, possibly grey, with one darker plank. The 'bank' in front may be made of large lumps of coal which sold at a premium! The tip has not yet grown to the point where rails and an incline are needed.

courtesy BRO

A BRIEF HISTORY OF FROG LANE COLLIERY

The Nineteenth Century

Anew 'sinking' was normally a major event both for the colliery owners and for local people and, as a result historical materials are often extensive. There are copious early records of coal mining in the parish of Westerleigh (of which Coalpit Heath is part) for the 18th century but very few for the 19th. Despite the absence of detailed records of the early history of Frog Lane Pit, it has been possible to work out from a wide range of sources (many of them contemporary maps), the main elements:

- A map entitled 'Outline Map of the Parish of Westerleigh shewing the outcrops of coal & c. In the Coalpit Heath Basin' dated November 7th 1850 by Thomas E. Blackwell anticipates quite accurately the shape and boundaries of Frog Lane Pits working area (known as its 'take'). Its date and structure suggests that it was part of the initial planning work for the pit. (Note that it shows Mayshill Pit.)

- The Mines Inspectorate reports the death of George Flook (a sinker) on July 7th 1853 as being the first documented evidence of the start of work.[1] No other references to pit sinking, normally carried out by a dedicated team of men specialising in this, have been found. Handel Cossham's diary[2] tells us that he used a team from Staffordshire to sink Parkfield Pit in the early 1850s, possibly they continued to sink Frog Lane. Frog Lane Pit surface was 194.82 feet above Ordnance Datum (OD) and the landing (where men and coal tubs came out the cages was 13 foot higher. Pit Bottom (High vein) was given as 417 feet below OD, a total depth of 612 feet Both shafts were oval with the winding shaft being 6ft 6in. x 9ft and the pumping shaft six inches narrower.

- Handel Cossham's notes[3] tell us that in August 1855 he went underground at Frog Lane in the High Vein with John Cook the Bailiff (the colliery agent or manager), reporting that sinking was still continuing to the Hard Vein a few yards below. Cossham was complimentary about the pits potential, it should be remembered that he had just finished sinking the adjacent Parkfield Colliery in the same seams on land leased from the Lords of Westerleigh.

During 1855 and 1856 The Coalpit Heath Colliery Company (CPHCC) appear to have commissioned a large body of survey work from Alex Bassett of Cardiff (Lord Tredegar's Surveyor) and a number of these very finely hand drawn and coloured maps survive. It was normal for such maps to show the surveyors name and date of drawing up. They were then updated, normally every six months, to show the panels of coal worked in different colours, thus helping understanding of the progress of development, notably the following :

- Maps of both the High[4] and Hard Veins[5] dated 31st March 1855 show the very early developments of working in both seams (the dates are those of the maps drawing up – they would have been added to over time). The High Vein Map (the lower seam) also gives the first detailed drawing of the Mayshill Colliery surface layout, Matt Southway asserts

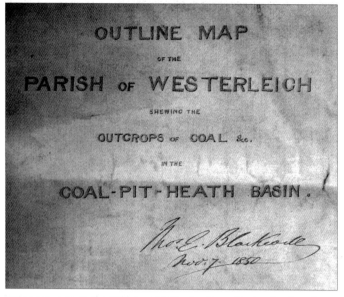

Title section from the 1850 map by Blackwell, understood to have been drawn up as part of the planning for Frog Lane Collieries sinking and layout. The section of the map showing the working area is on page 17.

that this pit was initially sunk in the 1780s and enlarged in 1847[6] to work the steeply inclined seams to the 'rise' towards Nibley. Certainly its equipment was older than that at Frog Lane and its large single shaft of 10ft x14ft with cage with a water tank underneath suggests it was sunk to de-water and work the seams to the rise. The shaft was 390 feet to the High Vein and because of its width was used to raise and lower large items, specifically equipment and horses.

- The history of the various Nibley workings is complex, the Coal Seams are steeply inclined and come to the surface here. There are references to Coal Mining here as far back as 1708.[7] Separate sections are shown on Bassett's Frog Lane High Vein 1865 plan for both Nibley High and Hard Vein Pits (overleaf) and the steep inclination of the seams is clearly shown. The abandonment plans for both the Nibley Pits[8] show a very long narrow band of workings between the deeper Mayshill workings and the surface, ventilated by a series of 'air pits'.

- Bassett produced an interesting map dated March 1856 covering the whole length of Frog Lane's intended High Vein

The title section from Alex Bassett's 1856 plan of the High Vein workings from Mayshill, through Frog Lane to Dudleys Pit.

courtesy Coal Authority (ref SWR3410)

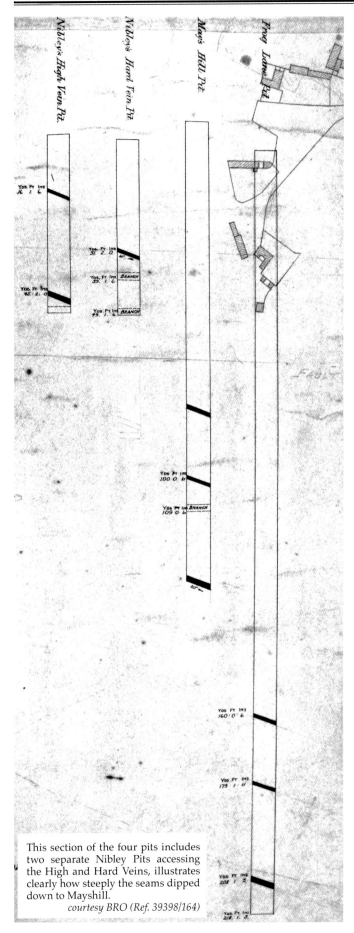

Nibley's High Vein Pit.

Nibley's Hard Vein Pit.

May's Hill Pit.

Frog Lane Pit

Yds. Ft. Ins
12. 1. 6

Yds. Ft. Ins
31. 2. 0

Yds. Ft. Ins
39. 1. 6

Yds. Ft. Ins
63. 2. 0

Yds. Ft. Ins
75. BRANCH

BRANCH

FAULT

Yds. Ft. Ins
100. 0. 6

Yds. Ft. Ins BRANCH
109. 0. 6

20"

Yds. Ft. Ins
160. 0. 6

Yds. Ft. Ins
179. 1. 11

Yds. Ft. Ins
203. 1. 3

Yds. Ft. Ins
214. 1. 3

This section of the four pits includes two separate Nibley Pits accessing the High and Hard Veins, illustrates clearly how steeply the seams dipped down to Mayshill.
courtesy BRO (Ref. 39398/164)

workings[9] from Nibley Gate to Dudleys Pit (a small earlier CPHCC Pit probably sunk in the late 18th century, adjacent to Parkfield) The dates recorded on the panels of coal worked suggests that work in the High Vein was initially concentrated towards the northern boundary, working uphill to the older Mayshill workings (known as working to 'the rise', much easier than working to 'the dip'). The dates on the map also suggest that this work was done in parallel with that of driving the 2,000 yard long 'engine plane', the main haulage road in the high vein. In other words short term production came from the northern section whilst the major haulage road was being driven. From the dates on other underground maps[10] this haulage road is understood to have continued to be extended until the 1890s.

• Bassett also produced in March 1856, separate maps of the three seams (High and Hard plus the Hollybush in the middle) for the previous generation of pits to the south of Frog Lane's 'take' (working area).[11] These clearly show that between 1860 and 1870 the remaining pillars of coal were removed, these pits would have then been abandoned and closed. Presumably the men working there transferred then to Frog Lane

The summary account s of the colliery for the twelve months to 3rd October 1865[12] shows the revenues being £8,265 for the year against costs of £2,765, included in which is the purchase of what is believed to be their first locomotive reported by the Industrial Railway Society (IRS) to be a four-coupled well tank by Fletcher Jennings of Whitehaven.

The earliest photograph of Frog Lane is believed to date from around 1870 and is the only one showing the original vertical winding engine house, no records of its size or origins are known. This engine was replaced in 1888 by a contempory horizontal steam winding engine of 450HP built by J. D. Leigh of Patricroft, with cylinders of 27in. x 48in. driving a 12ft diameter drum. The engine house lasted until 2004 when it was unfortunately demolished.

The splendid Cornish Pumping Engine (to the left in the 1870s photograph) was built by T. E. Bush of Bristol in 1852[13] at the time of pit sinking, its 85-inch diameter cylinder was larger than average.

Underground, once the main infrastructure was in place, work proceeded on extracting coal as efficiently as possible. The workings were divided up into districts with names such as Russell's, No. 1 and No. 2 West, Charity, Old Branch, New Branch, Engine Deep etc – not all were working concurrently. The working methods and details of life underground are covered subsequently.

THE GROWTH OF COMPETITION

The profitability enjoyed by Frog Lane in 1865 soon came under pressure from competing sources of coal as the railway infrastructure improved and the South Wales coalfield came 'on stream' – especially after the opening of the Severn Tunnel in 1886. 1913 is generally recognised as the peak of production for the UK Coal Industry as after World War One many export markets were lost forever. This was followed by the great depression of 1926 after which most pits struggled to make a profit. Frog Lane was no exception and there are some interesting accounts of annual production costs and revenues for this period that make it clear that the pit only covered its costs when it worked for six days a week.[14]

Other than the replacement of the vertical winding engine the surface changes were only those to be expected such as the tip growing in size, new boiler houses and screens and minor additions to buildings as required.

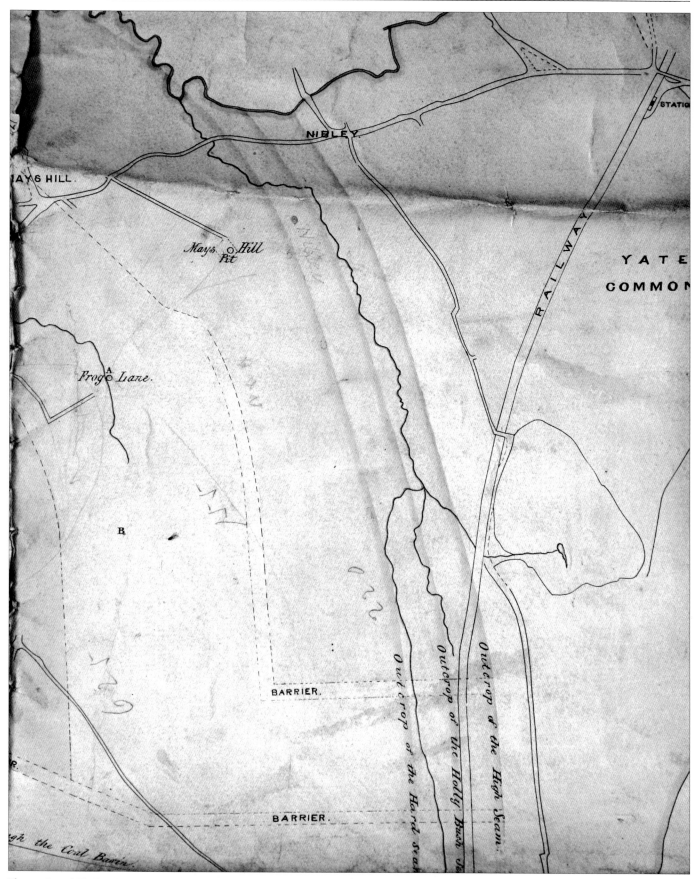

The section of Blackwells 1850 map showing the area to be occupied by the Frog Lane workings. It clearly shows Mayshill Pit as being established by this time as well as the planned barriers needed to prevent sudden inrushes of water. The position of the outcrops where the three seams come to the surface make it easy to understand why some of the earliest recorded coal workings were around Mayshill and Nibley.

	£	s	d
Oct 3 By Expenditure at Pits	155	14	2
„ d°. Surface labour	52	11	10
„ Iron	164	13	.
„ Timber.	270	15	7
„ Powder	49	15	
„ Grease & Oil	213	7	2
„ Hemp Ropes & Cordage	11	0	5
„ Lime	45	.	.
„ Stones	4	2	4
„ Hauling	42	16	.
„ Bricks & Tiles	8	1	
„ Taxes Rates & Tithes.	90	18	5
„ Rents & damages.	79	10	.
„ Horses Harness & Farriery	2	5	
„ Ironmongery	47	11	9
„ Stationery	6	2	
„ Hay Corn & Straw	48	0	1
„ Salaries & Pensions	47	15	6
„ Sundries	7	7	.
„ Tonnage	224	10	8
„ Waggon Hire	33	.	.
„ Discounts	62	7	9
„ Surveying	33	17	
„ Locomotive.	1064		
	2765	1	8

By Balance: —

Accounts due to the Colliery but not yet paid (as per list on 1ˢᵗ page — 755. 7. 1

Cash 4744. 15. 6   5500 2 7

£ 8265. 4. 3

Frog Lane Colliery annual accounts for the year ending November 1865. The less obvious entries include the substantial sum of £213 for grease and oil (lots of ropes and chains to lubricated), £45 worth of Lime (presumably for mortar) and what is understood to be their first locomotive (from Fletcher Jennings at £1,064). There is no entry for underground labour and whilst this may be covered by 'expenditure at pit' it seems a little low.
courtesy GA (Ref. GA 7399/12)

From the date on the engine house this horizontal winding engine was built by J. D. Leigh of Patricroft in 1888 and is seen here circa 1906. Note the winding engine man on the elevated platform (presumably to see over the drum) at the top of the photo.   *J. C. Burrow courtesy Anne Matson*

THE LAST YEARS OF WORKING

During the 1930s, as workable reserves were dwindling, attention appears to have been directed to the remaining unworked areas of coal. These included the lower quality High Vein workings, to the north west of the Pit under Mayshill Farm, and the area underneath the land adjacent to the Badminton Road held by Hills Charity Commissioners who had, presumably, previously resisted the approaches of the CPHCC.

Once the adjacent Parkfield Colliery closed in 1936, serious consideration was given to allowing the worked out lower part of Frog Lanes workings (those to the dip, furthest away from pit bottom and near to the Parkfield Boundary) to flood, as this would reduce pumping costs. There is a carefully surveyed plan[15] from this period that, in addition to showing the point to which the waters would rise, also shows a cross section of the fault and displacement of the seams between the two pits.

By the outbreak of World War Two both the High and the Hard vein were nearing exhaustion and the management started to make plans for exploratory work in the Holly Bush vein lying between them. Elsewhere in the coalfield this was

a good quality seam and intensively worked, at Frog Lane it was found to be badly faulted and difficult to work having a poor roof and a fireclay floor. These explorations started in 1944, and modern equipment was installed in a heading driven off the incline from the High to the Hard Vein. There was a considerable area of coal available and when the NCB took over in 1947 they continued this work. Ultimately it was not a success and the investment in this work must have contributed to the pits losses.

FROG LANE PIT NATIONALISED

Eventually the limited reserves in the two workable seams coupled with the increased pumping load following the closure of Parkfield in 1936, made closure of Frog Lane inevitable in 1949 by the NCB.

There is much anecdote locally about the role of Mr Davies, a Welshman bought in by the NCB to allegedly modernise the pit. The view generally being that this was not a success as large amounts of new investment was written off – was Davies wrong or was it the entrenched attitudes of the local men? Frank Britton gives us the following insight.[16]

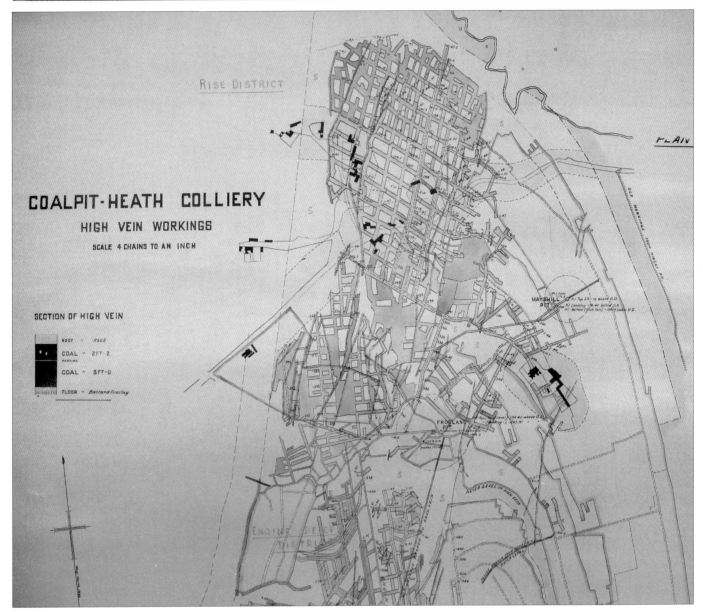

A 1940s map of the High Vein workings in the northern section – the southern section being mostly worked out. The northerly 'rise' district was one of the last to be worked, running nearly up to the River Frome. Note also the 'old nibley workings' on the left and the incline from Pit Bottom to the Hard Vein.

courtesy BRO (Ref. 33938/)

'He (Mr Davies) was talking about putting, if you understand you'd got roads where these horses were going like a snake, roads twisting and turning like old fashioned and some of these roads would be, well you couldn't go by the side of the dram, just the width of the dram sort of business. You'd go round a bend and then you'd go round another bend and sometimes you had to get there and as the horses were going you'd have to ease the drams round or he'd pull them, because he had to get up straight see to get round like. He'd pull them off if you weren't there to just guide them and all this nonsense, he was talking about putting wheels on. They were telling him like that it wouldn't work. We tried it in one place it didn't work, he held the pit up for, well that section up anyway, for a day and the animals was back there the next day'.

Interviewer: 'So what did they do? They put a little engine and some chain haulage/rope haulage'.

'Yes, well they don't pull round corners'.

Interviewer: 'Because presumably if you were going to do that you'd lay it out dead straight'.

'You'd have it more or less straight, you can have a gradual bend you ain't going to have a sharp bend. If you put a track down sometimes and you'd have a bend like this table, then you had to get there to guide them drams round when that horse was pulling he'd pull up straight round, he couldn't walk straight round. You'd have to get there and take the dram round like'.

Interviewer: 'So presumably Mr Davies came through when he told you he was going to try and modernise it'.

'He was going to do all sorts of things when he came there. I can honestly remember two or three old men telling him one day they said "You won't do that Mister." You know what some of these old men are they don't care if it was MrDavies was the King of England, "You won't do that Mister", and they were right see'.

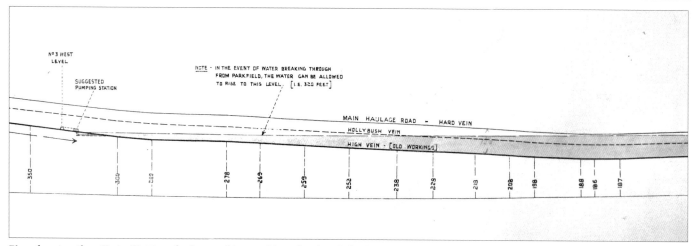

Plan showing the effect of letting the lower older workings flood and the location for a new pump station, presumably as a basis for reducing pumping costs.
courtesy BRO (Ref. 39398/86)

Nationalisation of the UK Coal Industry had been seriously considered at least twice since 1900 and the landslide election victory of Clement Attlee's labour party in 1945 meant that this was inevitable in 1947. The National Archives office in Kew [17] provides a fascinating inventory of what the NCB acquired from the owners of Frog Lane Pit, the less obvious items included:

- Sturden Court Farm of 122 acres in Winterbourne Parish.

- Serridge Farm of 39 acres in Westerleigh Parish (the inventory included a horse of 13 hands!) – originally the seat of the CPHCC from 1785.

- Serridge Cottage – understood to be the original office and pay house for the adjacent Orchard Pit at the southernmost dramway terminus.

- New Engine Cottage – originally the Engine House for New Engine Pit.

FROM CLOSURE TO THE PRESENT DAY

John Dando provided an interesting report from a local paper describing the very last underground visit:

'The last visitor to Coalpit Heath Colliery was 12 year old Raymond Stowe who spent four hours underground watching the last efforts in clearing up the coal mine. Mr George Dando, the engineman in charge of the winder that made the last movement of the cages is the grandson of the first engineman to be employed at the colliery when it was opened.'

It has not been possible to date this accurately but it is believed to been in January 1950.

Following closure in 1949, and the salvage of worthwhile materials from underground, the shafts would have been capped or filled and all scrap removed. By all accounts the main buildings were left standing for some time, photographs shows the Cornish Engine House after closure waiting demolition and also the southern face of the pit around the same period. Certain parts of the pit are also understood to have been used by the NCB for training in the 1950s.

The colliery tip was a prominent local landmark until it was reworked in the 1985 miners strike for coal and substantially reduced in height. At one stage, it attracted its own crew of 'flying pickets' who had followed the empty lorries returning

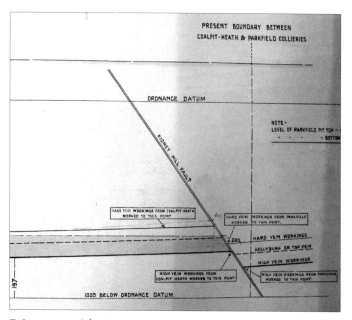

Enlargement of the far end of a plan from the 1940s showing the effect of letting the lower workings flood (Parkfield closed in 1936 and so Frog Lane would have had to bear the additional pumping load) This is of interest as it shows the effect of the "Kidney Hill Fault" which drops the seams on the Parkfield side.
courtesy BRO (Ref. 39398/86)

from taking the coal recovered to Aberthaw Power Station in South Wales back to Frog Lane. Much of the tip area has been subsequently landscaped and is nowadays occupied by the Willow Estate of mobile homes.

Much of the colliery site is occupied today by Danco Ltd who have for some time run a marquee hire business from here.

WHAT REMAINS

The most obvious feature was the horizontal winding engine house until its demolition in 2004. There are a couple of single storey workshop buildings remaining in situ on the northern boundary but they are not in a good state of repair and are not expected to survive for much longer (January 2009).

The colliery house where the caretaker used to live is still in existence and is a base for a boarding kennels business (Rock House).

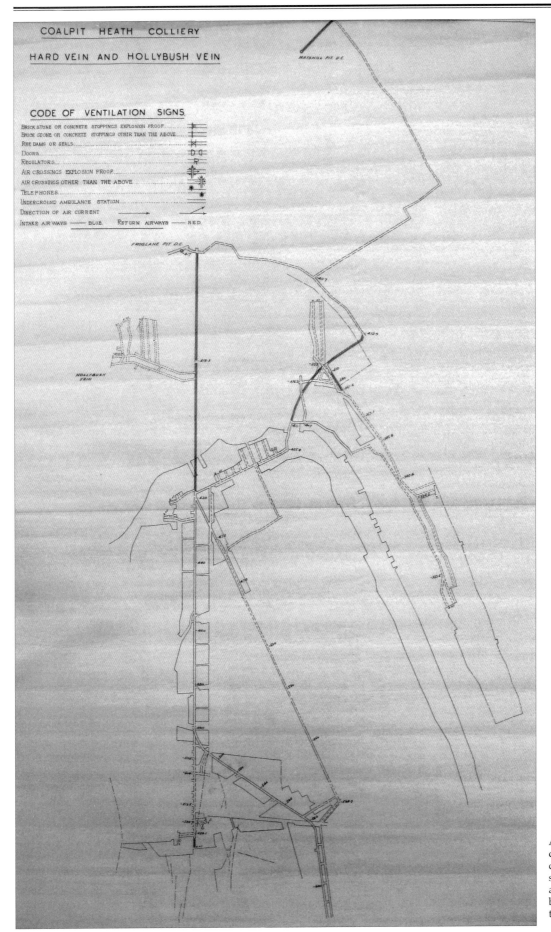

An NCB plan of the ventilation circuit at Frog Lane. Air was drawn down the Frog Lane shafts, through the workings and up the Mayshill Shafts by the powerful fans located there. *courtesy BRO*

Frog Lane Cornish Engine House around 1951, the whole site starting to look derelict. So far it has not been possible to find out who demolished it and when. Pity it's not still there!

courtesy FC&DLHS

Pictures of Miners apparently undergoing training at Frog Lane in 1951, presumably it was in use for short period as a training site whilst Harry Stoke Drift Mine was under construction. Fred Tovey second left on the left hand picture and middle back row on right hand picture.

courtesy Marlene Davis

At the rear of the site adjacent to the GWR weighbridge, the tip rises steeply above the field by 50 feet or so and this is also the point at which the culverted stream passes under the tip. This was surveyed some time ago when it was found that its floor and lower walls are constructed from redressed dramway blocks.

References

1. Page 127, *The Bristol Coalfield*, ISBN 184306 0949
2. BRO 9429-16
3. BRO 9429-16
4. BRO 39398-33
5. BRO 39398-164
6. *Kingswood Coal*, page 11
7. BRO AC/AS/87
8. CA SWR 3943
9. CA SWR 3410
10. BRO 39398 33
11. CA SWA 3412/3/4
12. GA D7399/12
13. BRO 39398 64 and 65
15. BRO 39398 86
16. YHC Oral History Transcript Dec 2008
17. Kew National Archives Coal 36/293

Left & below: The 1888 Horizontal Engine House after the roofing slates had been removed and not long before demolition in 2004.

The culvert underneath Frog Lane Tip being surveyed, the walls are stone and the arched roof is in brick. This was presumably built around 1870 as the tip began to increase in size.

The floor of the culvert appeared to have been built with redressed dramway blocks which appear to be lifting as a result of the weight of the tip.

Frog Lane Tip circa 1985, just after it had been reworked during the miners strike.

courtesy Stephen Dowle

Dorothy Hewitt is understood to have taken this superb photograph around 1906, probably whilst working with or inspired by J. C. Burrow. It shows clearly the beam of the pumping engine in its resting position, a dram stopped in mid journey on its way to be tipped, the tall timbers stacked ready to go underground and one of the Peckett Locos at the side. The gentleman looking at the camera is thought to be the manager Francis Eames.

courtesy Anne Matson

FROG LANE COLLIERY SURFACE

For those not familiar with mining processes, the purpose and layout of a collieries buildings and structures can be a bit of a puzzle. Every pit surface contains a jumble of large and small structures and buildings at various levels, the most obvious being headgear, engine houses, chimneys and boiler house – all intertwined with standard and narrow gauge railway tracks.

What even the best photographs of pits cannot capture is the background of noise, smells, smoke and steam. Pit yards were never quiet places, the requirement to raise, process and transport coal meant that there was always something moving. Winding and pumping engines chugging, ventilation fans whining, boilers gurgling, sawmills whining, railway wagons and locos clattering gave a continual background of noise with lots of dust, smoke and steam .

Most pits had between a third and a quarter of their labour force working on the surface on a wide range of tasks concerned with making sure coaling was not interrupted and output maximised, these jobs included:

- The winding engine man (commonly known as 'winder') was probably the most important job in the pit. The lives of the miners were literally in his hands as he controlled the steam engine winding the cages up and down the shaft. One of the last winding engine men at Frog Lane was George Dando, whose father John had been a winding man too. He shared this role with two others, Clem Varlow and Harold Skuse (father of the famous 'Tarzan' Skuse, performer at Bitterwell!) Apparently three winding men were needed, one for each eight hour shift to give 24 hour coverage. Harvey Hacker was the winder when the other three were sick or on holiday (Reference - personal comment by John Dando) Entry to winding engine houses was normally by invitation only and they were kept spotlessly clean.

- The safe and speedy loading and unloading of men and full and empty coal drams at pit top was crucial to effective production. The key men here were the onsetters or banksman, one at the top and one at the bottom of the shaft responsible for ensuring that the cages were properly loaded, unloaded and secured before signalling to the winding engine man to start winding. One of the onsetters in 1947 was Bryn Potter, who had previously worked at Six Bells Colliery in South Wales.

- The miners were paid by the amount of coal produced and Frank Britton tells us how this was recorded:

  'These men had a number, when they did fill their dram they did chalk their number on the front of the dram and they'd know how many drams they'd filled then. Then when they did go up the top they were weighed and they'd have their number on and they did know how much coal they did have, look'.

- One of the men responsible for weighing in the 1940s was William Crew (Ref - pers comm. Phyllis Taylor) Also at the pit top were one or two men responsible for moving the full drams of coal for screening and returning the empty drams.

John Dando, 1855-1918, winding engine man pictured in his working clothes around the turn of the century. *courtesy John Dando*

- The screens sorted the coal into different grades ready for loading into railway and road wagons, the latter were weighed in and out on the weighbridge at the entrance to the pit to establish the weight of coal to be billed for. All of these activities needed men to operate and oversee them. Jeff Sheppard of Mayshill Farm recalls being sent to collect coal with the horse and cart as a boy of eleven:

  'First of all they used to crash the coal down in the cart to try to make the horse start and then they would try and get the horse to go "go on, gee-up". Well of course the horse wouldn't go unless he heard his name, I'd just whisper "come on Sailor" and then he moved and they never sussed it out'.

- Railway operations needed a number of men. These including drivers, firemen, shunters, weighbridge men, wagon repair and track maintenance men.

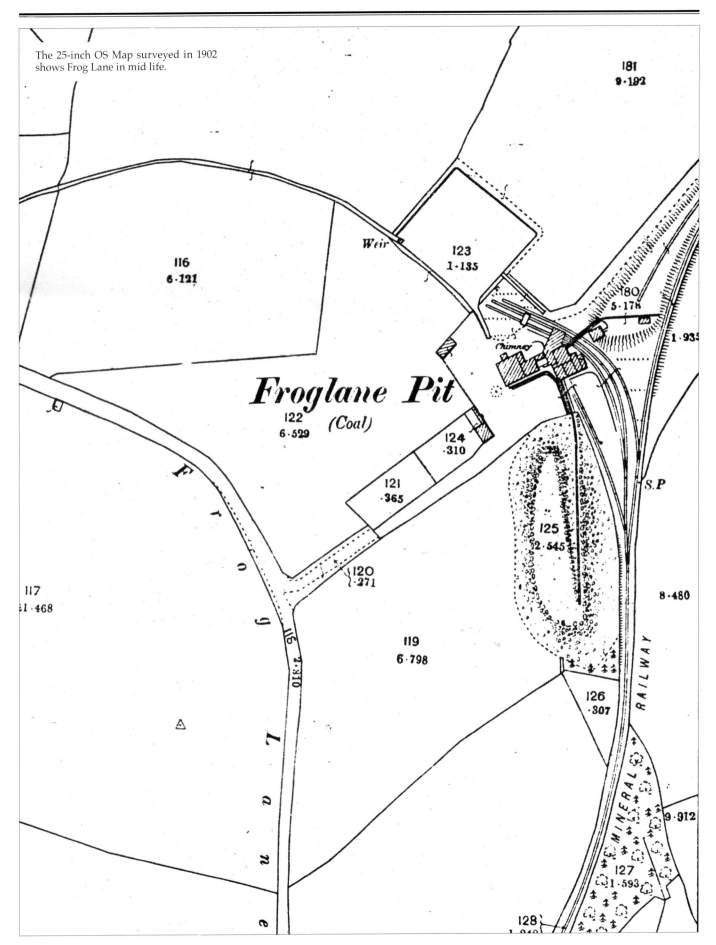

The 25-inch OS Map surveyed in 1902 shows Frog Lane in mid life.

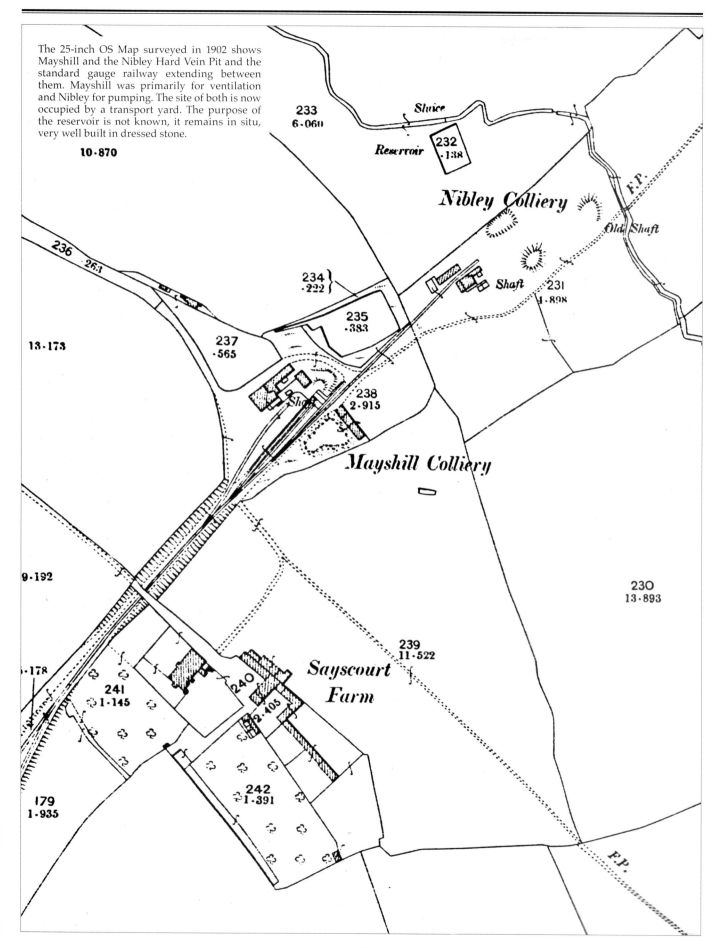

The 25-inch OS Map surveyed in 1902 shows Mayshill and the Nibley Hard Vein Pit and the standard gauge railway extending between them. Mayshill was primarily for ventilation and Nibley for pumping. The site of both is now occupied by a transport yard. The purpose of the reservoir is not known, it remains in situ, very well built in dressed stone.

10·870

233
6·060

232
·138

Sluice

Reservoir

Nibley Colliery

Old Shaft

F.P.

236
26·3

234
·222

Shaft

231
4·898

237
·565

235
·383

13·173

238
2·915

Shaft

Mayshill Colliery

9·192

230
13·893

239
11·522

178

Sayscourt
Farm

241
1·145

240

242·405

179
1·935

242
1·391

F.P.

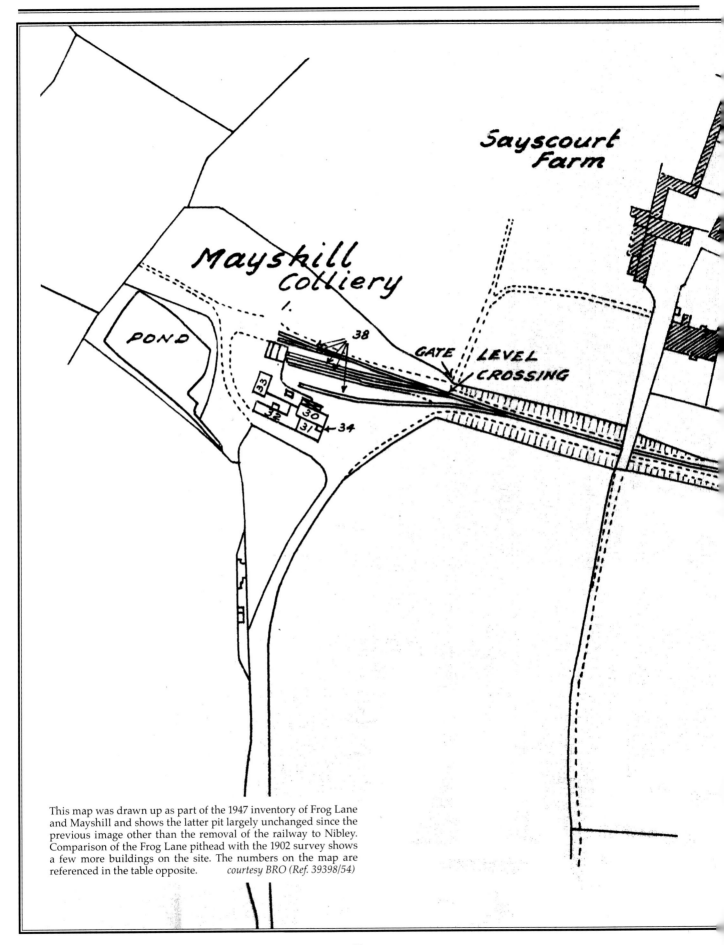

Sayscourt Farm

Mayshill Colliery

POND

38

GATE LEVEL CROSSING

33

32

30

31 → 34

This map was drawn up as part of the 1947 inventory of Frog Lane and Mayshill and shows the latter pit largely unchanged since the previous image other than the removal of the railway to Nibley. Comparison of the Frog Lane pithead with the 1902 survey shows a few more buildings on the site. The numbers on the map are referenced in the table opposite. *courtesy BRO (Ref. 39398/54)*

REFERENCE

No on Plan	Description	No on Plan	Description
1.	Colliery Surface & c – shaded pink, held under lease GL 78 c.c. file No 0/5	25.	Garage
2.	Winding Engine House	26.	Garage
3.	Winding Headgear and Stairway	27.	Stores Shed
4.	Ambulance House	28.	Wooden Capstan
5.	Portable House for Trainees Centre	29.	Magazine
6.	Stores Shed (Stone Built)	30.	Winding Engine House (Mayshill Pit)
7.	Stores Shed (Portable)	31.	Boiler House " "
8.	Boiler House	32.	Engine Room " "
9.	Beam Pump House	33.	Engine Room " "
10.	Screens and Washery Building	34.	Chimney Stack " "
11.	Motor House (adjoining)	35.	20 Ton Weighing Machine by Parsons, Bradford
12.	Land Sales Screen	36.	(3 no) Cycle Racks
13.	Old Screens and Hand Operated Tippler	37.	Electricity Sub Station
14.	Old Boiler House	38.	Railway Tracks, crossings switches and gates between Coalpit Heath Colliery and GWR and LMSR Sidings
15.	Laboratory		
16.	Laboratory Workshop	39.	Locomotive Shed
17.	Rail Sales Office	40.	Blacksmiths Shop
18.	Pit Top Weighbridge	41.	Fitting Shop
19.	Steam Winch	42.	Saw Shed
20.	Overhead Track from Pit-top to Boilers	43.	Carpenters Shop
21.	Overhead Track from Pit-top to Rubbish Heap	44.	Part of House used as Office
22.	Overhead Track from Pit-top to Winding Engine House &c	45.	Remainder of House including garden – Caretaker's Dwelling
23.	Brick Chimney Stack	46.	Additional Rubbish Tipping&c Land – Shaded Blue – Coalpit Heath Company's Freehold
24.	Brick Chimney Stack		

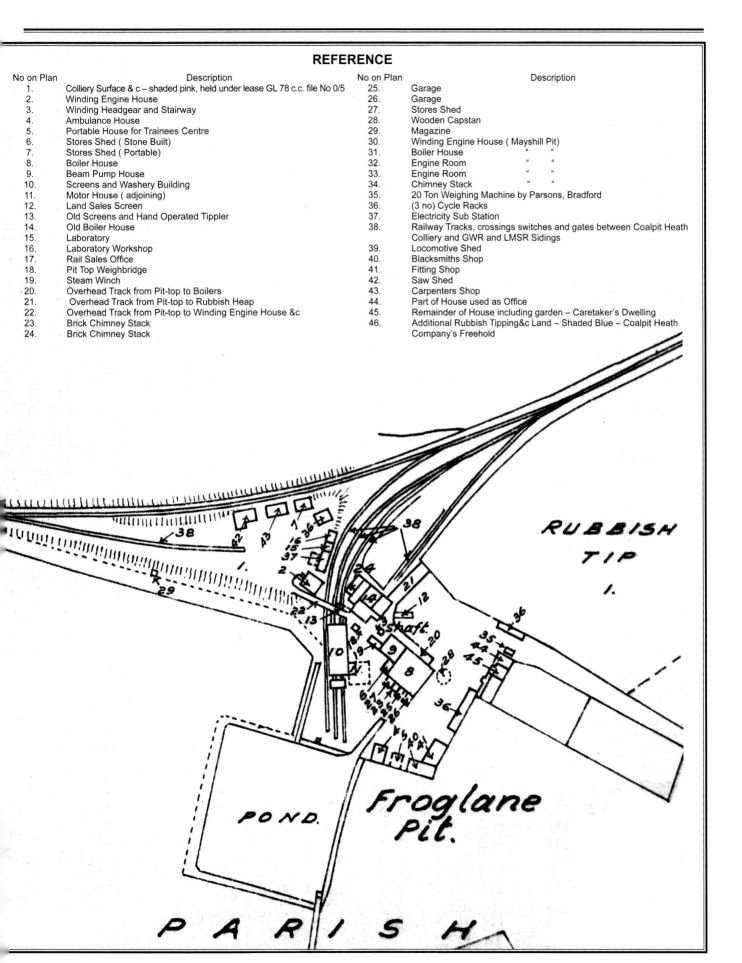

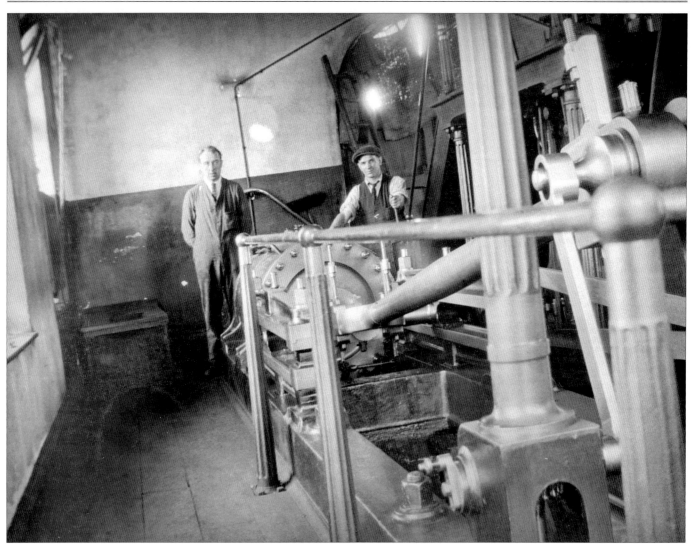

| No. | COAL MINES ACTS. | S1 |

Authorised Person.

Section

Coalpit Heath. Colliery. Date 21ˢᵗ Nov. 1947.

I hereby appoint you Bryn Potter. ~~to attend~~ to BF

Onsetter.

and in the exercise of this authority you are enjoined to do so strictly in accordance with the Coal Mines Acts and the General Regulations.

Signed A B Davies

MANAGER.

I hereby accept this authority.

Signed Bryn. Potter.

J. Boazman & Co., Ltd., Printers, &c., Newcastle.

Left: Bryn Potters 1947 certificate, signed by the manager Mr A. B. Davies confirming his appointment as onsetter. *courtesy Stephen Potter*

Opposite: The onsetter at pit bank circa 1906 (looking as if he has been told to keep still) The men in the cage appear clean so are probably going down, there are no gates visible on the cage. There are two empty drams waiting to go down with their different chalk marks (showing which miners filled them) The cages runs in parallel wooden guides the small gate on the left of the cage is to stop people and debris falling down the other side of the shaft. Note also the stack of long pit props outside.

J. C. Burrow, courtesy Anne Matson

A busy scene at Pit Bottom in 1906, a journey of loaded drams has been brought up for loading two at a time in the cage, two are already loaded and the onsetter appears ready to signal the 'all clear' (bowler hats are clearly a badge of office for onsetters in this period). Note the size of the lump coal in the dram on the right.

J. C. Burrow, courtesy Anne Matson

The drams of coal are reported to hold nine hundredweight each and this image circa 1906 shows one of them on the hand tippler. The offices and caretakers residence are in the background.

J. C. Burrow, courtesy Anne Matson

- Stoking the five boilers would have been a full time job, probably needing two men. The clinker and ash would need regular removal too. One boiler would not be working to enable it to be cleaned and maintained.

- The pit blacksmith was a key job, in addition to making any ironwork needed, he was responsible for shoeing the horses and would often go underground to do this. Phyllis Taylors grandfather, Albert Stone, was one of the blacksmiths in the 1930 and 40s. Jack Shaw was striker in the late 1930s for Les Davies, another of the Blacksmiths and Jack recalls that a lot of the work was repairing the ironwork on the drams. The NCB 1947 inventory listed three separate forges or hearths. Fred Drew describes the process for sharpening the miners picks:

    'Repair the picks, you know the picks you drive in to pick the coal out you had to sharpen those most days unless you were lucky in that you didn't break them off. It would depend how you'd harden them; if you hardened them too much they'd drive in the stone and break the ends off and they'd be useless and then you would have to temper them right as well otherwise and you'd harden them off, if you do it too hard then they'd break. So what you did, you put it in the fire, shaped the ends and then let him cool off, then get the heat going then, put them back in and bring them out, dip them in water quick and you'd rub the stone down, the pick down with the stone and watch the colours came and as the colours go down get to blue, in the water and that was it. We did it to save straw and dipping in the water guarantee to break the end off like with a chisel, we used to do chisels the same way and temper them in the same way, if you did see blue in the straw then it was OK that was the right thing that tempered them then, the blue came and then you'd test them on the anvil. Get the hammer and the chisel on the anvil and if it didn't break off they knew it was all right. If it broke off you had to do it all over again, it was as simple as that.'

- Sawmill workers had to deal with a continual demand for pit props and chocks (blocks of wood for packing and supporting the roof. Railway wagons delivered timber into the yard and after processing into sizes suitable for underground use these were loaded into special drams and taken to the pit top.

- One of the least popular jobs on the surface was the man stationed at the end of the incline at the top of the tip to supervise the tipping of the drams of waste stone and rubbish, the job was invariably windy, dusty and lonely.

- In addition to these there would be numbers of general fitters and labourers (day men) ready to deal with all eventualities that pit work required.

A busy scene at the Pit Bank around 1906, one dram is heading off to the right probably to be tipped directly into a railway wagon, on the left two others are in the process of being tipped onto the coal pile. Two more drams are visible under the roof and there is plenty of timber ready to go underground. One intriguing feature is that the narrow gauge railway tracks appear to be laid out with two different gauges. All our information indicates the gauge being the normal two foot, there appears to be a narrower one there as well, possibly the high and hard vein used different gauge drams.

Dorothy Hewitt, courtesy Anne Matson

Two of the CPHCC Shire Horses in full harness outside their stables at Serridge Farm, apparently posed for Dorothy Hewitt. The family Jack Russell dog watches over the proceedings. *courtesy Anne Matson*

- After the introduction of electricity probably sometime in the 1920s, skilled Electrical fitters were required too . Clerical staff would have included accounts and wages clerks as well as managers and surveyors. There would have been weighbridge men, a chemist, and a man to dispense carbide for the miners lamps. Frog Lane was the only pit in the NCBs area that still charged men for carbide!

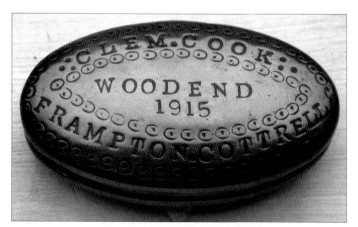

Clem Cook's brass tobacco tin, these tins were used to store chewing tobacco and are shaped thus for strength. According to the 1901 census, Clem was born in 1892, lived at 38 Woodend and his brother Ernest is listed as Colliery Engine Cleaner, another surface job. It is thought that Clem may have worked at Frog Lane but this remains to be proved.

- Deliveries of coal, both to paying customers and for the miners free entitlement are understood to have been made by horse and cart. The CPHCC had at least one cart that used to bring the hay and straw for the pit horses into Frog Lane from Serridge Farm and we presume this would also have been used for delivering coal to the miners.

Frog Lane only had a single wooden headgear with its winding wheel (the technical term is 'sheave') the other shaft being used for pumping. Underneath the headgear was the covered pit top with all the arrangements for winding men, coal and supplies (mostly pit props) in and out, the screens for sorting coal (stored in hoppers until ready for loading into road and rail wagons below). The stone and rubbish from the screens was loaded into drams and hauled up the incline to the spoil tip and dumped there, coal for the boilers was sent over in drams.

In additions to the offices for the manager and staff, there was a whole complex of workshops, stores and outbuildings to house the various items needed to run an efficient pit. Until the 1930s all machinery would have been powered by steam and all lighting would be by oil or gas lamps. There were no pithead baths at Coalpit Heath.

When the NCB took over the UK Coal Industry in 1947, a full inventory was taken of everything they acquired to establish a value for compensating the previous owners. These records for Frog Lane are in the National Archives at Kew and with the accompanying maps, give a very comprehensive record of what existed in 1947. The maps and the table are reproduced on pages 30-31.

The NCB Survey of the Frog Lane steam plant is interesting and includes:

- 450HP twin cylinder winding engine by J. D. Leigh of Manchester with 27in. x 48in. cylinders working pressure of 60psi, drum 12ft diameter, band brakes, rope 1in. diameter 644 yds long, one slow banker, one overwinder.

- Pumping Engine by T. E. Bush of Bristol with 85in. diameter cylinder and 10ft stroke. Working pressure was 22psi. This worked three lifts and delivered 13.5 gallons for every foot of stroke (so 135 gallons when working full stroke) The weight of the beam is given as 22 tons and there were two balance beams (to counteract the weight of the pump rods) one on the surface and another 170 yards down the shaft. There was a wooden capstan in the pit yard used to raise the heavy pitwork from the pumping shaft when repairs were needed.

- The drams were hauled up the spoil tip by a steam winch driving the steel ropes.

- The fitting shop contained an engine with a single cylinder of 9in. x 24in. This was the famous 'table engine' which has since been the subject of much attention by engineers and model makers. It powered all of the workshop and related machinery by belt drives.

- The Saw Mill was powered by an engine by Marshall of Gainsborough with a 11in. x 22in. cylinder (probably a portable or a traction engine).

- These were supplied with steam from five Lancashire boilers, 30ft by 8ft built by R. Marsden & Sons and working at 60psi. This steam was also pumped underground to power the incline haulage engines. The inventory lists an old boiler house with two boilers of the same size which were not in use.

Some of the other unusual features on the inventory included:

- A small laboratory and laboratory workshop, both brick with tin rooves, needed to analyse the coal quality.

- An explosives magazine – normally built well away from other buildings with three strong and one weak wall (to minimise the damage if it exploded!).

- A portable training centre.

At Mayshill the inventory showed the following engines:

- A Beam Winding Engine with a cylinder 30in. x 70in. powered by two 28ft x 7ft Lancashire boilers working at 55psi. This Engine is understood to have been built by Acraman of Bristol around 1840.

- Two fan engines are also listed as Mayshill was the 'upcast' shaft, one with 18in. x 36in cylinders and the other 12in. x18in. These worked fans with diameters of 8ft and 6ft respectively.

One of the CPHCCs shire horses with their cart posed for Miss Hewitt at Serridge Farm. The barn behind still exists and can be seen from Henfield Lane.
courtesy Anne Matson

Two views of the Lancashire boilers at Frog Lane. The insulated tops of the Lancashire Boilers and various valves and pipework are evident in the top picture whilst the firing aisle with the front of the boilers is seen below. Four of the boilers would have been in constant use with the fifth being washed out.
J. C. Burrow courtesy Anne Matson

A superb 1932 picture by George Watkins of the beam of Frog Lane's Cornish Pumping Engine built by T. E. Bush of Bristol in 1852, the makers name can be seen cast into the beam. The cylinder was 85″ diameter, on a par with some of the largest ones in Cornwall. The twin packs of wood on either side of the piston rod are there to cushion the 'T' piece mounted above the beam in the event of the pump rods breaking and so unweighting the beam, causing the piston to smash the cylinder below with its combined weight. Breakages of pump rods and also their removal for repair were frequent occurrences. *Reproduced by permission of English Heritage, NMR*

The 'table engine' that operated the machinery in the fitting shops. In the modern world if we want power, we plug it in and switch it on, until well after World War Two, much industrial machinery was powered by stationary engines (steam, oil and gas) driving through a complex series of pulleys and belts. This engine is thought to predate the pit. Photograph by George Watkins circa 1932. *Reproduced by permission of English Heritage, NMR*

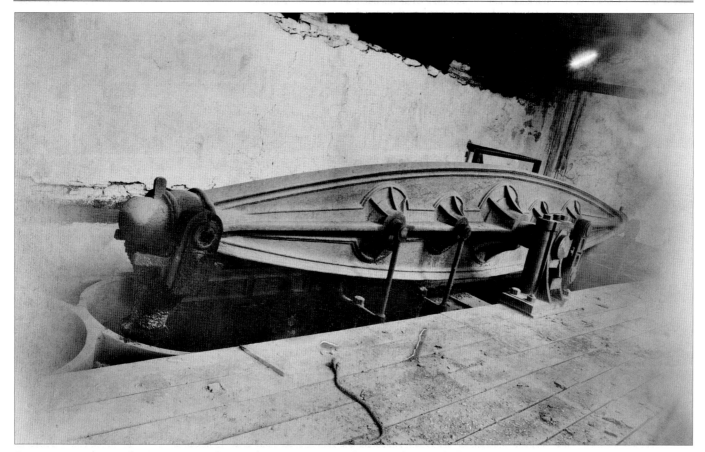

George Watkins visited the upper floor of the Mayshill winding engine house to photograph the engine beam in 1932. His notes suggest that the engine was similar to the one at New Engine Colliery which George reported as being built by Acraman of Bristol in 1832 (Acraman are also alleged to have built a very early steam locomotive for the CPHCC). The beam was enclosed entirely in the house and the engine was not thought to be heavily used.
Reproduced by permission of English Heritage, NMR

Opposite: On the floor below the engine beam at Mayshill was the flywheel (bottom left), connecting rod (centre) and depth indicators (middle left) for the winder – George Watkins did us proud with these images!
Reproduced by permission of English Heritage, NMR

The atmosphere at Mayshill would have been quieter, it was a smaller pit and although the railway reached it, we have no recollections of the locomotives working that far. In the pits later life, the winder is not understood to have been used regularly. Mayshill Pit's main purpose was as the 'upcast' shaft, with fans on site drawing the air though the workings, these were steam powered from the boilers listed (which the winder could use if needed).

Frank Thornell recalls messing about here and the details of the cage:

'Yes, the fans were out in the yard not actually in the shaft, and I know when I was there, a few of us from Yate working, messing around years ago, one of the chaps chucked a great big stone down there to see how deep it was and it stopped the fans. The manager had us all in the office and he said "Well which of you done it?" And of course we never split on nobody, not years ago like, and he said "If somebody don't split we'll sack the lot of ye." He tried to get round it that way but anyway nobody ever split and he never sacked us anyway. He was only too glad to get us to there like, that's what he intended. He needed to find out who done it. We knew who done it."

Interviewer: 'So what happened at Mayshill Frank? Did you go out, did you go up and down there or did you just…'

'Yes, up and down, but it wasn't a cage. It was like, pick water up in it, a great bucket affair like'.

Understood to be one of the Capell six-bladed fans installed in 1890 at Mayshill. The photo is taken from inside the fan 'drift' and when the the fan was in action it drew the air from the pit shaft behind the photographer and exhausting it through the aperture seen on the upper part of the fan housing.
J. C. Burrow, courtesy Anne Matson

WORKING UNDERGROUND

Working underground in a coal mine was unpleasant and dangerous. The light was poor, work was hard and dirty, space was limited and there was a continual risk of injury or death from moving objects, explosions or roof falls. In 1909, near the peak of UK coal production, there were over half a million coal miners. In 2009 there are less than ten remaining 'deep' mines (as distinct from drift mines) and conditions for the remaining few thousand working miners, whilst still dangerous, have improved vastly. Some of the surviving miners have been interviewed for the Frog Lane 2009 Project and their accounts of underground work provide a unique insight into this vanished world.

The Mining Community

Underground work is 'out of sight' to all of us and 'out of mind' to most. Coal miners have always been a separate and distinct community, you can't see them working and it's difficult to imagine what it is like working in darkness 600ft below ground with only a candle or carbide lamp for light. Colliers often worked on their knees or laying on their side, protective clothing being limited to boots. Working with such dangers required good co-operation between men. Fred Woodruff explains:

'Everybody worked together and everybody helped one another and that was it. There was nobody being nasty against one another. Same as when you got under that ground, down that ground and underneath, the atmosphere seemed to change, everybody was for one another and everybody helped one another'.

It was very much a 'macho' world too, this tone was set by the men working at the coal face where the hard and dangerous work made them the highest earners in the pit. For all these reasons it's no surprise that coal miners were therefore regarded with a little fear and awe even in their own communities. Coal miners were at the forefront of early workers movements such as Chartism, Trade Unionism and Communism.

Whilst the Frog Lane miners may not have been as numerous or as militant as their counterparts in the larger coalfields such as Wigan or the Rhondda, their disruptive reputation stretched back into the 17th century with a long period of unrest reported in the 1780s. Coal mining did not dominate male employment in Coalpit Heath in the way it did other coalfields, nevertheless it was a major employer and Frog Lane's miners came from as far afield as Mangotsfield and Pucklechurch – particularly after Parkfield Colliery closed in 1936.

When Frog Lane was sunk around 1852 the employment of very young children in the mines could still be recalled, having only been outlawed in 1842. By the time it closed in 1949, the first Labour Government had been in power for four years and miners could expect to retire by 65 and enjoy a state pension – some contrast!

Above: One of the few known postcards of Frog Lane, taken around the turn of the century from the corner by what is now the entrance to the Willows estate. We think that it shows miners (some with umbrellas) leaving after the morning shift. *courtesy Stephen Dowle*

Opposite: Drilling the rock above the coal face ready for blasting. The ratchet drive and the adjustable support for the drill are clearly shown. Note also the rails ready for extending further so the drams can get right up to the coal face for loading. *Dorothy Hewitt, courtesy Anne Matson*

Starting Work

Most of the miners who contributed to our Oral History Project started work as teenagers in the 1940s after a brief interview by the manager Mr Sage and most of our information comes from this period. Typically these boys, would be working alongside a more experienced person to learn their 'trade' with maintenance, masonry and attending to the horses being typical starting occupations. 258 men were employed underground at Frog Lane in 1947, our description of working underground includes a few of their stories.

The interview process for Frog Lane seems to have been fairly informal, approaches normally being made to the manager by a relative already working there. John Mills, who started in 1942, was an exception being an 'optant' (one who volunteered to help the war effort), and here he describes his interview:

'Mr. Sage who was the Manager interviewed me, he didn't have much to say, just accepted me as one that was being transferred and due arrangement was made for me to start at the colliery, no training mind, and on the appropriate day I left the office at Newman's. I was given a pair of boots and had to have a lamp and one or two other things, a pair of corduroy trousers and obviously changed my occupation'.

Frank Britton started work on the Frog Lane Railway and his interview was no longer:

'I started work when I was 14 and rode a bike from Harris' Barton to Clifton to work for a painter and decorator for 7/6d per week that was to start. I did that for a couple of months like and I came home one Saturday and my Uncle Sam said "I've got a job for you, boy, you ain't going to ride all that distance no more." Me father worked in the pit and Uncle Sam worked on the top of the pit. He took me on the Saturday afternoon to see Mr. Sage, the Manager, and Mr. Sage was cutting his lawn. "Mr. Sage" he said and he brought me up like to see him about the job on the loco. "Right" he said "Start Monday morning". So I started on the Monday morning'.

Interviewer: So no interview then, just straight in?

'No, no nonsense, I started straightaway on the Monday morning as fireman on the loco, I was on the loco then until I was just coming up 16; and then when I was 16 I went underground'.

Sid Horder's experience a few years earlier was similar:

'No training? "No". I think the first day I went down there I think the deputy came with me and showed me what to do and what not to do, and that was it. The only light I had was

This Dorothy Hewitt picture shows a curve on an underground haulage way, with a deputy or possibly Francis Eames himself (see the gold watch chain) checking that the haulage rope is correctly located on the roller. Note again the solid roof, suggesting the roadway is in the High Vein and the twin signal wires running between the props at top left.

courtesy Anne Matson

J. C. Burrow must have found this underground haulage engine house difficult to record properly but has managed to capture lots of detail, including steel beams with the makers name Steel, Peach and Tozer and date (1898 we think) clearly shown. This may indicate the date the engine was installed. In addition to the gears and drive, the indicator bell and oil lamp give some nice detail on the right hand wall. The shadow suggests that the lighting was on the photographers left. This engine would have worked one of the underground inclines, we have not yet identified which one.   *J. C. Burrow, courtesy Anne Matson*

on my helmet, well it wasn't a helmet, it was a trilby hat with the rim cut out and everything. Off I went and they took me to spot where there was some water and they said "We want you to work on this pump, pumping this water out" and that's what I was doing, hand pump'.

Working Times

The main shift at Frog Lane was between 6a.m. and 2p.m. and men who arrived late risked being turned away unpaid or incurring the wrath of the winding men who would have to stop winding coal to let them descend. Between 5.30 and 6 in the morning, Frog Lane would be filled with streams of men on bikes and foot, some of them coming some distance.
John Mills recalled:

'The men were taken down in the company's time between 6 o'clock and half past. If you weren't there by half past six they would take the gates off and they'd start the coal. They weren't very pleased if you arrived late and they had to put the gates on again. By the time everybody had got into their own place it was probably about 7 o'clock. By the time the pony boys had harnessed the pit ponies and the men had got to their coal face, the whole operation would start at about 7 o'clock.

We would then break for our little lunch and we then went on until about 2 o'clock. The men would start coming down just before 2 o'clock but we were taken up in our time from two until half past, that's how it was arranged and that happened over and over. I got quite used to it, I was very friendly with all the men that worked with me and they treated me quite well and I knew some of them and I formed quite a number of friendships in the colliery'.

The afternoon shift would start just after 2p.m. their work involved drilling the rock strata above the coal faces ready for blasting, the shots being fired ready for the next day's main shift. Saturday was normally a half day.
Again John Mills recollected:

'Another interesting part you might like me to describe. If a pair of miners working at the coalface they would, as you know, dig underneath ready for what they call a firing. They would bore, having dug underneath, they would bore a hole manually with a drill, bore a hole into the rock at a higher level and then there were two men that were employed specifically to visit these coalfaces to do what we call the firing. On an afternoon shift all the pit faces that had been prepared they would go and plug the holes with some kind of explosive and bring the coal down'.

How the work in the different coal seams was organised

A coal mine is like a factory, work needing to be carefully organised to maximise output. Everyone knows that colliers, at the face are important and highly paid just like production line workers, however to do their work efficiently they depend on the help of others who do specialised jobs including:

- The rock above the coal face would have to drilled and blasted with explosives to create a high enough space for the men to work in and advance the face.

- The roof would have to be propped, stone removed, empty drams bought up and 'fulls' taken away by men, horses or cable to pit bottom, loaded on the cage and 'empties' returned.

- Deputies (often called firemen) would inspect all areas for safety before the main shift started, reporting to the undermanager (Bob Sharpe in the 1940s).

- Ostlers would care for and feed the horses, clean the stables and the harnesses.

- Masons would build walls to direct ventilation and provide support, pumps men and engine men would work the haulage and pumping engines.

- 'Day men' would carry out the less specialised maintenance and labouring jobs.

Planning the underground layout and organisation of a Coal Mine is an important job and makes a huge difference to the effectiveness and therefore profitability of a pit. In the late Victorian era much attention was given to this and other specialised mining subjects as much of the industries literature shows! There was even a dedicated Bristol Mining School at which Handel Cossham was a regular speaker.

From the available underground plans it would appear that the Coalpit Heath Colliery Company went to some trouble to organise the layout of Frog Lane properly as it was a substantial investment. The three coal seams found at Frog Lane were already well known, having been worked extensively in the areas immediately surrounding Frog Lane's 'take' (the underground area that it was entitled to work). Whilst there would have been good knowledge of the local geography, these three seams were relatively thin and there were a number of faults (where ancient movements in the strata displaced the coal seams), so the investment was still speculative.

The seams and their characteristics were as follows:

- The uppermost was the Hard (or Top) Vein which was around two and half feet thick, a good quality coal which came out in large lumps and travelled well.

- Next came the Holly Bush Vein, for various reasons the geology of the this seam made it difficult to work, the floor was fireclay, the roof was poor and subject to collapse and therefore needed lots of support. The seam was subject to 'rolls' where the thickness of the coal varied, making it difficult to organise and lay out the working faces. Only in 1944 when the other two seams were nearing exhaustion were serious attempts made to work it and these were ultimately not successful.

- The lowest seam worked was the illogically named High Vein, total thickness of coal was four feet but with a band of dirt in between that needed to be separated. It was reckoned a good quality coal but not as good as the Hard Vein.

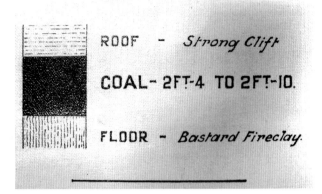

SECTION OF HARD VEIN

ROOF - *Strong Clift*

COAL - 2FT-4 TO 2FT-10.

FLOOR - *Bastard Fireclay.*

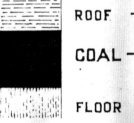

SECTION OF HOLLYBUSH VEIN

ROOF - *Clift - rather weak*

COAL - 2FT-0 TO 2FT-10.

FLOOR - *Strong Fireclay.*

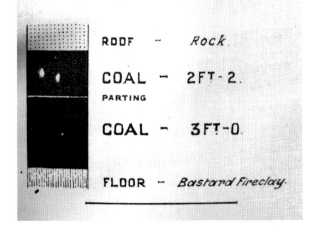

SECTION OF HIGH VEIN

ROOF - *Rock.*

COAL - 2FT-2.

PARTING

COAL - 3FT-0.

FLOOR - *Bastard Fireclay.*

Section of the three seams at Coalpit Heath taken from the respective maps held by the BRO. *courtesy BRO*

Dorothy Hewitt is understood to have taken this picture during her underground visit with J. C. Burrow. Women were not allowed underground but I expect her father, the Colliery Bailiff, indulged her on this. The image is well up to Burrow's professional standard. The workings are in the Hard Vein, note the short temporary pit props and the use of candles in holders (rather than oil lamps) for fixed lighting. The image helps understand why the face workers earned good money and why few lasted into old age! *courtesy Anne Matson*

Frog Lane's working areas or 'take' was roughly egg shaped with the narrower end of the egg around Nibley and the thicker end near Parkfield. In the central and southern areas the seams were fairly flat, sloping gently down towards the southern boundary with Parkfield at the Kidney Hill Fault. The south western boundary was defined by a fault too. To the north and west the seams became steeper as they rose to the surface and working methods were adapted to deal with these differences.

The workings were surveyed regularly so that an accurate record of them could be made for layout and planning purposes and as a basis for calculating the amount of coal extracted and therefore royalties due. From the 1870s it became a statutory requirement to maintain accurate records of underground workings. Whilst many pits had a resident surveyor, Frog Lane appeared from John Mills following account, to depend on an external one (possibly Messrs Dillwyn of Bridgend, who are listed in 1947 as being contracted to CPHCC):

Right: Local Historian Trevor Thompson showing how Francis Eames would have used his pocket miners dial for surveying underground. A miners dial is basically a robust compass with sights to be able to accurately record the directions of roadways. This is a pocket one, intended for quick use, tripod mounted ones were used for full surveys.

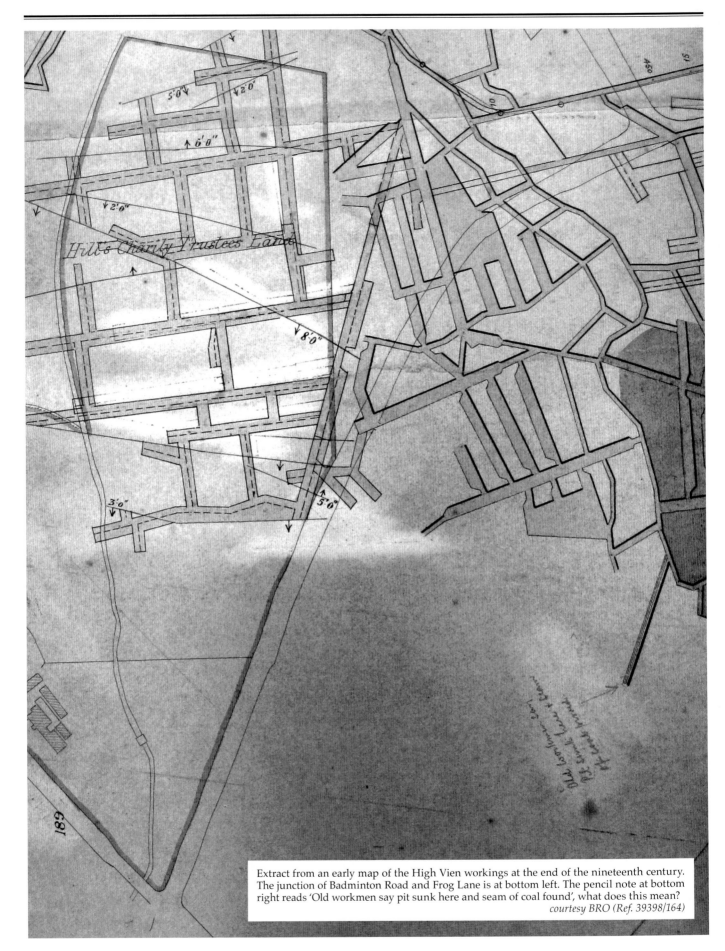

Extract from an early map of the High Vien workings at the end of the nineteenth century. The junction of Badminton Road and Frog Lane is at bottom left. The pencil note at bottom right reads 'Old workmen say pit sunk here and seam of coal found', what does this mean?
courtesy BRO (Ref. 39398/164)

'I hadn't been working very long underground and as I told you I'd met Mr. Sage the Manager and Mr. Sharpe the Underground Manager, and he approached me one day and he said "Would you like to work with a Surveyor?" I said "Yes, I would". The surveyor came about every three months to survey the pit and so when he came I was asked to report slightly later, 9 o'clock perhaps, surveyor's time, and another young man was there with me and we were given the job of accompanying the Surveyor. Very, very interesting, because the surveyor held his book and all the other things that he wanted. The other friend that I was with he held the tripod and the theodolite, and I was given the job of just holding the tape, that's all I had to do. But the interesting part was we visited every coalface in the mine'.

Interviewer: That does sound interesting, yes, I would have liked that job.

'Every coal face we visited; and he would ask me to go to the coalface with my tape measure and he would then write down what he wanted to, because he was checking the way in which they were going and how far they'd gone. Now when you come to the Mays Hill shaft I always remember the surveyor said to us "I want to check where we are to be sure", and he took us through all the old workings and he said "I want you to go now John, as far as you can see and take your tape to where I want you to." I took the end of the tape, he took his measurements and he said to me "You are at the bottom, the very bottom of Mays Hill shaft, underneath the cage, right at

the bottom. It was very interesting and I did that six or seven times with the surveyor'.

Interviewer: Did he come in just for a day?

'Just for the day.'

Interviewer: 'So he wasn't a colliery employee, he came from outside?'

'No he wasn't a colliery employee he came from, I don't really know, maybe South Wales or somewhere, but he wasn't employed by the colliery. He must have kept like these maps and all the details of where they were going and how far they'd gone'.

Interviewer: 'To read the instruments you must have had a light?'

'He had the same light as we did, a carbide light. He had a light the same as us'.

Workers at the Coal Face

Coal face workers normally worked in pairs on their particular 'stalls' and this work was the best paid (on a piecework basis) as well as being the hardest. Numbers of face workers were fixed and only when one 'stepped down' (either through age or infirmity) to take a less demanding underground job would 'vacancies' arise. These were much sought after and the younger men working with the horses were keen to be selected, they worked closely with the face workers, bringing up empty

J. C. Burrow took this well known image in 1906 of face workers in the High Vein (easily recognisable because of the middle 'dirt band' and its greater height. The picks are the early type with fixed heads.
courtesy Anne Matson

Colliers setting 'props and lids' presumably after the rock roof has been blasted down.

J. C. Burrow, courtesy Anne Matson

drams and moving fulls away, so had plenty of chances to show their mettle. These boys were often given money to ensure that particular colliers were well served with empties, so their output (and wages) were maximised.

We don't have any face workers contributing to our Oral History, so our accounts of underground work are based on deductions and photographs.

The sequence of coal face work appears to be as follows:

- The section of the rock above the coal face would be drilled in the afternoon shift and the rock then blasted down using small explosive charges to provide the height to access the coal face. Explosives are understood not to have been used directly in the coal seams themselves, as they shattered the coal; large lump coal commanding a better price than small coal.

- After 6.00 a.m. workers would first clear the stone bought down by blasting and wherever possible use it as packing for walls and supports, only sending it up the shaft if they had to. They would then undercut the face with pick axes, often working on their knees or sides as the seams were only two & a half and four feet thick. The coal was then wedged down to minimise breakage and loaded into drams. They would cut and fix timber props (which had been brought up according to their orders) to support the roof, short ones directly in the face, longer ones once the stone was blasted down.

- In the afternoon shift, the cycle of drilling and blasting would begin again

According to a *Colliery Guardian* account of 1891 the colliers would work stalls approximately 10 yards wide with 6 yard pillars, three stalls wide and three stalls deep on either side of the haulage road and then work the pillars back.[1]

Supporting the roof

Many of the underground photos at Frog Lane show a solid sandstone roof which did not need much propping, a great help in reducing costs and unusual in a coal mine. At the other extreme were those areas where both the sides and the roof needed supporting through broken ground. Timber in vast quantities was used for chocks, packing and pit props which, over time, would rot and if access to the area concerned was still needed, would have to be replaced. It was impossible to inspect all timber supports to ensure they were sound and it often took a fall or collapse to highlight the problem.

Sid Horder tells us about this:

'Oh, on one occasion my light went out and the golden rule down there was never to touch any of the beams, these were the sides of the passageway because some were loose. If you

Steel, Peech and Tozers Steel Beams are being used to create a permanent roadway through broken ground, note the ends of the timber used to make a roof over the beams and the two pit props being delivered on the flat wagon.   *Dorothy Hewitt courtesy Anne Matson*

Another photograph by Dorothy Hewitt. Thought to be near Pit Bottom and showing a Miner pushing a loaded dram. The dram wheels (made by Hadfields of Sheffield), the solid roof and the insulated steam pipe are clearly shown.   *courtesy Anne Matson*

touched one you would probably dislodge the one that was overhead and he'd come down on you. My light had gone out and I had no way of lighting it because the carbide had gone, and I had to crawl my way back in the dark. Half the time I was on my hands and knees trying to get back. I got back safe. Anyway to cut a long story short The last time I was there I sat down to have my food and I leaned against this upright and the wood on the top came down and hit me on the head. I thought "That's it, no more". So I turned it in'.

After the coal in a given area had been removed, the area was often sealed off to reduce the cost of ventilation and maintenance. The props would weaken and give way and the roof begin to collapse.

Masons were employed underground to build walls and other structures to provide permanent support, seal off worked out areas and build other underground structures. Frank Thornell describes working for one of these masons:

'The first job I did have when I went down the pit was, you might not believe it, was along with a brickie's mate. You wouldn't think that, brickies mate, because everywhere there was engines to pull and things like that and they used to brick it all out like this one here, like a house you know. Brick the places out and I used to mix it all up. The chappie I worked with he wasn't a very nice chap, and I used to go down early before he did come down and take his picks down like I told you. We took them down in the cage because they might have tipped up and gone on someone's head. I'd go down there and mix on the floor like, and have a lot of this stuff ready before we put the bricks

in and he used to chuck it away over the back. I'd say what's the matter then and he'd say "I can't put cement in between bricks that have bits of stone in". Well you couldn't help having bits of stone in could you because the roof did come down, he said it's rubbish all this. He'd go and have a smoke because you could smoke in Coalpit Heath because they had open lights, carbide lights down there. And he used to chuck it over the back, I'd watch and he would chuck it over the back'.

Different underground 'districts'

The pit was divided into a number of working areas or 'districts' with names like Old Branch, New Branch, Engine Deep, Russells, No. 1 and No. 2 West, Charity etc. Working conditions varied considerably, the shallower workings near Nibley were wetter than the deeper ones (it is not obvious but shallower workings are more susceptible to seepage of surface water). In the Old Branch and other areas to the north side of the pit where the seams were steeply inclined, the working method required the use of chain and horse haulage to get the empty tubs up to the face and the loaded ones back to the roadway. This method was called 'chain hatching'.

Fred Woodruff (started at Frog Lane in 1946) explains what it was like in one district:

'There was a lot of water trouble down there in Coalpit Heath. I worked in a place what they called Charity and that's the only place as I did work. There was several places down there like what they call the Holly Bush and stuff like that but I've never been down there, but it was so dusty and dry down there, it was different to what it was at Charity. They said to us when we were in Charity we were on an incline going up all the time. You went up one hatch to one level and then you went up to another one and they said the water was coming in, and they were saying then that it wasn't far from being up in Iron Acton in the River Frome there. Not too far up. That's why we had all the water'.

Haulage and Roadways

Digging the Coal out is an important job, but good transport arrangements to take the coal to the pit bottom are essential too. When you examine maps of underground workings, they often show a complex and sometime confusing series of passages, roadways and areas of coal that are not always easy to understand. We are fortunate that many of these maps have survived to be held by the Coal Authority and the Bristol Records Office. We have used these together with old photographs and descriptions from our oral history contributors to help understand more about the workings of Frog Lane.

The pit layout included from an early stage, a main 'haulage plane' in the high vein, this was eventually over 2,000 yards long, dipping gently and reaching nearly to the Parkfield Boundary at Dudley's Pit. It was worked by a large compound steam engine situated near pit bottom, using steam pumped down from the surface. Panels of coal were worked progressively outwards from here on either side of this 'trunk road' throughout the life of the pit. Where the haulage plane was close by, the colliers the tubs to the coal face without horses, as Frank Thornell explains:

'Because they had an endless rope, so they hitched the empties on back where I told you coming down that pit, going up towards Bitterwell and all that way, they did come out and they did hitch them on this endless rope. Just clip them on and send them all down, and these were the ones coming up; and you had a chap just here what did hit the clips when they were coming out. He had to hit the clips off and then push them round to that tip where I showed you in the front'.

The coal was worked on a 'pillar and stall' basis, which left a 'chequerboard' effect on the workings. All the roadways needed to be higher than the seams so men and horses could travel them easily. Gunpowder would have been used to blast the rock out above and below the coal seams to make roads of usable height, the main roads being 9 feet wide by 6 feet high according to John Cornwell[2] .These roadways were normally driven by specialists, called 'branchers'.

Horses were used to haul the drams on the longer journeys between the coalface and the point of connection to the haulage cables and the roadways used had to be both level and high enough for a horse (shown on the maps as 'horse road').

Towards the North and West where the seams were more

One of J. C. Burrow's best known pictures of Frog Lane, showing the compound haulage engine that worked the main haulage plane in the high vein. This well constructed brick and stone engine house was very near to pit bottom and hauled 'journeys' of twenty drams from over a mile away, taking seven minutes. The engine man appears to have his hand on the regulator and is keeping his eye on the pressure gauge. Note the large gimbal mounted peg and ball lamp giving illumination above the engine.
courtesy Anne Matson

One of our favourites from the newly discovered J. C. Burrow pictures of Frog Lane. This shows the dram being loaded with lump coal near the working face by the younger collier whilst his older colleague appears to be demonstrating the lever used to work the clutch or brake on the chain that controlled the descent of the loaded dram to the main haulage way. No peg and ball lamps appear in this view, the candle in its holder spiked to the prop giving the only light.

courtesy Anne Matson

This J. C. Burrow photo appears to show the same location as the previous one and is taken from the opposite direction looking towards the coal face. It clearly shows the rail ends and the chain return wheel secured to the bottom of the pit prop. *courtesy Anne Matson*

steeply inclined, different working methods were needed known as 'chain hatchings'. Frank Britton explains:

Interviewer: 'What are chain hatchings? I've heard the term chain hatchings but when you say chain hatchings I don't know what you mean'.

'Well you go up the inclines and you get to where all the mens' working and then there was these very steep places these were and they were wet and it was raining more or less quite a bit there all the time. Well now up the steep hatching like that it was too steep for these drams to come down [so] you had sticks in, we called it sticks but it's timber. You had that end there and then you had a chain the whole length of that hatching like, say from here to the bottom of our garden'.

Interviewer: 'So you can pull the empties up…'

'You'd have a whole chain all the length of that hatching there, and when you came with your full drams your horse would still be in the front, you'd hitch that chain on the back and then your horse had to pull that coal down the hill because he had to pull that chain up'.

Interviewer: 'Ah so that's sort of a brake is it to stop it running into the horse?'

'Yes. All your wheels spragged up and that chain was holding them back, if you missed the chain they four sprags and all would go down over there, they'd smash it all up'.

Interviewer: And they're on rails up and down those hatchings, so they lay rails right up to the face.

'Yes, all the way up right into the man's face and as the men did

go forward, as they did go forward a length they put another length of rails down'.

Interviewer: 'Got it. So presumably you'd do that where it's steep but where it's flat you don't need to do it because you can push them in and out by hand can't you?'

'Yes. That was the idea otherwise you would have killed horses all day long and that would have been the end of it'.

Inclines

There is no clear definition at what point a roadway becomes an incline! But they were organised differently and a number of long and short inclines connected the various levels throughout Frog Lane. The most important incline was that connecting the (upper) Hard Vein with the Pit Bottom.

The Hard vein was not accessed directly from the shaft by a separate 'landing' as might be expected, but rather by a 500 yard long self acting incline to the High Vein pit bottom. Full tubs going down and empties and supplies, mainly pit props going up. A description of this is given by John Mills who started work on the incline at Frog Lane in 1942:

'I'll explain it now if I may. The incline or the coal face was away in the distance but they were going towards the surface all the time. From the pit bottom in the other direction they were going downhill and they had an engine there that pulled the coal up; but where I worked the seam was going towards

Another of our favourites from the 'new' J. C. Burrow images, this one appears to show the drum housing at the top of one of the gravity worked inclines. The weight of the descending loaded drams will draw up a number of empty drams on the cable in the centre of the picture. The man on the right is probably controlling the brake that ensures this is done safely. His younger colleague is positioning the last dram on the 'journey'. Burrow lit this scene from the left and it works particularly well.

courtesy Anne Matson

the surface. Now that allowed a system, where the full drams were used to pull the empty drams'.

Interviewer: 'So it was double tracked was it?'

'It was a double track at the sidings and two pit ponies, one named Blondie, and one or two others, with two young men would bring two sixes of empty drams to the sidings where I worked, so I would have twelve empty drams on the sidings. They would then take twelve full drams away from the sidings back down to the pit bottom where they were taken up the shaft. My job was to handle these empty drams and secure them to the long cable that stretched all the way up the incline, and hitch six of these empty drams on the cable and when I had it all ready, all hitched up, not easy work because each one had to be pushed up a slight incline to hitch onto the cable'.

Interviewer: So you used to hitch each one on to the cable?

'Each, one at a time. The first dram was pinned onto the cable, [then] the next dram was hitched to that dram with a short chain. Each dram was hitched to the one in front; it wasn't a long cable. To arrange this you see, you were going uphill and you had to put the dram ready to hitch up but you had to hold the dram there. We used what was known as a sprag, that's a little piece of wood about a foot long which you threaded into the wheel of the dram to hold it for a moment, pinned it down ready, brought the next one up and the same thing until you had six ready; and then we had to signal to the man at the top of the incline. He controlled a very basic brake system, I'm never quite sure how it worked, but he had a brake there where the cable went round some kind of a drum and he could hold it up to a certain point'.

Interviewer: 'How did you signal to him?'

'Very interesting! Very basic! I'll show you a demonstration. It was a long wire going all the way up the incline and we had a ball, that were on the end of a piece of iron and it's a bit like a signal box. We'd pull this up, you see, and that would lift the ball actually at the top of the incline and we would drop it, that was signal one. You'd signal two when you were ready and the man at the top would do the same thing to signal back that he was ready, and when they were ready at the top of the incline, he had a man helping him there, they would push the six full ones off the platform and they would begin to come down the incline. And as they began to come down the incline so the six empties they would be pulled up. As you said about a double track; it was a double track at the sidings where I worked. It went into an interlock track all the way up until they'd passed half-way up'.

Interviewer: 'So you had a sort of loop in the middle?'

'A loop, and they passed and when they'd got to the top the man would put the brake on steady and he would land his six drams at the top and I would be left with the six full ones at the bottom. Having got those six full ones at the bottom, they were held by the cable. I had to run them onto the sidings, so what I would have to do was to handle them one at a time, take the first one pull the pin, separate it from the others, let it run steadily down the sidings until they were in the right place. Using again these sprags causing it to skid and the six of them would gradually, we would handle them six at a time, put the sprags in the six full trucks, pull the pin that held it to the cable and the six trucks would gradually slip down onto the sidings'.

'Blondie' the horse with a number of the Horse Boys around 1944, from left to right understood to be Raymond Gifford, Vernon Lewis, Bill Clark (upper), Frank Britton and John Mills.

Raymond Hawkins, courtesy Victor Close

'We had to stop them in the right place, there was a safety block there, and they were ready then for them to be taken to the pit bottom. The second six empties would then be handled and another six full ones came down. So that happened all day; twelve on the sidings coming up and twelve going down. I worked out that if we kept going we would handle them every quarter of an hour. There were breaks sometimes, because often the supply of coal at the top coming down from the coal-faces was held up so we had to wait until they had it ready. Sometimes the empties were held up because they were supplying other parts of the colliery as well and we had to wait. So on an average we would handle each load every quarter of an hour. Now that was quite a regular system'.

"In addition, we had to handle the pit props. The men at the coal-face would need certain pit props because they were using them as they advanced into the coal. The pit props were brought down the shaft at 5 o'clock, we started at 6, and the pit props having been brought down were distributed to one or two different places ready for distribution. Now my sidings that I worked on would be stacked with pit props when I arrived in the morning. If you look at the layout of the whole thing all the miners and all the ponies had to pass that sidings on their way to the coal-face. They'd leave the pit bottom through the stables down to where I worked, up the incline and spread right out to where they had to work. And the system was that as the men who worked at the coal-face passed the pit props, if they wanted some that day, they would put their number on the pit props because every pair of workers had their number and so by the time all the men had passed by all the pit props were numbered with a piece of chalk ready for distribution. Now I had a man working with me to help me there and he would then say after perhaps an hour "I'm ready to take the pit props up to the coal-face". Now when this was done instead of sending six empty drams up we sent four with a low loader in the middle. We had a low loader and we would load the pit props onto the low loader'.

'A low loader is a dram without any sides but with iron bars each side, and the pit props would be slipped in between and chained to hold them firm. And the man who worked with me, called Victor Hawkins, having got the pit props ready he would then walk up the incline and tell the people at the top "There's some pit props coming up". Now they're heavier you see than the empties so the man controlling the brake would allow the full drams to come down rather faster. It was fairly steep and as he let these four drams off, if he knew there was some pit props coming up, he would allow them to go faster so that they would pull the weight you see'.

'Now, Victor the man who had helped me load them, he would then follow those pit props and distribute them to the miners who had their chalk mark on them. He went with the low loader and the pit props and distributed them to the various…'.
Interviewer: 'Did he walk behind it John, or did he ride on it?'
'Oh he walked up in advance. Told them they were coming and then waited for them to get there because no one was allowed in the incline while the coal was moving'.
Interviewer: 'So it was like a delivery man, a pit prop delivery man?'
'That's right, a prop delivery man. He would come down having done that and we would perhaps repeat that three or four times a shift so that all the men were provided with their pit props'.

There were other inclines connecting the various seams and running up the workings on the northern side, there were three separate ones (called Mayshill, Giffords and an unnamed one) to reach the extremities of the later workings under Mayshill Farm.

A Frog Lane Puzzle

We have always been puzzled why Frog Lane used the main incline described above, from Pit Bottom up to the Hard Vein, instead of accessing it directly from a 'landing' or 'inset' directly off the shaft as was normal practice. It would appear that this was the original intention of the company and that such a 'landing' was built. This was suggested by Handel Cossham's notes[2] where he refers to work taking place in the Hard Vein, before the High Vein was reached and Bassett's 1856 plans shows early workings in both seams, without any apparent means of connection between the two other than the shaft. Fred Drew appears to confirm that there was an original landing directly into the Hard Vein:

'There was one thing about the pit that I don't think a lot of people knew, there was also halfway down the shaft roughly there was another level. I only went in there once because I knew the bloke who used to check the shaft out, there was two of them, that checked the shaft and [I] talked to him one day and asked him if he'd show it to me, so on the way down he said I'll ring the bell and stopped the cage just so we could step off and you could walk in then, must have been there from about the beginning of the pit I suppose. On the way in you had like offices on the left hand side, that was as far as we went, we was off the cage, looking round, got back in and then went down. How far that went or where it went, I don't know. Never come across anybody else that sort of knew anything about the hole half way down, but there was a proper sort of a little building on the left hand side let in like offices, apart from that I don't know'.
Interviewer: Was there anything in the office when you went there?
'No, it had just all been left, they'd gone so far down and gone in and worked one level out and apparently they'd gone down again to the base and started all over again, but I never come across anybody who ever knew much about it, how long it had been there I don't know'.
Interviewer: It was probably a different coal seam was it?
'Could have been there from the beginning of the pit. Perhaps they went down so far and eventually run out of coal. Maybe they went down to another level and then concentrated on the lower level; went halfway down and they went down again to the base. All I could see of it was it had been worked out and left and I've never known anyone who'd stop halfway down only, until I asked him all about it he stopped halfway down and showed me what it was'.

So it would appear that the pit was reorganised to wind coal from one landing only. It is interesting that the date of installation of the horizontal winder and the construction of the main incline are both thought to be somewhere around the 1880s.

Pit Bottom

Pit Bottom is the central hub of any pit and needs organising carefully if the flow of men, drams and materials is to run smoothly. Pit Bottom at Frog Lane was one of the few places where electric lights were used in later years. The onsetter worked here, supervising the movement of drams and men in and out of the cages, signalling up to the winder when the cage was clear to ascend. Bob Sharpe, the undermanager had a small office here to receive the reports of the deputy's inspections at the start of the shift, deal with any issues and generally keep an eye on operations. During the main shift, there would be a constant flow of full drams coming in to be

The onsetter at pit bottom. Lots of interesting details including the miners holding their peg and ball lamps as there is not much headroom in the cage. Pit bottom appears to be well built in stone and there is a notice by Mr Eames limiting the number of men in the cage. Note that the cage floor appears to be able to handle drams of two different gauges.

J. C. Burrow, courtesy Anne Matson

sent up the shaft, with the empties returning to be distributed to the working faces. The stables were just round the corner as was the compound haulage steam engine for the main haulage plane, it was not quiet for long!

The loading and unloading of tubs at pit bottom is also described by Frank Thornell:

'It was awkward really, because when the cages came down one side of Coalpit Heath Pit, they had a great big water thing where they pump all the water up, and you could just get the cage out one side enough before he'd hit that, and you had slewing plates, you had to slew the empties out as they came out. The full ones didn't go in but the full ones went the other side, but hit the empties out so you had to be there, pull this one, slew this one round the big pipes. Also I used to help this chap with, it wasn't the chap that did it regular, he was an oldish this chap, and he used to say "Come on, you going to give us a hand Frank?" "Well I ain't supposed to be with you I'm supposed to be helping the brickie", but any chance I got I'd go in and help him pull these drams and only one side because when they came out the other side, straight out, you could push them one way, which did go up towards Mays Hill or the other towards Bristol'.

Underground Machinery

Frog Lane was not a heavily mechanised mine and the 1947 underground inventory gives a good perspective on what the NCB inherited:

- 29 horses!
- 2 pairs of horizontal compound steam engines
- One vertical and one horizontal three throw pumps, plus two centrifugal pumps
- 770yards of high bridge rails @20lbs/yd for High Vein Haulage
- 2,400yards of high bridge rail @20lbs/yd for Hard Vein Haulage
- 5,140yards of low bridge service rails @16lbs/yd for High Vein Service Roads
- 3,000yards of low bridge service rails @16lbs/yd for Hard Vein Service Roads
- 1,000yards of $^7/_{16}$in. x 1.5in.x1.5in. chain used on horse roads
- 3,300yards of steel rope for high and hard vein haulage
- Apart from phones, the main electrical equipment was a 17-inch and two 12-inch longwall chain coal cutter and related switches and motors.

Another Raymond Hawkins image of the horse boys circa 1944, the picture being taken near the bottom of the main incline. Its interesting to compare the changes in miners clothing in the 40 years since J. C. Burrow and Dorothy Hewitt took their pictures, no moustaches either. The iron eye protectors over the horses eyes are typical. Left to right understood to be, Raymond Gifford, Bill Clark, Vernon Lewis and Frank Britton.

Raymond Hawkins. courtesy Victor Close

Working the Hollybush Seam

The NCB introduced more machinery, specifically on the Hollybush Seam workings which seem to have been organised by the CPHCC with mechanisation in mind from the outset. There is a good range of later underground maps of the Hollybush workings in the BRO and some are reproduced here. It would appear that the initial Hollybush workings were driven off either sides of the main incline from the High to the Hard Vein, obviously at the point where it intersected the seam in the central area of the Frog Lane take. It's not clear how traffic on the incline was adapted to deal with this.

The Hollybush workings appear to be laid out on a modern mechanised long wall basis (rather than Frog Lanes typical 'pillar and stall') coal cutters and gate end conveyers were used in these workings. The electrical power required to drive this machinery would have been substantial. Frank Thornell worked there for while and tells us what it was like:

'That's a good question because when they dug like at Charity, because Charity was up near up all round Yate, well they never had conveyor belts there. They'd get paid on how many drams like you said. The Holly Bush and all that they had belts. Perhaps you might be in a rough little place and you couldn't get all your coal off; stint of coal isn't it. Then you might get a nice little place where it was a bit easier so you'd got all yours off say an hour before, well you had to go and help this other chap get his off. I know you did get some that did try it a little bit, but you weren't going to get paid until you'd get that whole seam of coal off. Perhaps a hundred yards till all the coal was off. They used to cut it about 4ft 6in. underneath look, so you'd have to have it like that wall cleared so as they. Say the belt was here look, get the coal off first day, so they could put the belt over to here (7-8 feet distance) so that was gone, you know. Everyday, I'd shift it all over'.

Thre are accounts that the roof was poor, needing lots of labour and materials to support it, the floor was of fireclay and would soften quickly and the quality and thickness of the coal was variable so it's not surprising that these workings were discontinued. By this time (1947) Frog Lane had been working for over 90 years and was an unmodernised mine very much on its last legs. If the Hollybush workings had not been initiated the pit might have lost less money and closure might have been delayed a little, but not by much! Frank Thornell tells us about the management and workings after 1947:

'Two managers what come here they didn't like it round here, no birds about, no girls and that. I told one chap, Under-Manager, well Davies, got to be Welsh hasn't it and he couldn't sort of get the girls on a night like when he did to go out, and the other chap he was quite smart and he could get a few. A lot of them might have been married, I'm not saying but they kept that quiet about being married, but all the same for that, and in the end I think he got a bit fed up and then what they said, which was all lies was that they bought the three great big boilers which costs thousands and thousands in 1947. They bought all new coal cutters with what they cut the coal underneath with teeth on you know, and all that to make it expensive'.

Interviewer: Did they bring them in when you were there Frank? 'Yes, that was always in more or less bar when it was up Charity where they worked it by hand up the top. But all like in the Holly Bush and all that and places like that because what they had in places like that, when you go off the main sort of road, you had horses pulling the drams out as well then'.

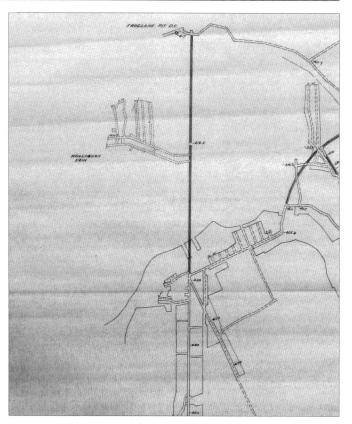

Map of initial workings in Holly Bush – note the heading accessing the new roadway coming off the left of the main incline from Pit Bottom to the Hard Vein. *courtesy BRO (Ref. 39398/46)*

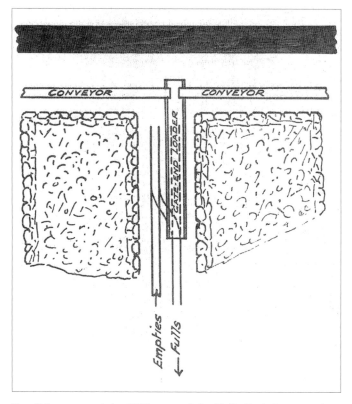

Detail from one of the NCB maps of the Holly Bush Seam working pattern. This image show the arrangement of conveyers, loader and seams. *courtesy BRO*

- 61 -

Lighting

Frog Lane was always a 'naked flame' mine, not being troubled with gas or explosions. Candles were used from the outset and continue to appear in use on the coal face in the photos taken by Burrows and Miss Hewitt in 1906. By this stage, most of the workers appeared to use 'peg and ball' oil lamps stuck on their hats. These were basically a circular vessel filled with oil, with a screw fitment underneath for the metal 'peg' which was used to locate and mount it and a wick and holder in the top side. Large versions of these were used in static positions along with the more conventional hanging and wall mounted oil lamps. Carbide cap lamps, initially American 'Justrite' and 'Autolite' models were introduced probably after World War One and continued in use until the pit closed. Frog Lane was the only NCB Pit in the area to charge the miners for Carbide. The pit bottom was reported to be electrically lit in later years as John Mills describes:

'The only fixed lighting in the Coalpit Heath Colliery, when you got to the pit bottom where the cages were loaded, they had a few electric light bulbs; and there was an office at the point where the Underground Manager operated from his office. His name was Mr. Sharpe he was the manager for the undermen, Mr. Sage was the over-all manager and Mr. Sharpe was the underground manager. And then the stables had about two lights as well and beyond that there was nothing. Nothing'.

It is a surprise to many people that miners were able to smoke underground at Frog Lane but this was the case as there was no gas.

Horses

The 1947 NCB inventory lists twenty-nine horses, this corresponds with our interviewees account that there were normally around thirty horses underground. They were housed in the stables near Pit Bottom with an Ostler in charge. Horses were the main motive power away from the main haulage roadways and inclines and were needed at all times.

Coalpit Heath was a mainly rural area and so a lot of the boys that started work would be familiar with horses from working with them on local farms. Fortunately there are a number of first hand accounts from these men. Frank Britton was one, and describes who was in charge:

'Well, Raymond Bisp was sort of in charge of the horse chaps, we know where we were working, he was more or less just had to keep it running. If there was a hitch he had to go and see what was the matter, what had gone wrong sort of business, and I suppose Fred Luton was sort of Under Foreman, and Fred Sharpe was Under Manager'.
Interviewer: 'They don't seem to figure much, you were largely left to yourselves?'
'You weren't never bothered much by them. Bisp used to be running round looking after the horse chaps to make sure that everything was running, because these coal men mind were on piece work like and be shouting "Hey in here like, with these drams". If they thought you was going into you like and not to them, there was some arguments with them like, and he was there to sort of keep things going'.

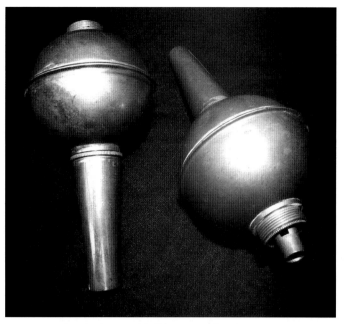

A pair of peg and ball lamps used at Frog Lane.

The late John Mills pictured in July 2008 demonstrating how his hat and lamp would have been fixed when he worked at Frog Lane.

Opposite: Smoking whilst hewing, probably from the 1940s. The seams are inclined upwards so the picture is likely to have been taken in the Charity District. *courtesy FC&DLHS*

Interviewer: 'So they're on piece work, how about you Frank?'
'We weren't on piece work we had a fixed wage, but some of the coalmen would just give you perhaps a shilling on a Friday and some of them might just give you a shilling not much more'.

Horses would have been purchased locally and needed careful training, firstly to get them used to being underground and secondly to become familiar with the requirements and routine of their work. Unless they were ill or there was strike, they stayed underground. If they were bought to surface it was via the larger Mayshill shaft and Fred Drew reports that they normally had a cloth put over their eyes. They would need regular shoeing, which the pit blacksmith would come down to the stables to do. They would need regular feeding, their hay and feed was transported on a daily basis from the CPHCCs Serridge Farm and sent down the shaft to the stables. In all the pictures of the horses underground, they appear to be well groomed and cared for and the boys were obviously fond of their charges.

Fred Drew describes the stables and mice:

'You go down get the horses, take the horses out and pull the dram tub when they were loaded. There were quite a few horse blokes down there, I can't remember how many horses we had cos it's so long ago I never counted the perishing things. There was one long stall and we were away first thing in the morning and put all the lights on, you'd see one black mass going up the walls, all cockroaches, they'd come out the feed bins where you'd put the hay in to feed the horses and you see these things coming out of the hay and up the wall as though they were coal, thousands of the perishing things. We used to have mice down there, a few mice, we didn't used to see those very often unless we were sat down eating food and we'd throw some bits out and see them come from God knows where, and get a stick like and then pomp, pomp, and we'd line them up, it was a potty place down there, it wasn't too bad'.

Fred Drew also describes how the horses were cared for:

'They had two men that was their job looking after the horses, look, they fed them, looked after them in general, one was pretty good he knew better than us, more than us what to do with them. Yes they looked after the horses, without the horses you wouldn't do very much work would you, it would all depend on the horses look'.

Horses temperaments, like people varied, Frank Thornell explained how he selected one to work with:

'When I used to go in some Sundays I used to, course I never drove horses a lot, but sometimes I go on a weekend I'd drive the horses. Anyway on weekends I'd always go and get a nice quiet

J. C. Burrow took this image of Frog Lane Stables showing cleaning in progress and a dram full of hay on the right. The horses needed to be well fed and cared for as without them the pit could not function.
courtesy Anne Matson

Forgive us for including another image of the horse boys circa 1944, this time with horses Ben and Jack. Perhaps 'more meat more coal' is a reference to wartime rationing. L-R Fred Tovey, Bill Clark, Raymond England. *Raymond Hawkins. courtesy Victor Close*

horse, you know what I mean, nice and quiet, and sometimes they knew it was Sunday more or less, and you had to catch em and pull 'em out the stables. They had a big stables at Coalpit Heath and you had a job to get 'em out, but obviously if you go in on a Sunday and you'd get a nice quite horse, which some was quiet, you got to take a quiet horse you're not going to take the boldest, and they knew near enough that it was Sunday as well mind. In a way you had to budge 'em and get hold of 'em'.

Whilst horses appeared to be used on a 'first come, first served basis' all the boys had their favourites and it is clear from their accounts that they were very fond of and cared for them. There were some that did not take so much care, as Frank Britton describes:

'Yes, I can remember I broke a little horse in underground, called Lion, I broke him in Old Branch and he was working on a level road just pulling the drams, he was only a young horse and he had only just started his work and I had him for a couple of months and he was working really well. This Fred Luton came one morning as I was putting the harness on and he said "Don't take he Frank he got to go up the chain hatching today." I said "Fred, he won't come back." He never done it he hadn't enough sense. I said "He's never done that Fred, that horse is going in a place he's never been before." Oh he knowed it, he was that sort of man like. They brought him back about ten o'clock back in a dram. They'd been and killed him down in the chain hatching. See these horses got used to

it that they'd come to the edge, it's like coming to the edge of that table, and he'd have to stop, he knowed if he hadn't have stopped he'd have some trouble. And they know, it's no good they know but he didn't know did he and he went on pulling and pulled over the edge'.

After Frank Britton left the pit, he spent much of his time involved with horses and his enthusiasm and affection for them stands out, he was also the only boy that could handle the most difficult one called 'Nigger' as Frank describes:

'Nigger, he was a devil mind and when we did come, the chaps that were wet had the preference to go up in the pit first when they were in the bottom of the pit and sometimes they coal men would get in the front seat see they wouldn't let we chaps come on down, coming down from up top because we did leave about half past one to get down to the stables and get ready to go out in the pit. The men would be in the front and they wouldn't let us go down there they'd say "They'm in the front now Frank" and I'd say "Go on" and he'd go down and he'd sort them out. He'd know he was going home he knew he was going to the stables see. He'd make they fly, he'd make they scream. He'd kick for the fun of it, he'd love it and the coal men, when I did go into the coal men they'd say "Watch that thing mind". He'd chase them you see, he'd drive them right up and under the coal. Oh, he was a villain, a villain. I couldn't put the harness on him in the stable I used to leave his harness

Ann Moulsdale with ex Pit Pony Charlie in 1953.

courtesy Ann Moulsdale

in the workings because if I put his harness on in the stable by the time I'd got to the workings there wouldn't be none left. He'd kick that all to pieces. He was a real boy'.

When the pit closed, the horses would have been sold too – Ann Moulsdale bought Charlie, one of the last ones and learned to ride on it. She recalls:

"He was the last pit pony to go down".
Audrey Dyer: "Oh was he?"
Ann: "And Mr. Denning took him down Tom Denning he came from Wales, love him, and he said it was absolutely disgusting to be taking him down because he was so young; he was about four".

Health and Safety

A coal mine is inherently dangerous and accidents and injury are a continual risk. In Frog Lane's early days, in common with most other industries of the time, only fatalities would be recorded, loss or damage to limb might result in compensation from the company, but little else. Because Frog Lane was not a 'gassy' pit, injuries and fatalities from explosions were not a risk, however roof falls and heavy machinery produced their own grim toll. This was one of the reasons why miners normally worked in pairs so that one could look out for and, if needed, dig out a colleague in the event of a fall. Roof falls are a regular occurrence in coal mines and many miners preferred to use wooden pit props, rather than the later steel one, as the former gave out a variety of noises when under stress that enabled the miners to beat a hasty retreat.

There was one particular characteristic of roof falls that Frog Lane was infamous for. These were the 'Bell Moulds', large bell shaped pieces of rock (possibly fossilised tree trunks) the base of which was exposed in the roof when the coal and rock was extracted. These were prone to fall without giving any warning and were heavy enough to kill you if you happened to be underneath at the time. Fred Drew describes what these were like:

'Well you got your fireman that would go round checking conditions, whether it was safe or not. They'd go round checking. They'd check the roofs, stuff like that, but up in the roof and that we used to get what you'd call the "bell mole" or bell, it was a block, shaped round, like an inverted corn, the corn would go nearly a foot that way and this thing was nearly up to the roof, part of it going that way; so we'd get a shock or something in the roof and this thing would suddenly pop out. If you were there, you'd had it, it was a simple as that'.

Last picture of the horse boys around 1944.

courtesy Victor Close

The last death at Frog Lane is described by Fred Drew:

'One of the last case was three men, one was a fireman, one was an under-manager and another man, walking back one day not long before the pit closed down, worse luck, and there was a bloke called Gilbert Moseley, this was the local paper man who used to write the piece in the local paper and he was in the middle walking back along the track, one was there and one was there and Gilbert in the middle, and this thing came down out of the roof, straight down on Gilbert and killed him, and the other two men sort of fell away, one went one side and one went the other and they came up all right but poor old Gilbert, it was just before the pit closed down and he was dead. Poor old Gilbert'.

The subject of underground accidents deserves a chapter in its own right. Here the local policeman's report to the Gloucester Coroner details two accidental deaths at Frog Lane on the 17th of September 1872:

'Sir, I respectfully beg to state that I received information of the above at 5 o'clock on the 17th inst and at once went to Westerleigh and made enquiry, found that the deceased men were employed at Frog Lane Colliery Westerleigh belonging to the Coalpit Heath Coal Company, they left their houses at Winterbourne Down yesterday evening and commenced their work at the colliery at 9 p.m. The two deceased with a man named Henry Bowyer was at work removing coal from under a massive stone rock or brow for the purpose of making a siding for empty trams. A little before 1 p.m. this morning the three men were in a stooping position coursing together when without the slightest notice a portion of the rock slipped and about six tons weight fell on deceased, Thomas Biggs, which caused instantaneous death and a portion of the debris severely injuring Thomas Cook. Henry Bowyer at once got assistance and removed the rock and Thomas Cook was at once conveyed to his house and died from the injuries he received at about seven this morning deceased Thomas Biggs was completely crushed…'

References

1. Page 127 *The Bristol Coalfield*, John Cornwell
2. BRO 9429/16

A J. C. Burrow image clearly intending to show the size of a Bell Mould and the aperture it left after dropping from the roof.

courtesy Anne Matson

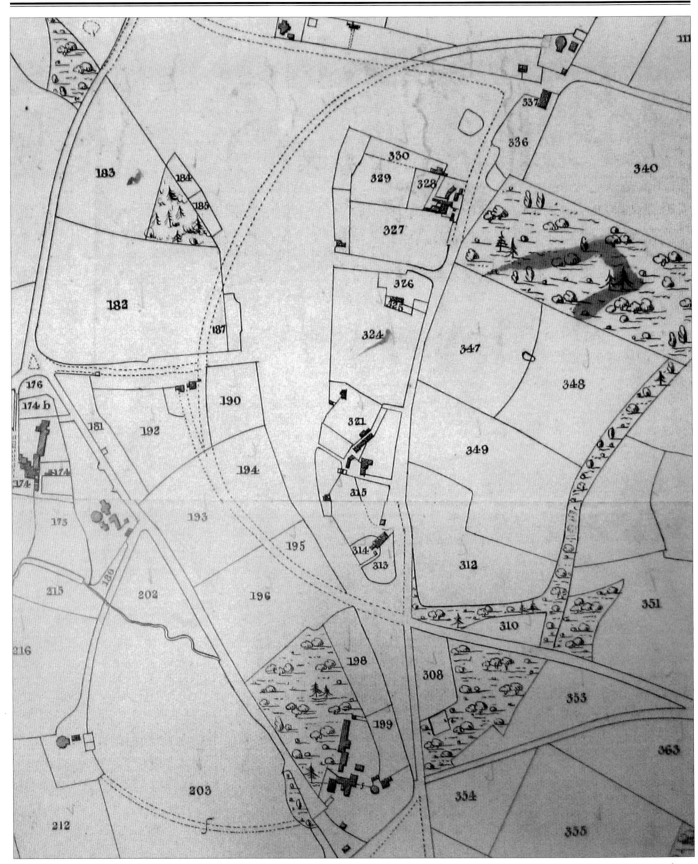

This 1843 map of the Parish of Westerleigh showing the route of the two original dramway branches. Bitterwell Engine shed was built in V the at bottom right (just above the number 363). From this point the northern branch performs an almost perfect 180 degree turn to finish at Ram Hill Pit (top right). The southern branch goes via the New Engine complex (just below the number 199) and then on across what is now Kendleshire golf course to finish up at Orchard Pit at the bottom left, the site of which is now Serridge Cottage. The dramway may have continued up to Serridge Engine Pit, 200 yards to the north but we have no evidence to confirm this.

courtesy BRO (Ref. STG 94)

THE FROG LANE COLLIERY RAILWAY

Before the widespread introduction of railways, the use of carts and pack horses to transport coal on poor roads and the damage that resulted was a continual problem in coal mining areas. Collieries were thus, one of the earliest users of railways, both under and above ground. By the mid 19th century the proprietors of most pits clamoured to be connected to the rapidly growing national railway network to send their coal to market quickly and cheaply.

EARLY HISTORY

Frog Lane Pit had been open for 10 years before the railway was built. From the details available it appears that an extension of the existing Midland Railway exchange sidings at Box Hedge Farm was constructed around 1865. This date is confirmed by the date stone on the line's major engineering feature, a bridge carrying the lane to Says Court Farm over the line between Mayshill and Frog Lane Pits, there is also an entry in the 1865 accounts for the purchase of a 'locomotive'.[1]

1865 date stone on Says Court Railway Bridge.

The reason for the delay in constructing the railway is assumed to be because the company wanted to be sure that the intended output of the pits was achievable before making further investment.

The earlier horse drawn 'dramway', officially the Bristol & Gloucestershire Railway (abbreviated to B+G), from Orchard and New Engine Pits was opened in 1832. These two branches joined at Bitterwell, continuing to Westerleigh and then down to Mangotsfield (where the Avon & Gloucestershire Railway from here to Willsbridge branched off) ending at Bristol's floating harbour.

The section from Westerleigh into Bristol was used for the B+G, and later Midand Railways main line from Bristol to Gloucester, opening in June 1844.[2] This line was built to Brunel's 7ft broad gauge and the earlier standard gauge lines were retained so this section was 'mixed gauge'. This arrangement was far from ideal as traffic on the horse drawn standard gauge 'dramway' had to be coordinated with the longer distance locomotive hauled broad gauge traffic. The broad gauge was extended from Westerleigh into the exchange sidings at Bitterwell in June 1847. By 1865 traffic on this isolated northern end of the dramway originating

from Ram Hill/Church Lease and Orchard pits would have been minimal, both being closed by 1870. The coal would probably have been transshipped into main line wagons at Box Hedge sidings for onward despatch on the B+G and its successor the Midland Railway.

The B+G was in the middle of the 'gauge battle' between Brunel's 7ft broad gauge and the eventually successful standard gauge of 4ft $8^{1}/_{2}$in. and this meant that the weighbridge at Box Hedge sidings had provision for both gauges. The conversion from horse drawn dramway with stone sleeper blocks and fish bellied rails to a modern style railway with conventional rails and sleepers, had the side effect of making lots of high quality dressed limestone sleeper blocks available for reuse. These redressed dramway blocks have been noted incorporated in the Brandy Bottom Colliery Heapstead, the lining of the culvert under Frog Lane tip and (most easily visible) in the twin arch railway bridge beside Says Court Farm.

Dressed dramway blocks used for capping stones on Says Court Bridge, 2009.

A well known J. C. Burrow photograph of Francis Eames and workman in the timber yard at Frog Lane in 1906. Standard gauge wagons loaded with timber came down the spur which branched off the line to Mayshill just before Says Court bridge for unloading here. Once the timber had been cut to the required sizes they were loaded onto flat narrow gauge wagons on the track on the right and taken to the pit head and stacked waiting loading into the cages.

courtesy Anne Matson

The weighbridge house at Bitterwell is understood to date from this period and to have been lived in by the weighbridge man and his family. Jack Shaw, the last loco driver on the railway lived in it with his family after World War Two for a while.

Mr and Mrs Jack Shaw outside Bitterwell weighbridge house c. 1946.
courtesy Jack Straw

THE ROUTE DESCRIBED

The new single track line ran up on a spur starting from the exchange sidings just after the road crossing to Box Hedge Farm, up behind the weighbridge house (all other lines being in front) and turning north through Martin Croft Brake and then Ram Hill Wood toward Frog Lane pit. After half a mile it crossed Broad lane (the crossing was gated in later years), through Burn Wood before passing Frog Lane Farm on the left (where there was another crossing) and then curving round to the left into the pit yard to terminate past the screens, a distance of less than 2 miles from the exchange sidings. Just before Frog Lane a branch headed due north finally entering Mayshill pit yard after passing underneath a substantially built twin arch bridge. A reversal from a point prior to this bridge headed down to Frog Lane's timber yard and sawmill area where incoming loads of timber for conversion into chocks and pit props were unloaded.

The 25-inch ordnance survey map (revised in 1919) shows the railway extended the short distance to Nibley Colliery, possibly to help transport of coal for the boilers.

When the GWR 'Badminton Extension' line from Wootton Bassett near Swindon, through Badminton to Stoke Gifford was built in 1903 to provide a direct route from London to South Wales[3], it crossed the Frog Lane Railway just north of and parallel to Broad Lane, but 30ft higher on an embankment. The opportunity was taken to put in a spur connecting the GWR's Coalpit Heath Station with the Frog Lane Colliery Railway. It is understood that the additional weighbridge house built just south of the tip dates from this period and was provided to avoid weighing coal destined for shipment via the GWR at Bitterwell and then returning.

GWR weighbridge house - interior remains.

The route of the southernmost dramway branch running west from the exchange sidings to Orchard Pit was retained as far as New Engine Yard, where there was an extensive workshop complex and saw mill serving New Engine and the related earlier pits nearby. The other branch (north of the Engine shed) to Church Lease and Ram Hill Pits was truncated and used for wagon storage.

LINE FEATURES AND BUILDINGS

Other than shallow cuttings, minor embankments and culverts the only major feature constructed was the twin arch stone bridge taking the lane from Says Court Farm to the Badminton Road over the line. This bridge is still in existence, complete with its 1865 date stone and whilst the cutting between the bridge and Mayshill has been filled the upper part of the bridges southern face remains visible. As described previously, this is constructed from redressed dramway sleeper blocks, the cap stones and 'stringers' showing the characteristic twin holes and rail chair imprints. The only other overbridge is the 1903 small girder bridge constructed to carry the GWR Badminton Extension Line over the Frog Lane Railway.

A substantial stone built, double track engine shed was constructed at the western end of the exchange sidings in between the fork of the original dramway route to Orchard Pit (retained for access to New Engine Yard) and the now truncated route to Church Leaze/Ram Hill pits (which was retained for wagon storage). This shed, three walls of which remain, was extended at some stage although it is not clear why this was needed as it is understood that there were never more than two locomotives present on the line. The end of an 'egg-ended' boiler reported to have originated from New Engine Yard was cut off, fitted with a base and mounted on a large circular stone plinth in the extension wall of the shed to serve as a water tank. A small fireplace was built into the base of this plinth, reportedly to prevent the water in the tank freezing. Water for the tank (and for the weighbridge cottage) was drawn from a well beside the engine shed using a small donkey pump.

The original weighbridge was a two storey building, the main structure of which remains. This was used as a dwelling and

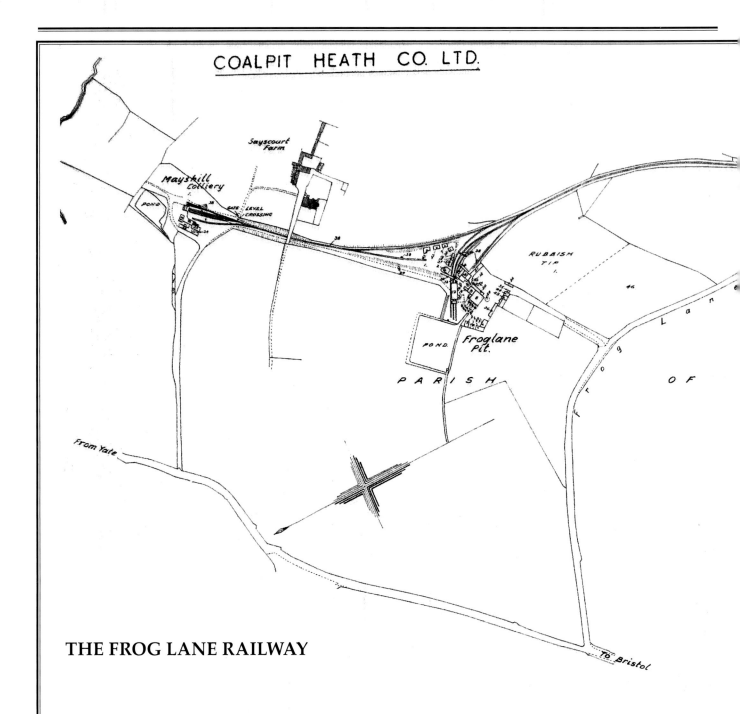

COALPIT HEATH CO. LTD.

THE FROG LANE RAILWAY

Lord Salisbury when at Norton Hill Colliery.
courtesy Ray Ashman

An enlargement of a 1906 photograph which shows a railway wagon at New Engine - presumably unloading timber.   *courtesy Anne Matson*

Twin archedbridge at Mayshill on the land to Says Court Farm.

Bitterwell engine shed from the back, 2007.

Loco shed water tank made from end of egg-ended boiler circa 1982.
courtesy David Pollard

Bitterwell Sidings looking west in 2005 from Box Hedge Lane. The weighbridge house can be made out above the two figures.

had a canopy in front over, the weighbridge platform. This became well known to railway enthusiasts in later years as one of the few places where you could still see broad gauge rail in its original setting (disused) alongside the standard gauge.

These buildings still survive, ivy grown and gradually deteriorating, their continued existence was due to the use of the railway line and loco shed as a linear scrapyard – although this has recently been cleaned up.

There was a workshops and sawmill complex at New Engine Yard and it has been suggested that the workshops here were capable of most repairs to the lines steam locos with the exception of wheel turning, which was done at Peckett's works at Fishponds. Some local residents report that the locos used to take on water from a tank beside the Engine House at New Engine Yard.

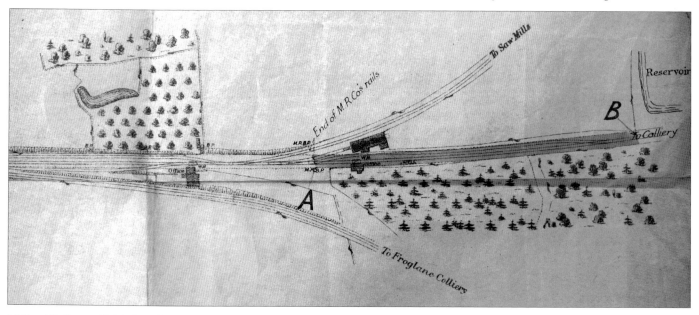

Midland Railway official plan of Bitterwell Sidings circa 1920.

courtesy BRO

Lord Salisbury in later life at Norton Hill Colliery Somerset in the 1950. *courtesy FC&DLHS*

THE LOCOMOTIVES

The Industrial Railway Society (IRS) gives the locomotives used at Frog Lane as follows[4]:

Fletcher Jennings 0-4-0 tank. Works No. 58 of 1866 delivered new and understood to have been scrapped or sold.

Fox Walker outside cylindered 0-6-0 saddle tank, works No. 326 of 1876. Sold to Pecketts in 1906, presumably in part exchange for *Lord Salisbury*. Later resold to James Pain, Glendon Ironstone Quarries, Northamptonshire

Peckett inside cylindered 0-6-0 saddle tank *Lord Roberts*, works No. 825 of 1900. Believed scrapped or sold probably in the mid 1940s.

Peckett inside cylindered 0-6-0 Saddle Tank *Lord Salisbury*, works No. 1041 of 1906. Sent to Radstock in 1950 and then to Norton Hill in 1953 from where it was scrapped by Wm Pike of Trowbridge in February 1965.

Ruston & Hornsby 4-wheeled diesel mechanical, works No. 242869 of 1946. Sent to Somerset where it worked for some time at Norton Hill and Kilmersdon before being despatched to Merthyr Vale Colliery in South Wales.

THE ROLLING STOCK

The CPHCC is understood to have purchased some wagons and hired others but the only known images of wagons are of Frank Eames, the pit manager, leaning on a nicely painted example that was supplied by the Midland Railway Carriage & Wagon Company of Birmingham.

The first record of wagons, with the then Midland Waggon Co., is in October 1857 when Mr Hewitt requested side safety chains to be fitted to thirty wagons on hire. In 1861 ten 6-ton wagons were purchased from Midland followed by fifty 7-tonners in June 1866 and twenty more in December 1869.

The more local Gloucester Railway Carriage & Wagon Co. were used to hire fifty 6-ton and twenty 10-ton wagons for one year in October 1892 and this was obviously renewed for at least a further two years.

The only other item of stock that a number of folks have referred to is a hand operated 'pump' trolley, used to travel the line and much loved by local children!

There are no records of brake vans or passenger carriages being resident on the line but we do have a very unusual anecdote from Mr Bennet of Says Court Farm passed down from his grandfather. Apparently in the 1890s Edward Colston, one of Frog Lane's principal shareholders used to load all his family, servants and luggage and equipment into a train once every year that would traverse the Colliery Railway and

Frank Eames the Colliery Manager and one of the companies wagons – circa 1930. The wagon, with fleet number 36 had been built by the Midland Railway Carriage & Wagon Co, and was either on hire from them or being bought on deferred purchase terms as it carries the distinctive Midland builder's plate on the far end. The wagon is probably black with plain white lettering.   *courtesy FC&DLHS*

deposit them right outside Says Court Farm where they stayed for a month. At the end of the month the train would return to collect them and the process would be reversed – let's hope a picture of this turns up!

WORKING THE LINE

The following description of railway operations is based on extracts from our oral history contributors Jack Shaw, Frank Britton and Fred Drew who worked on the railway. This has been supplemented by extracts from an article written by Roger Bird, based on his conversations in the 1960s with Mr Frank Eames (nephew of the Pit Manager of the same surname), a colliery fitter who worked on the locos in the 1930s (this article was published in SGMRG newsletter No. 12).

On a line that suffered from steep grades and overhanging trees, sanding was obviously important. Both locos were fitted with a large rear sandbox that extended right across the frames in front of the coal bunker. Both this and the front footplate boxes were normal gravity feed, the front boxes being operated by control rods on either side at the front of the cab and the rear box by a handle at waist height. Locos were always placed on the track facing from Frog Lane towards the engine shed yard. This enabled them to work all loaded trains from the colliery chimney first i.e. uphill, ensuring that the firebox crown was always covered with water.

The enginemen's quarters (or bothy) was an extension of the main shed. There was a fire grate with an oven on either side for drying the sand for the locomotives, each oven being fitted with a small chute under which buckets were placed into which the sand trickled as it dried. Coal was taken from wherever convenient, usually the colliery.

Routine loco repairs were carried out at the shed, more serious work was carried at Henfield Yard where the workshops were situated. The only job not done by the company was the turning or fitting of new tyres to the wheels, these being removed and sent to Pecketts for this work.

The line was worked on the 'one engine in steam' principle, the locos working alternative weeks. Locos were cleaned and the boiler emptied on Sunday mornings, the shunter and fireman were responsible for all actual cleaning (tubes and tube plate), while the driver supervised and ensured that boiler plugs and other parts removed during the work were replaced properly.

The course of the Frog Lane railway looking south west from Says Court railway bridge. The line went underneath the photographer and followed the line of the wood curving round to the left. Frog Lane Pit was in the trees and the telegraph pole marks the point where the sawmill spur branched off.

Frank Britton tells us what it was like:

'We did go in on a Sunday, I think it perhaps worked out about once a month and we did all the tubes and that. We did get there and push rod down through the tubes. My job was trying to get into the fire box and getting all the inside and Jack [Shaw] and they used to push the tubes through the rods'.

STARTING THE WORKING DAY

The loco fire was lit by the shunter who started work at 6 AM, he always travelled on the footplate, brake vans not being employed on the line. The fireman's first job was to collect the pit manager's mail from the post office and deliver it to his home (Bleak House, Ram Hill). He then proceeded to Broad Lane crossing gates, locked them in the 'rail clear' position and walked along the track to the shed. Broad Lane gates were always locked in both positions to prevent accidents or damage to them. (Roger Bird)

Jack Shaw started as fireman on the Frog Lane railway in the late 1930s, he had initially been working for Les Davies the pit blacksmith who was also stand in engine driver for Mr Cooke the normal driver and his move to the railway came about through this connection.

Jack tells us that the working day was normally from around 7 a.m. to 3 p.m. with a half day on Saturday. The steam locos worked 'bunker first' to the pit so reversed into the shed. He confirmed that it was the fireman's job, to light up the engine at around 5.30 a.m. using oily rags and scrap timber and then build up steam ready to start work at 7.15 a.m. The loco normally returned to the shed by around 3 p.m. and the fireman would rake out the fire at the end of work. Maintenance in later days

seems to have been limited to routine oiling and greasing and a fortnightly tube clean which involved the youngest or smallest person climbing into the firebox and pushing the long cleaning brushes through the tubes.

Frank Britton describes a typical mornings work:

'We would take some loads up to Coalpit Heath Station on a morning, that was the first load on a morning, roughly 10 or 11 o'clock time. Then come back down after taking that load up there; they'd come down and shunt about a bit and get the load ready for the afternoon, shunting empties back in for me Uncle Sam and they were loading the coal back into the hopper, then shunt the empties and that back in there, and they'd be shunting them up until they'd get the load ready and then it was dinner time, so everybody did have a bit of dinner, perhaps a little bit more shunting, then couple up and take them down to Westerleigh sidings'.

TRAFFIC ON THE LINE

By World War Two there were normally three daily trainloads of 10 wagons each coming from the pit, one going to the Bitterwell sidings for despatch on the LMS and two going to Coalpit Heath Station for the GWR. Inbound traffic was the corresponding empty wagons and substantial quantities of 'trees' which were shunted into the sawmill sidings for processing into pit props and 'chocks'.

The LMS engine usually came into the exchange sidings at Box Hedge Farm (they owned the line to the point just past the engine shed) to deliver empties and take away loaded wagons. On only one occasion do any of our 'railway men' recall working down this line into Westerleigh Yard. By this time *Lord*

Salisbury was the regular engine, *Lord Roberts* being much more 'difficult' according to Fred Drew, fireman in the 1940s. Up to this time the two Peckett saddle tanks are understood to have been used on alternating weeks. The 1947 NCB inventory[6] for Frog Lane makes no reference to *Lord Roberts* and it is assumed to have been scrapped sometime during World War Two.

Loaded wagons destined for the GWR at Coalpit Heath Station were always pushed from Frog lane whilst empties were pulled back. The reverse occurred with loaded wagons destined for the LMS at Westerleigh sidings which were pulled from Frog Lane by the locomotive and empties pushed back. The reason for this was to avoid running round the LMS train, and that the loco was always downgrade from the wagons on the steep grade up to Coalpit Heath station. Empty wagons coming in from the GWR had to be shunted into the weighbridge sidings at Frog Lane. This involved stopping the train back from the point to allow the fireman to walk to the point lever. Once the points were changed the loco accelerated quickly and momentarily slowed to allow the shunter to uncouple, after which the engine pulled briskly away past the fireman and stopped further down the main line. As soon as the loco had passed, the fireman switched the point to allow the rolling wagons to enter the weighbridge siding. Sometimes if the wagons were a poor running set, they would stop before the last wagon had cleared the point. In this event a long wire rope was hitched to the draw gear of the last wagon and to the front of the loco, the wagons thus being pulled by the loco from the adjacent line.

Wagons to and from the LMS were weighed at the engine shed yard. After weighing the loaded wagons were parked between the weighbridge and Box Hedge Lane to await collection by an LMS locomotive. Wagons awaiting movement to Henfield Yard were parked on the loop between the first point (from Westerleigh) and Box Hedge Lane (see map, pages 74 and 75).

A great assortment of wagons could be found on the line at any one time. As well as GW and LMS there were private owner wagons from South Wales and the Forest of Dean. The colliery company also owned a number of its own wagons, these were of varying capacities and lettered 'Coalpit Heath Colliery Co.' in white letters on black woodwork and strapping. These wagons were repaired at Henfield Yard.

The only signal on the line was at the Fishguard turnout controlling access into the timber yard. This was of the slotted post type and was connected to the point tie bar. When the loco was pushing a long line of wagons into the Fishguard it was impossible for the driver to see the shunter. The signal was there to indicate the direction the point was set.

The only recorded accident on the line occurred at engine shed yard when a fireman's hand was badly scalded by a passing loco. When changing a point he allowed his hand to rest on the lever waiting for the next movement. (Roger Bird)

MESSING ABOUT

The railway men were youngsters and always ready for a bit of fun as Frank Britton tells us:

'Jack [Shaw] was older than me I know but he was a young chap then but old Bert [Cooke] he was sort of the grumpy one of us three. When we did drive from Coalpit Heath Colliery to New Engine which was quite a little stretch up through there, Jack did sit on a coal box at the back, I'd be looking out up the line up this way and Bert would be looking up there; and we'd be singing you know how it is with young chaps. And Jack would clap his hands and hit the steam thing on a little bit and old Bert would be looking out and the old engine would start rattling away and old Jack would just tap it a little bit and it

would be picking speed up and then all at once the old man would realise'.

Many of our oral history contributors recall playing on the railway and the adjoining colliery waste tip. Anne Moulsdale recalls messing about on the line and one occasion when this went as far as pushing the engine out of the shed!

'Yes and we lost count of time and I can see June Burnett now stood upon the waste tip at Coalpit Heath because you didn't have shorts and tops to match in those days, you had what you could get, she had a peach jumper and white shorts, you could see her for miles. I can remember we came back and they had an old, well you know you've seen a track thing where they used to work it up and down, well this one wasn't but it was like that, and it was left and we used to get on it and go down and run along the tracks, the track was still there then jump and set off down to the pit, but the trouble was where it had pieces in the line, where the line wanted doing, you'd come off, and we'd get back on. Nobody ever knew, and after the paper chase we'd come back but we always used to end up here by the engine shed. Then you could sit on the engine with Dave Trott, they knew as much about the engine as the engine driver did they spent all their lives, they lived here. I can remember them opening the big doors and pushing it out, and Mrs. Shaw lived in the weighbridge along the line.
Audrey: She used to do a lot of knitting for me that Mrs. Shaw.
Anne: 'And she came out after us and what she was going to do to us and say too, was no odds to anybody. They got the thing back and banged the doors shut and they were gone. They never did it to hurt anybody else'.

THE DIESEL ARRIVES

After Jack Shaw's war service in the Royal Engineers (a separate story in itself, involving assembling American steam locomotives in Ghana[4]) he returned to the railway in 1946 as driver for their newly acquired Ruston and Hornsby Diesel loco. Because Jack had been working on diesel engines with the Royal Engineers he was presumably considered ideal for this task. Jack reports that Lord Salisbury was laid aside immediately and although not as strong as the steam engine, the diesel was reliable. Jack recalls one incident with the diesel when he left the handbrake off at Coalpit Heath Station, the loco ran back down the line into the pit yard and was halted by the rising gradient to Mayshill whence it returned, finally coming to rest in the middle of the line fortunately without damage, awaiting his rescue!

When the pit closed, the Lord Salisbury and the Ruston diesel were sent to the neighbouring NCB Somerset area, the wagons were scrapped, the line lifted during the early 1950s and the trackbed slowly returned to nature!

WALKING THE LINE TODAY

Surprisingly given that it closed over 50 years ago, much of the route is easy to follow and most of the trackbed remains, all is on private property and permission should be sought before entering. The best starting point is the very impressive Says Court Farm. As you enter the farmyard you cross the twin arch railway bridge constructed from redressed dramway sleeper blocks. The cutting and the northern face of the bridge have recently been completely filled in but the southern face is half clear (Jan. 2009) with the tops of the arches visible. This is an excellent point to look down over the fields, past the northern end of the tip where the timber yard used to be, the railway follows the field boundary curving slightly leftwards. The trackbed is mostly obscured but the occasional sleeper and rail are in use as fenceposts. Just past the end of the spoil heap after about a third of a mile, the railway runs on a small embankment over a culvert that continues under the remains of the spoil tip.

At this point the brick walls of the GWR weighbridge house still exist and the line then runs through a very overgrown cutting (full of primroses in the spring) until it crosses an open field where the route has been ploughed out. Its route becomes clear again in the form of a footpath through Burn Wood (widened to allow lorries to reach the main line railway embankment during its rebuilding in 2007) before passing under the main railway line and then crossing Broad Lane. From here to Bitterwell the route is now a muddy field and woodland.

The area around Bitterwell has some surprising remains. Three walls of the engine shed survive including the one with the boiler/water tank atop, complete with fire place below and the shed doors are still in situ. The engineman's bothy beside the shed still has the sand drying grates intact. The shed will probably fall down before long, indeed one side wall has fallen in that past 10 years. 200 yards away is the substantially complete, but overgrown and roofless weighbridge house, clearance in 2005 of some the scrap metal in the exchange sidings revealed the massive steel weighbridge supports.

The layout of the sidings is clear from here to Box Hedge Lane after which the route goes into as shallow cutting for half a mile before crossing the Westerleigh road and into the site of Westerleigh Yard, currently occupied by an oil depot.

Standard Gauge rail in use at fence post beside the route of the railway.

The loco shed door still in situ – just.

The Weighbridge House gable end from the north.

The sand drying grate with sand hoppers on either side.

The route of the railway after crossing Box Hedge Lane.

Opposite:

Top: Another view of the remains of the GWR weighbridge house.

Middle: The interior rear wall of the loco shed

Bottom: The fire grate at the base of the loco shed water tank.

References

1. GA D7399/12
2. *The Bristol and Gloucester Railway*, Colin Maggs, Oak wood Press
3. *The GWR Badminton Line portrait of a railway*, K. Robertson and D. Abbott, ISBN 0 86299-459-4
4. *Industrial Locomotives of South Western England*, IRS ISBN 0 901096-23-7
5. Oral History Transcipt - October 2008
6. National Archives, Kew, Coal 36/293

Dorothy Hewitt's photograph of Francis Eames surveying in a well timbered roadway. The tripod was used to ensure the miners dial was stable and level so that accurate readings could be taken.

courtesy Anne Matson

MINING MISCELLANY

This chapter is intended to cover those topics that have not fitted naturally into the other chapters on mining.

Mine Owners and Managers

The first Chapter described how the three Lords of the Manor of Westerleigh (LoW) came into a business partnership in the 1740s, Jarret Smith holding 50% and the Colston and Middleton Families 25% each. Jarret died in the 1780s and his properties were divided between his two sons of whom Thomas took over the family holding in the LoW partnership. Similarly the Middleton and Colston holdings were passed down the chain of succession. At some stage in the first half of the 19th century they set up a the Coalpit Heath Colliery Company (CPHCC) and the company commissioned the sinking of Frog Lane Pit. The Middleton family left the partnership in the mid 1860s, possibly to concentrate their energies on their growing coal mining operations around Nottingham. The Colston family remained involved for longer but by nationalisation in 1947 only the Smythe family were shown as shareholders.

From the 1820s, the direction and management of the CPHCCs activities appears to have been increasingly undertaken by various members of the Hewitt family according to local historian Trevor Thomson. The family came from the Ipswich area and were initially in business in Bristol as coal merchants, different parts of the family apparently had the use of both

Serridge House, home of the Hewitts circa 1906.
Dorothy Hewitt, courtesy Anne Matson

Heath Cottage, another Hewitt residence , just off Badminton Road.
Dorothy Hewitt, courtesy Anne Matson

Heath Cottage and Serridge House. The Hewitts remained active in management of the CPHCC until around the start of World War One.

John Cook is referred to as the Frog Lane Bailiff by Handel Cossham when he visited in 1855, Cook's relationship with the Hewitts is not clear. The manager in 1891 was J. Naysmith.

Francis Eames is probably the best known and longest serving manager at Frog Lane. Originating from Swadlingcote near Burton on Trent he is understood to have taken the management post sometime around 1898, continuing to his death in 1932. He and his wife Rosina are buried in St. Saviours Graveyard. Many of the pictures taken by Burrow and Dorothy Hewitt in 1906 include Francis Eames.

As far as we are aware, Eames was succeeded by Mr Sage, the interviewer of some of our oral history contributors. Mr Davies from Wales, appears to have taken over from Mr Sage in 1947, its is not known if he stayed through to closure.

There would always have been one or more undermanagers (so called because they work UNDER the overall manager and managed work UNDERground) the only name we have is Bob Sharpe who is fondly remembered by some of our interviewees from the 1940s. Unfortunately we do not have any pictures of any of these gentlemen.

The descendents of the Hewitt family, specifically Miss Dorothy are understood to have remained in residence at Serridge House

Understood to be Henry Hewitt in later years.   *courtesy Ann Matson*

until after 1947. Bleak House at Ram Hill was also one of the Frog Lane Management residences as was one on Badminton Road

Wages, what the miners earned

There are no reliable figures for the different wages levels, it has been mentioned previously that the face workers were normally the highest earners and were paid on a 'piecework' basis. Other workers wages would have been lower that this and would vary according to skills and age. Our oral history interviewees tell their own stories beginning with Fred Drew:

'Call it wages? Good God, you couldn't even buy a packet of fags with what we used to earn years ago down there, and I'm not kidding when I say that. I think I started off with roughly, the first job I had at Newmans ten shillings a week and you'd get fourpence stoppages. After the war started the marvellous thing was it went up to twelve shillings I thought I was married it went up as quick as that. And then it gradually went up over a period of time, that was the days when you couldn't smoke in Newmans except for half an hour in the mornings and half an hour in the afternoon and if you were caught smoking in between that you'd get the sack, it's as simple as that. Then down the pit, wages were poorish down there I can't remember exactly, I think when I did the job proper same as the rest of the men on the farriers business or the blacksmiths, I did earn roughly about three pounds a week something like that'.

Interviewer: Did the wages go up quite a bit when you became a farrier?

'Well, I got moved up, they couldn't pay me, what I done was exactly the same as the other men but married men and those, but you couldn't get the same money as them because almost the same wage but you weren't married, and there was a difference between single and married and married men got extra, common sense really I suppose, but I was given a bit of a rise, sort of boost me a little bit but never got the full amount of money, so it's as simple as that. I think about two pounds something I think and the men didn't get much more, underground they'd get about a fiver or something, but for the job they did, they did it for that well it was stupid. Then that's they way it was all those years ago, we're going back what, 'cor Lord what how many years?'

Frank Britton tells us of his Uncle Sams wage negotiation skills:

'Another thing, the very first week's wages I got I went over to the office where Jack showed me to get our wages and I had ten shillings. I thought that was alright and I hadn't had to ride all the way over Clifton and all that for half-a-crown and when I got back, me Uncle Sam who was always there said "How much you get boy?" Sam was like that you know. I said "Ten shillings Uncle Sam" and he said "That's no bloody good come along with me" and he took me back to see Mr. Sage. "Mr. Sage" he said "I can put him on the street singing for more money" and he gave me another half-a-crown a week rise straight away'.

Delivering the Coal

There was only two ways for Coal to leave the Pit, one was by road and the other by rail. We have not been able to find out in the time available exactly where the railway coal went. It was a good house and steam raising coal and would have found a ready market in Bristol's extensive industries, most of which, it is easy to forget were steam powered! Bristol's gas works would probably have provided a good market too. After the closure of the rail connected Yate No's 1 and 2 pits in 1886, Frog Lane (and Parkfield) would have been the nearest collieries to the rail served markets as far north as Gloucester (where Welsh and Forest of Dean Coal would start to have advantage) and to the east along the GWR Main line at least as far as Reading. Welsh coal would probably have been cheaper but this advantage may have been partially countered by the GWR's charges for the extra mileage.

Mr Noad's horse and cart delivering coal.   *courtesy Mr Noad*

The other way that coal got delivered was by horse and cart. It's difficult for us to imagine these days where electricity, gas and oil are so freely available (so far!), piped to our houses, but in the 1930s and 40s all heating and most cooking would have been done by coal and it was not unusual to keep a fire in all year. So lots of coal was used and if you had your own horse and cart like Jeff Sheppard's father who farmed Mayshill Farm, you would go down and collect what you needed.

If you did not have your own horse and cart, it would be delivered by the coal merchant. One of the well known local ones was William George Noad whose coal yard was at Winterbourne Station.

Pit Sights and Sounds

Unfortunately the sights and sounds of the pit cannot be recreated but some of our oral history interviewees can recall them:

'Where I lived round mum and dad if they heard that winding wheel which was about 2 miles away they said "it's going to rain". Of course that meant that the wind was blowing in a westerly direction'. *Sid Horder*

'Before the miners came along the lane we heard this shish foo shish foo with the winding engine and they eventually had a pit hooter and they sounded the hooter as well'.
Jeff Shepherd

'We could tell when the pit started pumping the water out and that was done regularly at 4 o'clock in the afternoon and of course if we were anywhere near the brook we could look over and say "Oh look it's 4 o'clock, the brooks pumping"'.
Jeff Shepherd

Local Characters Remembered

Many of our interviewees have strong memories of local characters, not all of them miners, here's a sample:

'My impressions of Yate in the twenties, I used to see lots of people walking about with a wooden leg, wooden legs and hook arms from the First War and often you would see somebody on the road, we used to call them "tramps" and they were always old people, old men mostly. You never saw any young men and there were quite a few characters in the area. One in particular his name was Brendan Blacker, he was quite a good character. I can remember on one occasion he was on his horse and he rode up to the Railway Hotel at Yate and rode his horse into the bar, ordered his drink, sat on the horse and drank his drink and off he went again. The kindest man he was'. *Sid Horder*

'You could go round here and on a Sunday go for a walk and the main walk was to go to Bitterwell after church, go down there and back. And the families used to go, sometimes you didn't get there you'd meet so many people and you'd stop talking that you wouldn't get there; we used to go down, mainly, down Bitterwell to see Tarzan, old Skuse, I forget his name now. He used to have his leopard skin and all, he used to wear his leopard skin and he used to live in the tree down there did Tarzan and people used to go down there every Sunday to see Tarzan'.
Interviewer: 'Who was he exactly?'
'Bernard Skuse was a local chap. His father drove the wheel, the engine at the pit, to let us up and down. People went down there regular to see him. He was down there years, he used to swing from the trees, swing from the branches and all down

there. He was good'.
Interviewer: Did he not work down the mines either as well as everyone then?
I don't think he worked anywhere, he was just Tarzan and that was it. His father used to drive the wheel. He had quite a few relatives, his brother was a tattooist down Eastville, Les Skuse, used to do tattoos on people down Eastvillle. I've got a tape here somewhere of Tarzan when he went down Somerset living and he married a schoolteacher from a grammar school. And he was in his canoe and had his dog and all on there going up the river. Quite a character he was. Yes, quite a character'.
Fred Woodruff

'I expect you've heard about the Bunting brothers, no, George Bunting, what was his brother's name and they lived together in the first council house up in Woodside Road real characters.
Interviewer: Were they miners?
'Oh yes, but they didn't talk to one another, they lived together and if one did go out and he'd lit the fire he'd put the fire out before he went out. They were characters you know, but as I say they were the salt of the earth. His brother's name was "Pretty" Bunting, I don't ever know why they called him "Pretty" Bunting'. *Stuart Ovens*

Jeff Shepherd remembers Albert Stone:

'Now next door there was a family called Stone and next door to the pub was a blacksmith's shop and Uncle Albert was a blacksmith, so if there was any trouble in the Half Moon, "send for Uncle Albert". Uncle Albert used to chuck them out. Of course they always had to give him a pint and if he had to chuck out more than one, that was two pints'.

Francis Eames, apparently taken in the same occasion as the picture in the railway chapter circa 1930. *courtesy FCLHS*

We don't know if it is a miners cottage but its such a superb image we wanted an excuse to include it. The house was just off the Badminton Road in Kendleshire.

Dorothy Hewitt, courtesy Anne Maston

LIVING IN A MINING COMMUNITY
FAMILY LIFE
by Kathyrn Sherrington

We have heard a lot about the men in the community and we know that work underground could be hard and dangerous. What also comes out from our oral history interviews is that life for the ladies was hard too – and without respite.

Basic Housing

Standards of living for most Frog Lane miners and their families were low and would remain so until well after 1949. Accommodation for mining families, was often owned by the colliery company, while other homes belonged to the Lords of the Manor of Westerleigh. Floors were normally bare and very cold, while some families made mats from rags and old clothes, creating make-shift carpets to walk on. Stan Williams of Coalpit Heath was born in 1928 and remembers his mother's floor coverings; rags sewn together in beautiful patterns to make floor mats.

Housing: Jean Blacker, 1930, a Frog Lane miner's daughter remembers the cottage she grew up:

'A little two up two down cottage. As you opened the front door you was straight into the front room. Beyond that you had a little small kitchen big black, open range fire place and that and beyond this was the lean to with the copper boiler'.

Water and Lighting: Another miner's daughter Margaret Curtis recalls standards of living were also very different to what we are used to today:

"We had no electricity and we had no running water, we had a pump outside… and my mother used to send the water twice a year to the university, have it analysed to make sure it was clean and pure to drink".

Phyllis Taylor remembers getting water from a garden well:

'It was a nice house, nice garden, a lovely garden and it had a well. A lovely well where you drew water with a bucket which I used to draw for my aunt; and it was beautiful to drink, lovely and cold, icy, and it never went dry, beautiful'.

Houses would be lit by burning paraffin. According to Margaret Curtis:

'We had a man come every week with the paraffin so you had to be careful not to burn out too much, with the cooking as well'.

The Powell family – a mining family living in Henfield c.1907.

courtesy FC&DLHS

Make do and Mend: Women would often sit beneath oil lamps or candles at their sewing machines altering clothes. Stan Williams remembers his mother being a wonderful seamstress, taking apart old clothes and making new trousers from the material for children around the village.

Hilda Winter-Alsop, born in the 1920s at Coalpit Heath notes:

'When I got a little bit older, crazy on knitting, you should see my things I've got knitted in there. He [husband] made some needles, we didn't buy any needles, we got the steel and done them off at the ends and put a cork on one end for me but that sometimes it used to drive him crazy at night. He used to say "For God's sake put those clattering needles down" because the needles just used to make a noise you know'.

Coal Heating: Coal fires would keep houses warm. For miners, coal was free. Stan Williams told us:

'By the time I left school I had father and three brothers all working at Coalpit Heath coal mine at the same time. I used to dread coming home from school and seeing about 1 ton of coal on the pavement outside of my home as the mine had no pit head baths and the miners were given an allowance of coal for the purpose of washing after a day working at the pit. It was my job to carry all the coal into the shed'.

Local people were proud of the quality of coal from Frog Lane:

'It had gold veins, it burnt lovely, it was so clean and so shiny, lovely coal' recalls Audrey Dyer.
Ann Moulsdale remembers her mother recognising poorer quality coal:
'She always used to know if it came from the Forest of Dean, she used to say "That's Forest coal", she always knew it'.

Holding Things Together: The woman's role

While the men were working hard in the pits, at ground level women were working equally hard to maintain the home. They also had to ensure that the workers were washed and fed and that the children were taken care of. Sid Horder remembers his mother sending him to work down the pit:

'My mother wrapped my sandwiches up in a newspaper, as they did in those days'.

Washday: For women, washing was particularly hard work. With no electricity a whole day each week was dedicated to washing, a physically demanding job. Margaret Curtis recalls her mother's washday every Monday:

'Mother used to keep all the rubbish to burn to get the water to boil and do her washing outside…Monday's was out for everything else it was washday… she had a scrubbing board and a big stick to push the washing down in the boiler'.

Staying Clean: Most homes did not enjoy a bathroom as we do now. Baths were made of tin and filled from wells, water pumps or butts. Toilets usually consisted of basic privies at the far end of the garden; one person we have spoken to remembers cycling to the farthest point in the garden to go to the toilet!

Miners would return home after their shifts and wash in tin baths in front of the fire. Without electricity, heating bath water was a big job. Families tended to bathe once a week, sharing the job of carrying buckets of water heated by the copper boiler and using them to fill the bath – time consuming work! Stan

Williams was one of four brothers who worked in Frog Lane with their father. Stan remembers bath time in their home being reminiscent of a production line!

Dinner on the Table: Men would return from work to hot baths and home cooked food, and as they worked hard to earn money is was generally understood that drinking, smoking and 'talking mining' were acceptable social behaviour, whether it be in the local pub or whilst drinking pints of cider in front of the fire at home.

Women, in the meantime, would be ensuring that the house was clean, tidy and as warm as possible, and that hot food was readily available for the workers. Given the never-ending work, large families were often considered a blessing; male offspring could work in the pits and provide the family with extra income and female offspring provided additional labour around the home.

Stan Williams, based on his mother's example, believes women to have been extremely hard working; *'women's place was at home – and they knew it!'*. He remembers men seeming to work hard and play hard, yet women's work seemed to be endless. Sid Horder reflects the same sentiment when thinking about how hard his mother worked:

'She had two brothers and I was only four when we left Yorkshire and I can remember she brought the four of us down on the train from Yorkshire on her own. Aren't you girls wonderful. How she ever managed it I don't know. My youngest sister she was in her arms and I suppose at the age of four I was toddling along, oh dear'.

Grow your Own

The general ethos of the time was to make the best of what was available, especially regarding food. Bob Williams, born in 1940 remembers home-baking as prevalent:

'There was a lot of baking done in the village then, people use to bake a lot at home and everything was grown in the garden in the season so you had potatoes, green beans, broad beans, radishes, cucumbers, marrows, everything you could think of. When it was in season you had it fresh'.

Many interviewees continue to grow their own vegetables today.

It seems that men tended to take care of the gardens, many being quite large. 'Living off the land' was the common philosophy and so hard work was not restricted to inside the home. Phyllis Taylor remembers her grandparents garden:

'They had fruit trees; he had the lot, blackberries, raspberries, loganberries, peach, plums and six kinds of different apple tree which you don't ever see now. He [grandfather] grew his own potatoes and everything and he used to do all that gardening when he came back from the pit. Yes, they were tough in those days but it was lovely and I used to enjoy it very much'.

As well as growing food, many families kept animals: *'Nearly everybody had a pigsty'* recalls Fred Woodruff and, as Audrey Dyer remembers: *'Of course everybody had a greenhouse where they grew their tomatoes and things like that'* and surplus produce would be shared or exchanged with neighbours to avoid waste.

Others were more crafty when it came to obtaining food. Sid Horder remembers some of the local characters:

'One in particular, if he was short of food he'd go down Yate Market and he'd look for a pen with some chickens in it. He'd grab one and kill it, he'd go round until he's found who it belonged to and say "Look, there's a dead chicken in your pen, do you want me to take it out for you"? "Yes" and that was their dinner when he got home. Oh yes, they were very cunning years ago, they had to be to survive, it wasn't easy one little bit'.

Coalpit Heath Community Spirit

The people we have spoken to have presented us with a real sense of community. There was a traditional village sentiment in which people achieved a sense of belonging by knowing those around them and by supporting the local area, whether that be through business or living off what the area had to offer.

Shopping: Without cars, local amenities were crucial. Local shops supplied villagers with everything they needed whilst supporting the village ideal of knowing one another. Maurice Ovens owned the local butcher shop, whilst Happy Tovey and Gladys Bateman's shop on the main road sold papers, tobacco and other 'bits and pieces'. Other memorable shops included a local cobblers – Smart's boot shop; Frankcombes the greengrocers; Kate Davies' shop where she sold sugar and such like, sold loose in little blue bags and, of course, the Co-op.

Ann Moulsdale, born 1930s recalls the exchange of money at the Co-op;

'That used to fascinate me, they used to put the money in a thing on a wire that would go across the shop to an office, and back it used to come'.

Rather than being pre-packed items would be cut to measure; Audrey Dyer born in the 1920s recalls:

'Nothing was packed in those days, they used to cut it, the cheese with a wire and the butter with a wire, it was all done up so neat'.

A Mining Childhood

Many children growing up before the 1950s had few restrictions governing where they played. In Coalpit Heath, the mining landscape was also a wonderful playground. Although most children had little or no disposable income, they had ample opportunity to play out.

As children, the people we have interviewed recall having a great deal of freedom. Many people remember playing on the railway line and riding in coal trucks. Bob Williams born in 1940 recalls: *'We used to play up and down the line backwards and forwards to the Coalpit Heath Pit until they closed it, on bogies. We shouldn't have done but it's a wonder I never had a broken leg'.*

Phyllis Taylor, also born in the 1920s, notes a country childhood:

'We always used to go up to the iron mine and play up there. It was quite adventuresome crawling through all these pipes. And we used to go round primrosing we didn't go round stabbing people and getting into mischief and doing horrible things. We used to find our own amusement and I was always keen on horse riding and of course we used to walk a lot and I had a bicycle.

We had plenty of fresh air. And my mother when she was alive was a great one for nature. She used to take me on my bicycle all over to Iron Acton all round the lanes and tell me all the names of the different birds and things ... and then we used to go down to the River Frome here and have picnics, lots of school children did that in the summer holidays, we used to go there and have picnics by the river, you know, and they used to swim in the River Frome as well'

Children of Industry: The industrial aspects of the surrounding environment proved both curious and enticing for local children. Slag heaps were a common sight. Frog Lane slag heap was quite

Happy and Gladys Tovey's shop on corner of Boundary road, c.1951.

courtesy FC&DLHS

Understood to be one of the local schools around 1900.

courtesy FC&DLHS

big and attracted attention from local children. Bob Williams, born 1940, remembers throwing tiles down the open shafts and counting the seconds before the tile splashed in the water below. Bob recalls the sense of freedom:

'We most went anywhere … most of the older people would talk to you, tell you things; if you asked the question they would tell you. There was no restrictions at all really; we were told there was a mine shaft, you don't get near it. In those days a lot of the mine shafts were still open. The actual things, although they had been in disuse for God knows how many years, they were still open shafts'.

Don Crew remembers playing on slag heaps as a boy:

'Yes we used to get up on the back of the tip so that no one could see us because there were trees there. We used to slide down there on a piece of galvanised tin'.

We asked Don if he and his friends were ever caught and told off:

'Well they would have done but it was when the shift had ended and there was no one around and all the coal was gone we used to get down there and slide down on the tip'.

Jeff Sheppard of Mayshill Farm also recalls playing near old mine workings: '

'The other ones [mine shafts] further along to Nibley which were not sealed when I was a boy, we used to go and play down there, and you could actually look down. It was overgrown with shrubbery and whatever but I remember a friend of mine, we were playing around there, and somebody had been dumping rubbish and the entrance was on a slope like that and across, and then it was on a drop; and he saw a hammer head down there so he thought he'd go down, kid-like, to get this hammer head. Of course the rubbish started moving, going down, so I grabbed the kid by the coat tails and dragged him back out, otherwise he would have gone down the mine. We used to call the place "double stiles" because there was two stiles over the little stream down the bottom right by the old pits. Like I say they were really quite dangerous. When the Coal Board took over they went round and sealed all these pits'.

Trust: Most of the people we have interviewed describe a reliance on local children to simply 'be sensible'. Whilst there were places that children were expected to stay away from, areas were not necessarily fenced off or segregated in any way. There was an element of trust that children would stay out of trouble and harms way whilst out playing.

Nevertheless, there was still mischief to be had as Bob Williams notes:

'Kids used to come up from school (to the Ring O'Bells) and they used to drink this damn cider which was neat and anyway the headmaster, Mr Coombes, came up and said that they'd have to stop giving them the cider 'cos they were going back to school and messing themselves. It was a good clearer out so they said…I don't know how they drunk the stuff because it was bloomin' horrible'.

Audrey Dyer remembers a trip down the mine, organised by pit manager and ARP member Mr Sage. Audrey remembers going down in the cage:

'It was queer really because it was a bit rocky, there was nothing firm about it at all, I just think you went down on ropes I think. It swayed from place to place until you got to the bottom with a bump I wasn't nervous it was just the fact that I'd got all this water dripping over me and wondered where it was coming from, so why that was I don't know. Mr. Skuse he was, I don't know what they called him, he did wind the cage up and down'.

The Miners' Institute played an important role for children as well as adults. Fred Drew remembers going to:

'... shows in there years ago when I was a kid, concerts and stuff like that, you know. Then the war came and they turfed everything out and put in the boilers for making food for the kids. Nowadays you don't get the shows like you used to: the comedy groups going round, the shows and concerts and things like that now it's all finished and gone. That was in the day when there was no televisions. You used to get a show down there and you thought that was brilliant to go and see a show down there or a magic lantern show, you remember the magic lantern with slides in?

We went to one, one night and we thought it was a marvellous thing after reading all about the tricks of the trade and to see it. They had one down there which was a bloke catching a bullet in his teeth, I'd never forgot that I, thought it was marvellous you know, brilliant, what a con job that was... Talk about con, oh dear oh dear, course when you think of it now it was blasted impossible, blew his head off'.

LIVING IN A MINING COMMUNITY
RELIGION, SPORT & LEISURE
by Sarah Morris and David Hardill

As you might expect, in the immediate pre and post war period, the pattern of life around Coalpit Heath was different from today. Whilst we all tend to see our past with nostalgia, it is clear from our interviewees accounts that life was harder, simpler and that the community was more close knit. What is easily forgotten is that cars were few and far between, everyone tended to work nearer to home and so inevitably people would see more of each other.

Many of our interviewees were brought up in the period immediately after the depression when work and money were extremely tight. They also lived through the Second World War, when there was a real threat from air raids and older relatives risked being killed or injured on active service. It's worth remembering too, that in the immediate post war period Britain was effectively bankrupt, rationing continued until 1953 and there was a general emphasis on 'getting the country back on its feet'.

The following section on church and chapel, sport and the local pubs provides some views of how the local people spent their time when not at work or home during this period.

CHURCH AND CHAPEL

Miners have a traditional association with non conformism. The Coalpit Heath miners were no exception and the chapels in the area were mostly built over the nineteenth century and continued to be an integral part of local life into the twentieth. Sunday was a day of rest taken up by the morning or evening services, and Sunday school for children in the afternoon. Life was influenced by religious traditions and the many activities available for congregations provided a social focus point for the village.

Origins of churches and chapels in the area: The non-conformist movement emerged from dissent with the Church of England, and became particularly strong in the late eighteenth and early nineteenth centuries. Nonconformists, who believed in a strong work ethic, were involved in creating industries in southern Gloucestershire: exploiting the mineral wealth of the area. Handel Cossham, a mine owner, was also a local preacher. Evangelicals later felt called to bring the gospel to the workers living in these new industrial areas described as 'heathen wastes'. Their success resulted in various chapels being built. Zion chapel was the first, built in 1795 to provide for the spiritual needs of the colliers and hatters of Frampton Cotterell and Coalpit Heath. Sunday Schools were then established nearby. A Wesleyan chapel was built on Church Road in Frampton in 1821 to meet local demand, then Bethel chapel, (free Methodist) was built on Woodend Road in 1851 followed by Hebron Chapel on the Ridgeway, in 1887. The Salvation Army church was built in 1882 and a Gospel Hall was set up by Christian Brethren in 1928.

Coalpit Heath's Anglican Church began in similar circumstances. The Coalpit Heath Colliery Company were concerned about miners drinking, the area being 'proverbial for vice and irreligion'! To counteract this, William Hewitt, the Colliery Bailiff (Manager and agent) collected money from residents of Westerleigh to build St. Saviour's church in the village in 1845 on land donated by the Colliery owners.

Some mining families did attend church. However most people say the area was predominantly chapel and the number of chapels built in relation to churches would support this idea. Jeff Shepherd concurs:

'They [the miners] were nearly all chapel. There were some church Anglicans but they were mostly chapel and there were three or four chapels in Coalpit Heath'.

For some it depended on family history and personal connections:

'We used to go to chapel, that was one thing we had to do. Not church, it had to be chapel because mum was a chapel person'
Hilda Winter-Alsop

Services and traditions at church and chapel were quite different. Chapel attendees liked to be involved in the services: singing lustily so there was no need for a choir. They viewed the chapel as more down to earth and democratic than the Anglican church. Margaret Curtis experienced services at both church and chapel and suggested:

'It was more laid back at chapel than what it was going to church. The children enjoyed the chapel more so than they enjoyed going to church because it was a bit "high" for them'.

Temperance was another important feature of life for chapel people.

Politics was one aspect of life where church and chapel people held strong and varying views. In the late 1800s there were some disturbances about who would be elected to local positions of authority, with non-conformists challenging the traditional control the Church of England had over these positions. By the twentieth century, these differences created little personal animosity. People mostly had respect for others' beliefs, and

St. Saviours Church circa 1906.

Dorothy Hewitt, courtesy Ann Matson

Zion Chapel.

courtesy FC&DLHS

would sometimes get together for joint events as Ann Moulsdale recalls:

'Everybody tolerated the fact that they were Baptists or Methodists and we were church. I mean, when it came to our Sunday school sports day everybody mixed and then they started an Eisteddfod … between the chapels and the churches and they used to have poetry and singing and all that type of thing, and that went on for years'.

Attendance: For many people, attending church or chapel with their family on a Sunday was a weekly tradition, so both were always pretty full. Many enjoyed the services and the music:

'I was in the choir for 20 years, yes I was in the choir, our mother made I go mostly. I enjoyed it, I was confirmed, I used to carry the banner around and the proudest moment of our mothers life was…when I got confirmed by the Bishop and we had the bread and wine'. *Frank Thornell*

Margaret Curtis enjoyed attending different church classes and services:

'They used to have Sunday School in the school, and then we went to church once a month and I was also in the Bible Class as well. We'd have our Bible Class in the belfry in Coalpit Heath Church'.

For some this may have seemed like a big commitment. Hilda Winter-Alsop remembers attending Sunday School in the afternoon then having to return for an evening service too. Some children resisted, preferring to spend their time on other activities. Don Crew suggests girls were expected to attend more than boys were: *'There was no pressure on me to go. I think there was a bit of pressure on my sister to go, but not on the boys, no.'*
And not all miners attended regularly:

'I don't think they [the miners] were really all that keen on church, theirs was the pigeon flying and the gardening, that was what they were more interested in than anything else… [it was more] The wives and children'. *Margaret Curtis*

Social activities: In some ways, church and chapel can be seen as a focal point for mining families. The many activities organised by different churches and chapels were a major part of village social life: from days out to Weston, to May Queen processions, to chapel anniversaries. Such events were a chance to enjoy time off with friends. Audrey Dyer remembers running off with the choir boys after church as a child! Church and chapel attendance was wrapped up in the life of the village and congregations would have known each other well. Ted Blacker describes how the chapel pastor knew his parishioners:

'Lewis used to do the sermon but it was all the subjects what were going on locally. Somebody was ill, somebody would die and he'd sort of discuss their life and things like that'.

Jeff Shepherd had a long association with St. Saviour's Scout group, both as a boy then later as a leader:

'I was in the First Coalpit Heath Boy Scouts and they were all miners' sons… The first patrol leader, Frank Hughes, is still

First Frampton Cotterell Scouts and Cubs in 1968. *courtesy FC&DLHS*

alive he's 85 or 6 and he still lives in the village. So we had a troop of about 28 boys: they were all miners' sons and I got on with them very well indeed… I went to many camps in Devon… we also had at weekends to go to Ford near Castle Combe. There was nine of us used to go and it really was a wonderful experience'.

Music was an important part of church and chapel life. Don Crew's brother and sister sang at Hebron chapel, and Frank Thornell sang in St. Saviour's Glee Men:

'I was in the Glee Men once and I had a good voice course to be in the Glee Men. I didn't know what I was like. Didn't know if I was a baritone, never heard of it'.

An important date for chapel attendees was the anniversary of when each one was built. The chapel would be packed at anniversary time and everyone would turn out in their best for the occasion: *'Only time of the year I got a new dress when it was anniversaries, got a bonnet'*. Jean Blacker

Another chapel celebration was the May Queen procession. Hilda Winter-Alsop remembers one at the Wesleyan chapel:

'All the way up was an avenue of trees and it was red May trees and golden chain and we were given permission to pick some of the golden chain and we had to fill baskets with blossom; and me and my friend, we were dressed in dresses and that, it was a pageant They had a Queen and she had to walk down and we had to walk backwards spreading these for the Queen to walk on… That was a fun day for us, it was really fun'.

The churches also had celebrations such as the flower festival.

Perhaps the most important social event of the year was the Sunday School outing to Weston super Mare. For many this was their one holiday and children in particular loved their trip to the seaside by train or charabanc, to play on the beach and visit the pier. At St. Saviour's church, participation depended on your weekly donation towards the trip, while Ted Blacker describes keeping up his attendance to ensure he went with the chapel:

'My luxury was a day out with the chapel down to Weston on a Sunday and that was once a year and that was it… every Sunday you got a text, a coloured text, a religious text, and you had to qualify with so many and if you didn't have those number of texts you couldn't apply for the trip to Weston. If you wanted to go to Weston you had to go to Chapel'.

Religion in daily life: The way people lived their lives was often governed by rules inherited from church teaching, or practices which developed into traditions over the years. Sunday was an enforced day of rest with its own particular activities. Ann Moulsdale was not allowed to play with friends on a Sunday, and Fred Woodruff suggests you shouldn't even clean a pair of shoes! Jeff Shepherd was dressed up and taken to pay social calls:

'After church we used to have to go to an old lady, a miner's widow, named Mrs. Moseley. We used to sit there with her daughter and mother and a couple of old ladies, and we'd sit round and one small miserable bored boy used to have to sit there for about an hour listening to these ladies talk'.

Ann Moulsdale and Audrey Dyer still don't wash clothes on Good Friday:

'Never do the washing on a Good Friday… I wouldn't now, they say you wash blood out of the family. It's very old fashioned… I think that's because our grandmothers didn't do it and our mothers didn't do it, so we don't do it'.

Yate Sunday School charabanc trip to Weston-super-Mare.

courtesy Y&DHC

Decline of church and chapel?: At first the new arrivals to the area after World War Two swelled the numbers attending church and chapels. However attendance started to decline from the 1940s, to the extent that the Salvation Army closed in the 1950s, and three of the chapels were pulled down in the 1960s, as Fred Woodruff describes:

'There were a lot of chapels about here then. There was the Wesleyan, he's gone. Hebron Chapel, that's gone. Bethel Chapel that's gone. There's only one chapel left round here now and that's Zion, the big chapel on top of the hill'.

The Gospel hall closed in 1976.

St. Peter's Church in Frampton, Zion Chapel and St. Saviour's are still going strong, and continue to be valued by those who worship there.

A contempory view of St. Saviours.

A SPORTING LIFE

The strong camaraderie and tight knit community spirit of Coalpit Heath ensured a thriving social life. Football and cricket were the sports of choice from the 19th century. Animals and garden produce were a source of great pride for Frog Lane miners.

Football in the winter and cricket in the summer months were easily the most popular sports. Miners seldom mentioned rugby and tennis, although a Coalpit Heath tennis team had existed. Both football and cricket could be played either in the street or a nearby grassy area. Children could improvise balls and goals or bats and wickets. Don Crew noted that in the 1940s:

'We used to play football with a pig's bladder because there was no [ball] From the farm, they used to kill on the farm in them days (to get the pig's bladder), and the cricket bat was made out of a plank of wood shaped to a cricket bat and the ball was a ball of rags 'cos there was no proper ball'.

Football and cricket teams featured heavily with miners around Coalpit Heath. It was competitive as Fred Woodruff noted:

'Oh I played football and cricket. Cricket for Coalpit Heath. I was President of Coalpit Heath Cricket Club for 3 or 4 years….. Oh yes. At that time we used to play in the village knock-out. I've got a cup there somewhere, but we won the village knock-out. We used to play all over the place, go down Somerset, up Gloucester, Forest Green'.

Gardening and pigeons were hugely popular within the mining community. Most miners had big gardens and depended on growing some of their food or exchanging produce for other items. As Bob Williams (born in 1940) recalls:

'I think that's what miners did more or less, it was pigeons and gardening. That was their hobbies really I think they were glad to be out of the darkness. So that's why they took to pigeons and gardening. It was freedom for them after they'd been down in the dark all the time, wasn't it'.

Cricket in front of the Manor School.

courtesy FC&DLHS

Miner's Welfare Football Team 1948.   *courtesy Frank Thornell*

Pigeon Racing was also enormously popular with the mining fraternity … and almost a full time hobby!:

'A lot of people kept pigeons as well, they used to race pigeons, that's something else that's gone, but that was quite a thing, pigeon fanciers they called them. They used to take these pigeons all over the place. I can remember when I first started at Coalpit Heath Station, pigeons would come in the baskets and we used to have to release them and fill out the time when we released them and send that off and then they would see how long it took them to get back from wherever they were going to. There was a lot of that. The railways used to carry phenomenal amounts of pigeons so it was quite a big thing that was, especially in the Coalpit Heath area and I think in Yate and everywhere else, everybody had a pigeon loft'. *Bob Williams*

Miners also took advantage of their surroundings for enjoyment. It was very much a rural existence away from the pit. Frank Thornell (born 1933) recalls local families:

'They had a dog, they had ferrets and they kept pigeons. That was their hobby, because they'd go rabbiting, you know catching rabbits, which I used to as well. And we had a dog for ferreting, there was hundreds of rabbits about years ago. Everybody had that years ago look. Everybody round here'.

Other miners took advantage of the local surroundings including Bitterwell Lake. Angling was popular here. Margaret Curtis (born 1941) notes:

'Apart from Bitterwell Lake, they used to drain it twice a year to clean it out, did you know that, and drain it over into where the hole is now, over that bank there to clean it out and make sure it was all clean. Then they used to re-stock with fish again after they re-flooded it'.

Bitterwell was initially used for swimming by many in the area. According to Fred Woodruff:

'Yes, they had those buildings down there and they were the changing rooms, the 2 big huts at the bottom. The women's was on the right and the men was on the left. That was proper changing rooms, they had diving board an' all down Bitterwell. They had a big diving board down the bottom end, lovely spring-board too, they used to dive over in there. Oh a lot of swimming done down Bitterwell all the summer down Bitterwell swimming'.

PUBS, SMOKING AND DRINKING

The pub, and from 1927, the Miners' Institute, were at the heart of mining life in Coalpit Heath. There had always been places for drinking, smoking and socialising for men but the pub was more than a mere drinking den. It was a focus for local business and a base for local clubs. The Miner's Institute provided amenities unavailable elsewhere in Coalpit Heath.

Even before Frog Lane Colliery opened in 1853, miners had a good choice of pubs and beer houses for such a small population. The Ring O' Bells and Half Moon were already well established. They offered a place to socialise and relax. The pub remained central to local miners. *'The Ring O'Bells was the main pub and that was where they used to take their cocks and their birds to be checked. That was the main miners one, the Ring O'Bells for the miners'.* Ted Blacker, North Road 1920s.

A 'macho' culture prevailed in the pubs. Men only! As Stan Williams (born 1928) recalls:

'You had big families, you used to boast about the size of your family – I've got four, you've got five, this went on a lot … No women in there. Men wanted to sit down and discuss mining. A woman's place was in the home.'

A Terrible Neighbourhood?: Before 1845, Coalpit Heath had acquired a doubtful reputation for drunkenness. It was described as a 'mining district near to Bristol, proverbial for vice and irreligion'. (FC&DLHS)

The reputation of the area gradually improved and during the early 20th century drinking remained part of the culture. Pubs and beer houses peppered the area. Drinking went hand in hand with mining! Yate miners travelling to Frog Lane in the

Coalpit Heath Cricket Six, 1972 – a determined looking Frank Thornell bottom left, Pete Seaman bottom right.   *courtesy Frank Thornell*

Ring O'Bells c.1910. *courtesy FC&DLHS*

1930s, received drinks at the Swan at Nibley, as Sid Horder of Frog Lane Colliery in the 1930s notes:

'They used to walk to the coal mine at Coalpit Heath, the landlord of the Swan at Nibley, his name was Dick Griffiths, he used to stand outside at half past five in a morning and any coal miner who walked by, if he wanted a drink he could have one. He could empty his can of tea, or whatever he had in his can and Dick Griffiths would fill it up with cider or whatever he wanted'.

Heavy drinking was part and parcel of life for many!

'They'd come out of the pubs three steps forwards and six steps back, there was lots of that. There wasn't fighting, well occasionally you'd get people fighting, but by and large they were merry drunk if you know what I mean, not fighting drunk. You'd get exceptions to the rule obviously but you'd see them about and they'd be trying to get on and ride their bikes. It was just comical really I suppose you would say'. *Bob Williams, Coalpit Heath 1940s*

What were people drinking?: Beer and 'Scrumpy' were the norm. Before World War II, cheap cider was the most common drink of all.

'There was lots of cider, because they had the apples and that there to do it with. Beer became more popular with George's beer coming in during the 1940s. There was still the cider drinkers though. They used to go into the pub, order a pint of cider and they'd stick a poker in the fire and they'd mull it. They'd stick the red hot poker into the cider and they'd drink it. They reckon it was good for curing colds.
   Out the back there was a cider house and when I was a kid they used to press the cider. Bill Blackmore's son who lives in America, I went out to see him, and he was telling me, I can remember making the cider to get the apples from the orchard and it went through like a mincer and they put it into like sacking, fold it all up and they put bars in it was like a big press and forced the cider out into like a big stone trough and that went down into barrels basically and then it was kept for about six months to mature'. *Bob Williams, landlord's son Ring O' Bells, 1940s.*

The Miners' Institute on Badminton Road became a central part of the community. The Institute began in 1927, and provided miners with a purpose built community hall. Workers paid six old pence from their weekly wages (Trevor Thompson) for sports and social facilities. Evening concerts and a bar gave Coalpit Heath a taste of the high life.

'They had the Miners' (Club) and that went on later on the Miners' when they had it up there. It was the Miners', always been the Miners' up there but they used to have a canteen like up there, you could have the milk and that years ago, and they had showers for when you played football down here. They had tennis courts and all up there'. *Frank Thornell, Coalpit Heath 1930s*

Smoking as well as drinking, was part of mining culture. Nearly all men smoked cigarettes, pipes or took snuff. They even smoked down the mine! Frank Thornell who moved from Frog Lane to work at Harry Stoke describes the difference:

'But at Harry Stoke, they had the same seams of coal like Coalpit Heath. Some of them did have a smoke see, which they weren't supposed to do, well there was no gas in there like. If you got caught smoking you'd get the sack. Well I've gone down there before now and what they used to do, was they used to put a couple of matches in the rim of your hat and then put one fag down your sock'.

Half Moon c.1968 *courtesy Roy Close*

Star Inn c.1902 *courtesy FC&DLHS*

The production area at Newmans Motors of Yate in the 1950s. The working environment here was vastly different to what the miners would have been previously used to. *courtesy Y&DHC*

COALPIT HEATH
SINCE 1949
by Sarah Morris

Coalpit Heath today is different in many ways to the village it was when Frog Lane was producing coal. This is partly due to changes to society in general, but the village has also been shaped by its mining heritage. How has Coal Pit Heath coped with the loss of the mine?

The end of mining at Frog lane

The closure of the pit had a big emotional impact on residents. Some found it hard to accept. Many believed there was good coal still underground. Ann Moulsdale was one resident who was shocked by the closure:

'They reckon there's as much coal left down in drams and things, any amount of coal was left down there…Other people might know better than me but one minute everything seemed to be going alright and the next minute they seemed to be closing it'.

It was the end of familiar sights and sounds such as miners walking together across the fields to the mine for their shift, and fathers coming home to a daily bath by the fire.

Employment: One major impact on the families of Coal pit Heath was the need for mine workers to look for other jobs. Some had mined all their lives and couldn't imagine anything else, as Audrey Dyer suggests:

'Lots of fathers and sons and grandsons went down there …and when you got older after what could you do. Mines closed and you weren't educated for anything else so what could you do?'

Some took up the offer of a position at Pensford colliery, and later at Harry Stoke as Frank Britton describes:

'They went to Pensford a lot of them. Several of the miners anyway, about a coach load did go away every morning. We all had chance if we wanted to go, they put our name down if we wanted to go to Pensford but I thought to myself I'd rather not go now and do all that travelling about on coaches'.

Others had to retrain for another profession. Ex miners have worked as farm labourers, surveyors, gas board engineers, many went to the Parnall's or Newman's motor factories in Yate, which was better paid than mining. Many later started to commute to Filton to work for BAE and Rolls-Royce. Don Crew's father evidently found it hard to adjust to life after mining, working in various different places:

'When he finished at Frog Lane he went working in the MOD place… Then he left there and he went down to Harry Stoke drilling further on the drilling with his Uncle, and then he left there and went in Parnalls and he finished there working on the assembly line'.

However he, like the rest of the miners, was pragmatic about the closure of the mine. Mine workers retrained and took what jobs they could to provide for their families.

Nowadays most residents commute to work in Bristol, the Filton factories or local business parks.

Community Life: In the 1950s many newcomers moved to the area and the village has continued to grow since then. Some older people who remember mining days miss the closeness of a small village where everyone was involved in the lives of their neighbours. Phyllis Taylor misses this friendliness and support:

'Everybody knew everybody else. It's not like it is today, I mean there are people here who I couldn't tell you their names

The Williams Brothers – Eddy, Jack, Colin, Ivor and Stan – all ex Frog Lane Miners, Coalpit Heath, 1950.
courtesy Stan Williams

and they never even speak…It's sad really, and it's not being nosey but everybody used to help one another'.

This is only one point of view, however. Audrey Dyer has friends in the village who support her and still share home grown produce:

'I'll tell you who grows the best kidney beans in Coalpit Heath. Stuart Ovens, they're straight and honestly you could draw a line with them where they are so straight they're lovely, and Heather his wife she always comes down with some'.

Many residents view the area as friendly and sociable and are engaged in the life of the village. Coalpit Heath is a peaceful and safe place, surrounded by beautiful countryside and within reach of larger towns. As Fred Drew says: *This is home really, you don't get any hassle or problems'.*

Social activities: The community used to be very much defined by mining work and miner's hobbies such as growing vegetables and pigeon racing. Though these became less popular, some village social activities have continued. The football and cricket clubs were always taken very seriously. Various groups and clubs still meet in the halls of Coalpit Heath. Phyllis Taylor is a member of local societies near Frampton Cotterell:

'They have got a Flower Arranging Society in Winterbourne but I belong to the Horticultural Society which is Winterbourne Down, not Winterbourne; and I also belong to the Theatre Club which is down at the Community Centre'.

There is not so much entertainment in the area for young people, but children are involved in school events and projects.

Egg and spoon race at the primary school fete, 2008.

St. Saviours bell ringers, 1953. *courtesy FC&DLHS*

The Miner's Institute still serves an important social role for ex miners who retain strong bonds and enjoy talking about the past and sharing memories.

'Yes I go in there on a Tuesday... I drop down and see, we'll probably Colin Dando he's a relation of mine, a distant relation, and we have a chat about old times, a laugh and a couple of pints and that. I go down there once a week like because I still like to feel a part of the community'. *Don Crew*

Church and chapel attendance has declined over the years and many of the chapels closed down in the 1960s:

'But then of course the chapels were gradually – well the only one that's left now is Zion they all went bit by bit which was a shame really'. *Ann Moulsdale*

However congregations enjoy worshipping at St. Peter's Church in Frampton Cotterell, Zion United Church and the thriving St. Saviour's in Coalpit Heath which organises social activities including a popular summer fayre. Bell ringing continues at the church today.

Services: Local shops and services in Coalpit Heath have dwindled since 1949, a picture which is shared by most British villages due to changing ways of life. Families in the village used to have bread, milk and meat delivered to the door, and there was a good range of stores in the village, as well as the much valued Co-operative. Some good facilities remain such as the Post Office, newsagents, minimarket and hairdressers, though many people choose to travel to larger supermarkets. Ann Moulsdale remarks on the closure of independent retailers:

'We go to Staple Hill to an old butchers over there don't we? The old fashioned one by the school, Haines I think is his name, just off the crossroads... We go over there now because there's no butcher left in the village. Stuart retired, Alan retired, Price retired'.

The railway station was dismantled under Beeching, and bus services have always been infrequent as Audrey Dyer explains: *'We have got a bus service but it's every 2 hours'.*

There are still local pubs frequented by villages, however Don Crew feels the style of service has changed:

'Well most of the pubs they were tenants and now they're all managed pubs, it's not the same. They don't greet you and you don't have the rapport and the laughs and that... I still go down there to 'The Live and Let Live' that's about all, I don't go anywhere else because there's people in there, one or two, that know me and we chat about old times'.

Landscape: Coalpit Heath looks very different in some ways from the mining village it used to be. There have been various periods of development up till recent times. The sixties saw

Coalpit Heath Post Office.   *courtesy Andy Brander*

older cottages pulled down and open spaces filled in to join together outlying hamlets as part of the village. Many mining families moved into new houses. This was followed by new roads and later builds such as the large recent development at Park Farm. This has allowed new families to move into and enjoy the area, but a regular comment from villagers who have lived in the village all their lives, is that they miss the fields and open spaces. Frank Britton recalls the fields where he used to hunt rabbits:

'I was a lurcher man see and I did come home from the pit, I had my lurchers, I had my dogs I used to go rabbiting every day me and the dogs just where I'm living now. I've killed dozens of rabbits just here. This used to be a market garden here, all up through here … Mr. Francombe had a big piece here, old man Nicholls had a big piece here and Nelson they had a big piece here … There used to be a pond down there, I knowed every ounce of ground in this area'.

Andy Brander agrees but suggests some areas have been smartened up:

'The odd small pockets of green are being filled in with houses; big gardens lost and a house built. Some of the old eyesores have been replaced with nice housing though, so that is good. I always feel that we under threat of another green field being given away to housing and that worries me'.

The local landscape continues to carry reminders of Coalpit Heath's mining heritage: the slag heap at Frog Lane which remained until 1984, the impressive remains at Ram Hill including the shaft, steam engine house and horse gin, and the dramway which is now a popular walk and cycleway. There have been recent investigations into mining history and archaeology with projects at different sites in the area. Such projects remind locals of the area's history. Ted and Jean Blacker found investigations on their land at North Road exciting: '*They came here and did a dig in the garden, it was quite amusing really*'.

Recent housing development.

courtesy Andy Brander

Above: Two views of the Miner's Institute at Coalpit Heath taken early in 2009. The Institute is still widely used by the community and ex Frog Lane men. *courtesy Andy Brander*

The South Gloucestershire Mines Research Group are doing a lot of recording work on the remains of the coalfield and its collieries. Here Andy Brander is seen digging at Serridge whilst Di Grudgings and Pete Hemmings look on!

INFORMATION & SOURCES

Information and Reference Sources

We want to provide full details of all of our information sources and this final section is intended to identify these as a basis for helping others wishing to do further research.

Sources of Text

The main sources of text have been the transcription of the oral history interviewees themselves . The original recordings and transcripts can be accessed via the Yate & District Heritage Centre. We have reproduced these materials with the approval of the interviewees themselves. The original recordings and their transcripts are held at the Y&DHC and can be consulted by arrangement with them.

Other text from external sources has been referenced within each chapter.

Sources of Photographs

We have been fortunate to have access to a wide range of photographs to choose from:

1. The main source of photographs have been the images taken by J. C. Burrow (the famous photographer of underground scenes in Cornish Mines) at Frog Lane. These are understood to have been in early May 1906 together with those taken at the same time by Dorothy Hewitt, daughter of the Colliery Bailiff and Agent.

These photographs have been loaned to the SGMRG with approval to reproduce them in our own publications by Anne Matson and Family. Ann kindly contacted me as a result of my appeal for information on Radio Bristol in November 2008 and after visiting Ann we were overwhelmed by the number and quality of the images. Some of the Burrows ones and all of the Hewitt ones being new to us. As this booklet goes to press work is continuing to catalogue and identify these images which deserve a separate publication in their own right.

2. The English Heritage, National Monuments Record (NMR) at Swindon have granted permission to reproduce the six George Watkins images of steam engines at Frog Lane and Mayshill. George Watkins was a Bristol based steam engine enthusiast, active from the 1930s, whose passion was to photograph steam engines and relate plant in their original location. There are additional images of engines at both collieries in the Watkins collection that we have not used, as well as photographs of other local steam plant at New Engine and Parkfield Pits. The Watkins collection and George's supporting notes can be consulted by arrangement with the NMR.

3. The Frampton Cotterell & District Local History Society (FC&DLHS) have kindly given us permission to reproduce a wide range of images of the area.

4. A number of local people and the oral history interviewees themselves have kindly loaned us photographic and other materials and these are gratefully credited accordingly.

5. Unless otherwise noted, all other photographs are from the SGMRG archives.

Sources of Maps and Documents

1. Many of the maps and documents we used have come from the extensive archives of the Bristol Records Office (BRO) and these are credited and referenced accordingly. The bulk of the Frog Lane maps fall in the 39398 reference series which numbers in excess of 100. The BRO also holds the Ashton Court Papers from which much of the pre 1800 materials were sourced. We are grateful for the continually helpful attitude of the BRO to our requests to access and reproduce their materials.

2. The Gloucestershire Archive kindly granted permission for us to reproduce the 1865 Colliery Accounts.

3. All other maps and documents are from the SGMRG archive.

Additional locations, known to contain Frog Lane related material but not used on this occasion:

1. The Coal Authority at Mansfield also hold a wide range of maps for Frog Lane and the earlier pits, only one has been used in this publication.

2. The Northumberland Records Office hold the Archives of the North of England Institute of Mining Engineers (NEIME).

3. The Somerset Records Office also hold materials on Frog Lane.

Areas where we need additional information:

We are always keen to be notified of additional images, information and artefacts, the main gaps being:

1. Any photographs of or information on Mayshill or Nibley Collieries.

2. Any pictures of the railway.

3. Any information about the customers of Frog Lanes Coal.

4. Any records or accounts of the colliery during the nineteenth century.

If you can help, please contact me at 31, Laverstoke Lane, Laverstoke, Whitchurch, Hants RG28 7NY or via SGMRG.com

THE BOOK ®

Citroën Xsara
Service and Repair Manual

John S. Mead

Models covered

(3751 - 448 - 5AH1)

Citroën Xsara Coupé, Hatchback and Estate models with petrol and diesel engines, including special/limited editions

1.4 litre (1360cc), 1.6 litre (1587cc), 1.8 litre (1761cc) and 2.0 litre (1998cc) petrol engines
1.9 litre (1868cc), 1.9 litre (1905cc) and 2.0 litre (1997cc) diesel and turbo diesel engines

Does not cover 2.0i, 16v VTS Coupé model, or Picasso

© Haynes Publishing 2004

A book in the **Haynes Service and Repair Manual Series**

ABCDE
FGHIJ
K

ISBN **978 0 85733 628 6**

British Library Cataloguing in Publication Data
A catalogue record for this book is available from the British Library.

Printed in the USA

Haynes Publishing
Sparkford, Yeovil, Somerset BA22 7JJ, England

Haynes North America, Inc
861 Lawrence Drive, Newbury Park, California 91320, USA

Haynes Publishing Nordiska AB
Box 1504, 751 45 UPPSALA, Sweden

Contents

LIVING WITH YOUR CITROËN XSARA

Safety first!	Page	**0•5**
Introduction to the Citroën Xsara	Page	**0•6**

Roadside repairs

If your car won't start	Page	**0•7**
Jump starting	Page	**0•8**
Wheel changing	Page	**0•9**
Identifying leaks	Page	**0•10**
Towing	Page	**0•10**

Weekly checks

Introduction	Page	**0•11**
Underbonnet check points	Page	**0•11**
Engine oil level	Page	**0•13**
Power steering fluid level	Page	**0•13**
Coolant level	Page	**0•14**
Screen washer fluid level	Page	**0•14**
Brake fluid level	Page	**0•15**
Wiper blades	Page	**0•15**
Tyre condition and pressure	Page	**0•16**
Battery	Page	**0•17**
Electrical systems	Page	**0•17**

Lubricants and fluids

	Page	**0•18**

Tyre pressures

	Page	**0•19**

MAINTENANCE

Routine maintenance and servicing

Citroën Xsara petrol engine models	Page	**1A•1**
Servicing specifications	Page	**1A•2**
Maintenance schedule	Page	**1A•6**
Maintenance procedures	Page	**1A•7**
Citroën Xsara diesel engine models	Page	**1B•1**
Servicing specifications	Page	**1B•2**
Maintenance schedule	Page	**1B•6**
Maintenance procedures	Page	**1B•7**

Contents

REPAIRS AND OVERHAUL

Engine and Associated Systems

TU series petrol engine in-car repair procedures   Page   2A•1

XU series petrol engine in-car repair procedures   Page   2B•1

XUD series diesel engine in-car repair procedures   Page   2C•1

DW series diesel engine in-car repair procedures   Page   2D•1

Petrol engine removal and overhaul procedures   Page   2E•1

Diesel engine removal and overhaul procedures   Page   2F•1

Cooling, heating and ventilation systems   Page   3•1

Fuel/exhaust systems – petrol engines   Page   4A•1

Fuel/exhaust systems – 1.9 litre diesel engines   Page   4B•1

Fuel/exhaust systems – 2.0 litre diesel engines   Page   4C•1

Emission control systems   Page   4D•1

Starting and charging systems   Page   5A•1

Ignition system (petrol engines)   Page   5B•1

Preheating system (diesel engines)   Page   5C•1

Transmission

Clutch   Page   6•1

Manual transmission   Page   7A•1

Automatic transmission   Page   7B•1

Driveshafts   Page   8•1

Brakes, Suspension and Steering

Braking system   Page   9•1

Suspension and steering   Page   10•1

Body Equipment

Bodywork and fittings   Page   11•1

Body electrical systems   Page   12•1

Wiring diagrams   Page   12•21

REFERENCE

Dimensions and weights   Page   REF•1

Conversion factors   Page   REF•2

Buying spare parts   Page   REF•3

Vehicle identification   Page   REF•3

General repair procedures   Page   REF•4

Jacking and vehicle support   Page   REF•5

Disconnecting the battery   Page   REF•6

Tools and working facilities   Page   REF•7

MOT test checks   Page   REF•9

Fault finding   Page   REF•13

Glossary of technical terms   Page   REF•21

Index

Index   Page   REF•26

Many people see the words 'advanced driving' and believe that it won't interest them or that it is a style of driving beyond their own abilities. Nothing could be further from the truth. Advanced driving is straightforward safe, sensible driving - the sort of driving we should all do every time we get behind the wheel.

An average of 10 people are killed every day on UK roads and 870 more are injured, some seriously. Lives are ruined daily, usually because somebody did something stupid. Something like 95% of all accidents are due to human error, mostly driver failure. Sometimes we make genuine mistakes - everyone does. Sometimes we have lapses of concentration. Sometimes we deliberately take risks.

For many people, the process of 'learning to drive' doesn't go much further than learning how to pass the driving test because of a common belief that good drivers are made by 'experience'.

Learning to drive by 'experience' teaches three driving skills:

☐ Quick reactions. (Whoops, that was close!)
☐ Good handling skills. (Horn, swerve, brake, horn).
☐ Reliance on vehicle technology. (Great stuff this ABS, stop in no distance even in the wet...)

Drivers whose skills are 'experience based' generally have a lot of near misses and the odd accident. The results can be seen every day in our courts and our hospital casualty departments.

Advanced drivers have learnt to control the risks by controlling the position and speed of their vehicle. They avoid accidents and near misses, even if the drivers around them make mistakes.

The key skills of advanced driving are **concentration,** effective all-round **observation, anticipation** and **planning.** When **good vehicle handling** is added to these skills, all driving situations can be approached and negotiated in a safe, methodical way, leaving nothing to chance.

Concentration means applying your mind to safe driving, completely excluding anything that's not relevant. Driving is usually the most dangerous activity that most of us undertake in our daily routines. It deserves our full attention.

Observation means not just looking, but seeing and seeking out the information found in the driving environment.

Anticipation means asking yourself what is happening, what you can reasonably expect to happen and what could happen unexpectedly. (One of the commonest words used in compiling accident reports is 'suddenly'.)

Planning is the link between seeing something and taking the appropriate action. For many drivers, planning is the missing link.

If you want to become a safer and more skilful driver and you want to enjoy your driving more, contact the Institute of Advanced Motorists at www.iam.org.uk, phone 0208 996 9600, or write to IAM House, 510 Chiswick High Road, London W4 5RG for an information pack.

Working on your car can be dangerous. This page shows just some of the potential risks and hazards, with the aim of creating a safety-conscious attitude.

General hazards

Scalding

• Don't remove the radiator or expansion tank cap while the engine is hot.
• Engine oil, automatic transmission fluid or power steering fluid may also be dangerously hot if the engine has recently been running.

Burning

• Beware of burns from the exhaust system and from any part of the engine. Brake discs and drums can also be extremely hot immediately after use.

Crushing

• When working under or near a raised vehicle, always supplement the jack with axle stands, or use drive-on ramps. *Never venture under a car which is only supported by a jack.*
• Take care if loosening or tightening high-torque nuts when the vehicle is on stands. Initial loosening and final tightening should be done with the wheels on the ground.

Fire

• Fuel is highly flammable; fuel vapour is explosive.
• Don't let fuel spill onto a hot engine.
• Do not smoke or allow naked lights (including pilot lights) anywhere near a vehicle being worked on. Also beware of creating sparks
(electrically or by use of tools).
• Fuel vapour is heavier than air, so don't work on the fuel system with the vehicle over an inspection pit.
• Another cause of fire is an electrical overload or short-circuit. Take care when repairing or modifying the vehicle wiring.
• Keep a fire extinguisher handy, of a type suitable for use on fuel and electrical fires.

Electric shock

• Ignition HT voltage can be dangerous, especially to people with heart problems or a pacemaker. Don't work on or near the ignition system with the engine running or the ignition switched on.

• Mains voltage is also dangerous. Make sure that any mains-operated equipment is correctly earthed. Mains power points should be protected by a residual current device (RCD) circuit breaker.

Fume or gas intoxication

• Exhaust fumes are poisonous; they often contain carbon monoxide, which is rapidly fatal if inhaled. Never run the engine in a confined space such as a garage with the doors shut.
• Fuel vapour is also poisonous, as are the vapours from some cleaning solvents and paint thinners.

Poisonous or irritant substances

• Avoid skin contact with battery acid and with any fuel, fluid or lubricant, especially antifreeze, brake hydraulic fluid and Diesel fuel. Don't syphon them by mouth. If such a substance is swallowed or gets into the eyes, seek medical advice.
• Prolonged contact with used engine oil can cause skin cancer. Wear gloves or use a barrier cream if necessary. Change out of oil-soaked clothes and do not keep oily rags in your pocket.
• Air conditioning refrigerant forms a poisonous gas if exposed to a naked flame (including a cigarette). It can also cause skin burns on contact.

Asbestos

• Asbestos dust can cause cancer if inhaled or swallowed. Asbestos may be found in gaskets and in brake and clutch linings. When dealing with such components it is safest to assume that they contain asbestos.

Special hazards

Hydrofluoric acid

• This extremely corrosive acid is formed when certain types of synthetic rubber, found in some O-rings, oil seals, fuel hoses etc, are exposed to temperatures above 400°C. The rubber changes into a charred or sticky substance containing the acid. *Once formed, the acid remains dangerous for years. If it gets onto the skin, it may be necessary to amputate the limb concerned.*
• When dealing with a vehicle which has suffered a fire, or with components salvaged from such a vehicle, wear protective gloves and discard them after use.

The battery

• Batteries contain sulphuric acid, which attacks clothing, eyes and skin. Take care when topping-up or carrying the battery.
• The hydrogen gas given off by the battery is highly explosive. Never cause a spark or allow a naked light nearby. Be careful when connecting and disconnecting battery chargers or jump leads.

Air bags

• Air bags can cause injury if they go off accidentally. Take care when removing the steering wheel and/or facia. Special storage instructions may apply.

Diesel injection equipment

• Diesel injection pumps supply fuel at very high pressure. Take care when working on the fuel injectors and fuel pipes.

⚠️ *Warning: Never expose the hands, face or any other part of the body to injector spray; the fuel can penetrate the skin with potentially fatal results.*

Remember...

DO

• Do use eye protection when using power tools, and when working under the vehicle.

• Do wear gloves or use barrier cream to protect your hands when necessary.

• Do get someone to check periodically that all is well when working alone on the vehicle.

• Do keep loose clothing and long hair well out of the way of moving mechanical parts.

• Do remove rings, wristwatch etc, before working on the vehicle – especially the electrical system.

• Do ensure that any lifting or jacking equipment has a safe working load rating adequate for the job.

DON'T

• Don't attempt to lift a heavy component which may be beyond your capability – get assistance.

• Don't rush to finish a job, or take unverified short cuts.

• Don't use ill-fitting tools which may slip and cause injury.

• Don't leave tools or parts lying around where someone can trip over them. Mop up oil and fuel spills at once.

• Don't allow children or pets to play in or near a vehicle being worked on.

The Citroën Xsara range was launched in five-door Hatchback form in the Autumn of 1997 as a replacement for the Citroën ZX. Originally, the Xsara was available with various engine options, depending on model and country of export. The initial engine line-up included 1.4 litre (1360cc), 1.6 litre (1587cc) and 1.8 litre (1761cc) petrol engines, and 1.9 litre (1905cc) diesel and turbo diesel engines.

In early 1998 the Xsara range was further enhanced by the addition of a three-door Coupé model, followed soon after by an Estate model. Further developments and improvements to the existing engines continued, mainly in the area of emission control to meet increasingly stringent European legislation.

In 1999 a new 1.9 litre (1868cc) diesel engine was introduced to replace the existing 1.9 litre non-turbo unit, and a 2.0 litre (1998cc) 16-valve petrol engine also became available for certain export countries.

For the 2000 model year another all new turbocharged diesel engine was introduced, this being the 2.0 litre (1997cc) high pressure diesel injection (HDi) unit.

All engines are derived from the well-proven TU and XU series petrol engines, and XUD series diesel engines, which have appeared in many Citroën and Peugeot vehicles (the DW series diesel engine is essentially an XUD unit with revised cylinder head). The engines are all of four-cylinder single- or double-overhead camshaft design, mounted transversely at the front of the car, with the transmission mounted on the left-hand side. All models have a five-speed manual transmission with the option of a four-speed automatic transmission on certain petrol engines.

All models have fully-independent front suspension. The rear suspension is semi-independent, with torsion bars and trailing arms.

A wide range of standard and optional equipment is available within the Xsara range to suit most tastes, including power steering, central locking, engine immobiliser, electric windows, electric sunroof, and air bags. An anti-lock braking system and air conditioning system are available as options, or standard equipment on certain models.

Provided that regular servicing is carried out in accordance with the manufacturer's recommendations, the Citroën Xsara should prove reliable and very economical. The engine compartment is well-designed, and most of the items requiring frequent attention are easily accessible.

Your Citroën Xsara Manual

The aim of this manual is to help you get the best value from your vehicle. It can do so in several ways. It can help you decide what work must be done (even should you choose to get it done by a garage), provide information on routine maintenance and servicing, and give a logical course of action and diagnosis when random faults occur. However, it is hoped that you will use the manual by tackling the work yourself. On simpler jobs it may even be quicker than booking the car into a garage and going there twice, to leave and collect it. Perhaps most important, a lot of money can be saved by avoiding the costs a garage must charge to cover its labour and overheads.

The manual has drawings and descriptions to show the function of the various components so that their layout can be understood. Tasks are described and photographed in a clear step-by-step sequence.

References to the 'left-hand' and 'right-hand' sides of the vehicle are always in the sense of when viewed by a person sat in the driver's seat, facing forwards.

Acknowledgements

Thanks are due to Draper Tools Limited, who provided some of the workshop tools, and to all those people at Sparkford who helped in the production of this Manual.

We take great pride in the accuracy of information given in this manual, but vehicle manufacturers make alterations and design changes during the production run of a particular vehicle of which they do not inform us. No liability can be accepted by the authors or publishers for loss, damage or injury caused by errors in, or omissions from, the information given.

Citroen Xsara 1.8 VTR Coupé

Citroen Xsara 2.0 HDi

Citroen Xsara Estate

The following pages are intended to help in dealing with common roadside emergencies and breakdowns. You will find more detailed fault finding information at the back of the manual, and repair information in the main chapters.

If your car won't start and the starter motor doesn't turn

- [ ] If it's a model with automatic transmission, make sure the selector is in P or N.
- [ ] Open the bonnet and make sure that the battery terminals are clean and tight.
- [ ] Switch on the headlights and try to start the engine. If the headlights go very dim when you're trying to start, the battery is probably flat. Get out of trouble by jump starting (see next page) using a friend's car.

If your car won't start even though the starter motor turns as normal

- [ ] Is there fuel in the tank?
- [ ] Is there moisture on electrical components under the bonnet? Switch off the ignition, then wipe off any obvious dampness with a dry cloth. Spray a water-repellent aerosol product (WD-40 or equivalent) on ignition and fuel system electrical connectors like those shown in the photos. Pay special attention to the ignition coil wiring connector and HT leads. (Note that Diesel engines don't normally suffer from damp.)

A Check that the spark plug HT leads (where applicable) are securely connected by pushing them home.

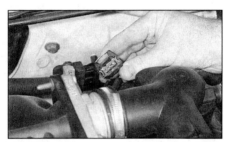

B The throttle potentiometer wiring plug may cause problems if not connected securely.

C Check the ECU multi-plug for security with the ignition switched off.

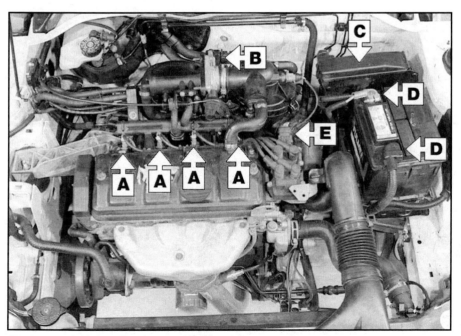

Check that electrical connections are secure (with the ignition switched off) and spray them with a water-dispersant spray like WD-40 if you suspect a problem due to damp.

D Check the security and condition of the battery connections.

E Check that the ignition coil wiring plug is secure, and spray with water-dispersant if necessary.

Jump starting

When jump-starting a car using a booster battery, observe the following precautions:

✔ Before connecting the booster battery, make sure that the ignition is switched off.

✔ Ensure that all electrical equipment (lights, heater, wipers, etc) is switched off.

✔ Take note of any special precautions printed on the battery case.

✔ Make sure that the booster battery is the same voltage as the discharged one in the vehicle.

✔ If the battery is being jump-started from the battery in another vehicle, the two vehicles MUST NOT TOUCH each other.

✔ Make sure that the transmission is in neutral (or PARK, in the case of automatic transmission).

Jump starting will get you out of trouble, but you must correct whatever made the battery go flat in the first place. There are three possibilities:

1 The battery has been drained by repeated attempts to start, or by leaving the lights on.

2 The charging system is not working properly (alternator drivebelt slack or broken, alternator wiring fault or alternator itself faulty).

3 The battery itself is at fault (electrolyte low, or battery worn out).

1 Connect one end of the red jump lead to the positive (+) terminal of the flat battery

2 Connect the other end of the red lead to the positive (+) terminal of the booster battery.

3 Connect one end of the black jump lead to the negative (-) terminal of the booster battery

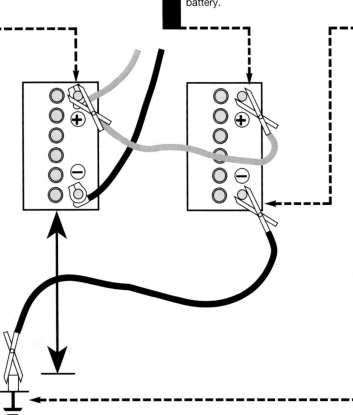

4 Connect the other end of the black jump lead to a bolt or bracket on the engine block, well away from the battery, on the vehicle to be started.

5 Make sure that the jump leads will not come into contact with the fan, drive-belts or other moving parts of the engine.

6 Start the engine using the booster battery and run it at idle speed. Switch on the lights, rear window demister and heater blower motor, then disconnect the jump leads in the reverse order of connection. Turn off the lights etc.

Wheel changing

Some of the details shown here will vary according to model. For instance, the location of the spare wheel and jack is not the same on all cars. However, the basic principles apply to all vehicles.

Warning: Do not change a wheel in a situation where you risk being hit by other traffic. On busy roads, try to stop in a lay-by or a gateway. Be wary of passing traffic while changing the wheel – it is easy to become distracted by the job in hand.

Preparation

☐ When a puncture occurs, stop as soon as it is safe to do so.
☐ Park on firm level ground, if possible, and well out of the way of other traffic.
☐ Use hazard warning lights if necessary.

☐ If you have one, use a warning triangle to alert other drivers of your presence.
☐ Apply the handbrake and engage first or reverse gear.
☐ Chock the wheel diagonally opposite the

one being removed – a chock is supplied as part of the car's tool kit.
☐ If the ground is soft, use a flat piece of wood to spread the load under the foot of the jack.

Changing the wheel

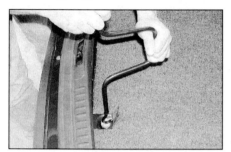

1 From inside the boot area, use the wheelbrace to lower the spare wheel cradle.

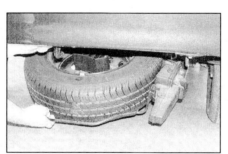

2 Slide the spare wheel and tool kit out from the underside of the car.

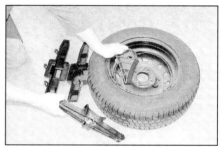

3 Open the box and take out the jack. Use the chock supplied to chock the wheel diagonally opposite the one being removed.

4 Slacken each wheel bolt by a half turn.

5 Locate the jack below the reinforced jacking point and on firm ground (don't jack the car at any other point on the sill).

6 Turn the jack handle clockwise until the wheel is raised clear of the ground, remove the bolts and wheel trim, then lift the wheel clear.

7 Position the spare wheel and the wheel trim, then fit the bolts.

8 Note that the tyre valve symbol (on the inside of the wheel trim) must be positioned adjacent to the tyre valve on the wheel. Tighten the bolts moderately with the wheelbrace, then lower the car to the ground. Tighten the wheel bolts in a diagonal sequence, then secure the punctured wheel in the spare wheel cradle.

Finally...

☐ Remove the wheel chocks. Stow the jack and tools in the appropriate locations in the car.
☐ Don't leave the spare wheel cradle empty and unsecured – it could drop onto the ground while the car is moving.
☐ Check the tyre pressure on the wheel just fitted. If it is low, or if you don't have a pressure gauge with you, drive slowly to the nearest garage and inflate the tyre to the correct pressure. Have the damaged tyre or wheel repaired, or renew it, as soon as possible.

Identifying leaks

Puddles on the garage floor or drive, or obvious wetness under the bonnet or underneath the car, suggest a leak that needs investigating. It can sometimes be difficult to decide where the leak is coming from, especially if the engine bay is very dirty already. Leaking oil or fluid can also be blown rearwards by the passage of air under the car, giving a false impression of where the problem lies.

 Warning: Most automotive oils and fluids are poisonous. Wash them off skin, and change out of contaminated clothing, without delay.

 The smell of a fluid leaking from the car may provide a clue to what's leaking. Some fluids are distinctively coloured. It may help to clean the car carefully and to park it over some clean paper overnight as an aid to locating the source of the leak.
Remember that some leaks may only occur while the engine is running.

Sump oil

Engine oil may leak from the drain plug...

Oil from filter

...or from the base of the oil filter.

Gearbox oil

Gearbox oil can leak from the seals at the inboard ends of the driveshafts.

Antifreeze

Leaking antifreeze often leaves a crystalline deposit like this.

Brake fluid

A leak occurring at a wheel is almost certainly brake fluid.

Power steering fluid

Power steering fluid may leak from the pipe connectors on the steering rack.

Towing

When all else fails, you may find yourself having to get a tow home – or of course you may be helping somebody else. Long-distance recovery should only be done by a garage or breakdown service. For shorter distances, DIY towing using another car is easy enough, but observe the following points:

☐ Use a proper tow-rope – they are not expensive. The vehicle being towed must display an ON TOW sign in its rear window.
☐ Always turn the ignition key to the 'on' position when the vehicle is being towed, so that the steering lock is released, and that the direction indicator and brake lights will work.

☐ Only attach the tow-rope to the towing eye provided. This can be found in the luggage compartment next to the wheelbrace, and is screwed into the front or rear towing locations on the body, as required. Use the wheelbrace to screw the towing eye firmly into place.
☐ Before being towed, release the handbrake and select neutral on the transmission.
☐ On models with automatic transmission, if towing with the wheels on the ground, special precautions apply. An additional 1.0 litre of the specified automatic transmission fluid must be added to the transmission before towing. The towing speed must be limited to 30 mph (48 kph) and the distance must not exceed 30 miles (48 km). On completion, the transmission fluid level must be returned to

the normal amount. If in doubt, do not tow, or transmission damage may result.
☐ Note that greater-than-usual pedal pressure will be required to operate the brakes, since the vacuum servo unit is only operational with the engine running.
☐ Greater-than-usual steering effort will also be required.
☐ The driver of the car being towed must keep the tow-rope taut at all times to avoid snatching.
☐ Make sure that both drivers know the route before setting off.
☐ Only drive at moderate speeds and keep the distance towed to a minimum. Drive smoothly and allow plenty of time for slowing down at junctions.

Introduction

There are some very simple checks which need only take a few minutes to carry out, but which could save you a lot of inconvenience and expense.

These 'Weekly checks' require no great skill or special tools, and the small amount of time they take to perform could prove to be very well spent, for example;

☐ Keeping an eye on tyre condition and pressures, will not only help to stop them wearing out prematurely, but could also save your life.

☐ Many breakdowns are caused by electrical problems. Battery-related faults are particularly common, and a quick check on a regular basis will often prevent the majority of these.

☐ If your car develops a brake fluid leak, the first time you might know about it is when your brakes don't work properly. Checking the level regularly will give advance warning of this kind of problem.

☐ If the oil or coolant levels run low, the cost of repairing any engine damage will be far greater than fixing the leak, for example.

Underbonnet check points

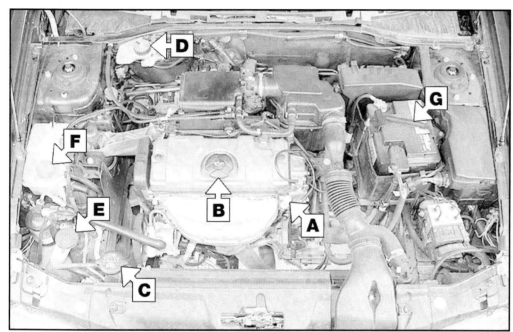

◀ 1.4 and 1.6 litre petrol

A *Engine oil level dipstick*

B *Engine oil filler cap*

C *Coolant expansion tank*

D *Brake fluid reservoir*

E *Screen washer fluid reservoir*

F *Power steering fluid reservoir*

G *Battery*

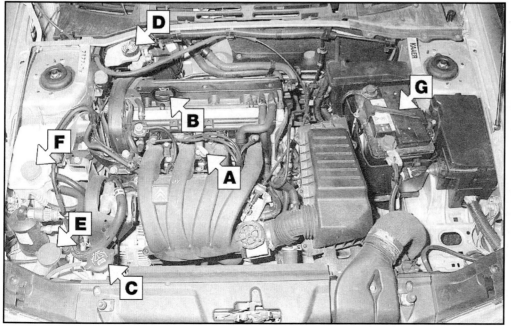

◀ 1.8 and 2.0 litre (16-valve) petrol

A *Engine oil level dipstick*

B *Engine oil filler cap*

C *Coolant expansion tank*

D *Brake fluid reservoir*

E *Screen washer fluid reservoir*

F *Power steering fluid reservoir*

G *Battery*

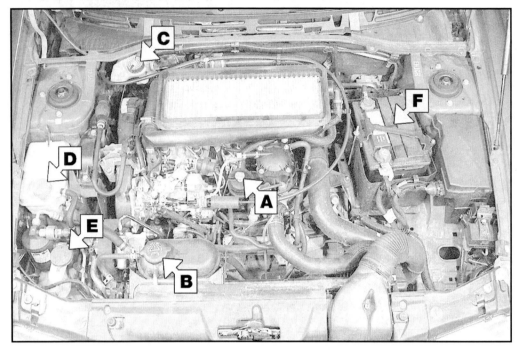

◀ 1.9 litre turbo diesel

A Engine oil level dipstick and filler cap

B Coolant expansion tank

C Brake fluid reservoir

D Power steering fluid reservoir

E Screen washer fluid reservoir

F Battery

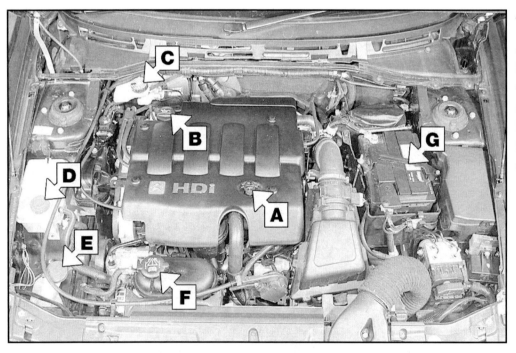

◀ 2.0 litre diesel

A Engine oil level dipstick

B Engine oil filler cap

C Brake fluid reservoir

D Power steering fluid reservoir

E Screen washer fluid reservoir

F Coolant expansion tank

G Battery

Engine oil level

Before you start
✔ Make sure that your car is on level ground.
✔ Check the oil level before the car is driven, or at least 5 minutes after the engine has been switched off.

 HAYNES HiNT *If the oil is checked immediately after driving the vehicle, some of the oil will remain in the upper engine components, resulting in an inaccurate reading on the dipstick.*

The correct oil
Modern engines place great demands on their oil. It is very important that the correct oil for your car is used (See 'Lubricants and fluids').

Car Care
● If you have to add oil frequently, you should check whether you have any oil leaks. Place some clean paper under the car overnight, and check for stains in the morning. If there are no leaks, the engine may be burning oil .

● Always maintain the level between the upper and lower dipstick marks (see photo 3). If the level is too low severe engine damage may occur. Oil seal failure may result if the engine is overfilled by adding too much oil.

1 The dipstick is often brightly coloured for easy identification. Withdraw the dipstick.

2 Using a clean rag or paper towel, wipe all the oil from the dipstick. Insert the clean dipstick into the tube as far as it will go, then withdraw it again.

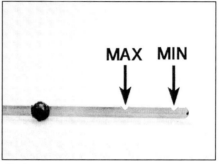
3 Note the oil level on the end of the dipstick, which should be between the upper (MAX) mark and lower (MIN) mark. Approximately 1.25 litres of oil will raise the level from the lower mark to the upper mark.

4 Oil is added through the filler cap. Unscrew the cap and top up the level; a funnel may help to reduce spillage. Add the oil slowly, checking the level on the dipstick often. Don't overfill (see *Car Care*).

Power steering fluid level

Before you start
✔ Park the vehicle on level ground.
✔ Set the steering wheel straight-ahead.
✔ The engine should be turned off.

 HAYNES HiNT *For the check to be accurate, the steering must not be turned once the engine has been stopped.*

Safety First!
● The need for frequent topping-up indicates a leak, which should be investigated immediately.

1 The power steering fluid reservoir is located on the right-hand side of the engine compartment. The fluid level should be checked with the engine stopped. A translucent reservoir is fitted, with MAX and MIN markings on the side of the reservoir.

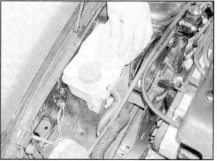
2 The fluid level should be between the MAX and MIN marks. If topping-up is necessary, and before removing the cap, wipe the surrounding area so that dirt does not enter the reservoir.

3 Unscrew the cap, allowing the fluid to drain from the bottom of the cap as it is removed. Top up the fluid level to the MAX mark, using the specified type of fluid (do not overfill the reservoir), then refit and tighten the filler cap.

Coolant level

Warning: DO NOT attempt to remove the expansion tank pressure cap when the engine is hot, as there is a very great risk of scalding. Do not leave open containers of coolant about, as it is poisonous.

Car Care

● Adding coolant should not be necessary on a regular basis. If frequent topping-up is required, it is likely there is a leak. Check the radiator, all hoses and joint faces for signs of staining or wetness, and rectify as necessary.

● It is important that antifreeze is used in the cooling system all year round, not just during the winter months. Don't top-up with water alone, as the antifreeze will become too diluted.

1 The coolant level varies with engine temperature. The level is checked in the expansion tank, which is built into the side of the radiator on petrol engine models. When the engine is cold, the coolant level should be between the MAXI and MINI marks.

2 On diesel engine models, the expansion tank is located at the front of the engine compartment, and the level can only be checked by removing the expansion tank cap (see next step). The coolant level is correct when it is just below the MAXI mark indicated on the side of the tank.

3 If topping-up is necessary, **wait until the engine is cold** then turn the expansion tank cap slowly anti-clockwise, and pause until any pressure remaining in the system is released. Unscrew the cap and lift off.

4 Add a mixture of water and antifreeze to the expansion tank, until the coolant level is up to the MAXI level mark. Refit the cap, turning it clockwise as far as it will go until it is secure.

Screen washer fluid level

Screenwash additives not only keep the windscreen clean during foul weather, they also prevent the washer system freezing in cold weather – which is when you are likely to need it most. Don't top up using plain water as the screenwash will become too diluted, and will freeze during cold weather. *On no account use coolant antifreeze in the washer system – this could discolour or damage paintwork.*

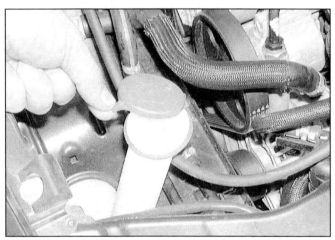

1 The windscreen/tailgate washer fluid reservoir is located at the right-hand side of the engine compartment. If topping-up is necessary, open the cap.

2 When topping-up the reservoir, a screenwash additive should be added in the quantities recommended on the bottle.

Brake fluid level

Warning:
● Brake fluid can harm your eyes and damage painted surfaces, so use extreme caution when handling and pouring it.
● Do not use fluid that has been standing open for some time, as it absorbs moisture from the air, which can cause a dangerous loss of braking effectiveness.

HAYNES HiNT
● Make sure that your car is on level ground.
● The fluid level in the reservoir will drop slightly as the brake pads wear down, but the fluid level must never be allowed to drop below the 'MIN' mark.

Safety First!
● If the reservoir requires repeated topping-up this is an indication of a fluid leak somewhere in the system, which should be investigated immediately.

● If a leak is suspected, the car should not be driven until the braking system has been checked. Never take any risks where brakes are concerned.

1 The MAX and MIN marks are indicated on the side of the reservoir, which is located on the front of the vacuum servo unit in the engine compartment. The fluid level must be kept between these two marks.

2 If topping-up is necessary, first wipe the area around the filler cap with a clean rag before removing the cap. When adding fluid, it's a good idea to inspect the reservoir. The system should be drained and refilled if dirt is seen in the fluid (see Chapter 9).

3 Carefully add fluid, avoiding spilling it on surrounding paintwork. Use only the specified hydraulic fluid; mixing different types of fluid can cause damage to the system and/or a loss of braking effectiveness. After filling to the correct level, refit the cap securely and wipe off any spilt fluid.

Wiper blades

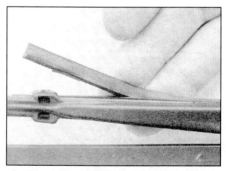

1 Check the condition of the wiper blades; if they are cracked or show any signs of deterioration, or if the glass swept area is smeared, renew them. Wiper blades should be renewed annually.

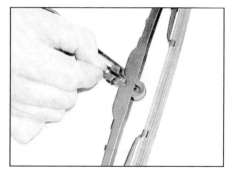

2 To remove a windscreen wiper blade, pull the arm fully away from the screen until it locks. Swivel the blade through 90°, then depress the locking clip at the base of the mounting block.

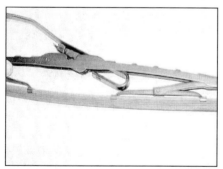

3 Move the blade down the arm to disengage the mounting block, then slide the blade from the arm. Don't forget to check the tailgate wiper blade as well (where applicable).

Tyre condition and pressure

It is very important that tyres are in good condition, and at the correct pressure - having a tyre failure at any speed is highly dangerous. Tyre wear is influenced by driving style - harsh braking and acceleration, or fast cornering, will all produce more rapid tyre wear. As a general rule, the front tyres wear out faster than the rears. Interchanging the tyres from front to rear ("rotating" the tyres) may result in more even wear. However, if this is completely effective, you may have the expense of replacing all four tyres at once!

Remove any nails or stones embedded in the tread before they penetrate the tyre to cause deflation. If removal of a nail does reveal that the tyre has been punctured, refit the nail so that its point of penetration is marked. Then immediately change the wheel, and have the tyre repaired by a tyre dealer.

Regularly check the tyres for damage in the form of cuts or bulges, especially in the sidewalls. Periodically remove the wheels, and clean any dirt or mud from the inside and outside surfaces. Examine the wheel rims for signs of rusting, corrosion or other damage. Light alloy wheels are easily damaged by "kerbing" whilst parking; steel wheels may also become dented or buckled. A new wheel is very often the only way to overcome severe damage.

New tyres should be balanced when they are fitted, but it may become necessary to re-balance them as they wear, or if the balance weights fitted to the wheel rim should fall off. Unbalanced tyres will wear more quickly, as will the steering and suspension components. Wheel imbalance is normally signified by vibration, particularly at a certain speed (typically around 50 mph). If this vibration is felt only through the steering, then it is likely that just the front wheels need balancing. If, however, the vibration is felt through the whole car, the rear wheels could be out of balance. Wheel balancing should be carried out by a tyre dealer or garage.

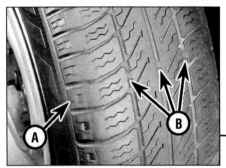

1 Tread Depth - visual check
The original tyres have tread wear safety bands (B), which will appear when the tread depth reaches approximately 1.6 mm. The band positions are indicated by a triangular mark on the tyre sidewall (A).

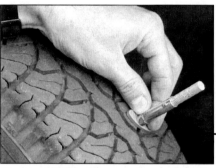

2 Tread Depth - manual check
Alternatively, tread wear can be monitored with a simple, inexpensive device known as a tread depth indicator gauge.

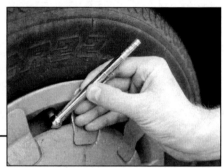

3 Tyre Pressure Check
Check the tyre pressures regularly with the tyres cold. Do not adjust the tyre pressures immediately after the vehicle has been used, or an inaccurate setting will result. Tyre pressures are shown on page 0•19.

Tyre tread wear patterns

Shoulder Wear

Underinflation (wear on both sides)
Under-inflation will cause overheating of the tyre, because the tyre will flex too much, and the tread will not sit correctly on the road surface. This will cause a loss of grip and excessive wear, not to mention the danger of sudden tyre failure due to heat build-up.
Check and adjust pressures
Incorrect wheel camber (wear on one side)
Repair or renew suspension parts
Hard cornering
Reduce speed!

Centre Wear

Overinflation
Over-inflation will cause rapid wear of the centre part of the tyre tread, coupled with reduced grip, harsher ride, and the danger of shock damage occurring in the tyre casing.
Check and adjust pressures

If you sometimes have to inflate your car's tyres to the higher pressures specified for maximum load or sustained high speed, don't forget to reduce the pressures to normal afterwards.

Uneven Wear

Front tyres may wear unevenly as a result of wheel misalignment. Most tyre dealers and garages can check and adjust the wheel alignment (or "tracking") for a modest charge.
Incorrect camber or castor
Repair or renew suspension parts
Malfunctioning suspension
Repair or renew suspension parts
Unbalanced wheel
Balance tyres
Incorrect toe setting
Adjust front wheel alignment
Note: *The feathered edge of the tread which typifies toe wear is best checked by feel.*

Battery

Caution: Before carrying out any work on the vehicle battery, read the precautions given in 'Safety first' at the start of this manual.

✔ Make sure that the battery tray is in good condition, and that the clamp is tight. Corrosion on the tray, retaining clamp and the battery itself can be removed with a solution of water and baking soda. Thoroughly rinse all cleaned areas with water. Any metal parts damaged by corrosion should be covered with a zinc-based primer, then painted.

✔ Periodically (approximately every three months), check the charge condition of the battery as described in Chapter 5A.

✔ If the battery is flat, and you need to jump start your vehicle, see *Roadside Repairs*.

Battery corrosion can be kept to a minimum by applying a layer of petroleum jelly to the clamps and terminals after they are reconnected.

1 The battery is located on the left-hand side of the engine compartment. The exterior of the battery should be inspected periodically for damage such as a cracked case or cover.

3 If corrosion (white, fluffy deposits) is evident, remove the cables from the battery terminals, clean them with a small wire brush, then refit them. Automotive stores sell a useful tool for cleaning the battery post and terminals.

2 Check the tightness of the battery cable clamps to ensure good electrical connections. You should not be able to move them. Also check each cable for cracks and frayed conductors.

4 Note that on certain models, the battery positive lead terminal can be disconnected by simply lifting the plastic cover.

Electrical systems

✔ Check all external lights and the horn. Refer to the appropriate Sections of Chapter 12 for details if any of the circuits are found to be inoperative.

✔ Visually check all accessible wiring connectors, harnesses and retaining clips for security, and for signs of chafing or damage.

If you need to check your brake lights and indicators unaided, back up to a wall or garage door and operate the lights. The reflected light should show if they are working properly.

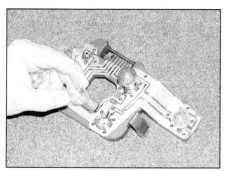

1 If a single indicator light, brake light or headlight has failed, it is likely that a bulb has blown and will need to be replaced. Refer to Chapter 12 for details. If both brake lights have failed, it is possible that the brake light switch operated by the brake pedal has failed. Refer to Chapter 9 for details.

2 If more than one indicator light or tail light has failed it is likely that either a fuse has blown or that there is a fault in the circuit (see Chapter 12). The main fuses are located in the fuse/relay boxes situated behind the cover in the facia on the driver's side, and in the engine compartment (refer to Chapter 12).

3 To replace a blown fuse, remove it, where applicable, using the plastic tool provided. Fit a new fuse of the same rating, available from car accessory shops. It is important that you find the reason that the fuse blew (see *Electrical fault finding* in Chapter 12).

Lubricants and fluids

Engine

Petrol	Multigrade engine oil, viscosity SAE 10W/30 to 15W/50, to API SJ or SJ-EC and ACEA-A3.96 or A1.98
Diesel	Multigrade engine oil, viscosity SAE 10W/30 to 15W/50, to API CF or CF-EC and ACEA-B3.96 or B1.98
Cooling system	Ethylene glycol-based antifreeze and soft water
Manual transmission	Total BV 75W/80 gear oil
Automatic transmission	
4 HP 14 transmission	Dexron type II ATF
AL4 transmission	Synthetic automatic transmission fluid, Citroën reference number 9736 22
Braking system	Hydraulic fluid to SAE J1703F or DOT 4
Power steering	Dexron type II ATF

Choosing your engine oil

Engines need oil, not only to lubricate moving parts and minimise wear, but also to maximise power output and to improve fuel economy.

HOW ENGINE OIL WORKS

• Beating friction

Without oil, the moving surfaces inside your engine will rub together, heat up and melt, quickly causing the engine to seize. Engine oil creates a film which separates these moving parts, preventing wear and heat build-up.

• Cooling hot-spots

Temperatures inside the engine can exceed 1000° C. The engine oil circulates and acts as a coolant, transferring heat from the hot-spots to the sump.

• Cleaning the engine internally

Good quality engine oils clean the inside of your engine, collecting and dispersing combustion deposits and controlling them until they are trapped by the oil filter or flushed out at oil change.

OIL CARE - FOLLOW THE CODE

To handle and dispose of used engine oil safely, always:

0800 66 33 66
www.oilbankline.org.uk

• *Avoid skin contact with used engine oil. Repeated or prolonged contact can be harmful.*
• *Dispose of used oil and empty packs in a responsible manner in an authorised disposal site. Call 0800 663366 to find the one nearest to you. Never tip oil down drains or onto the ground.*

Tyre pressures

Note: *The latest tyre pressure recommendations are marked on a label attached to the driver's door pillar. The following pressures are included as a guide, and apply to original-equipment tyres. The pressures may vary if any other make or type of tyre is fitted; check with the tyre manufacturer or supplier for correct pressures if necessary.*

	Front	Rear
Hatchback and Coupé models:		
Normal use:		
1.4 litre petrol engine models:		
175/65 R 14 tyres	2.2 bars (32 psi)	2.2 bars (32 psi)
185/65 TR 14 tyres	2.4 bars (35 psi)	2.3 bars (33 psi)
185/65 HR 14 tyres	2.4 bars (35 psi)	2.3 bars (33 psi)
All other models:	2.4 bars (35 psi)	2.3 bars (33 psi)
Fully laden:		
175/65 R 14 tyres	2.4 bars (35 psi)	2.4 bars (35 psi)
185/65 TR 14 tyres	2.4 bars (35 psi)	2.7 bars (39 psi)
185/65 HR 14 tyres	2.5 bars (36 psi)	2.6 bars (38 psi)
195/55 VR 15 tyres	2.4 bars (35 psi)	2.3 bars (33 psi)
Estate models:		
Normal use:		
1.4 litre petrol engine models:		
185/65 TR 14 tyres	2.3 bars (33 psi)	2.3 bars (33 psi)
185/65 HR 14 tyres	2.2 bars (32 psi)	2.1 bars (30 psi)
All other models:		
185/65 TR 14 tyres	2.4 bars (35 psi)	2.3 bars (33 psi)
185/65 HR 14 tyres	2.3 bars (33 psi)	2.1 bars (30 psi)
Fully laden:		
185/65 TR 14 tyres	2.4 bars (35 psi)	3.0 bars (44 psi)
185/65 HR 14 tyres	2.3 bars (33 psi)	3.0 bars (44 psi)

Notes

Chapter 1 Part A:
Routine maintenance and servicing – petrol engine models

Contents

Air bag(s) and seat belt pre-tensioner renewal 28
Air filter renewal 18
Automatic transmission fluid/oil level check 15
Automatic transmission fluid renewal – 4 HP 14 transmission 17
Auxiliary drivebelt check and renewal 5
Brake fluid renewal 21
Braking system check 24
Clutch control mechanism check 6
Coolant renewal 27
Driveshaft gaiter check 8
Engine oil and filter renewal 3
Exhaust gas emissions check 13
Exhaust system check 12
Front brake pad condition check 10

Fuel filter renewal 25
General information 1
Handbrake check and adjustment 20
Hinge and lock lubrication 16
Manual transmission oil level check 23
Pollen filter renewal 7
Rear brake pad condition check 11
Rear brake shoe condition check 19
Regular maintenance 2
Road test 14
Spark plug renewal 22
Steering and suspension check 9
Timing belt renewal 26
Underbonnet/underbody component/hose fluid leak check 4

Degrees of difficulty

Easy, suitable for novice with little experience	**Fairly easy,** suitable for beginner with some experience	**Fairly difficult,** suitable for competent DIY mechanic	**Difficult,** suitable for experienced DIY mechanic	**Very difficult,** suitable for expert DIY or professional 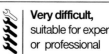

Lubricants and fluids .... Refer to end of *Weekly checks*

Capacities

Engine oil (including filter)
1.4 and 1.6 litre engines .... 3.50 litres
1.8 litre (8-valve) engines:
   Without air conditioning .... 4.75 litres
   With air conditioning .... 4.25 litres
1.8 litre (16-valve) engines:
   Without air conditioning .... 4.75 litres
   With air conditioning .... 4.25 litres
2.0 litre (16-valve engines) .... 4.25 litres
Difference between MAX and MIN dipstick marks (approx.) .... 1.25 litres

Cooling system (approximate)
1.4 and 1.6 litre engines .... 6.5 litres
1.8 and 2.0 litre engines .... 7.5 litres

Transmission
Manual .... 2.0 litres
Automatic:
   4 HP 14 transmission:
      From dry .... 6.2 litres
      Drain and refill .... 2.4 litres
   AL4 transmission:
      From dry .... 5.8 litres
      Drain and refill .... 3.0 litres

Fuel tank .... 54.0 litres

Engine
Auxiliary drivebelt tension (for use with electronic tension checking tool – see text):
   1.4 and 1.6 litre engines:
      Without air conditioning .... 55 ± 3 SEEM units
      With air conditioning .... 120 ± 3 SEEM units
   1.8 litre engines:
      Initial setting .... 94 ± 3 SEEM units
      Final setting .... 112 ± 3 SEEM units
   2.0 litre engines:
      Used belt .... 90 SEEM units
      New belt .... 120 SEEM units

Cooling system
Antifreeze mixture:
   28% antifreeze .... Protection down to −15°C
   50% antifreeze .... Protection down to −30°C
Note: *Refer to antifreeze manufacturer for latest recommendations.*

Fuel system

Idle speed*:
  1.4 litre engines:
    Without air conditioning .... 850 rpm
    With air conditioning .... 950 ± 50 rpm
  1.6 litre engines:
    Without air conditioning .... 850 ± 50 rpm
    With air conditioning .... 900 ± 50 rpm
  1.8 litre (8-valve) engines
    Without air conditioning .... 800 ± 50 rpm
    With air conditioning .... 900 ± 50 rpm
  1.8 and 2.0 litre (16-valve) engines .... 850 ± 50 rpm
Idle mixture CO content* .... Less than 0.5%

*Not adjustable – controlled by ECU. **Note**: See the relevant Part of Chapter 4 for further information.

Ignition system

Ignition timing	Refer to Chapter 5B	
Spark plugs:	**Type**	**Electrode gap**
All engines	Bosch FR 7 DE	0.9 mm

Brakes

Brake pad friction material minimum thickness .... 2.0 mm
Brake shoe friction material minimum thickness .... 1.5 mm

Tyre pressures .... Refer to end of *Weekly checks*

Torque wrench settings

	Nm	lbf ft
Automatic transmission drain plug (4 HP 14 type)	25	18
Automatic transmission fluid filler/level plugs	25	18
Manual transmission oil filler/level plug:		
BE3 type	20	15
MA type	25	18
Roadwheel bolts	85	63
Spark plugs	25	18

Underbonnet view of a 1.4 litre engine

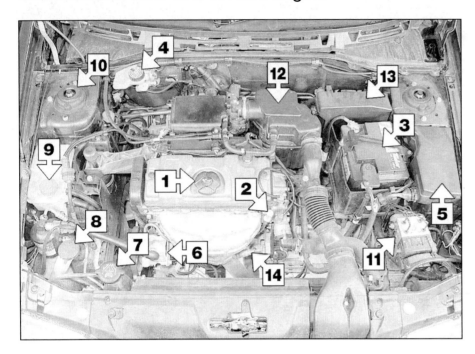

1 Engine oil filler cap
2 Engine oil dipstick
3 Battery
4 Brake master cylinder fluid reservoir
5 Engine compartment fuse/relay box
6 Power steering pump
7 Radiator filler cap
8 Windscreen/tailgate washer fluid reservoir filler cap
9 Power steering fluid reservoir filler cap
10 Suspension strut upper mounting
11 ABS hydraulic modulator
12 Air cleaner housing
13 Engine management ECU box
14 Lambda sensor

Underbonnet view of a 1.8 litre (16-valve) engine

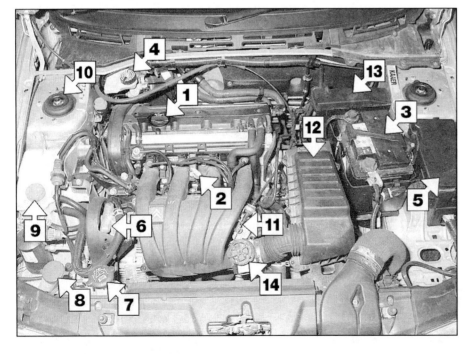

1 Engine oil filler cap
2 Engine oil dipstick
3 Battery
4 Brake master cylinder fluid reservoir
5 Engine compartment fuse/relay box
6 Power steering pump
7 Radiator filler cap
8 Windscreen/tailgate washer fluid reservoir filler cap
9 Power steering fluid reservoir filler cap
10 Suspension strut upper mounting
11 Accelerator cable
12 Air cleaner housing
13 Engine management ECU box
14 Throttle housing

Front underbody view (1.4 litre model)

1 Engine oil filter
2 Sump drain plug
3 Air conditioning compressor
4 Engine/transmission rear mounting
5 Exhaust front pipe
6 Front suspension subframe
7 Front brake caliper
8 Front suspension lower arm
9 Track rod balljoint
10 Front anti-roll bar
11 Steering gear assembly

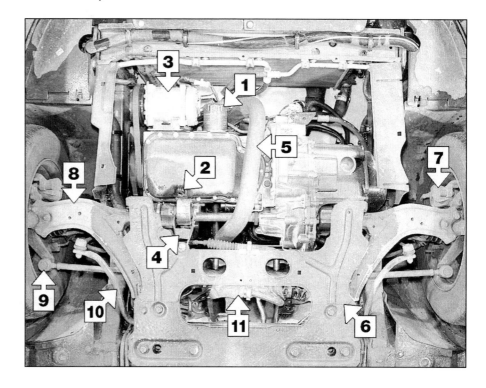

Rear underbody view (1.4 litre model)

1 Spare wheel
2 Rear silencer
3 Fuel tank
4 Handbrake cable
5 Rear suspension torsion bar
6 Rear suspension tubular crossmember
7 Rear shock absorber
8 Rear suspension trailing arm
9 Braking system compensator

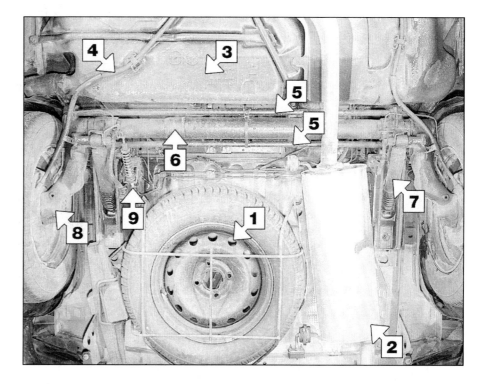

The maintenance intervals in this manual are provided with the assumption that you, not the dealer, will be carrying out the work. These are the minimum maintenance intervals recommended for vehicles driven daily. If you wish to keep your vehicle in peak condition at all times, you may wish to perform some of these procedures more often. We encourage frequent maintenance, because it enhances the efficiency, performance and resale value of your vehicle.

If the vehicle is driven in dusty areas, used to tow a trailer, or driven frequently at slow speeds (idling in traffic) or on short journeys, more frequent maintenance intervals are recommended.

When the vehicle is new, it should be serviced by a factory-authorised dealer service department, in order to preserve the factory warranty.

Valve clearance checking is no longer specified as part of the routine maintenance schedule. Check the valve clearances if there is any tapping or rattling from the top of the engine, or in the event of an unexplained lack of performance. The prudent owner may wish to check the clearances more often, perhaps at 25 000 mile (40 000 km) or two-yearly intervals.

Every 250 miles (400 km) or weekly
☐ Refer to *Weekly checks*

Every 12 500 miles (20 000 km) or 12 months – whichever comes first
☐ Renew the engine oil and filter (Section 3)*.
☐ Check all underbonnet/underbody components for fluid leaks (Section 4).
☐ Check the condition of the auxiliary drivebelt (Section 5).
☐ Check the clutch control mechanism (Section 6).
☐ Renew the pollen filter (Section 7).
☐ Check the condition of the driveshaft rubber gaiters (Section 8).
☐ Check the steering and suspension components (Section 9).
☐ Check the condition of the front brake pads (Section 10).
☐ Check the condition of the rear brake pads – models with rear disc brakes (Section 11).
☐ Check the condition of the exhaust system (Section 12).
☐ Check the exhaust gas emission level (Section 13).
☐ Road test (Section 14).
☐ Check the automatic transmission fluid level (Section 15).

*Note: *The engine oil renewal interval shown is based on the use of either a semi-synthetic or fully synthetic engine oil. If an inferior quality oil is used, the interval should be reduced. Consult your Citroën dealer for further information.*

Every 25 000 miles (40 000 km) or 2 years – whichever comes first
In addition to all the items listed above, carry out the following:
☐ Operate and lubricate all hinges and locks (Section 16).
☐ Renew the automatic transmission fluid – 4 HP 14 transmission only (Section 17).
☐ Renew the air filter (Section 18).
☐ Check the condition of the rear brake shoes – models with rear drum brakes (Section 19).
☐ Check the operation of the handbrake (Section 20).
☐ Renew the brake fluid (Section 21).

Every 37 500 miles (60 000 km) or 3 years – whichever comes first
In addition to all the items listed above, carry out the following:
☐ Renew the spark plugs (Section 22).
☐ Check the manual transmission oil level (Section 23).
☐ Check the condition and operation of the braking system components (Section 24).
☐ Renew the fuel filter (Section 25).
☐ Renew the timing belt (Section 26).

Note: *Although the normal interval for timing belt renewal is 75 000 miles (120 000 km), it is strongly recommended that the interval is halved to 37 500 miles (60 000 km) on vehicles which are subjected to intensive use, ie. mainly short journeys or a lot of stop-start driving. The actual belt renewal interval is therefore very much up to the individual owner, but bear in mind that severe engine damage will result if the belt breaks.*

Every 75 000 miles (120 000 km) or 5 years – whichever comes first
In addition to all the items listed above, carry out the following:
☐ Renew the coolant (Section 27).

Every 10 years – regardless of mileage
☐ Renew the air bag(s) and seat belt pre-tensioners (Section 28).

1 General information

This Chapter is designed to help the home mechanic maintain his/her vehicle for safety, economy, long life and peak performance.

The Chapter contains a master maintenance schedule, followed by Sections dealing specifically with each task in the schedule. Visual checks, adjustments, component renewal and other helpful items are included. Refer to the accompanying illustrations of the engine compartment and the underside of the vehicle for the locations of the various components.

Servicing your vehicle in accordance with the mileage/time maintenance schedule and the following Sections will provide a planned maintenance programme, which should result in a long and reliable service life. This is a comprehensive plan, so maintaining some items but not others at the specified service intervals will not produce the same results.

As you service your vehicle, you will discover that many of the procedures can – and should – be grouped together, because of the particular procedure being performed, or because of the proximity of two otherwise-unrelated components to one another. For example, if the vehicle is raised for any reason, the exhaust can be inspected at the same time as the suspension and steering components.

The first step in this maintenance programme is to prepare yourself before the actual work begins. Read through all the Sections relevant to the work to be carried out, then make a list and gather all the parts and tools required. If a problem is encountered, seek advice from a parts specialist, or a dealer service department.

Service interval display

Certain Xsara models are equipped with a service interval display indicator in the instrument panel. When the ignition is initially switched on, a spanner appears in the display window and the total number of miles remaining until the next service is due is also shown.

The display should not necessarily be used as a definitive guide to the servicing needs of your Xsara, but it is useful as a reminder, to ensure that servicing is not accidentally overlooked. Owners of older cars, or those covering a small annual mileage, may feel inclined to service their car more often, in which case the service interval display is perhaps less relevant.

The display should be reset whenever a service is carried out, and this is achieved using the trip meter reset button on the instrument panel as follows.

With the ignition switched off, press and hold down the trip meter reset button. Switch the ignition on and the mileage remaining until the next service will flash. Continue to hold the button down for a further ten seconds. The spanner symbol will disappear and the mileage will return to zero.

2 Regular maintenance

1 If, from the time the vehicle is new, the routine maintenance schedule is followed closely, and frequent checks are made of fluid levels and high-wear items, as suggested throughout this manual, the engine will be kept in relatively good running condition, and the need for additional work will be minimised.
2 It is possible that there will be times when the engine is running poorly due to the lack of regular maintenance. This is even more likely if a used vehicle, which has not received regular and frequent maintenance checks, is purchased. In such cases, additional work may need to be carried out, outside of the regular maintenance intervals.
3 If engine wear is suspected, a compression test (refer to relevant Part of Chapter 2) will provide valuable information regarding the overall performance of the main internal components. Such a test can be used as a basis to decide on the extent of the work to be carried out. If, for example, a compression test indicates serious internal engine wear, conventional maintenance as described in this Chapter will not greatly improve the performance of the engine, and may prove a waste of time and money, unless extensive overhaul work is carried out first.
4 The following series of operations are those most often required to improve the performance of a generally poor-running engine:

Primary operations

a) *Clean, inspect and test the battery (See Weekly checks).*
b) *Check all the engine-related fluids (See Weekly checks).*
c) *Check the condition of all hoses, and check for fluid leaks (Section 4).*
d) *Check the condition and tension of the auxiliary drivebelt (Section 5).*
e) *Check the condition of the air filter, and renew if necessary (Section 18).*
f) *Renew the spark plugs (Section 22).*
g) *Inspect the HT leads – where applicable (Section 22).*
h) *Renew the fuel filter (Section 25).*

5 If the above operations do not prove fully effective, carry out the following secondary operations:

Secondary operations

All items listed under *Primary operations*, plus the following:

a) *Check the charging system (Chapter 5A).*
b) *Check the ignition system (Chapter 5B).*
c) *Check the fuel system (Chapter 4A).*
d) *Renew the ignition HT leads – where applicable (Section 22).*

Every 12 500 miles (20 000 km) or 12 months – whichever comes first

3 Engine oil and filter renewal

Note: *A suitable square-section wrench may be required to undo the sump drain plug on some engines. These wrenches can be obtained from most motor factors or your Citroën dealer.*

1 Frequent oil and filter changes are the most important preventative maintenance procedures which can be undertaken by the DIY owner. As engine oil ages, it becomes diluted and contaminated, which leads to premature engine wear.
2 Before starting this procedure, gather together all the necessary tools and materials. Also make sure that you have plenty of clean rags and newspapers handy, to mop up any spills. Ideally, the engine oil should be warm, as it will drain better, and any impurities suspended in the oil will be removed with it. Take care, however, not to touch the exhaust or any other hot parts of the engine when working under the vehicle. To avoid any possibility of scalding, and to protect yourself from possible skin irritants and other harmful contaminants in used engine oils, it is advisable to wear gloves when carrying out this work. Access to the underside of the vehicle will be greatly improved if it can be raised on a lift, driven onto ramps, or jacked up and supported on axle stands (see *Jacking and vehicle support*). Whichever method is chosen, make sure that the vehicle remains level, or if it is at an angle, that the drain plug is at the lowest point.
3 Remove the engine undertray, then slacken the sump drain plug about half a turn; on some engines, a square-section wrench may be needed to slacken the plug **(see**

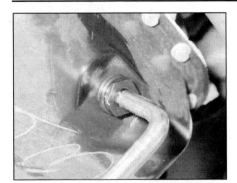

3.3 Slackening the sump drain plug with a square-section wrench

As the drain plug releases from the threads, move it away sharply so the stream of oil issuing from the sump runs into the container, not up your sleeve.

3.7 Using an oil filter removal tool to slacken the oil filter

illustration). Position the draining container under the drain plug, then remove the plug completely. If possible, try to keep the plug pressed into the sump while unscrewing it by hand the last couple of turns **(see Haynes Hint)**. Recover the sealing ring from the drain plug.

4 Allow some time for the old oil to drain, noting that it may be necessary to reposition the container as the oil flow slows to a trickle.

5 After all the oil has drained, wipe off the drain plug with a clean rag, and fit a new sealing washer. Clean the area around the drain plug opening, and refit the plug. Tighten the plug securely.

6 Move the container into position under the oil filter, which is located on the front facing side of the cylinder block.

7 Using an oil filter removal tool if necessary, slacken the filter initially, then unscrew it by hand the rest of the way **(see illustration)**. Empty the oil in the old filter into the container. To ensure that the old filter is completely empty before disposal, puncture the filter dome in at least two places and allow any remaining oil to drain through the punctures and into the container.

8 Use a clean rag to remove all oil and dirt from the filter sealing area on the engine. Check the old filter to make sure that the rubber sealing ring hasn't stuck to the engine. If it has, carefully remove it.

9 Apply a light coating of clean engine oil to the sealing ring on the new filter, then screw it into position on the engine. Tighten the filter firmly by hand only – do not use any tools.

10 Refit the engine undertray then remove the old oil and all tools from under the car. Lower the car to the ground (if applicable).

11 Remove the dipstick, then unscrew the oil filler cap from the cylinder head cover. Fill the engine, using the correct grade and type of oil (see *Weekly checks*). An oil can spout or funnel may help to reduce spillage. Pour in half the specified quantity of oil first, then wait a few minutes for the oil to fall to the sump. Continue adding oil a small quantity at a time until the level is up to the lower mark on the dipstick. Adding approximately 1.25 litres will bring the level up to the upper mark on the dipstick. Refit the filler cap.

12 Start the engine and run it for a few minutes; check for leaks around the oil filter seal and the sump drain plug. Note that there may be a delay of a few seconds before the oil pressure warning light goes out when the engine is first started, as the oil circulates through the engine oil galleries and the new oil filter before the pressure builds up.

13 Switch off the engine, and wait a few minutes for the oil to settle in the sump once more. With the new oil circulated and the filter completely full, recheck the level on the dipstick, and add more oil as necessary.

14 Dispose of the used engine oil and filter safely, with reference to *General repair procedures* at the rear of this manual. Do not discard the old filter with domestic household waste. The facility for waste oil disposal provided by many local council refuse tips generally has a filter receptacle alongside.

4 Underbonnet/underbody component/hose fluid leak check

⚠ *Warning: Refer to the safety information given in 'Safety First!' and Chapter 3 before disturbing any of the cooling system components.*

1 Carefully check the radiator and heater coolant hoses along their entire length. Renew any hose which is cracked, swollen or which shows signs of deterioration. Cracks will show up better if the hose is squeezed. Pay close attention to the clips that secure the hoses to the cooling system components. Hose clips that have been over-tightened can pinch and puncture hoses, resulting in cooling system leaks.

2 Inspect all the cooling system components (hoses, joint faces, etc) for leaks. Where any problems of this nature are found on system components, renew the component or gasket with reference to Chapter 3 **(see Haynes Hint)**.

Fuel

Warning: Refer to the safety information given in 'Safety First!' and the relevant Part of Chapter 4 before disturbing any of the fuel system components.

3 Petrol leaks are difficult to pinpoint, unless the leakage is significant and hence easily visible. Fuel tends to evaporate quickly once it comes into contact with air, especially in a hot engine bay. Small drips can disappear before you get a chance to identify the point of leakage. If you suspect that there is a fuel leak from the area of the engine bay, leave the vehicle overnight then start the engine from cold, with the bonnet open. Metal components tend to shrink when they are cold, and rubber seals and hoses tend to harden, so any leaks will be more apparent whilst the engine is warming up from a cold start.

4 Check all fuel lines at their connections to the fuel rail, fuel pressure regulator and fuel filter. Examine each rubber fuel hose along its length for splits or cracks. Check for leakage from the crimped joints between rubber and metal fuel lines. Examine the unions between the metal fuel lines and the fuel filter housing. Also check the area around the fuel injectors for signs of O-ring leakage.

5 To identify fuel leaks between the fuel tank and the engine bay, the vehicle should be raised and securely supported on axle stands (see *Jacking and vehicle support*). Inspect the

A leak in the cooling system will usually show up as white- or rust-coloured deposits on the area adjoining the leak.

petrol tank and filler neck for punctures, cracks and other damage. The connection between the filler neck and tank is especially critical. Sometimes a rubber filler neck or connecting hose will leak due to loose retaining clamps or deteriorated rubber.

6 Carefully check all rubber hoses and metal fuel lines leading away from the petrol tank. Check for loose connections, deteriorated hoses, kinked lines, and other damage. Pay particular attention to the vent pipes and hoses, which often loop up around the filler neck and can become blocked or kinked, making tank filling difficult. Follow the fuel supply and return lines to the front of the vehicle, carefully inspecting them all the way for signs of damage or corrosion. Renew damaged sections as necessary.

Engine oil

7 Inspect the area around the cylinder head cover, cylinder head, oil filter and sump joint faces. Bear in mind that, over a period of time, some very slight seepage from these areas is to be expected – what you are really looking for is any indication of a serious leak caused by gasket failure. Engine oil seeping from the base of the timing belt cover or the transmission bellhousing may be an indication of crankshaft or transmission input shaft oil seal failure. Should a leak be found, renew the failed gasket or oil seal by referring to the appropriate Chapter in this manual.

Automatic transmission fluid

8 Where applicable, check the hoses leading to the transmission fluid cooler for leakage. Check the transmission itself for any signs of leakage around the various joint faces and seals. Automatic transmission fluid is a thin oil and is usually red in colour making it easy to distinguish from engine oil.

Power steering fluid

9 Examine the hose running between the fluid reservoir and the power steering pump, and the return hose running from the steering rack to the fluid reservoir. Also examine the high pressure supply hose between the pump and the steering rack.

10 Check the condition of each hose carefully. Look for deterioration caused by corrosion and damage from grounding, or debris thrown up from the road surface.

11 Pay particular attention to crimped unions, and the area surrounding the hoses that are secured with adjustable worm drive clips. Like automatic transmission fluid, power steering fluid is a thin oil, and is usually red in colour.

Air conditioning refrigerant

 Warning: Refer to the safety information given in 'Safety First!' and Chapter 3, regarding the dangers of disturbing any of the air conditioning system components.

12 The air conditioning system is filled with a liquid refrigerant, which is retained under high pressure. If the air conditioning system is opened and depressurised without the aid of specialised equipment, the refrigerant will immediately turn into gas and escape into the atmosphere. If the liquid comes into contact with your skin, it can cause severe frostbite. In addition, the refrigerant contains substances which are environmentally damaging; for this reason, it should *never* be allowed to escape into the atmosphere.

13 Any suspected air conditioning system leaks should be immediately referred to a Citroën dealer or air conditioning specialist. Leakage will be shown up as a steady drop in the level of refrigerant in the system.

14 Note that water may drip from the condenser drain pipe, underneath the car, immediately after the air conditioning system has been in use. This is normal, and should not be cause for concern.

Brake fluid

 Warning: Refer to the safety information given in 'Safety First!' and Chapter 9, regarding the dangers of handling brake fluid.

15 With reference to Chapter 9, examine the area surrounding the brake pipe unions at the master cylinder for signs of leakage. Check the area around the base of fluid reservoir, for signs of leakage caused by seal failure. Also examine the brake pipe unions at the ABS hydraulic unit.

16 If fluid loss is evident, but the leak cannot be pinpointed in the engine bay, the brake calipers/wheel cylinders and underbody brake lines should be carefully checked with the vehicle raised and supported on axle stands (see *Jacking and vehicle support*). Leakage of fluid from the braking system is a serious fault that must be rectified immediately.

17 Brake hydraulic fluid is a toxic substance with a watery consistency. New fluid is almost colourless, but it becomes darker with age and use.

Unidentified fluid leaks

18 If there are signs that a fluid of some description is leaking from the vehicle, but you cannot identify the type of fluid or its exact origin, park the vehicle overnight and slide a large piece of card underneath it. Providing that the card is positioned in roughly the right location, even the smallest leak will show up on the card. Not only will this help you to pinpoint the exact location of the leak, it should be easier to identify the fluid from its colour. Bear in mind, though, that the leak may only be occurring when the engine is running.

Vacuum hoses

19 Although the braking system is hydraulically-operated, the brake servo unit amplifies the effort applied at the brake pedal,

by making use of the vacuum in the inlet manifold, generated by the engine. Vacuum is ported to the servo by means of a large-bore hose. Any leaks that develop in this hose will reduce the effectiveness of the braking system, and may affect the running of the engine.

20 In addition, a number of the underbonnet components, particularly the emission control components, are driven by vacuum supplied from the inlet manifold via narrow-bore hoses. A leak in a vacuum hose means that air is being drawn into the hose (rather than escaping from it) and this makes leakage very difficult to detect. One method is to use an old length of vacuum hose as a kind of stethoscope – hold one end close to (but not in) your ear and use the other end to probe the area around the suspected leak. When the end of the hose is directly over a vacuum leak, a hissing sound will be heard clearly through the hose. Care must be taken to avoid contacting hot or moving components, as the engine must be running when testing in this manner. Renew any vacuum hoses that are found to be defective.

5   Auxiliary drivebelt check and renewal

Note: *Citroën specify the use of an electronic tension checking tool (SEEM 4122-T) to accurately check the auxiliary drivebelt tension on manually adjusted drivebelts. If access to this equipment (or suitable alternative equipment calibrated to display belt tension in SEEM units) cannot be obtained, an approximate setting can be achieved as described below. If an approximate setting method is used, the tension must be checked using the electronic tool at the earliest possible opportunity.*

1 Depending on specification, either one or two auxiliary drivebelts are fitted. The belts drive the alternator, power steering pump and air conditioning compressor according to equipment fitted, and are adjusted either manually or by means of an automatic spring-loaded tensioning mechanism. Where a twin drivebelt arrangement is used, it will obviously be necessary to remove the outer belt in order to renew the inner belt.

Checking the auxiliary drivebelt condition

2 Chock the rear wheels then jack up the front of the vehicle and support it on axle stands (see *Jacking and vehicle support*). Remove the right-hand front roadwheel.

3 To gain access to the right-hand end of the engine, the wheelarch plastic liner must be removed. The liner is secured by various screws and clips under the wheelarch. Release all the fasteners, and remove the liner from under the front wing. Where necessary, unclip the coolant hoses from under the wing to improve access further.

5.9 Loosen the alternator mounting bolts, then slacken the adjuster bolt (arrowed) – models with manual tensioner on the alternator

4 Using a suitable socket and extension bar fitted to the crankshaft pulley bolt, rotate the crankshaft so that the entire length of the drivebelt can be examined. Examine the drivebelt for cracks, splitting, fraying or damage. Check also for signs of glazing (shiny patches) and for separation of the belt plies. Renew the belt if worn or damaged.

5 If the condition of the belt is satisfactory, on engines where the belt is adjusted manually, check the drivebelt tension as described below, bearing in mind the Note at the start of this Section. On engines with an automatic spring-loaded tensioner, there is no need to check the drivebelt tension.

Auxiliary drivebelt with manual adjuster on the alternator mounting

Removal

6 If not already done, proceed as described in paragraphs 2 and 3.

7 Disconnect the battery negative terminal (refer to *Disconnecting the battery* in the Reference Section of this manual).

8 Slacken the alternator upper and lower mounting bolts and, where applicable, the adjuster strap mounting bolt.

9 Turn the adjuster bolt as necessary to relieve the tension in the drivebelt, then slip the drivebelt from the pulleys **(see illustration)**.

Refitting

10 If the belt is being renewed, ensure that the correct type is used. Fit the belt around the pulleys, and take up the initial slack in the belt by means of the adjuster bolt.

11 Tension the drivebelt as described in the following paragraphs.

Tensioning

12 If not already done, proceed as described in paragraphs 2 and 3.

13 If the electronic tool is not being used, the belt should be tensioned so that, under firm thumb pressure, there is about 5.0 mm of free movement at the mid-point between the pulleys on the longest belt run. If the electronic tool is being used, the tool sensor should be positioned on the belt at a point midway between the crankshaft and alternator pulleys.

> **HAYNES HINT** *Correct tensioning of the drivebelt will ensure it has a long life. A belt which is too slack will slip and squeal. Beware of overtightening, as this can cause wear in the alternator bearings.*

14 To adjust, with the mounting bolts just holding the alternator, but still allowing slight movement, turn the adjuster bolt until the correct hand tension is achieved, or the specified number of SEEM units are displayed on the electronic tool. Refer to the Specifications for the SEEM unit tension settings according to model.

15 Remove the tool (if used), and rotate the crankshaft two or three times. Recheck and, if necessary, readjust the tension, then tighten the alternator mountings. Where applicable, also tighten the bolt securing the adjuster strap to its mounting bracket.

16 Reconnect the battery negative terminal.

17 Clip the coolant hoses into position (where necessary), then refit the wheelarch liner. Refit the roadwheel, and lower the vehicle to the ground.

Auxiliary drivebelt with a manually-adjusted tensioning pulley

Removal

18 If not already done, proceed as described in paragraphs 2 and 3.

19 Disconnect the battery negative terminal (refer to *Disconnecting the battery* in the Reference Section of this manual).

20 Slacken the two bolts securing the tensioning pulley assembly to the engine **(see illustrations)**.

21 Rotate the adjuster bolt to move the tensioner pulley away from the drivebelt until there is sufficient slack for the drivebelt to be removed from the pulleys.

Refitting

22 If the belt is being renewed, ensure that the correct type is used. Fit the belt around the pulleys, ensuring that the ribs on the belt are correctly engaged with the grooves in the pulleys, and that the drivebelt is correctly routed. Take all the slack out of the belt by turning the tensioner pulley adjuster bolt. Tension the belt as follows.

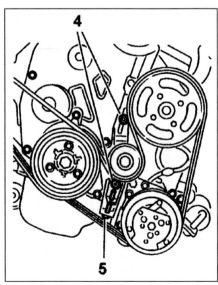

5.20a Tensioning pulley securing screws (4) and adjuster bolt (5) – models with low-mounted manual tensioner

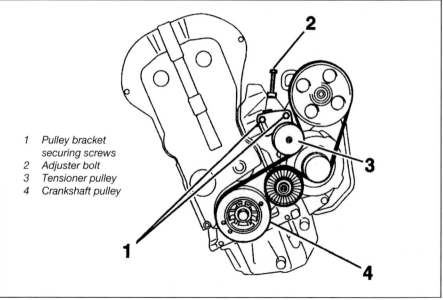

1 Pulley bracket securing screws
2 Adjuster bolt
3 Tensioner pulley
4 Crankshaft pulley

5.20b Tensioning pulley arrangement – models with high-mounted manual tensioner

Tensioning

23 If not already done, proceed as described in paragraphs 2 and 3.

24 If the electronic tool is not being used, the belt should be tensioned so that, under firm thumb pressure, there is about 5.0 mm of free movement at the mid-point between the pulleys on the longest belt run. If the electronic tool is being used, the tool sensor should be positioned on the belt according to engine type as follows:

- *1.4 and 1.6 litre engines – midway between the crankshaft pulley and air conditioning compressor pulley or power steering pump pulley, as applicable.*
- *1.8 and 2.0 litre engines – midway between the power steering pump pulley and alternator pulley.*

25 To adjust the tension, with the two tensioner pulley assembly retaining bolts slackened, rotate the adjuster bolt until the correct hand tension is achieved, or the specified number of SEEM units are displayed on the electronic tool. Refer to the Specifications for the SEEM unit tension settings according to model. Note that on 1.8 litre engines, if the electronic tool is being used, the belt tension should be set to the initial setting specified.

26 Remove the tool (if used), and fully tighten the two tensioner pulley assembly retaining bolts. Rotate the crankshaft through three complete revolutions in the normal direction of rotation.

27 If the electronic tool is not being used, recheck the belt tension and, if necessary, readjust.

28 If the electronic tool is being used, slacken the two tensioner pulley assembly retaining bolts and refit the tool sensor to the belt. Check that the specified number of SEEM units are displayed and adjust if necessary by means of the adjuster bolt. Note that on 1.8 litre engines, the tension should be set to the final setting specified.

29 Fully tighten the two tensioner pulley retaining bolts.

30 Reconnect the battery negative terminal.

31 Clip the coolant hoses into position (where necessary), then refit the wheelarch liner. Refit the roadwheel, and lower the vehicle to the ground.

Auxiliary drivebelt with an automatic spring-loaded tensioner pulley

Removal

32 If not already done, proceed as described in paragraphs 2 and 3.

33 Disconnect the battery negative terminal (refer to *Disconnecting the battery* in the Reference Section of this manual).

34 Where necessary, remove the retaining screws from the power steering pump pulley shield, and remove the shield to gain access to the top of the drivebelt.

35 Move the tensioner pulley away from the drivebelt, using a ratchet handle or extension bar with 3/8 inch square-section end engaged in the hole in the base of the automatic tensioner arm. Once the tensioner is released, retain it in the released position by inserting a 4.0 mm Allen key in the hole provided.

36 Undo the two mounting bolts and remove the automatic tensioner assembly from the engine.

37 Disengage the drivebelt from all the pulleys, noting its correct routing and remove the belt from the engine.

Refitting and tensioning

38 If the belt is being renewed, ensure that the correct type is used. Fit the belt around the pulleys, ensuring that the ribs on the belt are correctly engaged with the grooves in the pulleys, and that the drivebelt is correctly routed.

39 Refit the tensioner assembly and securely tighten the mounting bolts.

40 Take the load off the tensioner arm and remove the Allen key. Release the tensioner arm; the tensioner is spring-loaded, removing the need to manually adjust the belt tension.

41 Refit the power steering pump pulley shield (where removed), and securely tighten its retaining screws.

42 Reconnect the battery negative terminal.

43 Clip the coolant hoses into position (where necessary), then refit the wheelarch liner. Refit the roadwheel, and lower the vehicle to the ground.

6 Clutch control mechanism check

1 Check that the clutch pedal moves smoothly and easily through its full travel, and that the clutch itself functions correctly, with no trace of slip or drag.

2 If excessive effort is required to operate the clutch, check first that the cable is correctly routed and undamaged, then remove the pedal and check that its pivot is properly greased. See Chapter 6 for more information.

7 Pollen filter renewal

1 Working under the passenger's side of the facia, undo the three stud screws securing the carpet trim panel to the facia. Release the two studs and washers securing the trim panel to the floor and remove the panel **(see illustrations)**.

2 Remove the three securing screws, and withdraw the lid from the pollen filter housing **(see illustration)**. If no screws are visible, slide the lid sideways to release the internal retaining lugs.

3 Withdraw the filter **(see illustration)**.

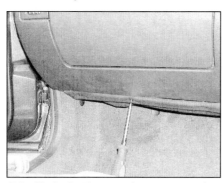

7.1a Undo the three stud screws securing the carpet trim panel to the facia . . .

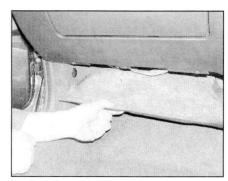

7.1b . . . release the two studs and washers securing the trim panel to the floor and remove the panel

7.2 Remove the three screws and withdraw the lid from the pollen filter housing

7.3 Withdraw the pollen filter from the housing

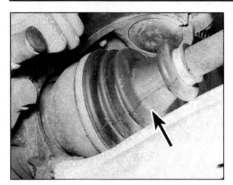

8.1 Check the condition of the driveshaft gaiters (arrowed)

9.4 Check for wear in the hub bearings by grasping the wheel and trying to rock it

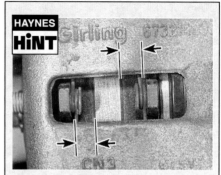

For a quick check, the thickness of friction material on each brake pad can be measured through the aperture in the caliper body.

4 Clean the filter housing and the lid, then fit the new filter using a reversal of the removal procedure.

8 Driveshaft gaiter check

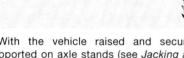

1 With the vehicle raised and securely supported on axle stands (see *Jacking and vehicle support*), turn the steering onto full lock, then slowly rotate the roadwheel. Inspect the condition of the outer constant velocity (CV) joint rubber gaiters, squeezing the gaiters to open out the folds **(see illustration)**. Check for signs of cracking, splits or deterioration of the rubber, which may allow the grease to escape, and lead to water and grit entry into the joint. Also check the security and condition of the retaining clips. Repeat these checks on the inner CV joints. If any damage or deterioration is found, the gaiters should be renewed (see Chapter 8).
2 At the same time, check the general condition of the CV joints themselves by first holding the driveshaft and attempting to rotate the wheel. Repeat this check by holding the inner joint and attempting to rotate the driveshaft. Any appreciable movement indicates wear in the joints, wear in the driveshaft splines, or a loose driveshaft retaining nut.

9 Steering and suspension check

Front suspension and steering check

1 Firmly apply the handbrake, then jack up the front of the car and support it securely on axle stands (see *Jacking and vehicle support*).
2 Visually inspect the balljoint dust covers and the steering rack-and-pinion gaiters for splits, chafing or deterioration. Any wear of these components will cause loss of lubricant, together with dirt and water entry, resulting in

rapid deterioration of the balljoints or steering gear.
3 On vehicles with power steering, check the fluid hoses for chafing or deterioration, and the pipe and hose unions for fluid leaks. Also check for signs of fluid leakage under pressure from the steering gear rubber gaiters, which would indicate failed fluid seals within the steering gear.
4 Grasp the roadwheel at the 12 o'clock and 6 o'clock positions, and try to rock it **(see illustration)**. Very slight free play may be felt, but if the movement is appreciable, further investigation is necessary to determine the source. Continue rocking the wheel while an assistant depresses the footbrake. If the movement is now eliminated or significantly reduced, it is likely that the hub bearings are at fault. If the free play is still evident with the footbrake depressed, then there is wear in the suspension joints or mountings.
5 Now grasp the wheel at the 9 o'clock and 3 o'clock positions, and try to rock it as before. Any movement felt now may again be caused by wear in the hub bearings or the steering track-rod balljoints. If the inner or outer balljoint is worn, the visual movement will be obvious.
6 Using a large screwdriver or flat bar, check for wear in the suspension mounting bushes by levering between the relevant suspension component and its attachment point. Some movement is to be expected as the mountings are made of rubber, but excessive wear should be obvious. Also check the condition of any visible rubber bushes, looking for splits, cracks or contamination of the rubber.
7 With the car standing on its wheels, have an assistant turn the steering wheel back and forth about an eighth of a turn each way. There should be very little, if any, lost movement between the steering wheel and roadwheels. If this is not the case, closely observe the joints and mountings previously described, but in addition, check the steering column universal joints for wear, and the rack-and-pinion steering gear itself.

Suspension strut/shock absorber check

8 Check for any signs of fluid leakage around the suspension strut/shock absorber body, or

from the rubber gaiter around the piston rod. Should any fluid be noticed, the suspension strut/shock absorber is defective internally, and should be renewed. **Note:** *Suspension struts/shock absorbers should always be renewed in pairs on the same axle.*
9 The efficiency of the suspension strut/shock absorber may be checked by bouncing the vehicle at each corner. Generally speaking, the body will return to its normal position and stop after being depressed. If it rises and returns on a rebound, the suspension strut/shock absorber is probably suspect. Examine also the suspension strut/shock absorber upper and lower mountings for any signs of wear.

10 Front brake pad condition check

1 Firmly apply the handbrake, then jack up the front of the car and support it securely on axle stands (see *Jacking and vehicle support*). Remove the front roadwheels.
2 It is now possible to check the thickness of the pad friction material **(see Haynes Hint)**. If any pad's friction material is worn to the specified thickness or less, *all four pads must be renewed as a set.*
3 For a comprehensive check, the brake pads should be removed and cleaned. The operation of the caliper can then be checked, and the brake disc itself can be fully examined on both sides. Refer to Chapter 9 for details.

11 Rear brake pad condition check

1 Chock the front wheels then jack up the rear of the car and support it on axle stands (see *Jacking and vehicle support*). Remove the rear roadwheels.
2 For a quick check, the thickness of friction material remaining on each brake pad can be measured through the top of the caliper body.

If any pad's friction material is worn to the specified thickness or less, all four pads must be renewed as a set.

3 For a comprehensive check, the brake pads should be removed and cleaned. This will permit the operation of the caliper to be checked, and the condition of the brake disc itself to be fully examined on both sides. Refer to Chapter 9 for further information.

12 Exhaust system check

1 With the engine cold (at least an hour after the vehicle has been driven), check the complete exhaust system from the engine to the end of the tailpipe. The exhaust system is most easily checked with the vehicle raised on a hoist, or suitably supported on axle stands, so that the exhaust components are readily visible and accessible (see *Jacking and vehicle support*).

2 Check the exhaust pipes and connections for evidence of leaks, severe corrosion and damage. Make sure that all brackets and mountings are in good condition, and that all relevant nuts and bolts are tight. Leakage at any of the joints or in other parts of the system will usually show up as a black sooty stain in the vicinity of the leak.

3 Rattles and other noises can often be traced to the exhaust system, especially the brackets and mountings. Try to move the pipes and silencers. If the components are able to come into contact with the body or suspension parts, secure the system with new mountings. Otherwise separate the joints (if possible) and twist the pipes as necessary to provide additional clearance.

13 Exhaust gas emissions check

1 The air/fuel mixture is controlled directly by the engine management system (refer to Chapter 4A for greater detail). As a result, the exhaust gas CO content is not manually adjustable without the aid of special test equipment.

2 However, experienced home mechanics equipped with an accurate tachometer and a calibrated exhaust gas analyser should be able to check the exhaust gas CO content, as described in the following sub-Section.

3 If the results of the test show that the CO content is different to that quoted in the Specifications, this indicates a fault within the fuel delivery, engine management or emission control systems (assuming the vehicle is otherwise in good mechanical order).

4 The engine management system wiring harness incorporates a diagnostic socket, which can be used in conjunction with a fault code reader or other suitable test equipment.

The socket allows the engine management system to be electronically 'interrogated' to establish the presence of faults detected by the ECU.

5 Testing the engine management system components individually, with standard workshop equipment, in an attempt to locate a fault by elimination is a time consuming operation that is unlikely to be fruitful (particularly if the fault occurs dynamically). It also carries a high risk of damage to the electronic control unit's internal components.

Exhaust emission level check

6 Start the engine and allow it to warm up to normal operating temperature. With the engine at idle, wait until the auxiliary cooling fan has cut in and out again, at least twice, before proceeding.

7 Switch on the CO meter and allow it to warm up and stabilise, in accordance with the manufacturer's instructions.

8 Insert the CO meter probe into the exhaust tailpipe. Connect a calibrated tachometer to the engine, again in accordance with the manufacturer's instructions.

9 Ensure that all electrical and mechanical loads (such as headlights, heater blower motor, air conditioning) are switched off.

10 Raise the engine speed and maintain it at 2500 to 3000 rpm for at least two minutes. If the auxiliary cooling fan cuts in, wait until it cuts out again.

11 Check the reading on the CO meter, when the display has stabilised.

12 Repeat the test procedure to obtain an average figure, then compare your result with the figure given in the Specifications.

14 Road test

Instruments and electrical equipment

1 Check the operation of all instruments and electrical equipment.

2 Make sure that all instruments read correctly, and switch on all electrical equipment in turn to check it functions properly.

Steering and suspension

3 Check for any abnormalities in the steering, suspension, handling or road 'feel'.

4 Drive the vehicle, and check that there are no unusual vibrations or noises.

5 Check that the steering feels positive, with no excessive 'sloppiness', or roughness, and check for any suspension noises when cornering, or when driving over bumps.

Drivetrain

6 Check the performance of the engine, clutch (where applicable), transmission and driveshafts.

7 Listen for any unusual noises from the engine, clutch and transmission.

8 Make sure that the engine runs smoothly when idling, and that there is no hesitation when accelerating.

9 Check that, where applicable, the clutch action is smooth and progressive, that the drive is taken up smoothly, and that the pedal travel is not excessive. Also listen for any noises when the clutch pedal is depressed.

10 On manual transmission models, check that all gears can be engaged smoothly without noise, and that the gear lever action is smooth and not abnormally vague or 'notchy'.

11 On automatic transmission models, make sure that all gearchanges occur smoothly, without snatching, and without an increase in engine speed between changes. Check that all the gear positions can be selected with the vehicle at rest. If any problems are found, they should be referred to a Citroën dealer.

12 Listen for a metallic clicking sound from the front of the vehicle, as the vehicle is driven slowly in a circle with the steering on full lock. Carry out this check in both directions. If a clicking noise is heard, this indicates lack of lubrication or wear in a driveshaft constant velocity joint (see Chapter 8).

Check the operation and performance of the braking system

13 Make sure that the vehicle does not pull to one side when braking, and that the wheels do not lock prematurely when braking hard.

14 Check that there is no vibration through the steering when braking.

15 Check that the handbrake operates correctly, without excessive movement of the lever, and that it holds the vehicle on a slope.

16 Test the operation of the brake servo unit as follows. With the engine off, depress the footbrake four or five times to exhaust the vacuum. Start the engine, holding the brake pedal depressed. As the engine starts, there should be a noticeable 'give' in the brake pedal as vacuum builds up. Allow the engine to run for at least two minutes, and then switch it off. If the brake pedal is depressed now, it should be possible to detect a hiss from the servo as the pedal is depressed. After about four or five applications, no further hissing should be heard, and the pedal should feel considerably firmer.

15 Automatic transmission fluid/oil level check

Note: *Refer to Chapter 7B for transmission identification according to model.*

4 HP 14 transmission

1 Take the vehicle on a moderate journey (at least 30 minutes), to warm the transmission up to normal operating temperature, then park the vehicle on level ground. Leave the engine

15.1 Withdrawing the automatic transmission dipstick – 4 HP 14 transmission

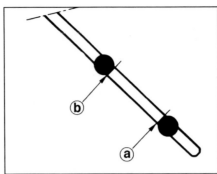

15.2 Automatic transmission fluid dipstick lower (a) and upper (b) fluid level markings – 4 HP 14 transmission

idling, apply the handbrake fully, and move the selector lever to the P (Park) position. The fluid level is checked using the dipstick located at the front of the engine compartment, directly in front of the engine unit **(see illustration)**. The dipstick top is brightly-coloured for easy identification.

2 With the engine idling and the footbrake applied, move the selector lever through all gear positions, stopping briefly in each position, then return the selector lever to the P position. Withdraw the dipstick from the tube, and wipe all the fluid from its end with a clean rag or paper towel. Insert the clean dipstick back into the tube as far as it will go, then withdraw it once more. Note the fluid level on the end of the dipstick. The fluid level should be between the two upper marks on the dipstick (the marks located on either side of the number '80') **(see illustration)**.

3 If topping-up is necessary, add the required quantity of the specified fluid to the transmission via the dipstick tube. Use a funnel with a fine-mesh gauze, to avoid spillage, and to ensure that no foreign matter enters the transmission. **Note:** *Never overfill the transmission so that the fluid level is above the upper mark.*

4 After topping-up, take the vehicle on a short run to distribute the fresh fluid, then recheck the level, topping-up if necessary.

5 Always maintain the level between the two upper dipstick marks. If the level is allowed to fall below the lower mark, fluid starvation may result, which could lead to severe transmission damage.

6 Frequent need for topping-up indicates that there is a leak, which should be found and corrected before it becomes serious.

AL4 transmission

7 Take the vehicle on a moderate journey (at least 30 minutes), to warm the transmission up to normal operating temperature, then park the vehicle on level ground.

8 The oil level is checked by removing the oil filler and oil level plugs from the transmission housing.

9 Remove the air cleaner air inlet duct as described in Chapter 4A.

10 To improve access to the oil level plug, which is on the base of the transmission housing, it may be preferable to jack up the front and rear of the car, and support it on axle stands (see *Jacking and vehicle support*); it is essential that the car is kept level for the check to be accurate. Remove the engine undertray for access to the plug.

11 Using a square-section wrench, remove the oil filler plug from the top of the transmission housing **(see illustration)**, and add 0.5 litres of the specified oil. As access to the filler plug is limited, Citroën mechanics use a filling bottle with a length of small-bore hose attached. The end of the hose is inserted into the filler orifice and the bottle (filled with the specified oil) is then suspended from the bonnet. A suitable alternative could easily be made up from, for example, a clean plastic drinks bottle with the base cut off and with a hose attached to the cap.

12 With the handbrake and footbrake firmly applied, start the engine and move the selector through all available positions several times. Finally, select P, and leave the engine running.

13 Working under the car, place a suitable container underneath the transmission, then remove the oil level plug **(see illustration)**. This is the smaller hex-head bolt inside the

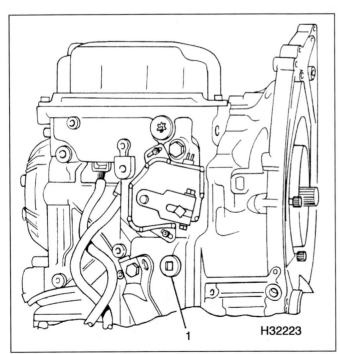

15.11 Automatic transmission oil filler plug (1), viewed from above – AL4 transmission

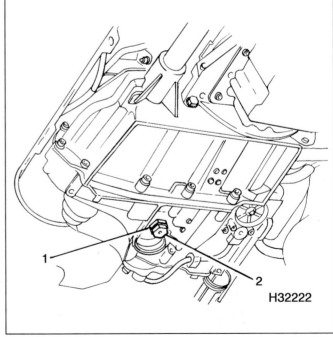

15.13 Automatic transmission oil level plug (2) is located inside the drain plug (1) – AL4 transmission

larger hex-headed transmission drain plug – do not loosen the larger, outer plug with the engine running, or the transmission oil will run out, resulting in transmission damage.

14 If the level is correct, oil will run from the level plug in a steady stream, quickly reducing to a sequence of drips. In theory, the amount of oil lost when the plug is removed should be the same as, or less than, the 0.5 litres just added. When the dripping stops, refit the level plug.

15 If little or no oil emerges, refit the level plug, then switch off the engine. Repeat paragraphs 11 to 14 until the level is correct.

16 On completion, tighten the filler and level plugs to the specified torque, then refit the engine undertray and air inlet duct.

17 Frequent need for topping-up indicates that there is a leak, which should be found and corrected before it becomes serious.

Every 25 000 miles (40 000 km) or 2 years – whichever comes first

16 Hinge and lock operation and lubrication

1 Work around the vehicle, and lubricate the hinges of the bonnet, doors and tailgate with a small amount of general-purpose oil.

2 Lightly lubricate the bonnet release mechanism and exposed section of inner cable with a smear of grease.

3 Check carefully the security and operation of all hinges, latches and locks, adjusting them where required. Check the operation of the central locking system (if fitted).

4 Check the condition and operation of the bonnet and tailgate struts, renewing them if they are leaking or no longer able to support the bonnet or tailgate securely when raised.

17 Automatic transmission fluid renewal – 4 HP 14 transmission

Note: *This procedure only applies to the 4 HP 14 automatic transmission. The AL4 type transmission is regarded as being 'lubricated for life' – refer to Chapter 7B.*

1 Take the vehicle on a short run, to warm the transmission up to operating temperature.

2 Park the car on level ground, then switch off the ignition and apply the handbrake firmly. Chock the rear wheels then jack up the front of the car and support it on axle stands (see *Jacking and vehicle support*). Note that, when refilling and checking the fluid level, the car must be level, to ensure accuracy.

3 Remove the engine undertray, then position a suitable container under the transmission. The transmission has two drain plugs: one on the sump, and another on the bottom of the differential housing **(see illustration)**.

⚠ *Warning: If the fluid is hot, take precautions against scalding.*

4 Remove the dipstick then unscrew both drain plugs, and allow the fluid to drain completely into the container. Clean the drain plugs, being especially careful to wipe any metallic particles off the magnetic insert. Discard the original sealing washers; these should be renewed whenever they are disturbed.

5 When the fluid has finished draining, clean the drain plug threads and those of the transmission casing. Fit a new sealing washer to each drain plug, and refit the plugs to the transmission, tightening each securely. If the car was raised for the draining operation, refit the engine undertray and lower the car to the ground. Make sure that the car is level (front-to-rear and side-to-side).

6 Refilling the transmission is an awkward operation, adding the specified type of fluid to the transmission a little at a time via the dipstick tube. Use a funnel with a fine-mesh gauze, to avoid spillage, and to ensure that no foreign matter enters the transmission. Allow plenty of time for the fluid level to settle properly. Fill the transmission until the level reaches the maximum cold mark. This is the middle notch of the three, next to the number '50'.

7 Once the level is up to the appropriate mark on the dipstick, refit the dipstick. Start the engine, and allow it to idle for a few minutes. Switch the engine off, then recheck the level, topping-up if necessary. Take the car on a moderate journey to fully distribute the new fluid around the transmission, then recheck the fluid level as described in Section 15.

18 Air filter renewal

1.4 and 1.6 litre engines

1 Slacken the retaining clip securing the air intake duct to the front of the air filter lid and the clip securing the lid to the throttle housing.

2 Disconnect the breather hose at the front of the air filter lid by slackening the retaining clip (where fitted) or disconnecting the quick-release connection.

3 Undo the screws securing the lid to the air filter housing. Release the lid from the air filter housing, air intake duct and throttle housing, then lift out the air filter element **(see illustration)**.

4 Wipe clean the inside of the filter housing and fit the new element.

5 Locate the air filter lid in position, engaging it with the throttle housing and air intake duct.

6 Secure the lid with the retaining screws and securely tighten the intake duct and throttle housing retaining clips.

7 Refit the breather hose and tighten the retaining clip (where fitted).

1.8 litre (8-valve) engines

8 Slacken the retaining clip, and disconnect the intake duct from the front of the air filter cover **(see illustration)**.

9 Slacken and remove the two retaining screws situated at the front of the cylinder head cover, then release the two air filter

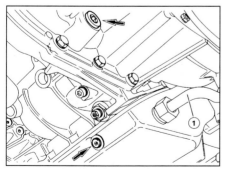

17.3 Automatic transmission fluid drain plugs (arrowed). Transmission is refilled via the dipstick tube (1) – 4 HP 14 transmission

18.3 Removing the air filter element on 1.4 litre engines

18.8 On 1.8 litre (8-valve) engines, disconnect the intake duct from the front of the cylinder head cover . . .

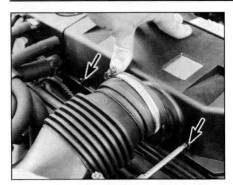

18.9a ... then slacken the retaining screws (arrowed) ...

18.9b ... and release the retaining clips

18.9c Lift off the filter cover ...

18.9d ... and withdraw the filter element

cover retaining clips. Remove the air filter cover from the cylinder head cover, and withdraw the filter element **(see illustrations)**.
10 Wipe clean the inside of the cylinder head cover and place the new element in position. Refit the filter cover, securing it in position with its retaining screws and clips.
11 Reconnect the intake duct to the air filter cover, and tighten its retaining clip.

1.8 and 2.0 litre (16-valve) engines

12 Slacken the retaining clip and disconnect the air intake duct from the air filter housing lid.
13 Undo the screws securing the lid to the air filter housing body and lift off the lid.
14 Lift out the filter element and wipe clean the housing body and lid.
15 Place the new element in position in the housing body. Refit the lid and secure it in position with the retaining screws.
16 Reconnect the inlet duct to the lid and tighten its retaining clip.

19 Rear brake shoe condition check

1 Chock the front wheels then jack up the rear of the car and support it on axle stands (see *Jacking and vehicle support*).
2 For a quick check, the thickness of friction material remaining on one of the brake shoes can be measured through the slot in the brake backplate that is exposed by prising out its sealing grommet **(see illustrations)**. If a rod of

the same diameter as the specified minimum thickness is placed against the shoe friction material, the amount of wear can quickly be assessed – a small mirror may help observation. If any shoe's friction material is worn to the specified thickness or less, all four shoes must be renewed as a set.
3 For a comprehensive check, the brake drums should be removed and cleaned. This will permit the wheel cylinders to be checked and the condition of the brake drum itself to be fully examined. Refer to Chapter 9 for further information.

20 Handbrake check and adjustment

Refer to Chapter 9.

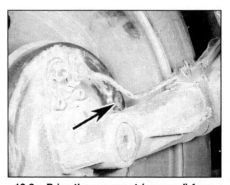

19.2a Prise the grommet (arrowed) from the rear drum brake backplate

19.2b Viewing the thickness of the brake shoe lining using a small mirror

21 Brake fluid renewal

> ⚠ *Warning: Brake hydraulic fluid can harm your eyes and damage painted surfaces, so use extreme caution when handling and pouring it. Do not use fluid that has been standing open for some time, as it absorbs moisture from the air. Excess moisture can cause a dangerous loss of braking effectiveness.*

1 The procedure is similar to that for the bleeding of the hydraulic system as described in Chapter 9, except that the brake fluid reservoir should be emptied by siphoning, using a clean poultry baster or similar before starting, and allowance should be made for the old fluid to be expelled when bleeding a section of the circuit.
2 Alternatively, to empty the reservoir, working as described in Chapter 9, open the first bleed screw in the sequence, and pump the brake pedal gently until nearly all the old fluid has been emptied from the master cylinder reservoir.

> **HAYNES HiNT** *Old hydraulic fluid is invariably much darker in colour than the new, making it easy to distinguish the two.*

3 Top-up to the MAX level with new fluid, and continue pumping until only the new fluid remains in the reservoir, and new fluid can be seen emerging from the bleed screw. Tighten the screw, and top the reservoir level up to the MAX level line.
4 Work through all the remaining bleed screws in the sequence until new fluid can be seen at all of them. Be careful to keep the master cylinder reservoir topped-up to above the MIN level at all times, or air may enter the system and increase the length of the task.
5 When the operation is complete, check that all bleed screws are securely tightened, and that their dust caps are refitted. Wash off all traces of spilt fluid, and recheck the master cylinder reservoir fluid level.
6 Check the operation of the brakes before taking the car on the road.

Every 37 500 miles (60 000 km) or 3 years – whichever comes first

22 Spark plug renewal

1 The correct functioning of the spark plugs is vital for the correct running and efficiency of the engine. It is essential that the plugs fitted are appropriate for the engine (a suitable type is specified at the start of this Chapter). If this type is used and the engine is in good condition, the spark plugs should not need attention between scheduled replacement intervals. Spark plug cleaning is rarely necessary, and should not be attempted unless specialised equipment is available, as damage can easily be caused to the firing ends.

1.4 and 1.6 litre engines

2 On early engines, if the marks on the original-equipment spark plug (HT) leads cannot be seen, mark the leads '1' to '4', to correspond to the cylinder the lead serves (No 1 cylinder is at the transmission end of the engine). Pull the leads from the plugs by gripping the end fitting, not the lead, otherwise the lead connection may be fractured.

3 On later engines fitted with a plug-top ignition coil module, remove the ignition coil module as described in Chapter 5B.

1.8 litre (8-valve) engines

4 With reference to Chapter 4A, remove the air intake duct for access to the spark plugs, then mark and disconnect the HT leads as described in paragraph 2.

1.8 and 2.0 litre (16-valve) engines

5 To gain access to the spark plugs, the ignition coil unit fitted in the centre of the cylinder head cover must first be removed. Disconnect the wiring connector at the left-hand end of the coil unit, then undo the six retaining bolts and lift the coil unit upwards, off the spark plugs and from its location in the cylinder head cover.

All engines

6 It is advisable to remove the dirt from the spark plug recesses using a clean brush, vacuum cleaner or compressed air before removing the plugs, to prevent dirt dropping into the cylinders.

7 Unscrew the plugs using a spark plug spanner, suitable box spanner or a deep socket and extension bar (see illustration). Keep the socket aligned with the spark plug – if it is forcibly moved to one side, the ceramic insulator may be broken off. As each plug is removed, examine it as follows.

8 Examination of the spark plugs will give a good indication of the condition of the engine. If the insulator nose of the spark plug is clean and white, with no deposits, this is indicative of a weak mixture or too hot a plug (a hot plug transfers heat away from the electrode slowly, a cold plug transfers heat away quickly).

9 If the tip and insulator nose are covered with hard black-looking deposits, then this is indicative that the mixture is too rich. Should the plug be black and oily, then it is likely that the engine is fairly worn, as well as the mixture being too rich.

10 If the insulator nose is covered with light tan to greyish-brown deposits, then the mixture is correct and it is likely that the engine is in good condition.

11 The spark plug electrode gap is of considerable importance as, if it is too large or too small, the size of the spark and its efficiency will be seriously impaired.

12 To set the gap on single-electrode spark plugs, measure the gap with a feeler blade, and then bend open, or closed, the outer plug electrode(s) until the correct gap is achieved (see illustration). The centre electrode should never be bent, as this may crack the insulator and cause plug failure, if nothing worse. If using feeler blades, the gap is correct when the appropriate-size blade is a firm sliding fit.

13 Special spark plug electrode gap adjusting tools are available from most motor accessory shops, or from spark plug manufacturers.

14 Check that the threaded connector sleeves are tight, and that the plug exterior and threads are clean, then insert the spark plugs into their locations (see Haynes Hint).

15 Remove the rubber hose (if used), and tighten the plug to the specified torque using the spark plug socket and a torque wrench. Refit the remaining spark plugs in the same manner.

16 On early 1.4 and 1.6 litre engines and all 1.8 litre (8-valve) engines, wipe the entire length of each spark plug HT lead to remove any built-up dirt and grease, using a clean rag. Once the leads are clean, check for burns, cracks and other damage. Do not bend the leads excessively, nor pull them lengthwise – the conductor inside is quite fragile, and might break. Connect the HT leads to the spark plugs in the correct order, and refit any components removed for access.

17 On later 1.4 and 1.6 litre engines, refit the ignition coil module as described in Chapter 5B.

18 On 1.8 and 2.0 litre (16-valve) engines, refit the ignition coil unit to the cylinder head cover and secure with the six bolts tightened securely. Reconnect the coil unit wiring connectors.

HAYNES HINT

It is very often difficult to insert spark plugs into their holes without cross-threading them. To avoid this possibility, fit a short length of 5/16 inch internal diameter rubber hose over the end of the spark plug. The flexible hose acts as a universal joint to help align the plug with the plug hole. Should the plug begin to cross-thread, the hose will slip on the spark plug, preventing thread damage to the cylinder head.

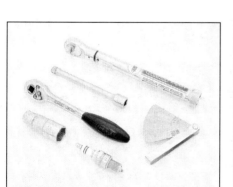

22.7 Tools required for spark plug removal, gap adjustment and refitting

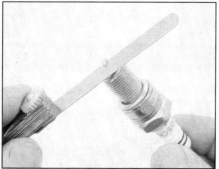

22.12 Measuring the spark plug gap with a feeler blade

23 Manual transmission oil level check

Note: *A suitable square-section wrench may be required to undo the transmission filler/level plugs. These wrenches can be obtained from most motor factors or your Citroën dealer. A new sealing washer will also be required when refitting the transmission filler/level plug.*

> **HAYNES HINT** *It may be possible to use the square end fitting on a ratchet handle (as found in a typical socket set) to undo the plug.*

1 The manual transmission oil does not need to be renewed as part of the regular maintenance schedule, but the oil level must be checked and if necessary topped-up at the interval specified here. To drain the transmission as part of a repair procedure, refer to the information given in Chapter 7A.
2 The oil level must be checked before the car is driven, or at least 5 minutes after the engine has been switched off. If the oil is checked immediately after driving the car, some of the oil will remain distributed around the transmission components, resulting in an inaccurate level reading.
3 With the car on level ground, firmly apply the handbrake, then jack up the front and rear of the car and support it securely on axle stands (see *Jacking and vehicle support*). Note that the car must be level, to ensure accuracy, when checking the oil level.
4 To gain access to the filler/level plug, remove the left-hand front roadwheel and the plastic wheelarch liner. The liner is secured by various screws and clips under the wheelarch. Release all the fasteners, and remove liner from under the front wing.
5 Wipe clean the area around the filler/level plug, which is on the left-hand end of the transmission **(see illustration)**. Unscrew the plug and clean it; discard the sealing washer.

6 The oil level should reach the lower edge of the filler/level hole. A certain amount of oil will have gathered behind the filler/level plug, and will trickle out when it is removed; this does **not** necessarily indicate that the level is correct. To ensure that a true level is established, wait until the initial trickle has stopped, then add oil as necessary until a trickle of new oil can be seen emerging **(see illustration)**. The level will be correct when the flow ceases; use only good-quality oil of the specified type (refer to *Lubricants and fluids*).
7 If the transmission has been overfilled so that oil flows out as soon as the filler/level plug is removed, check that the car is completely level (front-to-rear and side-to-side), and allow the surplus to drain off into a container.
8 When the level is correct, fit a new sealing washer to the filler/level plug, refit the plug and tighten it to the specified torque.
9 Refit the wheelarch liner and roadwheel, then lower the car to the ground. Tighten the roadwheel bolts to the specified torque.

24 Braking system check

1 Firmly apply the handbrake, then jack up the front of the car and support it securely on axle stands (see *Jacking and vehicle support*).
2 Inspect the area around both brake calipers for signs of brake fluid leakage, either from the piston seals, the brake pipe union or the bleed screw.
3 Examine the brake hoses leading to each caliper and check for signs of cracking, chafing or damage. Renew a hose which shows signs of deterioration without delay.
4 Ensure that the transmission is in neutral, then grasp each front wheel hub and turn it by hand. Slight resistance is normal, but if the hub is difficult to turn smoothly, this indicates that the brake pads are binding, possibly due to a seized or partially-seized brake caliper piston; refer to Chapter 9 for details of caliper removal and overhaul.

5 Remove the front brake pads as described in Chapter 9. Examine the brake pads and measure the depth of the remaining friction material. Renew all four pads, if any are worn below their minimum limit.
6 Using proprietary brake cleaning fluid and a stiff brush, wash all traces of dirt and brake dust from the brake calipers – take care to avoid inhaling any of the airborne brake dust. Examine the piston dust seal for signs of damage or deterioration and check that it is securely seated in its retaining groove.
7 Check the condition of the brake disc with reference to the information given in Chapter 9.
8 Refit the front brake pads as described in Chapter 9, then refit the roadwheels and lower the front of the car to the ground. Tighten the roadwheel bolts to the specified torque.
9 Chock the front wheels then jack up the rear of the car and support it on axle stands (see *Jacking and vehicle support*).
10 Ensure that the handbrake is released, then grasp each rear roadwheel and turn it by hand. Slight resistance is normal, but if the wheel is difficult to turn smoothly, this could be due to a seized or partially-seized wheel cylinder or brake caliper piston, or incorrect handbrake adjustment; refer to Chapter 9 for further details.

Models with rear drum brakes

11 Remove the rear roadwheels, then with reference to Chapter 9, remove the rear brake shoes. Examine the brake shoes and measure the depth of the remaining friction material. Renew all four brake shoes, if any are worn below their minimum limit.
12 Check the brake drums for wear and damage and check the area around the wheel cylinder piston seals for signs of fluid leakage. Check at the rear of the brake backplate for evidence of fluid leakage from the brake pipe union or bleed screw. Renew the wheel cylinder without delay if it shows signs of leakage; see Chapter 9 for details.
13 Using proprietary brake cleaning fluid and a stiff brush, wash all traces of dirt and brake dust from the wheel cylinders and backplates – take care to avoid inhaling any of the airborne brake dust.
14 On completion, refit the brake shoes, brake drums and roadwheels, then lower the car to the ground. Tighten the roadwheel bolts to the specified torque.

Models with rear disc brakes

15 Inspect the area around both brake calipers for signs of brake fluid leakage, either from the piston seals, the brake pipe union or the bleed screw.
16 Examine the brake hoses leading to each caliper and check for signs of cracking, chafing or damage. Renew a hose which shows signs of deterioration without delay.
17 Remove the rear brake pads as described in Chapter 9. Examine the brake pads and measure the depth of the remaining friction

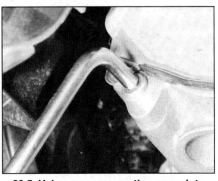

23.5 Using a square-section wrench to unscrew the transmission filler/level plug – MA transmission

23.6 Topping-up the transmission oil level

material. Renew all four pads, if any are worn below their minimum limit.

18 Using proprietary brake cleaning fluid and a stiff brush, wash all traces of dirt and brake dust from the brake calipers – take care to avoid inhaling any of the airborne brake dust. Examine the piston dust seal for signs of damage or deterioration and check that it is securely seated in its retaining groove.

19 Check the condition of the brake disc with reference to the information given in Chapter 9.

20 Refit the rear brake pads as described in Chapter 9, then refit the roadwheels and lower the car to the ground. Tighten the roadwheel bolts to the specified torque.

25 Fuel filter renewal

> **Warning: Before carrying out the following operation, refer to the precautions given in 'Safety first!' at the beginning of this manual, and follow them implicitly. Petrol is a highly-dangerous and volatile liquid, and the precautions necessary when handling it cannot be overstressed.**

1 The fuel filter is situated underneath the rear of the vehicle, on the side of the fuel tank. To gain access to the filter, chock the front wheels then jack up the rear of the car and support it on axle stands (see *Jacking and vehicle support*).

2 Seal off the fuel hoses leading to and from the filter, using proprietary hose clamps, with

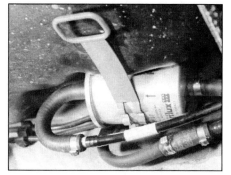

25.3 Release the fuel filter strap from the tank . . .

25.4 . . . then detach the hoses and remove the filter. Note the direction of the arrow on the filter body

rounded jaws – do not use G-clamps, self-locking grips, or similar with flat or square jaws as these could damage the hose internally, causing leakage later.

3 Unclip the filter retaining strap from the fuel tank **(see illustration)**.

4 Noting the direction of the arrow marked on the filter body, release the quick-release fittings and disconnect the fuel hoses from the filter **(see illustrations)**.

5 Remove the filter from the car. Dispose of the old filter safely; it will be highly flammable, and may explode if thrown on a fire.

6 Slide the new filter into position and clip the filter strap back onto the fuel tank. Ensure that the arrow on the filter body is pointing in the direction of the fuel flow, as noted when removing the old filter. The flow direction can otherwise be determined by tracing the fuel hoses back along their length.

7 Connect the fuel hoses to the filter by pressing each hose onto its respective filter

port until it 'snaps' into position. Remove the hose clamps.

8 Start the engine, check the filter hose connections for leaks, then lower the vehicle to the ground.

26 Timing belt renewal

Refer to Chapter 2A or 2B as applicable.
Note: *Although the normal interval for timing belt renewal is 75 000 miles (120 000 km), it is strongly recommended that the interval is halved to 37 500 miles (60 000 km) on vehicles which are subjected to intensive use, ie. mainly short journeys or a lot of stop-start driving. The actual belt renewal interval is therefore very much up to the individual owner, but bear in mind that severe engine damage will result if the belt breaks.*

Every 75 000 miles (120 000 km) or 5 years – whichever comes first

27 Coolant renewal

> **Warning: Wait until the engine is cold before starting this procedure. Do not allow antifreeze to come in contact with your skin, or with the painted surfaces of the vehicle. Rinse off spills immediately with plenty of water. Never leave antifreeze lying around in an open container, or in a puddle in the driveway or on the garage floor. Children and pets are attracted by its sweet smell, but antifreeze can be fatal if ingested.**

Cooling system draining

1 With the engine completely cold, remove the expansion tank filler cap. Turn the cap anti-clockwise until it reaches the first stop. Wait until any pressure remaining in the system is

released, then push the cap down, turn it anti-clockwise to the second stop, and lift it off.

2 Position a suitable container beneath the coolant drain outlet at the lower left-hand side of the radiator.

3 Loosen the drain plug (there is no need to remove it completely) and allow the coolant to drain into the container. If desired, a length of

tubing can be fitted to the drain outlet to direct the flow of coolant during draining.

4 To assist draining, open the cooling system bleed screws which are located on the top left-hand side of the radiator, in the heater matrix outlet hose union on the engine compartment bulkhead, and on the top of the thermostat housing **(see illustrations)**. On

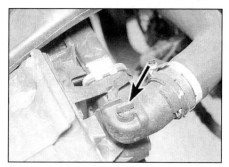

27.4a Radiator bleed screw (arrowed) – 1.4 litre engines

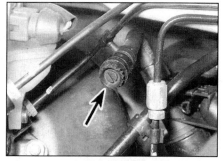

27.4b Heater hose bleed screw (arrowed) – 1.4 litre engines

1.8 litre (8-valve) engines, there may be an additional bleed screw adjacent to the thermostat housing.

5 To drain the cylinder block on 1.4 and 1.6 litre engines, reposition the container below the drain plug located at the front left-hand side of the cylinder block. Remove the drain plug, and allow the coolant to drain into the container.

6 To drain the cylinder block on 1.8 and 2.0 litre engines, firmly apply the handbrake, then jack up the front of the car and support it securely on axle stands (see *Jacking and vehicle support*). Remove the engine undertray and reposition the container below the radiator bottom hose connection at the rear right-hand side of the cylinder block. Disconnect the bottom hose and allow the coolant to drain into the container.

7 If the coolant has been drained for a reason other than renewal, then provided it is clean and less than five years old, it can be re-used, though this is not recommended.

8 Refit the radiator and cylinder block drain plugs and/or radiator bottom hose on completion of draining. Where applicable, refit the engine undertray and lower the car to the ground.

Cooling system flushing

9 If coolant renewal has been neglected, or if the antifreeze mixture has become diluted, then in time, the cooling system may gradually lose efficiency, as the coolant passages become restricted due to rust, scale deposits, and other sediment. The cooling system efficiency can be restored by flushing the system clean.

10 The radiator should be flushed separately from the engine, to avoid excess contamination.

Radiator flushing

11 To flush the radiator, disconnect the top and bottom hoses and any other relevant hoses from the radiator, with reference to Chapter 3.

12 Insert a garden hose into the radiator top inlet. Direct a flow of clean water through the radiator, and continue flushing until clean water emerges from the radiator bottom outlet.

13 If after a reasonable period, the water still does not run clear, the radiator can be flushed with a suitable proprietary cleaning agent, suitable for radiators of plastic/aluminium construction. It is important that the instructions provided with the product are followed carefully. If the contamination is particularly bad, insert the hose in the radiator bottom outlet, and reverse-flush the radiator.

Engine flushing

14 To flush the engine, tighten the cooling

system bleed screws, then remove the thermostat (see Chapter 3). Temporarily refit the thermostat cover, without the thermostat.

15 With the top and bottom hoses disconnected from the radiator, insert a garden hose into the radiator top hose. Direct a clean flow of water through the engine, and continue flushing until clean water emerges from the radiator bottom hose.

16 When flushing is complete, refit the thermostat and reconnect the hoses with reference to Chapter 3.

Cooling system filling

17 Before attempting to fill the cooling system, make sure that all hoses and clips are in good condition, and that the clips are tight. Note that an antifreeze mixture must be used all year round, to prevent corrosion of the engine components (see following sub-Section). Also check that the radiator and cylinder block drain plugs are in place and tight.

18 Remove the expansion tank filler cap.

19 Open all the cooling system bleed screws (see paragraph 4).

20 Some of the cooling system hoses are positioned at a higher level than the top of the radiator expansion tank. It is therefore necessary to use a 'header tank' when refilling the cooling system, to reduce the possibility of air being trapped in the system. Although Citroën dealers use a special header tank, the same effect can be achieved by using a suitable bottle, with a seal between the bottle and the expansion tank **(see Haynes Hint)**.

21 Fit the 'header tank' to the expansion tank and slowly fill the system. Coolant will emerge from each of the bleed screws in turn, starting with the lowest screw. As soon as coolant free from air bubbles emerges from the lowest screw, tighten that screw, and watch the next bleed screw in the system. Repeat the procedure until the coolant is emerging from the highest bleed screw in the cooling system and all bleed screws are securely tightened.

22 Ensure that the 'header tank' is full (at least 0.5 litres of coolant). Start the engine, and run it at a fast idle speed (do not exceed 2000 rpm) until the cooling fan cuts in, and then cuts out. Stop the engine. **Note:** *Take great care not to scald yourself.*

23 Allow the engine to cool, then remove the 'header tank'.

24 When the engine has cooled, check the coolant level with reference to *Weekly checks*. Top-up the level if necessary, and refit the expansion tank cap.

Antifreeze mixture

25 The antifreeze should always be renewed at the specified intervals. This is necessary not only to maintain the antifreeze properties,

Cut the bottom off an old antifreeze container to make a 'header tank' for use when refilling the cooling system. The seal at the point arrowed must be as airtight as possible.

but also to prevent corrosion which would otherwise occur as the corrosion inhibitors become progressively less effective.

26 Always use an ethylene-glycol based antifreeze which is suitable for use in mixed-metal cooling systems. A general guide to the quantity of antifreeze and levels of protection is given in the Specifications, but follow the instructions provided by the antifreeze manufacturer for exact requirements.

27 Before adding antifreeze, the cooling system should be completely drained, preferably flushed, and all hoses checked for condition and security.

28 After filling with antifreeze, a label should be attached to the expansion tank, stating the type and concentration of antifreeze used, and the date installed. Any subsequent topping-up should be made with the same type and concentration of antifreeze.

29 Do not use engine antifreeze in the windscreen/tailgate washer system, as it will damage the vehicle paintwork. A screenwash additive should be added to the washer system in the quantities stated on the bottle.

Every 10 years – regardless of mileage

28 Air bag(s) and seat belt pre-tensioner renewal

Due to the safety critical nature of the air bag and seat belt pre-tensioner components, these operations must be carried out by a Citroën dealer.

Chapter 1 Part B:
Routine maintenance and servicing – diesel engine models

Contents

Air bag(s) and seat belt pre-tensioner renewal 26
Air filter renewal 18
Auxiliary drivebelt check and renewal 6
Brake fluid renewal 21
Braking system check 23
Clutch control mechanism check 7
Coolant renewal 25
Driveshaft gaiter check 9
Engine oil and filter renewal 3
Exhaust smoke test 14
Exhaust system check 13
Front brake pad condition check 11
Fuel filter renewal 17

Fuel filter water draining 4
General information 1
Handbrake check and adjustment 20
Hinge and lock operation and lubrication 16
Manual transmission oil level check 22
Pollen filter renewal 8
Rear brake pad condition check 12
Rear brake shoe condition check 19
Regular maintenance 2
Road test 15
Steering and suspension check 10
Timing belt renewal 24
Underbonnet/underbody component/hose fluid leak check 5

Degrees of difficulty

		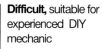		
Easy, suitable for novice with little experience	**Fairly easy,** suitable for beginner with some experience	**Fairly difficult,** suitable for competent DIY mechanic	**Difficult,** suitable for experienced DIY mechanic	**Very difficult,** suitable for expert DIY or professional

Lubricants and fluids . . . .   Refer to end of *Weekly checks*

Capacities

Engine oil (including filter)
1.9 litre engines:
   Without air conditioning . . . .   4.75 litres
   With air conditioning . . . .   4.50 litres
2.0 litre engines:
   Without air conditioning . . . .   4.50 litres
   With air conditioning . . . .   4.25 litres
Difference between MAX and MIN dipstick marks (approx.) . . . .   1.25 litres

Cooling system (approximate)
1.9 litre (XUD series) engines*:
   Non-turbo models without air conditioning . . . .   8.0 litres
   Non-turbo models with air conditioning . . . .   9.5 litres
   Turbo models without air conditioning . . . .   9.0 litres
   Turbo models with air conditioning . . . .   9.5 litres
1.9 litre (DW series) engines* . . . .   9.0 litres
2.0 litre engines . . . .   9.5 litres

Manual transmission . . . .   2.0 litres

Fuel tank . . . .   54.0 litres

Refer to Chapter 2C and 2D for information on engine identification

Engine
Auxiliary drivebelt tension (for use with electronic tension checking tool – see text):
   1.9 litre (XUD series) engines** . . . .   115 ± 10 SEEM units
   1.9 litre (DW series) engines**:
      Initial setting . . . .   144 ± 3 SEEM units
      Final setting . . . .   130 ± 4 SEEM units

**Refer to Chapter 2C and 2D for information on engine identification*

Cooling system
Antifreeze mixture:
   28% antifreeze . . . .   Protection down to –15°C
   50% antifreeze . . . .   Protection down to –30°C
Note: *Refer to antifreeze manufacturer for latest recommendations.*

Preheating system
Glow plugs type*:
   1.9 litre:
      Engine code WJZ . . . .   Bosch 0 250 202 020
      Engine code DJY . . . .   Bosch 0 250 201 039
      Engine code DHY . . . .   Bosch 0 250 201 039
      Engine code DHV . . . .   Bosch 0 250 201 042
   2.0 litre . . . .   Bosch 0 250 202 032

Refer to Chapter 2C and 2D for information on engine identification

Brakes

Brake pad friction material minimum thickness . . . . 2.0 mm
Brake shoe friction material minimum thickness . . . . 1.5 mm

Tyre pressures . . . . Refer to end of *Weekly checks*

Torque wrench settings	Nm	lbf ft
Auxiliary drivebelt eccentric tensioner pulley bolt (all engines)	44	32
Auxiliary drivebelt tensioner pulley arm retaining bolt		
(DW series engines)	95	70
Auxiliary drivebelt tensioner pulley bolts (XUD series engines)	22	16
Manual transmission oil filler/level plug	20	15
Roadwheel bolts	85	63

Component locations – diesel engine models

Underbonnet view of a 1.9 litre (XUD series) turbo engine

1 Engine oil filler cap/dipstick
2 Intercooler
3 Battery
4 Brake master cylinder fluid reservoir
5 Engine compartment fuse/relay box
6 Diesel preheating system control unit
7 Air cleaner air inlet duct
8 Fuel filter
9 Injection pump
10 Expansion tank filler cap
11 Power steering pump
12 Windscreen/tailgate washer fluid reservoir
    filler cap
13 Power steering fluid reservoir filler cap
14 Suspension strut upper mounting
15 Fuel system priming pump

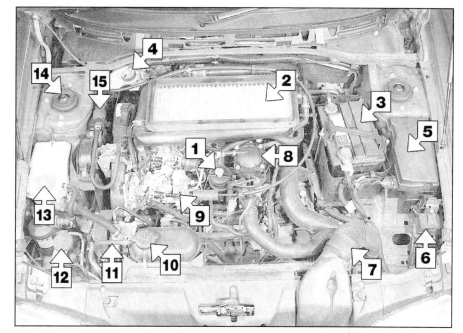

Underbonnet view of a 2.0 litre engine

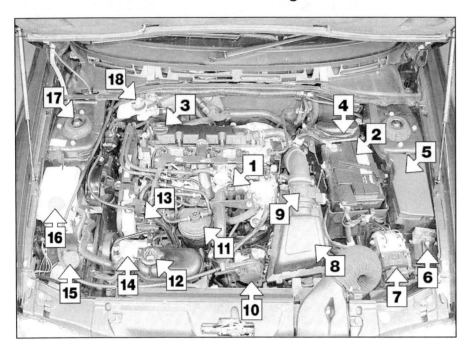

1 Engine oil dipstick
2 Battery
3 Engine oil filler cap
4 Engine management ECU box
5 Engine compartment fuse/relay box
6 Diesel preheating system control unit
7 ABS hydraulic modulator
8 Air cleaner housing
9 Air mass meter
10 Accelerator pedal position sensor
11 Fuel filter
12 Expansion tank filler cap
13 High pressure fuel pump
14 Power steering pump
15 Windscreen/tailgate washer fluid reservoir filler cap
16 Power steering fluid reservoir filler cap
17 Suspension strut upper mounting
18 Brake master cylinder fluid reservoir

Front underbody view of a 1.9 litre (XUD series) turbo engine model

1 Sump drain plug
2 Air conditioning compressor
3 Air conditioning refrigerant pipes
4 Air cleaner housing
5 Power steering pipe
6 Transmission oil drain plug
7 Front suspension lower arm
8 Front brake caliper
9 Track rod balljoint
10 Front anti-roll bar
11 Front suspension subframe
12 Steering gear assembly
13 Right-hand driveshaft
14 Engine/transmission rear mounting

Front underbody view of a 2.0 litre model

1 Sump drain plug
2 Alternator
3 Power steering pipe
4 Transmission oil drain plug
5 Front suspension lower arm
6 Front brake caliper
7 Track rod balljoint
8 Front anti-roll bar
9 Front suspension subframe
10 Steering gear assembly
11 Right-hand driveshaft
12 Engine/transmission rear mounting

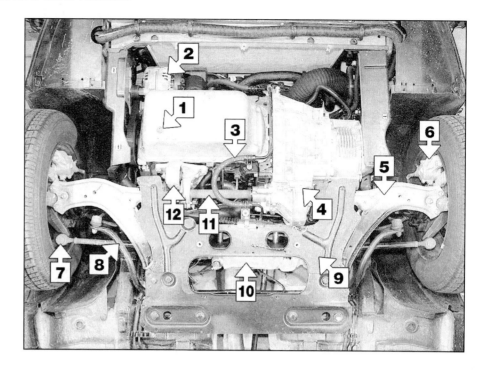

Rear underbody view of a 2.0 litre model

1 Spare wheel
2 Rear silencer
3 Fuel tank
4 Handbrake cable
5 Rear suspension torsion bar
6 Rear suspension tubular crossmember
7 Rear shock absorber
8 Rear suspension trailing arm

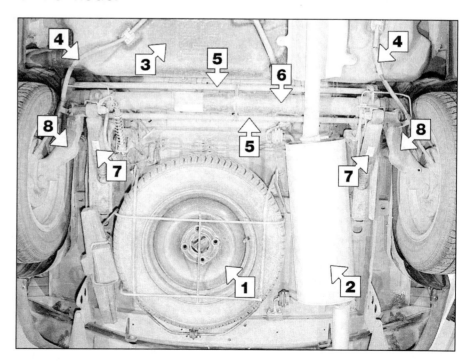

The maintenance intervals in this manual are provided with the assumption that you, not the dealer, will be carrying out the work. These are the minimum maintenance intervals recommended for vehicles driven daily. If you wish to keep your vehicle in peak condition at all times, you may wish to perform some of these procedures more often. We encourage frequent maintenance, because it enhances the efficiency, performance and resale value of your vehicle.

If the vehicle is driven in dusty areas, used to tow a trailer, or driven frequently at slow speeds (idling in traffic) or on short journeys, more frequent maintenance intervals are recommended.

When the vehicle is new, it should be serviced by a factory-authorised dealer service department, in order to preserve the factory warranty.

Valve clearance checking is no longer specified as part of the routine maintenance schedule. Check the valve clearances if there is any tapping or rattling from the top of the engine, or in the event of an unexplained lack of performance. The prudent owner may wish to check the clearances more often, perhaps at 20 000 mile (30 000 km) or two-yearly intervals.

Every 250 miles (400 km) or weekly

☐ Refer to *Weekly checks*

Every 10 000 miles (15 000 km) or 12 months – whichever comes first

☐ Renew the engine oil and filter (Section 3)*.
☐ Drain any water from the fuel filter (Section 4).
☐ Check all underbonnet/underbody components for fluid leaks (Section 5).
☐ Check the condition of the auxiliary drivebelt (Section 6).
☐ Check the clutch control mechanism (Section 7).
☐ Renew the pollen filter (Section 8).
☐ Check the condition of the driveshaft rubber gaiters (Section 9).
☐ Check the steering and suspension components (Section 10).
☐ Check the condition of the front brake pads (Section 11).
☐ Check the condition of the rear brake pads – models with rear disc brakes (Section 12).
☐ Check the condition of the exhaust system (Section 13).
☐ Carry out an exhaust smoke test (Section 14).
☐ Road test (Section 15).
*Note: *The engine oil renewal interval shown is based on the use of either a semi-synthetic or fully synthetic engine oil. If an inferior quality oil is used, the interval should be reduced. Consult your Citroën dealer for further information.*

Every 20 000 miles (30 000 km) or 2 years – whichever comes first

In addition to all the items listed above, carry out the following:
☐ Operate and lubricate all hinges and locks (Section 16).
☐ Renew the fuel filter (Section 17).
☐ Renew the air filter (Section 18).
☐ Check the condition of the rear brake shoes – models with rear drum brakes (Section 19).
☐ Check the operation of the handbrake (Section 20).
☐ Renew the brake fluid (Section 21).

Every 40 000 miles (60 000 km) or 4 years – whichever comes first

In addition to all the items listed above, carry out the following:
☐ Check the manual transmission oil level (Section 22).
☐ Check the condition and operation of the braking system components (Section 23).
☐ Renew the timing belt (Section 24).
Note: *Although the normal interval for timing belt renewal is 80 000 miles (120 000 km), it is strongly recommended that the interval is halved to 40 000 miles (60 000 km) on vehicles which are subjected to intensive use, ie. mainly short journeys or a lot of stop-start driving. The actual belt renewal interval is therefore very much up to the individual owner, but bear in mind that severe engine damage will result if the belt breaks.*

Every 80 000 miles (120 000 km) or 5 years – whichever comes first

In addition to all the items listed above, carry out the following:
☐ Renew the coolant (Section 25).

Every 10 years – regardless of mileage

☐ Renew the air bag(s) and seat belt pre-tensioners (Section 26).

1 General information

This Chapter is designed to help the home mechanic maintain his/her vehicle for safety, economy, long life and peak performance.

The Chapter contains a master maintenance schedule, followed by Sections dealing specifically with each task in the schedule. Visual checks, adjustments, component renewal and other helpful items are included. Refer to the accompanying illustrations of the engine compartment and the underside of the vehicle for the locations of the various components.

Servicing your vehicle in accordance with the mileage/time maintenance schedule and the following Sections will provide a planned maintenance programme, which should result in a long and reliable service life. This is a comprehensive plan, so maintaining some items but not others at the specified service intervals will not produce the same results.

As you service your vehicle, you will discover that many of the procedures can – and should – be grouped together, because of the particular procedure being performed, or because of the proximity of two otherwise-unrelated components to one another. For example, if the vehicle is raised for any reason, the exhaust can be inspected at the same time as the suspension and steering components.

The first step in this maintenance programme is to prepare yourself before the actual work begins. Read through all the Sections relevant to the work to be carried out, then make a list and gather all the parts and tools required. If a problem is encountered, seek advice from a parts specialist, or a dealer service department.

Service interval display

Certain Xsara models are equipped with a service interval display indicator in the instrument panel. When the ignition is initially switched on, a spanner appears in the display window and the total number of miles remaining until the next service is due, is also shown.

The display should not necessarily be used as a definitive guide to the servicing needs of your Xsara, but it is useful as a reminder, to ensure that servicing is not accidentally overlooked. Owners of older cars, or those covering a small annual mileage, may feel inclined to service their car more often, in which case the service interval display is perhaps less relevant.

The display should be reset whenever a service is carried out, and this is achieved using the trip meter reset button on the instrument panel as follows.

With the ignition switched off, press and hold down the trip meter reset button. Switch the ignition on and the mileage remaining until the next service will flash. Continue to hold the button down for a further ten seconds. The spanner symbol will disappear and the mileage will return to zero.

2 Regular maintenance

1 If, from the time the vehicle is new, the routine maintenance schedule is followed closely, and frequent checks are made of fluid levels and high-wear items, as suggested throughout this manual, the engine will be kept in relatively good running condition, and the need for additional work will be minimised.
2 It is possible that there will be times when the engine is running poorly due to the lack of regular maintenance. This is even more likely if a used vehicle, which has not received

regular and frequent maintenance checks, is purchased. In such cases, additional work may need to be carried out, outside of the regular maintenance intervals.
3 If engine wear is suspected, a compression test or leakdown test (refer to the relevant Part of Chapter 2) will provide valuable information regarding the overall performance of the main internal components. Such a test can be used as a basis to decide on the extent of the work to be carried out. If, for example, a compression or leakdown test indicates serious internal engine wear, conventional maintenance as described in this Chapter will not greatly improve the performance of the engine, and may prove a waste of time and money, unless extensive overhaul work is carried out first.
4 The following series of operations are those most often required to improve the performance of a generally poor-running engine:

Primary operations

a) Clean, inspect and test the battery (See Weekly checks).
b) Check all the engine-related fluids (see Weekly checks).
c) Check the fuel filter (Sections 4 and 17).
d) Check the condition of all hoses, and check for fluid leaks (Section 5).
e) Check the condition and tension of the auxiliary drivebelt (Section 6).
f) Check the condition of the air filter, and renew if necessary (Section 18).

5 If the above operations do not prove fully effective, carry out the following secondary operations:

Secondary operations

All items listed under *Primary operations*, plus the following:
a) Check the charging system (Chapter 5A).
b) Check the preheating system (Chapter 5C).
c) Check the fuel system (Chapter 4B or 4C).

Every 10 000 miles (15 000 km) or 12 months – whichever comes first

3 Engine oil and filter renewal

Note: *A suitable square-section wrench may be required to undo the sump drain plug on some engines. These wrenches can be obtained from most motor factors or your Citroën dealer.*

1 Frequent oil and filter changes are the most important preventative maintenance procedures which can be undertaken by the

DIY owner. As engine oil ages, it becomes diluted and contaminated, which leads to premature engine wear.
2 Before starting this procedure, gather together all the necessary tools and materials. Also make sure that you have plenty of clean rags and newspapers handy, to mop up any spills. Ideally, the engine oil should be warm, as it will drain better, and any impurities suspended in the oil will be removed with it. Take care, however, not to touch the exhaust or any other hot parts of the engine when working under the vehicle. To avoid any

possibility of scalding, and to protect yourself from possible skin irritants and other harmful contaminants in used engine oils, it is advisable to wear gloves when carrying out this work. Access to the underside of the vehicle will be greatly improved if it can be raised on a lift, driven onto ramps, or jacked up and supported on axle stands (see *Jacking and vehicle support*). Whichever method is chosen, make sure that the vehicle remains level, or if it is at an angle, that the drain plug is at the lowest point.
3 Remove the engine undertray, then slacken

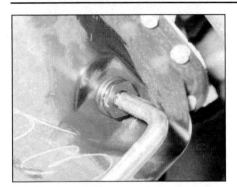

3.3 Slackening the sump drain plug with a square-section wrench

As the drain plug releases from the threads, move it away sharply so the stream of oil issuing from the sump runs into the container, not up your sleeve.

3.7 Using an oil filter removal tool to slacken the oil filter

the sump drain plug about half a turn; on some engines, a square-section wrench may be needed to slacken the plug **(see illustration)**. Position the draining container under the drain plug, then remove the plug completely. If possible, try to keep the plug pressed into the sump while unscrewing it by hand the last couple of turns **(see Haynes Hint)**. Recover the sealing ring from the drain plug.

4 Allow some time for the old oil to drain, noting that it may be necessary to reposition the container as the oil flow slows to a trickle.

5 After all the oil has drained, wipe off the drain plug with a clean rag, and fit a new sealing washer. Clean the area around the drain plug opening, and refit the plug. Tighten the plug securely.

6 Move the container into position under the oil filter, which is located on the front facing side of the cylinder block.

7 Using an oil filter removal tool if necessary, slacken the filter initially, then unscrew it by hand the rest of the way **(see illustration)**. Empty the oil in the old filter into the container. To ensure that the old filter is completely empty before disposal, puncture the filter dome in at least two places and allow any remaining oil to drain through the punctures and into the container.

8 Use a clean rag to remove all oil and dirt from the filter sealing area on the engine. Check the old filter to make sure that the rubber sealing ring hasn't stuck to the engine. If it has, carefully remove it.

9 Apply a light coating of clean engine oil to the sealing ring on the new filter, then screw it into position on the engine. Tighten the filter firmly by hand only – do not use any tools.

10 Refit the engine undertray then remove the old oil and all tools from under the car. Lower the car to the ground (if applicable).

11 Remove the dipstick, then unscrew the oil filler cap from the cylinder head cover or oil filler/breather neck (as applicable). Fill the engine, using the correct grade and type of oil (see *Lubricants and fluids*). An oil can spout or funnel may help to reduce

spillage. Pour in half the specified quantity of oil first, then wait a few minutes for the oil to fall to the sump. Continue adding oil a small quantity at a time until the level is up to the lower mark on the dipstick. Adding approximately 1.25 litres will bring the level up to the upper mark on the dipstick. Refit the filler cap.

12 Start the engine and run it for a few minutes; check for leaks around the oil filter seal and the sump drain plug. Note that there may be a delay of a few seconds before the oil pressure warning light goes out when the engine is first started, as the oil circulates through the engine oil galleries and the new oil filter before the pressure builds up.

13 Switch off the engine, and wait a few minutes for the oil to settle in the sump once more. With the new oil circulated and the filter completely full, recheck the level on the dipstick, and add more oil as necessary.

14 Dispose of the used engine oil and filter safely, with reference to *General repair procedures* at the rear of this manual. Do not discard the old filter with domestic household waste. The facility for waste oil disposal provided by many local council refuse tips generally has a filter receptacle alongside.

4 Fuel filter water draining

Note: *Refer to Chapter 2C and 2D for information on engine identification.*

1.9 litre (XUD series) engines

1 A water drain screw and tube are provided at the base of the fuel filter housing.

2 Place a suitable container beneath the drain tube and use rags to protect the surrounding area.

3 Open the drain screw by turning it anti-clockwise, and allow fuel and water to drain

until fuel, free from water, emerges from the end of the tube **(see illustration)**. Close the drain screw, and tighten it securely.

4 Dispose of the drained fuel and rags safely.

5 Start the engine. If difficulty is experienced, bleed the fuel system (see Chapter 4B).

1.9 litre (DW series) engines

6 Release the clip in the centre of the engine cover and undo the retaining screw on the right-hand side. Remove the engine oil dipstick then lift the cover off the engine.

7 Place a container and some clean rags beneath the fuel filter housing on the front of the engine.

8 Open the drain screw, located at the base of the filter, by turning it anti-clockwise.

9 Operate the priming pump on the side of the filter housing to allow fuel and water to drain. Continue until fuel, free from water, emerges from the drain screw. Close the drain screw, and tighten it securely.

10 Dispose of the drained fuel and rags safely.

11 Refit the engine cover and dipstick then start the engine. If difficulty is experienced, bleed the fuel system (see Chapter 4B).

2.0 litre engines

12 Release the four plastic fasteners and remove the engine cover from the top of the engine.

13 Place a container beneath the fuel filter housing on the front of the engine.

14 Open the drain screw, located at the base

4.3 Opening the fuel filter water drain plug – 1.9 litre (XUD series) engines

4.14 Fuel filter water drain plug location (arrowed) – 2.0 litre engines

A leak in the cooling system will usually show up as white- or rust-coloured deposits on the area adjoining the leak.

of the filter, by turning it anti-clockwise (see illustration).

15 Allow fuel and water to drain until fuel, free from water, emerges from the drain screw. Close the drain screw, and tighten it securely.

16 Dispose of the drained fuel safely.

17 Refit the engine cover and start the engine. Priming is not required as the fuel system is self-bleeding.

5 Underbonnet/underbody component/hose fluid leak check

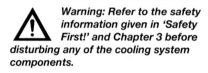

> **Warning: Refer to the safety information given in 'Safety First!' and Chapter 3 before disturbing any of the cooling system components.**

1 Carefully check the radiator and heater coolant hoses along their entire length. Renew any hose which is cracked, swollen or which shows signs of deterioration. Cracks will show up better if the hose is squeezed. Pay close attention to the clips that secure the hoses to the cooling system components. Hose clips that have been over-tightened can pinch and puncture hoses, resulting in cooling system leaks.

2 Inspect all the cooling system components (hoses, joint faces, etc) for leaks. Where any problems of this nature are found on system components, renew the component or gasket with reference to Chapter 3 **(see Haynes Hint)**.

Fuel

> **Warning: Refer to the safety information given in 'Safety First!' and Chapter 4B or 4C before disturbing any of the fuel system components.**

3 Unlike petrol leaks, diesel leaks are fairly easy to pinpoint; diesel fuel tends to settle on the surface around the point of leakage collecting dirt, rather than evaporate. If you suspect that there is a fuel leak from the area of the engine bay, leave the vehicle overnight then start the engine from cold, and allow it to

idle with the bonnet open. Metal components tend to shrink when they are cold, and rubber seals and hoses tend to harden, so any leaks may be more apparent whilst the engine is warming-up from a cold start.

4 Check all fuel lines at their connections to the fuel injection pump, or high pressure fuel pump, and fuel filter. Examine each rubber fuel hose along its length for splits or cracks. Check for leakage from the crimped joints between rubber and metal fuel lines. Examine the unions between the metal fuel lines and the fuel filter housing. Also check the area around the fuel injectors for signs of leakage.

5 To identify fuel leaks between the fuel tank and the engine bay, the vehicle should be raised and securely supported on axle stands (see *Jacking and vehicle support*). Inspect the fuel tank and filler neck for punctures, cracks and other damage. The connection between the filler neck and tank is especially critical. Sometimes a rubber filler neck or connecting hose will leak due to loose retaining clamps or deteriorated rubber.

6 Carefully check all rubber hoses and metal fuel lines leading away from the fuel tank. Check for loose connections, deteriorated hoses, kinked lines, and other damage. Pay particular attention to the vent pipes and hoses, which often loop up around the filler neck and can become blocked or kinked, making tank filling difficult. Follow the fuel supply and return lines to the front of the vehicle, carefully inspecting them all the way for signs of damage or corrosion. Renew damaged sections as necessary.

Engine oil

7 Inspect the area around the cylinder head cover, cylinder head, oil filter and sump joint faces. Bear in mind that, over a period of time, some very slight seepage from these areas is to be expected – what you are really looking for is any indication of a serious leak caused by gasket failure. Engine oil seeping from the base of the timing belt cover or the transmission bellhousing may be an indication of crankshaft or transmission input shaft oil seal failure. Should a leak be found, renew the

failed gasket or oil seal by referring to the appropriate Chapter in this manual.

Power steering fluid

8 Examine the hose running between the fluid reservoir and the power steering pump, and the return hose running from the steering rack to the fluid reservoir. Also examine the high pressure supply hose between the pump and the steering rack.

9 Check the condition of each hose carefully. Look for deterioration caused by corrosion and damage from grounding, or debris thrown up from the road surface.

10 Pay particular attention to crimped unions, and the area surrounding the hoses that are secured with adjustable worm drive clips. Power steering fluid is a thin oil, and is usually red in colour.

Air conditioning refrigerant

> **Warning: Refer to the safety information given in 'Safety First!' and Chapter 3, regarding the dangers of disturbing any of the air conditioning system components.**

11 The air conditioning system is filled with a liquid refrigerant, which is retained under high pressure. If the air conditioning system is opened and depressurised without the aid of specialised equipment, the refrigerant will immediately turn into gas and escape into the atmosphere. If the liquid comes into contact with your skin, it can cause severe frostbite. In addition, the refrigerant contains substances which are environmentally damaging; for this reason, it should not be allowed to escape into the atmosphere.

12 Any suspected air conditioning system leaks should be immediately referred to a Citroën dealer or air conditioning specialist. Leakage will be shown up as a steady drop in the level of refrigerant in the system.

13 Note that water may drip from the condenser drain pipe, underneath the car, immediately after the air conditioning system has been in use. This is normal, and should not be cause for concern.

Brake fluid

> **Warning: Refer to the safety information given in 'Safety First!' and Chapter 9, regarding the dangers of handling brake fluid.**

14 With reference to Chapter 9, examine the area surrounding the brake pipe unions at the master cylinder for signs of leakage. Check the area around the base of fluid reservoir, for signs of leakage caused by seal failure. Also examine the brake pipe unions at the ABS hydraulic unit.

15 If fluid loss is evident, but the leak cannot be pinpointed in the engine bay, the brake calipers/wheel cylinders and underbody brake lines should be carefully checked with the vehicle raised and supported on axle stands

6.3a Release the wheelarch plastic liner screws and retaining studs . . .

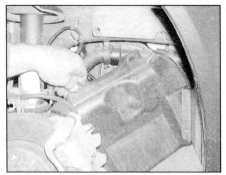

6.3b . . . and remove the liner from under the wheelarch

6.3c Unclip the coolant hoses for improved access to the crankshaft pulley

(see *Jacking and vehicle support*). Leakage of fluid from the braking system is a serious fault that must be rectified immediately.

16 Brake hydraulic fluid is a toxic substance with a watery consistency. New fluid is almost colourless, but it becomes darker with age and use.

Unidentified fluid leaks

17 If there are signs that a fluid of some description is leaking from the vehicle, but you cannot identify the type of fluid or its exact origin, park the vehicle overnight and slide a large piece of card underneath it. Providing that the card is positioned in roughly the right location, even the smallest leak will show up on the card. Not only will this help you to pinpoint the exact location of the leak, it should be easier to identify the fluid from its colour. Bear in mind, though, that the leak may only be occurring when the engine is running.

Vacuum hoses

18 Although the braking system is hydraulically-operated, the brake servo unit amplifies the effort applied at the brake pedal, by making use of the vacuum generated by the engine-driven vacuum pump. Vacuum is ported to the servo by means of a large-bore hose. Any leaks that develop in this hose will seriously reduce the effectiveness of the braking system.

19 In addition, a number of the underbonnet components, particularly the emission control components, are driven by vacuum supplied from the vacuum pump via narrow-bore hoses. A leak in a vacuum hose means that air is being drawn into the hose (rather than escaping from it) and this makes leakage very difficult to detect. One method is to use an old length of vacuum hose as a kind of stethoscope – hold one end close to (but not in) your ear and use the other end to probe the area around the suspected leak. When the end of the hose is directly over a vacuum leak, a hissing sound will be heard clearly through the hose. Care must be taken to avoid contacting hot or moving components, as the engine must be running, when testing in this manner. Renew any vacuum hoses that are found to be defective.

6 Auxiliary drivebelt check and renewal

Note: *Citroën specify the use of an electronic tension checking tool (SEEM 4122-T) to accurately check the auxiliary drivebelt tension on manually-adjusted drivebelts. If access to this equipment (or suitable alternative equipment calibrated to display belt tension in SEEM units) cannot be obtained, an approximate setting can be achieved as described below. If an approximate setting method is used, the tension must be checked using the electronic tool at the earliest possible opportunity.*

Note: *Refer to Chapter 2C and 2D for information on engine identification.*

1 On all engines, a single auxiliary drivebelt is fitted. The belt drives the alternator, power steering pump and air conditioning compressor according to equipment fitted, and is adjusted either manually, or by means of an automatic spring-loaded tensioning mechanism.

Checking the auxiliary drivebelt condition

2 Chock the rear wheels then jack up the front of the car and support it on axle stands (see *Jacking and vehicle support*). Remove the right-hand front roadwheel.

3 To gain access to the right-hand end of the engine, the wheelarch plastic liner must be removed. The liner is secured by various screws and clips under the wheelarch. Release all the fasteners, and remove liner

6.8 Slacken the two tensioner pulley retaining bolts (arrowed) . . .

from under the front wing. Where necessary, unclip the coolant hoses from under the wing to improve access further **(see illustrations)**.

4 Using a suitable socket and extension bar fitted to the crankshaft pulley bolt, rotate the crankshaft so that the entire length of the drivebelt can be examined. Examine the drivebelt for cracks, splitting, fraying or damage. Check also for signs of glazing (shiny patches) and for separation of the belt plies. Renew the belt if worn or damaged.

5 If the condition of the belt is satisfactory, on engines where the belt is adjusted manually, check the drivebelt tension as described below, bearing in mind the Note at the start of this Section. On engines with an automatic spring-loaded tensioner, there is no need to check the drivebelt tension.

Auxiliary drivebelt (XUD engines without air conditioning)

Removal

6 If not already done, proceed as described in paragraphs 2 and 3.

7 Disconnect the battery negative terminal (refer to *Disconnecting the battery* in the Reference Section of this manual).

8 Slacken the two bolts securing the tensioner pulley assembly to the engine **(see illustration)**.

9 Rotate the adjuster bolt at the base of the tensioner pulley assembly to move the pulley away from the drivebelt until there is sufficient slack for the drivebelt to be removed **(see illustration)**.

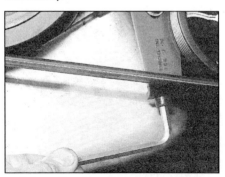

6.9 . . . then turn the tensioner pulley adjuster bolt to release the belt tension – 1.9 litre, XUD series engines without air conditioning

Refitting

10 If the belt is being renewed, ensure that the correct type is used. Fit the belt around the pulleys, ensuring that the ribs on the belt are correctly engaged with the grooves in the pulleys, and that the drivebelt is correctly routed. Take all the slack out of the belt by turning the tensioner pulley adjuster bolt. Tension the belt as follows.

Tensioning

11 If not already done, proceed as described in paragraphs 2 and 3.

12 If the electronic tool is not being used, the belt should be tensioned so that, under firm thumb pressure, there is about 5.0 mm of free movement at the mid-point between the pulleys on the longest belt run. If the electronic tool is being used, the tool sensor should be positioned on the belt midway between the power steering pump pulley and alternator pulley.

13 To adjust the tension, with the two tensioner pulley assembly retaining bolts slackened, rotate the adjuster bolt until the correct hand tension is achieved, or the specified number of SEEM units are displayed on the electronic tool. Refer to the Specifications for the SEEM unit tension settings.

> **HAYNES HiNT** *Correct tensioning of the drivebelt will ensure it has a long life. A belt which is too slack will slip and squeal. Beware of overtightening, as this can cause wear in the alternator bearings.*

14 Remove the tool (if used), and tighten the two tensioner pulley assembly retaining bolts to the specified torque.

15 Reconnect the battery negative terminal.

16 Clip the coolant hoses into position (where necessary), then refit the wheelarch liner. Refit the roadwheel, and lower the vehicle to the ground.

Auxiliary drivebelt (XUD engines with air conditioning)

Removal

17 If not already done, proceed as described in paragraphs 2 and 3.

18 Disconnect the battery negative terminal (refer to *Disconnecting the battery* in the Reference Section of this manual).

19 Working under the wheelarch, slacken the retaining bolt located in the centre of the eccentric tensioner pulley **(see illustration)**.

20 Insert a cranked 7.0 mm square section bar (a quarter inch square section drive socket bar for example) into the square hole on the front face of the eccentric tensioner pulley.

21 Using the bar, turn the eccentric tensioner pulley until the setting hole in the arm of the automatic tensioner pulley is aligned with the hole in the mounting bracket behind. When the holes are aligned, slide a suitable setting tool (a bolt or cranked length of bar of approximately 8.0 mm diameter) through the hole in the arm and into the mounting bracket.

22 With the automatic tensioner now locked, turn the eccentric tensioner pulley until the

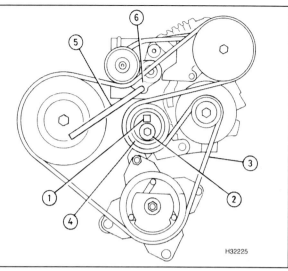

1 Eccentric tensioner pulley 7.0 mm square hole
2 Eccentric tensioner pulley retaining bolt
3 Auxiliary drivebelt
4 Eccentric tensioner pulley
5 Cranked 7.0 mm square section bar
6 Tensioner pulley arm 8.0 mm setting hole

6.19 Auxiliary drivebelt adjustment details – 1.9 litre, XUD series engines with air conditioning

drivebelt tension is released sufficiently to enable the belt to be removed.

Refitting and tensioning

23 Fit the drivebelt around the pulleys in the following order:
a) Air conditioning compressor.
b) Crankshaft.
c) Automatic tensioner pulley.
d) Power steering pump.
e) Alternator.
f) Eccentric tensioner pulley.

24 Ensure that the ribs on the belt are correctly engaged with the grooves on the pulleys.

25 Turn the eccentric tensioner pulley to apply tension to the drivebelt, until the load is released from the setting tool. Without altering the position of the eccentric tensioner pulley, tighten its retaining bolt to the specified torque.

26 Remove the setting tool from the automatic tensioner arm, then rotate the crankshaft four complete revolutions in the normal direction of rotation.

27 Check that the holes in the automatic adjuster arm and the mounting bracket are still aligned by re-inserting the setting tool. If the tool will not slide in easily, slacken the eccentric tensioner pulley retaining bolt and repeat the tensioning procedure from paragraph 24 onward.

28 On completion, clip the coolant hoses into position (where necessary), then refit the wheelarch liner. Refit the roadwheel, lower the car to the ground and reconnect the battery negative terminal.

Auxiliary drivebelt (1.9 litre DW engines without air conditioning)

Removal

29 If not already done, proceed as described in paragraphs 2 and 3.

30 Disconnect the battery negative terminal (refer to *Disconnecting the battery* in the Reference Section of this manual).

31 Slacken the bolt securing the arm of the tensioner pulley to the engine accessory mounting bracket **(see illustration)**.

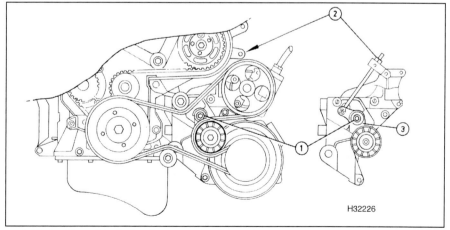

6.31 Auxiliary drivebelt adjustment details – 1.9 litre, DW series engines without air conditioning

1 Tensioner pulley arm securing bolt   2 Adjuster strut nut   3 Tensioner pulley arm

32 Working between the power steering pump and the engine, rotate the nut at the top of the adjuster strut until there is sufficient slack for the drivebelt to be removed.

Refitting

33 If the belt is being renewed, ensure that the correct type is used. Fit the belt around the pulleys, ensuring that the ribs on the belt are correctly engaged with the grooves in the pulleys, and that the drivebelt is correctly routed. Take all the slack out of the belt by turning the nut on the adjuster strut. Tension the belt as follows.

Tensioning

34 If not already done, proceed as described in paragraphs 2 and 3.
35 If the electronic tool is not being used, the belt should be tensioned so that, under firm thumb pressure, there is about 5.0 mm of free movement at the mid-point between the pulleys on the longest belt run. If the electronic tool is being used, the tool sensor should be positioned on the belt midway between the alternator pulley and the drivebelt lower guide roller.
36 To adjust the tension, with the tensioner pulley arm retaining bolt slackened, rotate the nut on the adjuster strut until the correct hand tension is achieved, or specified number of SEEM units are displayed on the electronic tool. Refer to the Specifications for the SEEM unit tension settings, noting that at this stage the belt tension should be set to the initial setting specified.
37 Remove the tool (if used), and tighten the tensioner pulley arm retaining bolt to the specified torque.
38 Reconnect the battery negative terminal.
39 If the electronic tool is being used, start the engine, allow it to run for approximately ten seconds then switch the engine off.
40 Refit the sensor of the electronic tool to the drivebelt and check that the tension is equal to the number of SEEM units specified for the final setting. If the tension is incorrect, slacken the tensioner pulley arm retaining bolt and adjust the tension by means of the adjuster strut nut. Tighten the tensioner pulley

arm retaining bolt to the specified torque when the tension is correct.
41 Remove the electronic tool (if used).
42 Clip the coolant hoses into position (where necessary), then refit the wheelarch liner. Refit the roadwheel, and lower the vehicle to the ground.

Auxiliary drivebelt (1.9 litre DW engines with air conditioning)

Note: *Later engines may be fitted with a revised tensioner assembly, similar to the unit fitted to 2.0 litre engines. Where the later tensioner arrangement is encountered, refer to the procedures described later in this Section for 2.0 litre engines.*

Removal

43 If not already done, proceed as described in paragraphs 2 and 3.
44 Disconnect the battery negative terminal (refer to *Disconnecting the battery* in the Reference Section of this manual).
45 Working under the wheelarch, slacken the retaining bolt located in the centre of the eccentric tensioner pulley **(see illustration 6.19)**.
46 Insert a cranked 7.0 mm square section bar (a quarter inch square section drive socket bar for example) into the square hole on the front face of the eccentric tensioner pulley.
47 Using the bar, turn the eccentric tensioner pulley until the setting hole at the base of the automatic tensioner pulley assembly is aligned with the corresponding hole in the mounting bracket behind. When the holes are aligned, slide a suitable setting tool (a bolt or cranked length of bar of approximately 8.0 mm diameter) through the hole in the pulley assembly and into the mounting bracket.
48 With the automatic tensioner locked, turn the eccentric tensioner pulley until the drivebelt tension is released sufficiently to enable the belt to be removed.

Refitting and tensioning

49 If the belt is being renewed, ensure that the correct type is used. Fit the belt around the pulleys, ensuring that the ribs on the belt are correctly engaged with the

grooves in the pulleys, and that the drivebelt is correctly routed.
50 Turn the eccentric tensioner pulley to apply tension to the drivebelt, until the load is released from the setting tool. Without altering the position of the eccentric tensioner pulley, tighten its retaining bolt to the specified torque.
51 Remove the setting tool from the automatic tensioner assembly.
52 Clip the coolant hoses into position (where necessary), then refit the wheelarch liner. Refit the roadwheel, lower the car to the ground and reconnect the battery negative terminal.

Auxiliary drivebelt (2.0 litre engines)

Note: *The following procedure is applicable to engines with and without air conditioning.*

Removal

53 If not already done, proceed as described in paragraphs 2 and 3.
54 Disconnect the battery negative terminal (refer to *Disconnecting the battery* in the Reference Section of this manual).
55 Using a suitable spanner engaged with the hexagonal stud in the centre of the automatic tensioner pulley, move the pulley toward the rear of the car to release the tension on the drivebelt, then slip the belt off the pulleys **(see illustration)**. Note that considerable effort will be needed to move the pulley against spring tension and it may be necessary to use some form of extension piece on the spanner to exert sufficient leverage.

Refitting and tensioning

56 Using the spanner on the hexagonal stud of the automatic tensioner pulley, move the pulley toward the rear of the car until the hole in the pulley arm is aligned with the hole in the mounting bracket behind. When the holes are aligned, slide a suitable locking tool (a bolt or cranked length of bar of approximately 4.0 mm diameter) through the hole in the arm and into the mounting bracket **(see illustrations)**. It is useful to have a small

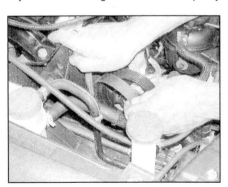

6.55 Using a spanner, move the automatic tensioner pulley rearwards, then slip the drivebelt off the pulleys – 2.0 litre engines

6.56a Turn the automatic tensioner pulley until the hole in the pulley arm (arrowed) is aligned with the hole in the mounting bracket . . .

6.56b . . . then insert a 4.0 mm locking tool through the hole and into the mounting bracket – 2.0 litre engines

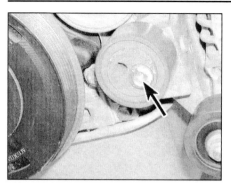

6.57 Slacken the retaining bolt (arrowed) located in the centre of the eccentric tensioner pulley – 2.0 litre engines

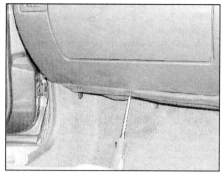

8.1a Undo the three stud screws securing the carpet trim panel to the facia . . .

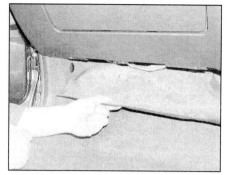

8.1b . . . release the two studs and washers securing the trim panel to the floor and remove the panel

mirror available to enable the alignment of the locking holes to be more easily seen in the limited space available.

57 Working under the wheelarch, slacken the retaining bolt located in the centre of the eccentric tensioner pulley **(see illustration)**.

58 If the belt is being renewed, ensure that the correct type is used. Fit the belt around the pulleys, ensuring that the ribs on the belt are correctly engaged with the grooves in the pulleys, and that the drivebelt is correctly routed.

59 Turn the eccentric tensioner pulley to apply tension to the drivebelt, until the load is released from the locking tool in the automatic tensioner. Without altering the position of the eccentric tensioner pulley, tighten its retaining bolt to the specified torque.

60 Remove the locking tool from the automatic tensioner, then rotate the crankshaft through four complete revolutions in the normal direction of rotation.

61 Check that the holes in the automatic adjuster and the mounting bracket are still aligned, and that it is now possible to insert a setting tool of 2.0 mm diameter through both holes. If the setting tool will not slide in easily, slacken the eccentric tensioner pulley retaining bolt and repeat the entire tensioning procedure.

62 On completion, clip the coolant hoses into position (where necessary), then refit the

wheelarch liner. Refit the roadwheel, lower the car to the ground and reconnect the battery negative terminal.

7 Clutch control mechanism check

1 Check that the clutch pedal moves smoothly and easily through its full travel, and that the clutch itself functions correctly, with no trace of slip or drag.

2 If excessive effort is required to operate the clutch, check first that the cable is correctly routed and undamaged, then remove the pedal and check that its pivot is properly greased. See Chapter 6 for more information.

8 Pollen filter renewal

1 Working under the passenger's side of the facia, undo the three stud screws securing the carpet trim panel to the facia. Release the two studs and washers securing the trim panel to the floor and remove the panel **(see illustrations)**.

2 Remove the three securing screws, and withdraw the lid from the pollen filter housing **(see illustration)**. If no screws are visible,

slide the lid sideways to release the internal retaining lugs.

3 Withdraw the filter **(see illustration)**.

4 Clean the filter housing and the lid, then fit the new filter using a reversal of the removal procedure.

9 Driveshaft gaiter check

1 With the vehicle raised and securely supported on stands (see *Jacking and vehicle support*), turn the steering onto full lock, then slowly rotate the roadwheel. Inspect the condition of the outer constant velocity (CV) joint rubber gaiters, squeezing the gaiters to open out the folds **(see illustration)**. Check for signs of cracking, splits or deterioration of the rubber, which may allow the grease to escape, and lead to water and grit entry into the joint. Also check the security and condition of the retaining clips. Repeat these checks on the inner CV joints. If any damage or deterioration is found, the gaiters should be renewed (see Chapter 8).

2 At the same time, check the general condition of the CV joints themselves by first holding the driveshaft and attempting to rotate the wheel. Repeat this check by holding the inner joint and attempting to rotate the driveshaft. Any appreciable movement

8.2 Remove the three screws and withdraw the lid from the pollen filter housing

8.3 Withdraw the pollen filter from the housing

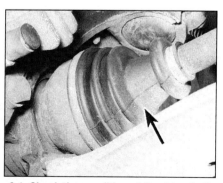

9.1 Check the condition of the driveshaft gaiters (arrowed)

10.4 Check for wear in the hub bearings by grasping the wheel and trying to rock it

indicates wear in the joints, wear in the driveshaft splines, or a loose driveshaft retaining nut.

10 Steering and suspension check

Front suspension and steering check

1 Firmly apply the handbrake, then jack up the front of the car and support it securely on axle stands (see *Jacking and vehicle support*).
2 Visually inspect the balljoint dust covers and the steering rack-and-pinion gaiters for splits, chafing or deterioration. Any wear of these components will cause loss of lubricant, together with dirt and water entry, resulting in rapid deterioration of the balljoints or steering gear.
3 On vehicles with power steering, check the fluid hoses for chafing or deterioration, and the pipe and hose unions for fluid leaks. Also check for signs of fluid leakage under pressure from the steering gear rubber gaiters, which would indicate failed fluid seals within the steering gear.
4 Grasp the roadwheel at the 12 o'clock and 6 o'clock positions, and try to rock it **(see illustration)**. Very slight free play may be felt, but if the movement is appreciable, further investigation is necessary to determine the source. Continue rocking the wheel while an assistant depresses the footbrake. If the movement is now eliminated or significantly reduced, it is likely that the hub bearings are at fault. If the free play is still evident with the footbrake depressed, then there is wear in the suspension joints or mountings.
5 Now grasp the wheel at the 9 o'clock and 3 o'clock positions, and try to rock it as before. Any movement felt now may again be caused by wear in the hub bearings or the steering track-rod balljoints. If the inner or outer balljoint is worn, the visual movement will be obvious.
6 Using a large screwdriver or flat bar, check for wear in the suspension mounting bushes by levering between the relevant suspension component and its attachment point. Some movement is to be expected as the mountings are made of rubber, but excessive wear

should be obvious. Also check the condition of any visible rubber bushes, looking for splits, cracks or contamination of the rubber.
7 With the car standing on its wheels, have an assistant turn the steering wheel back and forth about an eighth of a turn each way. There should be very little, if any, lost movement between the steering wheel and roadwheels. If this is not the case, closely observe the joints and mountings previously described, but in addition, check the steering column universal joints for wear, and the rack-and-pinion steering gear itself.

Suspension strut/shock absorber check

8 Check for any signs of fluid leakage around the suspension strut/shock absorber body, or from the rubber gaiter around the piston rod. Should any fluid be noticed, the suspension strut/shock absorber is defective internally, and should be renewed. **Note:** *Suspension struts/shock absorbers should always be renewed in pairs on the same axle.*
9 The efficiency of the suspension strut/shock absorber may be checked by bouncing the vehicle at each corner. Generally speaking, the body will return to its normal position and stop after being depressed. If it rises and returns on a rebound, the suspension strut/shock absorber is probably suspect. Examine also the suspension strut/shock absorber upper and lower mountings for any signs of wear.

11 Front brake pad condition check

1 Firmly apply the handbrake, then jack up the front of the car and support it securely on axle stands (see *Jacking and vehicle support*). Remove the front roadwheels.
2 It is now possible to check the thickness of the pad friction material **(see Haynes Hint)**. If any pad's friction material is worn to the specified thickness or less, *all four pads must be renewed as a set.*

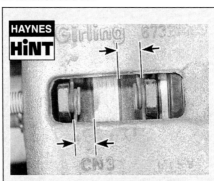

For a quick check, the thickness of friction material remaining on each brake pad can be measured through the aperture in the caliper body.

3 For a comprehensive check, the brake pads should be removed and cleaned. The operation of the caliper can then be checked, and the brake disc itself can be fully examined on both sides. Refer to Chapter 9 for details.

12 Rear brake pad condition check

1 Chock the front wheels then jack up the rear of the car and support it on axle stands (see *Jacking and vehicle support*). Remove the rear roadwheels.
2 For a quick check, the thickness of friction material remaining on each brake pad can be measured through the top of the caliper body. If any pad's friction material is worn to the specified thickness or less, all four pads must be renewed as a set.
3 For a comprehensive check, the brake pads should be removed and cleaned. This will permit the operation of the caliper to be checked, and the condition of the brake disc itself to be fully examined on both sides. Refer to Chapter 9 for further information.

13 Exhaust system check

1 With the engine cold (at least an hour after the vehicle has been driven), check the complete exhaust system from the engine to the end of the tailpipe. The exhaust system is most easily checked with the vehicle raised on a hoist, or suitably supported on axle stands, so that the exhaust components are readily visible and accessible (see *Jacking and vehicle support*).
2 Check the exhaust pipes and connections for evidence of leaks, severe corrosion and damage. Make sure that all brackets and mountings are in good condition, and that all relevant nuts and bolts are tight. Leakage at any of the joints or in other parts of the system will usually show up as a black sooty stain in the vicinity of the leak.
3 Rattles and other noises can often be traced to the exhaust system, especially the brackets and mountings. Try to move the pipes and silencers. If the components are able to come into contact with the body or suspension parts, secure the system with new mountings. Otherwise separate the joints (if possible) and twist the pipes as necessary to provide additional clearance.

14 Exhaust smoke test

Refer to the information given in the *MOT Test Checks* Section, in the Reference Section. The exhaust smoke test involves measuring the density of the soot particles leaving the exhaust pipe whilst the engine is under free acceleration. It involves the use of special test equipment and hence should be entrusted to a Citroën dealer or diesel fuel injection specialist.

15 Road test

Instruments and electrical equipment

1 Check the operation of all instruments and electrical equipment.
2 Make sure that all instruments read correctly, and switch on all electrical equipment in turn to check that it works properly.

Steering and suspension

3 Check for any abnormalities in the steering, suspension, handling or road 'feel'.
4 Drive the vehicle, and check that there are no unusual vibrations or noises.
5 Check that the steering feels positive, with no excessive 'sloppiness', or roughness, and check for any suspension noises when cornering, or when driving over bumps.

Drivetrain

6 Check the performance of the engine, clutch, transmission and driveshafts.
7 Listen for any unusual noises from the engine, clutch and transmission.
8 Make sure that the engine runs smoothly when idling, and that there is no hesitation when accelerating.
9 Check that the clutch action is smooth and progressive, that the drive is taken up smoothly, and that the pedal travel is not excessive. Also listen for any noises when the clutch pedal is depressed.
10 Check that all gears can be engaged smoothly, without noise, and that the gear lever action is smooth and not abnormally vague or 'notchy'.
11 Listen for a metallic clicking sound from the front of the vehicle, as the vehicle is driven slowly in a circle with the steering on full lock. Carry out this check in both directions. If a clicking noise is heard, this indicates lack of lubrication or wear in a driveshaft constant velocity joint (see Chapter 8).

Check the operation and performance of the braking system

12 Make sure that the vehicle does not pull to one side when braking, and that the wheels do not lock prematurely when braking hard.
13 Check that there is no vibration through the steering when braking.
14 Check that the handbrake operates correctly, without excessive movement of the lever, and that it holds the vehicle stationary on a slope.
15 Test the operation of the brake servo unit as follows. With the engine off, depress the footbrake four or five times to exhaust the vacuum. Start the engine, holding the brake pedal depressed. As the engine starts, there should be a noticeable 'give' in the brake pedal as vacuum builds up. Allow the engine to run for at least two minutes, and then switch it off. If the brake pedal is depressed now, it should be possible to detect a hiss from the servo as the pedal is depressed. After about four or five applications, no further hissing should be heard, and the pedal should feel considerably firmer.

Every 20 000 miles (30 000 km) or 2 years – whichever comes first

16 Hinge and lock operation and lubrication

1 Work around the vehicle, and lubricate the hinges of the bonnet, doors and tailgate with a small amount of general-purpose oil.
2 Lightly lubricate the bonnet release mechanism and exposed section of inner cable with a smear of grease.
3 Check carefully the security and operation of all hinges, latches and locks, adjusting them where required. Check the operation of the central locking system (if fitted).
4 Check the condition and operation of the bonnet and tailgate struts, renewing them if they are leaking or no longer able to support the bonnet or tailgate securely when raised.

17 Fuel filter renewal

Note: *Refer to Chapter 2C and 2D for information on engine identification.*

⚠️ **Warning: Refer to the safety information given in 'Safety First!' and Chapter 4B or 4C before disturbing any of the fuel system components.**

1.9 litre (XUD series) engines

1 The fuel filter is located in a plastic housing at the front of the engine.
2 Cover the area below the filter housing with rags or a piece of plastic sheeting, to protect against fuel spillage.
3 Thoroughly clean the exterior of filter housing, paying particular attention to the area around the cover-to-housing joint.
4 Position a suitable container under the end of the fuel filter drain hose. Open the drain screw on the front of the filter housing, and allow the fuel to drain completely.
5 Securely tighten the drain screw, then undo the four retaining screws and lift off the filter housing cover **(see illustration)**.
6 Lift the filter from the housing (see illustration). Ensure that the rubber sealing ring comes away with the filter, and does not stick to the housing/lid.
7 Remove all traces of dirt or debris from inside the filter housing then, making sure its sealing ring is in position, fit the new fuel filter.
8 Coat the threads of the filter cover securing bolts with thread-locking compound, then refit the cover and secure with the bolts.
9 Prime the fuel system (see Chapter 4B).
10 Open the drain screw until clean fuel flows from the hose, then close the drain screw and withdraw the container from under the hose.

1.9 litre (DW series) engines

11 Release the clip in the centre of the engine cover and undo the retaining screw on

17.5 Lift off the fuel filter cover . . .

17.6 . . . then lift the filter from the housing – 1.9 litre (XUD series) engines

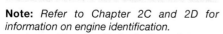

17.21 Release the four plastic fasteners and remove the engine cover – 2.0 litre engines

17.26 Disconnect the fuel supply and return hose quick-release fittings . . .

17.27 . . . then, using a socket, turn the filter housing cover anti-clockwise to release the locking lugs – 2.0 litre engines

the right-hand side. Remove the engine oil dipstick then lift the cover off the engine.

12 The fuel filter is located in a plastic housing at the front of the engine.

13 Cover the area below the filter housing with rags or a piece of plastic sheeting, to protect against fuel spillage.

14 Thoroughly clean the exterior of filter housing, paying particular attention to the area around the cover-to-housing joint.

15 Position a suitable container under the end of the fuel filter drain outlet. Open the drain screw on the underside of the filter housing, and allow the fuel to drain completely. Securely tighten the drain screw when the fuel has completely drained.

16 Release the retaining strap securing the filter housing cover to the housing.

17 Lift up the cover then remove the filter

from the housing. Ensure that the rubber sealing ring comes away with the filter, and does not stick to the housing lid.

18 Remove all traces of dirt or debris from inside the filter housing then, making sure its sealing ring is in position, fit the new fuel filter.

19 Locate the cover on the filter housing and secure with the retaining strap.

20 Prime the fuel system (see Chapter 4B).

2.0 litre engines

21 Release the four plastic fasteners and remove the engine cover from the top of the engine (see illustration).

22 The fuel filter is located in a plastic housing at the front of the engine.

23 Cover the area below the filter housing with rags or a piece of plastic sheeting, to protect against fuel spillage.

24 Thoroughly clean the exterior of filter housing, paying particular attention to the fuel hose unions and the area around the cover-to-housing joint.

25 Position a suitable container under the fuel filter drain outlet. Open the drain screw on the base of the filter housing, and allow the fuel to drain completely. Securely tighten the drain screw when the fuel has completely drained.

26 At the connections on the fuel pump cover, disconnect the fuel supply and return hose quick-release fittings using a small screwdriver to release the locking clip (see illustration). Suitably plug or cover the open hose unions to prevent dirt entry.

27 Using a suitable socket engaged with the hexagonal moulding on the filter housing cover, turn the cover approximately a quarter turn anti-clockwise to release the locking lugs (see illustration).

28 Lift off the housing cover, and collect the metal sealing ring and the O-ring seal, then lift out the filter (see illustrations).

29 Remove all traces of dirt or debris from inside the filter housing then fit the new fuel filter.

30 Locate the O-ring seal in position, followed by the metal sealing ring.

31 Refit the housing cover and turn it clockwise until the arrow on the housing cover is in line with the filter drain outlet (see illustration).

32 Reconnect the fuel supply and return hoses, then start the engine and check for fuel leaks.

33 On completion, refit the engine cover.

17.28a Lift off the filter housing cover . . .

17.28b . . . remove the metal sealing ring . . .

17.28c . . . and the sealing O-ring . . .

17.28d . . . then lift out the filter – 2.0 litre engines

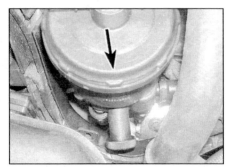

17.31 Refit the filter housing cover and turn it clockwise until the arrow is in line with the filter drain outlet – 2.0 litre engines

18.3a On 1.9 litre engines with the air cleaner accessible from above, release the clips securing the air cleaner cover . . .

18.3b . . . then lift off the cover . . .

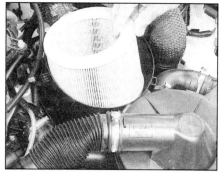

18.4 . . . and withdraw the air filter

18 Air filter renewal

Note: *Refer to Chapter 2C and 2D for information on engine identification.*

1.9 litre engines

Engine codes DJY, DHV and WJZ

1 Undo the bolt securing the air intake duct to the body front crossmember and move the duct slightly to one side.

2 On WJZ engines, slacken the retaining clip and disconnect the air duct from the air cleaner cover.

3 Release the retaining clips and lift off the air cleaner cover **(see illustrations)**.

4 Remove the filter element from the housing **(see illustration)**.

5 Wipe clean the inside of the filter housing and cover then fit the new filter element, making sure that it is correctly seated.

6 Refit the cover, and secure it in position with the retaining clips.

7 Refit the air intake duct to the crossmember and secure with the retaining bolt. On WJZ engines, reconnect the air duct to the air cleaner cover and tighten the retaining clip.

Engine code DHY

8 Access to the air filter is obtained from under the front of the vehicle. If necessary, to improve access, firmly apply the handbrake then jack up the front of the vehicle and support it on axle stands (see *Jacking and vehicle support*).

9 Remove the engine undertray.

10 Release the retaining clips, and remove the cover from the base of the air cleaner housing **(see illustration)**.

11 Withdraw the filter element from the housing **(see illustration)**.

12 Wipe clean the inside of the filter housing, then fit the new filter element.

13 Refit the cover to the base of the housing, and secure it in position with the retaining clips. Refit the engine undertray and lower the vehicle to the ground.

2.0 litre engines

14 Release the four plastic fasteners and remove the engine cover from the top of the engine.

15 Disconnect the wiring connector from the air mass meter.

16 Undo the screws securing the cover to the air filter housing **(see illustration)**.

17 Lift up the cover and withdraw the filter element from the housing **(see illustration)**.

18 Wipe clean the inside of the filter housing, then fit the new filter element.

19 Refit the cover and secure it in position with the retaining screws.

20 Reconnect the air mass meter wiring connector, then refit the engine cover.

19 Rear brake shoe condition check

1 Chock the front wheels then jack up the rear of the car and support it on axle stands (see *Jacking and vehicle support*).

2 For a quick check, the thickness of friction material remaining on one of the brake shoes can be measured through the slot in the brake backplate that is exposed by prising out its

18.10 On 1.9 litre engines with the air cleaner accessible from below, release the air cleaner cover clips . . .

18.11 . . . and withdraw the air filter element from the base of housing

18.16 On 2.0 litre engines, undo the screws securing the cover to the air filter housing . . .

18.17 . . . then lift up the cover and withdraw the filter element from the housing

sealing grommet **(see illustrations)**. If a rod of the same diameter as the specified minimum thickness is placed against the shoe friction material, the amount of wear can quickly be assessed – a small mirror may help observation. If any shoe's friction material is worn to the specified thickness or less, all four shoes must be renewed as a set.

3 For a comprehensive check, the brake drums should be removed and cleaned. This will permit the wheel cylinders to be checked and the condition of the brake drum itself to be fully examined. Refer to Chapter 9 for further information.

20 Handbrake check and adjustment

Refer to Chapter 9.

21 Brake fluid renewal

 Warning: Brake hydraulic fluid can harm your eyes and damage painted surfaces, so use extreme caution when handling and pouring it. Do not use fluid that has been standing open for some time, as it absorbs moisture from the air. Excess moisture can cause a dangerous loss of braking effectiveness.

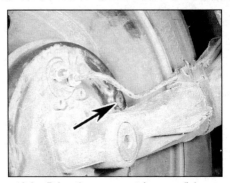

19.2a Prise the grommet (arrowed) from the rear drum brake backplate

1 The procedure is similar to that for the bleeding of the hydraulic system as described in Chapter 9, except that the brake fluid reservoir should be emptied by siphoning, using a clean poultry baster or similar before starting, and allowance should be made for the old fluid to be expelled when bleeding a section of the circuit.

2 Alternatively, to empty the reservoir, working as described in Chapter 9, open the first bleed screw in the sequence, and pump the brake pedal gently until nearly all the old fluid has been emptied from the master cylinder reservoir.

 HAYNES HiNT *Old hydraulic fluid is invariably much darker in colour than the new, making it easy to distinguish the two.*

19.2b Viewing the thickness of the brake shoe lining using a small mirror

3 Top-up to the MAX level with new fluid, and continue pumping until only the new fluid remains in the reservoir, and new fluid can be seen emerging from the bleed screw. Tighten the screw, and top the reservoir level up to the MAX level line.

4 Work through all the remaining bleed screws in the sequence until new fluid can be seen at all of them. Be careful to keep the master cylinder reservoir topped-up to above the MIN level at all times, or air may enter the system and increase the length of the task.

5 When the operation is complete, check that all bleed screws are securely tightened, and that their dust caps are refitted. Wash off all traces of spilt fluid, and recheck the master cylinder reservoir fluid level.

6 Check the operation of the brakes before taking the car on the road.

Every 40 000 miles (60 000 km) or 4 years – whichever comes first

22 Manual transmission oil level check

Note: *A suitable square-section wrench may be required to undo the transmission filler/level plug. These wrenches can be obtained from most motor factors or your Citroën dealer. A new sealing washer will also be required when refitting the transmission filler/level plug.*

HAYNES HiNT *It may be possible to use the square end fitting on a ratchet handle (as found in a typical socket set) to undo the plug.*

1 The manual transmission oil does not need to be renewed as part of the regular maintenance schedule, but the oil level must be checked and if necessary topped-up at the interval specified here. To drain the transmission as part of a repair procedure, refer to the information given in Chapter 7A.

2 The oil level must be checked before the car is driven, or at least 5 minutes after the engine has been switched off. If the oil is checked immediately after driving the car, some of the oil will remain distributed around the transmission components, resulting in an inaccurate level reading.

3 With the car on level ground, firmly apply the handbrake, then jack up the front and rear of the car and support it securely on axle stands (see *Jacking and vehicle support*). Note that the car must be level, to ensure accuracy, when checking the oil level.

4 To gain access to the filler/level plug, remove the left-hand front roadwheel and the plastic wheelarch liner. The liner is secured by various screws and clips under the wheelarch. Release all the fasteners, and remove liner from under the front wing.

5 Wipe clean the area around the filler/level plug, which is on the left-hand end of the transmission **(see illustration)**. Unscrew the

plug and clean it; discard the sealing washer.

6 The oil level should reach the lower edge of the filler/level hole. A certain amount of oil will have gathered behind the filler/level plug, and will trickle out when it is removed; this does **not** necessarily indicate that the level is correct. To ensure that a true level is established, wait until the initial trickle has

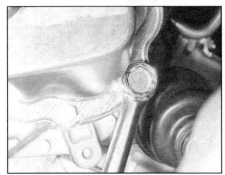

22.5 Removing the transmission filler/level plug

22.6a Topping-up the transmission oil level

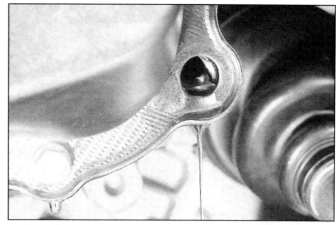

22.6b Oil level is correct when the oil stops flowing out of the filler/level hole

stopped, then add oil as necessary until a trickle of new oil can be seen emerging **(see illustrations)**. The level will be correct when the flow ceases; use only good-quality oil of the specified type (refer to *Lubricants and fluids*).

7 If the transmission has been overfilled so that oil flows out as soon as the filler/level plug is removed, check that the car is completely level (front-to-rear and side-to-side), and allow the surplus to drain off into a container.

8 When the level is correct, fit a new sealing washer to the filler/level plug, refit the plug and tighten it to the specified torque.

9 Refit the wheelarch liner and roadwheel, then lower the car to the ground. Tighten the roadwheel bolts to the specified torque.

23 Braking system check

1 Firmly apply the handbrake, then jack up the front of the car and support it securely on axle stands (see *Jacking and vehicle support*).

2 Inspect the area around both brake calipers for signs of brake fluid leakage, either from the piston seals, the brake pipe union or the bleed screw.

3 Examine the brake hoses leading to each caliper and check for signs of cracking, chafing or damage. Renew a hose which shows signs of deterioration without delay.

4 Ensure that the transmission is in neutral, then grasp each front wheel hub and turn it by hand. Slight resistance is normal, but if the hub is difficult to turn smoothly, this indicates that the brake pads are binding, possibly due to a seized or partially-seized brake caliper piston; refer to Chapter 9 for details of caliper removal and overhaul.

5 Remove the front brake pads as described in Chapter 9. Examine the brake pads and measure the depth of the remaining friction material. Renew all four pads, if any are worn below their minimum limit.

6 Using proprietary brake cleaning fluid and a stiff brush, wash all traces of dirt and brake dust from the brake calipers – take care to avoid inhaling any of the airborne brake dust. Examine the piston dust seal for signs of damage or deterioration and check that it is securely seated in its retaining groove.

7 Check the condition of the brake disc with reference to the information given in Chapter 9.

8 Refit the front brake pads as described in Chapter 9, then refit the roadwheels and lower the front of the car to the ground. Tighten the roadwheel bolts to the specified torque.

9 Chock the front wheels then jack up the rear of the car and support it on axle stands (see *Jacking and vehicle support*).

10 Ensure that the handbrake is released, then grasp each rear roadwheel and turn it by hand. Slight resistance is normal, but if the wheel is difficult to turn smoothly, this could be due to a seized or partially-seized wheel cylinder or brake caliper piston, or incorrect handbrake adjustment; refer to Chapter 9 for further details.

Models with rear drum brakes

11 Remove the rear roadwheels, then with reference to Chapter 9, remove the rear brake shoes. Examine the brake shoes and measure the depth of the remaining friction material. Renew all four brake shoes, if any are worn below their minimum limit.

12 Check the brake drums for wear and damage and check the area around the wheel cylinder piston seals for signs of fluid leakage. Check at the rear of the brake backplate for evidence of fluid leakage from the brake pipe union or bleed screw. Renew the wheel cylinder without delay if it shows signs of leakage; see Chapter 9 for details.

13 Using proprietary brake cleaning fluid and a stiff brush, wash all traces of dirt and brake dust from the wheel cylinders and backplates – take care to avoid inhaling any of the airborne brake dust.

14 On completion, refit the brake shoes, brake drums and roadwheels, then lower the

car to the ground. Tighten the roadwheel bolts to the specified torque.

Models with rear disc brakes

15 Inspect the area around both brake calipers for signs of brake fluid leakage, either from the piston seals, the brake pipe union or the bleed screw.

16 Examine the brake hoses leading to each caliper and check for signs of cracking, chafing or damage. Renew a hose which shows signs of deterioration without delay.

17 Remove the rear brake pads as described in Chapter 9. Examine the brake pads and measure the depth of the remaining friction material. Renew all four pads, if any are worn below their minimum limit.

18 Using proprietary brake cleaning fluid and a stiff brush, wash all traces of dirt and brake dust from the brake calipers – take care to avoid inhaling any of the airborne brake dust. Examine the piston dust seal for signs of damage or deterioration and check that it is securely seated in its retaining groove.

19 Check the condition of the brake disc with reference to the information given in Chapter 9.

20 Refit the rear brake pads as described in Chapter 9, then refit the roadwheels and lower the car to the ground. Tighten the roadwheel bolts to the specified torque.

24 Timing belt renewal

Refer to Chapter 2C or 2D as applicable.
Note: *Although the normal interval for timing belt renewal is 80 000 miles (120 000 km), it is strongly recommended that the interval is halved to 40 000 miles (60 000 km) on vehicles which are subjected to intensive use, ie. mainly short journeys or a lot of stop-start driving. The actual belt renewal interval is therefore very much up to the individual owner, but bear in mind that severe engine damage will result if the belt breaks.*

Every 80 000 miles (120 000 km) or 5 years – whichever comes first

25 Coolant renewal

Cooling system draining

 Warning: Wait until the engine is cold before starting this procedure. Do not allow antifreeze to come in contact with your skin, or with the painted surfaces of the vehicle. Rinse off spills immediately with plenty of water. Never leave antifreeze lying around in an open container, or in a puddle in the driveway or on the garage floor. Children and pets are attracted by its sweet smell, but antifreeze can be fatal if ingested.

1 With the engine completely cold, remove the expansion tank filler cap. Turn the cap anti-clockwise until it reaches the first stop. Wait until any pressure remaining in the system is released, then push the cap down, turn it anti-clockwise to the second stop, and lift it off.

2 Position a suitable container beneath the coolant drain outlet at the lower left-hand side of the radiator.

3 Loosen the drain plug (there is no need to remove it completely) and allow the coolant to drain into the container. If desired, a length of tubing can be fitted to the drain outlet to direct the flow of coolant during draining.

4 To assist draining, open the cooling system bleed screws which are located in the heater matrix outlet hose union on the engine compartment bulkhead, and on the top of, or adjacent to, the thermostat housing **(see illustrations)**.

5 To drain the cylinder block, firmly apply the handbrake, then jack up the front of the car and support it securely on axle stands (see *Jacking and vehicle support*). Remove the engine undertray and reposition the container below the drain plug located at the rear left-hand side of the cylinder block.

25.4a Open the cooling system bleed screws located in the heater matrix hose union on the bulkhead . . .

6 Remove the drain plug, and allow the coolant to drain into the container.

7 If the coolant has been drained for a reason other than renewal, then provided it is clean and less than five years old, it can be re-used, though this is not recommended.

8 Refit the radiator and cylinder block drain plugs on completion of draining.

Cooling system flushing

9 If coolant renewal has been neglected, or if the antifreeze mixture has become diluted, then in time, the cooling system may gradually lose efficiency, as the coolant passages become restricted due to rust, scale deposits, and other sediment. The cooling system efficiency can be restored by flushing the system clean.

10 The radiator should be flushed independently of the engine, to avoid unnecessary contamination.

Radiator flushing

11 To flush the radiator, disconnect the top and bottom hoses and any other relevant hoses from the radiator, with reference to Chapter 3.

12 Insert a garden hose into the radiator top inlet. Direct a flow of clean water through the radiator, and continue flushing until clean water emerges from the radiator bottom outlet.

13 If after a reasonable period, the water still does not run clear, the radiator can be flushed with a suitable proprietary cleaning agent, suitable for radiators of plastic/aluminium construction. It is important that the instructions provided with the product are followed carefully. If the contamination is particularly bad, insert the hose in the radiator bottom outlet, and reverse-flush the radiator.

Engine flushing

14 To flush the engine, tighten the cooling system bleed screws, then remove the thermostat (see Chapter 3). Temporarily refit the thermostat cover, without the thermostat.

15 With the top and bottom hoses disconnected from the radiator, insert a

25.4b . . . and on the thermostat housing

garden hose into the radiator top hose. Direct a clean flow of water through the engine, and continue flushing until clean water emerges from the radiator bottom hose.

16 When flushing is complete, refit the thermostat and reconnect the hoses with reference to Chapter 3.

Cooling system filling

17 Before attempting to fill the cooling system, make sure that all hoses and clips are in good condition, and that the clips are tight. An antifreeze mixture must be used all year round, to prevent corrosion of the engine components (see following sub-Section). Also check that the radiator and cylinder block drain plugs are in place and tight.

18 Remove the expansion tank filler cap.

19 Open all the cooling system bleed screws (see paragraph 4).

20 Some of the cooling system hoses are positioned at a higher level than the top of the radiator expansion tank. It is therefore necessary to use a 'header tank' when refilling the cooling system, to reduce the possibility of air being trapped in the system. Although Citroën dealers use a special header tank, the same effect can be achieved by using a suitable bottle, with a seal between the bottle and the expansion tank **(see Haynes Hint)**.

21 Fit the 'header tank' to the expansion tank and slowly fill the system. Coolant will emerge from each of the bleed screws in turn, starting with the lowest screw. As soon as coolant free from air bubbles emerges from the lowest screw, tighten that screw, and watch the next bleed screw in the system. Repeat the procedure until the coolant is emerging from the highest bleed screw in the cooling system and all bleed screws are securely tightened.

22 Ensure that the 'header tank' is full (at least 0.5 litres of coolant). Start the engine, and run it at a fast idle speed (do not exceed

Cut the bottom off an old antifreeze container to make a 'header tank' for use when refilling the cooling system. The seal at the point arrowed must be as airtight as possible.

2000 rpm) until the cooling fan cuts in, and then cuts out. Stop the engine. **Note:** *Take great care not to scald yourself with the hot coolant during this operation.*

23 Allow the engine to cool, then remove the 'header tank'.

24 When the engine has cooled, check the coolant level as described in *Weekly checks*. Top-up the level if necessary, and refit the expansion tank cap.

Antifreeze mixture

25 The antifreeze should always be renewed at the specified intervals. This is necessary not only to maintain the antifreeze properties, but also to prevent corrosion which would otherwise occur as the corrosion inhibitors become progressively less effective.

26 Always use an ethylene-glycol based antifreeze which is suitable for use in mixed-metal cooling systems. A general guide to the quantity of antifreeze and levels of protection is given in the Specifications, but follow the instructions provided by the antifreeze manufacturer for exact requirements.

27 Before adding antifreeze, the cooling system should be completely drained, preferably flushed, and all hoses checked for condition and security.

28 After filling with antifreeze, a label should be attached to the expansion tank, stating the type and concentration of antifreeze used, and the date installed. Any subsequent topping-up should be made with the same type and concentration of antifreeze.

29 Do not use engine antifreeze in the windscreen/tailgate washer system, as it will damage the vehicle paintwork. A screenwash additive should be added to the washer system in the quantities stated on the bottle.

Every 10 years – regardless of mileage

26 Air bag(s) and seat belt pre-tensioner renewal

Due to the safety critical nature of the air bag and seat belt pre-tensioner components, these operations must be carried out by a Citroën dealer.

Chapter 2 Part A:
TU series petrol engine in-car repair procedures

Contents

Camshaft and rocker arms – removal, inspection and refitting 10
Camshaft oil seal – renewal 8
Compression test – description and interpretation 2
Crankshaft oil seals – renewal 14
Cylinder head – removal and refitting 11
Cylinder head cover – removal and refitting 4
Engine assembly/valve timing holes – general information
    and usage 3
Engine oil and filter renewal ....See Chapter 1A
Engine oil level check ....See *Weekly checks*
Engine/transmission mountings – inspection and renewal 16
Flywheel/driveplate – removal, inspection and refitting 15
General information 1
Oil pump – removal, inspection and refitting 13
Sump – removal and refitting 12
Timing belt – general information, removal and refitting 6
Timing belt covers – removal and refitting 5
Timing belt tensioner and sprockets – removal,
    inspection and refitting 7
Valve clearances – checking and adjustment 9

Degrees of difficulty

Easy, suitable for novice with little experience	**Fairly easy,** suitable for beginner with some experience	**Fairly difficult,** suitable for competent DIY mechanic	**Difficult,** suitable for experienced DIY mechanic	**Very difficult,** suitable for expert DIY or professional

Specifications

Engine (general)

Designation:
    1.4 litre (1360cc) engine TU3
    1.6 litre (1587cc) engine TU5
Engine codes*:
    1.4 litre engine:
        Up to 1999 model year .... KFX (TU3JP)
        1999 model year onward .... KFX (TU3JP+)
    1.6 litre engine:
        Up to 1999 model year .... NFZ (TU5JP)
        1999 model year onward .... NFZ (TU5JP+)
Bore:
    1.4 litre engine .... 75.00 mm
    1.6 litre engine .... 78.50 mm
Stroke:
    1.4 litre engine .... 77.00 mm
    1.6 litre engine .... 82.00 mm
Direction of crankshaft rotation .... Clockwise (viewed from right-hand side of vehicle)
No 1 cylinder location .... At transmission end of block
Compression ratio (typical):
    1.4 litre engine .... 10.2 : 1
    1.6 litre engine .... 9.6 : 1
*The engine code is situated on front left-hand end of the cylinder block. It is either stamped on a plate which is riveted to the block (aluminium block engines) or stamped directly on the cylinder block (cast-iron block engines).

Timing belt

Tension setting (see text – Section 6):
    Initial setting .... 44 SEEM units
    Final setting .... 29 to 33 SEEM units

Camshaft

Drive	Toothed belt
Number of bearings	5

Camshaft bearing journal diameter (outside diameter):

No 1	36.950 to 36.925 mm
No 2	40.650 to 40.625 mm
No 3	41.250 to 41.225 mm
No 4	41.850 to 41.825 mm
No 5	42.450 to 42.425 mm

Cylinder head bearing journal diameter (inside diameter):

No 1	37.000 to 37.039 mm
No 2	40.700 to 47.739 mm
No 3	41.300 to 41.339 mm
No 4	41.900 to 41.939 mm
No 5	42.500 to 42.539 mm

Valve clearances (engine cold)

Inlet	0.20 mm
Exhaust	0.40 mm

Lubrication system

Oil pump type	Gear-type, chain-driven off the crankshaft
Minimum oil pressure at 90°C	4 bars at 4000 rpm
Oil pressure warning switch operating pressure	0.8 bars

Torque wrench settings

	Nm	lbf ft
Big-end bearing cap nuts	38	28
Camshaft sprocket retaining bolt	80	59
Camshaft thrust fork retaining bolt	16	12
Crankshaft pulley retaining bolts	8	6
Crankshaft sprocket retaining bolt	110	81
Cylinder head bolts (aluminium block engine):		
Stage 1	20	15
Stage 2	Angle-tighten a further 240°	
Cylinder head bolts (cast-iron block engine):		
Stage 1	20	15
Stage 2	Angle-tighten a further 120°	
Stage 3	Angle-tighten a further 120°	
Cylinder head cover nuts	16	12
Engine-to-transmission bolts	35	26
Engine/transmission left-hand mounting:		
Mounting bracket-to-transmission nuts	25	18
Mounting bracket-to-body bolts	25	18
Rubber mounting-to-bracket nuts	25	18
Rubber mounting centre nut	65	48
Engine/transmission rear mounting:		
Mounting bracket-to-cylinder block bolts	40	30
Connecting link-to-mounting bracket bolt	60	44
Connecting link-to-body bolt	50	37
Engine/transmission right-hand mounting:		
Upper mounting bracket-to-engine nuts	45	33
Upper mounting bracket-to-mounting rubber nut	45	33
Flywheel/driveplate retaining bolts	65	48
Main bearing cap bolts (cast-iron block engine):		
Stage 1	20	15
Stage 2	Angle-tighten a further 50°	
Main bearing ladder casting (aluminium block engine):		
11 mm bolts:		
Stage 1	20	15
Stage 2	Angle-tighten a further 50°	
6 mm bolts	8	6
Oil pump retaining bolts	8	6
Piston oil jet spray tube bolts (1.6 litre engines)	10	7
Sump drain plug	30	22
Sump retaining nuts and bolts	8	6
Timing belt cover bolts	8	6
Timing belt tensioner pulley nut	23	17

1 General information

Using this Chapter

This Part of Chapter 2 is devoted to in-car repair procedures for the TU series petrol engines. Similar information covering the XU series petrol engines, and the diesel engines will be found in Chapters 2B to 2D. All procedures concerning engine removal and refitting, and engine block/cylinder head overhaul for petrol and diesel engines can be found in Chapters 2E and 2F as applicable.

Refer to *Vehicle identification* in the Reference Section of this manual for details of engine code locations.

Most of the operations included in Chapter 2A are based on the assumption that the engine is still installed in the car. Therefore, if this information is being used during a complete engine overhaul, with the engine already removed, many of the steps included here will not apply.

TU series engine description

The TU series engine is a well-proven engine which has been fitted to many previous Citroën and Peugeot vehicles. The engine is of the in-line four-cylinder, overhead camshaft (OHC) type, mounted transversely at the front of the car, with the transmission attached to its left-hand end. The Xsara range is fitted with both 1.4 litre (1360cc) and 1.6 litre (1587cc) versions of the engine.

The crankshaft runs in five main bearings. Thrustwashers are fitted to No 2 main bearing (upper half) to control crankshaft endfloat.

The connecting rods rotate on horizontally-split bearing shells at their big-ends. The pistons are attached to the connecting rods by gudgeon pins, which are an interference fit in the connecting rod small-end eyes. The aluminium-alloy pistons are fitted with three piston rings – two compression rings and an oil control ring.

On 1.4 litre engines, the cylinder block is made from aluminium, and replaceable wet liners are fitted to the cylinder bores. Sealing

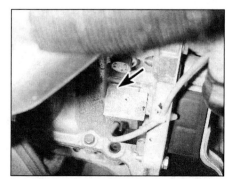

1.12 Engine code is stamped on a plate (arrowed) attached to the front of the cylinder block – viewed from above

O-rings are fitted at the base of each liner, to prevent the escape of coolant into the sump.

On 1.6 litre engines, the cylinder block is made from cast-iron, and the cylinder bores are an integral part of the cylinder block. On this type of engine, the cylinder bores are generally referred to as having dry liners.

The inlet and exhaust valves are each closed by coil springs, and operate in guides pressed into the cylinder head; the valve seat inserts are also pressed into the cylinder head, and can be renewed separately if worn.

The camshaft rotates directly in the cylinder head, is driven by a toothed timing belt, and operates the eight valves via rocker arms. Valve clearances are adjusted by a screw-and-locknut arrangement. The timing belt also drives the coolant pump.

Lubrication is by means of an oil pump, which is driven (via a chain and sprocket) off the right-hand end of the crankshaft. It draws oil through a strainer located in the sump, and then forces it through an externally-mounted filter into galleries in the cylinder block/crankcase. From there, the oil is distributed to the crankshaft (main bearings) and camshaft. The big-end bearings are supplied with oil via internal drillings in the crankshaft, while the camshaft bearings also receive a pressurised supply. The camshaft lobes and valves are lubricated by splash, as are all other engine components.

Throughout this manual, it is often necessary to identify the engines not only by their capacity, but also by their engine code which can be found on the left-hand end of the front face of the cylinder block. On engines with an aluminium cylinder block, the code is stamped on a plate which is riveted to the block; on engines with a cast-iron cylinder block, the number is stamped on a machined surface on the cylinder block, at the flywheel end. The first part of the engine number gives the engine code – eg KFX **(see illustration)**.

Repair operations possible with the engine in the car

The following work can be carried out with the engine in the car:
a) *Compression pressure – testing.*
b) *Cylinder head cover – removal and refitting.*
c) *Timing belt covers – removal and refitting.*
d) *Timing belt – removal, refitting and adjustment.*
e) *Timing belt tensioner and sprockets – removal and refitting.*
f) *Camshaft oil seal(s) – renewal.*
g) *Camshaft and rocker arms – removal, inspection and refitting.**
h) *Cylinder head – removal and refitting.*
i) *Cylinder head and pistons – decarbonising.*
j) *Sump – removal and refitting.*
k) *Oil pump – removal, overhaul and refitting.*
l) *Crankshaft oil seals – renewal.*

m) *Engine/transmission mountings – inspection and renewal.*
n) *Flywheel/driveplate – removal, inspection and refitting.*
*The cylinder head must be removed for the successful completion of this work. Refer to Section 10 for details.

2 Compression test – description and interpretation

1 When engine performance is down, or if misfiring occurs which cannot be attributed to the ignition or fuel systems, a compression test can provide diagnostic clues as to the engine's condition. If the test is performed regularly, it can give warning of trouble before any other symptoms become apparent.

2 The engine must be fully warmed-up to normal operating temperature, the battery must be fully charged, and all the spark plugs must be removed (see Chapter 1A). The aid of an assistant will also be required.

3 Disable and depressurise the fuel system, either by disconnecting the fuel pump wiring connector (refer to Chapter 4A) or by identifying and removing the fuel pump fuse from the fusebox. Start the engine, and run it until it cuts out.

4 Disable the ignition system by disconnecting the LT wiring connector from the ignition HT coil, or ignition coil module, referring to Chapter 5B for further information.

5 Fit a compression tester to the No 1 cylinder spark plug hole – the type of tester which screws into the plug thread is to be preferred.

6 Have the assistant hold the throttle wide open, and crank the engine on the starter motor; after one or two revolutions, the compression pressure should build up to a maximum figure, and then stabilise. Record the highest reading obtained.

7 Repeat the test on the remaining cylinders, recording the pressure in each.

8 All cylinders should produce very similar pressures; a difference of more than 2 bars between any two cylinders indicates a fault. Note that the compression should build up quickly in a healthy engine; low compression on the first stroke, followed by gradually-increasing pressure on successive strokes, indicates worn piston rings. A low compression reading on the first stroke, which does not build up during successive strokes, indicates leaking valves or a blown head gasket (a cracked head could also be the cause). Deposits on the undersides of the valve heads can also cause low compression.

9 Although Citroën do not specify exact compression pressures, as a guide, any cylinder pressure of below 10 bars can be considered as less than healthy. Refer to a Citroën dealer or other specialist if in doubt as to whether a particular pressure reading is acceptable.

3.4 Insert a 6 mm bolt (arrowed) through the hole in cylinder block flange and into the timing hole in the flywheel . . .

3.5 . . . then insert a 10 mm bolt through the cam sprocket timing hole, and locate it in the cylinder head

4 With the camshaft sprocket hole correctly positioned, insert a 6 mm diameter bolt or drill bit through the hole in the front, left-hand flange of the cylinder block, and locate it in the timing hole in the flywheel **(see illustration)**. Note that it may be necessary to rotate the crankshaft slightly, to get the holes to align.

5 With the flywheel correctly positioned, insert a 10 mm diameter bolt or drill bit through the timing hole in the camshaft sprocket, and locate it in the hole in the cylinder head **(see illustration)**.

6 The crankshaft and camshaft are now locked in position, preventing unnecessary rotation.

10 If the pressure in any cylinder is low, carry out the following test to isolate the cause. Introduce a teaspoonful of clean oil into that cylinder through its spark plug hole, and repeat the test.

11 If the addition of oil temporarily improves the compression pressure, this indicates that bore or piston wear is responsible for the pressure loss. No improvement suggests that leaking or burnt valves, or a blown head gasket, may be to blame.

12 A low reading from two adjacent cylinders is almost certainly due to the head gasket having blown between them; the presence of coolant in the engine oil will confirm this.

13 If the compression reading is unusually high, the combustion chambers are probably coated with carbon deposits. If this is the case, the cylinder head should be removed and decarbonised.

14 On completion of the test, refit the spark plugs and reconnect the ignition system.

place warning notices inside the vehicle, and in the engine compartment. This will reduce the possibility of the engine being accidentally cranked on the starter motor, which is likely to cause damage with the locking pins in place.

1 On all engines, timing holes are drilled in the camshaft sprocket and in the flywheel. The holes are used to ensure that the crankshaft and camshaft are correctly positioned when assembling the engine (to prevent the possibility of the valves contacting the pistons when refitting the cylinder head), or refitting the timing belt. When the timing holes are aligned with access holes in the cylinder head and the cylinder block, suitable diameter pins or bolts can be inserted to lock both the camshaft and crankshaft in position, preventing them from rotating. Proceed as follows.

2 Remove the timing belt upper cover as described in Section 5.

3 The crankshaft must now be turned until the timing hole in the camshaft sprocket is aligned with the corresponding hole in the cylinder head. The holes are aligned when the camshaft sprocket hole is in the 2 o'clock position, when viewed from the right-hand end of the engine. The crankshaft can be turned by using a spanner on the crankshaft sprocket bolt, noting that it should always be rotated in a clockwise direction (viewed from the right-hand end of the engine).

4 Cylinder head cover – removal and refitting

Removal

1 Disconnect the battery negative terminal (refer to *Disconnecting the battery* in the Reference Section of this manual).

2 Where necessary, undo the bolts securing the HT lead retaining clips to the rear of the cylinder head cover, and position the clips clear of the cover.

3 On early engines, slacken the retaining clip, and disconnect the breather hose from the left-hand end of the cylinder head cover **(see illustration)**. Where the original crimped-type Citroën hose clip is still fitted, cut it off and discard it. Use a standard worm drive clip on refitting.

4 On later engines, release the quick-release fitting and withdraw the breather assembly from the cylinder head cover.

5 Undo the two retaining nuts, and remove the washer from each of the cylinder head cover studs **(see illustration)**.

6 Lift off the cylinder head cover, and remove it along with its rubber seal **(see illustration)**. Examine the seal for signs of damage and deterioration, and if necessary, renew it.

7 Remove the spacer from each stud,

3 Engine assembly/valve timing holes – general information and usage

Note: *Do not attempt to rotate the engine whilst the crankshaft/camshaft are locked in position. If the engine is to be left in this state for a long period of time, it is a good idea to*

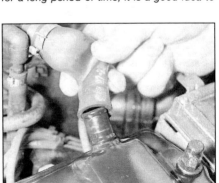

4.3 Disconnect the breather hose from the cylinder head cover

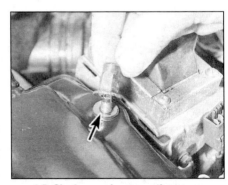

4.5 Slacken and remove the cover retaining nuts and washers (arrowed) . . .

4.6 . . . and lift off the cylinder head cover

4.7a Lift off the spacers (second one arrowed) . . .

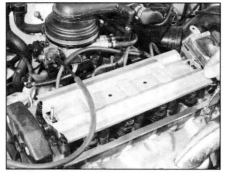

4.7b . . . and remove the oil baffle plate

4.9 On refitting, ensure the rubber seal is correctly located on the cylinder head cover

and lift off the oil baffle plate **(see illustrations)**.

Refitting

8 Carefully clean the cylinder head and cover mating surfaces, and remove all traces of oil.

9 Fit the rubber seal over the edge of the cylinder head cover, ensuring that it is correctly located along its entire length **(see illustration)**.

10 Refit the oil baffle plate to the engine, and locate the spacers in their recesses in the baffle plate.

11 Carefully refit the cylinder head cover to the engine, taking great care not to displace the rubber seal.

12 Check that the seal is correctly located, then refit the washers and cover retaining nuts, and tighten them to the specified torque.

13 Where necessary, refit the HT lead clips to the rear of the head cover, and securely tighten their retaining bolts.

14 On early engines, reconnect the breather hose to the cylinder head cover, securely tightening its retaining clip. On later engines, refit the breather assembly to the stub on the cylinder head cover, pushing it down until it locks into place.

15 Reconnect the battery negative terminal on completion.

5 Timing belt covers – removal and refitting

Removal

Upper cover

1 Unclip the hose from the top of the upper cover. Slacken and remove the two retaining bolts (one at the front and one at the rear), and remove the upper timing cover from the cylinder head **(see illustrations)**.

Centre cover

Note: *On later engines the centre cover is combined with the lower cover and is not a separate component.*

2 Remove the upper cover as described in paragraph 1, then free the wiring from its retaining clips on the centre cover **(see illustration)**.

3 Slacken and remove the three retaining bolts (one at the rear of the cover, beneath the engine mounting plate, and two directly above the crankshaft pulley), then manoeuvre the centre cover out from the engine compartment **(see illustration)**.

Lower cover

4 Remove the auxiliary drivebelt as described in Chapter 1A.

5.1a Undo the two retaining bolts (arrowed) . . .

5.1b . . . and remove the timing belt upper cover

5.2 Free the wiring loom from its clip . . .

5.3 . . . then undo the three bolts (locations arrowed) and remove the centre cover

5.6a Undo the three bolts (arrowed) . . .

5.6b . . . and remove the crankshaft pulley

5.7 Undo the retaining bolt and remove the timing belt lower cover

5 Remove the upper and, where applicable, the centre covers as described in paragraphs 1 to 3.
6 Undo the three crankshaft pulley retaining bolts and remove the pulley, noting which way round it is fitted **(see illustrations)**.
7 Slacken and remove the retaining bolt(s), and slide the lower cover off the end of the crankshaft **(see illustration)**.

Refitting

Upper cover

8 Refit the cover, ensuring it is correctly located with the centre cover, and tighten its retaining bolts.

Centre cover

9 Manoeuvre the centre cover back into position, ensuring it is correctly located with the lower cover, and tighten its retaining bolts.
10 Clip the wiring loom into its retaining clips on the front of the centre cover, then refit the upper cover as described in paragraph 8.

Lower cover

11 Locate the lower cover over the timing belt sprocket, and tighten its retaining bolt(s).
12 Fit the pulley to the end of the crankshaft, ensuring it is fitted the correct way round, and tighten its bolts to the specified torque.
13 Refit the centre and upper covers as described above, then refit and tension the auxiliary drivebelt as described in Chapter 1A.

6 Timing belt – general information, removal and refitting

Note: *Citroën specify the use of an electronic belt tension checking tool (SEEM 4122-T), and valve rocker contact plate (4533-T.Z.) to correctly set the timing belt tension. The following procedure assumes that this equipment (or suitable alternatives) is available. Accurate tensioning of the timing belt is essential, and if access to this equipment cannot be obtained, it is recommended that the work is entrusted to a Citroën dealer or suitably-equipped garage.*

General information

1 The timing belt drives the camshaft and coolant pump from a toothed sprocket on the right-hand end of the crankshaft. If the belt breaks or slips in service, the pistons are likely to hit the valve heads, resulting in extensive (and expensive) damage.
2 The timing belt should be renewed at the specified intervals (see Chapter 1A), or earlier if it is contaminated with oil or if it is at all noisy in operation (a 'scraping' noise due to uneven wear).
3 If the timing belt is being removed, it is a wise precaution to check the condition of the coolant pump at the same time (check for signs of coolant leakage). This may avoid the need to remove the timing belt again at a later stage, should the coolant pump fail.

Removal

4 Disconnect the battery negative terminal (refer to *Disconnecting the battery* in the Reference Section of this manual).
5 Align the engine assembly/valve timing holes as described in Section 3, and lock both the camshaft sprocket and the flywheel in position. *Do not* attempt to rotate the engine whilst the locking tools are in position.
6 Remove the timing belt centre and lower covers as described in Section 5.
7 Loosen the timing belt tensioner pulley retaining nut. Allow the pulley to pivot in a clockwise direction, to relieve the tension from the timing belt. Retighten the tensioner

6.8 Mark the direction of rotation on the belt, if it is to be re-used

pulley retaining nut to secure it in the slackened position.
8 If the timing belt is to be re-used, use white paint or similar to mark the dirction of rotation on the belt (if markings do not already exist) **(see illustration)**. Slip the belt off the sprockets.
9 Check the timing belt carefully for any signs of uneven wear, splitting, or oil contamination. Pay particular attention to the roots of the teeth. Renew the belt if there is the slightest doubt about its condition. If the engine is undergoing an overhaul, and has covered more than 37 500 miles (60 000 km) with the existing belt fitted, renew the belt as a matter of course, regardless of its apparent condition. The cost of a new belt is nothing when compared to the cost of repairs, should the belt break in service. If signs of oil contamination are found, trace the source of the oil leak, and rectify it. Wash down the engine timing belt area and all related components, to remove all traces of oil.

Refitting

10 Prior to refitting, thoroughly clean the timing belt sprockets. Check that the tensioner pulley rotates freely, without any sign of roughness. If necessary, renew the tensioner pulley as described in Section 7. Make sure that the locking tools are still in place, as described in Section 3.
11 Manoeuvre the timing belt into position, ensuring that the arrows on the belt are pointing in the direction of rotation (clockwise, when viewed from the right-hand end of the engine).
12 Do not twist the timing belt sharply while refitting it. Fit the belt over the crankshaft and camshaft sprockets. Make sure that the 'front run' of the belt is taut – ie, ensure that any slack is on the tensioner pulley side of the belt. Fit the belt over the coolant pump sprocket and tensioner pulley. Ensure that the belt teeth are seated centrally in the sprockets.
13 Loosen the tensioner pulley retaining nut. Pivot the pulley anti-clockwise to remove all free play from the timing belt, then retighten the nut. Tension the timing belt as follows.

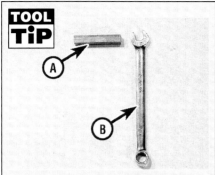

Tool Tip 1: A square section tool to fit the timing belt tensioner pulley can be made from a length of standard 8 mm door handle rod (A), obtained from a DIY shop, and then cut to size. Once the rod has been fitted to the tensioner, the timing belt can be tensioned by turning the rod with an 8 mm spanner (B).

Tensioning

14 Fit the sensor head of the electronic belt tensioning measuring equipment to the 'front run' of the timing belt, approximately midway between the camshaft and crankshaft sprockets.

15 Slacken the tensioner pulley retaining nut and insert a short length of 8.0 mm square bar into the square hole on the front face of the tensioner pulley **(see Tool Tip 1)**.

16 Using the square bar and a spanner, pivot the tensioner pulley anti-clockwise until an initial setting of 44 SEEM units is displayed on the tensioning measuring equipment **(see illustration)**. Hold the tensioner pulley in that position and retighten the retaining nut.

17 Remove the locking tools from the camshaft sprocket and flywheel, and remove the tension measuring equipment from the belt.

18 Using a suitable socket and extension bar on the crankshaft sprocket bolt, rotate the crankshaft through four complete rotations in a clockwise direction (viewed from the right-hand end of the engine). *Do not* at any time rotate the crankshaft anti-clockwise. Refit the locking tool to the flywheel and check that the camshaft sprocket timing hole is aligned.

19 To enable an accurate belt tension final setting to be achieved, all the load exerted on the camshaft lobes through the action of the valve springs and rocker arms must be removed. To do this, Citroën mechanics use a valve rocker contact plate (special tool 4533-T.Z.) which is simply a steel plate fitted over the rocker arms in place of the cylinder head cover, and secured using the cylinder head cover retaining nuts. Eight studs and locknuts are fitted to the plate, one located directly over the valve stem end of each rocker arm. The studs are then screwed down until they just lift the rocker arms away from the camshaft lobes and are then secured

6.16 Slacken the tensioner centre nut, then pivot the tensioner pulley anti-clockwise using the 8 mm bar and a spanner

A 8 mm bar   B Tensioner centre nut

in that position with the locknuts. This has the effect of removing all the load from the camshaft, allowing it to move very slightly as the belt tension is adjusted. If this is not done, the tension reading shown on the belt tension measuring equipment will be inaccurate. If the special tool cannot be obtained, a suitable alternative can be fabricated **(see Tool Tip 2)**.

20 Remove the cylinder head cover (see Section 4). Slacken the eight rocker arm contact bolts in the valve rocker contact plate and fit the contact plate to the cylinder head, observing the correct fitted direction. Tighten each rocker arm contact bolt until the rockers are just free of the camshaft lobes. Do not over-tighten the contact bolts otherwise the valves will contact the pistons.

21 Ensure that the flywheel locking tool is in place, but the camshaft sprocket locking tool is removed.

22 Refit the tension measuring equipment to the belt, slacken the tensioner pulley retaining nut, and turn the tensioner pulley until a setting of between 29 and 33 SEEM units is indicated on the measuring equipment. Hold the tensioner pulley in this position and tighten the retaining nut to the specified torque.

23 Remove the measuring equipment from the belt, the valve rocker contact plate from the cylinder head, and the locking tool from the flywheel. Rotate the crankshaft through another two complete rotations in a clockwise direction and check that both the camshaft sprocket and flywheel timing holes are realigned, and that the locking tools can be inserted. *Do not* at any time rotate the crankshaft anti-clockwise. If the locking tools cannot be inserted, repeat the refitting and tensioning procedure. If all is satisfactory, remove the locking tools.

24 With the belt tension correctly set, refit the cylinder head cover and timing belt covers, and reconnect the battery negative terminal.

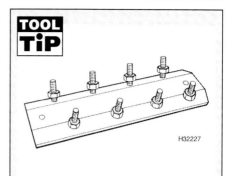

Tool Tip 2: A valve rocker contact plate can be made from steel sheet with eight studs and locknuts to contact the rocker arms.

7 Timing belt tensioner and sprockets – removal, inspection and refitting

Note 1: *This Section describes the removal and refitting of the components concerned as individual operations. If more than one of them is to be removed at the same time, start by removing the timing belt as described in Section 6; remove the component as described below, ignoring the preliminary dismantling steps.*

Note 2: *The following operations entail the slackening and then retensioning of the timing belt. Refer to Section 6 and ensure that the necessary equipment to accurately tension the timing belt is available, before proceeding.*

Removal

1 Disconnect the battery negative terminal (refer to *Disconnecting the battery* in the Reference Section of this manual).

2 Position the engine assembly/valve timing holes as described in Section 3, and lock both the camshaft sprocket and flywheel in position. *Do not* attempt to rotate the engine whilst the locking tools are in position.

Camshaft sprocket

3 On engines with a three-piece timing belt cover arrangement, remove the centre cover as described in Section 5. On engines with a two-piece cover, remove the lower cover.

4 Loosen the timing belt tensioner pulley retaining nut. Rotate the pulley in a clockwise direction, using a suitable square-section bar fitted to the hole in the pulley hub (see **Tool Tip 1** in Section 6). Retighten the retaining nut to hold the pulley in the slackened position.

5 Disengage the timing belt from the sprocket, and move the belt clear, taking care not to bend or twist it sharply. Remove the locking tool from the camshaft sprocket.

6 Slacken the camshaft sprocket retaining bolt and remove it, along with its washer. To prevent the camshaft rotating as the bolt is slackened, a sprocket-holding tool will be

2A•8 TU series petrol engine in-car repair procedures

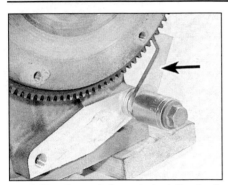

7.10 Use the tool shown to lock flywheel ring gear and prevent the crankshaft rotating

7.11a Remove the crankshaft sprocket bolt . . .

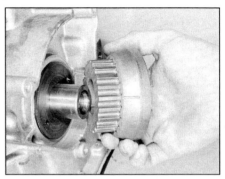

7.11b . . . then slide off the sprocket

required. In the absence of the special Citroën tool, an acceptable substitute can be easily fabricated (refer to the **Tool Tip** in the *Refitting* sub-Section). *Do not* attempt to use the locking tool inserted into the engine assembly/valve timing hole to prevent the sprocket from rotating whilst the bolt is slackened.

7 With the retaining bolt removed, slide the sprocket off the end of the camshaft. If the locating peg is a loose fit in the rear of the sprocket, remove it for safe-keeping. Examine the camshaft oil seal for signs of oil leakage and, if necessary, renew it as described in Section 8.

Crankshaft sprocket

8 Remove the centre (where fitted) and lower timing belt covers as described in Section 5.

9 Loosen the timing belt tensioner pulley retaining nut. Rotate the pulley in a clockwise direction, using a suitable square-section bar fitted to the hole in the pulley hub (see **Tool Tip 1** in Section 6). Retighten the retaining nut to hold the pulley in the slackened position.

10 To prevent crankshaft rotation whilst the sprocket retaining bolt is slackened on manual transmission models, select top gear, and have an assistant apply the brakes firmly. On automatic transmission models, remove the starter motor (Chapter 5A) and use a suitable tool in the driveplate teeth to stop crankshaft rotation. Alternatively, the flywheel ring gear can be locked using a suitable

tool made from steel angle; remove the cover plate from the base of the transmission bellhousing and bolt the tool to the bellhousing flange so it engages with the ring gear teeth. If the engine has been removed from the vehicle, lock the flywheel ring gear, using an arrangement similar to that shown **(see illustration)**. *Do not* be tempted to use the flywheel locking tool described in Section 3 to prevent the crankshaft from rotating; temporarily remove the locking tool from the flywheel prior to slackening the pulley bolt, then refit it once the bolt has been slackened.

11 Unscrew the retaining bolt and washer, then slide the sprocket off the end of the crankshaft **(see illustrations)**. Refit the locking tool to the flywheel.

12 If the Woodruff key is a loose fit in the crankshaft, remove it and store it with the sprocket for safe-keeping. If necessary, also slide the flanged spacer off the end of

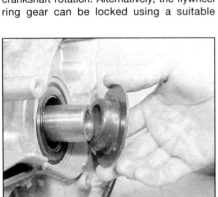

7.12 Remove the flanged spacer if necessary

the crankshaft **(see illustration)**. Examine the crankshaft oil seal for signs oil leakage and, if necessary, renew as described in Section 14.

Tensioner pulley

13 On engines with a three-piece timing belt cover arrangement, remove the centre cover as described in Section 5. On engines with a two-piece cover, remove the lower cover.

14 Slacken and remove the timing belt tensioner pulley retaining nut, and slide the pulley off its mounting stud. Examine the mounting stud for signs of damage and, if necessary, renew it.

Inspection

15 Clean the sprockets thoroughly, and renew any that show signs of wear, damage or cracks. If any of the sprockets are to be renewed, the timing belt should also be renewed as a matter of course.

16 Clean the tensioner assembly, but do not use any strong solvent which may enter the pulley bearing. Check that the pulley rotates freely about its hub, with no sign of stiffness or of free play. Renew the tensioner pulley if there is any doubt about its condition, or if there are any obvious signs of wear or damage.

Refitting

Camshaft sprocket

17 Refit the locating peg (where removed) to the rear of the sprocket, then locate the sprocket on the end of the camshaft. Ensure that the locating peg is correctly engaged with the cut-out in the camshaft end.

18 Refit the sprocket retaining bolt and washer. Tighten the bolt to the specified torque, whilst retaining the sprocket with the holding tool **(see Tool Tip)**.

19 Realign the timing hole in the camshaft sprocket (see Section 3) with the corresponding hole in the cylinder head, and refit the locking tool.

20 Refit the timing belt to the camshaft sprocket. Ensure that the 'front run' of the belt is taut – ie, ensure that any slack is on the tensioner pulley side of the belt. Do not twist the belt sharply while refitting it, and ensure

TOOL TIP

To make a camshaft sprocket holding tool, obtain two lengths of steel strip about 6 mm thick by 30 mm wide or similar, one 600 mm long, the other 200 mm long (all dimensions approximate). Bolt the two strips together to form a forked end, leaving the bolt slack so that the shorter strip can pivot freely. At the end of each 'prong' of the fork, secure a bolt with a nut and a locknut, to act as the fulcrums; these will engage with the cut-outs in the sprocket, and should protrude by about 30 mm.

that the belt teeth are seated centrally in the sprockets.

21 Loosen the tensioner pulley retaining nut. Using the square-section bar and a spanner, rotate the pulley anti-clockwise to remove all free play from the timing belt, then retighten the nut.

22 Tension the timing belt as described in Section 6.

23 Refit the timing belt covers as described in Section 5.

Crankshaft sprocket

24 Where removed, locate the Woodruff key in the crankshaft end, then slide on the flanged spacer, aligning its slot with the Woodruff key.

25 Align the crankshaft sprocket slot with the Woodruff key, and slide it onto the end of the crankshaft.

26 Temporarily remove the locking tool from the flywheel, then refit the crankshaft sprocket retaining bolt and washer. Tighten the bolt to the specified torque, whilst preventing crankshaft rotation using the method employed on removal. Refit the locking tool to the flywheel.

27 Relocate the timing belt on the crankshaft sprocket. Ensure that the 'front run' of the belt is taut – ie, ensure that any slack is on the tensioner pulley side of the belt. Do not twist the belt sharply while refitting it, and ensure that the belt teeth are seated centrally in the sprockets.

28 Loosen the tensioner pulley retaining nut. Using the square-section bar and a spanner, rotate the pulley anti-clockwise to remove all free play from the timing belt, then retighten the nut.

29 Tension the timing belt as described in Section 6.

30 Refit the timing belt covers as described in Section 5.

Tensioner pulley

31 Refit the tensioner pulley to its mounting stud, and fit the retaining nut.

32 Ensure that the 'front run' of the belt is taut – ie, ensure that any slack is on the pulley side of the belt. Check that the belt is centrally located on all its sprockets. Rotate the pulley anti-clockwise to remove all free play from the

timing belt, then tighten the pulley retaining nut securely.

33 Tension the belt as described in Section 6.

34 Refit the timing belt covers as described in Section 5.

8 Camshaft oil seal – renewal

Note: *If the camshaft oil seal is to be renewed with the timing belt still in place, check first that the belt is free from oil contamination. (Renew the belt as a matter of course if signs of oil contamination are found; see Section 6.) Cover the belt to protect it from oil contamination while work is in progress. Ensure that all traces of oil are removed from the area before the belt is refitted.*

1 Remove the camshaft sprocket as described in Section 7.

2 Punch or drill two small holes opposite each other in the oil seal. Screw a self-tapping screw into each, and pull on the screws with pliers to extract the seal. Alternatively, carefully prise the seal from its housing with a flat-bladed screwdriver **(see illustration)**. Take great care to avoid scoring the cylinder head and camshaft sealing surfaces.

3 Clean the seal housing, and polish off any burrs or raised edges, which may have caused the seal to fail in the first place.

4 Lubricate the lips of the new seal with clean engine oil, and drive it into position until it seats on its locating shoulder. Use a suitable tubular drift, such as a socket, which bears only on the hard outer edge of the seal. Take care not to damage the seal lips during fitting. Note that the seal lips should face inwards.

5 Refit the camshaft sprocket as described in Section 7.

9 Valve clearances – checking and adjustment

Note: *The valve clearances must be checked and adjusted only when the engine is cold.*

1 The importance of having the valve clearances correctly adjusted cannot be overstressed, as they vitally affect the performance of the engine. If the clearances are too big, the engine will be noisy (characteristic rattling or tapping noises) and engine efficiency will be reduced, as the valves open too late and close too early. A more serious problem arises if the clearances are too small, however. If this is the case, the valves may not close fully when the engine is hot, resulting in serious damage to the engine (eg, burnt valve seats and/or cylinder head warping/cracking). The clearances are checked and adjusted as follows.

2 Remove the cylinder head cover as described in Section 4.

3 The engine can now be turned using a suitable socket and extension bar fitted to the crankshaft sprocket/pulley bolt.

 Turning the engine will be easier if the spark plugs are removed first – see Chapter 1A.

4 It is important that the clearance of each valve is checked and adjusted only when the valve is fully closed, with the rocker arm resting on the heel of the cam (directly opposite the peak). This can be ensured by carrying out the adjustments in the following sequence, noting that No 1 cylinder is at the transmission end of the engine. The correct valve clearances are given in the Specifications at the start of this Chapter. The valve locations can be determined from the position of the manifolds.

Valve fully open	Adjust valves
No 1 exhaust	*No 3 inlet and No 4 exhaust*
No 3 exhaust	*No 4 inlet and No 2 exhaust*
No 4 exhaust	*No 2 inlet and No 1 exhaust*
No 2 exhaust	*No 1 inlet and No 3 exhaust*

5 Start by turning the crankshaft in the normal direction of rotation until the exhaust valve for No 1 cylinder is fully open. The clearances for No 3 cylinder inlet valve and No 4 cylinder exhaust valve can now be checked. The clearances are checked by inserting a feeler blade of the correct thickness between the valve stem and the rocker arm adjusting screw. The feeler blade should be a light, sliding fit, similar to a knife through butter. If adjustment is necessary, slacken the adjusting screw locknut, and turn the screw as necessary. Once the correct clearance is obtained, hold the adjusting screw and securely tighten the locknut. Recheck the valve clearance, and adjust again if necessary.

6 Rotate the crankshaft until the next valve in the sequence is fully open, and check the clearances of the next two specified valves.

7 Repeat the procedure until all eight valve clearances have been checked (and if necessary, adjusted), then refit the cylinder head cover as described in Section 4.

10 Camshaft and rocker arms – removal, inspection and refitting

General information

1 The rocker arm assembly is secured to the top of the cylinder head by the cylinder head bolts. Although in theory it is possible to undo the head bolts and remove the rocker arm assembly without removing the head, in practice, this is not recommended. Once the bolts have been removed, the head gasket will be disturbed, and the gasket will almost certainly leak or blow after refitting. For this

8.2 Carefully prise the camshaft oil seal from its housing with a flat-bladed screwdriver

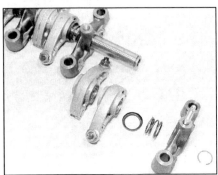

10.4 Remove the circlip, and slide the components off the end of the rocker arm

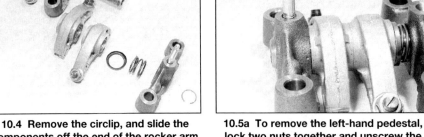

10.5a To remove the left-hand pedestal, lock two nuts together and unscrew the stud . . .

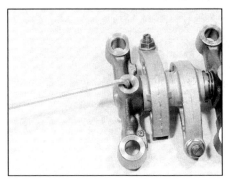

10.5b . . . then remove the grub screw

reason, removal of the rocker arm assembly cannot be done without removing the cylinder head and renewing the head gasket.

2 The camshaft is slid out of the right-hand end of the cylinder head, and it therefore cannot be removed without first removing the cylinder head, due to a lack of clearance.

Removal

Rocker arm assembly

3 Remove the cylinder head as described in Section 11.

4 To dismantle the rocker arm assembly, carefully prise off the circlip from the right-hand end of the rocker shaft; retain the rocker pedestal, to prevent it being sprung off the end of the shaft. Slide the various components off the end of the shaft, keeping all components in their correct fitted order **(see illustration)**. Make a note of each component's correct fitted position and orientation as it is removed, to ensure it is fitted correctly on reassembly.

5 To separate the left-hand pedestal and shaft, first unscrew the cylinder head cover retaining stud from the top of the pedestal; this can be achieved using a stud extractor, or two nuts locked together. With the stud removed, unscrew the grub screw from the top of the pedestal, and withdraw the rocker shaft **(see illustrations)**.

Camshaft

6 Remove the cylinder head as described in Section 11.

7 With the head on a bench, remove the sprocket locking tool, then remove the camshaft sprocket as described in Section 7.

8 Unbolt the ignition coil module and its mounting bracket, or the coolant housing (as applicable) from the left-hand end of the cylinder head. Undo the retaining bolt, and remove the camshaft thrust fork from the cylinder head **(see illustration)**.

9 Using a large flat-bladed screwdriver, carefully prise the oil seal out of the right-hand end of the cylinder head, then slide out the camshaft **(see illustrations)**. Discard the seal – a new one must be used on refitting.

Inspection

Rocker arm assembly

10 Examine the rocker arm bearing surfaces which contact the camshaft lobes for wear ridges and scoring. Renew any rocker arms on which these conditions are apparent. If a rocker arm bearing surface is badly scored, also examine the corresponding lobe on the camshaft for wear, as both will likely be worn. On later engines, roller rocker arms are used incorporating a roller bearing at the camshaft lobe contact point. On this type of rocker, check for any sign of excess play of the roller bearing or any roughness as it is rotated. Renew worn components as necessary. The rocker arm assembly can be dismantled as described in paragraphs 4 and 5.

11 Inspect the ends of the (valve clearance)

adjusting screws for signs of wear or damage, and renew as required.

12 If the rocker arm assembly has been dismantled, examine the rocker arm and shaft bearing surfaces for wear ridges and scoring. If there are obvious signs of wear, the relevant rocker arm(s) and/or the shaft must be renewed.

Camshaft

13 Examine the camshaft bearing surfaces and cam lobes for signs of wear ridges and scoring. Renew the camshaft if any of these conditions are apparent. Examine the condition of the bearing surfaces, both on the camshaft journals and in the cylinder head. If the head bearing surfaces are worn excessively, the cylinder head will need to be renewed. If the necessary measuring equipment is available, camshaft bearing journal wear can be checked by direct measurement, noting that No 1 journal is at the transmission end of the head.

14 Examine the thrust fork for signs of wear or scoring, and renew as necessary.

Refitting

Rocker arm assembly

15 If the rocker arm assembly was dismantled, refit the rocker shaft to the left-hand pedestal, aligning its locating hole with the pedestal threaded hole. Refit the grub screw, and tighten it securely. With the grub screw in position, refit the cylinder head

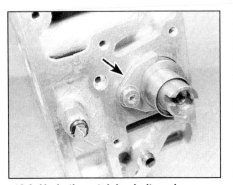

10.8 Undo the retaining bolt, and remove the camshaft thrust fork (arrowed) . . .

10.9a . . . prise out the oil seal . . .

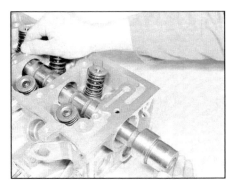

10.9b . . . and slide out the camshaft

cover mounting stud to the pedestal, and tighten it securely. Apply a smear of clean engine oil to the shaft, then slide on all removed components, ensuring each is correctly fitted in its original position. Once all components are in position on the shaft, compress the right-hand pedestal and refit the circlip. Ensure that the circlip is correctly located in its groove on the shaft.

16 Refit the cylinder head and rocker arm assembly as described in Section 11.

Camshaft

17 Ensure that the cylinder head and camshaft bearing surfaces are clean, then liberally oil the camshaft bearings and lobes. Slide the camshaft back into position in the cylinder head.

18 Locate the thrust fork with the left-hand end of the camshaft. Refit the fork retaining bolt, tightening it to the specified torque setting.

19 Ensure that the housing and cylinder head mating surfaces are clean and dry, with all traces of old sealant or gasket removed. Using a new gasket or suitable sealant, as applicable, refit the ignition coil module and its mounting bracket, or the coolant housing (according to model) to the left-hand end of the cylinder head. Tighten the retaining bolts securely in a progressive sequence.

20 Lubricate the lips of the new seal with clean engine oil, then drive it into position until it seats on its locating shoulder. Use a suitable tubular drift, such as a socket, which bears only on the hard outer edge of the seal. Take care not to damage the seal lips during fitting. Note that the seal lips should face inwards.

21 Refit the camshaft sprocket as described in Section 7.

22 Refit the cylinder head as described in Section 11.

11 Cylinder head – removal and refitting

Note: *The following operations entail the slackening and then retensioning of the timing belt. Refer to Section 6 and ensure that the necessary equipment to accurately tension the timing belt is available, before proceeding.*

Removal

1 Disconnect the battery negative terminal (refer to *Disconnecting the battery* in the Reference Section of this manual).

2 Drain the cooling system as described in Chapter 1A.

3 Remove the cylinder head cover as described in Section 4.

4 Align the engine assembly/valve timing holes as described in Section 3, and lock both the camshaft sprocket and flywheel in position. *Do not* attempt to rotate the engine whilst the locking tools are in position.

5 Note that the following text assumes that the cylinder head will be removed with both inlet and exhaust manifolds attached; this is easier, but makes it a bulky and heavy assembly to handle. If it is wished to remove the manifolds first, proceed as described in Chapter 4A.

6 Working as described in Chapter 4A, disconnect the exhaust system front pipe from the manifold. Where fitted, disconnect or release the lambda sensor wiring, so that it is not strained by the weight of the exhaust.

7 Remove the air cleaner housing and inlet duct assembly as described in Chapter 4A.

8 On later engines with secondary air injection, disconnect the intake air hose from the air injection valve on the front of the cylinder head.

9 Carry out the following operations as described in Chapter 4A:

a) *Depressurise the fuel system, and disconnect the fuel feed and return hoses from the fuel rail (plug all openings, to prevent loss of fuel and entry of dirt into the fuel system).*

b) *Disconnect the accelerator cable.*

c) *Disconnect the relevant electrical connectors from the throttle housing, fuel injectors and the idle speed auxiliary air valve/stepper motor.*

d) *Disconnect the vacuum servo unit hose, coolant hose(s) and all the other relevant/breather hoses from the manifold.*

10 Remove the remaining timing belt covers as described in Section 5.

11 Loosen the timing belt tensioner pulley retaining nut. Pivot the pulley in a clockwise direction, using an 8.0 mm square-section bar fitted to the hole in the pulley hub (see Section 6), then retighten the retaining nut.

12 Disengage the timing belt from the camshaft sprocket, and position the belt clear of the sprocket. Ensure that the belt is not bent or twisted sharply.

13 Slacken the retaining clips, and disconnect the coolant hoses from the thermostat housing (on the left-hand end of the cylinder head).

14 Depress the retaining clip(s), and disconnect the wiring connector(s) from the electrical switch and/or sensor(s) which are screwed into the thermostat housing/cylinder head (as appropriate).

15 Disconnect the wiring connector from the ignition HT coil, or ignition coil module. If the cylinder head is to be dismantled for overhaul, remove the ignition HT coil, or ignition coil module as described in Chapter 5B. On engines with spark plug HT leads, if the cylinder numbers are not already marked on the leads, number each lead, to avoid the possibility of the leads being incorrectly connected on refitting. Note that the HT leads should be disconnected from the spark plugs instead of the coil, and the coil and leads removed as an assembly.

16 Slacken and remove the bolt securing the engine oil dipstick tube to the cylinder head.

17 Working in the *reverse* of the sequence shown in illustration 11.35, progressively slacken the ten cylinder head bolts by half a turn at a time, until all bolts can be unscrewed by hand.

18 With all the cylinder head bolts removed, lift the rocker arm assembly off the cylinder head. Note the locating pins which are fitted to the base of each rocker arm pedestal. If any pin is a loose fit in the head or pedestal, remove it for safe-keeping.

19 On engines with a cast-iron cylinder block, lift the cylinder head away; seek assistance if possible, as it is a heavy assembly, especially if it is being removed complete with the manifolds.

20 On engines with an aluminium cylinder block, the joint between the cylinder head and gasket and the cylinder block/crankcase must now be broken without disturbing the wet liners. To break the joint, obtain two L-shaped metal bars which fit into the cylinder head bolt holes. Gently 'rock' the cylinder head free towards the front of the car. Do not try to swivel the head on the cylinder block/crankcase; it is located by dowels, as well as by the tops of the liners. **Note:** *If care is not taken and the liners are moved, there is also a possibility of the bottom seals being disturbed, causing leakage after refitting the head.* When the joint is broken, lift the cylinder head away; seek assistance if possible, as it is a heavy assembly, especially if it is being removed complete with the manifolds.

21 On all engines, remove the gasket from the top of the block, noting the two locating dowels. If the locating dowels are a loose fit, remove them and store them with the head for safe-keeping.

Caution: On aluminium block engines, do not attempt to rotate the crankshaft with the cylinder head removed, otherwise the wet liners may be displaced. Operations that require the rotation of the crankshaft (eg, cleaning the piston crowns), should only be carried out once the cylinder liners are firmly clamped in position. In the absence of the special Citroën liner clamps, the liners can be clamped in position using large flat washers positioned underneath suitable-length bolts. Alternatively, the original head bolts could be temporarily refitted, with suitable spacers fitted to their shanks.

22 If the cylinder head is to be dismantled for overhaul, remove the camshaft as described in Section 10, then refer to Part E of this Chapter.

Preparation for refitting

23 The mating faces of the cylinder head and cylinder block/crankcase must be perfectly clean before refitting the head. Citroën recommend the use of a scouring agent for this purpose, but acceptable results can be achieved by using a hard plastic or wood scraper to remove all traces of gasket and carbon. The same method can be used to clean the piston crowns, but refer to the *Caution* above before turning the crankshaft on aluminium block engines. Take particular care to avoid scoring or gouging the cylinder head/cylinder block mating surfaces during the cleaning operations, as aluminium alloy is easily damaged. Also, make sure that the carbon debris is not allowed to enter the oil and water passages – this is particularly important for the lubrication system, as carbon could block the oil supply to the engine's components. Using adhesive tape and paper, seal the water, oil and bolt holes in the cylinder block/crankcase.

 To prevent carbon debris entering the gap between the pistons and bores, smear a little grease in the gap. After cleaning each piston, use a small brush to remove all traces of grease and carbon from the gap, then wipe away the remainder with a clean rag.

24 Check the mating surfaces of the cylinder block/crankcase and the cylinder head for nicks, deep scratches and other damage. If slight, they may be removed carefully with a file, but if excessive, machining may be the only alternative to renewal.
25 Thoroughly clean the threads of the cylinder head bolt holes in the cylinder block. Ensure that the bolts run freely in their threads, and that all traces of oil and water are removed from each bolt hole.
26 If warpage of the cylinder head gasket surface is suspected, use a straight-edge to check it for distortion. Refer to Part E of this Chapter if necessary.
27 When purchasing a new cylinder head gasket, it is essential that a gasket of the correct thickness is obtained. At the time of writing, only one thickness of gasket was available, but confirm that this is still the case with your dealer or parts supplier. If you have any doubts, take the old gasket along to your dealer or parts supplier, and have him confirm the type of replacement gasket required.

11.30a Position a new gasket on the cylinder block/crankcase surface . . .

28 Check the condition of the cylinder head bolts, and particularly their threads, whenever they are removed. Wash the bolts in suitable solvent, and wipe them dry. Check each for any sign of visible wear or damage, renewing any bolt if necessary. Measure the length of each bolt, to check for stretching (although this is not a conclusive test, in the event that all ten bolts have stretched by the same amount).
Caution: Although Citroën do not actually specify that the cylinder head bolts must be renewed, it is strongly recommended that the bolts should be renewed as a complete set whenever they are disturbed.

Refitting

29 Wipe clean the mating surfaces of the cylinder head and cylinder block/crankcase. Check that the two locating dowels are in position at each end of the cylinder block/crankcase surface and, if necessary, remove the cylinder liner clamps.
30 Position a new gasket on the cylinder block/crankcase surface, ensuring that the manufacturer's identification markings face upwards **(see illustrations)**.
31 Check that the flywheel and camshaft sprocket are still correctly locked in position with their respective locking tools then, with the aid of an assistant, carefully refit the cylinder head assembly to the block, aligning it with the locating dowels.

11.33 Apply a smear of the grease supplied with the gasket set to the threads, and to the underside of the heads, of the cylinder head bolts

11.30b . . . ensuring that the manufacturers identification markings (HAUT – TOP) face upwards

32 Ensure that the locating pins are in position in the base of each rocker pedestal, then refit the rocker arm assembly to the cylinder head **(see illustration)**.
33 Apply a smear of grease to the threads, and to the underside of the heads, of the cylinder head bolts **(see illustration)**. Citroën specify Molykote G Rapid Plus grease (available from your Citroën dealer – a sachet is supplied with the top-end gasket set); in the absence of the specified grease, a good-quality high-melting-point grease may be used.
34 Carefully enter each bolt into its relevant hole (*do not drop them in*) and screw in, by hand only, until finger-tight.
35 Working progressively and in the sequence shown, tighten the cylinder head bolts to their Stage 1 torque setting, using a torque wrench and suitable socket **(see illustration)**.
36 Once all the bolts have been tightened to their Stage 1 setting, working again in the given sequence, angle-tighten the bolts through the specified Stage 2 angle, using a socket and extension bar. It is recommended that an angle-measuring gauge is used during this stage of the tightening, to ensure accuracy.
37 On cast-iron block engines, it will then be necessary to tighten the bolts through the specified Stage 3 angle setting.
38 With the cylinder head bolts correctly tightened, refit the dipstick tube retaining bolt and tighten it securely.
39 Refit the timing belt to the camshaft sprocket. Ensure that the 'front run' of the belt is taut – ie, ensure that any slack is on the

11.32 Refit the rocker arm assembly to the cylinder head

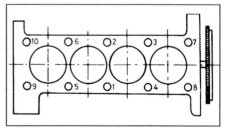
11.35 Cylinder head bolt tightening sequence

tensioner pulley side of the belt. Do not twist the belt sharply while refitting it, and ensure that the belt teeth are seated centrally in the sprockets.

40 Loosen the tensioner pulley retaining nut. Pivot the pulley anti-clockwise to remove all free play from the timing belt, then retighten the nut.

41 Tension the belt as described in Section 6, then refit the timing belt covers as described in Section 5.

42 If the head was stripped for overhaul, refit the ignition HT coil and leads, or ignition coil module, as described in Chapter 5, ensuring that the leads are correctly reconnected. If the head was not stripped, simply reconnect the wiring connector to the HT coil or coil module.

43 Reconnect the wiring connector(s) to the coolant switch/sensor(s) on the left-hand end of the head.

44 Reconnect the coolant hoses to the thermostat housing, securely tightening their retaining clips.

45 Where applicable, reconnect the intake air hose to the secondary air injection valve.

46 Working as described in Chapter 4A, carry out the following tasks:
 a) *Refit all disturbed wiring, hoses and control cable(s) to the inlet manifold and fuel system components.*
 b) *Reconnect and adjust the accelerator cable.*
 c) *Reconnect the exhaust system front pipe to the manifold. If applicable, reconnect the lambda sensor wiring connector.*
 d) *Refit the air cleaner housing and inlet duct.*

47 Check and, if necessary, adjust the valve clearances as described in Section 9.

48 On completion, reconnect the battery, and refill the cooling system as described in Chapter 1A.

12 Sump – removal and refitting

Removal

1 Disconnect the battery negative terminal (refer to *Disconnecting the battery* in the Reference Section of this manual). Chock the rear wheels then jack up the front of the vehicle and support it on axle stands (see *Jacking and vehicle support*).

2 Drain the engine oil, then clean and refit the engine oil drain plug, tightening it to the specified torque. If the engine is nearing its service interval when the oil and filter are due for renewal, it is recommended that the filter is also removed, and a new one fitted. After reassembly, the engine can then be refilled with fresh oil. Refer to Chapter 1A for further information.

3 Remove the exhaust system front pipe as described in Chapter 4A.

4 Progressively slacken and remove all the

sump nuts and bolts. On cast-iron block engines, it may be necessary to unbolt the flywheel cover plate from the transmission to gain access to the left-hand sump fasteners.

5 Try to break the joint by striking the sump with the palm of your hand, then lower and withdraw the sump from under the car **(see illustration)**. If the sump is stuck (which is quite likely) use a putty knife or similar, carefully inserted between the sump and block. Ease the knife along the joint until the sump is released.

6 While the sump is removed, take the opportunity to check the oil pump pick-up/strainer for signs of clogging or splitting. If necessary, remove the pump as described in Section 13, and clean or renew the strainer.

Refitting

7 Clean all traces of sealant from the mating surfaces of the cylinder block/crankcase and sump, then use a clean rag to wipe out the sump and the engine's interior.

8 Ensure that the sump and cylinder block/crankcase mating surfaces are clean and dry, then apply a coating of suitable sealant to the sump mating surface.

9 Offer up the sump, locating it on its retaining studs, and refit its retaining nuts and bolts. Tighten the nuts and bolts evenly and progressively to the specified torque.

10 Refit the exhaust front pipe as described in Chapter 4A.

11 Replenish the engine oil as described in Chapter 1A.

13 Oil pump – removal, inspection and refitting

Removal

1 Remove the sump as described in Section 12.

2 Slacken and remove the three bolts securing the oil pump in position **(see illustration)**. Disengage the pump sprocket from the chain, and remove the oil pump. If the pump locating dowel is a loose fit, remove and store it with the bolts for safe-keeping.

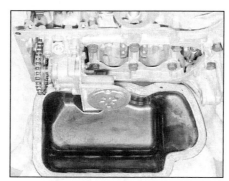

12.5 Slacken and remove the sump nuts and bolts, then remove the sump from the engine

Inspection

3 Examine the oil pump sprocket for signs of damage and wear, such as chipped or missing teeth. If the sprocket is worn, the pump assembly must be renewed, as the sprocket is not available separately. It is also recommended that the chain and drive sprocket, fitted to the crankshaft, are renewed at the same time. On aluminium block engines, renewal of the chain and drive sprocket is an involved operation requiring the removal of the main bearing ladder, and therefore cannot be carried out with the engine still fitted to the vehicle. On cast-iron block engines, the oil pump drive sprocket and chain can be removed with the engine *in situ*, once the crankshaft sprocket has been removed and the crankshaft oil seal housing has been unbolted. See Part E, Section 11, for further information.

4 Slacken and remove the bolts securing the strainer cover to the pump body, then lift off the strainer cover. Remove the relief valve piston and spring (and guide pin – cast-iron block engines only), noting which way round they are fitted.

5 Examine the pump rotors and body for signs of wear ridges and scoring. If worn, the complete pump assembly must be renewed.

6 Examine the relief valve piston for signs of wear or damage, and renew if necessary. The condition of the relief valve spring can only be measured by comparing it with a new one; if there is any doubt about its condition, it should also be renewed. Both the piston and spring are available individually.

7 Thoroughly clean the oil pump strainer with a suitable solvent, and check it for signs of clogging or splitting. If the strainer is damaged, the strainer and cover assembly must be renewed.

8 Locate the relief valve spring, piston and (where fitted) the guide pin in the strainer cover, then refit the cover to the pump body. Align the relief valve piston with its bore in the pump. Refit the cover retaining bolts, tightening them securely.

Refitting

9 Ensure that the locating dowel is in

13.2 Oil pump is retained by three bolts

14.2 Using a screwdriver to lever out the crankshaft right-hand oil seal

position, then engage the pump sprocket with its drive chain. Locate the pump on its dowel, and refit the pump retaining bolts, tightening them to the specified torque setting.
10 Refit the sump as described in Section 12.

14 Crankshaft oil seals – renewal

Right-hand oil seal

1 Remove the crankshaft sprocket and flanged spacer as described in Section 7. Secure the timing belt clear of the working area, so that it cannot be contaminated with oil. Make a note of the correct fitted depth of the seal in its housing.
2 Punch or drill two small holes opposite each other in the seal. Screw a self-tapping screw into each, and pull on the screws with pliers to extract the seal. Alternatively, the seal can be levered out of position using a suitable flat-bladed screwdriver, taking great care not to damage the crankshaft shoulder or seal housing **(see illustration)**.
3 Clean the seal housing, and polish off any burrs or raised edges, which may have caused the seal to fail in the first place.
4 Lubricate the lips of the new seal with clean engine oil, and carefully locate the seal on the end of crankshaft. Note that its sealing lip must face inwards. Take care not to damage the seal lips during fitting.
5 Using a suitable tubular drift (such as a socket) which bears only on the hard outer edge of the seal, tap the seal into position, to the same depth in the housing as the original was prior to removal. The inner face of the seal must be flush with the inner wall of the crankcase.
6 Wash off any traces of oil, then refit the crankshaft sprocket as described in Section 7.

Left-hand oil seal

7 Remove the flywheel as described in Section 15.
8 Make a note of the correct fitted depth of the seal in its housing. Punch or drill two small holes opposite each other in the seal. Screw a

self-tapping screw into each, and pull on the screws with pliers to extract the seal.
9 Clean the seal housing, and polish off any burrs or raised edges, which may have caused the seal to fail in the first place.
10 Lubricate the lips of the new seal with clean engine oil, and carefully locate the seal on the end of the crankshaft.
11 Using a suitable tubular drift, which bears only on the hard outer edge of the seal, drive the seal into position, to the same depth in the housing as the original was prior to removal.
12 Wash off any traces of oil, then refit the flywheel as described in Section 15.

15 Flywheel/driveplate – removal, inspection and refitting

Removal

Flywheel (manual transmission models)

1 Remove the transmission as described in Chapter 7A, then remove the clutch assembly as described in Chapter 6.
2 Prevent the flywheel from turning by locking the ring gear teeth with a similar arrangement to that shown in illustration 7.10. Alternatively, bolt a strap between the flywheel and the cylinder block/crankcase. *Do not* attempt to lock the flywheel in position using the locking tool described in Section 3.
3 Slacken and remove the flywheel retaining bolts, and remove the flywheel from the end of the crankshaft. Be careful not to drop it; it is heavy. If the flywheel locating dowel is a loose fit in the crankshaft end, remove it and store it with the flywheel for safe-keeping. Discard the flywheel bolts; new ones must be used on refitting.

Driveplate (automatic transmission models)

4 Remove the transmission as described in Chapter 7B. Lock the driveplate as described in paragraph 2. Mark the relationship between the torque converter plate and the driveplate, and slacken all the driveplate retaining bolts.
5 Remove the retaining bolts, along with the outer shim and torque converter plate. Discard the driveplate retaining bolts; new ones must be used on refitting.
6 Remove the driveplate from the end of the crankshaft and recover the inner shim. If the locating dowel is a loose fit in the crankshaft end, remove it and store it with the driveplate for safe-keeping.

Inspection

7 On models with manual transmission, examine the flywheel for scoring of the clutch face, and for wear or chipping of the ring gear teeth. If the clutch face is scored, the flywheel may be surface-ground, but renewal is preferable. Seek the advice of a Citroën dealer or engine reconditioning specialist to see if

machining is possible. If the ring gear is worn or damaged, the flywheel must be renewed, as it is not possible to renew the ring gear separately.
8 On models with automatic transmission, check the torque converter driveplate carefully for signs of distortion. Look for any hairline cracks around the bolt holes or radiating outwards from the centre, and inspect the ring gear teeth for signs of wear or chipping. If any sign of wear or damage is found, the driveplate must be renewed.

Refitting

Flywheel (manual transmission models)

9 Clean the mating surfaces of the flywheel and crankshaft. Remove any remaining locking compound from the threads of the crankshaft holes, using the correct size of tap, if available.

> **HAYNES HiNT**
> *If a suitable tap is not available, cut two slots along the threads of one of the old flywheel bolts, and use the bolt to remove the locking compound from the threads.*

10 If the new flywheel retaining bolts are not supplied with their threads already pre-coated, apply a suitable thread-locking compound to the threads of each bolt.
11 Ensure that the locating dowel is in position. Offer up the flywheel, locating it on the dowel, and fit the new retaining bolts.
12 Lock the flywheel using the method employed on dismantling, and tighten the retaining bolts to the specified torque.
13 Refit the clutch as described in Chapter 6. Remove the flywheel locking tool, and refit the transmission as described in Chapter 7A.

Driveplate (automatic transmission models)

14 Carry out the operations described above in paragraphs 9 and 10, substituting 'driveplate' for all references to the flywheel.
15 Fit the inner shim (the thinner of the two), then locate the driveplate on its locating dowel.
16 Offer up the torque converter plate, then fit the outer shim and the new retaining bolts. Lock the driveplate using the method employed on dismantling, and tighten the retaining bolts to the specified torque wrench setting.
17 Remove the driveplate locking tool, and refit the transmission as described in Chapter 7B.

16 Engine/transmission mountings – inspection and renewal

Inspection

1 If improved access is required, firmly apply the handbrake, then jack up the front of the

car and support it securely on axle stands (see *Jacking and vehicle support*).

2 Check the mounting rubber to see if it is cracked, hardened or separated from the metal at any point; renew the mounting if any such damage or deterioration is evident.

3 Check that all the mountings' fasteners are securely tightened; use a torque wrench to check if possible.

4 Using a large screwdriver or a crowbar, check for wear in the mounting by carefully levering against it to check for free play. Where this is not possible, enlist the aid of an assistant to move the engine/transmission back-and-forth, or from side-to-side, while you watch the mounting. While some free play is to be expected even from new components, excessive wear should be obvious. If excessive free play is found, check first that the fasteners are secure, then renew any worn components as described below.

Renewal

Right-hand mounting

5 Disconnect the battery negative terminal (refer to *Disconnecting the battery* in the Reference Section of this manual).

6 Place a jack beneath the engine, with a block of wood on the jack head. Raise the jack until it is supporting the weight of the engine.

7 Slacken and remove the three nuts securing the right-hand engine mounting upper bracket to the bracket on the cylinder block. According to model either unscrew the single nut, or the domed buffer and spacer nut, securing the bracket to the mounting rubber, and lift off the bracket.

8 Lift the buffer plate off the mounting rubber stud, then unscrew the rubber from the body. A strap wrench or similar may be used to unscrew the mounting, or alternatively fabricate a tool from suitable metal tube with projections to engage in the cut-outs in the mounting.

9 Check for signs of wear or damage on all components, and renew as necessary.

10 On reassembly, securely tighten the mounting rubber in the body.

11 Refit the buffer plate to the mounting rubber stud, then install the mounting bracket.

12 Tighten the mounting bracket retaining nuts to the specified torque wrench setting.

13 Remove the jack from under the engine, and reconnect the battery negative terminal.

Left-hand mounting

14 Remove the battery, battery tray and mounting plate as described in Chapter 5A.

15 Place a jack beneath the transmission, with a block of wood on the jack head. Raise the jack until it is supporting the weight of the transmission.

16 Slacken and remove the mounting rubber's centre nut, and two retaining nuts and remove the mounting from the engine compartment.

17 Disconnect the clutch cable from the transmission (see Chapter 6) then unscrew the retaining nuts and remove the bracket from the top of the transmission.

18 Check carefully for signs of wear or damage on all components, and renew them where necessary.

19 Refit the bracket to the transmission, tightening its mounting nuts to the specified torque. Reconnect the clutch cable as described in Chapter 6.

20 Fit the mounting rubber to the support bracket and tighten its retaining nuts to the specified torque. Refit the mounting centre nut, and tighten it to the specified torque.

21 Remove the jack from underneath the transmission, then refit the mounting plate, battery tray and battery as described in Chapter 5A.

Rear mounting

22 If not already done, firmly apply the handbrake, then jack up the front of the car and support it securely on axle stands (see *Jacking and vehicle support*).

23 Unscrew and remove the bolt securing the rear mounting link to the mounting on the rear of the cylinder block.

24 Remove the bolt securing the rear mounting link to the bracket on the subframe. Withdraw the link.

25 To remove the mounting assembly it will first be necessary to remove the right-hand driveshaft as described in Chapter 8.

26 With the driveshaft removed, undo the retaining bolts and remove the mounting from the rear of the cylinder block.

27 Check carefully for signs of wear or damage on all components, and renew them where necessary.

28 On reassembly, fit the rear mounting assembly to the rear of the cylinder block, and tighten its retaining bolts to the specified torque. Refit the driveshaft as described in Chapter 8.

29 Refit the rear mounting link, and tighten both its bolts to their specified torque settings.

30 Lower the vehicle to the ground.

Notes

Chapter 2 Part B:
XU series petrol engine in-car repair procedures

Contents

Camshaft oil seal(s) – renewal 10
Camshaft and followers – removal, inspection and refitting 11
Compression test – description and interpretation 2
Crankshaft oil seals – renewal 17
Crankshaft pulley – removal and refitting 5
Cylinder head – removal and refitting 13
Cylinder head cover – removal and refitting 4
Engine assembly/valve timing holes – general information
   and usage 3
Engine oil and filter renewal ....See Chapter 1A
Engine oil cooler – removal and refitting 16
Engine oil level check ....See *Weekly checks*
Engine/transmission mountings – inspection and renewal 19

Flywheel/driveplate – removal, inspection and refitting 18
General information 1
Oil pump – removal, inspection and refitting 15
Sump – removal and refitting 14
Timing belt (8-valve engines) – general information, removal and
   refitting 7
Timing belt (16-valve engines) – general information, removal and
   refitting 8
Timing belt covers – removal and refitting 6
Timing belt tensioner and sprockets – removal, inspection
   and refitting 9
Valve clearances (8-valve engines) – checking and adjustment 12

Degrees of difficulty

Easy, suitable for novice with little experience	Fairly easy, suitable for beginner with some experience	Fairly difficult, suitable for competent DIY mechanic	Difficult, suitable for experienced DIY mechanic	Very difficult, suitable for expert DIY or professional

Specifications

Engine (general)

Designation:
1.8 litre (1761cc) engine	XU7
2.0 litre (1998cc) engine	XU10

Engine codes*:
1.8 litre (8-valve) engine:	
Manual transmission models	LFX (XU7JB)
Automatic transmission models	LFZ (XU7JP)
1.8 litre (16-valve) engine	LFY (XU7JP4)
2.0 litre (16-valve) engine	RFV (XU10J4R)

Bore:
1.8 litre engine	83.00 mm
2.0 litre engine	86.00 mm

Stroke:
1.8 litre engine	81.40 mm
2.0 litre engine	86.00 mm

Direction of crankshaft rotation	Clockwise (viewed from the right-hand side of vehicle)
No 1 cylinder location	At the transmission end of block

Compression ratio (typical):
1.8 litre (8-valve) engine	9.25 : 1
1.8 litre (16-valve) engine	10.4 : 1
2.0 litre engine	10.4 : 1

The engine code is stamped on a plate attached to the front left-hand end of the cylinder block on 1.8 litre engines, and stamped directly onto the front face of the cylinder block (just to the left of the oil filter) on 2.0 litre engines.

Camshaft

Drive	Toothed belt
No of bearings	5
Camshaft bearing journal diameter	Not available at time of writing
Cylinder head bearing journal diameter	Not available at time of writing

Valve clearances (8-valve engines only)

Inlet	0.20 mm
Exhaust	0.40 mm

Lubrication system

Oil pump type	Gear-type, chain-driven off the crankshaft right-hand end
Minimum oil pressure at 80°C	5.0 to 6.0 bars (approximate) at 4000 rpm
Oil pressure warning switch operating pressure	0.8 bars

Torque wrench settings

	Nm	lbf ft
1.8 litre (8-valve) engine		
Big-end bearing cap nuts:*		
Stage 1	20	15
Stage 2	Angle-tighten a further 70°	
Camshaft bearing cap nuts	15	11
Camshaft sprocket retaining bolt	35	26
Crankshaft right-hand oil seal carrier bolts	16	12
Crankshaft pulley retaining bolt	120	89
Cylinder head bolts:		
Stage 1	60	44
Fully slacken then tighten to:		
Stage 2	20	15
Stage 3	Angle-tighten a further 300°	
Cylinder head cover nuts/bolts	10	7
Engine-to-transmission fixing bolts	45	33
Engine/transmission left-hand mounting:		
Rubber mounting-to-body bolts	21	15
Mounting stud to transmission	50	37
Rubber mounting centre nut	65	48
Engine/transmission rear mounting:		
Mounting assembly-to-block bolts	45	33
Connecting link-to-mounting assembly bolt	50	37
Connecting link-to-subframe bolt	50	37
Engine/transmission right-hand mounting:		
Manual transmission models:		
Upper mounting bracket-to-lower bracket nuts	45	33
Lower mounting bracket-to-engine bolts	45	33
Upper mounting bracket-to-mounting rubber nut	45	33
Automatic transmission models:		
Upper mounting bracket-to-lower bracket nuts	45	33
Upper mounting bracket-to-lower bracket bolts	60	44
Lower mounting bracket-to-engine bolts	45	33
Upper mounting bracket-to-rubber mounting nut	45	33
Flywheel/driveplate retaining bolts*	50	37
Main bearing cap nuts/bolts:		
Retaining nuts/bolts	54	40
Centre bearing cap side bolts	23	17
Oil pump retaining bolts	16	12
Sump retaining bolts	10	7
Timing belt cover bolts	8	6
Timing belt tensioner pulley bolt	20	15
New nuts/bolts must be used.		
1.8 litre (16-valve) engine		
Big-end bearing cap nuts:*		
Stage 1	20	15
Stage 2	Angle-tighten a further 70°	
Camshaft bearing housings:		
Stage 1	5	4
Stage 2	10	7
Camshaft sprocket-to-hub retaining bolts	10	7
Camshaft sprocket hub-to-camshaft retaining bolts	75	55
Crankshaft pulley retaining bolt	120	89
Crankshaft right-hand oil seal carrier bolts	16	12
Cylinder head cover nuts/bolts	10	7
Cylinder head bolts:		
Stage 1	60	44
Fully slacken then tighten to:		
Stage 2	20	15
Stage 3	Angle-tighten a further 300°	

Torque wrench settings

	Nm	lbf ft

1.8 litre (16-valve) engine (continued)

	Nm	lbf ft
Engine-to-transmission fixing bolts	45	33
Engine/transmission left-hand mounting:		
Rubber mounting-to-body bolts	21	15
Mounting stud to transmission	50	37
Rubber mounting centre nut	65	48
Engine/transmission rear mounting:		
Mounting assembly-to-block bolts	45	33
Connecting link-to-mounting assembly bolt	50	37
Connecting link-to-subframe bolt	50	37
Engine/transmission right-hand mounting:		
Upper mounting bracket-to-lower bracket nuts	45	33
Upper mounting bracket-to-lower bracket bolts	60	44
Lower mounting bracket-to-engine bolts	60	44
Upper mounting bracket-to-rubber mounting nut	45	33
Flywheel/driveplate retaining bolts*	50	37
Main bearing cap bolts:		
Bearing bolts	55	41
Side securing bolts	25	18
Oil pump retaining bolts	16	12
Piston oil jet spray tube bolt	10	7
Sump retaining bolts	16	12
Timing belt cover bolts	8	6
Timing belt idler pulley bolt	37	27
Timing belt tensioner pulley bolt	20	15

New nuts/bolts must be used.

2.0 litre engine

	Nm	lbf ft
Big-end bearing cap nuts:*		
Stage 1	20	15
Stage 2	Angle-tighten a further 70°	
Camshaft bearing housings:		
Stage 1	5	4
Stage 2	10	7
Camshaft sprocket-to-hub retaining bolts	10	7
Camshaft sprocket hub-to-camshaft retaining bolts	75	55
Crankshaft pulley retaining bolt	120	89
Crankshaft right-hand oil seal carrier bolts	16	12
Cylinder head cover nuts/bolts	10	7
Cylinder head bolts:		
Stage 1	35	26
Stage 2	70	52
Stage 3	Angle-tighten a further 160°	
Engine-to-transmission fixing bolts	45	33
Engine/transmission left-hand mounting:		
Rubber mounting-to-body bolts	21	15
Mounting stud to transmission	50	37
Rubber mounting centre nut	65	48
Engine/transmission rear mounting:		
Mounting assembly-to-block bolts	45	33
Connecting link-to-mounting assembly bolt	50	37
Connecting link-to-subframe bolt	50	37
Engine/transmission right-hand mounting:		
Upper mounting bracket-to-lower bracket nuts	45	33
Upper mounting bracket-to-lower bracket bolts	60	44
Lower mounting bracket-to-engine bolts	60	44
Upper mounting bracket-to-rubber mounting nut	45	33
Flywheel/driveplate retaining bolts*	50	37
Main bearing cap bolts	70	52
Oil pump retaining bolts	16	12
Piston oil jet spray tube bolt	10	7
Sump retaining bolts	10	7
Timing belt cover bolts	8	6
Timing belt idler pulley bolt	37	27
Timing belt tensioner pulley bolt	20	15

New nuts/bolts must be used.

1 General information

Using this Chapter

This Part of Chapter 2 is devoted to in-car repair procedures for the XU series petrol engines. Similar information covering the TU series petrol engines, and the diesel engines will be found in Chapters 2A, 2C and 2D. All procedures concerning engine removal and refitting, and engine block/cylinder head overhaul for petrol and diesel engines can be found in Chapters 2E and 2F as applicable.

Refer to *Vehicle identification* in the Reference Section of this manual for details of engine code locations.

Most of the operations included in Chapter 2B are based on the assumption that the engine is still installed in the car. Therefore, if this information is being used during a complete engine overhaul, with the engine already removed, many of the steps included here will not apply.

XU series engine description

The XU series engine is a well-proven power unit which has been fitted to many previous Citroën and Peugeot vehicles. The engine is of the in-line four-cylinder type, mounted transversely at the front of the car with the clutch and transmission attached to its left-hand end. The Xsara range is fitted with 1.8 litre (1761cc) and 2.0 litre (1998cc) engines. Both 8- and 16-valve versions of the 1.8 litre engine are available, whereas all 2.0 litre engines are of 16-valve configuration.

The crankshaft runs in five main bearings. Thrustwashers are fitted to No 2 main bearing cap, to control crankshaft endfloat.

The connecting rods rotate on horizontally-split bearing shells at their big-ends. The pistons are attached to the connecting rods by gudgeon pins which are an interference fit in the connecting rod small-end eyes. The aluminium alloy pistons are fitted with three piston rings – two compression rings and an oil control ring.

On 1.8 litre engines, the cylinder block is of the 'wet-liner' type. The block is cast in aluminium alloy, and the bores have replaceable cast-iron liners that are located from the top of the cylinder block. Sealing O-rings are fitted at the base of each liner, to prevent the escape of coolant into the sump.

On 2.0 litre engines, the cylinder block is of the conventional 'dry-liner' type. The block is of cast iron, and no separate bore liners are fitted.

On the 8-valve engines, the camshaft is driven by a toothed timing belt, and it operates the valves via followers located beneath each cam lobe. The valve clearances are adjusted by shims, positioned between the followers and the tip of the valve stem.

The camshafts on 16-valve engines are also driven by a common toothed timing belt; the front camshaft operates the inlet valves, and the rear camshaft operates the exhaust valves. The valve clearances are self-adjusting by means of hydraulic tappets.

Each camshaft runs in bearing caps which are bolted to the top of the cylinder head. The inlet and exhaust valves are each closed by coil springs, and operate in guides pressed into the cylinder head. Both the valve seats and guides can be renewed separately if worn.

The coolant pump is also driven by the timing belt, and is located in the right-hand end of the cylinder head.

Lubrication is by means of an oil pump which is driven (via a chain and sprocket) off the crankshaft right-hand end. It draws oil through a strainer located in the sump, and then forces it through an externally-mounted filter into galleries in the cylinder block/crankcase. From there, the oil is distributed to the crankshaft (main bearings) and camshaft. The big-end bearings are supplied with oil via internal drillings in the crankshaft; the camshaft bearings also receive a pressurised supply. The camshaft lobes and valves are lubricated by splash, as are all other engine components. On certain engines, an oil cooler is mounted beneath the oil filter cartridge, to keep the oil temperature constant under severe operating conditions. The oil cooler is supplied with coolant from the engine cooling system.

Throughout the manual, it is often necessary to identify the engines not only by their cubic capacity, but also by their engine code. The engine code, consists of three letters (eg. LFZ). On 1.8 litre engines the code is stamped on a plate attached to the front, left-hand end of the cylinder block, and on 2.0 litre engines the engine code is stamped directly onto the front face of the cylinder block, on the machined surface located just to the left of the oil filter (next to the crankcase vent hose union).

Repair operations possible with the engine in the car

The following work can be carried out with the engine in the car:
a) *Compression pressure – testing.*
b) *Cylinder head cover – removal and refitting.*
c) *Crankshaft pulley – removal and refitting.*
d) *Timing belt covers – removal and refitting.*
e) *Timing belt – removal, refitting and adjustment.*
f) *Timing belt tensioner and sprockets – removal and refitting.*
g) *Camshaft oil seal – renewal.*
h) *Camshaft and followers – removal, inspection and refitting.*
i) *Valve clearances – checking and adjustment.*
j) *Cylinder head – removal and refitting.*
k) *Cylinder head and pistons – decarbonising.*
l) *Sump – removal and refitting.*
m) *Oil pump – removal, overhaul and refitting.*
n) *Crankshaft oil seals – renewal.*
o) *Engine/transmission mountings – inspection and renewal.*
p) *Flywheel/driveplate – removal, inspection and refitting.*

2 Compression test – description and interpretation

Refer to Chapter 2A, Section 2.

3 Engine assembly/valve timing holes – general information and usage

Note: *Do not attempt to rotate the engine whilst the crankshaft/camshaft are locked in position. If the engine is to be left in this state for a long period of time, it is a good idea to place suitable warning notices inside the vehicle, and in the engine compartment. This will reduce the possibility of the engine being accidentally cranked on the starter motor, which is likely to cause damage with the locking pins in place.*

1 On all engines, timing holes are drilled in the camshaft sprocket(s) and crankshaft pulley. The holes are used to align the crankshaft and camshaft(s), to prevent the possibility of the valves contacting the pistons when refitting the cylinder head, or when refitting the timing belt. When the holes are aligned with their corresponding holes in the cylinder head and cylinder block (as appropriate), suitable diameter pins can be inserted to lock both the camshaft(s) and crankshaft in position, preventing them rotating unnecessarily. Proceed as follows.

2 Remove the timing belt upper cover as described in Section 6.

3 Firmly apply the handbrake, then jack up the front of the car and support it securely on axle stands (see *Jacking and vehicle support*). Remove the right-hand front roadwheel.

4 To gain access to the right-hand end of the engine, the wheelarch plastic liner must be removed. The liner is secured by various screws and clips under the wheelarch. Release all the fasteners, and remove liner from under the front wing. Where necessary, unclip the coolant hoses from under the wing to improve access further. The crankshaft can then be turned using a suitable socket and extension bar fitted to the pulley bolt. Note that the crankshaft must always be turned in a clockwise direction (viewed from the right-hand side of vehicle).

8-valve engines

5 Rotate the crankshaft pulley until the timing hole in the camshaft sprocket is aligned with its corresponding hole in the cylinder head.

3.6 8.0 mm drill inserted through the crankshaft pulley timing hole – 8-valve engines

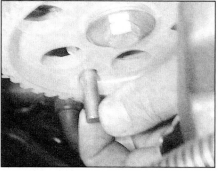

3.7 9.5 mm diameter drill inserted through the camshaft pulley timing hole – 8-valve engines

3.10 Drill bit (arrowed) inserted through the crankshaft pulley – 16-valve engines

Note that the holes are aligned when the sprocket hole is in the 8 o'clock position, when viewed from the right-hand end of the engine.

6 With the camshaft sprocket timing hole correctly positioned, insert an 8.0 mm diameter bolt or drill bit through the timing hole in the crankshaft pulley, and locate it in the corresponding hole in the end of the cylinder block **(see illustration)**. Note that it may be necessary to rotate the crankshaft slightly, to get the holes to align.

7 Once the crankshaft pulley is locked in position, insert a suitable 9.5 mm diameter (approximate) bolt or drill bit through the camshaft sprocket hole, and locate it in the cylinder head **(see illustration)**.

8 The crankshaft and camshaft are now locked in position, preventing unnecessary rotation.

16-valve engines

9 Rotate the crankshaft pulley until the timing holes in both camshaft sprocket hubs are aligned with their corresponding holes in the cylinder head. The holes are aligned when the inlet camshaft sprocket hole is in approximately the 5 o'clock position and the exhaust camshaft sprocket hole is in approximately the 7 o'clock position, when viewed from the right-hand end of the engine.

10 With the camshaft sprocket holes correctly positioned, insert a 6.0 mm diameter bolt or drill bit through the timing hole in the

crankshaft pulley, and locate it in the corresponding hole in the end of the engine **(see illustration)**. Note that the hole size may vary according to the type of pulley fitted and auxiliary drivebelt arrangement. If the bolt or drill is not a snug fit, try a larger size until a good fit is achieved in both the pulley and cylinder block.

11 With the crankshaft locked in position, insert a suitable bolt or drill through the timing hole in each camshaft sprocket hub and locate it in the cylinder head **(see illustration)**.

12 The crankshaft and camshafts are now locked in position, preventing rotation.

4 Cylinder head cover – removal and refitting

Removal

1 Disconnect the battery negative terminal (refer to *Disconnecting the battery* in the Reference Section of this manual).

8-valve engines

2 Slacken the retaining clips, and disconnect the breather hoses from the front right-hand end of the cover. Where the original crimped-type Citroën hose clips are still fitted, cut them off and discard them; use standard worm drive hose clips on refitting.

3 Slacken the retaining clip, and disconnect

the air cleaner-to-throttle housing duct from the front of the cylinder head cover. Also remove the inlet duct from the left-hand side of the cover.

4 Release the two retaining clips, then undo the two retaining screws located at the front, and remove the air cleaner element cover from the cylinder head cover. Remove the air cleaner element, and store it with the cover.

5 Evenly and progressively unscrew the ten cylinder head cover retaining nuts, lift off the cylinder head cover, and remove it along with its rubber seal **(see illustration)**. Examine the seal for signs of damage and deterioration, and if necessary, renew it.

16-valve engines

Note: *Later engines are fitted with plastic camshaft covers, rather than aluminium alloy as before. The procedure given below is not greatly affected by this change, except that the number of retaining bolts for each cover increases, and the bolts are located around the edge of each cover. No tightening sequence for the cover bolts is quoted by Citroën, so this stage can be ignored for later engines.*

6 Disconnect the wiring connector at the left-hand end of the ignition coil unit, located in the centre of the cylinder head covers. Undo the six retaining bolts and lift the coil unit upwards, off the spark plugs and from its location between the cylinder head covers **(see illustration)**.

3.11 Bolts (arrowed) inserted through the timing holes in each camshaft sprocket – 16-valve engines

4.5 Cylinder head cover retaining nuts (arrowed) – 8-valve engines

4.6 Removing the ignition coil unit – 16-valve engines

4.7a Remove the two Allen bolts . . .

4.7b . . . and lift off the fuel pipe cover – 16-valve engines

4.8a Disconnect the fuel supply pipe from the fuel pressure regulator . . .

7 Remove the Allen bolts from the fuel pipe cover, and remove the cover **(see illustrations)**.

8 Refer to Chapter 4A and depressurise the fuel system. Taking suitable precautions against fuel spillage, disconnect the fuel pipes

from the fuel pressure regulator as necessary. Detach the fuel supply and return pipes from the carrier bracket fitted across the cylinder head covers. Unscrew the retaining nuts and remove the fuel pipe carrier bracket **(see illustrations)**.

9 Slacken the retaining clips, and disconnect the breather hoses from the front left-hand side of the front cover **(see illustration)**. Where the original crimped-type hose clips are still fitted, cut them off and discard them; use standard worm drive hose clips on refitting.

10 Working in a spiral sequence starting from the outside and working inwards, progressively slacken, then remove the retaining studs and bolts from each cylinder head cover **(see illustrations)**.

11 Lift off each cover in turn and remove it. The cover seal should remain attached as the cover is removed – do not try to remove it, unless it is obviously damaged.

4.8b . . . and the return pipe, releasing it from the plastic clip

4.8c Unscrew the retaining nuts . . .

Refitting

8-valve engines

12 Clean the cylinder head and cover mating surfaces, and remove all traces of oil.

13 Locate the rubber seal in the cover groove, ensuring that it is correctly located along its entire length.

14 Apply a smear of suitable sealant to the each camshaft end bearing cap around the area where the cap contacts the cylinder head mating surface.

4.8d . . . and remove the fuel pipe carrier bracket – 16-valve engines

4.9 Disconnect the breather hoses from the front cylinder head cover – 16-valve engines

4.10a Remove the studs . . .

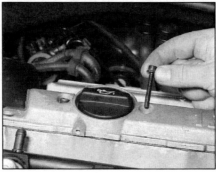

4.10b . . . and retaining bolts . . .

4.10c . . . and remove the cylinder head cover – note the short bolt which does not need to be removed – 16-valve engines

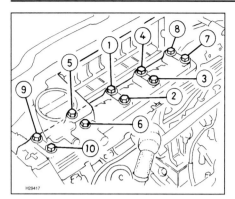

4.16 Tighten the cylinder head cover retaining nuts in the sequence shown – 8-valve engines

15 Carefully refit the cylinder head cover to the engine, taking great care not to displace the rubber seal.
16 Check that the seal is correctly located, then refit the cover retaining nuts and, working in the sequence shown, tighten them evenly and progressively to the specified torque **(see illustration)**.
17 Refit the air cleaner element, and install the element cover. Securely tighten the cover retaining screws, and secure it in position with the retaining clips.
18 Reconnect the breather hoses, inlet duct and throttle housing duct to the cover, tightening their retaining clips securely. Reconnect the battery negative terminal.

16-valve engines

19 Clean the cylinder head and cylinder head cover mating surfaces, and remove all traces of oil.
20 Check the condition of the rubber seal attached to each cover. The seal is designed to be re-usable, and so should not automatically be replaced unless its condition is suspect. If the seal is broken, it can be repaired using a bead of suitable sealant.
21 Carefully refit the cylinder head cover(s) to the engine.
22 Refit the cover retaining bolts and studs and, working in the sequence shown (where applicable), tighten them evenly and progressively to the specified torque **(see illustration)**.

5.3a Removing the crankshaft pulley retaining bolt

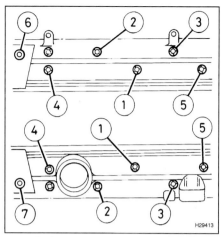

4.22 Tighten the aluminium cylinder head cover retaining nuts in the sequence shown – 16-valve engines

23 Reconnect the breather hoses to the front cover, and securely tighten the retaining clips.
24 Refit the ignition coil unit between the cylinder head covers. Refit the retaining bolts, tightening them securely, then reconnect the coil unit wiring connector.
25 Refit the fuel pipe carrier bracket to the covers, then refit the fuel pipes to their locations and secure with the fuel pipe cover.
26 Reconnect the battery negative terminal. On completion, start the engine and check the fuel hose unions for signs of leakage.

5 Crankshaft pulley – removal and refitting

Removal

1 Remove the auxiliary drivebelt as described in Chapter 1A.
2 To prevent crankshaft turning whilst the pulley retaining bolt is being slackened on manual transmission models, select top gear and have an assistant apply the brakes firmly. On automatic transmission models, remove the starter motor (Chapter 5A) and use a suitable tool in the driveplate teeth to stop crankshaft rotation. Alternatively, the flywheel

5.3b Removing the crankshaft pulley from the end of the crankshaft

Use a fabricated tool like this one to lock the flywheel ring gear and prevent crankshaft rotation.

ring gear can be locked using a suitable tool made from steel angle **(see Tool Tip)**. Remove the cover plate from the base of the transmission bellhousing and bolt the tool to the bellhousing flange so it engages with the ring gear teeth. *Do not* attempt to lock the pulley by inserting a bolt/drill through the timing hole. If the timing hole bolt/drill is in position, temporarily remove it prior to slackening the pulley bolt, then refit it once the bolt has been slackened.
3 Unscrew the retaining bolt and washer, then slide the pulley off the end of the crankshaft **(see illustrations)**. If the pulley locating roll pin or Woodruff key (as applicable) is a loose fit, remove it and store it with the pulley for safe-keeping. If the pulley is tight fit, it can be drawn off the crankshaft using a suitable puller.

Refitting

4 Ensure that the Woodruff key is correctly located in its crankshaft groove, or that the roll pin is in position (as applicable). Refit the pulley to the end of the crankshaft, aligning its locating groove or hole with the Woodruff key or pin.
5 Thoroughly clean the threads of the pulley retaining bolt, then apply a coat of locking compound to the bolt threads. Citroën recommend the use of Loctite (available from your Citroën dealer); in the absence of this, any good-quality locking compound may be used.
6 Refit the crankshaft pulley retaining bolt and washer. Tighten the bolt to the specified torque, preventing the crankshaft from turning using the method employed on removal.
7 Refit and tension the auxiliary drivebelt as described in Chapter 1A.

6 Timing belt covers – removal and refitting

1.8 litre (8-valve) engines with manual transmission

Upper cover

1 Release the retaining clips, and free the fuel hoses from the top of the cover.

2 Undo the two cover retaining bolts located on the front face of the cover.

3 Lift the cover upwards to disengage it from the lower cover, then remove the cover from the engine.

Lower cover

4 Remove the upper cover as previously described.

5 Remove the crankshaft pulley as described in Section 5.

6 Undo the three cover retaining bolts, one located in the centre of the cover and two located below the crankshaft, one on each side. Remove the cover from the engine.

1.8 litre (8-valve) engines with automatic transmission

Upper cover

7 Release the retaining clips, and free the fuel hoses from the top of the cover.

8 Undo the two cover retaining bolts (situated at the base of the cover), and remove the cover from the engine.

Centre cover

9 Remove the upper cover as previously described.

10 Undo the two cover retaining bolts located near the top of the cover. Move the cover upwards to free it from the two locating pins situated at the base of the cover, and remove it from the engine.

Lower cover

11 Remove the upper and centre covers as described previously.

12 Remove the crankshaft pulley as described in Section 5.

13 Undo the two cover retaining bolts, and remove the cover from the engine. Note that on some engines it may be necessary to unbolt the auxiliary drivebelt tensioner assembly and remove it from the engine in order to allow the cover to be removed.

1.8 and 2.0 litre (16-valve) engines

Upper (outer) cover

14 Unclip the wiring harness from its location in the shaped top of the engine right-hand mounting, and from the inlet manifold bracket. Where applicable, release the air conditioning hose which runs between the timing belt cover and the engine mounting. Move the hose and wiring harness to one side (*do not attempt to disconnect the air conditioning hose*).

15 Prise out the clips and remove the trim cover from the top of the engine right-hand mounting.

16 On early engines, lift the tab provided in the centre of the timing belt cover upwards to release the centre locating pegs. On later engines, undo the two nuts from the centre of the cover.

17 Unscrew and remove the three upper retaining screws. Move the cover upwards to

free it from the two locating pegs situated at the base of the cover, and remove it from the engine. Recover the rubber pads from the centre locating pegs, where applicable.

Lower cover

18 Remove the upper (outer) cover as described previously.

19 Remove the crankshaft pulley as described in Section 5.

20 Undo the two special peg bolts and the two conventional bolts, noting their locations, then remove the lower timing belt cover from the engine. Note that on some engines it may be necessary to unbolt the auxiliary drivebelt tensioner assembly and remove it from the engine in order to allow the cover to be removed.

Upper (inner) cover

21 Remove the timing belt as described in Section 8.

22 Remove both camshaft sprockets as described in Section 9.

23 Remove the six bolts securing the cover to the side of the cylinder head, and remove the cover from the engine.

Refitting

24 Refitting is a reversal of the relevant removal procedure, ensuring that each cover section is correctly located, and that the cover retaining nuts and/or bolts are securely tightened (to the specified torque, where given).

---

7 Timing belt (8-valve engines) – general information, removal and refitting

Note: *Citroën specify the use of an electronic belt tension checking tool (SEEM 4122-T) to correctly set the timing belt tension. The following procedure assumes that this equipment (or suitable alternative equipment calibrated to display belt tension in SEEM units) is available. Accurate tensioning of the timing belt is essential, and if the electronic equipment is not available, it is recommended that the work is entrusted to a Citroën dealer or suitably-equipped garage.*

General information

1 The timing belt drives the camshaft and coolant pump from a toothed sprocket on the right-hand end of the crankshaft. If the belt breaks or slips in service, the pistons are likely to hit the valve heads, resulting in extensive (and expensive) damage.

2 The timing belt should be renewed at the specified intervals (see Chapter 1A), or earlier if it is contaminated with oil or if it is at all noisy in operation (a 'scraping' noise due to uneven wear).

3 If the timing belt is being removed, it is a wise precaution to check the condition of the coolant pump at the same time (check for signs of coolant leakage). This may avoid the

need to remove the timing belt again at a later stage, should the coolant pump fail.

Removal

4 Disconnect the battery negative terminal (refer to *Disconnecting the battery* in the Reference Section of this manual).

5 Remove the centre and/or lower timing belt cover(s) as described in Section 6 (as applicable).

6 To improve access, refer to Section 19 and remove the engine right-hand mounting. This is not essential, but it does make several of the timing belt components much easier to remove with the engine in the car.

7 Align the engine assembly/valve timing holes as described in Section 3, and lock the camshaft sprocket and crankshaft pulley in position. *Do not* attempt to rotate the engine whilst the locking tools are in position.

8 Loosen the timing belt tensioner pulley retaining bolt. Allow the pulley to pivot in a clockwise direction, to relieve the tension from the timing belt. Retighten the tensioner pulley retaining bolt to secure it in the slackened position.

9 If the timing belt is to be re-used, use white paint or chalk to mark the direction of rotation on the belt (if markings do not already exist), then slip the belt off the sprockets. Note that the crankshaft must not be rotated whilst the belt is removed.

10 Check the timing belt carefully for any signs of uneven wear, splitting, or oil contamination. Pay particular attention to the roots of the teeth. Renew it if there is the slightest doubt about its condition. If the engine is undergoing an overhaul, and has covered more than 37 500 miles (60 000 km) with the existing belt fitted, renew the belt as a matter of course, regardless of its apparent condition. The cost of a new belt is nothing compared with the cost of repairs, should the belt break in service. If signs of oil contamination are found, trace the source of the oil leak and rectify it. Wash down the engine timing belt area and all related components, to remove all traces of oil.

Refitting

11 Before refitting, thoroughly clean the timing belt sprockets. Check that the tensioner pulley rotates freely, without any sign of roughness. If necessary, renew the tensioner pulley as described in Section 9.

12 Ensure that the camshaft sprocket locking tool is still in position. Temporarily refit the crankshaft pulley, and insert the locking tool through the pulley timing hole to ensure that the crankshaft is still correctly positioned.

13 Remove the crankshaft pulley. Manoeuvre the timing belt into position, ensuring that any arrows on the belt are pointing in the direction of rotation (clockwise when viewed from the right-hand end of the engine).

14 Do not twist the timing belt sharply while refitting it. Fit the belt over the crankshaft and camshaft sprockets. Ensure that the belt 'front run' is taut – ie, any slack should be on the tensioner pulley side of the belt. Fit the belt over the coolant pump sprocket and tensioner pulley. Ensure that the belt teeth are seated centrally in the sprockets.

15 Loosen the tensioner pulley retaining bolt. Pivot the pulley anti-clockwise to remove all free play from the timing belt, then retighten the bolt. Tension the timing belt as follows.

Tensioning

16 Fit the sensor head of the electronic belt tension measuring equipment to the 'front run' of the timing belt, approximately midway between the camshaft and crankshaft sprockets.

17 Slacken the tensioner pulley retaining bolt and insert a short length of 8.0 mm square bar into the square hole on the front face of the tensioner pulley **(see Tool Tip)**.

18 Using the square bar and a spanner, pivot the tensioner pulley anti-clockwise until an initial setting of 30 ± 2 SEEM units is displayed on the tension measuring equipment. Hold the tensioner pulley in that position and retighten the retaining bolt.

19 Remove the locking tool from the camshaft sprocket, and remove the tension measuring equipment from the belt.

20 Refit the crankshaft pulley and tighten the bolt moderately to allow the crankshaft to be rotated.

21 Using a suitable socket and extension bar on the crankshaft pulley bolt, rotate the crankshaft through two complete rotations in a clockwise direction (viewed from the right-hand end of the engine). *Do not* at any time rotate the crankshaft anti-clockwise. Both camshaft and crankshaft timing holes should be aligned so that the locking tools can be easily inserted. This indicates that the valve timing is correct. If all is well, remove the locking tools.

22 If the timing holes are not correctly positioned, repeat the fitting procedure so far.

23 Rotate the crankshaft two more turns without turning backwards and refit the camshaft locking tool. Refit the tension measuring equipment to the timing belt.

24 The final belt tension on the 'front run' of the belt should be 44 ± 2 SEEM units. Readjust the tensioner pulley position as required, then retighten the retaining bolt to the specified torque. Remove the tools and rotate the crankshaft through a further two rotations clockwise, and recheck the tension. Repeat this procedure as necessary until the correct tension reading is obtained after rotating the crankshaft.

25 With the belt tension correctly set remove the camshaft locking tool, then remove the crankshaft pulley and refit the timing cover(s).

26 Refit the crankshaft pulley as described in Section 5, and reconnect the battery negative terminal.

8 Timing belt (16-valve engines) – general information, removal and refitting

General information

1 The timing belt drives the camshafts and coolant pump from a toothed sprocket on the right-hand end of the crankshaft. If the belt breaks or slips in service, the pistons are likely to hit the valve heads, resulting in extensive (and expensive) damage.

2 The timing belt should be renewed at the specified intervals (see Chapter 1A), or earlier if it is contaminated with oil, or if it is at all noisy in operation (a 'scraping' noise due to uneven wear).

3 If the timing belt is being removed, it is a wise precaution to check the condition of the coolant pump at the same time (check for signs of coolant leakage). This may avoid the need to remove the timing belt again at a later stage, should the coolant pump fail.

4 Two types of timing belt tensioner pulley may be encountered. On early engines a manual tensioner pulley is used, and the belt tension must be set using an electronic tension checking tool. On later engines (from approximately mid-1999) a dynamic tensioner pulley is used which automatically adjusts the belt tension.

5 On engines with a manual tensioner pulley, Citroën specify the use of an electronic belt tension checking tool (SEEM 4122-T) to correctly set the timing belt tension. The following procedure assumes that this equipment (or suitable alternative equipment calibrated to display belt tension in SEEM units) is available. Accurate tensioning of the timing belt is essential, and if the electronic equipment is not available, it is recommended that the work is entrusted to a Citroën dealer or suitably-equipped garage.

Removal

6 Disconnect the battery negative terminal (refer to *Disconnecting the battery* in the Reference Section of this manual).

7 Remove the auxiliary drivebelt as described in Chapter 1A. Where applicable, unbolt and remove the auxiliary drivebelt tensioner.

8 Move the engine wiring harness and relevant hoses clear of the working area as necessary. This will entail the disconnection of certain connectors, and the removal of the harness from various cable clips and supports. Label any disconnected wiring and components as an aid to refitting.

9 Remove the timing belt upper (outer) cover as described in Section 6.

10 Determine the type of timing belt tensioner pulley fitted by referring to the accompanying illustrations, then proceed as described in the appropriate following sub-sections **(see illustrations)**.

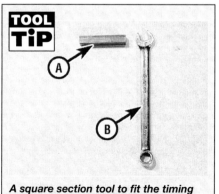

TOOL TiP

A square section tool to fit the timing belt tensioner pulley can be made from a length of standard 8 mm door handle rod (A), obtained from a DIY shop, and then cut to size. Once the rod has been fitted to the tensioner, the timing belt can be tensioned by turning the rod with an 8 mm spanner (B).

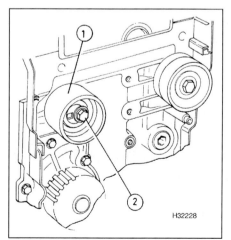

8.10a Early type manual timing belt tensioner pulley – 16-valve engines
1 Manual tensioner pulley
2 Retaining bolt

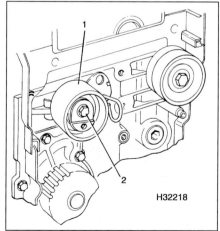

8.10b Later type dynamic timing belt tensioner pulley – 16-valve engines
1 Dynamic tensioner pulley
2 Retaining bolt

8.15 Loosen the manual timing belt tensioner retaining bolt . . .

8.16 . . . and slip the timing belt off the sprockets – 16-valve engines

Engines with a manual tensioner pulley

11 To improve access, refer to Section 19 and remove the engine right-hand mounting. This is not essential, but it does make several of the timing belt components much easier to remove with the engine in the car.

12 Align the engine assembly/valve timing holes as described in Section 3, and lock the camshaft sprocket hubs in position. *Do not* attempt to rotate the engine whilst the locking tools are in place.

13 Remove the crankshaft pulley as described in Section 5.

14 Unbolt and remove the timing belt lower cover (refer to Section 6 if necessary).

15 Loosen the timing belt tensioner pulley retaining bolt **(see illustration)**. Allow the pulley to pivot in a clockwise direction, to relieve the tension from the timing belt. Retighten the tensioner pulley retaining bolt to secure it in the slackened position.

16 If the timing belt is to be re-used, use white paint or chalk to mark the direction of rotation on the belt (if markings do not already exist), then slip the belt off the sprockets **(see illustration)**. Note that the crankshaft must not be rotated whilst the belt is removed.

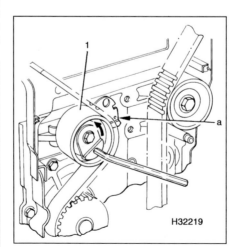

Using a home-made tool to retain the camshaft sprocket whilst the retaining bolt is slackened or tightened (TU engine shown).

17 Check the timing belt carefully for any signs of uneven wear, splitting, or oil contamination. Pay particular attention to the roots of the teeth. Renew it if there is the slightest doubt about its condition. If the engine is undergoing an overhaul, and has covered more than 37 500 miles (60 000 km) with the existing belt fitted, renew the belt as a matter of course, regardless of its apparent condition. The cost of a new belt is nothing compared with the cost of repairs, should the belt break in service. If signs of oil contamination are found, trace the source of the oil leak and rectify it. Wash down the engine timing belt area and all related components, to remove all traces of oil.

Engines with a dynamic tensioner pulley

18 To improve access, refer to Section 19 and remove the engine right-hand mounting. This is not essential, but it does make several of the timing belt components much easier to remove with the engine in the car.

![Diagram of dynamic tensioner pulley showing index pointer and reference hole, labelled 1 and a. H32219]

8.24 Rotate the dynamic tensioner pulley (1) anti-clockwise until the index pointer is below the reference hole (a) – 16-valve engines

19 Align the engine assembly/valve timing holes as described in Section 3, and lock the camshaft sprocket hubs in position. *Do not* attempt to rotate the engine whilst the locking tools are in position.

20 Remove the crankshaft pulley as described in Section 5.

21 Unbolt and remove the timing belt lower cover (refer to Section 6 if necessary).

22 Slacken the camshaft sprocket centre retaining bolt on each camshaft. To prevent the sprockets rotating as the bolts are slackened, a sprocket holding tool will be required. In the absence of the special Citroën tool, an acceptable substitute can be fabricated at home **(see Tool Tip)**. *Do not* attempt to use only the sprocket hub locking tools inserted in the engine assembly/valve timing holes to prevent the sprockets from rotating whilst the bolts are slackened.

23 Slacken the timing belt tensioner pulley retaining bolt and insert a suitable Allen key into the hexagonal hole on the front face of the tensioner pulley.

24 Using the Allen key, turn the tensioner pulley anti-clockwise (as viewed from the right-hand side of the car) until the index pointer is below the reference hole **(see illustration)**. Insert a small drill bit or short length of welding rod into the reference hole to retain the index pointer in this position.

25 Now turn the tensioner pulley clockwise until the hexagonal Allen key hole is positioned approximately adjacent to the upper edge of the coolant pump flange. Tighten the tensioner pulley retaining bolt to retain the pulley in this position.

26 If the timing belt is to be re-used, use white paint or chalk to mark the direction of rotation on the belt (if markings do not already exist), then slip the belt off the sprockets. Note that the crankshaft must not be rotated whilst the belt is removed.

27 Inspect the belt as described in paragraph 17.

8.30a Slacken the camshaft sprocket retaining bolts (arrowed) – 16-valve engines

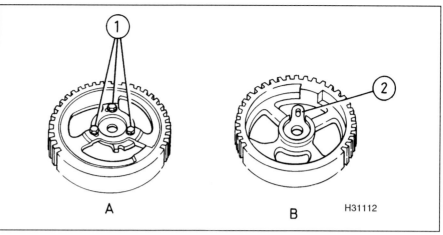

8.30b Camshaft sprocket details – early models (A) have three retaining bolts (1) in elongated slots, while later models (B) have a single bolt and a protruding lug (2) – 16-valve engines

Refitting and tensioning

Engines with a manual tensioner pulley

28 Before refitting, thoroughly clean the timing belt sprockets. Check that the tensioner and idler pulleys rotate freely, without any sign of roughness. If necessary, renew the pulleys as described in Section 9.

29 Ensure that the camshaft sprocket hub locking tools are still in position. Temporarily refit the crankshaft pulley, insert the locking tool through the pulley timing hole to ensure that the crankshaft is still correctly positioned, then remove the pulley.

30 Without removing the locking tools, on early engines, slacken the six camshaft sprocket retaining bolts (three on each sprocket). On later engines, only the single bolt securing each camshaft sprocket need be slackened. Check that both sprockets are free to turn within the limits of their elongated bolt holes, or that the protruding lug on single-bolt sprockets can move within its limits **(see illustrations)**. To prevent the single-bolt sprockets rotating as the bolts are slackened, a sprocket holding tool will be required. In the absence of the special Citroën tool, an acceptable substitute can be fabricated at home (see **Tool Tip** above). *Do not* attempt to use only the sprocket hub locking tools to prevent the sprockets from rotating whilst the bolts are slackened.

31 Tighten the camshaft sprocket retaining bolts finger-tight, then slacken them all by one sixth of a turn.

32 Again without removing the locking tools, turn each camshaft sprocket clockwise to the ends of their retaining bolt slots, or until the protruding lug reaches the end of its travel.

33 Ensuring that any arrows on the belt are pointing in the direction of rotation (clockwise when viewed from the right-hand end of the engine), manoeuvre the timing belt into position on the exhaust camshaft sprocket. Retain the belt on the sprocket using a cable tie.

34 With the sprockets still positioned fully clockwise as far as they will go, feed the belt over the inlet camshaft sprocket, keeping it tight on its top run.

35 Engage the belt around the idler pulley, crankshaft sprocket, coolant pump sprocket and finally around the tensioner pulley.

36 Fit the sensor head of the electronic belt tension measuring equipment to the 'front run' of the timing belt, approximately midway between the idler pulley and crankshaft sprockets.

37 Slacken the tensioner pulley retaining bolt and insert a short length of 8.0 mm square bar into the square hole on the front face of the tensioner pulley (see **Tool Tip** in Section 7).

38 Using the square bar and a spanner, pivot the tensioner pulley anti-clockwise until an initial setting of 45 SEEM units is displayed on the tension measuring equipment. Hold the tensioner pulley in that position and retighten the retaining bolt.

39 Check that the sprockets have not been turned so far that the retaining bolts are at the end of their slots, or that the protruding lug on single-bolt sprockets is at the end of its travel. If either condition is evident, repeat the refitting operation. If all is satisfactory, tighten the sprocket retaining bolts to the specified torque.

40 Remove the belt tension measuring equipment, the crankshaft and camshaft locking tools, and the cable tie used to retain the belt on the exhaust camshaft sprocket.

41 Refit the timing belt lower cover and the crankshaft pulley as described in Sections 6 and 5 respectively.

42 Rotate the crankshaft through two complete rotations in a clockwise direction (viewed from the right-hand end of the engine). Realign the engine assembly/valve timing holes and refit the crankshaft pulley and camshaft sprocket hub locking tools.

43 Slacken the camshaft sprocket retaining bolts, retighten them finger-tight, then slacken them all by one sixth of a turn.

44 Slacken the tensioner pulley retaining bolt once more. Refit the belt tension measuring equipment to the front run of the belt, and turn the tensioner pulley to give a final setting of

26 SEEM units (engines with three bolts per camshaft sprocket) or 32 SEEM units (single-bolt sprocket engines) on the tensioning gauge. Hold the tensioner pulley in this position and tighten the retaining bolt to the specified torque. Remove the tension measuring equipment.

45 Retighten all sprocket retaining bolts to the specified torque.

46 The belt tension must now be checked as follows. Remove the locking tools, then rotate the crankshaft once again through two complete rotations in a clockwise direction. Realign the engine assembly/valve timing holes and refit the crankshaft pulley and camshaft sprocket hub locking tools.

47 Slacken the camshaft sprocket retaining bolts, then retighten them to the specified torque.

48 Remove the camshaft and crankshaft locking tools. Turn the crankshaft approximately one quarter of a turn in the normal direction of rotation, until the locking tool hole in the crankshaft pulley is aligned with the timing belt lower cover front retaining bolt. It is important that this position is achieved ONLY by turning the belt forwards – if the belt is turned back at all to achieve alignment, the belt tension check will not be valid.

49 In this position, refit the tension measuring equipment to the front run of the belt, and check that the reading is between 32 and 40 SEEM units. If not, the entire belt tensioning procedure must be repeated from the start.

50 Once the belt tension has been correctly set, refit the engine right-hand mounting components (if removed) as described in Section 19.

51 Refit the timing belt upper (outer) cover as described in Section 6.

52 Reconnect any hoses and wiring disturbed for access.

53 Refit the auxiliary drivebelt tensioner then refit and tension the drivebelt with reference to Chapter 1A.

54 Reconnect the battery negative terminal.

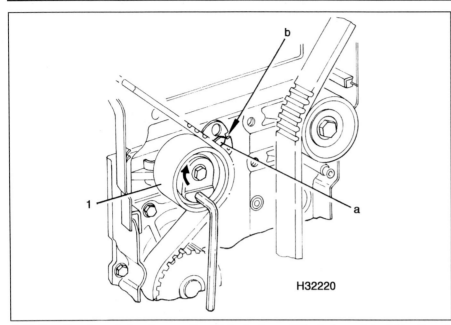

H32220

8.68 Turn the dynamic tensioner pulley (1) clockwise until the index pointer (a) is aligned with the slot (b) in the index plate – 16-valve engines

Engines with a dynamic tensioner pulley

55 Before refitting, thoroughly clean the timing belt sprockets. Check that the tensioner and idler pulleys rotate freely, without any sign of roughness. If necessary, renew the pulleys as described in Section 9.

56 Ensure that the camshaft sprocket hub locking tools are still in position. Temporarily refit the crankshaft pulley, insert the locking tool through the pulley timing hole to ensure that the crankshaft is still correctly positioned, then remove the pulley.

57 With the camshaft sprocket retaining bolts still slackened, turn each camshaft sprocket clockwise to the end of its travel. Tighten the sprocket retaining bolts slightly to hold the sprockets in this position.

58 Ensuring that any arrows on the belt are pointing in the direction of rotation (clockwise when viewed from the right-hand end of the engine), manoeuvre the timing belt into position on the exhaust camshaft sprocket. Retain the belt on the sprocket using a cable tie.

59 With the sprockets still positioned fully clockwise as far as they will go, feed the belt over the inlet camshaft sprocket, keeping it tight on its top run.

60 Engage the belt around the idler pulley, crankshaft sprocket, coolant pump sprocket and finally around the tensioner pulley.

61 With the timing belt in position, slacken the camshaft sprocket retaining bolts once more.

62 Remove the drill bit or welding rod from the reference hole in the tensioner pulley.

63 Slacken the tensioner pulley retaining bolt and turn the tensioner pulley, by means of the Allen key, so that the index pointer is positioned in its maximum position (ie, below

the reference hole). Hold the tensioner in this position and tighten the retaining bolt.

64 Hold the camshaft sprockets with the tool used during removal, and tighten the sprocket centre retaining bolts to the specified torque.

65 Refit the timing belt lower cover and the crankshaft pulley as described in Sections 6 and 5 respectively.

66 Remove the locking tools and rotate the crankshaft through four complete rotations in a clockwise direction (viewed from the right-hand end of the engine). Realign the engine assembly/valve timing holes and refit the crankshaft pulley and camshaft sprocket hub locking tools.

67 Hold the camshaft sprockets with the tool used during removal, and once again slacken the sprocket centre retaining bolts.

68 Hold the tensioner pulley in position by means of the Allen key and slacken the tensioner pulley retaining bolt. Turn the tensioner clockwise until the index pointer is aligned with the slot in the centre of the index plate, then tighten the retaining bolt to the specified torque **(see illustration)**.

69 Hold the camshaft sprockets and tighten the sprocket centre retaining bolts to the specified torque.

70 Remove the locking tools and rotate the crankshaft through two complete rotations in a clockwise direction (viewed from the right-hand end of the engine). Realign the engine assembly/valve timing holes and refit the crankshaft pulley and camshaft sprocket hub locking tools.

71 Check that the index pointer on the tensioner pulley is still aligned with the slot in the centre of the index plate. If not, repeat the procedure from paragraph 66 to 70.

72 Once the belt tension has been correctly set, refit the engine right-hand mounting

components (if removed) as described in Section 19.

73 Refit the timing belt upper (outer) cover as described in Section 6.

74 Reconnect any hoses and wiring disturbed for access.

75 Refit the auxiliary drivebelt tensioner then refit and tension the drivebelt with reference to Chapter 1A.

76 Reconnect the battery negative terminal.

---

9 Timing belt tensioner and sprockets – removal, inspection and refitting

Removal

Camshaft sprocket – 8-valve engines

1 Remove the timing belt as described in Section 7.

2 Remove the locking tool from the camshaft sprocket. Disengage the timing belt from the sprocket and position it clear, taking care not to bend or twist the belt sharply.

3 Remove the locking tool from the camshaft sprocket. Slacken the sprocket retaining bolt and remove it, along with its washer. To prevent the camshaft rotating as the bolt is slackened, a sprocket holding tool will be required. In the absence of the special Citroën tool, an acceptable substitute can be fabricated at home (see **Tool Tip** in Section 8). *Do not* attempt to use the engine assembly/valve timing hole locking tool to prevent the sprocket from rotating whilst the bolt is slackened.

4 With the retaining bolt removed, slide the sprocket off the end of the camshaft. If the locating peg is a loose fit in the rear of the sprocket, remove it for safe-keeping. Examine the camshaft oil seal for signs of oil leakage and, if necessary, renew it as described in Section 10.

Camshaft sprockets – early 16-valve engines

Note: *The early type camshaft sprockets have a large centre retaining bolt to secure the sprocket hub to the camshaft, and three smaller bolts that secure the sprocket to the hub. If the sprocket being worked on does not have the three smaller bolts, it is a later type – refer to the procedures contained in the following sub-Section.*

5 Remove the timing belt as described in Section 8.

6 If the sprockets are to be removed without their hubs, undo the three retaining bolts and remove the relevant sprocket. Suitably mark the sprockets 'inlet' and/or 'exhaust' as they are removed (although in fact the sprockets are identical).

7 If both the sprockets and the hubs are to be removed, remove the relevant sprocket hub locking tool, then slacken the sprocket hub centre retaining bolt. To prevent the sprocket rotating as the bolt is slackened, a sprocket holding tool will be required. In the absence of the special Citroën tool, an acceptable substitute can be fabricated at home (see **Tool Tip** in Section 8). *Do not* attempt to use the engine assembly/valve timing hole locking tool to prevent the sprocket from rotating whilst the bolt is slackened.

8 Undo the three retaining bolts and remove the relevant sprocket from its hub. Remove the previously-slackened hub retaining bolt, and withdraw the hub from the end of the camshaft. Note that the hubs are marked for identification with a single digit on their front face. On 1.8 litre engines, the inlet hub is marked '1' and the exhaust hub is marked '2'. On 2.0 litre engines, the inlet hub is marked '3' and the exhaust hub is marked '4'. Make your own markings if none are visible.

Camshaft sprockets – later 16-valve engines

Note: *The later type camshaft sprockets have only a centre sprocket/hub retaining bolt to secure the assembly to the camshaft. If the sprocket being worked on has three additional smaller bolts, securing the sprocket to the hub, it is an early type – refer to the procedures contained in the previous sub-Section.*

9 Remove the timing belt as described in Section 8.

10 Remove the relevant sprocket hub locking tool, then slacken the sprocket centre retaining bolt. To prevent the sprocket rotating as the bolt is slackened, a sprocket holding tool will be required. In the absence of the special Citroën tool, an acceptable substitute can be fabricated at home (see **Tool Tip** in Section 8). *Do not* attempt to use the engine assembly/valve timing hole locking tool to prevent the sprocket from rotating whilst the bolt is slackened.

11 Remove the previously-slackened hub retaining bolt, and withdraw the relevant sprocket and hub from the end of the camshaft. Suitably mark the sprockets and hubs 'inlet' and/or 'exhaust' as they are removed (although in fact they are identical).

Crankshaft sprocket – all engines

12 Remove the timing belt as described in Section 7 or 8 as applicable.

13 Slide the crankshaft sprocket off the end of the crankshaft. Remove the Woodruff key from the crankshaft, and store it with the sprocket for safe-keeping. Where necessary, also slide the spacer (where fitted) off the end of the crankshaft.

14 Examine the crankshaft oil seal for signs of oil leakage and, if necessary, renew it as described in Section 17.

Tensioner pulley – 8-valve engines

15 Remove the timing belt as described in Section 7.

16 Slacken and remove the timing belt tensioner pulley retaining bolt, and slide the pulley off its mounting stud. Examine the mounting stud for signs of damage and if necessary, renew it.

Tensioner and idler pulleys – 16-valve engines

17 Remove the timing belt as described in Section 8.

18 Undo the tensioner and idler pulley retaining bolts and remove the relevant pulley from the engine. On engines with a dynamic tensioner pulley, recover the small drill bit or welding rod inserted in the reference hole as the assembly is removed.

Inspection

19 Clean the camshaft/crankshaft sprockets thoroughly, and renew any that show signs of wear, damage or cracks.

20 Clean the tensioner/idler pulleys, but do not use any strong solvent which may enter the pulley bearings. Check that the pulleys rotate freely, with no sign of stiffness or free play. Renew them if there is any doubt about their condition, or if there are any obvious signs of wear or damage.

Refitting

Camshaft sprocket – 8-valve engines

21 Refit the locating peg (where removed) to the rear of the sprocket. Locate the sprocket on the end of the camshaft, ensuring that the locating peg is correctly engaged with the cut-out in the camshaft end.

22 Refit the sprocket retaining bolt and washer, and tighten it to the specified torque. Retain the sprocket with the tool used on removal.

23 Realign the hole in the camshaft sprocket with the corresponding hole in the cylinder head, and refit the locking tool. Check that the crankshaft pulley locking tool is still in position.

24 Refit and tension the timing belt as described in Section 7.

Camshaft sprockets – early 16-valve engines

25 If both the sprockets and the hubs have been removed, engage the sprocket hub with the camshaft. Ensure that the correct hub is fitted to the relevant camshaft by observing the hub identification markings described in paragraph 8.

26 Refit the sprocket retaining bolt and washer, and tighten it to the specified torque. Temporarily refit the sprocket to allow the hub to be held stationary, with the tool used on removal, as the bolt is tightened.

27 Turn the hub so that the locking tool can be engaged.

28 If the sprockets have been removed, leaving the hubs in place, position the sprocket on its hub and refit the three bolts finger tight only at this stage. Ensure that the correct sprocket is fitted to the relevant camshaft according to the identification made on removal.

29 Refit and tension the timing belt as described in Section 8.

Camshaft sprockets – later 16-valve engines

30 Engage the sprocket hub with the camshaft. Ensure that the correct hub is fitted to the relevant camshaft according to the identification made on removal.

31 Position the relevant sprocket on the hub and refit the sprocket retaining bolt and washer. Tighten the retaining bolt just tight enough to hold the sprocket/hub in place at this stage.

32 Turn the hub so that the locking tool can be engaged.

33 Refit and tension the timing belt as described in Section 8.

Crankshaft sprocket – all engines

34 Slide the spacer (where fitted) into position, taking great care not to damage the crankshaft oil seal, and refit the Woodruff key to its slot in the crankshaft end.

35 Slide on the crankshaft sprocket, aligning its slot with the Woodruff key.

36 Temporarily refit the crankshaft pulley, and insert the locking tool through the pulley timing hole, to ensure that the crankshaft is still correctly positioned.

37 Remove the crankshaft pulley, then refit and tension the timing belt as described in Section 7 or 8 as applicable.

Tensioner pulley – 8-valve engines

38 Refit the tensioner pulley to its mounting stud, and fit the retaining bolt.

39 Refit and tension the timing belt as described in Section 7.

Tensioner and idler pulleys – 16-valve engines

40 Refit the tensioner and idler pulleys and secure with the retaining bolts. On engines with a dynamic tensioner pulley, ensure that the pulley body correctly engages with the projection on the cylinder block, and position the index pointer as described in Section 8, paragraphs 24 and 25.

41 Relocate and tension the timing belt as described in Section 8.

10 Camshaft oil seal(s) – renewal

1 Remove the timing belt as described in Section 7 or 8 as applicable.

2 Remove the camshaft sprocket(s) as described in Section 9. On 16-valve engines, remove the sprockets and sprocket hubs.

3 Punch or drill two small holes opposite each other in the oil seal. Screw a self-tapping screw into each, and pull on the screws with pliers to extract the seal.

4 Clean the seal housing, and polish off any burrs or raised edges, which may have caused the seal to fail in the first place.

5 Lubricate the lips of the new seal with clean engine oil, and drive it into position until it seats on its locating shoulder. Use a suitable tubular drift, such as a socket, which bears only on the hard outer edge of the seal. Take care not to damage the seal lips during fitting. Note that the seal lips should face inwards.

6 Refit the camshaft sprocket(s) as described in Section 9.

7 Refit and tension the timing belt as described in Section 7 or 8 as applicable.

11 Camshaft and followers – removal, inspection and refitting

Removal

1 Disconnect the battery negative terminal (refer to *Disconnecting the battery* in the Reference Section of this manual), then proceed as described under the relevant sub-heading.

8-valve engines

2 Remove the cylinder head cover (Section 4) and the camshaft sprocket (Section 9).

3 Remove the ignition HT coil as described in Chapter 5B.

4 With the coil removed, slacken the upper bolt securing the thermostat housing to the left-hand end of the cylinder head. Remove the bolt, along with its sealing washer. This is necessary since the bolt screws into the left-hand (No 1) camshaft bearing cap.

5 Carefully ease the oil supply pipe out from the top of the camshaft bearing caps, and remove it **(see illustration)**. Note the O-ring seals fitted to each of the pipe unions.

6 The camshaft bearing caps should be numbered 1 to 5, number 1 being at the transmission end of the engine. If not, make identification marks on the caps, using white paint or a suitable marker pen. Also mark each cap in some way to indicate its correct fitted orientation. This will avoid the possibility of installing the caps the wrong way around on refitting.

7 Evenly and progressively slacken the camshaft bearing cap retaining nuts by one turn at a time. This will relieve the valve spring pressure on the bearing caps gradually and evenly. Once the pressure has been relieved, the nuts can be fully unscrewed and removed **(see illustration)**.

11.5 Removing the oil supply pipe from the camshaft bearing caps – 8-valve engines

8 Note the correct fitted orientation of the bearing caps, then remove them from the cylinder head **(see illustration)**.

9 Lift the camshaft away from the cylinder head, and slide the oil seal off the camshaft end **(see illustration)**.

10 Obtain eight small, clean plastic containers, and number them 1 to 8; alternatively, divide a larger container into eight compartments. Using a rubber sucker, withdraw each follower in turn, and place it in its respective container. Do not interchange the cam followers, or the rate of wear will be much increased. If necessary, also remove the shim from the top of the valve stem, and store it with its respective follower. Note that the shim may stick to the inside of the follower as it is withdrawn. If this happens, take care not to allow it to drop out as the follower is removed.

16-valve engines

11 Remove both cylinder head covers as described in Section 4.

12 Refer to Section 9 and remove both camshaft sprockets together with their hubs, and also remove the timing belt tensioner pulley.

13 Remove the timing belt upper (inner) cover as described in Section 6.

14 Progressively slacken, by a few turns at a time, the twelve bolts securing each camshaft bearing housing to the cylinder head. Release the bearing housings from their dowels and cylinder head locations. When each housing is

free, remove the bolts and washers completely, and lift off the bearing housings.

15 As both camshafts are identical, suitably mark them inlet and exhaust, or front and rear before removal.

16 Tilt the camshafts by pressing them down at their transmission end to release the centralising bearing at the timing belt end. Carefully lift the camshafts up and out of their locations and slide the oil seal off each camshaft end.

17 Obtain sixteen small, clean plastic containers, and number them inlet 1 to 8 and exhaust 1 to 8; alternatively, divide a larger container into sixteen compartments and number each compartment accordingly. Using a rubber sucker, withdraw each hydraulic tappet in turn, and place it in its respective container. Do not interchange the tappets, or the rate of wear will be much increased.

Inspection

18 Examine the camshaft bearing surfaces and cam lobes for signs of wear ridges and scoring. Renew the camshaft if any of these conditions are apparent. Examine the condition of the bearing surfaces, both on the camshaft journals and in the cylinder head/bearing caps. If the head bearing surfaces are worn excessively, the cylinder head will need to be renewed. If suitable measuring equipment is available, camshaft bearing journal wear can be checked by direct measurement (where the necessary specifications have been quoted by Citroën), noting that No 1 journal is at the transmission end of the head.

19 Examine the cam follower/hydraulic tappet bearing surfaces which contact the camshaft lobes for wear ridges and scoring. Renew any follower/tappet on which these conditions are apparent. If a follower/tappet bearing surface is badly scored, also examine the corresponding lobe on the camshaft for wear, as it is likely that both will be worn. Renew worn components as necessary.

Refitting

8-valve engines

20 Where removed, refit each shim to the top of its original valve stem. *Do not* interchange

11.7 Working as described in the text, unscrew the retaining nuts . . .

11.8 . . . and remove the camshaft bearing caps . . .

11.9 . . . then lift the camshaft away from the cylinder head – 8-valve engines

the shims, as this will upset the valve clearances.

21 Liberally oil the cylinder head cam follower bores and the followers. Carefully refit the followers to the cylinder head, ensuring that each follower is refitted to its original bore. Some care will be required to enter the followers squarely into their bores.

22 Liberally oil the camshaft bearings and lobes, then refit the camshaft to the cylinder head. Temporarily refit the sprocket to the end of the shaft, and position it so that the sprocket timing hole is aligned with the corresponding cut-out in the cylinder head. Also ensure that the crankshaft is still locked in position (see Section 3).

23 Ensure that the bearing cap and head mating surfaces are completely clean, unmarked, and free from oil. Apply a smear of sealant to the thermostat housing mating surface of the left-hand (No 1) bearing cap, then refit all the caps, using the identification marks noted on removal to ensure that each is installed correctly and in its original location.

24 Evenly and progressively tighten the camshaft bearing cap nuts by one turn at a time until the caps touch the cylinder head. Then go round again and tighten all the nuts to the specified torque setting. Work only as described, to impose the pressure of the valve springs gradually and evenly on the bearing caps.

25 Examine the oil supply pipe union O-rings for signs of damage or deterioration, and renew as necessary. Apply a smear of clean engine oil to the O-rings. Ease the pipe into position in the top of the bearing caps, taking great care not to displace the O-rings.

26 Examine the sealing washer for signs of damage or deterioration, and renew it if necessary. Refit the upper retaining bolt to the thermostat housing, tightening it securely.

27 Refit the ignition HT coil as described in Chapter 5B.

28 Fit a new camshaft oil seal, using the information given in Section 10, then refit the camshaft sprocket as described in Section 9.

29 Check the valve clearances as described in Section 12.

30 Refit the cylinder head cover as described in Section 4, and reconnect the battery negative terminal.

16-valve engines

31 Before refitting, remove all traces of oil from the bearing housing retaining bolt holes in the cylinder head, using a clean rag. Also ensure that both the cylinder head and bearing housing mating faces are clean and free from oil.

32 Liberally oil the cylinder head hydraulic tappet bores and the tappets. Carefully refit the tappets to the cylinder head, ensuring that each tappet is refitted to its original bore. Some care will be required to enter the tappets squarely into their bores. Check that each tappet rotates freely in its bore.

33 Liberally oil the camshaft bearings in the

cylinder head and the camshaft lobes, then lay the camshafts to the cylinder head. Turn the camshafts so that the cam lobes are positioned as follows:

Exhaust camshaft: *Cam lobes of No 1 cylinder pointing upwards.*
Inlet camshaft: *Cam lobes of No 2 cylinder pointing upwards.*

34 Ensure that the four locating dowels are in position, one at each corner of the cylinder head.

35 Apply a bead of silicone based jointing compound around the perimeter of the mating faces and around the retaining bolt hole locations.

36 Liberally oil the camshaft bearings and carefully locate the bearing housings over the camshafts. Refit the retaining bolts ensuring that each has a washer under its head.

37 Working in the order shown, progressively tighten the bearing housing retaining bolts to the Stage one torque setting then to the Stage two setting **(see illustration)**.

38 Refit the timing belt upper (inner) cover as described in Section 6.

39 Refit the timing belt tensioner pulley as described in Section 9.

40 Refit the cylinder head covers as described in Section 4.

41 Fit a new camshaft oil seal(s), using the information given in Section 10, then refit the camshaft sprocket(s) and hub(s) as described in Section 9.

---

12 Valve clearances (8-valve engines) – checking and adjustment

Note: *16-valve engines have hydraulic tappets – the valve clearances are self-adjusting on these engines.*

Checking

1 The importance of having the valve clearances correctly adjusted cannot be overstressed, as they vitally affect the

performance of the engine. Checking should not be regarded as a routine operation, however. It should only be necessary when the valve gear has become noisy, after engine overhaul, or when trying to trace the cause of power loss. The clearances are checked as follows. The engine must be cold for the check to be accurate.

2 Firmly apply the handbrake, then jack up the front of the car and support it securely on axle stands (see *Jacking and vehicle support*). Remove the right-hand front roadwheel.

3 To gain access to the crankshaft pulley bolt, the wheelarch plastic liner must be removed. The liner is secured by various screws and clips under the wheelarch. Release all the fasteners, and remove the liner from under the front wing. Where necessary, unclip the coolant hoses from under the wing to improve access further.

4 The engine can now be turned over using a suitable socket and extension bar fitted to the crankshaft pulley bolt.

5 Remove the cylinder head cover as described in Section 4.

6 Draw the outline of the engine on a piece of paper, numbering the cylinders 1 to 4, with No 1 cylinder at the transmission end of the engine. Show the position of each valve, together with the specified valve clearance (see paragraph 10). Above each valve, draw two lines for noting (1) the actual clearance and (2) the amount of adjustment required **(see illustration)**.

7 Turn the crankshaft until the inlet valve of No 1 cylinder (the cylinder nearest the transmission end) is fully closed, with the tip of the cam facing directly away from the cam follower.

8 Using feeler blades, measure the clearance between the base of the cam and the follower. Record the clearance on line (1).

9 Repeat the measurement for the other seven valves, turning the crankshaft as

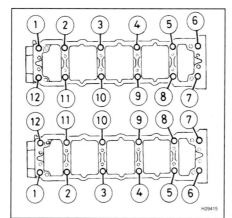

11.37 Camshaft bearing housing retaining bolt tightening sequence – 16-valve engines

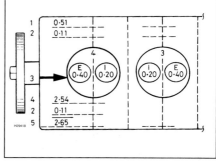

12.6 Example of valve shim thickness calculation

E   Exhaust
I   Inlet
1   Measured clearance
2   Difference between 1 and 3
3   Specified clearance
4   Thickness of original shim fitted
5   Thickness of new shim required

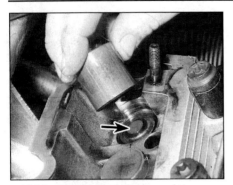

12.14a Lift out the follower and remove the shim (arrowed)

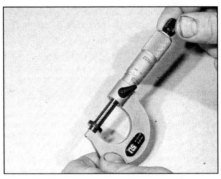

12.14b Using a micrometer to measure shim thickness

necessary so that the cam lobe in question is always facing directly away from the relevant follower.

10 Calculate the difference between each measured clearance and the desired value, and record it on line (2). Since the clearance is different for inlet and exhaust valves, make sure that you are aware which valve you are dealing with. The valve sequence from either end of the engine is:

Ex–In–In–Ex–Ex–In–In–Ex

11 If all the clearances are as specified, refit the cylinder head cover with reference to Section 4. Clip the coolant hoses into position (if removed) and refit the plastic wheelarch liner. Refit the roadwheel, and lower the vehicle to the ground.

12 If any clearance measured is not as specified, adjustment must be carried out as described in the following paragraphs.

Adjustment

13 Remove the camshaft as described in Section 11.

14 Withdraw the first follower from the cylinder head, and recover the shim from the top of the valve stem. Note that the shim may stick to the inside of the follower as it is withdrawn. If this happens, take care not to allow it to drop out as the follower is removed. Remove all traces of oil from the shim, and measure its thickness with a micrometer **(see illustrations)**. The shims usually carry thickness markings, but wear may have reduced the original thickness.

15 Refer to the clearance recorded for the valve concerned. If the clearance was more than that specified, the shim thickness must be *increased* by the difference recorded (2). If the clearance was less than that specified, the thickness of the shim must be *decreased* by the difference recorded (2).

16 Draw three more lines beneath each valve on the calculation paper, as shown in illustration 12.6. On line (4), note the measured thickness of the shim, then add or deduct the difference from line (2) to give the final shim thickness required on line (5).

17 Shims are available in thicknesses between 2.225 mm and 3.550 mm, in steps of 0.025 mm. Clean new shims before measuring or fitting them.

18 Repeat the procedure given in paragraphs 14 to 16 on the remaining valves, keeping each follower identified for position.

19 When reassembling, oil the shim, and fit it on the valve stem with the size marking face downwards. Oil the follower, and lower it onto the shim. Do not raise the follower after fitting, as the shim may become dislodged.

20 When all the followers are in position, complete with their shims, refit the camshaft as described in Section 11. Recheck the valve clearances before refitting the cylinder head cover, to make sure they are correct.

13 Cylinder head – removal and refitting

Removal

1 Disconnect the battery negative terminal (refer to *Disconnecting the battery* in the Reference Section of this manual).

2 Drain the cooling system as described in Chapter 1A.

3 Remove the timing belt as described in Section 7 or 8 as applicable.

8-valve engines

4 Remove the cylinder head cover as described in Section 4.

5 Remove the air cleaner-to-throttle housing duct as described in Chapter 4A.

6 Note that the following text assumes that the cylinder head will be removed with both inlet and exhaust manifolds attached; this is easier, but makes it a bulky and heavy assembly to handle. If it is wished first to remove the manifolds, proceed as described in Chapter 4A.

7 On automatic transmission models, refer to Section 19 and remove the engine right-hand mounting upper and lower mounting brackets.

8 Working as described in Chapter 4A, disconnect the exhaust system front pipe from the manifold. Where necessary, disconnect or release the lambda sensor wiring, so that it is not strained by the weight of the exhaust.

9 Carry out the following operations as described in Chapter 4A:

a) *Depressurise the fuel system, and disconnect the fuel feed and return hoses. Plug all openings, to prevent loss of fuel and the entry of dirt into the system.*

b) *Disconnect the accelerator cable.*

c) *Disconnect the vacuum servo unit vacuum hose, and all the other relevant vacuum/breather hoses, from the inlet manifold and throttle housing. Release the hoses from the retaining clips on the manifold.*

d) *Disconnect all the electrical connector plugs from the throttle housing.*

e) *Disconnect the wiring connectors from the fuel injectors, and free the wiring loom from the manifold.*

10 Slacken the retaining clips, and disconnect the coolant hoses from the thermostat housing (on the left-hand end of the cylinder head).

11 Depress the retaining clip(s), and disconnect the wiring connector(s) from the electrical switch(es) and/or sensor(s) which are screwed into the thermostat housing, or into the left-hand end of the cylinder head (as appropriate).

12 Slacken and remove the bolt securing the engine oil dipstick tube to the left-hand end of the cylinder head, and withdraw the tube from the cylinder block.

13 Disconnect the wiring connector from the ignition HT coil. If the cylinder head is to be dismantled for overhaul, remove the ignition HT coil as described in Chapter 5B. Note that the HT leads should be disconnected from the spark plugs instead of the coil, and the coil and leads removed as an assembly. If the cylinder numbers are not already marked on the HT leads, number each lead, to avoid the possibility of the leads being incorrectly connected on refitting.

16-valve engines

14 Remove the air cleaner assembly and intake ducting as described in Chapter 4A.

15 Remove the cylinder head covers as described in Section 4.

16 Remove the inlet manifold as described in Chapter 4A.

17 Working as described in Chapter 4A, disconnect the exhaust system front pipe from the manifold. Where necessary, disconnect or release the lambda sensor wiring, so that it is not strained by the weight of the exhaust.

18 Disconnect the radiator hose from the coolant outlet elbow.

19 Disconnect all remaining vacuum/breather hoses, and all electrical connector plugs from the cylinder head.

All engines

20 Working in the *reverse* of the sequence shown in illustration 13.39, progressively slacken the ten cylinder head bolts by half a turn at a time, until all bolts can be unscrewed by hand. Remove the bolts along with their washers (where fitted), noting the correct location of the spacer fitted to the bolt directly above the coolant pump on 1.8 litre engines.

21 With all the cylinder head bolts removed, the joint between the cylinder head and gasket and the cylinder block/crankcase must now be broken. On wet-liner engines, there is a risk of coolant and foreign matter leaking into the sump if the cylinder head is lifted carelessly. If care is not taken and the liners are moved, there is also a possibility of the bottom seals being disturbed, causing leakage after refitting the head.

22 To break the joint, obtain two L-shaped metal bars which fit into the cylinder head bolt holes, and gently 'rock' the cylinder head free towards the front of the car. *Do not* try to swivel the head on the cylinder block/crankcase; it is located by dowels.

23 When the joint is broken, lift the cylinder head away. Seek assistance if possible, as it is a heavy assembly, especially if it is complete with the manifolds. Remove the gasket from the top of the block, noting the two locating dowels. If the locating dowels are a loose fit, remove them and store them with the head for safe-keeping. Do not discard the gasket; it will be needed for identification purposes.

24 On wet-liner engines, *do not* attempt to turn the crankshaft with the cylinder head removed, otherwise the liners may be displaced. Operations that require the crankshaft to be turned (eg, cleaning the piston crowns), should only be carried out once the cylinder liners are firmly clamped in position. In the absence of the special Citroën liner clamps, the liners can be clamped in position as follows. Use large flat washers positioned underneath suitable-length bolts, or temporarily refit the original head bolts, with suitable spacers fitted to their shanks **(see illustration)**.

25 If the cylinder head is to be dismantled for overhaul, remove the camshaft(s) as described in Section 11, then refer to Part E of this Chapter.

Preparation for refitting

26 The mating faces of the cylinder head and cylinder block/crankcase must be perfectly clean before refitting the head. Citroën recommend the use of a scouring agent for

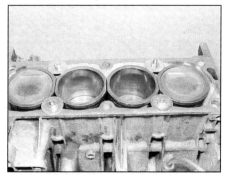

13.24 Cylinder liners clamped in position using suitable bolts and large flat washers

this purpose, but acceptable results can be achieved by using a hard plastic or wood scraper to remove all traces of gasket and carbon. The same method can be used to clean the piston crowns, but refer to paragraph 24 before turning the crankshaft on wet-liner engines. Take particular care to avoid scoring or gouging the cylinder head/cylinder block mating surfaces during the cleaning operations, as aluminium alloy is easily damaged. Make sure that the carbon is not allowed to enter the oil and water passages – this is particularly important for the lubrication system, as carbon could block the oil supply to the engine's components. Using adhesive tape and paper, seal the water, oil and bolt holes in the cylinder block/crankcase. To prevent carbon entering the gap between the pistons and bores, smear a little grease in the gap. After cleaning each piston, use a small brush to remove all traces of grease and carbon from the gap, then wipe away the remainder with a clean rag.

27 Check the mating surfaces of the cylinder block/crankcase and the cylinder head for nicks, deep scratches and other damage. If slight, they may be removed carefully with a file, but if excessive, machining may be the only alternative to renewal. If warpage of the cylinder head gasket surface is suspected, use a straight-edge to check it for distortion. Refer to Part E of this Chapter if necessary.

28 Thoroughly clean the threads of the cylinder head bolt holes in the cylinder block. Ensure that the bolts run freely in their threads, and that all traces of oil and water are removed from each bolt hole.

29 On wet-liner engines, check the cylinder liner protrusion as described in Part E, Section 12, of this Chapter.

30 When purchasing a new cylinder head gasket, it is essential that a gasket of the correct thickness is obtained. On some engines, only one thickness of gasket is available, so this is not a problem. However on other engines, there are two different thicknesses available – the standard gasket which is fitted at the factory, and a slightly thicker 'repair' gasket (+ 0.2 mm), for use once the head gasket face has been machined. If the cylinder head has been machined, it should have the letter R stamped adjacent to the No 3 exhaust port, and the gasket should also have the letter R stamped adjacent to No 3 cylinder on its front upper face. The gaskets can also be identified as described in the following paragraph, using the cut-outs on the left-hand end of the gasket.

31 With the gasket fitted the correct way up on the cylinder block, there will be either a single hole, or a series of holes, punched in the tab on the left-hand end of the gasket. The standard (1.2 mm) gasket has only one hole punched in it; the slightly thicker (1.4 mm) gasket has two holes punched in it. Identify

the gasket type, and ensure that the new gasket obtained is of the correct thickness. Note that modifications to the cylinder head gasket material, type, and manufacturer are constantly taking place; seek the advice of a Citroën dealer as to the latest recommendations.

32 Check the condition of the cylinder head bolts, and particularly their threads, whenever they are removed. Wash the bolts in a suitable solvent, and wipe them dry. Check each bolt for any sign of visible wear or damage, renewing them if necessary. Measure the length of each bolt (without the washer fitted) from the underside of its head to the end of the bolt. The bolts may be re-used if their length does not exceed the following dimensions.

> 1.8 litre (8-valve) engines   171.5 mm
> 1.8 litre (16-valve) engines 160.0 mm
> 2.0 litre engines   112.0 mm

33 If any one bolt is longer than the specified length, *all* of the bolts should be renewed as a complete set. Note that modifications to the cylinder head bolts are constantly taking place; seek the advice of a Citroën dealer as to the latest recommendations. Considering the stress which the cylinder head bolts are under, it is highly recommended that they are renewed, regardless of their apparent condition.

Refitting

34 Wipe clean the mating surfaces of the cylinder head and cylinder block/crankcase. Check that the two locating dowels are in position at each end of the cylinder block/crankcase surface. Where applicable, remove the cylinder liner clamps.

35 Position a new gasket on the cylinder block/crankcase surface, ensuring that its identification holes or the projecting tongue are at the left-hand (flywheel) end of the gasket.

1.8 litre (8- and 16-valve) engines

36 Check that the crankshaft pulley and camshaft sprocket(s) are still locked in position with their respective locking tools. With the aid of an assistant, carefully refit the cylinder head assembly to the block, aligning it with the locating dowels.

37 Apply a smear of grease to the threads, and to the underside of the heads, of the cylinder head bolts. Citroën recommend the use of Molykote G Rapid Plus (available from your Citroën dealer); in the absence of the specified grease, any good-quality high-melting-point grease may be used.

38 Carefully enter each bolt and washer (where fitted) into its relevant hole (*do not drop it in*) and screw it in finger-tight, not forgetting to fit the spacer to the bolt above the coolant pump on 1.8 litre engines.

39 Working progressively and in the sequence shown, tighten all the cylinder head bolts to their Stage 1 torque setting, using a

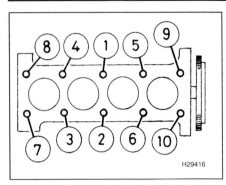

13.39 Cylinder head bolt tightening sequence

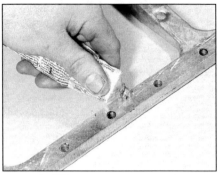

14.10a Where a sump spacer plate is fitted, apply sealant to the plate upper surface . . .

14.10b . . . then refit the plate to the base of the cylinder block/crankcase

torque wrench and a suitable socket **(see illustration)**.

40 Once all the bolts have been tightened to their Stage 1 torque setting, fully slacken all the head bolts, working in the reverse of the tightening sequence. Once the bolts are loose, and again working in the sequence shown, tighten all the bolts to the Stage 2 torque setting.

41 When all the bolts have been tightened to the Stage 2 torque setting, tighten each bolt in the sequence shown through the specified Stage 3 angle, using a socket and extension bar. It is recommended that an angle-measuring gauge is used during this stage of tightening, to ensure accuracy.

42 On 8-valve engines, once the cylinder head bolts are correctly tightened, reconnect the wiring connector to the ignition HT coil. Otherwise, if the head was stripped for overhaul, refit the HT coil as described in Chapter 5B.

43 Refit and tension the timing belt as described in Section 7 or 8 as applicable.

44 The remainder of the refitting procedure is a reversal of removal, noting the following points:

a) Ensure that all wiring is correctly routed, and that all connectors are securely reconnected to the correct components.

b) Ensure that the coolant hoses are correctly reconnected, and that their retaining clips are securely tightened.

c) Ensure that all vacuum/breather hoses are correctly reconnected.

d) Refit the cylinder head cover as described in Section 4.

e) Reconnect the exhaust system to the manifold, refit the air cleaner housing and ducts, and adjust the accelerator cable, as described in Chapter 4A. If the manifolds were removed, refit these as described in Chapter 4A.

f) On completion, refill the cooling system as described in Chapter 1A, and reconnect the battery.

2.0 litre engines

45 Refit the cylinder head as described above in paragraphs 36 to 38, ignoring the remark about the spacer fitted to the bolt above the coolant pump.

46 Working progressively and in the sequence shown in illustration 13.39, tighten the cylinder head bolts, to their Stage 1 torque setting using a torque wrench and suitable socket.

47 Once all the bolts have been tightened to their Stage 1 torque setting, tighten all bolts to their Stage 2 torque setting, again following the specified sequence.

48 With all the bolts tightened to their Stage 2 setting, working again in the specified sequence, angle-tighten the bolts through the specified Stage 3 angle, using a socket and extension bar. It is recommended that an angle-measuring gauge is used during this stage of tightening, to ensure accuracy.

49 Refit and tension the timing belt as described in Section 8.

50 The remainder of the refitting procedure is a reversal of removal, noting the points made in paragraph 44.

14 Sump – removal and refitting

Removal

1 Disconnect the battery negative terminal (refer to *Disconnecting the battery* in the Reference Section of this manual).

2 Drain the engine oil, then clean and refit the engine oil drain plug, tightening it securely. If the engine is nearing its service interval when the oil and filter are due for renewal, it is recommended that the filter is also removed, and a new one fitted. After reassembly, the engine can then be refilled with fresh oil. Refer to Chapter 1A for further information.

3 Chock the rear wheels then jack up the front of the vehicle and support it on axle stands (see *Jacking and vehicle support*).

4 On models with air conditioning, where the compressor is mounted onto the side of the sump, remove the drivebelt as described in Chapter 1A. Unbolt the compressor, and position it clear of the sump. Support the weight of the compressor by tying it to the vehicle, to prevent any excess strain being placed on the compressor lines. *Do not*

disconnect the refrigerant lines from the compressor (refer to the warnings given in Chapter 3).

5 Where necessary, disconnect the wiring connector from the oil temperature sender unit, which is screwed into the sump.

6 Progressively slacken and remove all the sump retaining bolts. Since the sump bolts vary in length, remove each bolt in turn, and store it in its correct fitted order by pushing it through a clearly-marked cardboard template. This will avoid the possibility of installing the bolts in the wrong locations on refitting.

7 Try to break the joint by striking the sump with the palm of your hand, then lower and withdraw the sump from under the car. If the sump is stuck (which is quite likely) use a putty knife or similar, carefully inserted between the sump and block. Ease the knife along the joint until the sump is released. Remove the gasket (where fitted), and discard it; a new one must be used on refitting. While the sump is removed, take the opportunity to check the oil pump pick-up/strainer for signs of clogging or splitting. If necessary, remove the pump as described in Section 15, and clean or renew the strainer.

8 On some engines, a large spacer plate is fitted between the sump and the base of the cylinder block/crankcase. If this plate is fitted, undo the two retaining screws from diagonally-opposite corners of the plate. Remove the plate from the base of the engine, noting which way round it is fitted.

Refitting

9 Clean all traces of sealant/gasket from the mating surfaces of the cylinder block/crankcase and sump, then use a clean rag to wipe out the sump and the engine's interior.

10 Where a spacer plate is fitted, remove all traces of sealant/gasket from the spacer plate, then apply a thin coating of suitable sealant to the plate upper mating surface. Offer up the plate to the base of the cylinder block/crankcase, and securely tighten its retaining screws **(see illustrations)**.

11 On engines where the sump was fitted without a gasket, ensure that the sump mating surfaces are clean and dry, then apply a thin coating of suitable sealant to the sump mating surface.

12 On engines where the sump was fitted with a gasket, ensure that all traces of the old gasket have been removed, and that the sump mating surfaces are clean and dry. Position the new gasket on the top of the sump, using a dab of grease to hold it in position.

13 Offer up the sump to the cylinder block/crankcase. Refit its retaining bolts, ensuring that each is screwed into its original location. Tighten the bolts evenly and progressively to the specified torque setting.

14 Where necessary, align the air conditioning compressor with its mountings on the sump, and insert the retaining bolts. Securely tighten the compressor retaining bolts, then refit the drivebelt as described in Chapter 1A.

15 Reconnect the wiring connector to the oil temperature sensor (where fitted).

16 Lower the vehicle to the ground, then refill the engine with oil as described in Chapter 1A.

15 Oil pump – removal, inspection and refitting

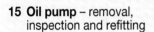

Removal

1 Remove the sump as described in Section 14.

2 Where necessary, undo the two retaining screws, and slide the sprocket cover off the front of the oil pump.

3 Slacken and remove the three bolts securing the oil pump to the base of the cylinder block/crankcase. Disengage the pump sprocket from the chain, and remove the oil pump **(see illustration)**. Where necessary, also remove the spacer plate which is fitted behind the oil pump.

Inspection

4 Examine the oil pump sprocket for signs of damage and wear, such as chipped or missing teeth. If the sprocket is worn, the

15.3 Removing the oil pump

pump assembly must be renewed, since the sprocket is not available separately. It is also recommended that the chain and drive sprocket, fitted to the crankshaft, be renewed at the same time. To renew the chain and drive sprocket, first remove the crankshaft timing belt sprocket as described in Section 9. Unbolt the oil seal carrier from the cylinder block. The sprocket, spacer (where fitted) and chain can then be slid off the end of the crankshaft. See Part E, Section 11, for further information.

5 Slacken and remove the bolts (along with the baffle plate, where fitted) securing the strainer cover to the pump body. Lift off the strainer cover, and take off the relief valve piston and spring, noting which way round they are fitted **(see illustrations)**.

6 Examine the pump rotors and body for signs of wear ridges or scoring. If worn, the complete pump assembly must be renewed.

7 Examine the relief valve piston for signs of wear or damage, and renew if necessary. The condition of the relief valve spring can only be measured by comparing it with a new one; if there is any doubt about its condition, it should also be renewed. Both the piston and spring are available individually.

8 Thoroughly clean the oil pump strainer with a suitable solvent, and check it for signs of clogging or splitting. If the strainer is damaged, the strainer and cover assembly must be renewed.

9 Locate the relief valve spring and piston in the strainer cover. Refit the cover to the pump

body, aligning the relief valve piston with its bore in the pump. Refit the baffle plate (where fitted) and the cover retaining bolts, and tighten them securely.

10 Prime the pump by filling it with clean engine oil before refitting.

Refitting

11 Offer up the spacer plate (where fitted), then locate the pump sprocket with its drive chain. Seat the pump on the base of the cylinder block/crankcase. Refit the pump retaining bolts, and tighten them to the specified torque setting.

12 Where necessary, slide the sprocket cover into position on the pump. Refit its retaining bolts, tightening them securely.

13 Refit the sump as described in Section 14.

16 Engine oil cooler – removal and refitting

Removal

1 Firmly apply the handbrake, then jack up the front of the car and support it securely on axle stands (see *Jacking and vehicle support*).

2 Drain the cooling system as described in Chapter 1A. Alternatively, clamp the oil cooler coolant hoses directly above the cooler, and be prepared for some coolant loss as the hoses are disconnected.

3 Position a suitable container beneath the oil filter. Unscrew the filter using an oil filter removal tool if necessary, and drain the oil into the container. If the oil filter is damaged or distorted during removal, it must be renewed. Given the low cost of a new oil filter relative to the cost of repairing the damage which could result if a re-used filter springs a leak, it is probably a good idea to renew the filter in any case.

4 Release the hose clips, and disconnect the coolant hoses from the oil cooler.

5 Unscrew the oil cooler/oil filter mounting bolt from the cylinder block, and withdraw the cooler. Note the locating notch in the cooler

15.5a Remove the oil pump cover retaining bolts . . .

15.5b . . . then lift off the cover and remove the spring . . .

15.5c . . . and relief valve piston, noting which way round it is fitted

16.5 Oil cooler/oil filter mounting bolt (A) and locating notch (B)

17.2 Using a self-tapping screw and pliers to remove the crankshaft oil seal

flange, which fits over the lug on the cylinder block **(see illustration)**. Discard the oil cooler sealing ring; a new one must be used on refitting.

Refitting

6 Fit a new sealing ring to the recess in the rear of the cooler, then offer the cooler to the cylinder block.

7 Ensure that the locating notch in the cooler flange is correctly engaged with the lug on the cylinder block, then refit the mounting bolt and tighten it securely.

8 Fit the oil filter, then lower the vehicle to the ground. Top-up the engine oil level as described in *Weekly checks*.

9 Refill or top-up the cooling system as described in Chapter 1A or *Weekly checks*. Start the engine, and check the oil cooler for signs of leakage.

17 Crankshaft oil seals – renewal

Right-hand oil seal

1 Remove the crankshaft sprocket and (where fitted) the spacer as described in Section 9.

2 Make a note of the correct fitted depth of the seal in its housing, the punch or drill two small holes opposite each other in the seal. Screw a self-tapping screw into each, and pull on the screws with pliers to extract the seal **(see illustration)**. Alternatively, the seal can be levered out of position. Use a flat-bladed screwdriver, and take great care not to damage the crankshaft shoulder or seal housing.

3 Clean the seal housing, and polish off any burrs or raised edges, which may have caused the seal to fail in the first place.

4 Lubricate the lips of the new seal with clean engine oil, and carefully locate the seal on the end of crankshaft. Note that its sealing lip

must be facing inwards. Take care not to damage the seal lips during fitting.

5 Fit the new seal using a suitable tubular drift, such as a socket, which bears only on the hard outer edge of the seal. Tap the seal into position, to the same depth in the housing as the original was prior to removal.

6 Wash off any traces of oil, then refit the crankshaft sprocket as described in Section 9.

Left-hand oil seal

7 Remove the flywheel/driveplate as described in Section 18. Make a note of the correct fitted depth of the seal in its housing.

8 Punch or drill two small holes opposite each other in the seal. Screw a self-tapping screw into each, and pull on the screws with pliers to extract the seal.

9 Clean the seal housing, and polish off any burrs or raised edges, which may have caused the seal to fail in the first place.

10 Lubricate the lips of the new seal with clean engine oil, and carefully locate the seal on the end of the crankshaft.

11 Fit the new seal using a suitable tubular drift, which bears only on the hard outer edge of the seal. Drive the seal into position, to the same depth in the housing as the original was prior to removal.

12 Wash off any traces of oil, then refit the flywheel/driveplate as described in Section 18.

18 Flywheel/driveplate – removal, inspection and refitting

Removal

Flywheel (manual transmission models)

1 Remove the transmission as described in Chapter 7A, then remove the clutch assembly as described in Chapter 6.

2 Prevent the flywheel from turning by locking the ring gear teeth (see **Tool Tip** in Section 5). Alternatively, bolt a strap between the flywheel and the cylinder block/crankcase. *Do not* attempt to lock the flywheel in position using the crankshaft pulley locking tool described in Section 3.

3 Slacken and remove the flywheel retaining bolts, and remove the flywheel from the end of the crankshaft. Be careful not to drop it; it is heavy. If the flywheel locating dowel is a loose fit in the crankshaft end, remove it and store it with the flywheel for safe-keeping. Discard the flywheel bolts; new ones must be used on refitting.

Driveplate (automatic transmission models)

4 Remove the transmission as described in Chapter 7B. Lock the driveplate as described in paragraph 2. Mark the relationship between the torque converter plate and the driveplate, and slacken all the driveplate retaining bolts.

5 Remove the retaining bolts, along with the torque converter plate and the two shims (one fitted on each side of the torque converter plate). Note that the shims are of different thickness, the thicker one being on the outside of the torque converter plate. Discard the driveplate retaining bolts; new ones must be used on refitting.

6 Remove the driveplate from the end of the crankshaft. If the locating dowel is a loose fit in the crankshaft end, remove it and store it with the driveplate for safe-keeping.

Inspection

7 On models with manual transmission, examine the flywheel for scoring of the clutch face, and for wear or chipping of the ring gear teeth. If the clutch face is scored, the flywheel may be surface-ground, but renewal is preferable. Seek the advice of a Citroën dealer or engine reconditioning specialist to see if machining is possible. If the ring gear is worn or damaged, the flywheel must be renewed, as it is not possible to renew the ring gear separately.

18.10 If the new flywheel bolt threads are not supplied with their threads pre-coated, apply a suitable thread-locking compound to them . . .

18.12 . . . then refit the flywheel, and tighten the bolts to the specified torque

8 On models with automatic transmission, check the torque converter driveplate carefully for signs of distortion. Look for any hairline cracks around the bolt holes or radiating outwards from the centre, and inspect the ring gear teeth for signs of wear or chipping. If any sign of wear or damage is found, the driveplate must be renewed.

Refitting

Flywheel (manual transmission models)

9 Clean the mating surfaces of the flywheel and crankshaft. Remove any remaining locking compound from the threads of the crankshaft holes, using the correct size of tap, if available.

> **HAYNES HiNT** *If a suitable tap is not available, cut two slots along the threads of one of the old flywheel bolts, and use the bolt to remove the locking compound from the threads.*

10 If the new flywheel retaining bolts are not supplied with their threads already pre-coated, apply a suitable thread-locking compound to the threads of each bolt **(see illustration)**.
11 Ensure that the locating dowel is in position. Offer up the flywheel, locating it on the dowel, and fit the new retaining bolts.
12 Lock the flywheel using the method employed on dismantling, and tighten the retaining bolts to the specified torque **(see illustration)**.
13 Refit the clutch as described in Chapter 6. Remove the flywheel locking tool, and refit the transmission as described in Chapter 7A.

Driveplate (automatic transmission models)

14 Carry out the operations described above in paragraphs 9 and 10, substituting 'driveplate' for all references to the flywheel.

15 Locate the driveplate on its locating dowel.
16 Offer up the torque converter plate, with the thinner shim positioned behind the plate and the thicker shim on the outside, and align the marks made prior to removal.
17 Fit the new retaining bolts, then lock the driveplate using the method employed on dismantling. Tighten the retaining bolts to the specified torque wrench setting.
18 Remove the driveplate locking tool, and refit the transmission (see Chapter 7B).

19 Engine/transmission mountings – inspection and renewal

Inspection

1 If improved access is required, firmly apply the handbrake, then jack up the front of the car and support it securely on axle stands (see *Jacking and vehicle support*).
2 Check the mounting rubbers to see if they are cracked, hardened or separated from the metal at any point; renew the mounting if any such damage or deterioration is evident.
3 Check that all the mountings' fasteners are securely tightened; use a torque wrench to check if possible.
4 Using a large screwdriver or a crowbar, check for wear in each mounting by carefully levering against it to check for free play. Where this is not possible, enlist the aid of an assistant to move the engine/transmission back-and-forth, or from side-to-side, while you watch the mounting. While some free play is to be expected even from new components, excessive wear should be obvious. If excessive free play is found, check first that the fasteners are correctly secured, then renew any worn components as described below.

Renewal

Right-hand mounting – 1.8 litre engines

5 Disconnect the battery negative terminal (refer to *Disconnecting the battery* in the Reference Section of this manual). Release all the relevant hoses and wiring from their retaining clips, and position them clear of the mounting so that they do not hinder the removal procedure.
6 Place a jack beneath the engine, with a block of wood on the jack head. Raise the jack until it is supporting the weight of the engine.
7 Slacken and remove the three nuts, or the two nuts and two bolts, securing the upper mounting bracket to the lower (engine) bracket. Remove the single nut securing the upper bracket to the mounting rubber, and lift off the bracket. If necessary, the lower mounting bracket can be unbolted and removed from the engine.
8 Lift the rubber buffer plate off the mounting rubber stud, then unscrew the mounting rubber from the body and remove it from the vehicle. A strap wrench or similar may be used to unscrew the mounting, or alternatively fabricate a tool from suitable metal tube with projections to engage in the cut-outs in the mounting.
9 Check all components carefully for signs of wear or damage, and renew them where necessary.
10 On reassembly, screw the mounting rubber into the vehicle body, and tighten it securely. Where removed, refit the lower mounting bracket to the engine, apply a drop of locking compound to the retaining bolts and tighten them to the specified torque.
11 Refit the rubber buffer plate to the mounting rubber stud, and install the upper mounting bracket.
12 Tighten the upper mounting bracket retaining nuts/bolts to the specified torque setting.

13 Remove the jack from underneath the engine, and reconnect the battery negative terminal.

Right-hand mounting – 2.0 litre engines

14 Disconnect the battery negative terminal (refer to *Disconnecting the battery* in the Reference Section of this manual). Release all the relevant hoses and wiring from their retaining clips. Place the hoses/wiring clear of the mounting so that the removal procedure is not hindered.

15 Place a jack beneath the engine, with a block of wood on the jack head. Raise the jack until it is supporting the weight of the engine.

16 Slacken and remove the two nuts and two bolts securing the upper mounting bracket to the lower (engine) bracket.

17 Undo the two bolts securing the curved mounting retaining plate to the body and lift off the plate. Unscrew the domed buffer nut, then unscrew the single nut securing the upper bracket to the mounting rubber, and lift off the bracket. If necessary, the lower mounting bracket can be unbolted and removed from the engine.

18 Lift the rubber buffer plate off the mounting rubber stud, then unscrew the mounting rubber from the body and remove it from the vehicle. A strap wrench or similar may be used to unscrew the mounting, or alternatively fabricate a tool from suitable metal tube with projections to engage in the cut-outs in the mounting.

19 Check all components carefully for signs of wear or damage, and renew them where necessary.

20 On reassembly, screw the mounting rubber into the vehicle body, and tighten it securely. Where removed, refit the lower mounting bracket to the engine, apply a drop of locking compound to the retaining bolts and tighten them to the specified torque.

21 Refit the rubber buffer plate to the mounting rubber stud, and install the upper mounting bracket.

22 Tighten the upper mounting bracket retaining nuts/bolts to the specified torque setting.

23 Refit the domed buffer nut and curved mounting retaining plate, then remove the jack from underneath the engine, and reconnect the battery negative terminal.

Left-hand mounting

24 Remove the battery, battery tray, and mounting plate as described in Chapter 5A.

25 Place a jack beneath the transmission, with a block of wood on the jack head. Raise the jack until it is supporting the weight of the transmission.

26 Slacken and remove the centre nut and washer from the left-hand mounting, then undo the nuts securing the mounting in position and remove it from the engine compartment.

27 If necessary, slide the spacer (where fitted) off the mounting stud, then unscrew the stud from the top of the transmission housing, and remove it along with its washer. If the mounting stud is tight, a universal stud extractor can be used to unscrew it.

28 Check all components carefully for signs of wear or damage, and renew as necessary.

29 Clean the threads of the mounting stud, and apply a coat of thread-locking compound to its threads. Refit the stud and washer to the top of the transmission, and tighten it to the specified torque setting.

30 Slide the spacer (where fitted) onto the mounting stud, then refit the rubber mounting. Tighten both the mounting-to-body bolts and the mounting centre nut to their specified torque settings, and remove the jack from underneath the transmission.

31 Refit the battery mounting plate, battery tray and battery as described in Chapter 5A.

Rear mounting

32 If not already done, firmly apply the handbrake, then jack up the front of the car and support it securely on axle stands (see *Jacking and vehicle support*). Remove the engine undertray.

33 Unscrew and remove the bolt securing the rear mounting link to the mounting on the rear of the cylinder block.

34 Remove the bolt securing the rear mounting link to the bracket on the subframe/underbody. Withdraw the link.

35 To remove the mounting assembly it will first be necessary to remove the right-hand driveshaft as described in Chapter 8.

36 With the driveshaft removed, undo the retaining bolts and remove the mounting from the rear of the cylinder block.

37 Check carefully for signs of wear or damage on all components, and renew them where necessary.

38 On reassembly, fit the rear mounting assembly to the rear of the cylinder block, and tighten its retaining bolts to the specified torque. Refit the driveshaft as described in Chapter 8.

39 Refit the rear mounting link, and tighten both its bolts to their specified torque settings.

40 Lower the vehicle to the ground.

Chapter 2 Part C:
XUD series diesel engine in-car repair procedures

Contents

Camshaft and followers – removal, inspection and refitting 11	General information 1
Compression and leakdown tests – description and interpretation . 2	Oil pump and drive chain – removal, inspection and refitting 15
Crankshaft pulley – removal and refitting 5	Oil seals – renewal 16
Cylinder head – removal and refitting 13	Right-hand engine mounting bracket and timing belt tensioner –
Cylinder head cover – removal and refitting 4	removal and refitting 9
Engine assembly/valve timing holes – general information	Sump – removal and refitting 14
and usage 3	Timing belt – removal, inspection, refitting and tensioning 7
Engine oil and filter renewal . . . . .See Chapter 1B	Timing belt covers – removal and refitting 6
Engine oil cooler – removal and refitting 19	Timing belt idler roller – removal and refitting 10
Engine oil level check . . . . .See Weekly checks	Timing belt sprockets – removal and refitting 8
Engine/transmission mountings – inspection and renewal 18	Valve clearances – checking and adjustment 12
Flywheel – removal, inspection and refitting 17	

Degrees of difficulty

Easy, suitable for novice with little experience	**Fairly easy,** suitable for beginner with some experience	**Fairly difficult,** suitable for competent DIY mechanic	**Difficult,** suitable for experienced DIY mechanic	**Very difficult,** suitable for expert DIY or professional

Specifications

Engine (general)

Designation (1905cc)	XUD9
Engine codes*:	
Non-turbo models	DJY (XUD9A)
Turbo models	DHY (XUD9TE) and DHV (XUD9BSD)
Bore	83.00 mm
Stroke	88.00 mm
Direction of crankshaft rotation	Clockwise (viewed from the right-hand side of vehicle)
No 1 cylinder location	At the transmission end of block
Compression ratio:	
Non-turbo models	23 : 1
Turbo models:	
DHY (XUD9TE) engine	21.8 : 1
DHV (XUD9BSD) engine	21.1 : 1

*The engine code is stamped on a plate attached to the front of the cylinder block.

Compression pressures (engine hot, at cranking speed)

Normal	25 to 30 bars (363 to 435 psi)
Minimum	18 bars (261 psi)
Maximum difference between any two cylinders	5 bars (73 psi)

Camshaft

Drive	Toothed belt
No of bearings	3
Endfloat	0.07 to 0.16 mm

Valve clearances (engine cold)

Inlet	0.15 ± 0.05 mm
Exhaust	0.30 ± 0.05 mm

Lubrication system

Oil pump type	Gear-type, chain-driven off the crankshaft right-hand end
Minimum oil pressure at 90°C:	
Non-turbo models	3.5 bars at 4000 rpm
Turbo models	4.9 bars at 4000 rpm
Oil pressure warning switch operating pressure	0.8 bars

Torque wrench settings

	Nm	lbf ft
Big-end bearing cap nuts:*		
Stage 1	20	15
Stage 2	Tighten through a further 70°	
Camshaft bearing cap nuts	20	15
Camshaft sprocket bolt	45	33
Crankshaft right-hand oil seal housing bolts	16	12
Crankshaft pulley bolt:		
Stage 1	40	30
Stage 2	Tighten through a further 60°	
Cylinder head bolts:		
DJY (XUD9A) and DHV (XUD9BSD) engines:		
Stage 1	20	15
Stage 2	60	44
Stage 3	Tighten through a further 180°	
DHY (XUD9TE) engine:		
Stage 1	20	15
Stage 2	60	44
Stage 3	Tighten through a further 220°	
Cylinder head cover bolts	20	15
Engine-to-transmission fixing bolts	45	33
Engine/transmission left-hand mounting:		
Rubber mounting-to-body bolts	21	15
Mounting stud to transmission	50	37
Rubber mounting centre nut	65	48
Engine/transmission rear mounting:		
Mounting assembly-to-block bolts	45	33
Connecting link-to-mounting assembly bolt	50	37
Connecting link-to-subframe bolt	50	37
Engine/transmission right-hand mounting:		
Engine (tensioner assembly) bracket bolts	18	13
Mounting bracket retaining nuts	45	33
Curved retaining plate bolts	20	15
Flywheel bolts*	50	37
Injection pump sprocket nut	50	37
Main bearing cap bolts	70	52
Oil pump mounting bolts	13	10
Piston oil jet spray tube bolt (turbo models)	10	7
Sump bolts	19	14
Timing belt tensioner adjustment bolt	18	13
Timing belt tensioner pivot nut	18	13

New nuts/bolts must be used.

1 General information

Using this Chapter

This Part of Chapter 2 is devoted to in-car repair procedures for the XUD series diesel engines. Similar information covering the DW series diesel engines, and the petrol engines will be found in Chapters 2A, 2B and 2D. All procedures concerning engine removal and refitting, and engine block/cylinder head overhaul for petrol and diesel engines can be found in Chapters 2E and 2F as applicable.

Refer to *Vehicle identification* in the Reference Section of this manual for details of engine code locations.

Most of the operations included in Chapter 2C are based on the assumption that the engine is still installed in the car. Therefore, if this information is being used during a complete engine overhaul, with the engine already removed, many of the steps included here will not apply.

XUD series engine description

The XUD series engine is a well-proven modern unit which has appeared in many Citroën and Peugeot vehicles. The engine is of four-cylinder overhead camshaft design, mounted transversely, with the transmission mounted on the left-hand side.

A toothed timing belt drives the camshaft, fuel injection pump and coolant pump. Followers are fitted between the camshaft and valves. Valve clearance adjustment is by means of shims. The camshaft is supported by three bearings machined directly in the cylinder head.

The crankshaft runs in five main bearings of the usual shell type. Endfloat is controlled by thrustwashers either side of No 2 main bearing.

The pistons are selected to be of matching weight, and incorporate fully-floating gudgeon pins retained by circlips.

The oil pump is chain-driven from the right-hand end of the crankshaft. An oil cooler is fitted to all engines.

The design of the turbo engine is the same as the normally-aspirated (non-turbo) version,

but components such as the crankshaft, pistons and connecting rods are uprated. It also incorporates oil jets which spray oil onto the undersides of the pistons to keep them cool.

Throughout the manual, it is often necessary to identify the engines not only by their cubic capacity, but also by their engine code. The engine code, consists of three letters (eg, DJY). The code is stamped on a plate attached to the front of the cylinder block.

Repair operations possible with the engine in the vehicle

The following work can be carried out with the engine in the car:
a) Compression pressure – testing.
b) Cylinder head cover – removal and refitting.
c) Crankshaft pulley – removal and refitting.
d) Timing belt covers – removal and refitting.
e) Timing belt – removal, refitting and adjustment.
f) Timing belt tensioner and sprockets – removal and refitting.
g) Camshaft oil seal – renewal.
h) Camshaft and followers – removal, inspection and refitting.
i) Valve clearances – checking and adjustment.
j) Cylinder head – removal and refitting.
k) Cylinder head and pistons – decarbonising.
l) Sump – removal and refitting.
m)Oil pump – removal and refitting.
n) Crankshaft oil seals – renewal.
o) Engine/transmission mountings – inspection and renewal.
p) Flywheel – removal, inspection and refitting.

2 Compression and leakdown tests – description and interpretation

Compression test

Note: *A compression tester specifically designed for diesel engines must be used for this test.*

1 When engine performance is down, or if misfiring occurs which cannot be attributed to the fuel system, a compression test can provide diagnostic clues as to the engine's condition. If the test is performed regularly, it can give warning of trouble before any other symptoms become apparent.

2 A compression tester specifically intended for diesel engines must be used, because of the higher pressures involved. The tester is connected to an adapter which screws into the glow plug or injector hole. On these engines, an adapter suitable for use in the injector holes will be required, due to the limited access to the glow plug holes **(see illustration)**. It is unlikely to be worthwhile buying such a tester for occasional use, but it

may be possible to borrow or hire one – if not, have the test performed by a garage.

3 Unless specific instructions to the contrary are supplied with the tester, observe the following points:
a) *The battery must be in a good state of charge, the air filter must be clean, and the engine should be at normal operating temperature.*
b) *All the injectors or glow plugs should be removed before starting the test. If removing the injectors, also remove the flame shield washers, otherwise they may be blown out. Refer to Chapters 4B and 5C for further information.*
c) *The anti-theft system electronic engine immobiliser unit wiring connector at the rear of the injection pump must be disconnected.*

4 There is no need to hold the accelerator pedal down during the test, because the diesel engine air inlet is not throttled.

5 The compression pressures measured are not so important as the balance between cylinders. Values are given in the Specifications.

6 The cause of poor compression is less easy to establish on a diesel engine than on a petrol one. The effect of introducing oil into the cylinders ('wet' testing) is not conclusive, because there is a risk that the oil will sit in the swirl chamber or in the recess on the piston crown instead of passing to the rings. However, the following can be used as a rough guide to diagnosis.

7 All cylinders should produce very similar pressures; any difference greater than that specified indicates the existence of a fault. Note that the compression should build up quickly in a healthy engine; low compression on the first stroke, followed by gradually-increasing pressure on successive strokes, indicates worn piston rings. A low compression reading on the first stroke, which does not build up during successive strokes, indicates leaking valves or a blown head gasket (a cracked head could also be the cause). Deposits on the undersides of the valve heads can also cause low compression.

8 A low reading from two adjacent cylinders is almost certainly due to the head gasket having blown between them; the presence of coolant in the engine oil will confirm this.

9 If the compression reading is unusually high, the cylinder head surfaces, valves and pistons are probably coated with carbon deposits. If this is the case, the cylinder head should be removed and decarbonised (see Part F).

Leakdown test

10 A leakdown test measures the rate at which compressed air fed into the cylinder is lost. It is an alternative to a compression test, and in many ways it is better, since the escaping air provides easy identification of where pressure loss is occurring (piston rings, valves or head gasket).

2.2 Performing a compression test

11 The equipment needed for leakdown testing is unlikely to be available to the home mechanic. If poor compression is suspected, have the test performed by a suitably-equipped garage.

3 Engine assembly/valve timing holes – general information and usage

Note: *Do not attempt to rotate the engine whilst the crankshaft/camshaft/injection pump are locked in position. If the engine is to be left in this state for a long period of time, it is a good idea to place suitable warning notices inside the vehicle, and in the engine compartment. This will reduce the possibility of the engine being accidentally cranked on the starter motor, which is likely to cause damage with the locking pins in place.*

1 On all engines, timing holes are drilled in the camshaft sprocket, injection pump sprocket and flywheel. The holes are used to align the crankshaft, camshaft and injection pump, and to prevent the possibility of the valves contacting the pistons when refitting the cylinder head, or when refitting the timing belt. When the holes are aligned with their corresponding holes in the cylinder head and cylinder block (as appropriate), suitable diameter bolts/pins can be inserted to lock both the camshaft, injection pump and crankshaft in position, preventing them from rotating unnecessarily. Proceed as follows.

Note: *With the timing holes aligned, No 4 cylinder is at TDC on its compression stroke.*

2 Remove the upper timing belt covers as described in Section 6.

3 Firmly apply the handbrake, then jack up the front of the car and support it securely on axle stands (see *Jacking and vehicle support*). Remove the right-hand front roadwheel.

4 The crankshaft must now be turned until the three bolt holes in the camshaft and injection pump sprockets (one hole in the camshaft sprocket, two holes in the injection pump sprocket) are aligned with the corresponding holes in the engine front plate. To gain access to the right-hand end of the engine, the wheelarch plastic liner must be removed. The liner is secured by various screws and clips under the wheelarch. Release all the fasteners, and remove liner from under the front wing. Where necessary, unclip the coolant hoses from under the wing to improve access further. The crankshaft can then be turned using a suitable socket and extension bar fitted to the pulley bolt. Note that the crankshaft must always be turned in a clockwise direction (viewed from the right-hand side of vehicle).

5 Insert an 8 mm diameter rod or drill through the hole in the left-hand flange of the cylinder block by the starter motor; if necessary, carefully turn the crankshaft either way until the rod enters the timing hole in the flywheel **(see illustrations)**.

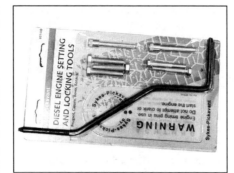

3.5a Suitable tools available for locking the engine in the TDC position

3.6a Bolt (arrowed) inserted through timing hole in the camshaft sprocket

6 Insert three 8 mm bolts through the holes in the camshaft and fuel injection pump sprockets, and screw them into the engine finger-tight **(see illustrations)**.

7 The crankshaft, camshaft and injection pump are now locked in position, preventing unnecessary rotation.

4 Cylinder head cover – removal and refitting

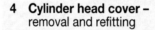

Removal

1 On DHY (XUD9TE engine) models remove the intercooler, on DJY (XUD9A engine) models, remove the air distribution

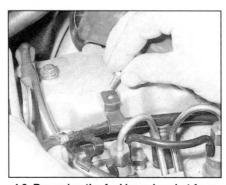

4.3 Removing the fuel hose bracket from the cylinder head cover

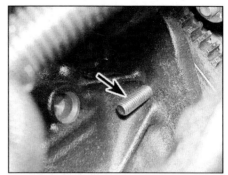

3.5b Rod (arrowed) inserted through cylinder block into timing hole in the flywheel

3.6b Bolts (arrowed) inserted through timing holes in the injection pump sprocket

housing, and on DHV (XUD9BSD engine) models, remove the air inlet ducts with reference to the procedures contained in Chapter 4B.

2 Disconnect the breather hose from the front of the cylinder head cover.

3 Unscrew the securing bolt and remove the fuel hose bracket from the right-hand end of the cylinder head cover **(see illustration)**.

4 Note the locations of any brackets secured by the three cylinder head cover bolts, then unscrew the bolts. Recover the metal and fibre washers under each bolt **(see illustration)**.

5 Carefully move any hoses clear of the cylinder head cover.

6 Lift off the cover, and recover the rubber

4.4 Remove the retaining bolts and washers . . .

4.6 . . . and lift off the cylinder head cover

seal **(see illustration)**. Examine the seal for signs of damage and deterioration, and if necessary, renew it.

Refitting

7 Refitting is a reversal of removal, bearing in mind the following points:
a) *Refit any brackets in their original positions noted before removal.*
b) *Refit the intercooler, air distribution housing, or inlet ducts, as applicable, with reference to Chapter 4B.*

5 Crankshaft pulley – removal and refitting

Removal

1 Remove the auxiliary drivebelt as described in Chapter 1B.
2 To prevent crankshaft turning whilst the pulley retaining bolt is being slackened, select top gear and have an assistant apply the brakes firmly. Alternatively, the flywheel ring gear can be locked using a suitable tool made from steel angle **(see illustration)**. Remove the cover plate from the base of the transmission bellhousing and bolt the tool to the bellhousing flange so it engages with the ring gear teeth. *Do not* attempt to lock the pulley by inserting a bolt/drill through the timing hole. If the timing hole bolt/drill is in position, temporarily remove it prior to slackening the pulley bolt, then refit it once the bolt has been slackened.

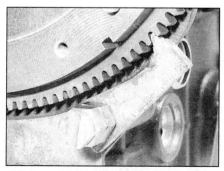

5.2 Use a fabricated tool similar to this to lock the flywheel ring gear and prevent crankshaft rotation

3 Unscrew the retaining bolt and washer, then slide the pulley off the end of the crankshaft. If the pulley locating roll pin or Woodruff key (as applicable) is a loose fit, remove it and store it with the pulley for safe-keeping. If the pulley is tight fit, it can be drawn off the crankshaft using a suitable puller.

Refitting

4 Ensure that the Woodruff key is correctly located in its crankshaft groove, or that the roll pin is in position (as applicable). Refit the pulley to the end of the crankshaft, aligning its locating groove or hole with the Woodruff key or pin.
5 Thoroughly clean the threads of the pulley retaining bolt, then apply a coat of locking compound to the bolt threads. Citroën recommend the use of Loctite (available from your Citroën dealer); in the absence of this, any good-quality locking compound may be used.
6 Refit the crankshaft pulley retaining bolt and washer. Tighten the bolt to the specified torque, then through the specified angle, preventing the crankshaft from turning using the method employed on removal.
7 Refit and tension the auxiliary drivebelt as described in Chapter 1B.

6 Timing belt covers – removal and refitting

Removal

Upper covers

1 If procedures are to be carried out which involve removal of the timing belt, remove the right-hand engine mounting-to-body bracket as described in Section 9. This will greatly improve access.
2 Undo the two bolts securing the camshaft sprocket cover and the nut and bolt securing the injection pump sprocket cover.
3 Release the covers from their locations and lift them off the engine.

Lower cover

4 Remove the crankshaft pulley as described in Section 5.
5 Remove both upper covers as described previously.
6 Undo the two remaining securing nuts, and remove the lower cover.

Refitting

7 Refitting is a reversal of the relevant removal procedure, ensuring that each cover section is correctly located, and that the cover retaining nuts and/or bolts are tightened securely.

7 Timing belt – removal, inspection, refitting and tensioning

General

1 The timing belt drives the camshaft, injection pump, and coolant pump from a toothed

sprocket on the right-hand end of the crankshaft. The belt also drives the brake servo vacuum pump indirectly via the rear ('flywheel') end of the camshaft. If the belt breaks or slips in service, the pistons are likely to hit the valve heads, resulting in expensive damage.
2 The timing belt should be renewed at the specified intervals, or earlier if it is contaminated with oil or at all noisy in operation (a 'scraping' noise due to uneven wear).
3 If the timing belt is being removed, it is a wise precaution to check the condition of the coolant pump at the same time (check for signs of coolant leakage). This may avoid the need to remove the timing belt again at a later stage, should the coolant pump fail.

Removal

4 Disconnect the battery negative terminal (refer to *Disconnecting the battery* in the Reference Section of this manual).
5 Remove the crankshaft pulley as described in Section 5.
6 Remove the timing belt covers as described in Section 6.
7 Temporarily refit the crankshaft pulley to enable the engine to be turned, then align the engine assembly/valve timing holes as described in Section 3, and lock the camshaft sprocket, injection pump sprocket and flywheel in position. *Do not* attempt to rotate the engine whilst the pins are in position.
8 Remove the right-hand engine mounting-to-body bracket as described in Section 9.
9 Loosen the timing belt tensioner pivot nut and adjustment bolt, then turn the tensioner bracket anti-clockwise to release the tension. Retighten the adjustment bolt to hold the tensioner in the released position. If available, use a 10 mm square drive extension in the hole provided, to turn the tensioner bracket against the spring tension **(see illustration)**.

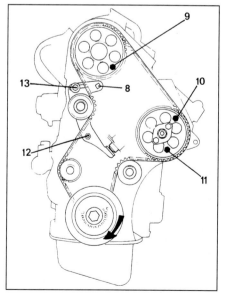

7.9 Removing the timing belt

8 Square hole	12 Tensioner pivot nut
9 to 11 Bolts	13 Adjustment bolt

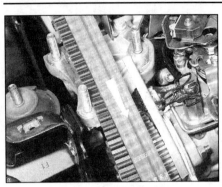

7.10a Mark the timing belt with an arrow to indicate its running direction

7.10b Removing the timing belt

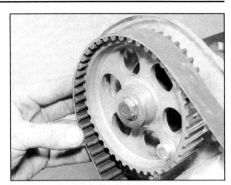

7.15 Locate the timing belt on the sprockets as described in text

10 Mark the timing belt with an arrow to indicate its running direction, if it is to be re-used. Remove the belt from the sprockets **(see illustrations)**.

Inspection

11 Check the timing belt carefully for any signs of uneven wear, split or oil contamination. Pay particular attention to the roots of the teeth. Renew it if there is the slightest doubt about its condition. If the engine is undergoing an overhaul, and has covered more than 40 000 miles (60 000 km) with the existing belt fitted, renew the belt as a matter of course, regardless of its apparent condition. The cost of a new belt is nothing compared with the cost of repairs, should the belt break in service. If signs of oil contamination are found, trace the source of the oil leak and rectify it. Wash down the engine timing belt area and all related components, to remove all traces of oil. Check that the tensioner and idler pulley rotates freely, without any sign of roughness. If necessary, renew as described in Sections 9 and 10 (as applicable).

Refitting and tensioning

12 Commence refitting by ensuring that the 8 mm bolts are still fitted to the camshaft and fuel injection pump sprockets, and that the rod/drill is positioned in the timing hole in the flywheel.
13 Locate the timing belt on the crankshaft sprocket, making sure that, where applicable, the direction of rotation arrow is facing the correct way.
14 Engage the timing belt with the crankshaft sprocket, hold it in position, then feed the belt over the remaining sprockets in the following order:
a) Idler roller.
b) Fuel injection pump.
c) Camshaft.
d) Tensioner roller.
e) Coolant pump.
15 Be careful not to kink or twist the belt. To ensure correct engagement, locate only a half-width on the injection pump sprocket before feeding the timing belt onto the camshaft sprocket, keeping the belt taut and fully engaged with the crankshaft sprocket. Locate the timing belt fully onto the sprockets **(see illustration)**.

16 Unscrew and remove the 8 mm locking bolts from the camshaft and fuel injection pump sprockets, and remove the rod/drill from the timing hole in the flywheel.
17 With the pivot nut loose, slacken the tensioner adjustment bolt while holding the bracket against the spring tension. Slowly release the bracket until the roller presses against the timing belt. Retighten the adjustment bolt and the pivot nut.
18 Rotate the crankshaft through two complete turns in the normal running direction (clockwise). *Do not* rotate the crankshaft backwards, as the timing belt must be kept tight between the crankshaft, fuel injection pump and camshaft sprockets.
19 Loosen the tensioner adjustment bolt and the pivot nut to allow the tensioner spring to push the roller against the timing belt, then tighten both the adjustment bolt and pivot nut to the specified torque.
20 Check that the timing holes are all correctly positioned by reinserting the sprocket locking bolts and the rod/drill in the flywheel timing hole, as described in Section 3. If the timing holes are not correctly positioned, the timing belt has been

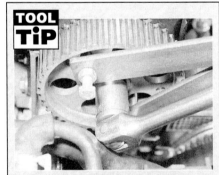

Tool Tip 1: To prevent a sprocket from turning as its retaining bolt is slackened, make up a sprocket holding tool. Obtain two lengths of steel strip (one long, the other short), and three nuts and bolts; one nut and bolt forms the pivot of the forked tool, with the remaining two nuts and bolts at the tips of the 'forks' to engage with the sprocket holes.

incorrectly fitted (possibly one tooth out on one of the sprockets) – in this case, repeat the refitting procedure from the beginning.
21 Refit the timing belt covers as described in Section 6.
22 Refit the right-hand engine mounting-to-body bracket, with reference to Section 9.
23 Refit the crankshaft pulley as described in Section 5.

8 Timing belt sprockets –
removal and refitting

Camshaft sprocket
Removal

1 Remove the upper timing belt covers as described in Section 6.
2 The camshaft sprocket bolt must now be loosened. The camshaft must be prevented from turning as the sprocket bolt is unscrewed, and this can be done in one of two ways, as follows. Do not remove the camshaft sprocket bolt at this stage.
a) *Make up a tool similar to that shown (see Tool Tip 1), and use it to hold the sprocket stationary by means of the holes in the sprocket.*
b) *Remove the cylinder head cover as described in Section 4. Prevent the camshaft from turning by holding it with a suitable spanner on the lug between Nos 3 and 4 camshaft lobes (see illustration).*

8.2 Holding the camshaft using a spanner on the lug between Nos 3 and 4 lobes

8.7 Withdrawing the camshaft sprocket

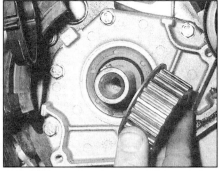

8.18 Withdrawing the crankshaft sprocket

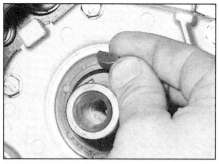

8.19 Removing the Woodruff key from the
end of the crankshaft

3 Align the engine assembly/valve timing holes as described in Section 3, and lock the camshaft sprocket, injection pump sprocket and flywheel in position. *Do not* attempt to rotate the engine whilst the pins are in position.
4 Loosen the timing belt tensioner pivot nut and adjustment bolt, then turn the tensioner bracket anti-clockwise to release the tension, and retighten the adjustment bolt to hold the tensioner in the released position. If available, use a 10 mm square drive extension in the hole provided, to turn the tensioner bracket against the spring tension. Slip the timing belt off the sprocket.
5 Remove the previously slackened camshaft sprocket retaining bolt and washer.
6 Remove the locking bolt securing the camshaft sprocket in the TDC position.
7 Slide the sprocket off the end of the camshaft **(see illustration)**. If the locating peg is a loose fit in the rear of the sprocket, remove it for safe-keeping. Examine the camshaft oil seal for signs of oil leakage and, if necessary, renew it as described in Section 16.

Refitting

8 Where applicable, refit the Woodruff key to the end of the camshaft, then refit the camshaft sprocket. Note that the sprocket will only fit one way round (with the protruding centre boss against the camshaft), as the end of the camshaft is tapered.
9 Refit the sprocket retaining bolt and washer. Tighten the bolt to the specified torque, preventing the camshaft from turning as during removal.
10 Where applicable, refit the cylinder head cover as described in Section 4.
11 Align the holes in the camshaft sprocket and the engine front plate, and refit the 8 mm bolt to lock the camshaft in the TDC position.
12 Fit the timing belt around the fuel injection pump sprocket (where applicable) and the camshaft sprocket, and tension the timing belt as described in Section 7.
13 Refit the upper timing belt covers as described in Section 6.

Crankshaft sprocket

Removal

14 Remove the crankshaft pulley as described in Section 5.

15 Remove the timing belt covers as described in Section 6.
16 Align the engine assembly/valve timing holes as described in Section 3, and lock the camshaft sprocket, injection pump sprocket and flywheel in position. *Do not* attempt to rotate the engine whilst the pins are in position.
17 Loosen the timing belt tensioner pivot nut and adjustment bolt, then turn the tensioner bracket anti-clockwise to release the tension, and retighten the adjustment bolt to hold the tensioner in the released position. If available, use a 10 mm square drive extension in the hole provided, to turn the tensioner bracket against the spring tension. Slip the timing belt off the sprocket.
18 Disengage the timing belt from the crankshaft sprocket, and slide the sprocket off the end of the crankshaft **(see illustration)**.
19 Remove the Woodruff key from the crankshaft, and store it with the sprocket for safe-keeping **(see illustration)**.
20 Examine the crankshaft oil seal for signs of oil leakage and, if necessary, renew it as described in Section 16.

Refitting

21 Refit the Woodruff key to the end of the crankshaft, then refit the crankshaft sprocket (with the flange nearest the cylinder block).
22 Fit the timing belt around the crankshaft sprocket, and tension the timing belt as described in Section 7.
23 Remove the timing belt covers as described in Section 6.
24 Refit the crankshaft pulley as described in Section 5.

8.30 Using a home-made tool to prevent
the injection pump sprocket from turning

Fuel injection pump sprocket

Removal

25 Remove the upper timing belt covers as described in Section 6.
26 Align the engine assembly/valve timing holes as described in Section 3, and lock the camshaft sprocket, injection pump sprocket and flywheel in position. *Do not* attempt to rotate the engine whilst the pins are in position.
27 Loosen the timing belt tensioner pivot nut and adjustment bolt, then turn the tensioner bracket anti-clockwise to release the tension, and retighten the adjustment bolt to hold the tensioner in the released position. If available, use a 10 mm square drive extension in the hole provided, to turn the tensioner bracket against the spring tension.
28 Make alignment marks on the fuel injection pump sprocket and the timing belt, to ensure that the sprocket and timing belt are correctly aligned on refitting. Slip the timing belt off the sprocket.
29 Remove the 8 mm bolts securing the fuel injection pump sprocket in the TDC position.
30 Using a suitable socket, undo the injection pump sprocket retaining nut **(see illustration)**. The sprocket can be held stationary as the nut is slackened using a suitable forked tool engaged with the holes in the sprocket **(see Tool Tip 1)**.
31 The sprocket is a taper fit on the injection pump shaft and it will be necessary to make up another tool to release it from the taper **(see Tool Tip 2)**.

TOOL TiP

Tool Tip 2: Make a sprocket releasing tool from a short strip of steel. Drill two holes in the strip to correspond with the two holes in the sprocket. Drill a third hole just large enough to accept the flats of the sprocket retaining nut.

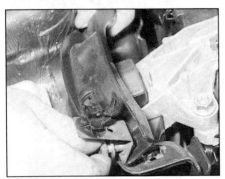

9.4 Remove the curved retaining plate ...

9.5 ... and lift the rubber buffer out from the engine mounting

9.6 Removing the engine mounting-to-body bracket

32 Partially unscrew the sprocket retaining nut, fit the home-made tool, and secure it to the sprocket with two suitable bolts. Prevent the sprocket from rotating as before, and unscrew the sprocket retaining nut. The nut will bear against the tool as it is undone, forcing the sprocket off the shaft taper. Once the taper is released, remove the tool, unscrew the nut fully, and remove the sprocket from the pump shaft.

33 Recover the Woodruff key from the end of the pump shaft if it is loose and remove the puller from the sprocket.

Refitting

34 Where applicable, refit the Woodruff key to the pump shaft, ensuring that it is correctly located in its groove.

35 Refit the sprocket, then tighten the securing nut to the specified torque, preventing the pump shaft from turning as during removal.

36 Make sure that the 8 mm bolts securing the sprockets in the TDC position are fitted to the camshaft and fuel injection pump sprockets, and that the rod/drill is positioned in the flywheel timing hole.

37 Fit the timing belt around the fuel injection pump sprocket, ensuring that the marks made on the belt and sprocket before removal are aligned.

38 Tension the timing belt as described in Section 7.

39 Refit the upper timing belt covers as described in Section 6.

Coolant pump sprocket

40 The coolant pump sprocket is integral with the pump, and cannot be removed.

---

9 Right-hand engine mounting bracket and timing belt tensioner – removal and refitting

General

1 The timing belt tensioner is operated by a spring and plunger housed in the right-hand engine mounting bracket, which is bolted to the end face of the engine. The engine

mounting is attached to the mounting on the body via the engine mounting-to-body bracket.

Right-hand engine mounting-to-body bracket

Removal

2 Before removing the bracket, the engine must be supported, preferably using a suitable hoist and lifting tackle attached to the lifting bracket at the right-hand end of the engine. Alternatively, the engine can be supported using a trolley jack and interposed block of wood beneath the sump, in which case, be prepared for the engine to tilt backwards when the bracket is removed.

3 Release the retaining clips and brackets, and position the diesel priming pump, and all the relevant hoses and cables, clear of the engine mounting assembly and suspension top mounting.

4 Unscrew the two retaining bolts, and remove the curved retaining plate from the top of the mounting **(see illustration)**.

5 Lift out the rubber buffer to expose the engine mounting bracket-to-body securing nut **(see illustration)**.

6 Unscrew the three nuts securing the bracket to the engine mounting, and the single nut securing the bracket to the body, then lift off the bracket **(see illustration)**.

Refitting

7 Refitting is a reversal of removal. Tighten the nuts and bolts to the specified torque.

Timing belt tensioner and right-hand engine mounting bracket

Note: *A suitable tool will be required to retain the timing belt tensioner plunger during this operation.*

Removal

8 Remove the engine mounting-to-body bracket as described previously in this Section, and remove the auxiliary drivebelt as described in Chapter 1B.

9 If not already done, support the engine with a trolley jack and interposed block of wood beneath the sump.

10 Where applicable, disconnect the hoist

and lifting tackle supporting the engine from the right-hand lifting bracket (this is necessary because, on some engines, the lifting bracket is attached to the engine mounting bracket, and must be removed).

11 Unscrew the two retaining bolts and remove the engine lifting bracket, if necessary.

12 Align the engine assembly/valve timing holes as described in Section 3, and lock the camshaft sprocket, injection pump sprocket and flywheel in position. *Do not* rotate the engine whilst the pins are in position.

13 Loosen the timing belt tensioner pivot nut and adjustment bolt, then turn the tensioner bracket anti-clockwise until the adjustment bolt is in the middle of the slot, and retighten the adjustment bolt. Use a 10 mm square drive extension in the hole provided, to turn the tensioner bracket against the spring tension.

14 Mark the timing belt with an arrow to indicate its running direction, if it is to be re-used. Remove the belt from the sprockets.

15 A tool must now be obtained in order to hold the tensioner plunger in the engine mounting bracket.

16 The Citroën tool is designed to slide in the two lower bolt holes of the mounting bracket. It should be easy to fabricate a similar tool out of sheet metal, using 10 mm bolts and nuts instead of metal rods **(see Tool Tip)**.

17 Unscrew the two lower engine mounting

Fabricated tool for holding tensioner plunger in the engine mounting bracket.

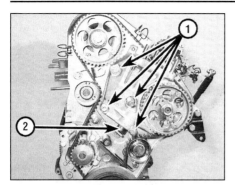

9.17a View of timing belt end of engine

1 *Engine mounting bracket retaining bolts*
2 *Timing belt tensioner plunger*

9.17b Tool in place to hold tensioner plunger in engine mounting bracket – timing belt removed for clarity

11.4 Camshaft bearing cap identification mark (arrowed)

bracket bolts, then fit the special tool **(see illustrations)**. Grease the inner surface of the tool, to prevent any damage to the end of the tensioner plunger. Unscrew the pivot nut and adjustment bolt, and withdraw the tensioner assembly.

18 Remove the two remaining engine mounting bracket bolts, and withdraw the bracket.

19 Compress the tensioner plunger into the engine mounting bracket, remove the special tool, then withdraw the plunger and spring.

Refitting

20 Refitting is a reversal of removal, bearing in mind the following points:
  a) *Tighten all fixings to the specified torque.*
  b) *Refit and tension the timing belt as described in Section 7.*
  c) *Refit and tighten the auxiliary drivebelt as described in Chapter 1B.*

10 Timing belt idler roller – removal and refitting

Removal

1 Remove the auxiliary drivebelt as described in Chapter 1B.

2 Align the engine assembly/valve timing holes as described in Section 3, and lock the camshaft sprocket, injection pump sprocket and flywheel in position. *Do not* rotate the engine whilst the pins are in position.

3 Loosen the timing belt tensioner pivot nut and adjustment bolt, then turn the tensioner bracket anti-clockwise to release the tension, and retighten the adjustment bolt to hold the tensioner in the released position. If available, use a 10 mm square drive extension in the hole provided, to turn the tensioner bracket against the spring tension.

4 Unscrew the two bolts and the stud securing the idler roller assembly to the cylinder block, noting that the upper bolt also secures the engine mounting bracket.

5 Slightly loosen the remaining four engine mounting bolts, noting that the uppermost bolt is on the inside face of the engine front

plate, and also secures the engine lifting bracket. Slide out the idler roller assembly.

Refitting

6 Refitting is a reversal of removal, bearing in mind the following points:
  a) *Tighten all fixings to the specified torque.*
  b) *Tension the timing belt as described in Section 7.*
  c) *Refit and tension the auxiliary drivebelt as described in Chapter 1B.*

11 Camshaft and followers – removal, inspection and refitting

Removal

1 Remove the cylinder head cover as described in Section 4.

2 Remove the camshaft sprocket as described in Section 8.

3 Remove the braking system vacuum pump as described in Chapter 9.

4 The camshaft bearing caps should be numbered from the flywheel end of the engine **(see illustration)**. If the caps are not already numbered, identify them, numbering them from the flywheel end of the engine, and making the marks on the manifold side.

5 Progressively unscrew the nuts, then remove the bearing caps.

6 Lift the camshaft from the cylinder head. Remove the oil seal from the timing belt end of the camshaft. Discard the seal, a new one should be used on refitting.

7 Obtain eight small, clean plastic containers, and number them 1 to 8; alternatively, divide a larger container into eight compartments. Using a rubber sucker, withdraw each follower in turn, and place it in its respective container. Do not interchange the cam followers, or the rate of wear will be much increased. If necessary, also remove the shim from the top of the valve stem, and store it with its respective follower. Note that the shim may stick to the inside of the follower as it is withdrawn. If this happens, take care not to allow it to drop out as the follower is removed.

Inspection

8 Examine the camshaft bearing surfaces and cam lobes for signs of wear ridges and scoring. Renew the camshaft if any of these conditions are apparent. Examine the condition of the bearing surfaces, both on the camshaft journals and in the cylinder head/bearing caps. If the head bearing surfaces are worn excessively, the cylinder head will need to be renewed. If suitable measuring equipment is available, camshaft bearing journal wear can be checked by direct measurement (where the necessary specifications have been quoted by Citroën), noting that No 1 journal is at the transmission end of the head.

9 Examine the cam follower bearing surfaces which contact the camshaft lobes for wear ridges and scoring. Renew any follower on which these conditions are apparent. If a follower bearing surface is badly scored, also examine the corresponding lobe on the camshaft for wear, as it is likely that both will be worn. Renew worn components as necessary.

Refitting

10 To prevent any possibility of the valves contacting the pistons as the camshaft is refitted, remove the locking rod/drill from the flywheel and turn the crankshaft a quarter turn in the *opposite* direction to normal rotation, to position all the pistons at mid-stroke. Release the timing belt from the injection pump sprocket while turning the crankshaft.

11 Where removed, refit each shim to the top of its original valve stem. *Do not* interchange the shims, as this will upset the valve clearances (see Section 12).

12 Liberally oil the cylinder head cam follower bores and the followers. Carefully refit the followers to the cylinder head, ensuring that each follower is refitted to its original bore. Some care will be required to enter the followers squarely into their bores.

13 Lubricate the cam lobes and bearing journals with clean engine oil of the specified grade.

14 Position the camshaft in the cylinder

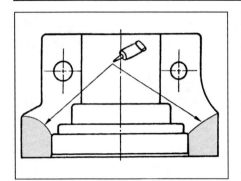

11.17 Apply sealing compound to the end camshaft bearing caps on the areas shown

11.19 Checking the camshaft endfloat using a feeler blade

head, passing it through the engine front plate.

15 Temporarily locate the sprocket on the end of the camshaft, and turn the shaft so that the sprocket timing hole is aligned with the corresponding cut-out in the cylinder head. Remove the sprocket.

16 Fit the centre bearing cap the correct way round as previously noted, then screw on the nuts and tighten them two or three turns.

17 Apply sealing compound to the end bearing caps on the areas shown **(see illustration)**. Fit them in the correct positions, and tighten the nuts two or three turns.

18 Tighten all the nuts progressively to the specified torque, making sure that the camshaft remains correctly positioned.

19 Check that the camshaft endfloat is as given in the Specifications, using a feeler blade. If not, the camshaft and/or the cylinder head must be renewed. To check the endfloat, push the camshaft fully towards one end of the cylinder head, and insert a feeler blade between the thrust faces of one of the camshaft lobes and a bearing cap **(see illustration)**.

20 If the original camshaft is being refitted, and it is known that the valve clearances are

correct, proceed to the next paragraph. Otherwise, check and adjust the valve clearances as described in Section 12.

21 Smear the lips of the new oil seal with clean engine oil and fit it onto the camshaft end, making sure its sealing lip is facing inwards. Press the oil seal in until it is flush with the end face of the camshaft bearing cap.

22 Refit the braking system vacuum pump as described in Chapter 9.

23 Again, temporarily locate the sprocket on the end of the camshaft, and make sure that the sprocket timing hole is aligned with the corresponding cut-out in the cylinder head.

24 Turn the crankshaft a quarter turn in the normal direction of rotation so that pistons 1 and 4 are again at TDC.

25 Refit the rod/drill to the flywheel timing hole.

26 Refit the camshaft sprocket as described in Section 8.

27 Refit the cylinder head cover as described in Section 4.

12 Valve clearances –
checking and adjustment

Checking

1 The importance of having the valve clearances correctly adjusted cannot be overstressed, as they vitally affect the performance of the engine. Checking should

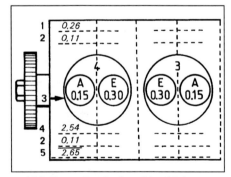

12.6 Example of valve shim thickness calculation

A   *Inlet*
E   *Exhaust*
1   *Measured clearance*
2   *Difference between 1 and 3*
3   *Specified clearance*
4   *Thickness of shim fitted*
5   *Thickness of shim required*

12.8 Measuring a valve clearance using a feeler blade

not be regarded as a routine operation, however. It should only be necessary when the valve gear has become noisy, after engine overhaul, or when trying to trace the cause of power loss. The clearances are checked as follows. The engine must be cold for the check to be accurate.

2 Chock the rear wheels then jack up the front of the car and support it on axle stands (see *Jacking and vehicle support*). Remove the right-hand front roadwheel.

3 From underneath the front of the car, remove the wheelarch plastic liner, which is secured by various screws and clips under the wheelarch. Release all the fasteners, and remove liner from under the front wing. Where necessary, unclip the coolant hoses from under the wing to improve access to the crankshaft pulley.

4 The engine can now be turned over using a suitable socket and extension bar fitted to the crankshaft pulley bolt.

> **HAYNES HiNT** *The engine will be easier to turn if the fuel injectors or glow plugs are removed.*

5 Remove the cylinder head cover as described in Section 4.

6 On a piece of paper, draw the outline of the engine with the cylinders numbered from the flywheel end. Show the position of each valve, together with the specified valve clearance. Above each valve, draw lines for noting (1) the actual clearance and (2) the amount of adjustment required **(see illustration)**.

7 Turn the crankshaft until the inlet valve of No 1 cylinder (nearest the transmission) is fully closed, with the tip of the cam facing directly away from the follower.

8 Using feeler blades, measure the clearance between the base of the cam and the cam follower **(see illustration)**. Record the clearance on line (1).

9 Repeat the measurement for the other seven valves, turning the crankshaft as necessary so that the cam lobe in question is always facing directly away from the relevant follower.

10 Calculate the difference between each measured clearance and the desired value, and record it on line (2). Since the clearance is different for inlet and exhaust valves – make sure that you are aware which valve you are dealing with. The valve sequence from either end of the engine is:

In–Ex–Ex–In–In–Ex–Ex–In

11 If all the clearances are within tolerance, refit the cylinder head cover with reference to Section 4. Refit the wheelarch liner and roadwheel, then lower the vehicle to the ground. If any clearance measured is outside the specified tolerance, adjustment must be carried out as described in the following paragraphs.

Adjustment

12 Remove the camshaft as described in Section 11.

13.4 Disconnecting the vacuum hose from the braking system vacuum pump

13.5 Disconnecting a fuel injector leak-off hose

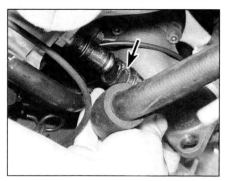

13.8 Disconnecting the coolant hose (arrowed) from the rear of the cylinder head

13 Withdraw the first follower and its shim. Be careful that the shim does not fall out of the follower. Clean the shim, and measure its thickness with a micrometer. The shims carry thickness markings, but wear may have reduced the original thickness, so be sure to check.

14 Refer to the clearance recorded for the valve concerned. If the clearance was more than that specified, the shim thickness must be increased by the difference recorded (2). If the clearance was less than that specified, the thickness of the shim must be decreased by the difference recorded (2).

15 Draw three more lines beneath each valve on the calculation paper, as shown in illustration 12.6. On line (4) note the measured thickness of the shim, then add or deduct the difference from line (2) to give the final shim thickness required on line (5).

16 Repeat the procedure given in paragraphs 13 to 15 on the remaining valves, keeping each follower identified for position.

17 When reassembling, oil the shim and fit it into the valve retainer, with the size marking face downwards. Oil the follower, and lower it onto the shim. Do not raise the follower after fitting, as the shim may become dislodged.

18 When all the followers are in position, complete with their shims, refit the camshaft as described in Section 11. Recheck the valve clearances before refitting the cylinder head cover, to make sure they are correct.

13 Cylinder head –
removal and refitting

Note: *This is an involved procedure, and it is suggested that the Section is read thoroughly before starting work. To aid refitting, make notes on the locations of all relevant brackets and the routing of hoses and cables before removal.*

Removal

1 Disconnect the battery negative terminal (refer to *Disconnecting the battery* in the Reference Section of this manual).

2 Drain the cooling system as described in Chapter 1B.

3 Remove the inlet and exhaust manifolds as described in Chapter 4B.

4 Slacken the retaining clip and disconnect the vacuum hose from the braking system vacuum pump **(see illustration)**.

5 Disconnect and remove the fuel injector leak-off hoses **(see illustration)**.

6 Disconnect the fuel pipes from the fuel injectors and the fuel injection pump, and remove the pipes as described in Chapter 4B.

7 Unscrew the securing nut and disconnect the feed wire from the relevant glow plug. Recover the washers.

8 Disconnect the coolant hose from the rear, left-hand end of the cylinder head **(see illustration)**.

9 Disconnect the small coolant hose from the

front timing belt end of the cylinder head **(see illustration)**.

10 Unclip the fuel return hose from the brackets on the cylinder head, and move it to one side **(see illustration)**.

11 Disconnect the accelerator cable from the fuel injection pump (refer to Chapter 4B if necessary), and move the cable clear of the cylinder head.

12 Remove the thermostat/fuel filter housing as described in Chapter 3.

13 Unscrew the nut or stud securing the coolant hose bracket and the engine lifting bracket to the transmission end of the cylinder head.

14 Remove the camshaft sprocket as described in Section 8.

15 Remove the timing belt tensioner and the right-hand engine mounting bracket as described in Section 9.

16 Remove the timing belt idler roller as described in Section 10.

17 Remove the bolt securing the engine front plate to the fuel injection pump mounting bracket.

18 Remove the nut and bolt securing the engine front plate and the alternator mounting bracket to the fuel injection pump mounting bracket, then remove the engine front plate.

19 Progressively unscrew the cylinder head bolts, in the reverse order to that shown in illustration 13.37.

20 Lift out the bolts and recover the spacers **(see illustration)**.

13.9 Disconnecting the coolant hose (arrowed) from the front of the head

13.10 Unclip the fuel return hose from its brackets

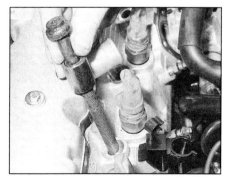

13.20 Removing a cylinder head bolt and spacer

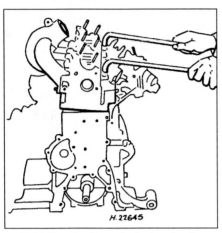

13.21 Freeing the cylinder head using angled rods

21 Release the cylinder head from the cylinder block and location dowel by rocking it. The Citroën tool for doing this consists simply of two metal rods with 90-degree angled ends **(see illustration)**. Do not prise between the mating faces of the cylinder head and block, as this may damage the gasket faces.

22 Lift the cylinder head from the block, and recover the gasket **(see illustration)**.

Preparation for refitting

23 The mating faces of the cylinder head and cylinder block/crankcase must be perfectly clean before refitting the head. Citroën recommend the use of a scouring agent for this purpose, but acceptable results can be achieved by using a hard plastic or wood scraper to remove all traces of gasket and carbon. The same method can be used to clean the piston crowns. Take particular care to avoid scoring or gouging the cylinder head/cylinder block mating surfaces during the cleaning operations, as aluminium alloy is easily damaged. Make sure that the carbon is not allowed to enter the oil and water passages – this is particularly important for the lubrication system, as carbon could block the

13.22 Removing the cylinder head

oil supply to the engine's components. Using adhesive tape and paper, seal the water, oil and bolt holes in the cylinder block/crankcase. To prevent carbon entering the gap between the pistons and bores, smear a little grease in the gap. After cleaning each piston, use a small brush to remove all traces of grease and carbon from the gap, then wipe away the remainder with a clean rag.

24 Check the mating surfaces of the cylinder block/crankcase and the cylinder head for nicks, deep scratches and other damage. If slight, they may be removed carefully with a file, but if excessive, machining may be the only alternative to renewal. If warpage of the cylinder head gasket surface is suspected, use a straight-edge to check it for distortion. Refer to Part F of this Chapter if necessary.

25 Thoroughly clean the threads of the cylinder head bolt holes in the cylinder block. Ensure that the bolts run freely in their threads, and that all traces of oil and water are removed from each bolt hole.

Gasket selection

26 Check that the timing belt is clear of the fuel injection pump sprocket, then turn the crankshaft until pistons 1 and 4 are at TDC. Position a dial test indicator (dial gauge) on

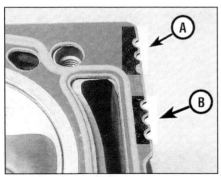

13.29 Cylinder head gasket thickness identification notches (A). Also note engine capacity and type identification notches (B)

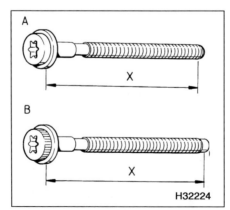

13.31 Measure the length (X) of the cylinder head bolts, to determine whether renewal is required

A Bolts without guiding end-piece
B Bolts with guiding end-piece

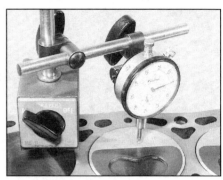

13.27 Measuring piston protrusion

the cylinder block, and zero it on the block face. Transfer the probe to the centre of No 1 piston, then slowly turn the crankshaft back and forth past TDC, noting the highest reading on the indicator. Record this reading.

27 Repeat this measurement procedure on No 4 piston, then turn the crankshaft half a turn (180°) and repeat the procedure on Nos 2 and 3 pistons **(see illustration)**.

28 If a dial test indicator is not available, piston protrusion may be measured using a straight-edge and feeler blades or vernier calipers. However, this is much less accurate, and cannot therefore be recommended.

29 Note down the greatest piston protrusion measurement, and use this to determine the correct cylinder head gasket from the following table. The series of notches on the edge of the gasket are used for thickness identification. On gaskets where the notches are in two adjacent groups, the series nearest to the corner are used for thickness identification **(see illustration)**. On gaskets where the notches are in two distinctly separate groups, the series nearest to the centre are used for thickness identification. On all gaskets, the remaining series of notches identify the engine capacity and type, and have no significance for the gasket thickness.

Piston protrusion	Gasket identification
0.56 to 0.67 mm	1 notch
0.68 to 0.71 mm	2 notches
0.72 to 0.75 mm	3 notches
0.76 to 0.79 mm	4 notches
0.80 to 0.83 mm	5 notches

Cylinder head bolt examination

30 The Torx head type cylinder head bolts are supplied in two versions, one version with an unthreaded guiding end-piece at the base of the thread, and one version without an end-piece. It is permissible to re-use either type providing that their length does not exceed the figures shown below. Note that, if a bolt is modified to locate the gasket (see paragraph 33), a new bolt will be required when finally refitting the cylinder head.

31 Measure the length of each bolt from the base of the head to the end of the thread (or guiding end-piece) **(see illustration)**.

Compare the results with the values given in the following table, to determine whether the bolts and spacers should be renewed. **Note:** *Considering the stress which the cylinder head bolts are under, it is highly recommended that they are renewed, regardless of their apparent condition.*

Non-turbo models

Bolt length	Action required
Bolts without guiding end-piece:	
Less than 121.5 mm	Re-use bolts and spacers
Greater than 121.5 mm	Renew bolts and spacers
Bolts with guiding end-piece:	
Less than 124.5 mm	Re-use bolts and spacers
Greater than 124.5 mm	Renew bolts and spacers

Turbo models

Bolt length	Action required
Bolts without guiding end-piece:	
Less than 146.5 mm	Re-use bolts and spacers
Greater than 146.5 mm	Renew bolts and spacers
Bolts with guiding end-piece:	
Less than 150.5 mm	Re-use bolts and spacers
Greater than 150.5 mm	Renew bolts and spacers

Refitting

32 Turn the crankshaft clockwise (viewed from the timing belt end) until Nos 1 and 4 pistons pass bottom dead centre (BDC) and begin to rise, then position them halfway up their bores. Nos 2 and 3 pistons will also be at their mid-way positions, but descending their bores.

33 Fit the correct gasket the right way round on the cylinder block, with the identification notches at the flywheel end of the engine. Make sure that the locating dowel is in place at the timing belt end of the block. Note that, as there is only one locating dowel, it is possible for the gasket to move as the cylinder head is fitted, particularly when the cylinder head is fitted with the engine in the car (due to the inclination of the engine). In the worst instance, this can allow the pistons and/or the valves to

hit the gasket, causing engine damage. To avoid this problem, saw the head off a cylinder head bolt, and file (or cut) a slot in the end of the bolt, to enable it to be turned with a screwdriver. Screw the bolt into one of the bolt holes at the flywheel end of the cylinder block, then fit the gasket over the bolt and location dowel. This will ensure that the gasket is held in position as the cylinder head is fitted.

34 Lower the cylinder head onto the block.

35 Apply a smear of grease to the threads, and to the underside of the heads, of the cylinder head bolts. Citroën recommend the use of Molykote G Rapid Plus (available from your Citroën dealer); in the absence of the specified grease, any good-quality high-melting-point grease may be used.

36 Carefully enter each bolt and spacer (convex sides uppermost, where applicable) into its relevant hole (*do not drop it in*) and screw it in finger-tight. Where applicable, after fitting three or four bolts to locate the cylinder head, unscrew the modified bolt fitted in paragraph 33, and fit a new bolt in its place.

37 Working progressively and in the sequence shown, tighten the cylinder head bolts to their Stage 1 torque setting, using a torque wrench and suitable socket **(see illustration)**.

38 Once all the bolts have been tightened to their Stage 1 torque setting, working again in the specified sequence, tighten each bolt to the specified Stage 2 setting. Finally, angle-tighten the bolts through the specified Stage 3 angle. It is recommended that an angle-measuring gauge is used during this stage of tightening, to ensure accuracy.

39 The remainder of the refitting procedure is a reversal of removal, noting the following points:

a) *Refit the camshaft sprocket, timing belt tensioner and idler roller, and timing belt as described earlier in this Chapter.*

b) *Refit the thermostat/fuel filter housing as described in Chapter 3.*

c) *Ensure that all wiring is correctly routed, and that all connectors are securely reconnected to the correct components.*

d) *Ensure that the coolant hoses are correctly reconnected, and that their retaining clips are securely tightened.*

e) *Ensure that all vacuum/breather hoses are correctly reconnected.*

f) *Refit the exhaust and inlet manifolds as described in Chapter 4B.*

g) *Refit the cylinder head cover as described in Section 4.*

h) *Refit the fuel system components, accelerator cable, and air cleaner housing and ducts as described in Chapter 4B.*

i) *Refill the cooling system as described in Chapter 1B.*

j) *Reconnect the battery and bleed the fuel system as described in Chapter 4B.*

14 Sump – removal and refitting

Refer to Chapter 2B, Section 14, but substitute Chapter 1B for all references to Chapter 1A.

15 Oil pump and drive chain – removal, inspection and refitting

Refer to Chapter 2B, Section 15.

16 Oil seals – renewal

Crankshaft right-hand oil seal

1 Remove the crankshaft sprocket as described in Section 8.

2 Note the fitted depth of the oil seal.

3 Pull the oil seal from the housing using a hooked instrument. Alternatively, drill a small hole in the oil seal, and use a self-tapping screw and a pair of pliers to remove it **(see illustration)**.

4 Clean the oil seal housing and the crankshaft sealing surface.

5 Dip the new oil seal in clean engine oil, and press it into the housing (open end first) to the previously-noted depth, using a suitable tube or socket. A piece of thin plastic or tape wound around the right-hand end of the crankshaft is useful to prevent damage to the oil seal as it is fitted.

6 Where applicable, remove the plastic or tape from the end of the crankshaft.

7 Refit the crankshaft sprocket as described in Section 8.

Crankshaft left-hand oil seal

8 Remove the flywheel as described in Section 17.

9 Proceed as described in paragraphs 2 to 6, noting that when fitted, the outer lip of the oil seal must point outwards; if it is pointing inwards, use a piece of bent wire to pull it out. Take care not to damage the oil seal.

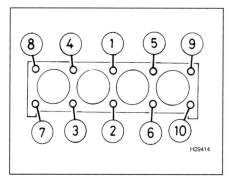

13.37 Cylinder head bolt tightening sequence

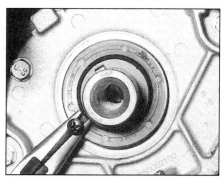

16.3 Self-tapping screw and pliers used to remove the crankshaft right-hand oil seal

16.12 Removing the camshaft right-hand oil seal

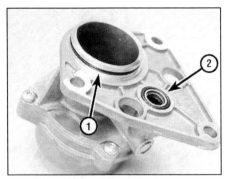

16.18 Camshaft left-hand oil seal (1) and oil feed gallery O-ring (2) on rear of the brake vacuum pump

10 Refit the flywheel as described in Section 17.

Camshaft right-hand oil seal

11 Remove the camshaft sprocket as described in Section 8. In principle there is no need to remove the timing belt completely, but remember that if the belt has been contaminated with oil, it must be renewed.

12 Pull the oil seal from the housing using a hooked instrument **(see illustration)**. Alternatively, drill a small hole in the oil seal and use a self-tapping screw and a pair of pliers to remove it.

13 Clean the oil seal housing and the camshaft sealing surface.

14 Smear the new oil seal with clean engine oil, then fit it over the end of the camshaft, open end first. A piece of thin plastic or tape wound round the right-hand end of the camshaft should prevent damage to the oil seal as it is fitted.

15 Press the seal into the housing until it is flush with the end face of the cylinder head. Use an M10 bolt (screwed into the end of the camshaft), washers and a suitable tube or socket to press the seal into position.

16 Refit the camshaft sprocket as described in Section 8.

17 Where applicable, fit a new timing belt as described in Section 7.

Camshaft left-hand oil seal

18 No oil seal is fitted to the left-hand end of the camshaft. The sealing is provided by an O-ring fitted to the vacuum pump flange. The O-ring can be renewed after unbolting the pump from the cylinder head (see Chapter 9). Note the smaller O-ring which seals the oil feed gallery to the pump – this may also cause leakage from the pump/cylinder head mating faces if it deteriorates or fails **(see illustration)**.

17 Flywheel – removal, inspection and refitting

Refer to Chapter 2B, Section 18.

18 Engine/transmission mountings – inspection and renewal

Inspection

1 Refer to Chapter 2B, Section 19.

Renewal

Right-hand mounting

2 Refer to Section 9.

Left-hand mounting

3 Refer to Chapter 2B, Section 19.

Rear mounting

4 Refer to Chapter 2B, Section 19.

19 Engine oil cooler – removal and refitting

Refer to Chapter 2B, Section 16, but substitute Chapter 1B for all references to Chapter 1A.

Chapter 2 Part D:
DW series diesel engine in-car repair procedures

Contents

Camshaft and followers (1.9 litre engines) – removal and refitting . . 10
Camshaft, tappets and rocker arms (2.0 litre engines) –
  removal and refitting 11
Compression and leakdown tests – description and
  interpretation 2
Crankshaft pulley – removal and refitting 5
Cylinder head (1.9 litre engines) – removal and refitting 13
Cylinder head cover – removal and refitting 4
Engine assembly/valve timing holes –
  general information and usage 3
Engine oil and filter renewal . . . . .See Chapter 1B
Engine oil cooler – removal and refitting 19
Engine oil level check . . . . .See Weekly checks

Engine/transmission mountings – inspection and renewal 18
Flywheel – removal, inspection and refitting 17
General information and precautions 1
Oil pump and drive chain – removal, inspection and refitting 15
Oil seals – renewal 16
Sump – removal and refitting 14
Timing belt (1.9 litre engines) – removal, inspection,
  refitting and tensioning 7
Timing belt (2.0 litre engines) – removal, inspection,
  refitting and tensioning 8
Timing belt covers – removal and refitting 6
Timing belt sprockets and tensioner – removal and refitting 9
Valve clearances (1.9 litre engines) – checking and adjustment 12

Degrees of difficulty

Easy, suitable for novice with little experience	**Fairly easy,** suitable for beginner with some experience	**Fairly difficult,** suitable for competent DIY mechanic 	**Difficult,** suitable for experienced DIY mechanic 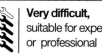	**Very difficult,** suitable for expert DIY or professional 

Specifications

Engine (general)

Designation:
   1.9 litre (1868cc) engine DW8
   2.0 litre (1997cc) engine DW10TD
Engine codes*:
   1.9 litre engine . . . . WJZ
   2.0 litre engine . . . . RHY
Bore:
   1.9 litre engine . . . . 82.20 mm
   2.0 litre engine . . . . 85.00 mm
Stroke . . . . 88.00 mm
Direction of crankshaft rotation . . . . Clockwise (viewed from the right-hand side of vehicle)
No 1 cylinder location . . . . At the transmission end of block
Compression ratio:
   1.9 litre engine . . . . 23 : 1
   2.0 litre engine . . . . 17.6 : 1
*The engine code is stamped on a plate attached to the front of the cylinder block.

Compression pressures (engine hot, at cranking speed)

Normal . . . . 25 to 35 bars (363 to 508 psi)
Maximum difference between any two cylinders . . . . 5 bars (73 psi)

Valve clearances (1.9 litre engine only)

Inlet . . . . 0.15 ± 0.05 mm
Exhaust . . . . 0.30 ± 0.05 mm

Timing belt

Tension setting:
1.9 litre engine (see text – Section 7):	
Initial setting	106 ± 2 SEEM units
Final setting	42 ± 2 SEEM units
2.0 litre engine (see text – Section 8):	
Initial setting	98 ± 2 SEEM units
Final setting	54 ± 3 SEEM units

Camshaft

Drive	Toothed belt
No of bearings:	
1.9 litre engine	3
2.0 litre engine	6
Endfloat:	
1.9 litre engine	0.025 to 0.07 mm
2.0 litre engine	Not available

Lubrication system

Oil pump type	Gear-type, chain-driven off the crankshaft right-hand end
Minimum oil pressure at 90°C:	
1.9 litre engine	4.5 bars at 4000 rpm
2.0 litre engine	4.0 bars at 4000 rpm
Oil pressure warning switch operating pressure	0.8 bars

Torque wrench settings

	Nm	lbf ft
1.9 litre engine		
Big-end bearing cap nuts:*		
Stage 1	20	15
Stage 2	Tighten through a further 70°	
Camshaft bearing cap nuts	20	15
Camshaft sprocket-to-hub bolts	23	17
Camshaft sprocket hub-to-camshaft bolts	43	32
Crankshaft right-hand oil seal housing bolts	14	10
Crankshaft pulley-to-sprocket bolts	10	7
Crankshaft sprocket bolt:		
Stage 1	40	30
Stage 2	Tighten through a further 55°	
Cylinder head bolts:		
Stage 1	20	15
Stage 2	60	44
Stage 3	Tighten through a further 180°	
Cylinder head lower cover bolts	5	4
Cylinder head upper cover bolts	10	7
Engine-to-transmission fixing bolts	45	33
Engine/transmission left-hand mounting:		
Rubber mounting-to-body bolts	21	15
Mounting stud to transmission	50	37
Rubber mounting centre nut	65	48
Engine/transmission rear mounting:		
Mounting assembly-to-block bolts	45	33
Connecting link-to-mounting assembly bolt	50	37
Connecting link-to-subframe bolt	50	37
Engine/transmission right-hand mounting:		
Engine bracket bolts	45	33
Mounting bracket retaining nuts	45	33
Curved retaining plate bolts	20	15
Flywheel bolts*	50	37
Injection pump sprocket bolts	23	17
Main bearing cap bolts	70	52
Oil pump mounting bolts	18	13
Piston oil jet spray tube bolt	10	7
Sump bolts	16	12
Timing belt idler roller bolt	43	32
Timing belt tensioner pulley bolt	21	15

*New nuts/bolts must be used.

Torque wrench settings (continued)

2.0 litre engine

	Nm	lbf ft
Big-end bearing cap nuts:*		
Stage 1	20	15
Stage 2	Tighten through a further 70°	
Camshaft bearing housing bolts	10	7
Camshaft sprocket-to-hub bolts	20	15
Camshaft sprocket hub-to-camshaft bolts	43	32
Crankshaft right-hand oil seal housing bolts	14	10
Crankshaft pulley bolt:		
Stage 1	40	30
Stage 2	Tighten through a further 51°	
Cylinder head bolts:		
Stage 1	20	15
Stage 2	60	44
Stage 3	Tighten through a further 220°	
Cylinder head cover bolts	8	6
Engine-to-transmission fixing bolts	45	33
Engine/transmission left-hand mounting:		
Rubber mounting-to-body bolts	21	15
Mounting bracket-to-transmission bolts	50	37
Rubber mounting centre nut	65	48
Engine/transmission rear mounting:		
Mounting assembly-to-block bolts	45	33
Connecting link-to-mounting assembly nut/bolt	45	33
Connecting link-to-subframe nut/bolt	45	33
Engine/transmission right-hand mounting:		
Engine bracket bolts	45	33
Upper mounting bracket-to-engine bracket bolts	61	45
Upper mounting bracket-to-rubber mounting nut	45	33
Curved retaining plate bolts	20	15
Flywheel bolts*	50	37
High pressure fuel pump sprocket nut	50	37
Main bearing cap bolts:		
Stage 1	25	18
Stage 2	Tighten through a further 60°	
Oil pump mounting bolts	18	13
Piston oil jet spray tube bolt	10	7
Sump bolts	16	12
Timing belt idler roller bolt	25	18
Timing belt tensioner pulley bolt	25	18

*New nuts/bolts must be used.

1 General information and precautions

Using this Chapter

This Part of Chapter 2 is devoted to in-car repair procedures for the DW series diesel engines. Similar information covering the XUD series diesel engines, and the petrol engines will be found in Chapters 2A, 2B and 2C. All procedures concerning engine removal and refitting, and engine block/cylinder head overhaul for petrol and diesel engines can be found in Chapters 2E and 2F as applicable.

Refer to Vehicle identification in the Reference Section of this manual for details of engine code locations.

Most of the operations included in Chapter 2D are based on the assumption that the engine is still installed in the car. Therefore, if this information is being used during a complete engine overhaul, with the engine already removed, many of the steps included here will not apply.

DW series engine description

The DW series engine is a relatively new power unit based on the well-proven XUD series engine which has appeared in many Citroën and Peugeot vehicles. The 1.9 litre (DW8) engine is virtually identical to the 1.9 litre XUD unit apart from revisions to the cylinder head cover and fuel system components. The 2.0 litre (DW10TD) engine is very similar to the XUD engine in terms of the cylinder block components, but the remainder of the engine has been completely redesigned. Both engines are of four-cylinder single overhead camshaft design, mounted transversely, with the transmission mounted on the left-hand side.

On the 1.9 litre engine, a toothed timing belt drives the camshaft, fuel injection pump and coolant pump. Followers are fitted between the camshaft and valves, with valve clearance adjustment being by means of shims. The camshaft is supported by three bearings machined directly in the cylinder head.

On the 2.0 litre engine, a toothed timing belt drives the camshaft, high pressure fuel pump and coolant pump. The camshaft operates the inlet and exhaust valves via rocker arms which are supported at their pivot ends by hydraulic self-adjusting tappets. The camshaft is supported by six bearings machined directly in the cylinder head and camshaft bearing housing.

The crankshaft runs in five main bearings of the usual shell type. Endfloat is controlled by thrustwashers either side of No 2 main bearing.

The pistons are selected to be of matching weight, and incorporate fully-floating gudgeon pins retained by circlips.

The oil pump is chain-driven from the right-hand end of the crankshaft and an oil cooler is fitted to all engines.

Throughout the manual, it is often necessary to identify the engines not only by their cubic capacity, but also by their engine code. The engine code, consists of three letters (eg, DW8). The code is stamped on a plate attached to the front of the cylinder block.

Repair operations – precaution

The 2.0 litre engine is a complex unit with numerous accessories and ancillary components. The design of the engine compartment is such that every conceivable space has been utilised, and access to virtually all of the engine components is extremely limited. In many cases, ancillary components will have to be removed, or moved to one side, and wiring, pipes and hoses will have to be disconnected or removed from various cable clips and support brackets.

When working on this engine, read through the entire procedure first, look at the car and engine at the same time, and establish whether you have the necessary tools, equipment, skill and patience to proceed. Allow considerable time for any operation, and be prepared for the unexpected. Any major work on this engines is not for the faint-hearted!

Because of the limited access, many of the 2.0 litre engine photographs appearing in this Chapter were, by necessity, taken with the engine removed from the vehicle.

 Warning: It is essential to observe strict precautions when working on the fuel system components of the 2.0 litre engine, particularly the high pressure side of the system. Before carrying out any engine operations that entail working on, or near, any part of the fuel system, refer to the special information given in Chapter 4C, Section 2.

Repair operations possible with the engine in the vehicle

1.9 litre engine

a) Compression pressure – testing.
b) Cylinder head covers – removal and refitting.
c) Crankshaft pulley – removal and refitting.
d) Timing belt covers – removal and refitting.
e) Timing belt – removal, refitting and adjustment.
f) Timing belt tensioner and sprockets – removal and refitting.
g) Camshaft oil seal – renewal.
h) Camshaft and followers – removal, inspection and refitting.
i) Valve clearances – checking and adjustment.
j) Cylinder head – removal and refitting.
k) Cylinder head and pistons – decarbonising.
l) Sump – removal and refitting.
m) Oil pump – removal and refitting.
n) Crankshaft oil seals – renewal.

o) Engine/transmission mountings – inspection and renewal.
p) Flywheel – removal, inspection and refitting.

2.0 litre engine

a) Compression pressure – testing.
b) Cylinder head cover – removal and refitting.
c) Crankshaft pulley – removal and refitting.
d) Timing belt covers – removal and refitting.
e) Timing belt – removal, refitting and adjustment.
f) Timing belt tensioner and sprockets – removal and refitting.
g) Camshaft oil seal – renewal.
h) Camshaft, rocker arms and hydraulic tappets – removal, inspection and refitting.
i) Sump – removal and refitting.
j) Oil pump – removal and refitting.
k) Crankshaft oil seals – renewal.
l) Engine/transmission mountings – inspection and renewal.
m) Flywheel – removal, inspection and refitting.

Note: On 2.0 litre engines, access between the cylinder head and engine compartment bulkhead, and to the rear underside of the engine is so restricted that it is impossible to remove the cylinder head with the engine in the car unless considerable additional dismantling is carried out first (eg, removal of the front suspension subframe and related components). Cylinder head removal and refitting procedures are therefore contained in Part F, assuming that the engine/transmission has been removed from the vehicle.

2 Compression and leakdown tests – description and interpretation

Compression test

Note: A compression tester specifically designed for diesel engines must be used for this test.

1 When engine performance is down, or if misfiring occurs which cannot be attributed to the fuel system, a compression test can provide diagnostic clues as to the engine's condition. If the test is performed regularly, it can give warning of trouble before any other symptoms become apparent.

2 A compression tester specifically intended for diesel engines must be used, because of the higher pressures involved. The tester is connected to an adapter which screws into the glow plug or injector hole. On these engines, an adapter suitable for use in the glow plug holes will be required, so as not to disturb the fuel system components. It is unlikely to be worthwhile buying such a tester for occasional use, but it may be possible to borrow or hire one – if not, have the test performed by a garage.

3 Unless specific instructions to the contrary are supplied with the tester, observe the following points:
a) The battery must be in a good state of charge, the air filter must be clean, and the engine should be at normal operating temperature.
b) All the glow plugs should be removed as described in Chapter 5C before starting the test.
c) On 1.9 litre engines the ant-theft system electronic engine immobiliser unit wiring connector at the rear of the injection pump must be disconnected.
d) On 2.0 litre engines the wiring connector on the engine management system ECU (located in the plastic box behind the battery) must be disconnected.

4 The compression pressures measured are not so important as the balance between cylinders. Values are given in the Specifications.

5 The cause of poor compression is less easy to establish on a diesel engine than on a petrol one. The effect of introducing oil into the cylinders ('wet' testing) is not conclusive, because there is a risk that the oil will sit in the swirl chamber or in the recess on the piston crown instead of passing to the rings. However, the following can be used as a rough guide to diagnosis.

6 All cylinders should produce very similar pressures; any difference greater than that specified indicates the existence of a fault. Note that the compression should build up quickly in a healthy engine; low compression on the first stroke, followed by gradually-increasing pressure on successive strokes, indicates worn piston rings. A low compression reading on the first stroke, which does not build up during successive strokes, indicates leaking valves or a blown head gasket (a cracked head could also be the cause). Deposits on the undersides of the valve heads can also cause low compression.

7 A low reading from two adjacent cylinders is almost certainly due to the head gasket having blown between them; the presence of coolant in the engine oil will confirm this.

8 If the compression reading is unusually high, the cylinder head surfaces, valves and pistons are probably coated with carbon deposits. If this is the case, the cylinder head should be removed and decarbonised (see Part F).

Leakdown test

9 A leakdown test measures the rate at which compressed air fed into the cylinder is lost. It is an alternative to a compression test, and in many ways it is better, since the escaping air provides easy identification of where pressure loss is occurring (piston rings, valves or head gasket).

10 The equipment needed for leakdown testing is unlikely to be available to the home mechanic. If poor compression is suspected, have the test performed by a suitably-equipped garage.

3 Engine assembly/valve timing holes – general information and usage

General

Note: *Do not attempt to rotate the engine whilst the crankshaft, camshaft and, where applicable, injection pump are locked in position. If the engine is to be left in this state for a long period of time, it is a good idea to place suitable warning notices inside the vehicle, and in the engine compartment. This will reduce the possibility of the engine being accidentally cranked on the starter motor, which is likely to cause damage with the locking pins in place.*

1 On 1.9 litre engines, timing holes or slots are located in the flywheel, camshaft sprocket hub and injection pump hub. The holes/slots are used to align the crankshaft, camshaft and injection pump at the TDC position for Nos 1 and 4 pistons. This will ensure that the valve timing and injection pump timing are maintained during operations that require removal and refitting of the timing belt. When the holes/slots are aligned with their corresponding holes in the cylinder block, cylinder head and injection pump, suitable diameter bolts/pins can be inserted to lock the crankshaft, camshaft and injection pump in position, preventing rotation. **Note:** *With the timing holes aligned, No 4 piston is at TDC on its compression stroke.*

2 On 2.0 litre engines, the timing holes or slots are only located in the flywheel and camshaft sprocket hub. The HDi type fuel system used on these engines does not have a conventional diesel injection pump, but instead uses a high pressure fuel pump that does not have to be timed. The alignment of the fuel pump sprocket (and hence the fuel pump itself) with respect to crankshaft and camshaft position, is therefore irrelevant.

3 To align the engine assembly/valve timing holes, proceed as follows according to engine type.

1.9 litre engines

4 Remove the upper and intermediate timing belt covers as described in Section 6.

5 Firmly apply the handbrake, then jack up the front of the car and support it securely on axle stands (see *Jacking and vehicle support*). Remove the right-hand front roadwheel.

6 To gain access to the crankshaft pulley, to enable the engine to be turned, the wheelarch plastic liner must be removed. The liner is secured by various screws and clips under the wheelarch. Release all the fasteners, and remove liner from under the front wing. Where necessary, unclip the coolant hoses from under the wing to improve access further. The crankshaft can then be turned using a suitable socket and extension bar fitted to the pulley bolt.

7 Turn the crankshaft until the timing slot in

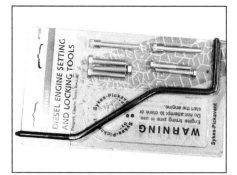

3.8a Suitable tools available for locking the engine in the TDC position

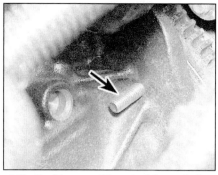

3.8b Rod (arrowed) inserted through the cylinder block into the flywheel timing hole

the camshaft sprocket hub, and the timing hole in the injection pump sprocket hub, are aligned with the corresponding holes in the cylinder head and pump. Note that the crankshaft must always be turned in a clockwise direction (viewed from the right-hand side of vehicle). Use a small mirror, if necessary, so that the position of the camshaft sprocket timing slot can be observed. When the slot is aligned with the corresponding hole in the cylinder head, the engine is positioned at TDC for Nos 1 and 4 pistons.

8 Insert an 8 mm diameter bolt, rod or drill through the hole in the left-hand flange of the cylinder block by the starter motor; if necessary, carefully turn the crankshaft either way until the rod enters the timing hole in the flywheel **(see illustrations)**.

9 Insert an 8 mm bolt through the slot in the camshaft sprocket hub and screw it into the engine finger tight. Insert a 6 mm rod or drill through the hole in the injection pump sprocket hub and into engagement with the pump **(see illustration)**.

10 The crankshaft, camshaft and injection pump are now locked in position, preventing unnecessary rotation.

2.0 litre engines

11 Carry out the operations described in paragraphs 4, 5 and 6.

12 Turn the crankshaft until the timing slot in the camshaft sprocket hub is aligned with the corresponding hole in the cylinder head. Note that the crankshaft must always be turned in a clockwise direction (viewed from the right-hand side of vehicle). Use a small mirror so

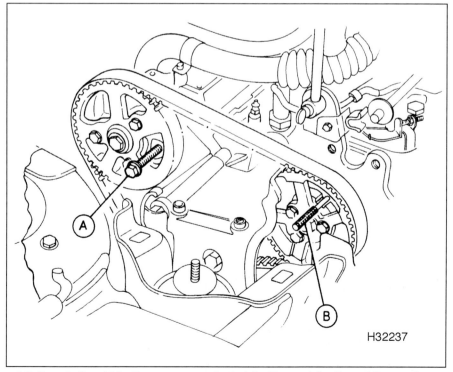

3.9 Camshaft and injection pump sprocket hub locking tool details – 1.9 litre engines

A   *8 mm bolt inserted through the timing slot in the camshaft sprocket hub*
B   *6 mm rod or drill bit inserted through the timing slot in the injection pump sprocket hub*

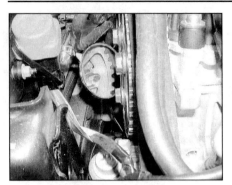

3.12a Use a mirror to observe the camshaft sprocket hub timing slot – 2.0 litre engines

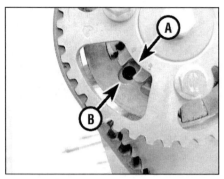

3.12b Camshaft sprocket hub timing slot (A) aligned with the cylinder head timing hole (B) – 2.0 litre engines

3.14 Insert an 8 mm bolt (arrowed) through the sprocket timing slot and into the cylinder head to lock the camshaft – 2.0 litre engines

that the position of the sprocket hub timing slot can be observed **(see illustrations)**. When the slot is aligned with the corresponding hole in the cylinder head, the engine is positioned at TDC for Nos 1 and 4 pistons.

13 Insert an 8 mm diameter bolt, rod or drill through the hole in the left-hand flange of the cylinder block by the starter motor; if necessary, carefully turn the crankshaft either way until the rod enters the timing hole in the flywheel **(see illustration 3.8b)**.

14 Insert an 8 mm bolt, rod or drill through the slot in the camshaft sprocket hub and into engagement with the cylinder head **(see illustration)**.

15 The crankshaft and camshaft are now locked in position, preventing unnecessary rotation.

4 Cylinder head cover – removal and refitting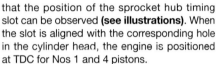

1.9 litre engines

Removal

1 Disconnect the battery negative terminal (refer to *Disconnecting the battery* in the Reference Section of this manual).

2 Release the clip in the centre of the engine cover and undo the retaining screw on the right-hand side. Remove the engine oil dipstick then lift the cover off the engine.

3 Remove the air distribution housing as described in Chapter 4B, Section 3.

4 Remove the timing belt upper cover as described in Section 6.

5 Slacken the retaining clip and disconnect the crankcase ventilation hose from the cylinder head upper cover.

6 Undo the eight bolts securing the cylinder head upper cover to the lower cover. Lift off the upper cover and recover the seal.

7 Undo the bolt securing the EGR pipe retaining clip to the cylinder head lower cover. Carefully move the pipe and any additional hoses clear of the cover.

8 Undo the three bolts securing the lower

cover to the cylinder head, noting the location of the seal on the right-hand bolt.

9 Lift the lower cover off the cylinder head and recover the seal.

Refitting

10 Refitting is a reversal of removal, bearing in mind the following points:

a) *Examine the upper and lower cover seals for signs of damage and deterioration, and renew if necessary.*

b) *Tighten the cylinder head cover bolts to the specified torque.*

c) *Refit the timing belt upper cover as described in Section 6.*

d) *Refit the air distribution housing as described in Chapter 4B, Section 3.*

2.0 litre engines

Removal

11 Remove the timing belt upper cover as described in Section 6.

12 Slacken or release the clips securing the crankcase ventilation hoses to the centre and left-hand end of the cylinder cover and disconnect the hoses.

13 Undo the bolts as necessary and move the engine cover and cable guide support bracket clear of the right-hand end of the cylinder head cover.

14 Disconnect the camshaft sensor wiring connector.

15 Release the wiring harness from the clip on the cylinder head cover and move the harness to one side.

16 Undo the bolts securing the cylinder head cover to the camshaft carrier and collect the washers. Carefully lift off the cover taking care not to damage the camshaft position sensor as the cover is removed. Recover the seal from the cover.

Refitting

17 Refitting is a reversal of removal, bearing in mind the following points:

a) *Examine the cover seal for signs of damage and deterioration, and renew if necessary.*

b) *Tighten the cylinder head cover bolts to the specified torque.*

c) *Before refitting the timing belt upper*

cover, adjust the camshaft position sensor air gap as described in Chapter 4C, Section 13.

5 Crankshaft pulley – removal and refitting

1.9 litre engines

Removal

1 Remove the auxiliary drivebelt as described in Chapter 1B.

2 Undo the four crankshaft pulley retaining bolts and remove the pulley, noting which way round it is fitted.

Refitting

3 Refitting is a reversal of removal, but tighten the pulley retaining bolts to the specified torque.

2.0 litre engines

Removal

4 Remove the auxiliary drivebelt as described in Chapter 1B.

5 To prevent crankshaft turning whilst the pulley retaining bolt is being slackened, select top gear and have an assistant apply the brakes firmly. Alternatively, the flywheel ring gear can be locked using a suitable tool made from steel angle **(see illustration)**. Remove

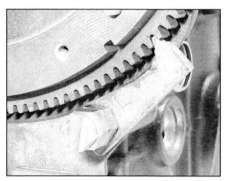

5.5 Use a fabricated tool similar to this to lock the flywheel ring gear and prevent crankshaft rotation

the cover plate from the base of the transmission bellhousing and bolt the tool to the bellhousing flange so it engages with the ring gear teeth. *Do not* attempt to lock the pulley by inserting a bolt/drill through the timing hole. If the timing hole bolt/drill is in position, from a previous operation, temporarily remove it prior to slackening the pulley bolt, then refit it once the bolt has been slackened.

6 Using a suitable socket and extension bar, unscrew the retaining bolt, remove the washer, then slide the pulley off the end of the crankshaft **(see illustration)**. If the pulley is tight fit, it can be drawn off the crankshaft using a suitable puller. If a puller is being used, refit the pulley retaining bolt without the washer, to avoid damaging the crankshaft as the puller is tightened.

7 If the pulley locating Woodruff key is a loose fit, remove it and store it with the pulley for safe-keeping.

Refitting

8 Ensure that the Woodruff key is correctly located in its crankshaft groove, then refit the pulley to the end of the crankshaft.

9 Thoroughly clean the threads of the pulley retaining bolt, then apply a coat of locking compound to the bolt threads. Citroën recommend the use of Loctite (available from your Citroën dealer); in the absence of this, any good-quality locking compound may be used.

10 Refit the crankshaft pulley retaining bolt and washer. Tighten the bolt to the specified torque, then through the specified angle, preventing the crankshaft from turning using the method employed on removal **(see illustrations)**.

11 Refit and tension the auxiliary drivebelt as described in Chapter 1B.

6 Timing belt covers – removal and refitting

1.9 litre engines

Upper cover – removal

1 Disconnect the battery negative terminal (refer to *Disconnecting the battery* in the Reference Section of this manual).

2 Release the clip in the centre of the engine cover and undo the retaining screw on the right-hand side. Remove the engine oil dipstick then lift the cover off the engine.

3 Disconnect the fuel supply and return hose quick-release fittings using a small screwdriver to release the locking clip. Cover the open unions to prevent dirt entry, using small plastic bags, or fingers cut from clean rubber gloves. Release the two hoses from the retaining clips on the upper timing belt cover and move them to one side.

4 Undo the bolt securing the upper cover to the cylinder head cover **(see illustration)**.

5.6 Removing the crankshaft pulley – 2.0 litre engines

5.10a Refit the crankshaft pulley retaining bolt after applying locking compound to the threads – 2.0 litre engines

5.10b Tighten the pulley bolt to the specified Stage 1 torque . . .

5.10c . . . then through the specified Stage 2 angle – 2.0 litre engines

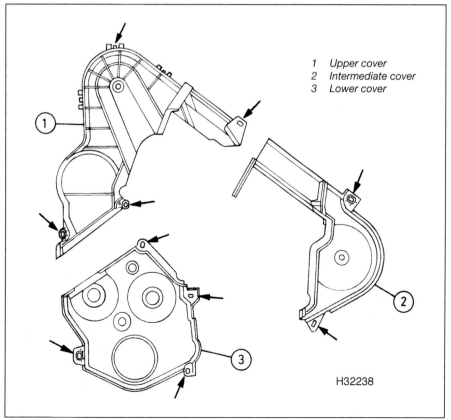

1 Upper cover
2 Intermediate cover
3 Lower cover

H32238

6.4 Timing belt cover retaining bolt locations (arrowed) – 1.9 litre engines

6.17 Disconnect the fuel supply and return hose quick-release fittings – 2.0 litre engines

6.18 Release the two fuel hoses from the retaining clips on the timing belt upper cover – 2.0 litre engines

5 Undo the two bolts at the joint between the upper cover and lower cover; one in the centre just below the engine mounting bracket, and one on the outer edge. Note that the bolt on the outer edge also retains the coolant pump. To avoid coolant leakage, after the cover is removed, refit the bolt fitted with a 5.0 mm spacer, and tighten it securely.
6 Undo the remaining bolt directly above the injection pump sprocket.
7 Release the locating lugs, ease the upper section out from behind the intermediate cover and manipulate the upper cover from its location.

Intermediate cover – removal

8 Remove the upper cover as described previously.
9 Undo the remaining bolt at the base of the cover just below the engine mounting bracket.
10 Release the locating lugs and manipulate the intermediate cover from its location.

Lower cover – removal

11 Remove the upper and intermediate covers as described previously.
12 Remove the crankshaft pulley as described in Section 5.
13 Undo the two remaining bolts on the edge of the cover, one on either side of the crankshaft pulley location.
14 Lift the cover off the front of the engine.

Refitting

15 Refitting of all the covers is a reversal of

the relevant removal procedure, ensuring that each cover section is correctly located, and that the cover retaining bolts are securely tightened. Ensure that all disturbed hoses are reconnected and retained by their relevant clips. On completion, prime and bleed the fuel system as described in Chapter 4B.

2.0 litre engines

⚠️ **Warning: Refer to the precautionary information contained in Section 1 before proceeding.**

Upper cover – removal

16 Disconnect the battery negative terminal (refer to *Disconnecting the battery* in the Reference Section of this manual).
17 At the connections above the fuel pump, disconnect the fuel supply and return hose quick-release fittings using a small screwdriver to release the locking clip **(see illustration)**. Cover the open unions to prevent dirt entry, using small plastic bags, or fingers cut from clean rubber gloves.
18 Release the two hoses from the retaining clips on the upper timing belt cover and move them to one side **(see illustration)**.
19 Release the EGR solenoid valve vacuum hose from the clip on the upper cover.
20 Undo the bolt securing the upper cover to the cylinder head cover.
21 Undo the upper bolt on the edge of the cover nearest to the engine compartment bulkhead.

22 Undo the lower bolt on the bulkhead side of the cover, at the join between the upper and lower covers. Note that this bolt also retains the coolant pump. To avoid coolant leakage, after the upper cover is removed, refit the bolt fitted with a 17.0 mm spacer, and tighten it securely.
23 Undo the remaining bolt in the centre of the cover, just above the engine mounting bracket.
24 Disengage the upper cover from the intermediate cover and manipulate the upper cover from its location **(see illustration)**.

Intermediate cover – removal

25 Remove the upper cover as described previously.
26 Undo the upper bolt on the top edge of the intermediate cover.
27 Undo the two remaining bolts at the join between the intermediate cover and lower cover, then manipulate the intermediate cover from its location **(see illustration)**.

Lower cover – removal

28 Remove the upper and intermediate covers as described previously.
29 Remove the crankshaft pulley as described in Section 5.
30 Undo the two remaining bolts on the edge of the cover, one on either side of the crankshaft pulley location.
31 Lift the cover off the front of the engine **(see illustration)**.

Refitting

32 Refitting of all the covers is a reversal of the relevant removal procedure, ensuring that each cover section is correctly located, and that the cover retaining bolts are securely tightened. Ensure that all disturbed hoses are reconnected and retained by their relevant clips.

---

7 Timing belt (1.9 litre engines) – removal, inspection, refitting and tensioning 🔧

Note: *Citroën specify the use of an electronic belt tension checking tool (SEEM 4122-T) to correctly set the timing belt tension. The*

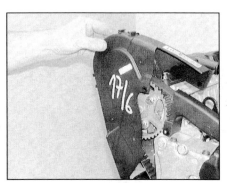

6.24 Removing the timing belt upper cover . . .

6.27 . . . intermediate cover . . .

6.31 . . . and lower cover – 2.0 litre engines

following procedure assumes that this equipment (or suitable alternative equipment calibrated to display belt tension in SEEM units) is available. Accurate tensioning of the timing belt is essential, and if the electronic equipment is not available, it is recommended that the work is entrusted to a Citroën dealer or suitably-equipped garage.

General

1 The timing belt drives the camshaft, injection pump, and coolant pump from a toothed sprocket on the right-hand end of the crankshaft. The belt also drives the brake vacuum pump indirectly via the rear ('flywheel') end of the camshaft. If the belt breaks or slips in service, the pistons are likely to hit the valve heads, resulting in expensive damage.

2 The timing belt should be renewed at the specified intervals, or earlier if it is contaminated with oil, or at all noisy in operation (a 'scraping' noise due to uneven wear).

3 If the timing belt is being removed, it is a wise precaution to check the condition of the coolant pump at the same time (check for signs of coolant leakage). This may avoid the need to remove the timing belt again at a later stage, should the coolant pump fail.

Removal

4 Remove the upper, intermediate and lower timing belt covers as described in Section 6.

5 Align the engine assembly/valve timing holes as described in Section 3, and lock the camshaft sprocket hub, injection pump hub, and flywheel in position. *Do not* attempt to rotate the engine whilst the pins are in position.

6 Remove the right-hand engine mounting as described in Section 18.

7 Slacken the three bolts securing the camshaft sprocket to the sprocket hub **(see illustration)**.

8 Similarly slacken the three bolts securing the injection pump sprocket to the pump hub.

9 Loosen the timing belt tensioner pulley retaining bolt. Allow the pulley to pivot in a clockwise direction, to relieve the tension from the timing belt. Retighten the tensioner pulley retaining bolt to secure it in the slackened position.

10 If the timing belt is to be re-used, use white paint or chalk to mark the direction of rotation on the belt (if markings do not already exist), then slip the belt off the sprockets. Note that the crankshaft must not be rotated whilst the belt is removed.

Inspection

11 Check the timing belt carefully for any signs of uneven wear, split or oil contamination. Pay particular attention to the roots of the teeth. Renew it if there is the slightest doubt about its condition. If the engine is undergoing an overhaul, and has covered more than 40 000 miles (60 000 km)

with the existing belt fitted, renew the belt as a matter of course, regardless of its apparent condition. The cost of a new belt is nothing compared with the cost of repairs, should the belt break in service. If signs of oil contamination are found, trace the source of the oil leak and rectify it. Wash down the engine timing belt area and all related components, to remove all traces of oil. Check that the tensioner pulley and idler roller rotate freely, without any sign of roughness. If necessary, renew as described in Section 9.

Refitting

12 Commence refitting by ensuring that the engine assembly/valve timing holes are still aligned as described in Section 3, and the camshaft sprocket hub, injection pump hub, and flywheel are locked in position.

13 Tighten the camshaft sprocket and injection pump sprocket retaining bolts lightly so that the sprockets can still move within

their elongated slots. Turn both sprockets fully anti-clockwise to the ends of the slots.

14 Locate the timing belt on the crankshaft sprocket, making sure that, where applicable, the direction of rotation arrow is facing the correct way.

15 Retain the timing belt on the crankshaft sprocket, then feed the belt over the remaining sprockets in the following order:
  a) Idler roller.
  b) Fuel injection pump.
  c) Camshaft.
  e) Coolant pump.
  f) Tensioner pulley.

Tensioning

16 Fit the sensor head of the electronic belt tension measuring equipment to the 'top run' of the timing belt, approximately midway between the camshaft and injection pump sprockets.

17 Slacken the tensioner pulley retaining bolt

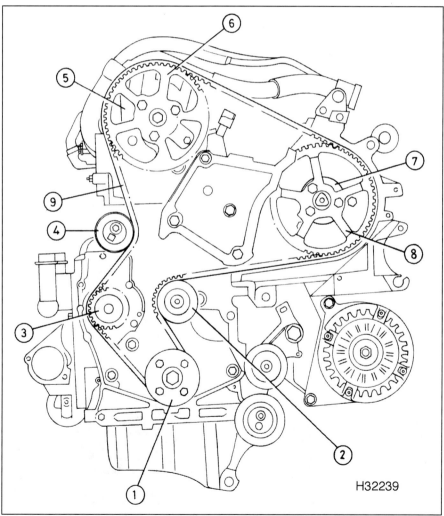

7.7 Timing belt, sprocket and tensioner details – 1.9 litre engines

1 Crankshaft sprocket	5 Camshaft sprocket hub	8 Injection pump
2 Idler roller	6 Camshaft sprocket	sprocket
3 Coolant pump sprocket	7 Injection pump sprocket	9 Timing belt
4 Tensioner pulley	hub	

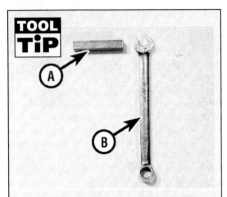

TOOL TIP

A square section tool to fit the timing belt tensioner pulley can be made from a length of standard 8 mm door handle rod (A), obtained from a DIY shop, and then cut to size. Once the rod has been fitted to the tensioner, the timing belt can be tensioned by turning the rod with an 8 mm spanner (B).

and insert a short length of 8.0 mm square bar into the square hole on the front face of the tensioner pulley. The bar can then be used to turn the pulley and tension the belt **(see Tool Tip)**. Alternatively, although clearance is restricted, the square end of a 1/4 inch drive socket bar can also be used.

18 Using the square bar and a spanner, pivot the tensioner pulley anti-clockwise until an initial setting of 106 ± 2 SEEM units is displayed on the tension measuring equipment. Hold the tensioner pulley in that position and retighten the retaining bolt.

19 Check that the sprockets have not been turned so far that the retaining bolts are at the end of their slots. If this is the case, repeat the refitting operation. If all is satisfactory, tighten the camshaft and injection pump sprocket retaining bolts to the specified torque.

20 Remove the belt tension measuring equipment and the crankshaft, camshaft sprocket hub and injection pump hub locking tools.

21 Rotate the crankshaft through eight complete rotations in a clockwise direction (viewed from the right-hand end of the engine). Realign the engine assembly/valve timing holes and refit the crankshaft, camshaft and injection pump locking tools.

22 Slacken the camshaft and injection pump sprocket retaining bolts, retighten them finger-tight, then slacken them all by one sixth of a turn.

23 Slacken the tensioner pulley retaining bolt once more. Refit the belt tension measuring equipment to the top run of the belt, and turn the tensioner pulley to give a final setting of 42 ± 2 SEEM units on the tensioning gauge. Hold the tensioner pulley in this position and tighten the retaining bolt to the specified torque.

24 Retighten all sprocket retaining bolts to the specified torque.

25 Release the sensor head of the belt

tension measuring equipment, then refit it again and check that a reading of between 38 and 46 SEEM units is indicated. Remove the tension measuring equipment.

26 Remove the locking tools, then rotate the crankshaft once again through two complete rotations in a clockwise direction. Realign the engine assembly/valve timing holes and refit the crankshaft locking tool.

27 Check that it is possible to insert the camshaft sprocket hub and injection pump hub locking tools. If the tools cannot be inserted, check that the offset between the timing holes in the sprocket hubs and the corresponding holes in the cylinder head and injection pump is not greater than 1.0 mm. If it is, repeat the complete timing belt refitting and tensioning procedure.

28 Refit the right-hand engine mounting as described in Section 18.

29 Refit the lower, intermediate and upper timing belt covers as described in Section 6.

30 Refit the crankshaft pulley as described in Section 5.

8 Timing belt (2.0 litre engines) – removal, inspection, refitting and tensioning

Note: *Citroën specify the use of an electronic belt tension checking tool (SEEM 4122-T) to correctly set the timing belt tension. The following procedure assumes that this equipment (or suitable alternative equipment calibrated to display belt tension in SEEM units) is available. Accurate tensioning of the timing belt is essential, and if the electronic equipment is not available, it is recommended that the work is entrusted to a Citroën dealer or suitably-equipped garage.*

General

1 The timing belt drives the camshaft, high pressure fuel pump, and coolant pump from a toothed sprocket on the right-hand end of the crankshaft. The belt also drives the brake vacuum pump indirectly via the rear ('flywheel') end of the camshaft. If the belt breaks or slips in service, the pistons are likely to hit the valve heads, resulting in expensive damage.

2 The timing belt should be renewed at the specified intervals, or earlier if it is contaminated with oil, or at all noisy in operation (a 'scraping' noise due to uneven wear).

3 If the timing belt is being removed, it is a wise precaution to check the condition of the coolant pump at the same time (check for signs of coolant leakage). This may avoid the need to remove the timing belt again at a later stage, should the coolant pump fail.

Removal

4 Remove the crankshaft pulley as described in Section 5. Refit the pulley retaining bolt to allow the engine to be turned in subsequent operations.

5 Remove the upper, intermediate and lower timing belt covers as described in Section 6.

6 Align the engine assembly/valve timing holes as described in Section 3, and lock the flywheel and camshaft sprocket in position. *Do not* attempt to rotate the engine whilst the locking pins are in position.

7 Remove the right-hand engine mounting as described in Section 18.

8 Slacken the three bolts securing the camshaft sprocket to the sprocket hub **(see illustration)**.

9 Loosen the timing belt tensioner pulley retaining bolt. Allow the pulley to pivot in a clockwise direction, to relieve the tension from the timing belt. Retighten the tensioner pulley retaining bolt to secure it in the slackened position.

10 If the timing belt is to be re-used, use white paint or chalk to mark the direction of rotation on the belt (if markings do not already exist), then slip the belt off the sprockets **(see illustration)**. Note that the crankshaft must not be rotated whilst the belt is removed.

Inspection

11 Refer to Section 7, paragraph 11.

Refitting

12 Commence refitting by ensuring that the engine assembly/valve timing holes are still aligned as described in Section 3, and the flywheel, and camshaft sprocket hub are locked in position.

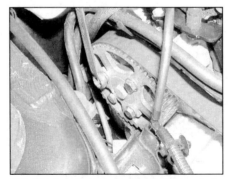

8.8 Slacken the three camshaft sprocket-to-sprocket hub retaining bolts – 2.0 litre engines

8.10 Removing the timing belt – 2.0 litre engines

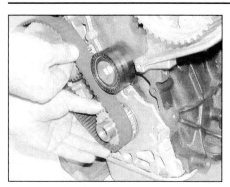

8.15a Retain the timing belt on the crankshaft sprocket and feed it around the idler roller . . .

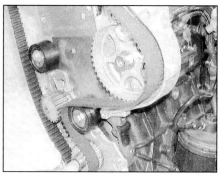

8.15b . . . high pressure fuel pump sprocket . . .

8.15c . . . camshaft sprocket . . .

13 Tighten the camshaft sprocket retaining bolts lightly so that the sprocket can still move within the elongated slots. Turn the sprocket fully clockwise to the ends of the slots.

14 Locate the timing belt on the crankshaft sprocket, making sure that, where applicable, the direction of rotation arrow is facing the correct way.

15 Retain the timing belt on the crankshaft sprocket, then feed the belt over the remaining sprockets in the following order **(see illustrations)**:
  a) Idler roller.
  b) High pressure fuel pump.
  c) Camshaft.
  e) Coolant pump.
  f) Tensioner pulley.

Tensioning

16 Fit the sensor head of the electronic belt tension measuring equipment to the 'top run' of the timing belt, approximately midway between the camshaft and injection pump sprockets.

17 Slacken the tensioner pulley retaining bolt and insert a short length of 8.0 mm square bar into the square hole on the front face of the tensioner pulley. The bar can then be used to turn the pulley and tension the belt (see **Tool Tip** in Section 7). Alternatively, although clearance is restricted, the square end of a 1/4 inch drive socket bar can also be used.

18 Using the square bar and a spanner, pivot the tensioner pulley anti-clockwise until an initial setting of 98 ± 2 SEEM units is displayed on the tension measuring equipment **(see illustrations)**. Hold the tensioner pulley in that position and retighten the retaining bolt.

19 Check that the camshaft sprocket retaining bolts are not at the ends of their slots (if necessary, remove one of the sprocket bolts to check this). If they are, repeat the refitting operation. If all is satisfactory, refit the removed bolt and tighten all three sprocket retaining bolts to the specified torque.

20 Remove the belt tension measuring equipment and the crankshaft and camshaft sprocket hub locking tools.

21 Rotate the crankshaft through eight complete rotations in a clockwise direction (viewed from the right-hand end of the engine). Realign the engine assembly/valve timing holes and refit the crankshaft locking tool.

22 Slacken the camshaft sprocket retaining bolts, retighten them finger-tight, then slacken them all by one sixth of a turn.

23 Refit the camshaft sprocket hub locking tool.

24 Slacken the tensioner pulley retaining bolt once more. Refit the belt tension measuring equipment to the top run of the belt, and turn the tensioner pulley to give a final setting of

54 ± 2 SEEM units on the tensioning gauge. Hold the tensioner pulley in this position and tighten the retaining bolt to the specified torque.

25 Retighten the camshaft sprocket retaining bolts to the specified torque.

26 Release the sensor head of the belt tension measuring equipment, then refit it again and check that a reading of 54 ± 3 SEEM units is indicated. Remove the tension measuring equipment.

27 Remove the locking tools, then rotate the crankshaft once again through two complete rotations in a clockwise direction. Realign the engine assembly/valve timing holes and refit the crankshaft locking tool.

28 Check that it is possible to insert the camshaft sprocket hub locking tool. If the tool cannot be inserted, check that the offset between the timing slot in the sprocket hub and the corresponding hole in the cylinder head is not greater than 1.0 mm. If it is, repeat the complete timing belt refitting and tensioning procedure.

29 Refit the right-hand engine mounting as described in Section 18.

30 Refit the lower, intermediate and upper timing belt covers as described in Section 6.

31 Refit the crankshaft pulley as described in Section 5.

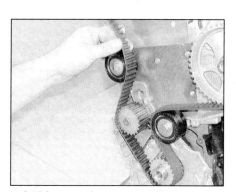

8.15d . . . coolant pump and tensioner pulley – 2.0 litre engines

8.18a Pivot the tensioner pulley anti-clockwise, then tighten the retaining bolt . . .

8.18b . . . when the specified tension value is shown on the tensioning measuring equipment – 2.0 litre engines

9 Timing belt sprockets and tensioner – removal and refitting

Camshaft sprocket

Removal

1 Remove the crankshaft pulley as described in Section 5. On 2.0 litre engines, refit the pulley retaining bolt to allow the engine to be turned in subsequent operations.

2 Remove the upper, intermediate and lower timing belt covers as described in Section 6.

3 Align the engine assembly/valve timing holes as described in Section 3, and lock the camshaft sprocket hub, injection pump sprocket hub (1.9 litre engines) and flywheel in position.

4 Loosen the timing belt tensioner pulley retaining bolt. Allow the pulley to pivot in a clockwise direction, to relieve the tension from the timing belt. Retighten the tensioner pulley retaining bolt to secure it in the slackened position.

5 Disengage the timing belt from the camshaft sprocket and position it clear, taking care not to bend or twist the belt sharply.

6 Remove the locking tool from the camshaft sprocket hub. Slacken the sprocket hub retaining bolt, and the three sprocket-to-hub retaining bolts. To prevent the camshaft rotating as the bolts are slackened, a sprocket holding tool will be required. In the absence of the special Citroën tool, an acceptable substitute can be fabricated at home **(see Tool Tip 1)**. *Do not* attempt to use the engine assembly/valve timing locking tool to prevent the sprocket from rotating whilst the bolt is slackened.

7 Remove the sprocket hub retaining bolt and washer, and slide the sprocket and hub off the end of the camshaft. If the Woodruff key is a loose fit in the camshaft, remove it for safekeeping. Examine the camshaft oil seal for signs of oil leakage and, if necessary, renew it as described in Section 16.

8 If necessary, the sprocket can be separated from the hub after removing the three retaining bolts.

9 Clean the camshaft sprocket thoroughly, and renew it if there are any signs of wear, damage or cracks.

Refitting

10 If removed, refit the sprocket to the hub and secure with the three retaining bolts, tightened finger tight only at this stage.

11 Where applicable, refit the Woodruff key to the end of the camshaft, then refit the camshaft sprocket and hub.

12 Refit the sprocket hub retaining bolt and washer. Tighten the bolt to the specified torque, preventing the camshaft from turning as during removal.

13 Align the engine assembly/valve timing

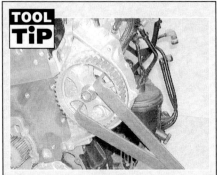

Tool Tip 1: A sprocket holding tool can be made from two lengths of steel strip bolted together to form a forked end. Bend the ends of the strip through 90° to form the fork 'prongs'.

slot in the camshaft sprocket hub with the hole in the cylinder head and refit the 8 mm bolt to lock the camshaft in position.

14 Fit the timing belt around the pump sprocket and camshaft sprocket, and tension the timing belt as described in Sections 7 or 8, as applicable.

Crankshaft sprocket – 1.9 litre engines

Removal

15 Remove the timing belt upper, intermediate and lower covers as described in Section 6.

16 Align the engine assembly/valve timing holes as described in Section 3, but do not lock the camshaft sprocket hub, injection pump sprocket hub or flywheel in position at this stage.

17 Using a suitable socket and extension bar, slacken the crankshaft sprocket retaining bolt. To prevent crankshaft turning whilst the sprocket retaining bolt is being slackened, select top gear and have an assistant apply the brakes firmly. Alternatively, the flywheel ring gear can be locked using a suitable tool made from steel angle **(see illustration 5.5)**. Remove the cover plate from the base of the transmission bellhousing and bolt the tool to the bellhousing flange so it engages with the ring gear teeth.

18 Check that the engine assembly/valve timing holes are still aligned as described in Section 3, and lock the camshaft sprocket hub, injection pump sprocket hub, and flywheel in position.

19 Loosen the timing belt tensioner pulley retaining bolt. Allow the pulley to pivot in a clockwise direction, to relieve the tension from the timing belt. Retighten the tensioner pulley retaining bolt to secure it in the slackened position.

20 Disengage the timing belt from the crankshaft sprocket and position it clear, taking care not to bend or twist the belt sharply.

21 Unscrew the previously slackened crankshaft sprocket retaining bolt and remove the washer. Slide the sprocket off the end of the crankshaft and collect the Woodruff key.

22 Examine the crankshaft oil seal for signs of oil leakage and, if necessary, renew it as described in Section 16.

23 Clean the crankshaft sprocket thoroughly, and renew it if there are any signs of wear, damage or cracks.

Refitting

24 Refit the Woodruff key to the end of the crankshaft, then refit the crankshaft sprocket.

25 Temporarily remove the engine assembly/valve timing hole locking tools.

26 Thoroughly clean the threads of the sprocket retaining bolt, then apply a coat of locking compound to the bolt threads. Citroën recommend the use of Loctite (available from your Citroën dealer); in the absence of this, any good-quality locking compound may be used.

27 Refit the sprocket retaining bolt and washer. Tighten the bolt to the specified torque, then through the specified angle, preventing the crankshaft from turning using the method employed on removal.

28 Check that the engine assembly/valve timing holes are still aligned as described in Section 3, and again lock the camshaft sprocket hub, injection pump sprocket hub and flywheel in position.

29 Fit the timing belt around the crankshaft sprocket, and tension the timing belt as described in Section 7.

Crankshaft sprocket – 2.0 litre engines

Removal

30 Align the engine assembly/valve timing holes as described in Section 3, but do not lock the camshaft sprocket hub or flywheel in position at this stage.

31 Remove the crankshaft pulley as described in Section 5. Refit the pulley retaining bolt to allow the engine to be turned in subsequent operations.

32 Remove the timing belt upper, intermediate and lower covers as described in Section 6.

33 Check that the engine assembly/valve timing holes are still aligned as described in Section 3, and lock the camshaft sprocket hub and flywheel in position.

34 Loosen the timing belt tensioner pulley retaining bolt. Allow the pulley to pivot in a clockwise direction, to relieve the tension from the timing belt. Retighten the tensioner pulley retaining bolt to secure it in the slackened position.

35 Disengage the timing belt from the crankshaft sprocket and position it clear, taking care not to bend or twist the belt sharply.

36 Slide the sprocket off the end of the

9.36a Slide the crankshaft sprocket off the end of the crankshaft . . .

9.36b . . . and collect the Woodruff key – 2.0 litre engines

Tool Tip 2: Make a sprocket releasing tool from a short strip of steel. Drill two holes in the strip to correspond with the two holes in the sprocket. Drill a third hole just large enough to accept the flats of the sprocket retaining nut.

crankshaft and collect the Woodruff key **(see illustrations)**.

37 Examine the crankshaft oil seal for signs of oil leakage and, if necessary, renew it as described in Section 16.

38 Clean the crankshaft sprocket thoroughly, and renew it if there are any signs of wear, damage or cracks.

Refitting

39 Refit the Woodruff key to the end of the crankshaft, then refit the crankshaft sprocket (with the flange nearest the cylinder block).

40 Fit the timing belt around the crankshaft sprocket, and tension the timing belt as described in Section 8.

Fuel injection pump sprocket – 1.9 litre engines

Removal

41 Remove the upper, intermediate and lower timing belt covers as described in Section 6.

42 Align the engine assembly/valve timing holes as described in Section 3, and lock the camshaft sprocket hub, injection pump sprocket hub and flywheel in position.

43 Loosen the timing belt tensioner pulley retaining bolt. Allow the pulley to pivot in a clockwise direction, to relieve the tension from the timing belt. Retighten the tensioner pulley retaining bolt to secure it in the slackened position.

44 Disengage the timing belt from the injection pump sprocket and position it clear, taking care not to bend or twist the belt sharply.

45 Unscrew and remove the three bolts securing the injection pump sprocket to the pump hub and remove the sprocket.

46 Clean the sprocket thoroughly, and renew it if there are any signs of wear, damage or cracks.

Refitting

47 Position the injection pump sprocket on the hub and refit the three retaining bolts. Tighten the bolts hand tight only at this stage.

48 Fit the timing belt around the injection pump sprocket, and tension the timing belt as described in Section 7.

High pressure fuel pump sprocket – 2.0 litre engines

Removal

49 Remove the crankshaft pulley as described in Section 5. Refit the pulley retaining bolt to allow the engine to be turned in subsequent operations.

50 Remove the upper, intermediate and lower timing belt covers as described in Section 6.

51 Align the engine assembly/valve timing holes as described in Section 3, and lock the camshaft sprocket hub and flywheel in position.

52 Loosen the timing belt tensioner pulley retaining bolt. Allow the pulley to pivot in a clockwise direction, to relieve the tension from the timing belt. Retighten the tensioner pulley retaining bolt to secure it in the slackened position.

53 Disengage the timing belt from the high pressure fuel pump sprocket and position it clear, taking care not to bend or twist the belt sharply.

54 Using a suitable socket, undo the pump sprocket retaining nut. The sprocket can be held stationary as the nut is slackened using a suitable forked tool engaged with the holes in the sprocket **(see Tool Tip 1)**.

55 The pump sprocket is a taper fit on the pump shaft and it will be necessary to make up another tool to release it from the taper **(see Tool Tip 2)**.

9.56 Using the home-made tools to remove the fuel pump sprocket – 2.0 litre engines

56 Partially unscrew the sprocket retaining nut, fit the home-made tool, and secure it to the sprocket with two suitable bolts. Prevent the sprocket from rotating as before, and unscrew the sprocket retaining nut **(see illustration)**. The nut will bear against the tool as it is undone, forcing the sprocket off the shaft taper. Once the taper is released, remove the tool, unscrew the nut fully, and remove the sprocket from the pump shaft.

57 Clean the sprocket thoroughly, and renew it if there are any signs of wear, damage or cracks.

Refitting

58 Refit the pump sprocket and retaining nut, and tighten the nut to the specified torque. Prevent the sprocket rotating as the nut is tightened using the sprocket holding tool.

59 Fit the timing belt around the pump sprocket, and tension the timing belt as described in Section 8.

Coolant pump sprocket

60 The coolant pump sprocket is integral with the pump, and cannot be removed.

Tensioner pulley

Removal

61 Remove the upper and intermediate timing belt covers as described in Section 6.

62 Align the engine assembly/valve timing holes as described in Section 3, and lock the camshaft sprocket hub, injection pump sprocket hub (1.9 litre engines) and flywheel in position.

63 Loosen the timing belt tensioner pulley retaining bolt. Allow the pulley to pivot in a clockwise direction, to relieve the tension from the timing belt.

64 Remove the tensioner pulley retaining bolt, and slide the pulley off its mounting stud.

65 Clean the tensioner pulley, but do not use any strong solvent which may enter the pulley bearings. Check that the pulley rotates freely, with no sign of stiffness or free play. Renew the pulley if there is any doubt about its condition, or if there are any obvious signs of wear or damage.

66 Examine the pulley mounting stud for signs of damage and if necessary, renew it.

Refitting

67 Refit the tensioner pulley to its mounting stud, and fit the retaining bolt.

68 Fit the timing belt around the pulley, and tension the timing belt as described in Sections 7 or 8, as applicable.

Idler roller

Removal

69 Remove the crankshaft pulley as described in Section 5. On 2.0 litre engines, refit the pulley retaining bolt to allow the engine to be turned in subsequent operations.

70 Remove the upper, intermediate and lower timing belt covers as described in Section 6.

71 Align the engine assembly/valve timing holes as described in Section 3, and lock the camshaft sprocket hub, injection pump sprocket hub (1.9 litre engines) and flywheel in position.

72 Loosen the timing belt tensioner pulley retaining bolt. Allow the pulley to pivot in a clockwise direction, to relieve the tension from the timing belt. Retighten the tensioner pulley retaining bolt to secure it in the slackened position.

73 Undo the retaining bolt and withdraw the idler roller from the engine.

74 Clean the idler roller, but do not use any strong solvent which may enter the bearings. Check that the roller rotates freely, with no sign of stiffness or free play. Renew the idler roller if there is any doubt about its condition, or if there are any obvious signs of wear or damage.

Refitting

75 Locate the idler roller on the engine, and fit the retaining bolt. Tighten the bolt to the specified torque.

76 Fit the timing belt around the idler roller, and tension the timing belt as described in Sections 7 or 8, as applicable.

10 Camshaft and followers (1.9 litre engines) – removal and refitting

Removal

1 Remove the cylinder head cover as described in Section 4.

2 Remove the camshaft sprocket as described in Section 9.

3 Remove the braking system vacuum pump as described in Chapter 9.

4 The camshaft bearing caps should be numbered from the flywheel end of the engine **(see illustration)**. If the caps are not already numbered, identify them, numbering them

from the flywheel end of the engine, and making the marks on the manifold side.

5 Progressively unscrew the nuts, then remove the bearing caps.

6 Lift the camshaft from the cylinder head. Remove the oil seal from the timing belt end of the camshaft. Discard the seal, a new one should be used on refitting.

7 Obtain eight small, clean plastic containers, and number them 1 to 8; alternatively, divide a larger container into eight compartments. Using a rubber sucker, withdraw each follower in turn, and place it in its respective container. Do not interchange the cam followers, or the rate of wear will be much increased. If necessary, also remove the shim from the top of the valve stem, and store it with its respective follower. Note that the shim may stick to the inside of the follower as it is withdrawn. If this happens, take care not to allow it to drop out as the follower is removed.

Inspection

8 Examine the camshaft bearing surfaces and cam lobes for signs of wear ridges and scoring. Renew the camshaft if any of these conditions are apparent. Examine the condition of the bearing surfaces, both on the camshaft journals and in the cylinder head/bearing caps. If the head bearing surfaces are worn excessively, the cylinder head will need to be renewed.

9 Examine the cam follower bearing surfaces which contact the camshaft lobes for wear ridges and scoring. Renew any follower on which these conditions are apparent. If a follower bearing surface is badly scored, also examine the corresponding lobe on the camshaft for wear, as it is likely that both will be worn. Renew worn components as necessary.

Refitting

10 To prevent any possibility of the valves contacting the pistons as the camshaft is refitted, remove the locking rod/drill from the flywheel and turn the crankshaft a quarter turn in the *opposite* direction to normal rotation, to position all the pistons at mid-stroke. Release the timing belt from the injection pump sprocket while turning the crankshaft.

11 Where removed, refit each shim to the top of its original valve stem. *Do not* interchange the shims, as this will upset the valve clearances.

12 Liberally oil the cylinder head cam follower bores and the followers. Carefully refit the followers to the cylinder head, ensuring that each follower is refitted to its original bore. Some care will be required to enter the followers squarely into their bores.

13 Lubricate the cam lobes and bearing journals with clean engine oil of the specified grade.

14 Position the camshaft in the cylinder head.

15 Temporarily locate the sprocket on the end of the camshaft, and turn the shaft so that the sprocket hub timing slot is aligned with the corresponding cut-out in the cylinder head. Remove the sprocket.

16 Fit the centre bearing cap the correct way round as previously noted, then screw on the nuts and tighten them two or three turns.

17 Apply sealing compound to the end bearing caps on the areas shown **(see illustration)**. Fit them in the correct positions, and tighten the nuts two or three turns.

18 Tighten all the nuts progressively to the specified torque, making sure that the camshaft remains correctly positioned.

19 Check that the camshaft endfloat is as given in the Specifications, using a feeler blade. If not, the camshaft and/or the cylinder head must be renewed. To check the endfloat, push the camshaft fully towards one end of the cylinder head, and insert a feeler blade between the thrust faces of one of the camshaft lobes and a bearing cap.

20 If the original camshaft is being refitted, and it is known that the valve clearances are correct, proceed to the next paragraph. Otherwise, check and adjust the valve clearances as described in Section 12.

21 Smear the lips of the new oil seal with clean engine oil and fit it onto the camshaft end, making sure its sealing lip is facing inwards. Press the oil seal in until it is flush with the end face of the camshaft bearing cap.

22 Refit the braking system vacuum pump as described in Chapter 9.

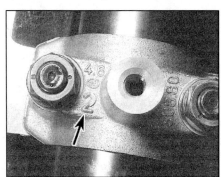

10.4 Camshaft bearing cap identification mark (arrowed) – 1.9 litre engines

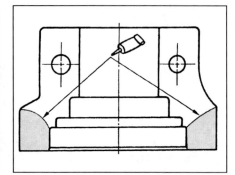

10.17 Apply sealing compound to the end camshaft bearing caps on the areas shown – 1.9 litre engines

23 Again, temporarily locate the sprocket on the end of the camshaft, and make sure that the sprocket hub timing slot is aligned with the corresponding cut-out in the cylinder head.
24 Turn the crankshaft a quarter turn in the normal direction of rotation so that pistons 1 and 4 are again at TDC.
25 Refit the rod/drill to the flywheel timing hole.
26 Refit the camshaft sprocket as described in Section 9.
27 Refit the cylinder head cover as described in Section 4.

11 Camshaft, tappets and rocker arms (2.0 litre engines) – removal and refitting

Removal

1 Remove the cylinder head cover as described in Section 4.
2 Remove the camshaft sprocket as described in Section 9.
3 Remove the braking system vacuum pump as described in Chapter 9.
4 Progressively slacken the camshaft bearing housing retaining bolts, working in a spiral pattern in the reverse order to that shown in illustration 11.25. When all the bolts have been slackened, unscrew and remove them from their locations.
5 Carefully release the camshaft bearing housing from the cylinder head. The housing is likely to be initially tight to release as it is located by two dowels on the forward facing side of the cylinder head. If necessary, very carefully prise up the housing using a screwdriver inserted in the slotted lug adjacent to each dowel location.
6 Once the bearing housing is free, lift it squarely from the cylinder head **(see illustration)**. The camshaft will rise up slightly under the pressure of the valve springs – be careful it doesn't tilt and jam in the cylinder head or bearing housing section.
7 Lift the camshaft from the cylinder head and remove the oil seal **(see illustration)**. Discard the seal, a new one should be used on refitting.
8 Have ready a suitable box divided into eight

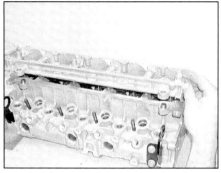

11.6 Remove the camshaft bearing housing from the cylinder head . . .

segments, or some containers or other means of storing and identifying the rocker arms and hydraulic tappets after removal. The box or containers for the hydraulic tappets must be oil tight and deep enough to allow the tappets to be almost totally submerged in oil. Mark the segments in the boxes or the containers with the number for each rocker arm and tappet (ie, 1 to 8).
9 Lift out each rocker arm and release it from the spring clip on the tappet. Place the rocker arms in their respective positions in the box or containers **(see illustration)**.
10 Similarly lift out the tappets and place them in their respective positions in the box or containers **(see illustrations)**. Once all the tappets have been removed, add clean engine oil to the box or container so that the tappet is submerged.

Inspection

11 Inspect the cam lobes and the camshaft bearing journals for scoring or other visible evidence of wear. Once the surface hardening of the cam lobes has been eroded, wear will occur at an accelerated rate. **Note:** *If these symptoms are visible on the tips of the camshaft lobes, check the corresponding rocker arm, as it will probably be worn as well.*
12 Examine the condition of the bearing surfaces in the cylinder head and camshaft bearing housing. If wear is evident, the cylinder head and bearing housing will both have to be renewed, as they are a matched assembly.

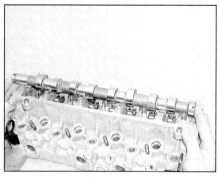

11.7 . . . then lift out the camshaft – 2.0 litre engines

13 Inspect the rocker arms and tappets for scuffing, cracking or other damage and renew any components as necessary. Also check the condition of the tappet bores in the cylinder head. As with the camshafts, any wear in this area will necessitate cylinder head renewal.

Refitting

14 Thoroughly clean the sealant from the mating surfaces of the cylinder head and camshaft bearing housing. Use a suitable liquid gasket dissolving agent (available from Citroën dealers) together with a soft putty knife; do not use a metal scraper or the faces will be damaged. As there is no conventional gasket used, the cleanliness of the mating faces is of the utmost importance.
15 Clean off any oil, dirt or grease from both components and dry with a clean lint-free cloth. Ensure that all the oilways are completely clean.
16 To prevent any possibility of the valves contacting the pistons as the camshaft is refitted, remove the locking rod/drill from the flywheel and turn the crankshaft a quarter turn in the *opposite* direction to normal rotation, to position all the pistons at mid-stroke.
17 Liberally lubricate the tappet bores in the cylinder head with clean engine oil.
18 Insert the tappets into their original bores in the cylinder head unless they have been renewed.
19 Lubricate the rocker arms and place them

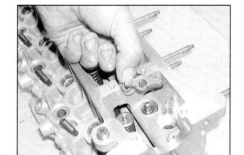

11.9 Lift out the rocker arms . . .

11.10a . . . followed by the hydraulic tappets . . .

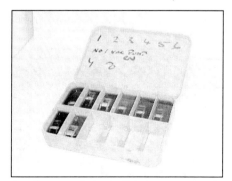

11.10b . . . and place all the components in their respective positions in a segmented box – 2.0 litre engines

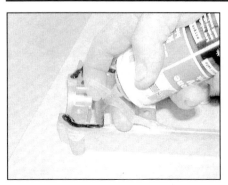

11.23 Apply a bead of silicone sealant to the mating face of the camshaft bearing housing – 2.0 litre engines

11.26a Locate a new oil seal over the camshaft, with its sealing lip facing inwards . . .

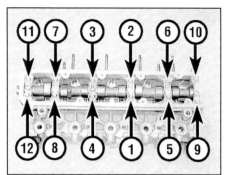

11.25 Camshaft bearing housing retaining bolt tightening sequence – 2.0 litre engines

11.26b . . . then use a bolt and socket or similar arrangement to press the seal into place – 2.0 litre engines

over their respective tappets and valve stems. Ensure that the ends of the rocker arms engage with the spring clips on the tappets.

20 Lubricate the camshaft bearing journals in the cylinder head sparingly with oil, taking care not to allow the oil to spill over onto the camshaft bearing housing contact areas.

21 Lay the camshaft in the cylinder head and temporarily locate the camshaft sprocket in position. Turn the camshaft so that the engine assembly/valve timing slot in the sprocket hub is approximately aligned with the timing hole in the cylinder head. Remove the sprocket.

22 Ensure that the mating faces of the cylinder head and camshaft bearing housing are clean and free of any oil or grease.

23 Sparingly apply a bead of silicone sealant to the mating face of the camshaft bearing housing, taking care not to allow the product to contaminate the camshaft bearing journal areas **(see illustration)**.

24 Locate the bearing housing over the camshaft and into position on the cylinder head.

25 Insert all the bearing housing retaining bolts and progressively tighten them to the specified torque, in the sequence shown **(see illustration)**.

26 Smear the lips of the new oil seal with clean engine oil and fit it over the camshaft, making sure its sealing lip is facing inwards. Press the seal into position until it is flush with the end face of the cylinder head. Use a suitable bolt (screwed into the end of the

camshaft), washers and a tube or socket to press the seal into position **(see illustrations)**.

27 Refit the braking system vacuum pump as described in Chapter 9.

28 Again, temporarily locate the sprocket on the end of the camshaft, and make sure that the sprocket hub timing slot is aligned with the corresponding cut-out in the cylinder head.

29 Turn the crankshaft a quarter turn in the normal direction of rotation so that pistons 1 and 4 are again at TDC.

30 Refit the rod/drill to the flywheel timing hole.

31 Refit the camshaft sprocket as described in Section 9.

32 Refit the cylinder head cover as described in Section 4.

12 Valve clearances (1.9 litre engines) – checking and adjustment

Checking

1 The importance of having the valve clearances correctly adjusted cannot be overstressed, as they vitally affect the performance of the engine. Checking should not be regarded as a routine operation, however. It should only be necessary when the valve gear has become noisy, after engine overhaul, or when trying to trace the cause of power loss. The clearances are checked as follows. The engine must be cold for the check to be accurate.

2 Remove the cylinder head cover as described in Section 4.

3 Chock the rear wheels then jack up the front of the car and support it on axle stands (see *Jacking and vehicle support*). Remove the right-hand front roadwheel.

4 From underneath the front of the car, remove the wheelarch plastic liner, which is secured by various screws and clips under the wheelarch. Release all the fasteners, and remove liner from under the front wing. Where necessary, unclip the coolant hoses from under the wing to improve access to the crankshaft pulley.

5 The engine can now be turned over using a suitable socket and extension bar fitted to the crankshaft pulley bolt.

> **HAYNES HINT** *The engine will be easier to turn if the fuel injectors or glow plugs are removed.*

6 On a piece of paper, draw the outline of the engine with the cylinders numbered from the flywheel end. Show the position of each valve, together with the specified valve clearance. Above each valve, draw lines for noting (1) the actual clearance and (2) the amount of adjustment required **(see illustration)**.

7 Turn the crankshaft until the inlet valve of No 1 cylinder (nearest the transmission) is fully closed, with the tip of the cam facing directly away from the follower.

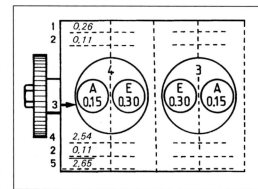

12.6 Example of valve shim thickness calculation – 1.9 litre engines

A   Inlet
E   Exhaust
1   Measured clearance
2   Difference between 1 and 3
3   Specified clearance
4   Thickness of shim fitted
5   Thickness of shim required

12.8 Measuring a valve clearance using a feeler blade – 1.9 litre engines

8 Using feeler blades, measure the clearance between the base of the cam and the follower **(see illustration)**. Record the clearance on line (1).

9 Repeat the measurement for the other seven valves, turning the crankshaft as necessary so that the cam lobe in question is always facing directly away from the relevant follower.

10 Calculate the difference between each measured clearance and the desired value, and record it on line (2). Since the clearance is different for inlet and exhaust valves – make sure that you are aware which valve you are dealing with. The valve sequence from either end of the engine is:

In–Ex–Ex–In–In–Ex–Ex–In

11 If all the clearances are within tolerance, refit the cylinder head cover with reference to Section 4. Refit the wheelarch liner and roadwheel, then lower the vehicle to the ground. If any clearance measured is outside the specified tolerance, adjustment must be carried out as described in the following paragraphs.

Adjustment

12 Remove the camshaft as described in Section 10.

13 Withdraw the first follower and its shim. Be careful that the shim does not fall out of the follower. Clean the shim, and measure its thickness with a micrometer. The shims carry thickness markings, but wear may have reduced the original thickness, so be sure to check.

14 Refer to the clearance recorded for the valve concerned. If the clearance was more than that specified, the shim thickness must be increased by the difference recorded (2). If the clearance was less than that specified, the thickness of the shim must be decreased by the difference recorded (2).

15 Draw three more lines beneath each valve on the calculation paper, as shown in illustration 12.6. On line (4) note the measured thickness of the shim, then add or deduct the difference from line (2) to give the final shim thickness required on line (5).

16 Repeat the procedure given in paragraphs 13 to 15 on the remaining valves, keeping each follower identified for position.

17 When reassembling, oil the shim and fit it into the valve retainer, with the size marking face downwards. Oil the follower, and lower it onto the shim. Do not raise the follower after fitting, as the shim may become dislodged.

18 When all the followers are in position, complete with their shims, refit the camshaft as described in Section 10. Recheck the valve clearances before refitting the cylinder head cover, to make sure they are correct.

13 Cylinder head (1.9 litre engines) – removal and refitting

Note 1: *This is an involved procedure, and it is suggested that the Section is read thoroughly before starting work. To aid refitting, make notes on the locations of all relevant brackets and the routing of hoses and cables before removal.*

Note 2: *On 2.0 litre engines, due to the limited access, it is impossible to remove the cylinder head with the engine in the car unless considerable additional dismantling is carried out first (eg. removal of the front suspension subframe and related components). Cylinder head removal and refitting procedures are therefore contained in Part F, assuming that the engine/transmission has been removed from the vehicle.*

Removal

1 Drain the cooling system as described in Chapter 1B.

2 Remove the cylinder head cover as described in Section 4.

3 Remove the timing belt as described in Section 7.

4 Undo the two bolts securing the EGR pipe to the exhaust manifold and remove the pipe. On certain installations there may be insufficient clearance to remove the pipe completely, in which case move the pipe clear of the cylinder head.

5 Disconnect the catalytic converter from the exhaust manifold with reference to Chapter 4B.

6 Remove the braking system vacuum pump as described in Chapter 9.

7 Disconnect and remove the fuel injector leak-off hoses.

8 Disconnect the fuel pipes from the fuel injectors and the fuel injection pump, and remove the pipes as described in Chapter 4B.

9 Unscrew the securing nut and disconnect the feed wire from the relevant glow plug. Recover the washers.

10 Remove the thermostat/fuel filter housing as described in Chapter 3.

11 Disconnect the coolant hose from the rear, left-hand end of the cylinder head.

12 Remove the right-hand engine mounting bracket from the engine.

13 Check that all pipes, hoses and wiring connectors and attachments likely to impede

cylinder head removal are disconnected and moved clear.

14 Progressively unscrew the cylinder head bolts, in the reverse order to that shown in illustration 13.31.

15 Lift out the bolts and, where fitted recover the washers.

16 Release the cylinder head from the cylinder block and location dowel by rocking it. The Citroën tool for doing this consists simply of two metal rods with 90-degree angled ends **(see illustration)**. Do not prise between the mating faces of the cylinder head and block, as this may damage the gasket faces.

17 Lift the cylinder head from the block, and recover the gasket.

Preparation for refitting

18 The mating faces of the cylinder head and cylinder block/crankcase must be perfectly clean before refitting the head. Citroën recommend the use of a scouring agent for this purpose, but acceptable results can be achieved by using a hard plastic or wood scraper to remove all traces of gasket and carbon. The same method can be used to clean the piston crowns. Take particular care to avoid scoring or gouging the cylinder head/cylinder block mating surfaces during the cleaning operations, as aluminium alloy is easily damaged. Make sure that the carbon is not allowed to enter the oil and water passages – this is particularly important for the lubrication system, as carbon could block the oil supply to the engine's components. Using adhesive tape and paper, seal the water, oil and bolt holes in the cylinder block/crankcase. To prevent carbon entering the gap between the pistons and bores, smear a little grease in the gap. After cleaning each piston, use a small brush to remove all traces of grease and carbon from the gap, then wipe away the remainder with a clean rag.

19 Check the mating surfaces of the cylinder block/crankcase and the cylinder head for nicks, deep scratches and other damage. If

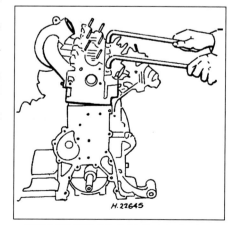

13.16 Freeing the cylinder head using angled rods – 1.9 litre engines

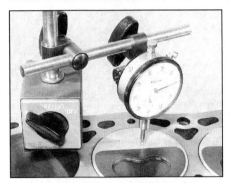

**13.22 Measuring piston protrusion –
1.9 litre engines**

slight, they may be removed carefully with a file, but if excessive, machining may be the only alternative to renewal. If warpage of the cylinder head gasket surface is suspected, use a straight-edge to check it for distortion. Refer to Part F of this Chapter if necessary.
20 Thoroughly clean the threads of the cylinder head bolt holes in the cylinder block. Ensure that the bolts run freely in their threads, and that all traces of oil and water are removed from each bolt hole.

Gasket selection

21 Check that the timing belt is clear of the fuel injection pump sprocket, then turn the crankshaft until pistons 1 and 4 are at TDC. Position a dial test indicator (dial gauge) on the cylinder block, and zero it on the block face. Transfer the probe to the centre of No 1 piston, then slowly turn the crankshaft back and forth past TDC, noting the highest reading on the indicator. Record this reading.
22 Repeat this measurement procedure on No 4 piston, then turn the crankshaft half a turn (180º) and repeat the procedure on Nos 2 and 3 pistons **(see illustration)**.
23 If a dial test indicator is not available, piston protrusion may be measured using a straight-edge and feeler blades or vernier calipers. However, this is much less accurate, and cannot therefore be recommended.
24 Note down the greatest piston protrusion measurement, and use this to determine the correct cylinder head gasket from the following table. The series of holes on the side of the gasket are used for thickness identification. The holes are in two adjacent groups, and the series of up to five holes

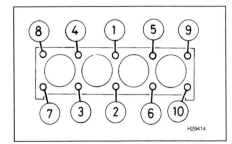

**13.31 Cylinder head bolt tightening
sequence – 1.9 litre engines**

nearest to the edge of the gasket are the ones used for thickness identification. The remaining two holes identify the engine capacity and type, and have no significance for gasket thickness selection **(see illustration)**.

Piston protrusion	Gasket identification
0.51 to 0.55 mm	1 hole
0.55 to 0.59 mm	2 holes
0.59 to 0.63 mm	3 holes
0.63 to 0.67 mm	4 holes
0.67 to 0.71 mm	5 holes

Cylinder head bolt examination

25 Carefully examine the cylinder head bolts for signs of damage to the threads or head, and for any sign of corrosion. If the bolts are in a satisfactory condition, measure the length of each bolt from the underside of the head, to the end of the unthreaded portion at the base of the shank. The bolts may be re-used providing that the measured length does not exceed 125.5 mm. Note that, if a bolt is modified to locate the gasket (see paragraph 27), a new bolt will be required when finally refitting the cylinder head. **Note:** *Considering the stress to which the cylinder head bolts are subjected, it is highly recommended that they are all renewed, regardless of their apparent condition.*

Refitting

26 Turn the crankshaft clockwise (viewed from the timing belt end) until Nos 1 and 4 pistons pass bottom dead centre (BDC) and begin to rise, then position them halfway up their bores. Nos 2 and 3 pistons will also be at their mid-way positions, but descending their bores.
27 Fit the correct gasket the right way round

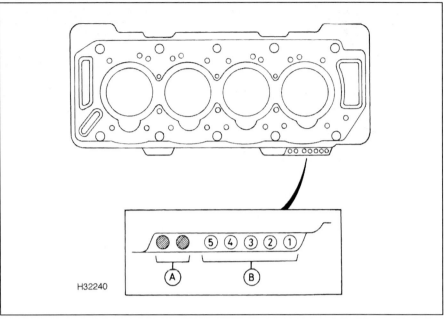

13.24 Cylinder head gasket identification holes – 1.9 litre engines

A Engine identification holes   *B Gasket thickness identification holes*

on the cylinder block, with the identification holes toward the front facing side of the engine, and adjacent to cylinder No 1 (flywheel end). Make sure that the locating dowel is in place at the timing belt end of the block. Note that, as there is only one locating dowel, it is possible for the gasket to move as the cylinder head is fitted, particularly when the cylinder head is fitted with the engine in the car (due to the inclination of the engine). In the worst instance, this can allow the pistons and/or the valves to hit the gasket, causing engine damage. To avoid this problem, saw the head off an old cylinder head bolt, and file (or cut) a slot in the end of the bolt, to enable it to be turned with a screwdriver. Screw the bolt into one of the bolt holes at the flywheel/driveplate end of the cylinder block, then fit the gasket over the bolt and location dowel. This will ensure that the gasket is held in position as the cylinder head is fitted.
28 Lower the cylinder head onto the block.
29 Apply a smear of grease to the threads, and to the underside of the heads, of the cylinder head bolts. Citroën recommend the use of Molykote G Rapid Plus (available from your Citroën dealer); in the absence of the specified grease, any good-quality high-melting-point grease may be used.
30 Carefully enter each bolt and washer (where applicable) into its relevant hole (*do not drop it in*) and screw it in finger-tight. After fitting three or four bolts to locate the cylinder head, unscrew the modified bolt fitted in paragraph 27, and fit a new bolt in its place.
31 Working progressively and in the sequence shown, tighten the cylinder head bolts to their Stage 1 torque setting, using a torque wrench and suitable socket **(see illustration)**.

32 Once all the bolts have been tightened to their Stage 1 torque setting, working again in the specified sequence, tighten each bolt to the specified Stage 2 setting. Finally, angle-tighten the bolts through the specified Stage 3 angle. It is recommended that an angle-measuring gauge is used during this stage of tightening, to ensure accuracy.

33 The remainder of the refitting procedure is a reversal of removal, noting the following points:

a) Refit the timing belt as described in Section 7.
b) Refit the fuel system components as described in Chapter 4B.
c) Reconnect the catalytic converter to the exhaust manifold as described in Chapter 4B.
d) Refit the braking system vacuum pump as described in Chapter 9.
e) Refit the thermostat/fuel filter housing as described in Chapter 3.
f) Refit the cylinder head cover as described in Section 4.
g) Ensure that all wiring is correctly routed, and that all connectors are securely reconnected to the correct components.
h) Ensure that the coolant hoses are correctly reconnected, and that their retaining clips are securely tightened.
i) Ensure that all vacuum/breather hoses are correctly reconnected.
j) Refill the cooling system as described in Chapter 1B.
k) Reconnect the battery and bleed the fuel system as described in Chapter 4B.

14 Sump – removal and refitting

Refer to Chapter 2B, Section 14, but substitute Chapter 1B for all references to Chapter 1A.

15 Oil pump and drive chain – removal, inspection and refitting

Refer to Chapter 2B, Section 15.

16 Oil seals – renewal

Crankshaft right-hand oil seal

1 Remove the crankshaft sprocket as described in Section 9.
2 Note the fitted depth of the oil seal.
3 Pull the oil seal from the housing using a hooked instrument. Alternatively, drill a small hole in the oil seal, and use a self-tapping screw and a pair of pliers to remove it **(see illustration)**.

4 Clean the oil seal housing and the crankshaft sealing surface.
5 Dip the new oil seal in clean engine oil, and press it into the housing (open end first) to the previously-noted depth, using a suitable tube or socket. A piece of thin plastic or tape wound around the right-hand end of the crankshaft is useful to prevent damage to the oil seal as it is fitted.
6 Where applicable, remove the plastic or tape from the end of the crankshaft.
7 Refit the crankshaft sprocket as described in Section 9.

Crankshaft left-hand oil seal

8 Remove the flywheel as described in Section 17.
9 Proceed as described in paragraphs 2 to 6, noting that when fitted, the outer lip of the oil seal must point outwards; if it is pointing inwards, use a piece of bent wire to pull it out. Take care not to damage the oil seal.
10 Refit the flywheel as described in Section 17.

Camshaft right-hand oil seal

11 Remove the camshaft sprocket as described in Section 9. In principle there is no need to remove the timing belt completely, but remember that if the belt has been contaminated with oil, it must be renewed.
12 Pull the oil seal from the housing using a hooked tool **(see illustration)**. Alternatively, drill a small hole in the oil seal and use a self-tapping screw and a pair of pliers to remove it.
13 Clean the oil seal housing and the camshaft sealing surface.
14 Smear the lips of the new oil seal with clean engine oil, then fit it over the end of the camshaft, open end first. A piece of thin plastic or tape wound round the right-hand end of the camshaft should prevent damage to the oil seal as it is fitted.
15 Press the seal into the housing until it is flush with the end face of the cylinder head. Use a suitable bolt (screwed into the end of the camshaft), washers and a tube or socket to press the seal into position.
16 Refit the camshaft sprocket as described in Section 9.
17 Where applicable, fit a new timing belt as described in Sections 7 or 8, according to engine type.

Camshaft left-hand oil seal

18 No oil seal is fitted to the left-hand end of the camshaft. The sealing is provided by an O-ring fitted to the braking system vacuum pump flange. The O-ring can be renewed after unbolting the pump from the cylinder head (see Chapter 9). Note the smaller O-ring which seals the oil feed gallery to the pump – this may also cause leakage from the pump/cylinder head mating faces if it deteriorates or fails.

17 Flywheel – removal, inspection and refitting

Refer to Chapter 2B, Section 18.

18 Engine/transmission mountings – inspection and renewal

Inspection

1 If improved access is required, firmly apply the handbrake, then jack up the front of the car and support it securely on axle stands (see *Jacking and vehicle support*).
2 Check the mounting rubbers to see if they are cracked, hardened or separated from the metal at any point; renew the mounting if any such damage or deterioration is evident.
3 Check that all the mountings' fasteners are securely tightened; use a torque wrench to check if possible.
4 Using a large screwdriver or a crowbar, check for wear in each mounting by carefully levering against it to check for free play. Where this is not possible, enlist the aid of an assistant to move the engine/transmission back-and-forth, or from side-to-side, while you watch the mounting. While some free play is to be expected even from new components, excessive wear should be obvious. If excessive free play is found, check first that the fasteners are correctly secured, then renew any worn components as described below.

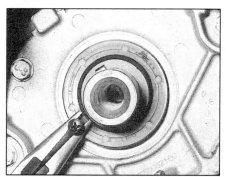

16.3 Self-tapping screw and pliers used to remove the crankshaft right-hand oil seal

16.12 Using a hooked tool to remove the camshaft oil seal

18.11 Removing the right-hand engine mounting upper bracket and rubber buffer plate

18.21a Remove the centre nut and washer from the left-hand mounting . . .

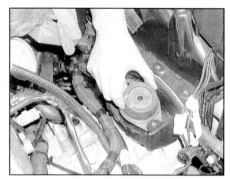

18.21b . . . then undo the two nuts and remove the mounting

Renewal

Right-hand mounting

5 Disconnect the battery negative terminal (refer to *Disconnecting the battery* in the Reference Section of this manual).

6 Remove the timing belt upper and intermediate covers as described in Section 6.

7 Release all the relevant hoses and wiring from their retaining clips. Place the hoses/wiring clear of the mounting so that the removal procedure is not hindered.

8 Place a jack beneath the engine, with a block of wood on the jack head. Raise the jack until it is supporting the weight of the engine.

9 Slacken and remove the three bolts securing the upper mounting bracket to the lower (engine) bracket.

10 Undo the two bolts securing the curved mounting retaining plate to the body and lift off the plate. Unscrew the domed buffer nut, then unscrew the single nut securing the upper bracket to the mounting rubber.

11 Lift off the upper bracket and the rubber buffer plate off the mounting rubber stud, then remove the washer, unscrew the mounting rubber from the body, and remove it from the

vehicle **(see illustration)**. A strap wrench or similar may be used to unscrew the mounting, or alternatively fabricate a tool from suitable metal tube with projections to engage in the cut-outs in the mounting.

12 If necessary, the lower mounting bracket can be unbolted and removed from the engine.

13 Check all components carefully for signs of wear or damage, and renew them where necessary.

14 On reassembly, screw the mounting rubber into the vehicle body, and tighten it securely. Where removed, refit the lower mounting bracket to the engine, apply a drop of locking compound to the retaining bolts and tighten them to the specified torque.

15 Refit the rubber buffer plate to the mounting rubber stud, and install the upper mounting bracket.

16 Tighten the upper mounting bracket retaining nuts/bolts to the specified torque setting.

17 Refit the domed buffer nut and curved mounting retaining plate, then remove the jack from underneath the engine.

18 Refit the timing belt covers as described in Section 6, then reconnect the battery.

Left-hand mounting

19 Remove the battery, battery tray, and mounting plate as described in Chapter 5A.

20 Place a jack beneath the transmission, with a block of wood on the jack head. Raise the jack until it is supporting the weight of the transmission.

21 Slacken and remove the centre nut and washer from the left-hand mounting, then undo the nuts securing the mounting in position and remove it from the engine compartment **(see illustrations)**.

22 If necessary, slide the spacer and small washer off the mounting stud, then unscrew the stud from the top of the transmission housing, and remove it along with its large washer **(see illustrations)**. To improve access to the mounting stud, undo the retaining bolts and remove the mounting bracket from the body.

23 Check all components carefully for signs of wear or damage, and renew as necessary.

24 Clean the threads of the mounting stud, and apply a coat of thread-locking compound to its threads. Refit the stud and washer to the top of the transmission, and tighten it to the specified torque setting.

25 Slide the spacer (where fitted) onto the

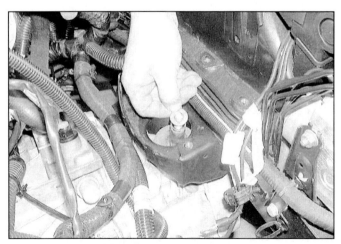

18.22a Remove the washer . . .

18.22b . . . and spacer to allow the mounting stud to be unscrewed

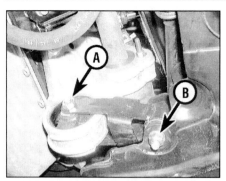

18.28 Rear engine mounting connecting link attachments

A   *Connecting link-to-mounting nut*
B   *Connecting link-to-subframe nut*

mounting stud, then refit the rubber mounting. Tighten both the mounting-to-body bolts and the mounting centre nut to their specified torque settings, and remove the jack from underneath the transmission.

26 Refit the battery mounting plate, battery tray and battery as described in Chapter 5A.

Rear mounting

27 If not already done, firmly apply the handbrake, then jack up the front of the car and support it securely on axle stands (see *Jacking and vehicle support*). Remove the engine undertray.

28 Unscrew and remove the bolt securing the rear mounting connecting link to the mounting on the rear of the cylinder block **(see illustration)**.

29 Remove the bolt securing the rear mounting connecting link to the bracket on the subframe/underbody. Withdraw the link.

30 To remove the mounting assembly it will first be necessary to remove the right-hand driveshaft as described in Chapter 8.

31 With the driveshaft removed, undo the retaining bolts and remove the mounting from the rear of the cylinder block.

32 Check carefully for signs of wear or damage on all components, and renew them where necessary.

33 On reassembly, fit the rear mounting assembly to the rear of the cylinder block, and tighten its retaining bolts to the specified torque. Refit the driveshaft as described in Chapter 8.

34 Refit the connecting link, and tighten both its bolts to their specified torque settings.

35 Refit the engine undertray and lower the vehicle to the ground.

19 Engine oil cooler – removal and refitting

Refer to Chapter 2B, Section 16, but substitute Chapter 1B for all references to Chapter 1A.

Notes

Chapter 2 Part E:
Petrol engine removal and overhaul procedures

Contents

Crankshaft – inspection 14
Crankshaft – refitting and main bearing running clearance check . . 18
Crankshaft – removal 11
Cylinder block/crankcase – cleaning and inspection 12
Cylinder head – dismantling 7
Cylinder head – reassembly 9
Cylinder head and valves – cleaning and inspection 8
Engine – initial start-up after overhaul 20
Engine and automatic transmission – removal, separation
   and refitting 5
Engine and manual transmission – removal, separation and
   refitting 4

Engine overhaul – dismantling sequence 6
Engine overhaul – general information 2
Engine overhaul – reassembly sequence 16
Engine/transmission removal – methods and precautions 3
General information 1
Main and big-end bearings – inspection 15
Piston/connecting rod assembly – inspection 13
Piston/connecting rod assembly – refitting and big-end bearing
   running clearance check 19
Piston/connecting rod assembly – removal 10
Piston rings – refitting 17

Degrees of difficulty

| **Easy,** suitable for novice with little experience | | **Fairly easy,** suitable for beginner with some experience | | **Fairly difficult,** suitable for competent DIY mechanic | | **Difficult,** suitable for experienced DIY mechanic | | **Very difficult,** suitable for expert DIY or professional | |

Specifications

Note: *At the time of writing, many specifications for certain engines were not available. Where the relevant specifications are not given here, refer to your Citroën dealer for further information.*

Cylinder head
Maximum gasket face distortion . . . . 0.05 mm

Cylinder block
Cylinder bore diameter:
   1.4 litre engine:
      Size group A . . . . 75.000 to 75.010 mm
      Size group B . . . . 75.010 to 75.020 mm
      Size group C . . . . 75.020 to 75.030 mm
   1.6 litre engine . . . . Not available (78 mm nominal)
   1.8 litre engine:
      Size group A . . . . 83.000 to 83.010 mm
      Size group B . . . . 83.010 to 83.020 mm
      Size group C . . . . 83.020 to 83.030 mm
   2.0 litre engine . . . . Not available (86 mm nominal)
Liner protrusion above block mating surface – aluminium-block engine only:
   Standard . . . . 0.03 to 0.10 mm
   Maximum difference between any two liners . . . . 0.05 mm

Valves

Valve head diameter:
Inlet:
    1.4 litre engine . . . . 36.8 mm
    1.6 litre engine . . . . 39.5 mm
    1.8 litre (8-valve) engine . . . . 41.6 mm
    1.8 litre (16-valve) engine . . . . 34.7 mm
    2.0 litre engine . . . . 34.7 mm
Exhaust:
    1.4 litre engine . . . . 29.4 mm
    1.6 litre engine . . . . 31.4 mm
    1.8 litre (8-valve) engine . . . . 34.5 mm
    1.8 litre (16-valve) engine . . . . 29.7 mm
    2.0 litre engine . . . . 29.7 mm
Valve stem diameter:
Inlet:
    1.4 litre engine . . . . 6.84 to 6.99 mm
    1.6 litre engine . . . . Not available
    1.8 litre (8-valve) engine . . . . 7.96 to 7.98 mm
    1.8 litre (16-valve) engine . . . . 6.96 to 6.98 mm
    2.0 litre engine . . . . 6.96 to 6.98 mm
Exhaust:
    1.4 litre engine . . . . 6.83 to 6.98 mm
    1.6 litre engine . . . . Not available
    1.8 litre (8-valve) engine . . . . 7.95 to 7.97 mm
    1.8 litre (16-valve) engine . . . . 6.94 to 6.96 mm
    2.0 litre engine . . . . 6.94 to 6.96 mm
Overall length:
Inlet:
    1.4 litre engine . . . . 112.51 to 113.01 mm
    1.6 litre engine . . . . Not available
    1.8 litre (8-valve) engine . . . . 108.59 to 108.99 mm
    1.8 litre (16-valve) engine . . . . 104.38 to 104.78 mm
    2.0 litre engine . . . . 104.38 to 104.78 mm
Exhaust:
    1.4 litre engine . . . . 112.31 to 112.81 mm
    1.6 litre engine . . . . Not available
    1.8 litre (8-valve) engine . . . . 108.20 to 108.54 mm
    1.8 litre (16-valve) engine . . . . 102.90 to 103.30 mm
    2.0 litre engine . . . . 102.90 to 103.30 mm

Pistons

Piston diameter:
1.4 litre engine:
    Size group A . . . . 74.950 ± 0.010 mm
    Size group B . . . . 74.960 ± 0.010 mm
    Size group C . . . . 74.970 ± 0.010 mm
1.6 litre engine . . . . Not available
1.8 litre engine:
    .Size group A . . . . 82.960 ± 0.007 mm
    .Size group B . . . . 82.970 ± 0.007 mm
    .Size group C . . . . 82.980 ± 0.007 mm
2.0 litre engine . . . . Not available

Piston rings

End gaps:
Top compression ring:
    1.4 litre engine . . . . 0.3 to 0.5 mm
    1.6, 1.8 and 2.0 litre engines* . . . . 0.3 to 0.5 mm
Second compression ring:
    1.4 litre engine . . . . 0.3 to 0.5 mm
    1.6, 1.8 and 2.0 litre engines* . . . . 0.3 to 0.5 mm
Oil control ring* . . . . 0.3 to 0.5 mm
*These are suggested figures, typical for this type of engine – no exact values are stated by Citroën.

Connecting rods

Maximum weight difference between any two piston/connecting rod assemblies:
    1.4 and 1.6 litre engines . . . . 5.0 g
    1.8 litre engine . . . . 13.0 g
    2.0 litre engine . . . . 7.0 g

Crankshaft

Endfloat	0.07 to 0.32 mm
Main bearing journal diameter:	
1.4 and 1.6 litre engines:	
Standard	49.965 to 49.981 mm
Repair size	49.665 to 49.681 mm
1.8 litre engine:	
Standard	59.981 to 60.000 mm
Repair size	59.681 to 59.700 mm
2.0 litre engine:	
Standard	59.975 to 60.000 mm
Repair size	59.675 to 59.700 mm
Big-end bearing journal diameter:	
1.4 and 1.6 litre engines:	
Standard	44.992 to 45.008 mm
Repair size	44.692 to 44.708 mm
1.8 litre engine:	
Standard	44.975 to 44.991 mm
Repair size	44.475 to 44.491 mm
2.0 litre engine:	
Standard	49.984 to 50.000 mm
Repair size	49.684 to 49.700 mm
Maximum bearing journal out-of-round (all engines)	0.007 mm
Main bearing running clearance:	
1.4 and 1.6 litre engines	0.023 to 0.048 mm
1.8 litre engine	0.025 to 0.062 mm
2.0 litre engine	0.038 to 0.069 mm
Big-end bearing running clearance – all engines*	0.025 to 0.050 mm

*These are suggested figures, typical for this type of engine – no exact values are stated by Citroën.

Torque wrench settings

TU series engines

Refer to Chapter 2A Specifications.

XU series engines

Refer to Chapter 2B Specifications.

1 General information

Included in this Part of Chapter 2 are details of removing the engine/transmission from the car and general overhaul procedures for the cylinder head, cylinder block/crankcase and all other engine internal components.

The information given ranges from advice concerning preparation for an overhaul and the purchase of replacement parts, to detailed step-by-step procedures covering removal, inspection, renovation and refitting of engine internal components.

After Section 6, all instructions are based on the assumption that the engine has been removed from the car. For information concerning in-car engine repair, as well as the removal and refitting of those external components necessary for full overhaul, refer to Part A or B of this Chapter (as applicable) and to Section 6. Ignore any preliminary dismantling operations described in Part A or B that are no longer relevant once the engine has been removed from the car.

Apart from torque wrench settings, which are given at the beginning of Part A or B (as applicable), all specifications relating to engine overhaul are at the beginning of this Part of Chapter 2.

2 Engine overhaul – general information

It is not always easy to determine when, or if, an engine should be completely overhauled, as a number of factors must be considered.

High mileage is not necessarily an indication that an overhaul is needed, while low mileage does not preclude the need for an overhaul. Frequency of servicing is probably the most important consideration. An engine which has had regular and frequent oil and filter changes, as well as other required maintenance, should give many thousands of miles of reliable service. Conversely, a neglected engine may require an overhaul very early in its life.

Excessive oil consumption is an indication that piston rings, valve seals and/or valve guides are in need of attention. Make sure that oil leaks are not responsible before deciding that the rings and/or guides are worn. Perform a compression test, as described in Part A of this Chapter, to determine the likely cause of the problem.

Check the oil pressure with a gauge fitted in place of the oil pressure switch, and compare it with that specified in Part A or B of this Chapter. If it is extremely low, the main and big-end bearings, and/or the oil pump, are probably worn out.

Loss of power, rough running, knocking or metallic engine noises, excessive valve gear noise, and high fuel consumption may also point to the need for an overhaul, especially if they are all present at the same time. If a complete service does not remedy the situation, major mechanical work is the only solution.

An engine overhaul involves restoring all internal parts to the specification of a new engine. During an overhaul, the cylinder liners (where applicable), the pistons and the piston rings are renewed. New main and big-end bearings are generally fitted; if necessary, the crankshaft may be reground to restore the journals. The valves are also serviced as well, since they are usually in less-than-perfect condition at this point. The end result should be an as-new engine that will give many trouble-free miles.

Note: *Critical cooling system components such as the hoses, thermostat and coolant pump should be renewed when an engine is overhauled. The radiator should be checked* *carefully, to ensure that it is not clogged or leaking. Also, it is a good idea to renew the oil pump whenever the engine is overhauled.*

Before beginning the engine overhaul, read through the entire procedure, to familiarise yourself with the scope and requirements of the job. Overhauling an engine is not difficult if you follow carefully all of the instructions, have the necessary tools and equipment, and pay close attention to all specifications. It can, however, be time-consuming. Plan on the car being off the road for a minimum of two weeks, especially if parts must be taken to an engineering works for repair or reconditioning. Check on the availability of parts and make sure that any necessary special tools and equipment are obtained in advance. Most work can be done with typical hand tools, although a number of precision measuring tools are required for inspecting parts to determine if they must be renewed. Often the engineering works will handle the inspection of parts and offer advice concerning reconditioning and renewal.

Always wait until the engine has been completely dismantled, and until all components (especially the cylinder block/crankcase and the crankshaft) have been inspected, before deciding what service and repair operations must be performed by an engineering works. The condition of these components will be the major factor to consider when determining whether to overhaul the original engine, or to buy a reconditioned unit. Do not, therefore, purchase parts or have overhaul work done on other components until they have been thoroughly inspected. As a general rule, time is the primary cost of an overhaul, so it does not pay to fit worn or sub-standard parts.

As a final note, to ensure maximum life and minimum trouble from a reconditioned engine, everything must be assembled with care, in a spotlessly-clean environment.

3 Engine/transmission removal – methods and precautions

If you have decided that the engine must be removed for overhaul or major repair work, several preliminary steps should be taken.

Locating a suitable place to work is extremely important. Adequate work space, along with storage space for the car, will be needed. If a workshop or garage is not available, at the very least, a flat, level, clean work surface is required.

Cleaning the engine compartment and engine/transmission before beginning the removal procedure will help keep tools clean and organised.

An engine hoist will also be necessary. Make sure the equipment is rated in excess of the combined weight of the engine and transmission. Safety is of primary importance, considering the potential hazards involved in lifting the engine/transmission out of the car.

If this is the first time you have removed an engine, an assistant should ideally be available. Advice and aid from someone more experienced would also be helpful. There are many instances when one person cannot simultaneously perform all of the operations required when lifting the engine out of the vehicle.

Plan the operation ahead of time. Before starting work, arrange for the hire of or obtain all of the tools and equipment you will need. Some of the equipment necessary to perform engine/transmission removal and installation safely (in addition to an engine hoist) is as follows: a heavy duty trolley jack, complete sets of spanners and sockets as described at the rear of this manual, wooden blocks, and plenty of rags and cleaning solvent for mopping up spilled oil, coolant and fuel. If the hoist must be hired, make sure that you arrange for it in advance, and perform all of the operations possible without it beforehand. This will save you money and time.

Plan for the car to be out of use for quite a while. An engineering works will be required to perform some of the work which the do-it-yourselfer cannot accomplish without special equipment. These places often have a busy schedule, so it would be a good idea to consult them before removing the engine, in order to accurately estimate the amount of time required to rebuild or repair components that may need work.

During the engine removal procedure, it is advisable to make notes of the locations of all brackets, cable ties, earthing points, etc, as well as how the wiring harnesses, hoses and electrical connections are attached and routed around the engine and engine compartment. An effective way of doing this is to take a series of photographs of the various components before they are disconnected or removed. A simple inexpensive disposable camera is ideal for this and the resulting photographs will prove invaluable when the engine is refitted.

Always be extremely careful when removing and refitting the engine/transmission. Serious injury can result from careless actions. Plan ahead and take your time, and a job of this nature, although major, can be accomplished successfully.

The engine and transmission unit is removed upwards from the engine compartment on all models described in this manual.

4 Engine and manual transmission – removal, separation and refitting

Removal

Note: *The engine can be removed from the car only as a complete unit with the transmission; the two are then separated for overhaul.*

1 Disconnect the battery negative terminal (refer to *Disconnecting the battery* in the Reference Section of this manual).

2 Chock the rear wheels then jack up the front of the vehicle and support it on axle stands (see *Jacking and vehicle support*). Remove the front roadwheels.

3 Disconnect the bonnet support struts as described in Chapter 11, and tie or support the bonnet in the vertical position.

4 Remove the air cleaner assembly and air inlet ducts as described in Chapter 4A.

5 If the engine is to be dismantled, working as described in Chapter 1A, first drain the oil and remove the oil filter. Clean and refit the drain plug, tightening it securely.

6 Drain the transmission oil as described in Chapter 7A. Refit the filler/level and drain plugs, and tighten them to their specified torque settings.

7 Drain the cooling system as described in Chapter 1B.

8 Remove the alternator as described in Chapter 5A, and the power steering pump as described in Chapter 10.

9 On models with air conditioning, unbolt the compressor, and position it clear of the engine. Support the weight of the compressor by tying it to the vehicle body, to prevent any excess strain being placed on the compressor lines whilst the engine is removed. *Do not* disconnect the refrigerant lines from the compressor (refer to the warnings given in Chapter 3).

10 Remove the battery, battery tray and mounting plate as described in Chapter 5A.

11 Carry out the following operations, using the information given in Chapter 4A and 4C (as applicable):

a) *Depressurise the fuel system, and disconnect the fuel feed and return hoses.*

b) *Disconnect the accelerator cable.*

c) *Disconnect the fuel system wiring connectors.*

d) *Disconnect the purge valve and/or braking system servo vacuum hoses from the inlet manifold (as applicable).*

e) *Remove the exhaust system front pipe.*

12 Referring to Chapter 3, release the retaining clip and disconnect the heater matrix hoses from their connection on the engine compartment bulkhead. Also disconnect the radiator bottom hose connection on the engine, and any remaining coolant hoses.

13 Remove the radiator as described in Chapter 3. Note that this is not strictly necessary, but greatly improves the clearance, and removes the risk of damaging the radiator as the engine is removed.

14 Working as described in Chapter 6, disconnect the clutch cable from the transmission, and position it clear of the working area.

15 Carry out the following operations, using the information given in Chapter 7A:

a) *Disconnect the gearchange selector rod/link rods (as applicable) from the transmission.*

b) Disconnect the wiring connector from the vehicle speed sensor.

c) Release the power steering pipe from the underside of the transmission.

d) Disconnect the wiring connector(s) from the reversing light switch.

16 Remove both driveshafts as described in Chapter 8.

17 Trace the wiring harness back from the engine to the main harness connectors at the fuse/relay box, and behind the battery tray location. Release the locking rings by twisting them anti-clockwise and disconnect the connectors. Also trace the wiring connectors back to the transmission and disconnect all engine related wiring and earth leads in this area. Check that all the relevant connectors have been disconnected, and that the harness is released from any relevant clips or ties, so that it is free to be removed with the engine/transmission.

18 Manoeuvre the engine hoist into position, and attach it to the engine lifting brackets. Raise the hoist until it is supporting the weight of the engine.

19 Slacken and remove the centre nut and washer from the engine/transmission left-hand mounting. Undo the two nuts and washers securing the mounting to its bracket, and remove the mounting from the engine compartment and recover the spacer (where fitted). Undo the remaining retaining bolts and remove the mounting bracket from the body.

20 From underneath the vehicle, slacken and remove the nuts and bolts securing the rear mounting connecting link to the mounting assembly and subframe, and remove the connecting link.

21 Working on the right-hand engine/transmission mounting, undo the two bolts and remove the curved retaining plate and rubber damper (where fitted) from the top of the mounting. Slacken and remove the mounting bracket retaining nuts/bolts (as applicable) and lift off the bracket. Remove the rubber damper plate from the mounting, and store it with the bracket for safe-keeping.

22 Make a final check that any components which would prevent the removal of the engine/transmission from the car have been removed or disconnected. Ensure that components such as the gearchange selector rod are secured so that they cannot be damaged on removal.

23 Lift the engine/transmission out of the car, ensuring that nothing is trapped or damaged. Enlist the help of an assistant during this procedure, as it will be necessary to tilt the assembly slightly to clear the body panels. On models equipped with anti-lock brakes, great care must be taken to ensure that the anti-lock braking system unit is not damaged during the removal procedure.

24 Once the engine is high enough, lift it out over the front of the body, and lower the unit to the ground.

Separation

25 With the engine/transmission assembly removed, support the assembly on suitable blocks of wood on a workbench (or failing that, on a clean area of the workshop floor).

26 Undo the retaining bolts, and remove the flywheel lower cover plate (where fitted) from the transmission.

27 On models with a 'pull-type' clutch release mechanism (see Chapter 6 for further information), tap out the retaining pin or unscrew the retaining bolt (as applicable), and remove the clutch release lever from the top of the release fork shaft. This is necessary to allow the fork shaft to rotate freely, so that it disengages from the release bearing as the transmission is pulled away from the engine. Make an alignment mark across the centre of the clutch release fork shaft, using a scriber, paint or similar, and mark its relative position on the transmission housing (see Chapter 7A for further information).

28 Slacken and remove the retaining bolts, and remove the starter motor from the transmission.

29 Ensure that both engine and transmission are adequately supported, then slacken and remove the remaining bolts securing the transmission housing to the engine. Note the correct fitted positions of each bolt (and the relevant brackets) as they are removed, to use as a reference on refitting.

30 Carefully withdraw the transmission from the engine, ensuring that the weight of the transmission is not allowed to hang on the input shaft while it is engaged with the clutch friction plate.

31 If they are loose, remove the locating dowels from the engine or transmission, and keep them in a safe place.

32 On models with a 'pull-type' clutch, make a second alignment mark on the transmission housing, marking the relative position of the release fork mark after removal. This should indicate the angle at which the release fork is positioned. The mark can then be used to position the release fork prior to installation, to ensure that the fork correctly engages with the clutch release bearing as the transmission is installed.

Refitting

33 If the engine and transmission have been separated, perform the operations described below in paragraphs 34 to 42. If not, proceed as described from paragraph 43 onwards.

34 Apply a smear of high-melting-point grease (Citroën recommend the use of Molykote BR2 plus – available from your Citroën dealer) to the splines of the transmission input shaft. Do not apply too much, otherwise there is a possibility of the grease contaminating the clutch friction plate.

35 Ensure that the locating dowels are correctly positioned in the engine or transmission.

36 On models with a 'pull-type' clutch, before refitting, position the clutch release bearing so that its arrow mark is pointing upwards (bearing fork slots facing towards the

front of the engine), and align the release fork shaft mark with the second mark made on the transmission housing (release fork positioned at approximately 60° to clutch housing face). This will ensure that the release fork and bearing will engage correctly as the transmission is refitted to the engine.

37 Carefully offer the transmission to the engine, until the locating dowels are engaged. Ensure that the weight of the transmission is not allowed to hang on the input shaft as it is engaged with the clutch friction disc.

38 On models with a 'pull-type' clutch, with the transmission fully engaged with the engine, check that the release fork and bearing are correctly engaged. If the release fork and bearing are correctly engaged, the mark on the release fork should be aligned with the original mark made on the transmission housing (see Chapter 7A for further information).

39 Refit the transmission housing-to-engine bolts, ensuring that all the necessary brackets are correctly positioned, and tighten them securely.

40 Refit the starter motor, and securely tighten its retaining bolts.

41 On models with a 'pull-type' clutch release mechanism, refit the clutch release lever to the top of the release fork shaft, securing it in position with its retaining pin or bolt (as applicable).

42 Where necessary, refit the lower flywheel cover plate to the transmission, and securely tighten its retaining bolts.

43 Reconnect the hoist and lifting tackle to the engine lifting brackets. With the aid of an assistant, lift the assembly over the engine compartment.

44 The assembly should be tilted as necessary to clear the surrounding components, as during removal; lower the assembly into position in the engine compartment, manipulating the hoist and lifting tackle as necessary.

45 With the engine/transmission in position, refit the right-hand engine/transmission mounting bracket, tightening the nuts and bolts (as applicable) by hand only at this stage.

46 Working on the left-hand mounting, refit the mounting bracket to the body and tighten its retaining bolts to the specified torque. Refit the mounting rubber and refit the mounting retaining nuts and washers and the centre nut and washer, tightening them lightly only.

47 From underneath the vehicle, refit the rear mounting link and install both its bolts.

48 Rock the engine to settle it on its mountings, then go around and tighten all the mounting nuts and bolts to their specified torque settings. Where necessary, once the right-hand mounting bracket nuts have been tightened, refit the rubber damper and curved retaining plate, tightening its retaining bolts to the specified torque. The hoist can then be detached from the engine and removed.

49 The remainder of the refitting procedure is

a direct reversal of the removal sequence, noting the following points:

a) *Ensure that the wiring loom is correctly routed and retained by all the relevant retaining clips; all connectors should be correctly and securely reconnected.*

b) *Prior to refitting the driveshafts to the transmission, renew the driveshaft oil seals as described in Chapter 7A.*

c) *Ensure that all coolant hoses are correctly reconnected, and securely retained by their retaining clips.*

d) *Adjust the accelerator cable as described in Chapter 4A.*

e) *Refill the engine and transmission with the correct quantity and type of lubricant, as described in Chapters 1A and 7A.*

f) *Refill the cooling system as described in Chapter 1A.*

g) *Bleed the power steering system as described in Chapter 10.*

5 Engine and automatic transmission – removal, separation and refitting

Removal

Note: *The engine can be removed from the car only as a complete unit with the transmission; the two are then separated for overhaul.*

1 Disconnect the battery negative terminal (refer to *Disconnecting the battery* in the Reference Section of this manual).

2 Chock the rear wheels then jack up the front of the vehicle and support it on axle stands (see *Jacking and vehicle support*). Remove the front roadwheels.

3 Disconnect the bonnet support struts as described in Chapter 11, and tie or support the bonnet in the vertical position.

4 Remove the air cleaner assembly and air inlet ducts as described in the Chapter 4A.

5 If the engine is to be dismantled, working as described in Chapter 1A, first drain the oil and remove the oil filter. Clean and refit the drain plug, tightening it securely.

6 On the 4 HP 14 transmission, drain the transmission fluid as described in Chapter 1A, then refit the drain plugs, tightening them securely.

7 Drain the cooling system as described in Chapter 1A.

8 Remove the alternator as described in Chapter 5A, and the power steering pump as described in Chapter 10.

9 On models with air conditioning, unbolt the compressor, and position it clear of the engine. Support the weight of the compressor by tying it to the vehicle body, to prevent any excess strain being placed on the compressor lines whilst the engine is removed. *Do not disconnect the refrigerant lines from the compressor (refer to the warnings given in Chapter 3).*

10 Remove the battery, battery tray and mounting plate as described in Chapter 5A.

11 Carry out the following operations, using the information given in Chapter 4A and 4C (as applicable):

a) *Depressurise the fuel system, and disconnect the fuel feed and return hoses.*

b) *Disconnect the accelerator cable.*

c) *Disconnect the fuel system wiring connectors.*

d) *Disconnect the purge valve and/or braking system servo vacuum hoses from the inlet manifold (as applicable).*

e) *Remove the exhaust system front pipe.*

12 Referring to Chapter 3, release the retaining clip and disconnect the heater matrix hoses from their connection on the engine compartment bulkhead. Also disconnect the radiator bottom hose connection on the engine.

13 Using a hose clamp or similar, clamp the transmission fluid cooler coolant hoses to minimise coolant loss during subsequent operations.

14 Slacken the retaining clips, and disconnect both coolant hoses from the fluid cooler.

15 Remove the radiator as described in Chapter 3. Note that this is not strictly necessary, but greatly improves the clearance, and removes the risk of damaging the radiator as the engine is removed.

16 On models equipped with the 4 HP 14 transmission, carry out the following operations, using the information given in Chapter 7B:

a) *Remove the transmission dipstick tube.*

b) *Disconnect the wiring from the starter inhibitor/reversing light switch and the vehicle speed sensor. Release the earth strap(s) from the top of the transmission housing.*

c) *Disconnect the selector cable.*

d) *Release the power steering pipe from the underside of the transmission.*

17 On models equipped with the AL4 transmission, carry out the following operations, using the information given in Chapter 7B:

a) *Disconnect the transmission ECU wiring connector, undo the ECU mounting bracket screws and remove the mounting bracket and ECU as an assembly.*

b) *Disconnect the wiring harness from the modular connector located at the rear of the transmission.*

c) *Disconnect the output speed sensor wiring plug located behind the modular connector.*

d) *Disconnect the vehicle speed sensor wiring plug.*

e) *Release the earth strap(s) from the transmission housing.*

f) *Disconnect the selector cable.*

18 Remove both driveshafts as described in Chapter 8.

19 Trace the wiring harness back from the engine to the main harness connectors at the fuse/relay box, and behind the battery tray location. Release the locking rings by twisting them anti-clockwise and disconnect the connectors. Also trace the wiring connectors back to the transmission and disconnect all engine related wiring and earth leads in this area. Check that all the relevant connectors have been disconnected, and that the harness is released from any relevant clips or ties, so that it is free to be removed with the engine/transmission.

20 Manoeuvre the engine hoist into position, and attach it to the engine lifting brackets. Raise the hoist until it is supporting the weight of the engine.

21 Slacken and remove the centre nut and washer from the engine/transmission left-hand mounting. Undo the two nuts and washers securing the mounting to its bracket, and remove the mounting from the engine compartment and recover the spacer (where fitted). Undo the remaining retaining bolts and remove the mounting bracket from the body.

22 From underneath the vehicle, slacken and remove the nuts and bolts securing the rear mounting link to the mounting assembly and subframe, and remove the link.

23 Working on the right-hand engine/transmission mounting, undo the two bolts and remove the curved retaining plate and rubber damper (where fitted) from the top of the mounting. Slacken and remove the mounting bracket retaining nuts/bolts (as applicable) and lift off the bracket. Remove the rubber damper plate from the mounting, and store it with the bracket for safe-keeping.

24 Make a final check that any components which would prevent the removal of the engine/transmission from the car have been removed or disconnected.

25 Lift the engine/transmission out of the car, ensuring that nothing is trapped or damaged. Enlist the help of an assistant during this procedure, as it will be necessary to tilt the assembly slightly to clear the body panels. On models equipped with anti-lock brakes, great care must be taken to ensure that the anti-lock braking system unit is not damaged during the removal procedure.

26 Once the engine is high enough, lift it out over the front of the body, and lower the unit to the ground.

Separation

27 With the engine/transmission assembly removed, support the assembly on suitable blocks of wood on a workbench (or failing that, on a clean area of the workshop floor).

28 On the 4 HP 14 transmission, detach the kickdown cable from the throttle cam. Work back along the cable, freeing it from any retaining clips, and noting its correct routing.

29 Undo the retaining bolts and remove the driveplate lower cover plate from the transmission, to gain access to the torque converter retaining bolts/nuts. Slacken and remove the visible bolt/nut. Rotate the crankshaft using a socket and extension bar on the pulley bolt, and undo the remaining bolts/nuts securing the torque converter to the driveplate as they become accessible. There are three bolts or three nuts in total.

30 Slacken and remove the retaining bolts, and remove the starter motor from the transmission.

31 To ensure that the torque converter does not fall out as the transmission is removed, secure it in position using a length of metal strip bolted to one of the starter motor bolt holes.

32 Ensure that both the engine and transmission are adequately supported, then slacken and remove the remaining bolts securing the transmission housing to the engine. Note the correct fitted positions of each bolt (and any relevant brackets) as they are removed, to use as a reference on refitting.

33 Carefully withdraw the transmission from the engine. If the locating dowels are a loose fit in the engine/transmission, remove them and keep them in a safe place.

Refitting

34 If the engine and transmission have been separated, perform the operations described below in paragraphs 35 to 43. If not, proceed as described from paragraph 44 onwards.

35 Ensure that the bush fitted to the centre of the crankshaft is in good condition. Apply a little Molykote G1 grease (available from your Citroën dealer) to the torque converter centring pin. Do not apply too much, otherwise there is a possibility of the grease contaminating the torque converter.

36 Ensure that the locating dowels are correctly positioned in the engine or transmission.

37 On the AL4 transmission, turn the torque converter so that one of the mounting studs is positioned opposite the right-hand driveshaft output shaft (approximately the 9 o-clock position). Turn the engine crankshaft so that the corresponding mounting hole in the driveplate is in the same position. The torque converter mounting studs and the corresponding holes in the driveplate should then be in alignment when the transmission is fitted.

38 Carefully offer the transmission to the engine, until the locating dowels are engaged.

39 Refit the transmission housing-to-engine bolts, ensuring that all the necessary brackets are correctly positioned, and tighten them to the specified torque setting.

40 Remove the torque converter retaining strap installed prior to removal.

41 On the 4 HP 14 transmission, align the torque converter threaded holes with the retaining plate, and refit the three retaining bolts. On the AL4 transmission, refit the three torque converter retaining nuts.

42 Tighten the torque converter retaining bolts/nuts to the specified torque setting, then refit the driveplate lower cover.

43 Refit the starter motor, and securely tighten its retaining bolts.

44 Refit the engine to the vehicle as described in paragraphs 43 to 48 of Section 4.

45 The remainder of the refitting procedure is

a reversal of the removal sequence, noting the following points:

a) Ensure that the wiring loom is correctly routed, and retained by all the relevant retaining clips; all connectors should be correctly and securely reconnected.

b) On the 4 HP 14 transmission, prior to refitting the driveshafts to the transmission, renew the driveshaft oil seals as described in Chapter 7B, Section 8.

c) Ensure that all coolant hoses are correctly reconnected, and securely retained by their retaining clips.

d) Adjust the selector cable and, on the 4 HP 14 transmission, the kickdown cable, as described in Chapter 7B.

e) Adjust the accelerator cable as described in Chapter 4A.

f) Refill the engine and transmission with correct quantity and type of lubricant, as described in Chapters 1A and 7B.

g) Refill the cooling system as described in Chapter 1A.

h) Bleed the power steering system as described in Chapter 10.

6 Engine overhaul – dismantling sequence

1 It is much easier to dismantle and work on the engine if it is mounted on a portable engine stand. These stands can often be hired from a tool hire shop. Before the engine is mounted on a stand, the flywheel/driveplate should be removed, so that the stand bolts can be tightened into the end of the cylinder block/crankcase.

2 If a stand is not available, it is possible to dismantle the engine with it blocked up on a sturdy workbench, or on the floor. Be extra careful not to tip or drop the engine when working without a stand.

3 If you are going to obtain a reconditioned engine, all the external components must be removed first, to be transferred to the replacement engine (just as they will if you are doing a complete engine overhaul yourself). These components include the following:

a) Alternator mounting brackets.

b) Power steering pump and air conditioning compressor brackets (where fitted).

c) Thermostat and housing, and coolant outlet chamber/elbow (Chapter 3).

d) Dipstick tube.

e) Fuel system components (Chapter 4A).

f) All electrical switches and sensors.

g) Inlet and exhaust manifolds (Chapter 4A).

h) Oil filter (Chapter 1A).

i) Flywheel/driveplate (Chapter 2A or 2B).

Note: When removing the external components from the engine, pay close attention to details that may be helpful or important during refitting. Note the fitted position of gaskets, seals, spacers, pins, washers, bolts, and other small items.

4 If you are obtaining a 'short' engine

(cylinder block/crankcase, crankshaft, pistons and connecting rods all assembled), then the cylinder head, sump, oil pump, and timing belt will have to be removed also.

5 If you are planning a complete overhaul, the engine can be dismantled, and the internal components removed, in the order given below, referring to Part A or B of this Chapter unless otherwise stated.

a) Inlet and exhaust manifolds (Chapter 4A).

b) Timing belt, sprockets and tensioner(s).

c) Cylinder head.

d) Flywheel/driveplate.

e) Sump.

f) Oil pump.

g) Pistons/connecting rods (Section 10 of this Chapter).

h) Crankshaft (Section 11 of this Chapter).

6 Before beginning the dismantling and overhaul procedures, make sure that you have all of the tools necessary. Refer to *Tools and working facilities* for further information.

7 Cylinder head – dismantling

Note: *New and reconditioned cylinder heads are available from the manufacturer, and from engine overhaul specialists. Some specialist tools are required for dismantling and inspection, and new components may not be readily available. It may therefore be more practical and economical for the home mechanic to purchase a reconditioned head, rather than dismantle, inspect and recondition the original head.*

1 Remove the cylinder head as described in Part A or B of this Chapter (as applicable).

2 If not already done, remove the inlet and exhaust manifolds with reference to Chapter 4A.

3 Remove the camshaft(s), followers and shims (as applicable) as described in Part A or B of this Chapter.

4 Using a valve spring compressor, compress each valve spring in turn until the split collets can be removed. Release the compressor, and lift off the spring retainer, spring and spring seat. Using a pair of pliers, carefully extract the valve stem oil seal from the top of the guide **(see illustrations)**.

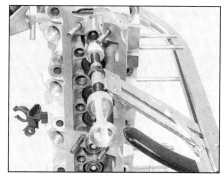

7.4a Compress the valve spring using a spring compressor . . .

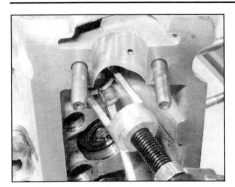

7.4b . . . then extract the collets and release the spring compressor

7.4c Remove the spring retainer . . .

7.4d . . . followed by the valve spring . . .

7.4e . . . and the spring seat

7.4f Remove the valve stem oil seal using a pair of pliers

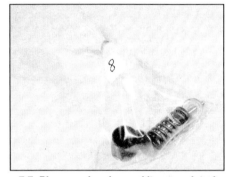

7.7 Place each valve and its associated components in a labelled polythene bag

5 If, when the valve spring compressor is screwed down, the spring retainer refuses to free and expose the split collets, gently tap the top of the tool, directly over the retainer, with a light hammer. This will free the retainer.
6 Withdraw the valve through the combustion chamber.
7 It is essential that each valve is stored together with its collets, retainer, spring, and spring seat. The valves should also be kept in their correct sequence, unless they are so badly worn that they are to be renewed. If they are going to be kept and used again, place each valve assembly in a labelled polythene bag or similar small container **(see illustration)**. Note that No 1 valve is nearest to the transmission (flywheel/driveplate) end of the engine.

8 Cylinder head and valves – cleaning and inspection

1 Thorough cleaning of the cylinder head and valve components, followed by a detailed inspection, will enable you to decide how much valve service work must be carried out during the engine overhaul. **Note:** *If the engine has been severely overheated, it is best to assume that the cylinder head is warped – check carefully for signs of this.*

Cleaning

2 Remove all traces of old gasket material

from the cylinder head. Citroën recommend the use of a scouring agent for this purpose, but acceptable results can be achieved by using a hard plastic or wood scraper to remove all traces of gasket and carbon.
3 Similarly, remove the carbon from the combustion chambers and ports, then wash the cylinder head thoroughly with paraffin or a suitable solvent.
4 Scrape off any heavy carbon deposits that may have formed on the valves, then use a power-operated wire brush to remove deposits from the valve heads and stems.

Inspection

Note: *Be sure to perform all the following inspection procedures before concluding that the services of a machine shop or engine overhaul specialist are required. Make a list of all items that require attention.*

Cylinder head

5 Inspect the head very carefully for cracks, evidence of coolant leakage, and other damage. If cracks are found, a new cylinder head should be obtained.
6 Use a straight-edge and feeler blade to check that the cylinder head gasket surface is not distorted **(see illustration)**. If it is, it may be possible to have it machined, provided that the cylinder head height is not significantly reduced.
7 Examine the valve seats in each of the combustion chambers. If they are severely pitted, cracked, or burned, they will need to

be renewed or re-cut by an engine overhaul specialist. If they are only slightly pitted, this can be removed by grinding-in the valve heads and seats with fine valve-grinding compound, as described below.
8 Check the valve guides for wear by inserting the relevant valve, and checking for side-to-side motion of the valve. A very small amount of movement is acceptable. If the movement seems excessive, remove the valve. Measure the valve stem diameter (see below), and renew the valve if it is worn. If the valve stem is not worn, the wear must be in the valve guide, and the guide must be renewed. The renewal of valve guides is best carried out by an engine overhaul specialist, who will have the necessary tools available. Where no valve stem diameter is specified,

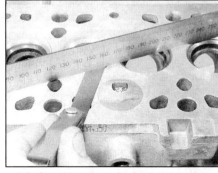

8.6 Checking the cylinder head gasket surface for distortion

seek the advice of the specialist carrying out the work, or a Citroën dealer on the best course of action.

9 If renewing the valve guides, the valve seats should be re-cut or re-ground only *after* the guides have been fitted.

Valves

10 Examine the head of each valve for pitting, burning, cracks, and general wear. Check the valve stem for scoring and wear ridges. Rotate the valve, and check for any obvious indication that it is bent. Look for pits or excessive wear on the tip of each valve stem. Renew any valve that shows any such signs of wear or damage.

11 If the valve appears satisfactory at this stage, measure the valve stem diameter at several points using a micrometer **(see illustration)**. Any significant difference in the readings obtained indicates wear of the valve stem. Should any of these conditions be apparent, the valve(s) must be renewed.

12 If the valves are in satisfactory condition, they should be ground (lapped) into their respective seats, to ensure a smooth, gas-tight seal. If the seat is only lightly pitted, or if it has been re-cut, fine grinding compound *only* should be used to produce the required finish. Coarse valve-grinding compound should *not* be used, unless a seat is badly burned or deeply pitted. If this is the case, the cylinder head and valves should be inspected by an expert, to decide whether seat re-cutting, or even the renewal of the valve or seat insert (where possible) is required.

13 Valve grinding is carried out as follows. Place the head upside-down on blocks, on a bench.

14 Smear a trace of (the appropriate grade of) valve-grinding compound on the seat face, and press a suction grinding tool onto the valve head **(see illustration)**. With a semi-rotary action, grind the valve head to its seat, lifting the valve occasionally to redistribute the grinding compound. A light spring placed under the valve head will greatly ease this operation.

15 If coarse grinding compound is being used, work only until a dull, matt even surface is produced on both the valve seat and the valve, then wipe off the used compound, and repeat the process with fine compound. When a smooth unbroken ring of light grey matt finish is produced on both the valve and seat, the grinding operation is complete. *Do not* grind-in the valves any further than absolutely necessary, or the seat will be prematurely sunk into the cylinder head.

16 When all the valves have been ground-in, carefully wash off *all* traces of grinding compound using paraffin or a suitable solvent, before reassembling the cylinder head.

Valve components

17 Examine the valve springs for signs of damage and discoloration. No minimum free

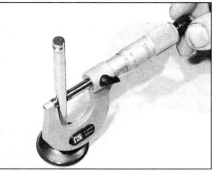

8.11 Measuring a valve stem diameter

length is specified by Citroën, so the only way of judging valve spring wear is by comparison with a new component.

18 Stand each spring on a flat surface, and check it for squareness. If any of the springs are damaged, distorted or have lost their tension, obtain a complete new set of springs. It is normal to fit new springs as a matter of course if a major overhaul is being carried out.

19 Renew the valve stem oil seals regardless of their apparent condition.

9 Cylinder head – reassembly

1 Lubricate the stems of the valves, and insert the valves into their original locations **(see illustration)**. If new valves are being fitted, insert them into the locations to which they have been ground.

2 Refit the spring seat then, working on the first valve, dip the new valve stem seal in fresh engine oil. Carefully locate it over the valve and onto the guide. Take care not to damage the seal as it is passed over the valve stem. Use a suitable socket or tube to press the seal firmly onto the guide **(see illustration)**.

3 Locate the valve spring on top of its seat, then refit the spring retainer.

4 Compress the valve spring, and locate the split collets in the recess in the valve stem. Release the compressor, then repeat the procedure on the remaining valves.

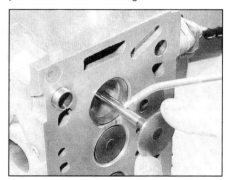

9.1 Lubricate the valve stems prior to refitting

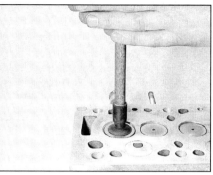

8.14 Grinding-in a valve

> **HAYNES HINT**
>
> *Use a little dab of grease to hold the collets in position on the valve stem while the spring compressor is released.*

5 With all the valves installed, place the cylinder head on blocks on the bench and, using a hammer and interposed block of wood, tap the end of each valve stem to settle the components.

6 Refit the camshaft(s), followers and shims (as applicable) as described in Part A or B of this Chapter.

7 The cylinder head can then be refitted as described in Part A or B of this Chapter.

10 Piston/connecting rod assembly – removal

1 Remove the cylinder head, sump and oil pump as described in Part A or B of this Chapter (as applicable).

2 If there is a pronounced wear ridge at the top of any bore, it may be necessary to remove it with a scraper or ridge reamer, to avoid piston damage during removal. Such a ridge indicates excess bore wear.

3 Using quick-drying paint or similar, mark each connecting rod and big-end bearing cap with its respective cylinder number on the flat machined surface provided; if the engine has been dismantled before, note carefully any

9.2 Fitting a valve stem oil seal using a socket

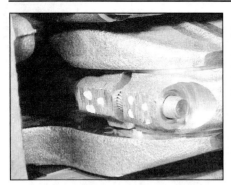

10.3 Connecting rod and big-end bearing cap identification marks (No 3 shown)

10.5 Removing a big-end bearing cap and shell

10.6 To protect the crankshaft journals, tape over the connecting rod stud threads

identifying marks made previously **(see illustration)**. Note that No 1 cylinder is at the transmission (flywheel/driveplate) end of the engine.

4 Turn the crankshaft to bring pistons 1 and 4 to BDC (bottom dead centre).

5 Unscrew the nuts from No 1 piston big-end bearing cap. Take off the cap, and recover the bottom half bearing shell **(see illustration)**. If the bearing shells are to be re-used, tape the cap and the shell together.

6 To prevent the possibility of damage to the crankshaft bearing journals, tape over the connecting rod stud threads **(see illustration)**.

7 Using a hammer handle, push the piston up through the bore, and remove it from the top of the cylinder block. Recover the bearing shell, and tape it to the connecting rod for safe-keeping.

8 Loosely refit the big-end cap to the connecting rod, and secure with the nuts – this will help to keep the components in their correct order.

9 Remove No 4 assembly in the same way.

10 Turn the crankshaft through 180° to bring pistons 2 and 3 to BDC (bottom dead centre), and remove them in the same way.

11 Crankshaft – removal

1 Remove the crankshaft sprocket and the oil pump as described in Part A or B of this Chapter (as applicable).

2 Remove the pistons and connecting rods, as described in Section 10. If no work is to be done on the pistons and connecting rods, there is no need to remove the cylinder head, or to push the pistons out of the cylinder bores. The pistons should just be pushed far enough up the bores so that they are positioned clear of the crankshaft journals.

3 Check the crankshaft endfloat as described in Section 14, then proceed as follows.

TU series aluminium block engines

4 Work around the outside of the cylinder block, and unscrew all the small (6 mm) bolts

securing the main bearing ladder to the base of the cylinder block. Note the correct fitted depth of both the left- and right-hand crankshaft oil seals in the cylinder block/main bearing ladder.

5 Working in a diagonal sequence, evenly and progressively slacken the ten large (11 mm) main bearing ladder retaining bolts by a turn at a time. Once all the bolts are loose, remove them from the ladder.

6 With all the retaining bolts removed, carefully lift the main bearing ladder casting away from the base of the cylinder block. Recover the lower main bearing shells, and tape them to their respective locations in the casting. If the two locating dowels are a loose fit, remove them and store them with the casting for safe-keeping.

7 Lift out the crankshaft, and discard both the oil seals. Remove the oil pump drive chain from the end of the crankshaft. Where necessary, slide off the drive sprocket, and recover the Woodruff key.

8 Recover the upper main bearing shells, and store them along with the relevant lower bearing shell. Also recover the two thrustwashers (one fitted either side of No 2 main bearing) from the cylinder block.

TU series cast-iron block engines

9 Unbolt and remove the crankshaft left- and right-hand oil seal housings from each end of the cylinder block, noting the correct fitted locations of the locating dowels. If the locating dowels are a loose fit, remove them

11.15 Removing the oil seal carrier from the block – XU series engines

and store them with the housings for safe-keeping.

10 Remove the oil pump drive chain, and slide the drive sprocket off the end of the crankshaft. Remove the Woodruff key, and store it with the sprocket for safe-keeping.

11 The main bearing caps should be numbered 1 to 5 from the transmission (flywheel/driveplate) end of the engine. If not, mark them accordingly using quick-drying paint.

12 Unscrew and remove the main bearing cap retaining bolts, and withdraw the caps. Recover the lower main bearing shells, and tape them to their respective caps for safe-keeping.

13 Carefully lift out the crankshaft, taking care not to displace the upper main bearing shell.

14 Recover the upper bearing shells from the cylinder block, and tape them to their respective caps for safe-keeping. Remove the thrustwasher halves from the side of No 2 main bearing, and store them with the bearing cap.

XU series engines

15 Slacken and remove the retaining bolts, and remove the oil seal carrier from the right-hand end of the cylinder block, along with its gasket (where fitted) **(see illustration)**.

16 Remove the oil pump drive chain, and slide the drive sprocket and spacer (where fitted) off the end of the crankshaft. Remove the Woodruff key, and store it with the sprocket for safe-keeping **(see illustrations)**.

11.16a Remove the oil pump drive chain . . .

11.16b ... then slide off the drive sprocket ...

11.16c ... and remove the Woodruff key from the crankshaft – XU series engines

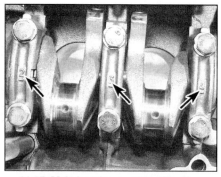

11.17 Main bearing cap identification markings (arrowed) – XU series engines

11.19 Removing No 2 main bearing cap. Note the thrustwasher (arrowed) – XU series engines

11.20 Lifting out the crankshaft – XU series engines

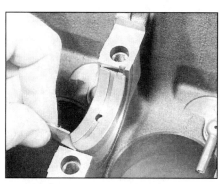

11.21 Remove the upper main bearing shells and store them with their lower shells – XU series engines

17 The main bearing caps should be numbered 1 to 5, starting from the transmission (flywheel/driveplate) end of the engine **(see illustration)**. If not, mark them accordingly using quick-drying paint. Also note the correct fitted depth of the left-hand crankshaft oil seal in the bearing cap.

18 On 1.8 litre engines, undo the two bolts (one at the front of the block, and one at the rear) securing the centre main bearing cap to the block. Remove the bolts, along with their sealing washers.

19 On all engines, slacken and remove the main bearing cap retaining bolts/nuts, and lift off each bearing cap. Recover the lower bearing shells, and tape them to their respective caps for safe-keeping. Also recover the lower thrustwasher halves from

the side of No 2 main bearing cap **(see illustration)**. Remove the sealing strips from the sides of No 1 main bearing cap, and discard them.

20 Lift out the crankshaft **(see illustration)**, and discard the left-hand oil seal.

21 Recover the upper bearing shells from the cylinder block **(see illustration)**, and tape them to their respective caps for safe-keeping. Remove the upper thrustwasher halves from the side of No 2 main bearing, and store them with the lower halves.

12 Cylinder block/crankcase – cleaning and inspection

Cleaning

1 Remove all external components and electrical switches/sensors from the block. For complete cleaning, the core plugs should ideally be removed **(see illustration)**. Drill a small hole in the plugs, then insert a self-tapping screw into the hole. Pull out the plugs by pulling on the screw with a pair of grips, or by using a slide hammer.

2 On aluminium block engines with wet liners, remove the liners – see paragraph 18.

3 Where fitted, undo the retaining bolt and remove the piston oil jet spray tube from inside the cylinder block.

4 Scrape all traces of gasket from the cylinder block/crankcase, and from the main bearing ladder (where fitted), taking care not to damage the gasket/sealing surfaces.

5 Remove all oil gallery plugs (where fitted). The plugs are usually very tight – they may have to be drilled out, and the holes re-tapped. Use new plugs when the engine is reassembled.

6 If any of the castings are extremely dirty, all should be steam-cleaned.

7 After the castings are returned, clean all oil holes and oil galleries one more time. Flush all internal passages with warm water until the water runs clear. Dry thoroughly, and apply a light film of oil to all mating surfaces, to prevent rusting. On cast-iron block engines, also oil the cylinder bores. If you have access to compressed air, use it to speed up the drying process, and to blow out all the oil holes and galleries.

⚠️ **Warning: Wear eye protection when using compressed air.**

8 If the castings are not very dirty, you can do an adequate cleaning job with very hot, soapy water and a stiff brush. Take plenty of time, and do a thorough job. Regardless of the cleaning method used, be sure to clean all oil holes and galleries very thoroughly, and to dry all components well. On cast-iron block engines, protect the cylinder bores as described above, to prevent rusting.

9 All threaded holes must be clean, to ensure

12.1 Cylinder block core plugs (arrowed)

12.9 Cleaning a cylinder block threaded hole using a suitable tap

12.18a On aluminium block engines, remove each liner . . .

12.18b . . . and recover the bottom O-ring seal (arrowed)

accurate torque readings during reassembly. To clean the threads, run the correct-size tap into each of the holes to remove rust, corrosion, thread sealant or sludge, and to restore damaged threads **(see illustration)**. If possible, use compressed air to clear the holes of debris produced by this operation.

 Warning: Wear eye protection when using compressed air.

10 Apply suitable sealant to the new oil gallery plugs, and insert them into the holes in the block. Tighten them securely.

11 On engines with a piston oil jet spray tube, clean the threads of the oil jet retaining bolt, and apply a drop of thread-locking compound to the bolt threads. Refit the piston oil jet spray tube to the cylinder block, and tighten its retaining bolt to the specified torque setting.

12 If the engine is not going to be reassembled right away, cover it with a large plastic bag to keep it clean; protect all mating surfaces and the cylinder bores as described above, to prevent rusting.

Inspection

Cast-iron cylinder block

13 Visually check the castings for cracks and corrosion. Look for stripped threads in the threaded holes. If there has been any history of internal water leakage, it may be worthwhile having an engine overhaul specialist check the cylinder block/crankcase with special equipment. If defects are found, have them repaired if possible, or renew the assembly.

14 Check each cylinder bore for scuffing and scoring. Check for signs of a wear ridge at the top of the cylinder, indicating that the bore is excessively worn.

15 If the necessary measuring equipment is available, measure the bore diameter of each cylinder liner at the top (just under the wear ridge), centre, and bottom of the cylinder bore, parallel to the crankshaft axis.

16 Next, measure the bore diameter at the same three locations, at right-angles to the crankshaft axis. Compare the results with the figures given in the Specifications. Where no figures are stated by Citroën, if there is any doubt about the condition of the cylinder

bores, seek the advice of an engine reconditioning specialist or Citroën dealer.

17 At the time of writing, it was not clear whether oversize pistons were available for all engines. Consult your Citroën dealer for the latest information on piston availability. If oversize pistons are available, then it may be possible to have the cylinder bores rebored and fit the oversize pistons. If oversize pistons are not available, and the bores are worn, renewal of the block seems to be the only option.

Aluminium cylinder block with wet liners

18 Remove the liner clamps (where used), then use a hard wood drift to tap out each liner from the inside of the cylinder block. When all the liners are released, tip the cylinder block/crankcase on its side and remove each liner from the top of the block. As each liner is removed, stick masking tape on its left-hand (transmission side) face, and write the cylinder number on the tape. No 1 cylinder is at the transmission (flywheel/driveplate) end of the engine. Remove the O-ring from the base of each liner, and discard **(see illustrations)**.

19 Check each cylinder liner for scuffing and scoring. Check for signs of a wear ridge at the top of the liner, indicating that the bore is excessively worn.

20 If the necessary measuring equipment is available, measure the bore diameter of each cylinder liner at the top (just under the wear ridge), centre, and bottom of the cylinder bore, parallel to the crankshaft axis.

21 Next, measure the bore diameter at the same three locations, at right-angles to the crankshaft axis. Compare the results with the figures given in the Specifications.

22 Repeat the procedure for the remaining cylinder liners.

23 If the liner wear exceeds the permitted tolerances at any point, or if the cylinder liner walls are badly scored or scuffed, then renewal of the relevant liner assembly will be necessary. If there is any doubt about the condition of the cylinder bores, seek the advice of an engine reconditioning specialist or Citroën dealer.

24 If renewal is necessary, new liners, complete with pistons and piston rings, can be purchased from a Citroën dealer. Note that it is not possible to buy liners individually – they are supplied only as a matched assembly complete with piston and rings.

25 To allow for manufacturing tolerances, pistons and liners are separated into three size groups. The size group of each piston is indicated by a letter (A, B or C) stamped onto its crown, and the size group of each liner is indicated by a series of 1 to 3 notches on the upper lip of the liner; a single notch for group A, two notches for group B, and three notches for group C. Ensure that each piston and its respective liner are both of the same size group. It is permissible to have different size group piston and liner assemblies fitted to the same engine, but never fit a piston of one size group to a liner in a different group. On some later engine, pistons and liners are manufactured in only one size group.

26 Prior to installing the liners, thoroughly clean the liner mating surfaces in the cylinder block, and use fine abrasive paper to polish away any burrs or sharp edges which might damage the liner O-rings. Clean the liners and wipe dry, then fit a new O-ring to the base of each liner. To aid installation, apply a smear of oil to each O-ring and to the base of the liner.

27 If the original liners are being refitted, use the marks made on removal to ensure that each is refitted the correct way round, and is inserted into its original bore. Insert each liner into the cylinder block, taking care not to damage the O-ring, and press it home as far as possible by hand. Using a hammer and a block of wood, tap each liner lightly but fully onto its locating shoulder. Wipe clean, then lightly oil all exposed liner surfaces, to prevent rusting.

28 With all four liners correctly installed, use a dial gauge (or a straight-edge and feeler blade) to check that the protrusion of each liner above the upper surface of the cylinder block is within the limits given in the Specifications. The maximum difference between any two liners must not be exceeded.

29 If new liners are being fitted, it is permissible to interchange them to bring the

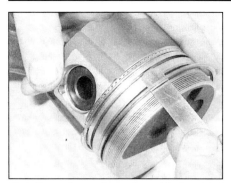

13.2 Removing a piston ring with the aid of a feeler blade

14.2 Checking crankshaft endfloat using a dial gauge

14.3 Checking crankshaft endfloat using feeler blades

difference in protrusion within limits. Remember to keep each piston with its respective liner.

30 If liner protrusion cannot be brought within limits, seek the advice of an engine reconditioning specialist or Citroën dealer before proceeding with the engine rebuild.

13 Piston/connecting rod assembly – inspection

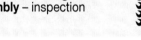

1 Before the inspection process can begin, the piston/connecting rod assemblies must be cleaned, and the original piston rings removed from the pistons.

2 Carefully expand the old rings over the top of the pistons. The use of two or three old feeler blades will be helpful in preventing the rings dropping into empty grooves **(see illustration)**. Be careful not to scratch the piston with the ends of the ring. The rings are brittle, and will snap if they are spread too far. They are also very sharp – protect your hands and fingers. Note that the third ring incorporates an expander. Always remove the rings from the top of the piston. Keep each set of rings with its piston if the old rings are to be re-used.

3 Scrape away all traces of carbon from the top of the piston. A hand-held wire brush (or a piece of fine emery cloth) can be used, once the majority of the deposits have been scraped away.

4 Remove the carbon from the ring grooves in the piston, using an old ring. Break the ring in half to do this (be careful not to cut your fingers – piston rings are sharp). Be careful to remove only the carbon deposits – do not remove any metal, and do not nick or scratch the sides of the ring grooves.

5 Once the deposits have been removed, clean the piston/connecting rod assembly with paraffin or a suitable solvent, and dry thoroughly. Make sure that the oil return holes in the ring grooves are clear.

6 If the pistons and cylinder bores are not damaged or worn excessively, and if the cylinder block does not need to be rebored, the original pistons can be refitted. Normal piston wear shows up as even vertical wear on the piston thrust surfaces, and slight looseness of the top ring in its groove. New piston rings should always be used when the engine is reassembled.

7 Carefully inspect each piston for cracks around the skirt, around the gudgeon pin holes, and at the piston ring 'lands' (between the ring grooves).

8 Look for scoring and scuffing on the piston skirt, holes in the piston crown, and burned areas at the edge of the crown. If the skirt is scored or scuffed, the engine may have been suffering from overheating, and/or abnormal combustion which caused excessively high operating temperatures. The cooling and lubrication systems should be checked thoroughly. Scorch marks on the sides of the pistons show that blow-by has occurred. A hole in the piston crown, or burned areas at the edge of the piston crown, indicates that abnormal combustion (pre-ignition, knocking, or detonation) has been occurring. If any of the above problems exist, the causes must be investigated and corrected, or the damage will occur again.

9 Corrosion of the piston, in the form of pitting, indicates that coolant has been leaking into the combustion chamber and/or the crankcase. Again, the cause must be corrected, or the problem may persist in the rebuilt engine.

10 On aluminium-block engines with wet liners, it is not possible to renew the pistons separately; pistons are only supplied with piston rings and a liner, as a part of a matched assembly (see Section 12). On iron-block engines, pistons can be purchased from a Citroën dealer.

11 Examine each connecting rod carefully for signs of damage, such as cracks around the big-end and small-end bearings. Check that the rod is not bent or distorted. Damage is highly unlikely, unless the engine has been seized or badly overheated. Detailed checking of the connecting rod assembly can only be carried out by an engine specialist or Citroën dealer with the necessary equipment.

12 On XU series engines, the big-end cap nuts and bolts must be renewed as a complete set prior to refitting. This should be done after the big-end bearing running clearance check has been carried out (see Section 19). The bolts can be simply tapped out of the connecting rods and new bolts fitted in the same way.

13 On all engines, the gudgeon pins are an interference fit in the connecting rod small-end bearing. Therefore, piston and/or connecting rod renewal should be entrusted to an engine repair specialist who will have the necessary tooling to remove and install the gudgeon pins.

14 Crankshaft – inspection

Checking crankshaft endfloat

1 If the crankshaft endfloat is to be checked, this must be done when the crankshaft is still installed in the cylinder block/crankcase, but is free to move (see Section 11).

2 Check the endfloat using a dial gauge in contact with the end of the crankshaft. Push the crankshaft fully one way, and then zero the gauge. Push the crankshaft fully the other way, and check the endfloat. The result can be compared with the specified amount, and will give an indication as to whether new thrustwashers are required **(see illustration)**.

3 If a dial gauge is not available, feeler blades can be used. First push the crankshaft fully towards the flywheel end of the engine, then use feeler blades to measure the gap between the web of No 2 crankpin and the thrustwasher **(see illustration)**.

Inspection

4 Clean the crankshaft using paraffin or a suitable solvent, and dry it, preferably with compressed air if available. Be sure to clean the oil holes with a pipe cleaner or similar probe, to ensure that they are not obstructed.

 Warning: Wear eye protection when using compressed air.

5 Check the main and big-end bearing journals for uneven wear, scoring, pitting and cracking.

6 Big-end bearing wear is accompanied by distinct metallic knocking when the engine is running (particularly noticeable when the engine is pulling from low speed) and some loss of oil pressure.

7 Main bearing wear is accompanied by severe engine vibration and rumble – getting progressively worse as engine speed increases – and again by loss of oil pressure.

8 Check the bearing journal for roughness by running a finger lightly over the bearing surface. Any roughness (which will be accompanied by obvious bearing wear) indicates that the crankshaft requires regrinding (where possible) or renewal.

9 If the crankshaft has been reground, check for burrs around the crankshaft oil holes (the holes are usually chamfered, so burrs should not be a problem unless regrinding has been carried out carelessly). Remove any burrs with a fine file or scraper, and thoroughly clean the oil holes as described previously.

10 Using a micrometer, measure the diameter of the main and big-end bearing journals, and compare the results with the Specifications **(see illustration)**. By measuring the diameter at a number of points around each journal's circumference, you will be able to determine whether or not the journal is out-of-round. Take the measurement at each end of the journal, near the webs, to determine if the journal is tapered. Compare the results obtained with those given in the Specifications. Where no specified journal diameters are quoted, seek the advice of a Citroën dealer.

11 Check the oil seal contact surfaces at each end of the crankshaft for wear and damage. If the seal has worn a deep groove in the surface of the crankshaft, consult an engine overhaul specialist; repair may be possible, but otherwise a new crankshaft will be required.

14.10 Measuring a crankshaft big-end journal diameter

12 Citroën produce a set of oversize bearing shells for both the main and big-end bearings for most engines. Where oversize bearing shells are available, and if the crankshaft journals have not already been reground, it may be possible to have the crankshaft reconditioned, and to fit oversize shells (see Section 18). If no oversize shells are available and the crankshaft has worn beyond the specified limits, it will have to be renewed. Consult your Citroën dealer or engine specialist for further information on parts availability.

15 Main and big-end bearings – inspection

1 Even though the main and big-end bearings should be renewed during the engine overhaul, the old bearings should be retained for close examination, as they may reveal valuable information about the condition of the engine. The bearing shells are graded by thickness, the grade of each shell being indicated by the colour code, or size identification, marked on it.

2 Bearing failure can occur due to lack of lubrication, the presence of dirt or other foreign particles, overloading the engine, or corrosion **(see illustration)**. Regardless of the cause of bearing failure, the cause must be corrected (where applicable) before the engine is reassembled, to prevent it from happening again.

3 When examining the bearing shells, remove them from the cylinder block/crankcase, the main bearing ladder/caps (as appropriate), the connecting rods and the connecting rod big-end bearing caps. Lay them out on a clean surface in the same general position as their location in the engine. This will enable you to match any bearing problems with the corresponding crankshaft journal. *Do not* touch any shell's bearing surface with your fingers while checking it, or the delicate surface may be scratched.

4 Dirt and other foreign matter gets into the engine in a variety of ways. It may be left in the engine during assembly, or it may pass through filters or the crankcase ventilation

system. It may get into the oil, and from there into the bearings. Metal chips from machining operations and normal engine wear are often present. Abrasives are sometimes left in engine components after reconditioning, especially when parts are not thoroughly cleaned using the proper cleaning methods. Whatever the source, these foreign objects often end up embedded in the soft bearing material, and are easily recognised. Large particles will not embed in the bearing, and will score or gouge the bearing and journal. The best prevention for this cause of bearing failure is to clean all parts thoroughly, and keep everything spotlessly-clean during engine assembly. Frequent and regular engine oil and filter changes are also recommended.

5 Lack of lubrication (or lubrication breakdown) has a number of interrelated causes. Excessive heat (which thins the oil), overloading (which squeezes the oil from the bearing face) and oil leakage (from excessive bearing clearances, worn oil pump or high engine speeds) all contribute to lubrication breakdown. Blocked oil passages, which usually are the result of misaligned oil holes in a bearing shell, will also oil-starve a bearing, and destroy it. When lack of lubrication is the cause of bearing failure, the bearing material is wiped or extruded from the steel backing of the bearing. Temperatures may increase to the point where the steel backing turns blue from overheating.

6 Driving habits can have a definite effect on bearing life. Full-throttle, low-speed operation (labouring the engine) puts very high loads on bearings, tending to squeeze out the oil film. These loads cause the bearings to flex, which produces fine cracks in the bearing face (fatigue failure). Eventually, the bearing material will loosen in pieces, and tear away from the steel backing.

7 Short-distance driving leads to corrosion of bearings, because insufficient engine heat is produced to drive off the condensed water and corrosive gases. These products collect in the engine oil, forming acid and sludge. As the oil is carried to the engine bearings, the acid attacks and corrodes the bearing material.

8 Incorrect bearing installation during engine assembly will lead to bearing failure as well. Tight-fitting bearings leave insufficient bearing running clearance, and will result in oil starvation. Dirt or foreign particles trapped behind a bearing shell result in high spots on the bearing, which lead to failure.

9 *Do not* touch any shell's bearing surface with your fingers during reassembly; there is a risk of scratching the delicate surface, or of depositing particles of dirt on it.

10 As mentioned at the beginning of this Section, the bearing shells should be renewed as a matter of course during engine overhaul; to do otherwise is false economy. Refer to Section 18 for details of bearing shell selection.

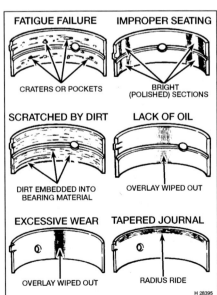

FATIGUE FAILURE	IMPROPER SEATING
CRATERS OR POCKETS	BRIGHT (POLISHED) SECTIONS
SCRATCHED BY DIRT	LACK OF OIL
DIRT EMBEDDED INTO BEARING MATERIAL	OVERLAY WIPED OUT
EXCESSIVE WEAR	TAPERED JOURNAL
OVERLAY WIPED OUT	RADIUS RIDE

H 28395

15.2 Typical bearing failures

16 Engine overhaul – reassembly sequence

1 Before reassembly begins, ensure that all new parts have been obtained, and that all necessary tools are available. Read through the entire procedure to familiarise yourself with the work involved, and to ensure that all items necessary for reassembly of the engine are at hand. In addition to all normal tools and materials, thread-locking compound will be needed. A suitable tube of liquid sealant will also be required for the joint faces that are fitted without gaskets. It is recommended that Citroën's own products are used, which are specially formulated for this purpose; the relevant product names are quoted in the text of each Section where they are required.

2 In order to save time and avoid problems, engine reassembly can be carried out in the following order:
a) Crankshaft (See Section 18).
b) Piston/connecting rod assemblies (See Section 19).
c) Oil pump (See Part A or B – as applicable).
d) Sump (See Part A or B – as applicable).
e) Flywheel/driveplate (See Part A or B – as applicable).
f) Cylinder head (See Part A or B – as applicable).
g) Timing belt tensioner and sprockets, and timing belt (See Part A or B – as applicable).
h) Engine external components.

3 At this stage, all engine components should be absolutely clean and dry, with all faults repaired. The components should be laid out (or in individual containers) on a completely clean work surface.

17 Piston rings – refitting

1 Before fitting new piston rings, the ring end gaps must be checked as follows.

2 Lay out the piston/connecting rod assemblies and the new piston ring sets, so that the ring sets will be matched with the same piston and cylinder during the end gap measurement and subsequent engine reassembly.

3 Insert the top ring into the first cylinder, and push it down the bore using the top of the piston. This will ensure that the ring remains square with the cylinder walls. Position the ring near the bottom of the cylinder bore, at the lower limit of ring travel. Note that the top and second compression rings are different. The second ring is easily identified by the step on its lower surface, and by the fact that its outer face is tapered.

4 Measure the end gap using feeler blades.

5 Repeat the procedure with the ring at the

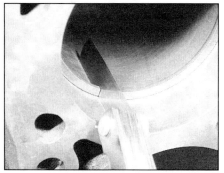

17.5 Measuring a piston ring end gap

top of the cylinder bore, at the upper limit of its travel and compare the measurements with the figures given in the Specifications **(see illustration)**.

6 If the gap is too small (unlikely if genuine Citroën parts are used), it must be enlarged, or the ring ends may contact each other during engine operation, causing serious damage. Ideally, new piston rings providing the correct end gap should be fitted. As a last resort, the end gap can be increased by filing the ring ends very carefully with a fine file. Mount the file in a vice equipped with soft jaws, slip the ring over the file with the ends contacting the file face, and slowly move the ring to remove material from the ends. Take care, as piston rings are sharp, and are easily broken.

7 With new piston rings, it is unlikely that the end gap will be too large. If the gaps are too large, check that you have the correct rings for your engine and for the cylinder bore size.

8 Repeat the checking procedure for each ring in the first cylinder, and then for the rings in the remaining cylinders. Remember to keep rings, pistons and cylinders matched up.

9 Once the ring end gaps have been checked and if necessary corrected, the rings can be fitted to the pistons.

10 Fit the piston rings using the same technique as for removal. Fit the bottom (oil control) ring first, and work up. When fitting the oil control ring, first insert the expander

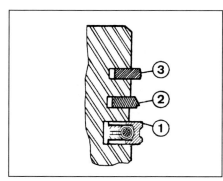

17.10 Piston ring fitting diagram (typical)

1   Oil control ring
2   Second compression ring
3   Top compression ring

(where fitted), then fit the ring with its gap positioned 180° from the expander gap. Ensure that the second compression ring is fitted the correct way up, with its identification mark (either a dot of paint or the word TOP stamped on the ring surface) at the top, and the stepped surface at the bottom **(see illustration)**. Arrange the gaps of the top and second compression rings 120° either side of the oil control ring gap. **Note:** *Always follow any instructions supplied with the new piston ring sets – different manufacturers may specify different procedures. Do not mix up the top and second compression rings, as they have different cross-sections.*

18 Crankshaft – refitting and main bearing running clearance check

Selection of new bearing shells

TU series engines

1 To ensure that the main bearing running clearance can be accurately set, the bearing shells are supplied in different thicknesses (grades). On cast iron block engines there are three different grades of bearing shell, and on aluminium block engines there are six different grades. The grades are indicated by a colour-coding marked on the edge of each shell, which denotes the shell's thickness, as listed in the following table. The upper shell on all bearings is of the same size (class B, colour code black), and the running clearance is controlled by fitting a lower bearing shell of the required thickness.

Aluminium block engine

Bearing colour code	Thickness (mm)	
	Standard	Undersize
Blue (class A)	1.823	1.973
Orange (class B)	1.829	1.979
Black (class C)	1.835	1.985
Yellow (class D)	1.841	1.991
Green (class E)	1.847	1.998
White (class F)	1.853	2.003

Cast-iron block engine

Bearing colour code	Thickness (mm)	
	Standard	Undersize
Blue (class A)	1.844	1.994
Black (class B)	1.858	2.008
Green (class C)	1.869	2.019

2 New bearing shells can be selected using the reference marks on the cylinder block/crankcase. The cylinder block marks identify the diameter of the bearing bores and the crankshaft marks, the diameter of the crankshaft journals.

3 The cylinder block reference marks are on the right-hand (timing belt) end of the block, and the crankshaft reference marks are on the right-hand (timing belt) end of the crankshaft,

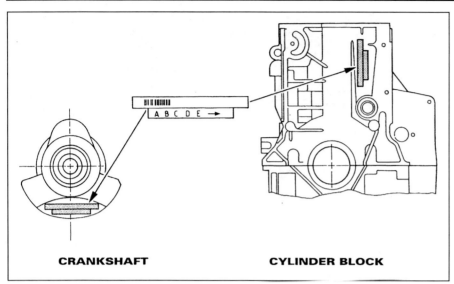

18.3 Cylinder block and crankshaft main bearing reference markings – TU series engines

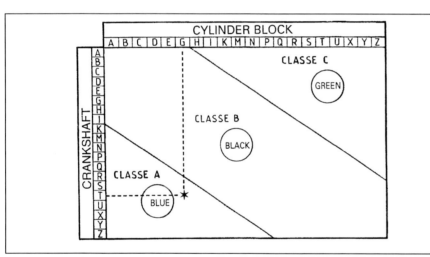

18.5a Three class main bearing shell selection chart – TU series engines

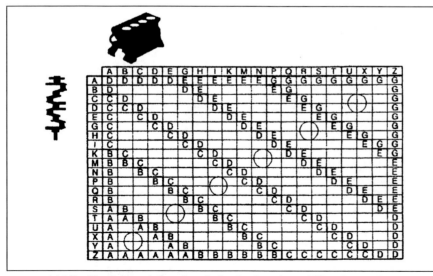

18.5b Six class main bearing shell selection chart – TU series engines

on the right-hand web of No 4 crankpin **(see illustration)**. These marks can be used to select bearing shells of the required thickness as follows.

4 On both the crankshaft and block there are two lines of identification: a bar code, which is used by Citroën during production, and a row of five letters. The first letter in the sequence refers to the size of No 1 bearing (at the flywheel/driveplate end). The last letter in the sequence (which is followed by an arrow) refers to the size of No 5 main bearing. These marks can be used to select the required bearing shell grade as follows.

5 Obtain the identification letter of both the relevant crankshaft journal and the cylinder block bearing bore. Noting that the cylinder block letters are listed across the top of the chart, and the crankshaft letters down the side, trace a vertical line down from the relevant cylinder block letter, and a horizontal line across from the relevant crankshaft letter, and find the point at which both lines cross. This crossover point will indicate the grade of lower bearing shell required to give the correct main bearing running clearance. For example, illustration 18.5a shows cylinder block reference G, and crankshaft reference T, crossing at a point within the area of Class A, indicating that a blue-coded (Class A) lower bearing shell is required to give the correct main bearing running clearance **(see illustrations)**.

6 Repeat this procedure so that the required bearing shell grade is obtained for each of the five main bearing journals.

7 Seek the advice of your Citroën dealer for the latest information on parts availability when ordering new bearing shells.

XU series engines

8 To ensure that the main bearing running clearance can be accurately set on XU series engines, the bearing shells are supplied in four different thicknesses (grades). The grades are indicated by a colour-coding marked on the edge of each shell, which denotes the shell's thickness, as listed in the following table. The upper shell on all bearings is of the same size, and the running clearance is controlled by fitting a lower bearing shell of the required thickness. **Note:** *On all XU series engines, upper shells are easily distinguished from lower shells, by their grooved bearing surface; the lower shells have a plain surface.*

1.8 litre engine

Bearing colour code	Thickness (mm)	
	Standard	Undersize
Upper bearing:		
Yellow	1.856	2.006
Lower bearing:		
Blue (class A)	1.836	1.986
Black (class B)	1.848	1.998
Green (class C)	1.859	2.009
Red (Class D)	1.870	2.020

2.0 litre engine

Bearing colour code	Thickness (mm) Standard	Undersize
Upper bearing:		
Black 1.847	1.997	
Lower bearing:		
Blue (class A)	1.844	1.994
Black (class B)	1.857	2.007
Green (class C)	1.866	2.016
Red (Class D)	1.877	2.027

9 On most engines, new bearing shells can be selected using the reference marks on the cylinder block/crankcase.

10 The cylinder block marks identify the diameter of the bearing bores and the crankshaft marks, the diameter of the crankshaft journals. Where no marks are present, the bearing shells can only be selected by checking the running clearance (see below).

11 The cylinder block reference marks are on the left-hand (flywheel/driveplate) end of the block, and the crankshaft reference marks are on the end web of the crankshaft **(see illustration)**. These marks can be used to select bearing shells of the required thickness as follows.

12 On both the crankshaft and block there are two lines of identification: a bar code, which is used by Citroën during production, and a row of five letters. The first letter in the sequence refers to the size of No 1 bearing (at the flywheel/driveplate end). The last letter in the sequence (which is followed by an arrow) refers to the size of No 5 main bearing. These marks can be used to select the required bearing shell grade as follows.

13 Obtain the identification number/letter of both the relevant crankshaft journal and the cylinder block bearing bore. Noting that the crankshaft references are listed across the top of the chart, and the cylinder block references down the side, trace a vertical line down from the relevant crankshaft reference, and a horizontal line across from the relevant cylinder block reference, and find the point at which both lines cross. This crossover point

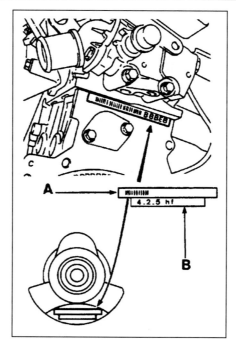

18.11 Cylinder block and crankshaft main bearing reference markings – XU series engines

A *Bar code (for production use only)*
B *Reference marks*

will indicate the grade of lower bearing shell required to give the correct main bearing running clearance. For example, illustration 18.13 shows crankshaft reference 6, and cylinder block reference H, crossing at a point within the RED area, indicating that a Red-coded (Class D) lower bearing shell is required to give the correct main bearing running clearance **(see illustration)**.

14 Repeat this procedure so that the required bearing shell grade is obtained for each of the five main bearing journals.

15 Seek the advice of your Citroën dealer on parts availability, and on the best course of action when ordering new bearing shells.

Main bearing running clearance check

TU series aluminium block engines

16 The running clearance check can be carried out using the original bearing shells. However, it is preferable to use a new set, since the results obtained will be more conclusive.

17 Clean the backs of the bearing shells, and the bearing locations in both the cylinder block/crankcase and the main bearing ladder.

18 Press the bearing shells into their locations, ensuring that the tab on each shell engages in the notch in the cylinder block/crankcase or main bearing ladder location. Take care not to touch any shell's bearing surface with your fingers. Note that the grooved bearing shells, both upper and lower, are fitted to Nos 2 and 4 main bearings **(see illustration)**. If the original bearing shells are being used for the check, ensure that they are refitted in their original locations. The clearance can be checked in either of two ways.

19 One method (which will be difficult to achieve without a range of internal micrometers or internal/external expanding calipers) is to refit the main bearing ladder casting to the cylinder block/crankcase, with the bearing shells in place. With the casting retaining bolts correctly tightened, measure the internal diameter of each assembled pair of bearing shells. If the diameter of each corresponding crankshaft journal is measured and then subtracted from the bearing internal diameter, the result will be the main bearing running clearance.

20 The second (and more accurate) method is to use an American product known as Plastigauge. This consists of a fine thread of perfectly-round plastic, which is compressed between the bearing shell and the journal. When the shell is removed, the plastic is deformed, and can be measured with a special card gauge supplied with the kit. The running clearance is determined from this gauge. Plastigauge should be available from your Citroën dealer; otherwise, enquiries at one of the larger specialist motor factors should produce the name of a stockist in your

	0	1	2	3	4	5	6	7	8	9	A	B	C	D	E	F	G	H	J	L	N	P	R	T	U	Y
0	C	C	C	B	B	B	I	B	B	B	B	B	B	A	A	A	A	A	A	A	A	A	A	A	A	A
1	C			C	B								B	A												A
2	C			C	B	I						B	A													A
3	C				C	I						B	A													A
4	C				C	B							B	A												A
5	C					C	B						B	A												A
6	C						C	B						B	A											A
7	C						C	B						B	A											A
8	C						I	C	B						B	A										A
9	D	C						C	B						B	A										A
A	D	D	C						C	B						B	A									A
B	D		D	C						C	B						B	A								A
C	D			D	C						C	B						B								B
D	D			D	C	I					C	B						B								B
E	D				D	C						C	B						B							B
F	D				D	C							C	B												B
G	D					D	C							C	B											B
H	D	—	—	—	—	J	D	C							C	B										B
J	D						D	C								C	B									B
L	D	D	D	D	D	D	D	D	D	D	C	C	C	C	C	C	C	C	C	B	B	B	B	B		

18.13 Main bearing shell selection chart – XU series engines

18.18 On TU series engines, the grooved bearing shells are fitted to Nos 2 and 4 main bearing journals

18.22 Plastigauge in place on a crankshaft main bearing journal

18.25 Measure the width of the deformed Plastigauge using the scale on the card

18.38 Refitting a crankshaft thrustwasher – TU series aluminium block engines

area. The procedure for using Plastigauge is as follows.

21 With the main bearing upper shells in place, carefully lay the crankshaft in position. Do not use any lubricant; the crankshaft journals and bearing shells must be perfectly clean and dry.

22 Cut several lengths of the appropriate-size Plastigauge (they should be slightly shorter than the width of the main bearings), and place one length on each crankshaft journal axis **(see illustration)**.

23 With the main bearing lower shells in position, refit the main bearing ladder casting, tightening its retaining bolts as described in paragraph 43. Take care not to disturb the Plastigauge, and *do not* rotate the crankshaft at any time during this operation.

24 Remove the main bearing ladder casting, again taking great care not to disturb the Plastigauge or rotate the crankshaft.

25 Compare the width of the crushed Plastigauge on each journal to the scale printed on the Plastigauge envelope, to obtain the main bearing running clearance **(see illustration)**. Compare the clearance measured with that in the Specifications at the start of this Chapter.

26 If the clearance is significantly different from that expected, the bearing shells may be the wrong size (or excessively worn, if the original shells are being re-used). Before deciding that different-size shells are required, make sure that no dirt or oil was trapped between the bearing shells and the caps or block when the clearance was measured. If the Plastigauge was wider at one end than at the other, the crankshaft journal may be tapered.

27 If the clearance is not as specified, use the reading obtained, along with the shell thicknesses quoted above, to calculate the necessary grade of bearing shells required. When calculating the bearing clearance required, bear in mind that it is always better to have the running clearance towards the lower end of the specified range, to allow for wear in use.

28 Where necessary, obtain the required grades of bearing shell, and repeat the running clearance checking process described above.

29 On completion, carefully scrape away all traces of the Plastigauge material from the crankshaft and bearing shells. Use your fingernail, or a wooden or plastic scraper which is unlikely to score the bearing surfaces.

TU series cast-iron block engines

30 The procedure is similar to that described in paragraphs 16 to 29, except that each main bearing has a separate cap, which must be fitted and the bolts tightened to the specified torque.

XU series engines

31 The running clearance check can be carried out using the original bearing shells. However, it is preferable to use a new set, since the results obtained will be more conclusive.

32 Clean the backs of the bearing shells, and the bearing locations in both the cylinder block/crankcase and the main bearing caps.

33 Press the bearing shells into their locations, ensuring that the tab on each shell engages in the notch in the cylinder block/crankcase or bearing cap. Take care not to touch any shell's bearing surface with your fingers. Note that the upper bearing shells all have a grooved bearing surface, whereas the lower shells have a plain bearing surface. If the original bearing shells are being used for the check, ensure that they are refitted in their original locations.

34 The clearance can be checked in either of two ways.

18.39 Ensure each bearing shell tab is located (arrowed), and apply clean oil – TU series aluminium block engines

35 One method (which will be difficult to achieve without a range of internal micrometers or internal/external expanding calipers) is to refit the main bearing caps to the cylinder block/crankcase, with bearing shells in place. With the cap retaining bolts tightened to the specified torque, measure the internal diameter of each assembled pair of bearing shells. If the diameter of each corresponding crankshaft journal is measured and then subtracted from the bearing internal diameter, the result will be the main bearing running clearance.

36 The second, and more accurate, method is to use Plastigauge. The method is as described above in paragraphs 20 to 29, substituting 'main bearing caps' for all references to the main bearing ladder casting.

Final crankshaft refitting

TU series aluminium block engines

37 Carefully lift the crankshaft out of the cylinder block once more.

38 Using a little grease, stick the upper thrustwashers to each side of the No 2 main bearing upper location; ensure that the oilway grooves on each thrustwasher face outwards (away from the block) **(see illustration)**.

39 Place the bearing shells in their locations as described earlier. If new shells are being fitted, ensure that all traces of protective grease are cleaned off using paraffin. Wipe dry the shells and connecting rods with a lint-

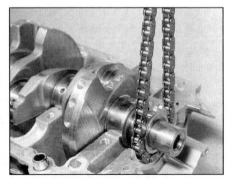

18.40 Refitting the oil pump drive chain and sprocket – TU series aluminium block engines

18.41 Apply a thin film of sealant to the cylinder block/crankcase mating surface . . .

18.42 . . . then lower the main bearing ladder into position – TU series aluminium block engines

18.43a Tighten the ten 11 mm main bearing bolts to the Stage 1 torque setting . . .

free cloth. Liberally lubricate each bearing shell in the cylinder block/crankcase with clean engine oil **(see illustration)**.

40 Refit the Woodruff key, then slide on the oil pump drive sprocket, and locate the drive chain on the sprocket **(see illustration)**. Lower the crankshaft into position so that Nos 2 and 3 cylinder crankpins are at TDC; Nos 1 and 4 cylinder crankpins will be at BDC, ready for fitting No 1 piston. Check the crankshaft endfloat as described in Section 14.

41 Thoroughly degrease the mating surfaces of the cylinder block/crankcase and the main bearing ladder. Apply a thin bead of suitable sealant to the cylinder block/crankcase mating surface of the main bearing ladder casting, then spread to an even film **(see illustration)**.

42 Lubricate the lower bearing shells with clean engine oil, then refit the main bearing ladder, ensuring that the shells are not displaced, and that the locating dowels engage correctly **(see illustration)**.

43 Install the ten 11 mm main bearing ladder retaining bolts, and tighten them all by hand only. Working progressively outwards from the centre bolts, tighten the ten bolts, by a turn at a time, to the specified Stage 1 torque wrench setting. Once all the bolts have been tightened to the Stage 1 setting, angle-tighten the bolts through the specified Stage 2 angle using a socket and extension bar. It is

recommended that an angle-measuring gauge is used during this stage of the tightening, to ensure accuracy **(see illustrations)**. If a gauge is not available, use a dab of white paint to make alignment marks between the bolt head and casting prior to tightening; the marks can then be used to check that the bolt has been rotated sufficiently during tightening.

44 Refit all the 6 mm bolts securing the main bearing ladder to the base of the cylinder block, and tighten them to the specified torque. Check that the crankshaft rotates freely.

45 Refit the piston/connecting rod assemblies to the crankshaft as described in Section 19.

46 Ensuring that the drive chain is correctly located on the sprocket, refit the oil pump and sump as described in Part A of this Chapter.

47 Fit two new crankshaft oil seals as described in Part A of this Chapter.

48 Refit the flywheel as described in Part A of this Chapter.

49 Where removed, refit the cylinder head, also as described in Part A, then refit the crankshaft sprocket and timing belt.

TU series cast-iron block engines

50 Carefully lift the crankshaft out of the cylinder block once more.

51 Using a little grease, stick the upper thrustwashers to each side of the No 2 main

bearing upper location. Ensure that the oilway grooves on each thrustwasher face outwards (away from the cylinder block) **(see illustration)**.

52 Place the bearing shells in their locations as described earlier **(see illustration)**. If new shells are being fitted, ensure that all traces of protective grease are cleaned off using paraffin. Wipe dry the shells and connecting rods with a lint-free cloth. Liberally lubricate each bearing shell in the cylinder block/crankcase and cap with clean engine oil.

53 Lower the crankshaft into position so that Nos 2 and 3 cylinder crankpins are at TDC; Nos 1 and 4 cylinder crankpins will be at BDC, ready for fitting No 1 piston. Check the crankshaft endfloat as described in Section 14.

54 Lubricate the lower bearing shells in the main bearing caps with clean engine oil. Make sure that the locating lugs on the shells engage with the corresponding recesses in the caps.

55 Fit the main bearing caps to their correct locations, ensuring that they are fitted the correct way round (the bearing shell lug recesses in the block and caps must be on the same side). Insert the bolts loosely.

56 Tighten the main bearing cap bolts to the specified Stage 1 torque wrench setting. Once all the bolts have been tightened to the

18.43b . . . then angle-tighten them through the specified Stage 2 angle – TU series aluminium block engines

18.51 Fitting a thrustwasher to No 2 main bearing upper location – TU series cast-iron block engines

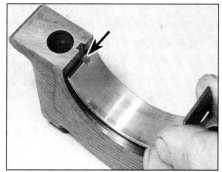

18.52 Ensure that the tab (arrowed) is correctly located in the cap when fitting the bearing shells – TU series cast-iron block engines

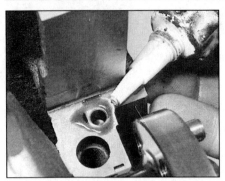

18.69 Applying sealant to the cylinder block No 1 main bearing cap mating face – XU series engines

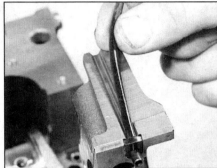

18.70 Fitting a sealing strip to No 1 main bearing cap – XU series engines

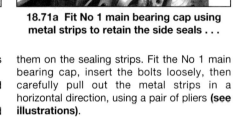

18.71a Fit No 1 main bearing cap using metal strips to retain the side seals . . .

Stage 1 setting, angle-tighten the bolts through the specified Stage 2 angle, using a socket and extension bar. It is recommended that an angle-measuring gauge is used during this stage of the tightening, to ensure accuracy.

57 Check that the crankshaft rotates freely.

58 Refit the piston/connecting rod assemblies to the crankshaft as described in Section 19.

59 Refit the Woodruff key to the crankshaft groove, and slide on the oil pump drive sprocket. Locate the drive chain on the sprocket.

60 Ensure that the mating surfaces of the right-hand oil seal housing and cylinder block are clean and dry. Note the correct fitted depth of the oil seal then, using a large flat-bladed screwdriver, lever the seal out of the housing.

61 Apply a smear of suitable sealant to the oil seal housing mating surface, and make sure that the locating dowels are in position. Slide the housing over the end of the crankshaft, and into position on the cylinder block. Tighten the housing retaining bolts securely.

62 Repeat the operations in paragraphs 60 and 61, and fit the left-hand oil seal housing.

63 Fit a new right-hand and left-hand crankshaft oil seal as described in Part A of this Chapter.

64 Ensuring that the chain is correctly located on the drive sprocket, refit the oil

pump and sump as described in Part A of this Chapter.

65 Refit the flywheel/driveplate as described in Part A of this Chapter.

66 Where removed, refit the cylinder head and install the crankshaft sprocket and timing belt as described in the relevant Sections of Part A.

XU series engines

67 Carry out the operations described above in paragraphs 50 to 54.

68 Fit main bearing caps Nos 2 to 5 to their correct locations, ensuring that they are fitted the correct way round (the bearing shell tab recesses in the block and caps must be on the same side). Insert the bolts/nuts, tightening them only loosely at this stage.

69 Apply a small amount of sealant to the No 1 main bearing cap mating face on the cylinder block, around the sealing strip holes **(see illustration)**.

70 Locate the tab of each sealing strip over the pins on the base of No 1 bearing cap, and press the strips into the bearing cap grooves. It is now necessary to obtain two thin metal strips, of 0.25 mm thickness or less, in order to prevent the strips moving when the cap is being fitted. Metal strips, such as old feeler blades, can be used, provided all burrs which may damage the sealing strips are first removed **(see illustration)**.

71 Oil both sides of the metal strips, and hold

them on the sealing strips. Fit the No 1 main bearing cap, insert the bolts loosely, then carefully pull out the metal strips in a horizontal direction, using a pair of pliers **(see illustrations)**.

72 Tighten all the main bearing cap bolts/nuts evenly to the specified torque. Using a sharp knife, trim off the ends of the No 1 bearing cap sealing strips, so that they protrude above the cylinder block/crankcase mating surface by approximately 1 mm **(see illustrations)**.

73 On 1.8 litre engines, refit the centre main bearing side retaining bolts and sealing washers (one at the front of the block, and one at the rear) and tighten them both to the specified torque.

74 Fit a new crankshaft left-hand oil seal as described in Chapter 2B.

75 Refit the piston/connecting rod assemblies to the crankshaft as described in Section 19.

76 Refit the Woodruff key, then slide on the oil pump drive sprocket and spacer (where fitted), and locate the drive chain on the sprocket.

77 Ensure that the mating surfaces of the right-hand oil seal carrier and cylinder block are clean and dry. Note the correct fitted depth of the oil seal then, using a large flat-bladed screwdriver, lever the old seal out of the housing.

78 Apply a smear of suitable sealant to the oil seal carrier mating surface. Ensure that the

18.71b . . . then remove the metal strips using a pair of pliers – XU series engines

18.72a With all bearing caps installed, tighten their retaining nuts and bolts to the specified torque . . .

18.72b . . . then trim the ends of No 1 bearing cap sealing strips, so they protrude by approximately 1 mm – XU series engines

locating dowels are in position, then slide the carrier over the end of the crankshaft and into position on the cylinder block. Tighten the carrier retaining bolts to the specified torque.

79 Fit a new crankshaft right-hand oil seal as described in Part B of this Chapter.

80 Ensuring that the drive chain is correctly located on the sprocket, refit the oil pump and sump as described in Part B of this Chapter.

81 Where removed, refit the cylinder head as described in Part B of this Chapter.

19 Piston/connecting rod assembly – refitting and big-end bearing running clearance check

Selection of bearing shells

1 On most engines, there are two sizes of big-end bearing shell produced by Citroën; a standard size for use with the standard crankshaft, and an oversize for use once the crankshaft journals have been reground.

2 Consult your Citroën dealer for the latest information on parts availability. Always quote the diameter of the crankshaft big-end crankpins when ordering bearing shells.

3 Before refitting the piston/connecting rod assemblies, we recommend that the big-end bearing running clearance is checked as follows.

Big-end bearing running clearance check

4 Clean the backs of the bearing shells, and the bearing locations in both the connecting rod and bearing cap.

5 Press the bearing shells into their locations, ensuring that the tab on each shell engages in the notch in the connecting rod and cap. Take care not to touch any shell's bearing surface with your fingers (see illustration). If the original bearing shells are being used for the check, ensure that they are refitted in their original locations. The clearance can be checked in either of two ways.

6 One method is to refit the big-end bearing cap to the connecting rod, ensuring that they are fitted the correct way around (see paragraph 21), with the bearing shells in place. With the cap retaining nuts correctly tightened, use an internal micrometer or vernier caliper to measure the internal diameter of each assembled pair of bearing shells. If the diameter of each corresponding crankshaft journal is measured and then subtracted from the bearing internal diameter, the result will be the big-end bearing running clearance.

7 The second, and more accurate method is to use Plastigauge (see Section 18).

8 Ensure that the bearing shells are correctly fitted. Place a strand of Plastigauge on each (cleaned) crankpin journal.

9 Refit the (clean) piston/connecting rod assemblies to the crankshaft, and refit the big-end bearing caps, using the marks made or noted on removal to ensure that they are fitted the correct way around.

19.5 Fitting a bearing shell to a connecting rod – ensure the tab (arrowed) engages with the recess in the connecting rod

10 Tighten the bearing cap nuts as described below in paragraph 22, or 23 and 24 (as applicable). Take care not to disturb the Plastigauge, nor rotate the connecting rod during the tightening sequence.

11 Dismantle the assemblies without rotating the connecting rods. Use the scale printed on the Plastigauge envelope to obtain the big-end bearing running clearance.

12 If the clearance is significantly different from that expected, the bearing shells may be the wrong size (or excessively worn, if the original shells are being re-used). Make sure that no dirt or oil was trapped between the bearing shells and the caps or block when the clearance was measured. If the Plastigauge was wider at one end than at the other, the crankshaft journal may be tapered.

13 Note that Citroën do not specify a recommended big-end bearing running clearance. The figure given in the Specifications is a guide figure, which is typical for this type of engine. Before condemning the components concerned, refer to your Citroën dealer or engine reconditioning specialist for further information on the specified running clearance. Their advice on the best course of action to be taken can then also be obtained.

14 On completion, carefully scrape away all traces of the Plastigauge material from the crankshaft and bearing shells. Use your fingernail, or some other object which is unlikely to score the bearing surfaces.

15 On XU series engines, fit the new bearing

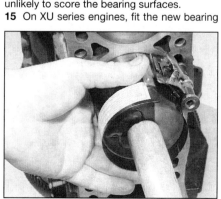

19.20 Tap the piston into the bore using a hammer handle

cap retaining bolts to the connecting rods as described in Section 13.

Final piston/connecting rod refitting

16 Note that the following procedure assumes that the cylinder liners (where fitted) are in position in the cylinder block/crankcase as described in Section 12, and that the crankshaft and main bearing ladder/caps are in place (see Section 18).

17 Ensure that the bearing shells are correctly fitted as described earlier. If new shells are being fitted, ensure that all traces of the protective grease are cleaned off using paraffin. Wipe dry the shells and connecting rods with a lint-free cloth.

18 Lubricate the cylinder bores, the pistons, and piston rings, then lay out each piston/connecting rod assembly in its respective position.

19 Start with assembly No 1. Make sure that the piston rings are still spaced as described in Section 17, then clamp them in position with a piston ring compressor.

20 Insert the piston/connecting rod assembly into the top of cylinder/liner No 1, ensuring that the arrow on the piston crown is pointing towards the timing belt end of the engine. Using a block of wood or hammer handle against the piston crown, tap the assembly into the cylinder/liner until the piston crown is flush with the top of the cylinder/liner (see illustration).

21 Ensure that the bearing shell is still correctly installed. Liberally lubricate the crankpin and both bearing shells. Taking care not to mark the cylinder/liner bores, pull the piston/connecting rod assembly down the bore and onto the crankpin. Refit the big-end bearing cap, tightening the nuts finger-tight at first. Note that the faces with the identification marks must match (which means that the bearing shell locating tabs abut each other).

TU series engines

22 On TU series engines, tighten the bearing cap retaining nuts evenly and progressively to the specified torque setting.

XU series engines

23 On XU series engines, tighten the bearing cap retaining nuts evenly and progressively to the Stage 1 torque setting (see illustration).

19.23 Tighten the big-end bearing cap nuts to the specified Stage 1 torque . . .

19.24 . . . then through the specified Stage 2 angle – XU series engines

24 Once both nuts have been tightened to the Stage 1 setting, angle-tighten them through the specified Stage 2 angle, using a socket and extension bar. It is recommended that an angle-measuring gauge is used during this stage of the tightening, to ensure accuracy **(see illustration)**.

All engines

25 Once the bearing cap retaining nuts have been correctly tightened, rotate the crankshaft. Check that it turns freely; some stiffness is to be expected if new components have been fitted, but there should be no signs of binding or tight spots.

26 Refit the other three piston/connecting rod assemblies in the same way.

27 Refit the cylinder head and oil pump as described in Part A or B of this Chapter (as applicable).

20 Engine –
initial start-up after overhaul

1 With the engine refitted in the vehicle, double-check the engine oil and coolant levels. Make a final check that everything has been reconnected, and that there are no tools or rags left in the engine compartment.

2 Disable the fuel system by identifying and removing the fuel pump fuse from the fusebox (see Chapter 12).

3 Remove the spark plugs, and disable the ignition system by disconnecting the LT wiring connector from the ignition HT coil, or ignition coil module referring to Chapter 5B for further information.

4 Turn the engine on the starter until the oil pressure warning light goes out. Refit the spark plugs, and reconnect the spark plug (HT) leads. Refit the fuel pump fuse and reconnect the wiring disconnected in paragraph 2.

5 Start the engine, noting that this may take a little longer than usual, due to the fuel system components having been disturbed.

6 While the engine is idling, check for fuel, water and oil leaks. Don't be alarmed if there are some odd smells and smoke from parts getting hot and burning off oil deposits.

7 Assuming all is well, keep the engine idling until hot water is felt circulating through the top hose, then switch off the engine.

8 After a few minutes, recheck the oil and coolant levels as described in *Weekly checks*, and top-up as necessary.

9 If they were tightened as described, there is no need to re-tighten the cylinder head bolts once the engine has first run after reassembly.

10 If new pistons, rings or crankshaft bearings have been fitted, the engine must be treated as new, and run-in for the first 500 miles (800 km). *Do not* operate the engine at full-throttle, or allow it to labour at low engine speeds in any gear. It is recommended that the oil and filter be changed at the end of this period.

Chapter 2 Part F:
Diesel engine removal and overhaul procedures

Contents

1.9 litre engine and transmission – removal, separation and refitting . . 4
2.0 litre engine and transmission – removal, separation and refitting . . 5
Crankshaft – inspection 15
Crankshaft – refitting and main bearing running clearance check . . 19
Crankshaft – removal 12
Cylinder block/crankcase – cleaning and inspection 13
Cylinder head – dismantling 8
Cylinder head – reassembly 10
Cylinder head (2.0 litre engines) – removal and refitting 6
Cylinder head and valves – cleaning and inspection 9
Engine – initial start-up after overhaul 21
Engine overhaul – dismantling sequence 7
Engine overhaul – general information 2
Engine overhaul – reassembly sequence 17
Engine/transmission removal – methods and precautions 3
General information 1
Main and big-end bearings – inspection 16
Piston/connecting rod assembly – inspection 14
Piston/connecting rod assembly – refitting and big-end bearing
    running clearance check 20
Piston/connecting rod assembly – removal 11
Piston rings – refitting 18

Degrees of difficulty

| **Easy,** suitable for novice with little experience | | **Fairly easy,** suitable for beginner with some experience | | **Fairly difficult,** suitable for competent DIY mechanic | | **Difficult,** suitable for experienced DIY mechanic | | **Very difficult,** suitable for expert DIY or professional | |

Specifications

Note: *At the time of writing, many specifications for certain engines were not available. Where the relevant specifications are not given here, refer to your Citroën dealer for further information.*

Cylinder head

Maximum gasket face distortion	0.03 mm
Cylinder head height:	
1.9 litre engine	140.0 mm
2.0 litre engine	133.0 mm
Swirl chamber protrusion	0 to 0.03 mm

Valves

Valve head diameter:	
Inlet:	
1.9 litre engine	38.5 mm
2.0 litre engine	Not available
Exhaust:	
1.9 litre engine	33.0 mm
2.0 litre engine	Not available
Valve stem diameter:	
Inlet:	
1.9 litre engine	7.96 to 7.99 mm
2.0 litre engine	Not available
Exhaust:	
1.9 litre engine	7.95 to 7.98 mm
2.0 litre engine	Not available
Overall length:	
Inlet:	
1.9 litre engine	112.40 mm
2.0 litre engine	Not available
Exhaust:	
1.9 litre engine	111.85 mm
2.0 litre engine	Not available

2F•2 Diesel engine removal and overhaul procedures

Cylinder block

Cylinder bore diameter:
  1.9 litre (XUD series) engine:
    Non-turbo models:

Standard	83.000 to 83.018 mm
Repair size	83.800 to 83.818 mm

    Turbo models:

Standard	83.000 to 83.018 mm
Repair size 1	83.500 to 83.518 mm
Repair size 2	83.800 to 83.818 mm

  1.9 litre (DW series) engine:

Standard	82.200 to 82.218 mm
Repair size	82.800 to 82.818 mm

  2.0 litre engine:

Standard	85.000 to 85.018 mm

Pistons

Piston diameter:
  1.9 litre (XUD series) engine:
    Non-turbo models:

Standard	82.930 to 82.939 mm
Repair size	83.730 to 83.739 mm

    Turbo models:

Standard	82.930 to 82.939 mm
Repair size 1	83.430 to 83.448 mm
Repair size 2	83.730 to 83.739 mm

  1.9 litre (DW series) engine:

Standard	82.121 to 82.139 mm
Repair size	82.721 to 82.739 mm

  2.0 litre engine:

Standard	84.210 to 84.228 mm
Maximum weight difference between any two pistons	4.0 g

Piston rings

End gaps:

Top compression ring	0.20 to 0.35 mm
2nd compression ring	0.40 to 0.60 mm
Oil control ring	0.25 to 0.50 mm

Crankshaft

Endfloat	0.07 to 0.32 mm

Main bearing journal diameter:

Standard	59.977 to 60.000 mm
Repair size	59.677 to 59.700 mm

Big-end bearing journal diameter:
  1.9 litre engine:

Standard	49.980 to 50.000 mm
Repair size	49.680 to 49.700 mm

  2.0 litre engine:

Standard	49.980 to 50.000 mm
Maximum bearing journal out-of-round	0.007 mm
Main bearing running clearance*	0.025 to 0.050 mm
Big-end bearing running clearance*	0.025 to 0.050 mm

These are suggested figures, typical for these types of engine – no exact values are stated by Citroën.

Torque wrench settings

XUD series engine

Refer to Chapter 2C Specifications.

DW series engine

Refer to Chapter 2D Specifications.

1 General information

Included in this Part of Chapter 2 are details of removing the engine/transmission from the car and general overhaul procedures for the cylinder head, cylinder block/crankcase and all other engine internal components.

The information given ranges from advice concerning preparation for an overhaul and the purchase of replacement parts, to detailed step-by-step procedures covering removal, inspection, renovation and refitting of engine internal components.

After Section 5, all instructions are based on the assumption that the engine has been removed from the car. For information concerning in-car engine repair, as well as the removal and refitting of those external components necessary for full overhaul, refer to Part C or D of this Chapter (as applicable) and to Section 7. Ignore any preliminary dismantling operations described in Part C or D that are no longer relevant once the engine has been removed from the car.

Apart from torque wrench settings, which are given at the beginning of Part C or D (as applicable), all specifications relating to engine overhaul are at the beginning of this Part of Chapter 2.

2 Engine overhaul – general information

It is not always easy to determine when, or if, an engine should be completely overhauled, as a number of factors must be considered.

High mileage is not necessarily an indication that an overhaul is needed, while low mileage does not preclude the need for an overhaul. Frequency of servicing is probably the most important consideration. An engine which has had regular and frequent oil and filter changes, as well as other required maintenance, should give many thousands of miles of reliable service. Conversely, a neglected engine may require an overhaul very early in its life.

Excessive oil consumption is an indication that piston rings, valve seals and/or valve guides are in need of attention. Make sure that oil leaks are not responsible before deciding that the rings and/or guides are worn. Perform a compression or leakdown test, as described in Part C or D of this Chapter, to determine the likely cause of the problem.

Check the oil pressure with a gauge fitted in place of the oil pressure switch, and compare it with that specified. If it is extremely low, the main and big-end bearings, and/or the oil pump, are probably worn out.

Loss of power, rough running, knocking or metallic engine noises, excessive valve gear noise, and high fuel consumption may also point to the need for an overhaul, especially if they are all present at the same time. If a complete service does not remedy the situation, major mechanical work is the only solution.

An engine overhaul involves restoring all internal parts to the specification of a new engine. During an overhaul, the cylinder bores are rebored (where necessary), and the pistons and the piston rings are renewed. New main and big-end bearings are generally fitted; if necessary, the crankshaft may be reground, to restore the journals. The valves are also serviced as well, since they are usually in less-than-perfect condition at this point. The end result should be an as-new engine that will give many trouble-free miles.

Note: *Critical cooling system components such as the hoses, thermostat and coolant pump should be renewed when an engine is overhauled. The radiator should be checked carefully, to ensure that it is not clogged or leaking. Also, it is a good idea to renew the oil pump whenever the engine is overhauled.*

Before beginning the engine overhaul, read through the entire procedure, to familiarise yourself with the scope and requirements of the job. Overhauling an engine is not difficult if you follow carefully all of the instructions, have the necessary tools and equipment, and pay close attention to all specifications. It can, however, be time-consuming. Plan on the car being off the road for a minimum of two weeks, especially if parts must be taken to an engineering works for repair or reconditioning. Check on the availability of parts and make sure that any necessary special tools and equipment are obtained in advance. Most work can be done with typical hand tools, although a number of precision measuring tools are required for inspecting parts to determine if they must be renewed. Often the engineering works will handle the inspection of parts and offer advice concerning reconditioning and renewal.

Always wait until the engine has been completely dismantled, and until all components (especially the cylinder block/crankcase and the crankshaft) have been inspected, before deciding what service and repair operations must be performed by an engineering works. The condition of these components will be the major factor to consider when determining whether to overhaul the original engine, or to buy a reconditioned unit. Do not, therefore, purchase parts or have overhaul work done on other components until they have been thoroughly inspected. As a general rule, time is the primary cost of an overhaul, so it does not pay to fit worn or sub-standard parts.

As a final note, to ensure maximum life and minimum trouble from a reconditioned engine, everything must be assembled with care, in a spotlessly-clean environment.

3 Engine/transmission removal – methods and precautions

If you have decided that the engine must be removed for overhaul or major repair work, several preliminary steps should be taken.

Locating a suitable place to work is extremely important. Adequate work space, along with storage space for the car, will be needed. If a workshop or garage is not available, at the very least, a flat, level, clean work surface is required.

Cleaning the engine compartment and engine/transmission before beginning the removal procedure will help keep tools clean and organised.

An engine hoist will also be necessary. Make sure the equipment is rated in excess of the combined weight of the engine and transmission. Safety is of primary importance, considering the potential hazards involved in lifting the engine/transmission out of the car.

If this is the first time you have removed an engine, an assistant should ideally be available. Advice and aid from someone more experienced would also be helpful. There are many instances when one person cannot simultaneously perform all of the operations required when lifting the engine out of the vehicle.

Plan the operation ahead of time. Before starting work, arrange for the hire of or obtain all of the tools and equipment you will need. Some of the equipment necessary to perform engine/transmission removal and installation safely (in addition to an engine hoist) is as follows: a heavy duty trolley jack, complete sets of spanners and sockets as described at the rear of this manual, wooden blocks, and plenty of rags and cleaning solvent for mopping up spilled oil, coolant and fuel. If the hoist must be hired, make sure that you arrange for it in advance, and perform all of the operations possible without it beforehand. This will save you money and time.

Plan for the car to be out of use for quite a while. An engineering works will be required to perform some of the work which the do-it-yourselfer cannot accomplish without special equipment. These places often have a busy schedule, so it would be a good idea to consult them before removing the engine, in order to accurately estimate the amount of time required to rebuild or repair components that may need work.

During the engine removal procedure, it is advisable to make notes of the locations of all brackets, cable ties, earthing points, etc, as well as how the wiring harnesses, hoses and electrical connections are attached and routed around the engine and engine compartment. An effective way of doing this is to take a series of photographs of the various components before they are disconnected or removed. A simple inexpensive disposable camera is ideal for this and the resulting photographs will prove invaluable when the engine is refitted.

Always be extremely careful when removing and refitting the engine/transmission. Serious injury can result from careless actions. Plan ahead and take your time, and a job of this nature, although major, can be accomplished successfully.

The engine and transmission unit is removed upwards from the engine compartment on all models described in this manual.

4 1.9 litre engine and transmission – removal, separation and refitting

Removal

Note: *The engine can be removed from the car only as a complete unit with the transmission; the two are then separated for overhaul.*

1 Disconnect the battery negative terminal (refer to *Disconnecting the battery* in the Reference Section of this manual).

2 Chock the rear wheels then jack up the front of the vehicle and support it on axle stands (see *Jacking and vehicle support*). Remove the front roadwheels.

3 Disconnect the bonnet support struts as described in Chapter 11, and tie or support the bonnet in the vertical position.

4 Remove the air cleaner assembly, air inlet ducts and, where fitted, the intercooler as described in Chapter 4B.

5 If the engine is to be dismantled, drain the engine oil and remove the oil filter as described in Chapter 1B. Clean and refit the drain plug, tightening it securely.

6 Drain the cooling system as described in Chapter 1B.

7 Drain the transmission oil as described in Chapter 7A. Refit the drain and filler plugs, and tighten them to their specified torque settings.

8 Remove the radiator as described in Chapter 3.

9 Remove the alternator as described in Chapter 5A.

10 Remove the power steering pump as described in Chapter 10.

11 Release the power steering pipe from the retaining clips on the underside of the transmission.

12 On models with air conditioning, unbolt the compressor, and position it clear of the engine. Support the weight of the compressor by tying it to the vehicle body, to prevent any excess strain being placed on the compressor lines whilst the engine is removed. *Do not disconnect the refrigerant lines from the compressor* (refer to the warnings given in Chapter 3).

13 Remove the battery, battery tray and mounting plate as described in Chapter 5A.

14 Carry out the following operations with reference to Chapter 3 and Chapter 4B:

a) *Disconnect the fuel supply hose from the thermostat/fuel filter housing and the return hose from the fuel injection pump.*

b) *Release the fuel hoses and priming pump from their retaining clips and move them clear of the engine.*

c) *Disconnect the accelerator cable from the fuel injection pump.*

d) *Disconnect the catalytic converter from the exhaust manifold.*

15 Referring to Chapter 3, release the retaining clip and disconnect the heater matrix hoses from their connection on the engine compartment bulkhead. Also disconnect the radiator bottom hose connection on the engine, and any remaining coolant hoses at their engine connections.

16 Disconnect the vacuum hose from the braking system vacuum pump.

17 Disconnect the vacuum hoses and wiring connector at the EGR solenoid valve.

18 Working as described in Chapter 6, disconnect the clutch cable from the transmission, and position it clear of the working area.

19 Carry out the following operations with reference to Chapter 7A:

a) *Disconnect the three gearchange selector link rods from the transmission levers.*

b) *Disconnect the wiring connector from the vehicle speed sensor.*

d) *Disconnect the wiring connector(s) from the reversing light switch.*

20 Remove both driveshafts as described in Chapter 8.

21 On models equipped with anti-lock brakes, disconnect the wiring connector from the ECU located on the ABS hydraulic modulator.

22 Unbolt the preheating system control unit from the mounting bracket at the front of the engine compartment fuse/relay box.

23 Open the engine compartment fuse/relay box and disconnect the engine related wiring connectors.

24 Trace the wiring harness back from the engine to the main harness connectors at the fuse/relay box, and/or at the bulkhead connection behind the battery tray location. Release the locking rings by twisting them anti-clockwise and disconnect the connectors. Also trace the wiring connectors back to the transmission and disconnect all engine related wiring and earth leads in this area. Check that all the relevant connectors have been disconnected, and that the harness is released from all the clips or ties, so that it is free to be removed with the engine/transmission.

25 Manoeuvre the engine hoist into position, and attach it to the engine lifting brackets. Arrange the chains or slings so that the engine/transmission unit can adopt approximately a 45° angle during removal, with the transmission end lowest. Temporarily place a jack beneath the transmission and raise the jack to contact the transmission.

26 Slacken and remove the centre nut and washer from the engine/transmission left-hand mounting. Undo the two nuts and washers securing the mounting to its bracket, remove the mounting from the engine compartment and recover the washer and spacer. Undo the remaining retaining bolts and remove the mounting bracket from the body.

27 From underneath the vehicle, slacken and remove the nuts and bolts securing the rear engine mounting connecting link to the mounting assembly and subframe, and remove the connecting link.

28 Working on the right-hand engine/transmission mounting, undo the two bolts and remove the curved retaining plate and rubber damper from the top of the mounting. Undo the nut securing the engine bracket to the stud on the rubber mounting.

29 Make a final check that any components which would prevent the removal of the engine/transmission from the car have been removed or disconnected. Ensure that components such as the gearchange selector rod are secured so that they cannot be damaged on removal.

30 Lower the jack under the transmission, and at the same time raise the engine hoist, until the complete assembly is supported by the hoist. Carefully lift the engine/transmission out of the car, ensuring that nothing is trapped or damaged. Enlist the help of an assistant during this procedure, as it will be necessary to tilt and twist the assembly slightly to clear the body panels and adjacent components.

31 Once the engine is high enough, lift it out over the front of the body, and lower the unit to the ground.

Separation

32 With the engine/transmission assembly removed, support the assembly on suitable blocks of wood on a workbench (or failing that, on a clean area of the workshop floor).

33 Undo the retaining bolts, and remove the flywheel lower cover plate (where fitted) from the transmission.

34 On models with a 'pull-type' clutch release mechanism (see Chapter 6 for further information), tap out the retaining pin or unscrew the retaining bolt (as applicable), and remove the clutch release lever from the top of the release fork shaft. This is necessary to allow the fork shaft to rotate freely, so that it disengages from the release bearing as the transmission is pulled away from the engine. Make an alignment mark across the centre of the clutch release fork shaft, using a scriber, paint or similar, and mark its relative position on the transmission housing (see Chapter 7A for further information).

35 Slacken and remove the retaining bolts, and remove the starter motor from the transmission.

36 Ensure that both engine and transmission are adequately supported, then slacken and remove the remaining bolts securing the transmission housing to the engine. Note the correct fitted positions of each bolt (and the relevant brackets) as they are removed, to use as a reference on refitting.

37 Carefully withdraw the transmission from the engine, ensuring that the weight of the transmission is not allowed to hang on the input shaft while it is engaged with the clutch friction plate.

38 If they are loose, remove the locating dowels from the engine or transmission, and keep them in a safe place.

39 On models with a 'pull-type' clutch, make a second alignment mark on the transmission housing, marking the relative position of the release fork mark after removal. This should indicate the angle at which the release fork is positioned. The mark can then be used to position the release fork prior to installation, to ensure that the fork correctly engages with the clutch release bearing as the transmission is installed.

Refitting

40 If the engine and transmission have been separated, perform the operations described below in paragraphs 41 to 49. If not, proceed as described from paragraph 50 onwards.

41 Apply a smear of high-melting-point grease (Citroën recommend the use of Molykote BR2 plus – available from your Citroën dealer) to the splines of the transmission input shaft. Do not apply too much, otherwise there is a possibility of the grease contaminating the clutch friction plate.

42 Ensure that the locating dowels are correctly positioned in the engine or transmission.

43 On models with a 'pull-type' clutch, before refitting, position the clutch release bearing so that its arrow mark is pointing upwards (bearing fork slots facing towards the front of the engine), and align the release fork shaft mark with the second mark made on the transmission housing (release fork positioned at approximately 60° to clutch housing face). This will ensure that the release fork and bearing will engage correctly as the transmission is refitted to the engine.

44 Carefully offer the transmission to the engine, until the locating dowels are engaged. Ensure that the weight of the transmission is not allowed to hang on the input shaft as it is engaged with the clutch friction plate.

45 On models with a 'pull-type' clutch, with the transmission fully engaged with the engine, check that the release fork and bearing are correctly engaged. If the release fork and bearing are correctly engaged, the mark on the release fork should be aligned with the original mark made on the transmission housing (see Chapter 7A for further information).

46 Refit the transmission housing-to-engine bolts, ensuring that all the necessary brackets are correctly positioned, and tighten them securely.

47 Refit the starter motor, and securely tighten its retaining bolts.

48 On models with a 'pull-type' clutch release mechanism, refit the clutch release lever to the top of the release fork shaft, securing it in position with its retaining pin or bolt (as applicable).

49 Where necessary, refit the lower flywheel cover plate to the transmission, and securely tighten its retaining bolts.

50 Reconnect the hoist and lifting tackle to the engine lifting brackets. With the aid of an assistant, lift the assembly over the engine compartment.

51 The assembly should be tilted as necessary to clear the surrounding components, as during removal; lower the assembly into position in the engine compartment, manipulating the hoist and lifting tackle as necessary. Engage the right-hand engine mounting bracket over the rubber mounting stud then, using the jack, raise the transmission until the engine/transmission assembly is approximately horizontal.

52 With the engine/transmission in position, refit the retaining nut to the right-hand engine/transmission mounting, tightening the nut by hand only at this stage.

53 Working on the left-hand mounting, refit the mounting bracket to the body and tighten its retaining bolts to the specified torque. Refit the mounting rubber and refit the mounting retaining nuts and washers and the centre nut and washer, tightening them lightly only.

54 From underneath the vehicle, refit the rear mounting connecting link and install both its bolts.

55 Rock the engine to settle it on its mountings, then go around and tighten all the mounting nuts and bolts to their specified torque settings. Once the right-hand mounting bracket nut has been tightened, refit the rubber damper and curved retaining plate, tightening its retaining bolts to the specified torque. The hoist can then be detached from the engine and removed.

56 The remainder of the refitting procedure is a direct reversal of the removal sequence, noting the following points:

a) *Ensure that the wiring loom is correctly routed and retained by all the relevant retaining clips; all connectors should be correctly and securely reconnected.*

b) *Prior to refitting the driveshafts to the transmission, renew the driveshaft oil seals as described in Chapter 7A.*

c) *Ensure that all coolant hoses are correctly reconnected, and securely retained by their retaining clips.*

d) *Adjust the accelerator cable as described in Chapter 4B.*

e) *Refill the engine and transmission with the correct quantity and type of lubricant, as described in Chapters 1B and 7A.*

f) *Refill the cooling system as described in Chapter 1B.*

g) *Bleed the fuel system as described in Chapter 4B.*

h) *Bleed the power steering system as described in Chapter 10.*

5   2.0 litre engine and transmission – removal, separation and refitting

> ⚠ *Warning: It is essential to observe strict precautions when working on the fuel system components of the 2.0 litre engine. Before carrying out any of the following operations, refer to the special information given in Chapter 4C, Section 2.*

Removal

Note: *The engine can be removed from the car only as a complete unit with the transmission; the two are then separated for overhaul.*

1 Disconnect the battery negative terminal (refer to *Disconnecting the battery* in the Reference Section of this manual).

2 Chock the rear wheels then jack up the front of the vehicle and support it on axle stands (see *Jacking and vehicle support*). Remove the front roadwheels.

3 Disconnect the bonnet support struts as described in Chapter 11, and tie or support the bonnet in the vertical position.

4 Remove the air cleaner assembly and air inlet ducts as described in Chapter 4C.

5 Remove the auxiliary drivebelt as described in Chapter 1B.

6 If the engine is to be dismantled, drain the engine oil and remove the oil filter as described in Chapter 1B. Clean and refit the drain plug, tightening it securely.

7 Drain the cooling system as described in Chapter 1B.

8 Drain the transmission oil as described in Chapter 7A. Refit the drain and filler plugs, and tighten them to their specified torque settings.

9 Remove the battery, battery tray and mounting plate as described in Chapter 5A.

10 Carry out the following operations with reference to Chapter 3:

a) *Remove the radiator.*

b) *Remove the electric cooling fans.*

c) *Release the retaining clip and disconnect the heater matrix hoses from their connection on the engine compartment bulkhead.*

d) *Disconnect the radiator bottom hose connection at the rear of the engine.*

e) *Disconnect the coolant hoses at the thermostat housing, and any remaining coolant hoses at their engine connections.*

11 Remove the front body panel as described in Chapter 11.

12 Remove the power steering pump as described in Chapter 10.

13 Undo the nuts and release the power steering pipe retaining clips on the

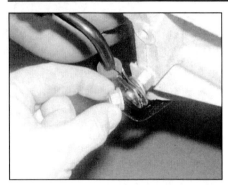

5.13a Release the power steering pipe retaining clips on the transmission . . .

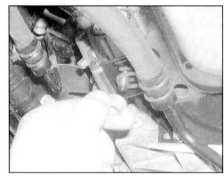

5.13b . . . and on the underside of the engine

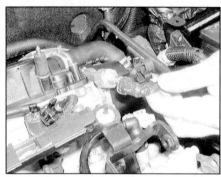

5.16 Disconnect the vacuum hose from the braking system vacuum pump

transmission and underside of the engine **(see illustrations)**.

14 On models with air conditioning, unbolt the compressor and position it clear of the engine. Support the weight of the compressor by tying it to the vehicle body, to prevent any excess strain being placed on the compressor lines whilst the engine is removed. *Do not disconnect the refrigerant lines from the compressor (refer to the warnings given in Chapter 3).*

15 Carry out the following operations with reference to Chapter 4C:

a) *At the connections above the fuel pump, disconnect the fuel supply and return hose quick-release fittings using a small*

5.17 Disconnect the EGR solenoid valve vacuum hoses and wiring connector

screwdriver to release the locking clip. Suitably plug or cover the open unions to prevent dirt entry.

b) *Release the fuel hoses from their retaining clips and move them clear of the engine.*

c) *Disconnect the catalytic converter from the exhaust manifold.*

16 Disconnect the vacuum hose from the braking system vacuum pump **(see illustration)**.

17 Disconnect the vacuum hoses and wiring connector at the EGR solenoid valve **(see illustration)**.

18 Working as described in Chapter 6, disconnect the clutch cable from the transmission, and position it clear of the working area.

19 Carry out the following operations with reference to Chapter 7A:

a) *Disconnect the three gearchange selector link rods from the transmission levers.*

b) *Disconnect the wiring connector from the vehicle speed sensor.*

c) *Disconnect the wiring connector(s) from the reversing light switch.*

20 Remove both driveshafts as described in Chapter 8.

21 Unbolt the preheating system control unit from the mounting bracket at the front of the engine compartment fuse/relay box.

22 Open the engine compartment fuse/relay

box and disconnect the engine related wiring connectors.

23 Trace the wiring harness back from the engine to the main harness connectors at the fuse/relay box, and/or at the bulkhead connection behind the battery tray location. Release the locking rings by twisting them anti-clockwise and disconnect the connectors **(see illustration)**. Also trace the wiring connectors back to the transmission and disconnect all engine related wiring and earth leads in this area. Check that all the relevant connectors have been disconnected, and that the harness is released from all the clips or ties, so that it is free to be removed with the engine/transmission.

24 Manoeuvre the engine hoist into position, and attach it to the engine lifting brackets.

25 Slacken and remove the centre nut and washer from the engine/transmission left-hand mounting. Undo the two nuts and washers securing the mounting to its bracket, remove the mounting from the engine compartment and recover the washer and spacer. Undo the remaining retaining bolts and remove the mounting bracket from the body **(see illustrations)**.

26 From underneath the vehicle, slacken and remove the nuts and bolts securing the rear engine mounting connecting link to the mounting assembly and subframe,

5.23 Release the engine main wiring harness connectors by turning the locking rings anti-clockwise

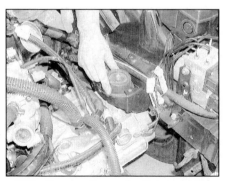

5.25a Remove the engine/transmission left-hand mounting . . .

5.25b . . . then undo the bolts and remove the mounting bracket from the body

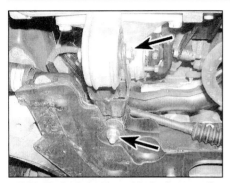

5.26 Undo the nuts and bolts (arrowed) and remove the rear engine mounting connecting link

5.27a Remove the right-hand engine mounting curved retaining plate . . .

5.27b . . . then undo the domed buffer nut, and the upper bracket retaining nut

and remove the connecting link **(see illustration)**.

27 Working on the right-hand engine/transmission mounting, undo the two bolts securing the curved mounting retaining plate to the body and lift off the plate. Unscrew the domed buffer nut, then unscrew the single nut securing the upper bracket to the mounting rubber **(see illustrations)**.

28 Make a final check that any components which would prevent the removal of the engine/transmission from the car have been removed or disconnected. Ensure that components such as the gearchange selector rod are secured so that they cannot be damaged on removal.

29 Raise the engine hoist and carefully lift the engine/transmission upwards, clear of the mountings, ensuring that nothing is trapped or damaged **(see illustration)**. Enlist the help of an assistant during this procedure, as it will be necessary to tilt and twist the assembly slightly to clear the body panels and adjacent components.

30 Once the engine/transmission assembly is high enough to clear the front crossmember, withdraw the unit forward and out of the engine compartment. Move the unit clear of the car and lower it to the ground.

Separation

31 With the engine/transmission assembly removed, support the assembly on suitable blocks of wood on a workbench (or

5.29 Removing the engine/transmission from the front of the car

failing that, on a clean area of the workshop floor).

32 Undo the retaining bolts, and remove the flywheel lower cover plate from the transmission.

33 Slacken and remove the retaining bolts, and remove the starter motor from the transmission.

34 Undo the bolts and release the coolant heating housing from the transmission, noting the location of the earth leads and cable clips also secured by the housing retaining bolts.

35 Disconnect any remaining wiring connectors at the transmission, then move the main engine wiring harness to one side.

36 Ensure that both engine and transmission are adequately supported, then slacken and remove the remaining bolts securing the transmission housing to the engine. Note the correct fitted positions of each bolt (and the relevant brackets) as they are removed, to use as a reference on refitting.

37 Carefully withdraw the transmission from the engine, ensuring that the weight of the transmission is not allowed to hang on the input shaft while it is engaged with the clutch friction plate.

38 If they are loose, remove the locating dowels from the engine or transmission, and keep them in a safe place.

Refitting

39 If the engine and transmission have been separated, perform the operations described below in paragraphs 40 to 47. If not, proceed as described from paragraph 48 onwards.

40 Apply a smear of high-melting-point grease (Citroën recommend the use of Molykote BR2 plus – available from your Citroën dealer) to the splines of the transmission input shaft. Do not apply too much, otherwise there is a possibility of the grease contaminating the clutch friction plate.

41 Ensure that the locating dowels are correctly positioned in the engine or transmission.

42 Carefully offer the transmission to the engine, until the locating dowels are engaged. Ensure that the weight of the transmission is not allowed to hang on the input shaft as it is engaged with the clutch friction plate.

43 Refit the transmission housing-to-engine bolts, ensuring that all the necessary brackets are correctly positioned, and tighten them securely.

44 Locate the main engine wiring harness on the transmission and reconnect the relevant wiring connectors.

45 Refit the coolant heating housing to the transmission, ensuring that the earth leads and cable clips are correctly attached.

46 Refit the starter motor, and securely tighten its retaining bolts.

47 Refit the lower flywheel cover plate to the transmission, and securely tighten its retaining bolts.

48 Reconnect the hoist and lifting tackle to the engine lifting brackets. With the aid of an assistant, lift the assembly into the engine compartment.

49 Manoeuvre the unit as necessary to clear the surrounding components, and engage the right-hand engine mounting bracket over the rubber mounting stud. Refit the retaining nut to the stud and tighten it by hand only at this stage.

50 Working on the left-hand mounting, refit the mounting bracket to the body and tighten its retaining bolts to the specified torque. Refit the mounting rubber and refit the mounting retaining nuts and washers and the centre nut and washer, tightening them lightly only.

51 From underneath the vehicle, refit the rear mounting connecting link and install both its bolts.

52 Rock the engine to settle it on its mountings, then go around and tighten all the mounting nuts and bolts to their specified torque settings. Once the right-hand mounting bracket nut has been tightened, refit the domed buffer nut and curved retaining plate, tightening the retaining bolts to the specified torque. The hoist can then be detached from the engine and removed.

53 The remainder of the refitting procedure is a direct reversal of the removal sequence, noting the following points:

a) *Ensure that the wiring loom is correctly routed and retained by all the relevant retaining clips; all connectors should be correctly and securely reconnected.*

b) *Prior to refitting the driveshafts to the*

transmission, renew the driveshaft oil seals as described in Chapter 7A.

c) Ensure that all coolant hoses are correctly reconnected, and securely retained by their retaining clips.

d) Adjust the accelerator cable as described in Chapter 4C.

e) Refill the engine and transmission with the correct quantity and type of lubricant, as described in Chapters 1B and 7A.

f) Refill the cooling system as described in Chapter 1B.

g) Bleed the power steering system as described in Chapter 10.

6 Cylinder head (2.0 litre engines) – removal and refitting

Note: Due to the limited access at the rear of the engine, it is impossible to remove the cylinder head with the engine in the car unless considerable additional dismantling is carried out first (eg, removal of the front suspension subframe and related components). The following information describes the cylinder head removal and refitting procedure with the engine/transmission removed from the car.

Removal

1 Remove the engine/transmission assembly as described in Section 5.

2 Remove the timing belt as described in Chapter 2D.

3 Carry out the following operations as described in Chapter 4C:

a) Remove the exhaust manifold and turbocharger.

b) Remove the inlet manifold.

c) Remove the fuel system accumulator rail.

4 Undo the three bolts and remove the right-hand engine mounting upper bracket from the engine bracket. Undo the bolts securing the engine bracket to the cylinder head and block and remove the bracket.

5 Remove the braking system vacuum pump as described in Chapter 9.

6 Disconnect the wiring connectors and coolant hoses at the thermostat housing on the left-hand end of the cylinder head.

7 Undo the bolts and release the wiring harness guide from the thermostat housing.

8 Undo the retaining nuts and bolts and remove the fuel injector wiring harness guide left-hand support bracket.

9 Undo the mounting bolt and release the dipstick tube from the cylinder head.

10 Move all the adjacent components clear, then undo the three bolts and two nuts securing the thermostat housing to the cylinder head. Lift off the hose and cable support bracket, then withdraw the thermostat housing. Recover the housing gasket.

11 Remove the cylinder head cover as described in Chapter 2D.

12 Progressively slacken the cylinder head bolts, in the reverse order to that shown in illustration 6.29.

13 When all the bolts are loose, unscrew them fully and remove them from the cylinder head.

14 Release the cylinder head from the cylinder block and location dowels by rocking it. The Citroën tool for doing this consists simply of two metal rods with 90-degree angled ends **(see illustration)**. Do not prise between the mating faces of the cylinder head and block, as this may damage the gasket faces.

15 Lift the cylinder head from the block, and recover the gasket.

Preparation for refitting

16 The mating faces of the cylinder head and cylinder block must be perfectly clean before refitting the head. Citroën recommend the use of a scouring agent for this purpose, but acceptable results can be achieved by using a hard plastic or wood scraper to remove all traces of gasket and carbon. The same method can be used to clean the piston crowns. Take particular care to avoid scoring or gouging the cylinder head/cylinder block mating surfaces during the cleaning operations, as aluminium alloy is easily

damaged. Make sure that the carbon is not allowed to enter the oil and water passages – this is particularly important for the lubrication system, as carbon could block the oil supply to the engine's components. Using adhesive tape and paper, seal the water, oil and bolt holes in the cylinder block. To prevent carbon entering the gap between the pistons and bores, smear a little grease in the gap. After cleaning each piston, use a small brush to remove all traces of grease and carbon from the gap, then wipe away the remainder with a clean rag.

17 Check the mating surfaces of the cylinder block and the cylinder head for nicks, deep scratches and other damage. If slight, they may be removed carefully with a file, but if excessive, machining may be the only alternative to renewal. If warpage of the cylinder head gasket surface is suspected, use a straight-edge to check it for distortion. Refer to Section 9 if necessary.

18 Thoroughly clean the threads of the cylinder head bolt holes in the cylinder block. Ensure that the bolts run freely in their threads, and that all traces of oil and water are removed from each bolt hole.

Gasket selection

19 Turn the crankshaft until pistons 1 and 4 are at TDC. Position a dial test indicator (dial gauge) on the cylinder block, and zero it on the block face. Transfer the probe to the edge of No 1 piston, then slowly turn the crankshaft back and forth past TDC, noting the highest reading on the indicator. Record this reading.

20 Repeat this measurement procedure on No 4 piston, then turn the crankshaft half a turn (180°) and repeat the procedure on Nos 2 and 3 pistons **(see illustration)**.

21 If a dial test indicator is not available, piston protrusion may be measured using a straight-edge and feeler blades or vernier calipers. However, this is much less accurate, and cannot therefore be recommended.

22 Note down the greatest piston protrusion measurement, and use this to determine the correct cylinder head gasket from the following table. The series of up to five notches on the side of the gasket are used for thickness identification **(see illustration)**.

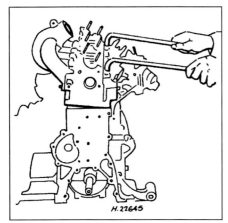

6.14 Freeing the cylinder head using angled rods

6.20 Measuring piston protrusion

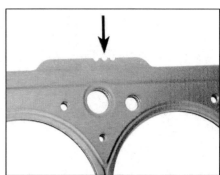

6.22 Cylinder head gasket thickness identification notches (arrowed)

Piston protrusion	Gasket identification
0.470 to 0.605 mm	1 notch
0.605 to 0.655 mm	2 notches
0.655 to 0.705 mm	3 notches
0.705 to 0.755 mm	4 notches
0.755 to 0.830 mm	5 notches

Cylinder head bolt examination

23 Carefully examine the cylinder head bolts for signs of damage to the threads or head, and for any sign of corrosion. If the bolts are in a satisfactory condition, measure the length of each bolt from the underside of the head, to the end of the shank. The bolts may be re-used providing that the measured length does not exceed 133.3 mm. **Note:** *Considering the stress to which the cylinder head bolts are subjected, it is highly recommended that they are all renewed, regardless of their apparent condition.*

Refitting

24 Turn the crankshaft clockwise (viewed from the timing belt end) until Nos 1 and 4 pistons pass bottom dead centre (BDC) and begin to rise, then position them halfway up their bores. Nos 2 and 3 pistons will also be at their mid-way positions, but descending their bores.

25 Make sure that the locating dowels are in place, then fit the correct gasket the right way round on the cylinder block, with the identification notches toward the fuel pump side of the engine.

26 Lower the cylinder head onto the block.

27 Apply a smear of grease to the threads, and to the underside of the heads, of the cylinder head bolts. Citroën recommend the use of Molykote G Rapid Plus (available from your Citroën dealer); in the absence of the specified grease, any good-quality high-melting-point grease may be used.

28 Carefully enter each bolt into its relevant hole (*do not drop it in*) and screw it in finger-tight.

29 Working progressively and in the sequence shown, tighten the cylinder head bolts to their Stage 1 torque setting, using a torque wrench and suitable socket **(see illustration)**.

30 Once all the bolts have been tightened to their Stage 1 torque setting, working again in

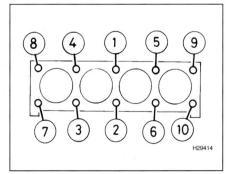

6.29 Cylinder head bolt tightening sequence

the specified sequence, tighten each bolt to the specified Stage 2 setting. Finally, angle-tighten the bolts through the specified Stage 3 angle. It is recommended that an angle-measuring gauge is used during this stage of tightening, to ensure accuracy.

31 Refit the cylinder head cover as described in Chapter 2D.

32 Ensure that the mating face of the cylinder head and thermostat housing are clean then refit the housing using a new gasket. Refit the hose and cable support bracket and the thermostat housing retaining nuts and bolts. Tighten the nuts and bolts securely.

33 Refit and tighten the dipstick tube retaining bolt.

34 Refit the wiring harness guide support brackets.

35 Reconnect the coolant hoses to the thermostat housing.

36 Refit the timing belt as described in Chapter 2D.

37 Refit the accumulator rail, inlet manifold, and the exhaust manifold and turbocharger, in strict accordance with the procedures described in Chapter 4C.

38 Refit the braking system vacuum pump as described in Chapter 9.

39 Refit the right-hand engine mounting components with reference to Chapter 2D.

40 Refit the engine/transmission assembly as described in Section 5.

7 Engine overhaul – dismantling sequence

1 It is much easier to dismantle and work on the engine if it is mounted on a portable engine stand. These stands can often be hired from a tool hire shop. Before the engine is mounted on a stand, the flywheel should be removed, so that the stand bolts can be tightened into the end of the cylinder block/crankcase.

2 If a stand is not available, it is possible to dismantle the engine with it blocked up on a sturdy workbench, or on the floor. Be extra-careful not to tip or drop the engine when working without a stand.

3 If you are going to obtain a reconditioned engine, all the external components must be removed first, to be transferred to the replacement engine (just as they will if you are doing a complete engine overhaul yourself). These components include the following:
  a) *Engine wiring harness and support brackets.*
  b) *Alternator, power steering pump and air conditioning compressor mounting brackets (as applicable).*
  c) *Coolant inlet housing.*
  d) *Fuel filter/thermostat housing.*
  e) *Dipstick tube.*
  f) *Fuel system components.*
  g) *All electrical switches and sensors.*

  h) *Inlet and exhaust manifolds and turbocharger (where fitted).*
  i) *Oil filter and oil cooler.*
  j) *Flywheel.*

Note: *When removing the external components from the engine, pay close attention to details that may be helpful or important during refitting. Note the fitted position of gaskets, seals, spacers, pins, washers, bolts, and other small items.*

4 If you are obtaining a 'short' engine (cylinder block/crankcase, crankshaft, pistons and connecting rods all assembled), then the cylinder head, sump, oil pump, and timing belt will have to be removed also.

5 If you are planning a complete overhaul, the engine can be dismantled, and the internal components removed, in the order given below, referring to Part C or D of this Chapter unless otherwise stated.
  a) *Inlet and exhaust manifolds (Chapter 4B or 4C).*
  b) *Timing belt, sprockets and tensioner.*
  c) *Cylinder head (Section 6 – 2.0 litre engines).*
  d) *Flywheel.*
  e) *Sump.*
  f) *Oil pump.*
  g) *Pistons/connecting rods (Section 11).*
  h) *Crankshaft (Section 12).*

6 Before beginning the dismantling and overhaul procedures, make sure that you have all of the tools necessary. Refer to *Tools and working facilities* for further information.

8 Cylinder head – dismantling

Note: *New and reconditioned cylinder heads are available from the manufacturer, and from engine overhaul specialists. Some specialist tools are required for dismantling and inspection, and new components may not be readily available. It may therefore be more practical and economical for the home mechanic to purchase a reconditioned head, rather than dismantle, inspect and recondition the original head.*

1 Remove the cylinder head as described in Part C or D of this Chapter, or in Section 6 of this Part (as applicable).

2 If not already done, remove the inlet and exhaust manifolds with reference to Chapter 4B or 4C.

3 On 1.9 litre engines, remove the camshaft, followers and shims as described in Part C or D of this Chapter.

4 On 2.0 litre engines, remove the camshaft, rocker arms and hydraulic tappets as described in Part D of this Chapter.

5 On all engines, remove the glow plugs as described in Chapter 5C and the injectors as described in Chapter 4B or 4C.

6 Using a valve spring compressor, compress each valve spring in turn until the split collets

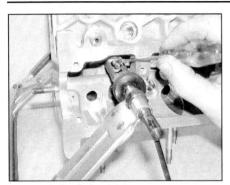

8.6a Compress the valve spring with a spring compressor and extract the split collets

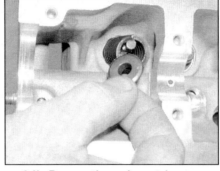

8.6b Remove the spring retainer . . .

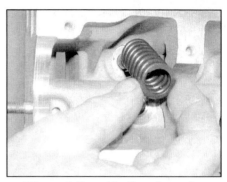

8.6c . . . followed by the valve spring

can be removed. Release the compressor, and lift off the spring retainer, and spring **(see illustrations)**.

7 If, when the valve spring compressor is screwed down, the spring retainer refuses to free and expose the split collets, gently tap the top of the tool, directly over the retainer, with a light hammer. This will free the retainer.

8 Withdraw the valve through the combustion chamber, remove the valve stem oil seal from the top of the guide, then lift out the spring seat **(see illustrations)**.

9 It is essential that each valve is stored together with its collets, retainer, spring, and spring seat. The valves should also be kept in their correct sequence, unless they are so badly worn that they are to be renewed. If they are going to be kept and used again,

place each valve assembly in a labelled polythene bag or similar small container **(see illustration)**. Note that No 1 valve is nearest to the transmission (flywheel) end of the engine.

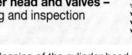

9 Cylinder head and valves – cleaning and inspection

1 Thorough cleaning of the cylinder head and valve components, followed by a detailed inspection, will enable you to decide how much valve service work must be carried out during the engine overhaul. **Note:** *If the engine has been severely overheated, it is best to assume that the cylinder head is warped – check carefully for signs of this.*

Cleaning

2 Remove all traces of old gasket material from the cylinder head. Citroën recommend the use of a scouring agent for this purpose, but acceptable results can be achieved by using a hard plastic or wood scraper to remove all traces of gasket and carbon.

3 Similarly, remove the carbon from the combustion chambers and ports, then wash the cylinder head thoroughly with paraffin or a suitable solvent.

4 Scrape off any heavy carbon deposits that may have formed on the valves, then use a power-operated wire brush to remove deposits from the valve heads and stems.

Inspection

Note: *Be sure to perform all the following inspection procedures before concluding that the services of a machine shop or engine overhaul specialist are required. Make a list of all items that require attention.*

Cylinder head

5 Inspect the head very carefully for cracks, evidence of coolant leakage, and other damage. If cracks are found, a new cylinder head should be obtained.

6 Use a straight-edge and feeler blade to check that the cylinder head gasket surface is not distorted **(see illustration)**. If it is, it may be possible to have it machined, provided that the cylinder head height is not significantly reduced. **Note:** *On 1.9 litre engines, it will be*

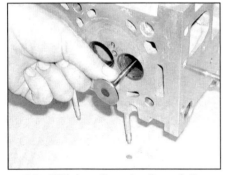

8.8a Withdraw the valve through the combustion chamber . . .

8.8b . . . remove the valve stem oil seal . . .

8.8c . . . then lift out the spring seat

8.9 Place each valve and its associated components in a labelled polythene bag

9.6 Checking the cylinder head gasket surface for distortion

9.10 Checking a swirl chamber protrusion

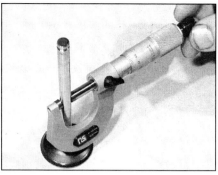

9.12 Measuring a valve stem diameter

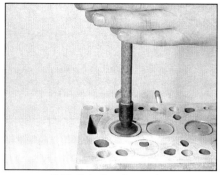

9.15 Grinding-in a valve

necessary to re-cut the combustion chambers and valve seats if more than 0.1 mm has been machined off the cylinder head. This is necessary in order to maintain the correct dimensions between the valve heads, valve guides and cylinder head gasket face.

7 Examine the valve seats in each of the combustion chambers. If they are severely pitted, cracked, or burned, they will need to be renewed or re-cut by an engine overhaul specialist. If they are only slightly pitted, this can be removed by grinding-in the valve heads and seats with fine valve-grinding compound, as described below.

8 Check the valve guides for wear by inserting the relevant valve, and checking for side-to-side motion of the valve. A very small amount of movement is acceptable. If the movement seems excessive, remove the valve. Measure the valve stem diameter (see below), and renew the valve if it is worn. If the valve stem is not worn, the wear must be in the valve guide, and the guide must be renewed. The renewal of valve guides is best carried out by an engine overhaul specialist, who will have the necessary tools available. Where no valve stem diameter is specified, seek the advice of the specialist carrying out the work, or a Citroën dealer on the best course of action.

9 If renewing the valve guides, the valve seats should be re-cut or re-ground only *after* the guides have been fitted.

10 On 1.9 litre engines, inspect the swirl chambers for burning or damage such as cracking. Small cracks in the chambers are acceptable; renewal of the chambers will only be required if the chamber tracts are badly burned and disfigured, or if they are no longer a tight fit in the cylinder head. If there is any doubt as to the swirl chamber condition, seek the advice of a Citroën dealer or a suitable repairer who specialises in diesel engines. Swirl chamber renewal should be entrusted to a specialist. Using a dial test indicator, check that the swirl chamber protrusion is within the limits given in the Specifications **(see illustration)**. Zero the dial test indicator on the gasket surface of the cylinder head, then measure the protrusion of the swirl chamber. If the protrusion is not within the specified

limits, the advice of a Citroën dealer or suitable repairer who specialises in diesel engines should be sought.

Valves

11 Examine the head of each valve for pitting, burning, cracks, and general wear. Check the valve stem for scoring and wear ridges. Rotate the valve, and check for any obvious indication that it is bent. Look for pits or excessive wear on the tip of each valve stem. Renew any valve that shows any such signs of wear or damage.

12 If the valve appears satisfactory at this stage, measure the valve stem diameter at several points using a micrometer **(see illustration)**. Any significant difference in the readings obtained indicates wear of the valve stem. Should any of these conditions be apparent, the valve(s) must be renewed.

13 If the valves are in satisfactory condition, they should be ground (lapped) into their respective seats, to ensure a smooth, gas-tight seal. If the seat is only lightly pitted, or if it has been re-cut, fine grinding compound *only* should be used to produce the required finish. Coarse valve-grinding compound should *not* be used, unless a seat is badly burned or deeply pitted. If this is the case, the cylinder head and valves should be inspected by an expert, to decide whether seat re-cutting, or even the renewal of the valve or seat insert (where possible) is required.

14 Valve grinding is carried out as follows. Place the head upside-down on blocks, on a bench.

15 Smear a trace of (the appropriate grade of) valve-grinding compound on the seat face, and press a suction grinding tool onto the valve head **(see illustration)**. With a semi-rotary action, grind the valve head to its seat, lifting the valve occasionally to redistribute the grinding compound. A light spring placed under the valve head will greatly ease this operation.

16 If coarse grinding compound is being used, work only until a dull, matt even surface is produced on both the valve seat and the valve, then wipe off the used compound, and repeat the process with fine compound. When a smooth unbroken ring of light grey matt

finish is produced on both the valve and seat, the grinding operation is complete. *Do not grind-in the valves any further than absolutely necessary, or the seat will be prematurely sunk into the cylinder head.*

17 When all the valves have been ground-in, carefully wash off *all* traces of grinding compound using paraffin or a suitable solvent, before reassembling the cylinder head.

Valve components

18 Examine the valve springs for signs of damage and discoloration. No minimum free length is specified by Citroën, so the only way of judging valve spring wear is by comparison with a new component.

19 Stand each spring on a flat surface, and check it for squareness. If any of the springs are damaged, distorted or have lost their tension, obtain a complete new set of springs. It is normal to fit new springs as a matter of course if a major overhaul is being carried out.

20 Renew the valve stem oil seals regardless of their apparent condition.

10 Cylinder head – reassembly

1 Working on the first valve assembly, refit the spring seat then dip the new valve stem oil seal in fresh engine oil. Locate the seal on the valve guide and press the seal firmly onto the guide using a suitable socket **(see illustrations)**.

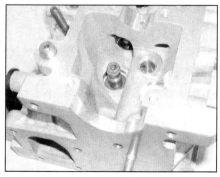

10.1a Locate the valve stem oil seal on the valve guide . . .

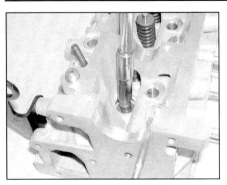

10.1b ... and press the seal firmly onto the guide using a suitable socket

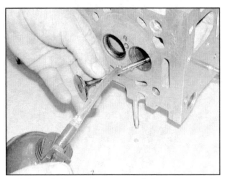

10.2 Lubricate the stem of the valve and insert it in the guide

2 Lubricate the stem of the first valve, and insert it in the guide **(see illustration)**.

3 Locate the valve spring on top of its seat, then refit the spring retainer.

4 Compress the valve spring, and locate the split collets in the recess in the valve stem. Release the compressor, then repeat the procedure on the remaining valves. Ensure that each valve is inserted into its original location. If new valves are being fitted, insert them into the locations to which they have been ground.

> **HAYNES HiNT** *Use a little dab of grease to hold the collets in position on the valve stem while the spring compressor is released.*

5 With all the valves installed, place the cylinder head on blocks on the bench and, using a hammer and interposed block of wood, tap the end of each valve stem to settle the components.

6 Refit the camshaft, followers, shims, hydraulic tappets and rocker arms (as applicable) as described in Part C or D of this Chapter.

7 The cylinder head can then be refitted as described in Part C or D of this Chapter (1.9 litre engines), or in Section 6 of this Part (2.0 litre engines).

11 Piston/connecting rod assembly – removal

1 Remove the cylinder head, sump and oil pump as described in this Part, or in Part C or D of this Chapter (as applicable).

2 If there is a pronounced wear ridge at the top of any bore, it may be necessary to remove it with a scraper or ridge reamer, to avoid piston damage during removal. Such a ridge indicates excess bore wear.

3 Using quick-drying paint, mark each connecting rod and big-end bearing cap with its respective cylinder number on the flat machined surface provided; if the engine has been dismantled before, note carefully any identifying marks made previously **(see illustration)**. Note that No 1 cylinder is at the transmission (flywheel) end of the engine.

4 Turn the crankshaft to bring pistons 1 and 4 to BDC (bottom dead centre).

5 Unscrew the nuts from No 1 piston big-end

bearing cap. Take off the cap, and recover the bottom half bearing shell **(see illustration)**. If the bearing shells are to be re-used, tape the cap and the shell together.

6 To prevent the possibility of damage to the crankshaft bearing journals, tape over the connecting rod stud threads.

7 Using a hammer handle, push the piston up through the bore, and remove it from the top of the cylinder block. Recover the bearing shell, and tape it to the connecting rod for safe-keeping.

8 Loosely refit the big-end cap to the connecting rod, and secure with the nuts – this will help to keep the components in their correct order.

9 Remove No 4 assembly in the same way.

10 Turn the crankshaft through 180° to bring pistons 2 and 3 to BDC (bottom dead centre), and remove them in the same way.

12 Crankshaft – removal

1 Remove the crankshaft sprocket and the oil pump as described in Part C or D of this Chapter (as applicable).

2 Remove the pistons and connecting rods, as described in Section 11. If no work is to be done on the pistons and connecting rods, there is no need to remove the cylinder head, or to push the pistons out of the cylinder bores. The pistons should just be pushed far enough up the bores so that they are positioned clear of the crankshaft journals.

3 Check the crankshaft endfloat as described in Section 15, then proceed as follows.

4 Slacken and remove the retaining bolts, and remove the oil seal carrier from the right-

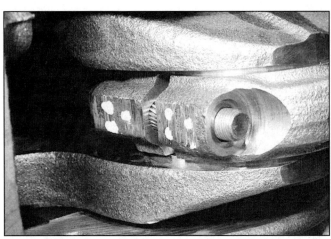

11.3 Connecting rod and big-end bearing cap identification marks (No 3 shown)

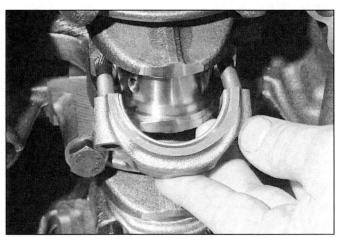

11.5 Removing a big-end bearing cap and shell

12.4 Removing the oil seal carrier from the right-hand end of the block

12.5a Remove the oil pump drive chain . . .

12.5b . . . then slide off the drive sprocket . . .

12.5c . . . and remove the Woodruff key from the crankshaft

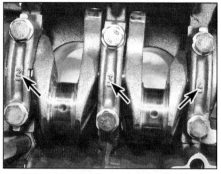

12.6 Main bearing cap identification markings (arrowed)

12.7 Removing No 2 main bearing cap. Note the thrustwasher (arrowed)

hand end of the cylinder block, along with its gasket (where fitted) **(see illustration)**.

5 Remove the oil pump drive chain, and slide the drive sprocket and spacer (where fitted) off the end of the crankshaft. Remove the Woodruff key, and store it with the sprocket for safe-keeping **(see illustrations)**.

6 The main bearing caps should be numbered 1 to 5, starting from the transmission (flywheel) end of the engine **(see illustration)**. If not, mark them accordingly using quick-drying paint. Also note the correct fitted depth of the left-hand crankshaft oil seal in the bearing cap.

7 Slacken and remove the main bearing cap retaining bolts, and lift off each bearing cap.

Recover the lower bearing shells, and tape them to their respective caps for safe-keeping. Also recover the lower thrustwasher halves from the side of No 2 main bearing cap **(see illustration)**. Remove the sealing strips from the sides of No 1 main bearing cap, and discard them.

8 Lift out the crankshaft **(see illustration)**, and discard the left-hand oil seal.

9 Recover the upper bearing shells from the cylinder block **(see illustration)**, and tape them to their respective caps for safe-keeping. Remove the upper thrustwasher halves from the side of No 2 main bearing, and store them with the lower halves.

13 Cylinder block/crankcase – cleaning and inspection

Cleaning

1 Remove all external components and electrical switches/sensors from the block. For complete cleaning, the core plugs should ideally be removed **(see illustration)**. Drill a small hole in the plugs, then insert a self-tapping screw into the hole. Pull out the plugs by pulling on the screw with a pair of grips, or by using a slide hammer.

2 Where fitted, undo the retaining bolt and remove the piston oil jet spray tube from inside the cylinder block.

3 Scrape all traces of gasket from the cylinder

12.8 Lifting out the crankshaft

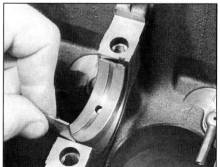

12.9 Remove the upper main bearing shells from the cylinder block/crankcase, and store them with their lower shells

13.1 Cylinder block core plugs (arrowed)

13.8 Cleaning a cylinder block threaded hole using a suitable tap

block/crankcase, taking care not to damage the gasket/sealing surfaces.

4 Remove all oil gallery plugs (where fitted). The plugs are usually very tight – they may have to be drilled out, and the holes re-tapped. Use new plugs when the engine is reassembled.

5 If the cylinder block is extremely dirty, it should be steam-cleaned.

6 After steam-cleaning, clean all oil holes and oil galleries one more time. Flush all internal passages with warm water until the water runs clear. Dry thoroughly, and apply a light film of oil to the cylinder bores and all mating surfaces, to prevent rusting. If you have access to compressed air, use it to speed up the drying process, and to blow out all the oil holes and galleries.

 Warning: Wear eye protection when using compressed air.

7 If the cylinder block is not very dirty, you can do an adequate cleaning job with very hot, soapy water and a stiff brush. Take plenty of time, and do a thorough job. Regardless of the cleaning method used, be sure to clean all oil holes and galleries very thoroughly, and to dry all components well. Protect the cylinder bores as described above, to prevent rusting.

8 All threaded holes must be clean, to ensure accurate torque readings during reassembly. To clean the threads, run the correct-size tap into each of the holes to remove rust, corrosion, thread sealant or sludge, and to restore damaged threads **(see illustration)**. If

14.2 Removing a piston ring with the aid of a feeler blade

possible, use compressed air to clear the holes of debris produced by this operation.

 Warning: Wear eye protection when using compressed air.

9 Apply sealant to new oil gallery plugs and tighten them securely in the block. Similarly apply sealant to new core plugs and drive them squarely into the block.

10 On engines with a piston oil jet spray tube, clean the threads of the oil jet retaining bolt, and apply a drop of thread-locking compound to the bolt threads. Refit the piston oil jet spray tube to the cylinder block, and tighten its retaining bolt to the specified torque setting.

11 If the engine is not going to be reassembled right away, cover it with a large plastic bag to keep it clean; protect all mating surfaces and the cylinder bores as described above, to prevent rusting.

Inspection

12 Visually check the block for cracks and corrosion. Look for stripped threads in the threaded holes. If there has been any history of internal water leakage, it may be worthwhile having an engine overhaul specialist check the cylinder block/crankcase with special equipment. If defects are found, have them repaired if possible, or renew the assembly.

13 Check each cylinder bore for scuffing and scoring. Check for signs of a wear ridge at the top of the cylinder, indicating that the bore is excessively worn.

14 If the necessary measuring equipment is available, measure the bore diameter of each cylinder at the top (just under the wear ridge), centre, and bottom of the cylinder bore, parallel to the crankshaft axis.

15 Next, measure the bore diameter at the same three locations, at right-angles to the crankshaft axis. Compare the results with the figures given in the Specifications. If there is any doubt about the condition of the cylinder bores, seek the advice of an engine reconditioning specialist or Citroën dealer.

16 Oversize pistons are available for 1.9 litre engines, but not for 2.0 litre engines. Where oversize pistons are available, it should be possible to have the cylinder bores rebored, and to fit the oversize pistons. Where oversize pistons are not available, or if the cylinder block has already been rebored, then if the bores are worn, renewal of the block is the only option.

14 Piston/connecting rod assembly – inspection

1 Before the inspection process can begin, the piston/connecting rod assemblies must be cleaned, and the original piston rings removed from the pistons.

2 Carefully expand the old rings over the top of the pistons. The use of two or three old feeler blades will be helpful in preventing the rings dropping into empty grooves **(see illustration)**.

Be careful not to scratch the piston with the ends of the ring. The rings are brittle, and will snap if they are spread too far. They are also very sharp – protect your hands and fingers. Note that the third ring incorporates an expander. Always remove the rings from the top of the piston. Keep each set of rings with its piston if the old rings are to be re-used.

3 Scrape away all traces of carbon from the top of the piston. A hand-held wire brush (or a piece of fine emery cloth) can be used, once the majority of the deposits have been scraped away.

4 Remove the carbon from the ring grooves in the piston, using an old ring. Break the ring in half to do this (be careful not to cut your fingers – piston rings are sharp). Be careful to remove only the carbon deposits – do not remove any metal, and do not nick or scratch the sides of the ring grooves.

5 Once the deposits have been removed, clean the piston/connecting rod assembly with paraffin or a suitable solvent, and dry thoroughly. Make sure that the oil return holes in the ring grooves are clear.

6 If the pistons and cylinder bores are not damaged or worn excessively, and if the cylinder block does not need to be rebored, the original pistons can be refitted. Normal piston wear shows up as even vertical wear on the piston thrust surfaces, and slight looseness of the top ring in its groove. New piston rings should always be used when the engine is reassembled.

7 Carefully inspect each piston for cracks around the skirt, around the gudgeon pin holes, and at the piston ring 'lands' (between the ring grooves).

8 Look for scoring and scuffing on the piston skirt, holes in the piston crown, and burned areas at the edge of the crown. If the skirt is scored or scuffed, the engine may have been suffering from overheating, and/or abnormal combustion which caused excessively high operating temperatures. The cooling and lubrication systems should be checked thoroughly. Scorch marks on the sides of the pistons show that blow-by has occurred. A hole in the piston crown, or burned areas at the edge of the piston crown, indicates that abnormal combustion has been occurring. If any of the above problems exist, the causes must be investigated and corrected, or the damage will occur again. The causes may include incorrect injection pump timing, or a faulty injector (as applicable).

9 Corrosion of the piston, in the form of pitting, indicates that coolant has been leaking into the combustion chamber and/or the crankcase. Again, the cause must be corrected, or the problem may persist in the rebuilt engine.

10 Examine each connecting rod carefully for signs of damage, such as cracks around the big-end and small-end bearings. Check that the rod is not bent or distorted. Damage is highly unlikely, unless the engine has been seized or badly overheated. Detailed checking

14.14a Prise out the circlip . . .

14.14b . . . and withdraw the gudgeon pin

19 Apply a smear of clean engine oil to the gudgeon pin and slide it into the piston and through the connecting rod small-end. Check that the piston pivots freely on the rod, then secure the gudgeon pin in position with two new circlips. Ensure that each circlip is correctly located in its groove in the piston.

15 Crankshaft – inspection

Checking crankshaft endfloat

1 If the crankshaft endfloat is to be checked, this must be done when the crankshaft is still installed in the cylinder block/crankcase, but is free to move (see Section 12).

2 Check the endfloat using a dial gauge in contact with the end of the crankshaft. Push the crankshaft fully one way, and then zero the gauge. Push the crankshaft fully the other way, and check the endfloat. The result can be compared with the specified amount, and will give an indication as to whether new thrustwashers are required **(see illustration)**.

3 If a dial gauge is not available, feeler blades can be used. First push the crankshaft fully towards the flywheel end of the engine, then use feeler blades to measure the gap between the web of No 2 crankpin and the thrustwasher **(see illustration)**.

Inspection

4 Clean the crankshaft using paraffin or a suitable solvent, and dry it, preferably with compressed air if available. Be sure to clean the oil holes with a pipe cleaner or similar probe, to ensure that they are not obstructed.

> ⚠ **Warning: Wear eye protection when using compressed air.**

5 Check the main and big-end bearing journals for uneven wear, scoring, pitting and cracking.

6 Big-end bearing wear is accompanied by

of the connecting rod assembly can only be carried out by an engine specialist with the necessary equipment.

11 Note that the big-end cap nuts and bolts must be renewed as a complete set prior to refitting. This should be done after the big-end bearing running clearance check has been carried out (see Section 20). The bolts can be simply tapped out of the connecting rods and new bolts fitted in the same way.

12 On all diesel engines, the gudgeon pins are of the floating type, secured in position by two circlips. The pistons and connecting rods can be separated as follows.

13 On 2.0 litre engines, before separating the piston and connecting rod, check the position of the valve recesses on the piston crown in relation to the connecting rod big-end bearing shell cut-outs and make a note of the orientation. On the new engine dismantled in the Haynes workshop during the preparation

of this manual, the piston-to-connecting rod orientation did not agree with the manufacturer's technical documentation.

14 Using a small flat-bladed screwdriver, prise out the circlips, and push out the gudgeon pin **(see illustrations)**. Hand pressure should be sufficient to remove the pin. Identify the piston and rod to ensure correct reassembly. Discard the circlips – new ones *must* be used on refitting.

15 Examine the gudgeon pin and connecting rod small-end bearing for signs of wear or damage. Wear can be cured by renewing both the pin and bush. Bush renewal, however, is a specialist job – press facilities are required, and the new bush must be reamed accurately.

16 The connecting rods themselves should not be in need of renewal, unless seizure or some other major mechanical failure has occurred. Check the alignment of the connecting rods visually, and if the rods are not straight, take them to an engine overhaul specialist for a more detailed check.

17 Examine all components, and obtain any new parts from your Citroën dealer. If new pistons are purchased, they will be supplied complete with gudgeon pins and circlips. Circlips can also be purchased individually.

18 On 1.9 litre engines, position the piston so that the cut-out on the piston crown is positioned as shown in relation to the connecting rod big-end bearing shell cut-outs **(see illustration)**. On 2.0 litre engines, position the piston in relation to the connecting rod as noted during separation.

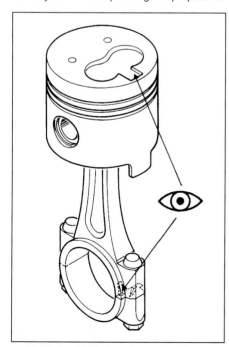

14.18 On 1.9 litre engines, on refitting ensure that the piston cut-out is positioned as shown, in relation to the connecting rod bearing shell cut-out

15.2 Checking crankshaft endfloat using a dial gauge

15.3 Checking crankshaft endfloat using feeler blades

15.10 Measuring a crankshaft big-end journal diameter

distinct metallic knocking when the engine is running (particularly noticeable when the engine is pulling from low speed) and some loss of oil pressure.

7 Main bearing wear is accompanied by severe engine vibration and rumble – getting progressively worse as engine speed increases – and again by loss of oil pressure.

8 Check the bearing journal for roughness by running a finger lightly over the bearing surface. Any roughness (which will be accompanied by obvious bearing wear) indicates that the crankshaft requires regrinding (where possible) or renewal.

9 If the crankshaft has been reground, check for burrs around the crankshaft oil holes (the holes are usually chamfered, so burrs should not be a problem unless regrinding has been carried out carelessly). Remove any burrs with a fine file or scraper, and thoroughly clean the oil holes as described previously.

10 Using a micrometer, measure the diameter of the main and big-end bearing journals, and compare the results with the

Specifications **(see illustration)**. By measuring the diameter at a number of points around each journal's circumference, you will be able to determine whether or not the journal is out-of-round. Take the measurement at each end of the journal, near the webs, to determine if the journal is tapered. Compare the results obtained with those given in the Specifications.

11 Check the oil seal contact surfaces at each end of the crankshaft for wear and damage. If the seal has worn a deep groove in the surface of the crankshaft, consult an engine overhaul specialist; repair may be possible, but otherwise a new crankshaft will be required.

12 Oversize main bearing shells are available for all engines, but oversize big-end bearing shells are available for 1.9 litre engines only. Where oversize bearing shells are available, if the crankshaft journals have not already been reground, it may be possible to have the crankshaft reconditioned, and to fit the oversize shells. Where oversize shells are not available, or if the crankshaft has already been reconditioned, it will have to be renewed if worn beyond the specified limits. Consult your Citroën dealer or engine specialist for further information on parts availability.

16 Main and big-end bearings – inspection

1 Even though the main and big-end bearings should be renewed during the engine overhaul, the old bearings should be retained for close examination, as they may reveal valuable information about the condition of the engine. The bearing shells are graded by thickness, the grade of each shell being indicated by the colour code, or size identification, marked on it.

2 Bearing failure can occur due to lack of lubrication, the presence of dirt or other foreign particles, overloading the engine, or corrosion **(see illustration)**. Regardless of the cause of bearing failure, the cause must be corrected (where applicable) before the engine is reassembled, to prevent it from happening again.

3 When examining the bearing shells, remove them from the cylinder block/crankcase, the main bearing ladder/caps (as appropriate), the connecting rods and the connecting rod big-end bearing caps. Lay them out on a clean surface in the same general position as their location in the engine. This will enable you to match any bearing problems with the corresponding crankshaft journal. *Do not* touch any shell's bearing surface with your fingers while checking it, or the delicate surface may be scratched.

4 Dirt and other foreign matter gets into the engine in a variety of ways. It may be left in the engine during assembly, or it may pass

through filters or the crankcase ventilation system. It may get into the oil, and from there into the bearings. Metal chips from machining operations and normal engine wear are often present. Abrasives are sometimes left in engine components after reconditioning, especially when parts are not thoroughly cleaned using the proper cleaning methods. Whatever the source, these foreign objects often end up embedded in the soft bearing material, and are easily recognised. Large particles will not embed in the bearing, and will score or gouge the bearing and journal. The best prevention for this cause of bearing failure is to clean all parts thoroughly, and keep everything spotlessly-clean during engine assembly. Frequent and regular engine oil and filter changes are also recommended.

5 Lack of lubrication (or lubrication breakdown) has a number of interrelated causes. Excessive heat (which thins the oil), overloading (which squeezes the oil from the bearing face) and oil leakage (from excessive bearing clearances, worn oil pump or high engine speeds) all contribute to lubrication breakdown. Blocked oil passages, which usually are the result of misaligned oil holes in a bearing shell, will also oil-starve a bearing, and destroy it. When lack of lubrication is the cause of bearing failure, the bearing material is wiped or extruded from the steel backing of the bearing. Temperatures may increase to the point where the steel backing turns blue from overheating.

6 Driving habits can have a definite effect on bearing life. Full-throttle, low-speed operation (labouring the engine) puts very high loads on bearings, tending to squeeze out the oil film. These loads cause the bearings to flex, which produces fine cracks in the bearing face (fatigue failure). Eventually, the bearing material will loosen in pieces, and tear away from the steel backing.

7 Short-distance driving leads to corrosion of bearings, because insufficient engine heat is produced to drive off the condensed water and corrosive gases. These products collect in the engine oil, forming acid and sludge. As the oil is carried to the engine bearings, the acid attacks and corrodes the bearing material.

8 Incorrect bearing installation during engine assembly will lead to bearing failure as well. Tight-fitting bearings leave insufficient bearing running clearance, and will result in oil starvation. Dirt or foreign particles trapped behind a bearing shell result in high spots on the bearing, which lead to failure.

9 *Do not* touch any shell's bearing surface with your fingers during reassembly; there is a risk of scratching the delicate surface, or of depositing particles of dirt on it.

10 As mentioned at the beginning of this Section, the bearing shells should be renewed as a matter of course during engine overhaul; to do otherwise is false economy.

FATIGUE FAILURE	IMPROPER SEATING
CRATERS OR POCKETS	BRIGHT (POLISHED) SECTIONS
SCRATCHED BY DIRT	LACK OF OIL
DIRT EMBEDDED INTO BEARING MATERIAL	OVERLAY WIPED OUT
EXCESSIVE WEAR	TAPERED JOURNAL
OVERLAY WIPED OUT	RADIUS RIDE

H 28395

16.2 Typical bearing failures

17 Engine overhaul – reassembly sequence

1 Before reassembly begins, ensure that all new parts have been obtained, and that all necessary tools are available. Read through the entire procedure to familiarise yourself with the work involved, and to ensure that all items necessary for reassembly of the engine are at hand. In addition to all normal tools and materials, thread-locking compound will be needed. A suitable tube of liquid sealant will also be required for the joint faces that are fitted without gaskets. It is recommended that Citroën's own products are used, which are specially formulated for this purpose; the relevant product names are quoted in the text of each Section where they are required.

2 In order to save time and avoid problems, engine reassembly can be carried out in the following order:

a) *Crankshaft (See Section 19).*
b) *Piston/connecting rod assemblies (See Section 20).*
c) *Oil pump (See Part C or D – as applicable).*
d) *Sump (See Part C or D – as applicable).*
e) *Flywheel (See Part C or D – as applicable).*
f) *Cylinder head (See Part C, Part D or Section 6 of this Part – as applicable).*
g) *Timing belt tensioner and sprockets, and timing belt (See Part C or D – as applicable).*
h) *Engine external components.*

3 At this stage, all engine components should be absolutely clean and dry, with all faults repaired. The components should be laid out (or in individual containers) on a completely clean work surface.

18 Piston rings – refitting

1 Before fitting new piston rings, the ring end gaps must be checked as follows.
2 Lay out the piston/connecting rod

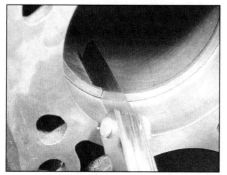

18.5 Measuring a piston ring end gap

assemblies and the new piston ring sets, so that the ring sets will be matched with the same piston and cylinder during the end gap measurement and subsequent engine reassembly.

3 Insert the top ring into the first cylinder, and push it down the bore using the top of the piston. This will ensure that the ring remains square with the cylinder walls. Position the ring near the bottom of the cylinder bore, at the lower limit of ring travel. Note that the top and second compression rings are different. The second ring is easily identified by the fact that its outer face is tapered.

4 Measure the end gap using feeler blades.

5 Repeat the procedure with the ring at the top of the cylinder bore, at the upper limit of its travel, and compare the measurements with the figures given in the Specifications **(see illustration)**. Where no figures are given, seek the advice of a Citroën dealer or engine reconditioning specialist.

6 If the gap is too small (unlikely if genuine Citroën parts are used), it must be enlarged, or the ring ends may contact each other during engine operation, causing serious damage. Ideally, new piston rings providing the correct end gap should be fitted. As a last resort, the end gap can be increased by filing the ring ends very carefully with a fine file. Mount the file in a vice equipped with soft jaws, slip the ring over the file with the ends contacting the file face, and slowly move the ring to remove material from the ends. Take care, as piston rings are sharp, and are easily broken.

7 With new piston rings, it is unlikely that the end gap will be too large. If the gaps are too large, check that you have the correct rings for your engine and for the cylinder bore size.

8 Repeat the checking procedure for each ring in the first cylinder, and then for the rings in the remaining cylinders. Remember to keep rings, pistons and cylinders matched up.

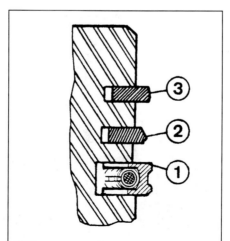

18.10 Piston ring fitting diagram (typical)
1   *Oil control ring*
2   *Second compression ring*
3   *Top compression ring*

9 Once the ring end gaps have been checked and if necessary corrected, the rings can be fitted to the pistons.

10 Fit the piston rings using the same technique as for removal. Fit the bottom (oil control) ring first, and work up. When fitting the oil control ring, first insert the expander (where fitted), then fit the ring with its gap positioned 180° from the expander gap. Ensure that the second compression ring is fitted the correct way up, with its identification mark (either a dot of paint or the word TOP stamped on the ring surface) at the top, and the stepped surface, or the larger diameter of the taper at the bottom **(see illustration)**. Arrange the gaps of the top and second compression rings 120° either side of the oil control ring gap. **Note:** *Always follow any instructions supplied with the new piston ring sets – different manufacturers may specify different procedures. Do not mix up the top and second compression rings, as they have different cross-sections.*

19 Crankshaft – refitting and main bearing running clearance check

Note: *It is recommended that new main bearing shells are fitted regardless of the condition of the original ones.*

Selection of bearing shells

1 There are two different sizes of main bearing shell available; the standard size shell for use with an original crankshaft and an oversize shell for use once the crankshaft has been reground.

2 The relevant set of bearing shells required can be obtained by measuring the diameter of the crankshaft main bearing journals (see Section 15). This will show if the crankshaft is original or whether its journals have been reground, identifying if either standard or oversize bearing shells are required.

3 If the access to the necessary measuring equipment cannot be gained, the size of the bearing shells can be identified by the markings stamped on the rear of each shell. Details of these markings should be supplied to your Citroën dealer who will then be able to identify the size of shell fitted.

4 Whether the original shells or new shells are being fitted, it is recommended that the running clearance is checked as follows prior to installation.

Main bearing running clearance check

5 The running clearance check can be carried out using the original bearing shells. However, it is preferable to use a new set, since the results obtained will be more conclusive.

6 Clean the backs of the bearing shells, and the bearing locations in both the cylinder block/crankcase and the main bearing caps.

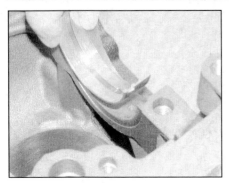

19.7a Fit the bearing shells, ensuring that the tab engages in the notch in the cylinder block/crankcase . . .

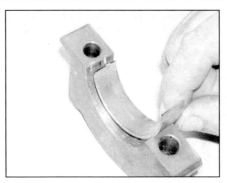

19.7b . . . and in the bearing cap

19.12 Plastigauge in place on a crankshaft main bearing journal

7 Press the bearing shells into their locations, ensuring that the tab on each shell engages in the notch in the cylinder block/crankcase or bearing cap **(see illustrations)**. Take care not to touch any shell's bearing surface with your fingers. Note that the upper bearing shells all have a grooved bearing surface, whereas the lower shells have a plain bearing surface. If the original bearing shells are being used for the check, ensure that they are refitted in their original locations.

8 The clearance can be checked in either of two ways.

9 One method (which will be difficult to achieve without a range of internal micrometers or internal/external expanding calipers) is to refit the main bearing caps to the cylinder block/crankcase, with bearing shells in place. With the cap retaining bolts tightened to the specified torque, measure the internal diameter of each assembled pair of bearing shells. If the diameter of each corresponding crankshaft journal is measured and then subtracted from the bearing internal diameter, the result will be the main bearing running clearance.

10 The second (and more accurate) method is to use an American product known as Plastigauge. This consists of a fine thread of perfectly-round plastic, which is compressed between the bearing shell and the journal. When the shell is removed, the plastic is deformed, and can be measured with a special card gauge supplied with the kit. The running clearance is determined from this gauge. Plastigauge should be available from your Citroën dealer; otherwise, enquiries at one of the larger specialist motor factors should produce the name of a stockist in your area. The procedure for using Plastigauge is as follows.

11 With the main bearing upper shells in place, carefully lay the crankshaft in position. Do not use any lubricant; the crankshaft journals and bearing shells must be perfectly clean and dry.

12 Cut several lengths of the appropriate-size Plastigauge (they should be slightly shorter than the width of the main bearings), and place one length on each crankshaft journal axis **(see illustration)**.

13 With the main bearing lower shells in position, refit the main bearing caps, tightening their retaining bolts to the specified torque. Take care not to disturb the Plastigauge, and *do not* rotate the crankshaft at any time during this operation.

14 Remove the main bearing caps, again taking great care not to disturb the Plastigauge or rotate the crankshaft.

15 Compare the width of the crushed Plastigauge on each journal to the scale printed on the Plastigauge envelope, to obtain the main bearing running clearance **(see illustration)**. Compare the clearance measured with that in the Specifications at the start of this Chapter.

16 If the clearance is significantly different from that expected, the bearing shells may be the wrong size (or excessively worn, if the original shells are being re-used). Before deciding that different-size shells are required, make sure that no dirt or oil was trapped between the bearing shells and the caps or block when the clearance was measured. If the Plastigauge was wider at one end than at the other, the crankshaft journal may be tapered.

17 Note that Citroën do not specify a running clearance for these engines. The figure given in the Specifications is a guide figure which is typical for this type of engine. Before condemning the components concerned, seek the advice of your Citroën dealer or suitable engine repair specialist. They will also

be able to inform as to the best course of action and whether it is possible to have the crankshaft journals reground (where possible) or whether renewal will be necessary.

18 Where necessary, obtain the correct size of bearing shell and repeat the running clearance checking procedure as described above.

19 On completion, carefully scrape away all traces of the Plastigauge material from the crankshaft and bearing shells using a fingernail or other object which is unlikely to score the bearing surfaces.

Final crankshaft refitting

20 Carefully lift the crankshaft out of the cylinder block once more.

21 Using a little grease, stick the upper thrustwashers to each side of the No 2 main bearing upper location. Ensure that the oilway grooves on each thrustwasher face outwards (away from the cylinder block) **(see illustration)**.

22 Place the bearing shells in their locations as described earlier. If new shells are being fitted, ensure that all traces of protective grease are cleaned off using paraffin. Wipe dry the shells and connecting rods with a lint-free cloth. Liberally lubricate each bearing shell in the cylinder block/crankcase and cap with clean engine oil.

23 Lower the crankshaft into position so that Nos 2 and 3 cylinder crankpins are at TDC; Nos 1 and 4 cylinder crankpins will be

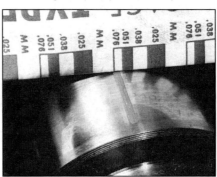

19.15 Measure the width of the deformed Plastigauge using the scale on the card

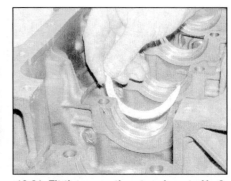

19.21 Fit the upper thrustwashers to No 2 main bearing location with the oilway grooves facing outwards

19.23 Lower the crankshaft into position in the cylinder block/crankcase

19.26 Apply sealant to the No 1 main bearing cap mating face on the cylinder block, around the sealing strip holes and in the corners

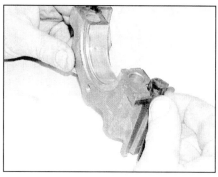

19.27 Fit the sealing strips to No 1 main bearing cap

at BDC, ready for fitting No 1 piston **(see illustration)**. Check the crankshaft endfloat as described in Section 15.

24 Lubricate the lower bearing shells in the main bearing caps with clean engine oil. Make sure that the locating lugs on the shells engage with the corresponding recesses in the caps.

25 Fit main bearing caps Nos 2 to 5 to their correct locations, ensuring that they are fitted the correct way round (the bearing shell tab recesses in the block and caps must be on the same side). Insert the bolts, tightening them only loosely at this stage.

26 Apply a small amount of sealant to the No 1 main bearing cap mating face on the cylinder block, around the sealing strip holes and in the corners **(see illustration)**.

27 Locate the tab of each sealing strip over the pins on the base of No 1 bearing cap, and press the strips into the bearing cap grooves **(see illustration)**. It is now necessary to obtain two thin metal strips, of 0.25 mm thickness or less, in order to prevent the strips moving when the cap is being fitted. Metal strips, such as old feeler blades, can be used, provided all burrs which may damage the sealing strips are first removed.

28 Oil both sides of the metal strips, and hold them on the sealing strips. Fit the No 1 main bearing cap, insert the bolts loosely, then carefully pull out the metal strips in a horizontal direction, using a pair of pliers **(see illustration)**.

29 Tighten all the main bearing cap bolts evenly to the specified torque and, on 2.0 litre engines, additionally through the specified angle. Using a sharp knife, trim off the ends of the No 1 bearing cap sealing strips, so that they protrude above the cylinder block/crankcase mating surface by approximately 1 mm **(see illustrations)**.

30 Fit a new crankshaft left-hand oil seal as described in Part C or D of this Chapter.

31 Refit the piston/connecting rod assemblies to the crankshaft as described in Section 20.

32 Refit the Woodruff key, then slide on the oil pump drive sprocket and spacer (where fitted), and locate the drive chain on the sprocket.

33 Ensure that the mating surfaces of the right-hand oil seal carrier and cylinder block are clean and dry. Note the correct fitted depth of the oil seal then, using a large flat-bladed screwdriver, lever the old seal out of the housing.

34 Apply a smear of suitable sealant to the oil seal carrier mating surface. Ensure that the locating dowels are in position, then slide the carrier over the end of the crankshaft and into position on the cylinder block. Tighten the carrier retaining bolts to the specified torque.

35 Fit a new crankshaft right-hand oil seal as described in Part C or D of this Chapter.

36 Ensuring that the drive chain is correctly

located on the sprocket, refit the oil pump and sump as described in Part C or D of this Chapter.

37 Where removed, refit the cylinder head as described in Part C or D of this Chapter, or in Section 6 of this Part.

20 Piston/connecting rod assembly – refitting and big-end bearing running clearance check

Selection of bearing shells

1 On most engines, there are two sizes of big-end bearing shell produced by Citroën; a standard size for use with the standard

19.28 Use two metal strips (arrowed) to hold the sealing strips in place as the bearing cap is fitted

19.29a Tighten all the main bearing cap bolts to the specified torque . . .

19.29b . . . and, on 2.0 litre engines, additionally through the specified angle

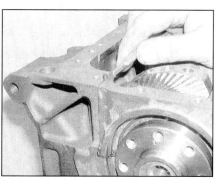

19.29c Trim off the ends of No 1 bearing cap sealing strips, so that they protrude by approximately 1 mm

20.5a Fit the big-end bearing shells ensuring that the tab engages in the notch in the connecting rod . . .

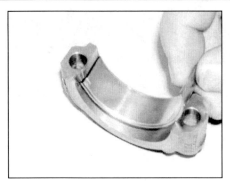

20.5b . . . and in the connecting rod cap

crankshaft, and an oversize for use once the crankshaft journals have been reground.

2 Consult your Citroën dealer for the latest information on parts availability. Always quote the diameter of the crankshaft big-end crankpins when ordering bearing shells.

3 Before refitting the piston/connecting rod assemblies, we recommend that the big-end bearing running clearance is checked as follows.

Big-end bearing running clearance check

4 Clean the backs of the bearing shells, and the bearing locations in both the connecting rod and bearing cap.

5 Press the bearing shells into their locations, ensuring that the tab on each shell engages in the notch in the connecting rod and cap **(see illustrations)**. Take care not to touch any shell's bearing surface with your fingers. If the original bearing shells are being used for the check, ensure that they are refitted in their original locations. The clearance can be checked in either of two ways.

6 One method is to refit the big-end bearing cap to the connecting rod, ensuring that they are fitted the correct way around (see paragraph 20), with the bearing shells in place. With the cap retaining nuts correctly tightened, use an internal micrometer or vernier caliper to measure the internal diameter of each assembled pair of bearing shells. If the diameter of each corresponding

crankshaft journal is measured and then subtracted from the bearing internal diameter, the result will be the big-end bearing running clearance.

7 The second, and more accurate method is to use Plastigauge (see Section 19).

8 Ensure that the bearing shells are correctly fitted. Place a strand of Plastigauge on each (cleaned) crankpin journal.

9 Refit the (clean) piston/connecting rod assemblies to the crankshaft, and refit the big-end bearing caps, using the marks made or noted on removal to ensure that they are fitted the correct way around.

10 Tighten the bearing cap nuts to the specified torque. Take care not to disturb the Plastigauge, nor rotate the connecting rod during the tightening sequence.

11 Dismantle the assemblies without rotating the connecting rods. Use the scale printed on the Plastigauge envelope to obtain the big-end bearing running clearance.

12 If the clearance is significantly different from that expected, the bearing shells may be the wrong size (or excessively worn, if the original shells are being re-used). Make sure that no dirt or oil was trapped between the bearing shells and the caps or block when the clearance was measured. If the Plastigauge was wider at one end than at the other, the crankshaft journal may be tapered.

13 Note that Citroën do not specify a recommended big-end bearing running clearance. The figure given in the

Specifications is a guide figure, which is typical for this type of engine. Before condemning the components concerned, refer to your Citroën dealer or engine reconditioning specialist for further information on the specified running clearance. Their advice on the best course of action to be taken can then also be obtained.

14 On completion, carefully scrape away all traces of the Plastigauge material from the crankshaft and bearing shells. Use your fingernail, or some other object which is unlikely to score the bearing surfaces.

15 Fit the new bearing cap retaining bolts to the connecting rods as described in Section 14.

Final piston/connecting rod refitting

16 Ensure that the bearing shells are correctly fitted as described earlier. If new shells are being fitted, ensure that all traces of the protective grease are cleaned off using paraffin. Wipe dry the shells and connecting rods with a lint-free cloth.

17 Lubricate the cylinder bores, the pistons, and piston rings, then lay out each piston/connecting rod assembly in its respective position.

18 Make sure that the piston rings are still spaced as described in Section 18, then clamp them in position with a piston ring compressor.

19 Insert the first piston/connecting rod assembly into the top of its corresponding cylinder. On 1.9 litre engines, ensure that the cloverleaf-shaped cut-out on the piston crown is towards the front (oil filter side) of the cylinder block, and on 2.0 litre engines, ensure that the arrow on the piston crown is pointing towards the timing belt end of the engine. Using a block of wood or hammer handle against the piston crown, tap the assembly into the cylinder until the piston crown is flush with the top of the block **(see illustrations)**.

20 Ensure that the bearing shell is still correctly installed. Liberally lubricate the crankpin and both bearing shells. Taking care not to mark the cylinder bores, pull the

20.19a Insert the piston/connecting rod assembly into the top of the relevant cylinder

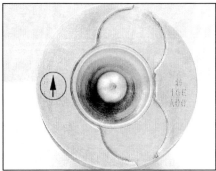

20.19b On 2.0 litre engines the arrow on the piston crown must point towards the timing belt end of the engine

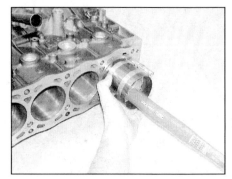

20.19c Tap the assembly into the cylinder bore until the piston crown is flush with the top of the block

piston/connecting rod assembly down the bore and onto the crankpin. Refit the big-end bearing cap, tightening the nuts finger-tight at first. Note that the faces with the identification marks must match (which means that the bearing shell locating tabs abut each other).

21 Tighten the bearing cap retaining nuts evenly and progressively to the Stage 1 torque setting **(see illustration)**.

22 Once both nuts have been tightened to the Stage 1 setting, angle-tighten them through the specified Stage 2 angle, using a socket and extension bar. It is recommended that an angle-measuring gauge is used during this stage of the tightening, to ensure accuracy **(see illustration)**.

23 Once the bearing cap retaining nuts have been correctly tightened, rotate the crankshaft. Check that it turns freely; some stiffness is to be expected if new components have been fitted, but there should be no signs of binding or tight spots.

24 Refit the other three piston/connecting rod assemblies in the same way.

25 Refit the cylinder head and oil pump as described in as described in Part C or D of this Chapter, and/or in Section 6 of this Part (as applicable).

21 Engine – initial start-up after overhaul

1 With the engine refitted in the vehicle, double-check the engine oil and coolant levels. Make a final check that everything has been reconnected, and that there are no tools

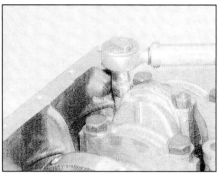

20.21 Tighten the bearing cap retaining nuts evenly and progressively to the Stage 1 torque setting . . .

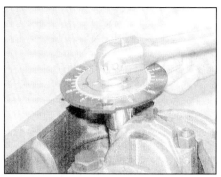

20.22 . . . then angle-tighten them through the specified Stage 2 angle

or rags left in the engine compartment.

2 On 1.9 litre engines, disconnect the anti-theft system electronic engine immobiliser unit wiring connector at the rear of the injection pump. On 2.0 litre engines, disconnect the wiring connector on the engine management system ECU (located in the plastic box behind the battery).

3 Turn the engine on the starter motor until the oil pressure warning light goes out. Ensure that the ignition is switched off and reconnect the wiring connectors.

4 On 1.9 litre engines, prime the fuel system as described in Chapter 4B.

5 Fully depress the accelerator pedal, turn the ignition key to position M, and wait for the preheating warning light to go out.

6 Start the engine, noting that this may take a little longer than usual, due to the fuel system components having been disturbed.

7 While the engine is idling, check for fuel, water and oil leaks. Don't be alarmed if there are some odd smells and smoke from parts getting hot and burning off oil deposits.

8 Assuming all is well, keep the engine idling until hot water is felt circulating through the top hose, then switch off the engine.

9 After a few minutes, recheck the oil and coolant levels as described in *Weekly checks*, and top-up as necessary.

10 If they were tightened as described, there is no need to re-tighten the cylinder head bolts once the engine has first run after reassembly.

11 If new pistons, rings or crankshaft bearings have been fitted, the engine must be treated as new, and run-in for the first 500 miles (800 km). *Do not* operate the engine at full-throttle, or allow it to labour at low engine speeds in any gear. It is recommended that the oil and filter be changed at the end of this period.

Notes

Chapter 3
Cooling, heating and ventilation systems

Contents

Air conditioning system – general information and precautions 11
Air conditioning system components – removal and refitting 12
Antifreeze mixture . . . . .See Chapter 1A or 1B
Coolant level check . . . . .See Weekly checks
Coolant pump – removal and refitting 7
Cooling system – draining . . . . .See Chapter 1A or 1B
Cooling system – filling . . . . .See Chapter 1A or 1B
Cooling system – flushing . . . . .See Chapter 1A or 1B
Cooling system electrical switches and sensors –
    removal and refitting 6

Cooling system hoses – disconnection and renewal 2
Electric cooling fan(s) – removal and refitting 5
General information and precautions 1
Heater/ventilation components – removal and refitting 10
Heating and ventilation system – general information 9
Pollen filter renewal . . . . .See Chapter 1A or 1B
Radiator – removal, inspection and refitting 3
Thermostat – removal, testing and refitting 4
Thermostat/fuel filter housing (1.9 litre diesel engine models) –
    removal and refitting 8

Degrees of difficulty

Easy, suitable for novice with little experience	Fairly easy, suitable for beginner with some experience	Fairly difficult, suitable for competent DIY mechanic	Difficult, suitable for experienced DIY mechanic	Very difficult, suitable for expert DIY or professional

Specifications

General

Maximum system pressure . . . . 1.4 bars

Thermostat

Opening temperatures:
  Starts to open:
    1.4 and 1.6 litre petrol engine models . . . . 88°C
    All other models . . . . 83°C
  Fully-open:
    1.4 and 1.6 litre petrol engine models . . . . 95°C
    All other models . . . . 89°C

Torque wrench settings	Nm	lbf ft
Coolant pump housing bolts (aluminium block engine):		
Smaller bolts	30	22
Larger bolts	65	48
Coolant pump securing bolts (cast iron block engine)	15	11

1 General information and precautions

General information

The cooling system is of pressurised type, comprising a coolant pump driven by the timing belt, an aluminium crossflow radiator, expansion tank, electric cooling fan(s), a thermostat, heater matrix, and all associated hoses and switches.

The system functions as follows. Cold coolant in the bottom of the radiator passes through the bottom hose to the coolant pump, where it is pumped around the cylinder block and head passages, and through the oil cooler(s) (where fitted). After cooling the cylinder bores, combustion surfaces and valve seats, the coolant reaches the underside of the thermostat, which is initially closed. The coolant passes through the heater, and is returned via the cylinder block to the coolant pump.

When the engine is cold, the coolant circulates only through the cylinder block, cylinder head, and heater. When the coolant reaches a predetermined temperature, the thermostat opens, and the coolant passes through the top hose to the radiator. As the coolant circulates through the radiator, it is cooled by the in-rush of air when the car is in forward motion. The airflow is supplemented by the action of the electric cooling fan(s) when necessary. Upon reaching the bottom of the radiator, the coolant has now cooled, and the cycle is repeated.

When the engine is at normal operating temperature, the coolant expands, and some of it is displaced into the expansion tank. Coolant collects in the tank, and is returned to the radiator when the system cools.

On models with automatic transmission, a proportion of the coolant is recirculated from the bottom of the radiator through the transmission fluid cooler mounted on the transmission. On models fitted with an engine oil cooler, the coolant is also passed through the oil cooler.

The electric cooling fan(s) mounted adjacent to the radiator are controlled by a thermostatic switch/sensor. At a predetermined coolant temperature, the switch/sensor actuates the fan.

Precautions

⚠ **Warning: Do not attempt to remove the expansion tank filler cap, or to disturb any part of the cooling system, while the engine is hot, as there is a high risk of scalding. If the expansion tank filler cap must be removed before the engine and radiator have fully cooled (even though this is not recommended), the pressure in the cooling system must first be relieved. Cover the cap with a thick layer of cloth to avoid scalding, and slowly unscrew the filler cap**

until a hissing sound is heard. When the hissing has stopped, indicating that the pressure has reduced, slowly unscrew the filler cap until it can be removed; if more hissing sounds are heard, wait until they have stopped before unscrewing the cap. At all times, keep well away from the filler cap opening, and protect your hands.

⚠ **Warning: Do not allow antifreeze to come into contact with your skin, or with the painted surfaces of the vehicle. Rinse off spills immediately, with plenty of water. Never leave antifreeze lying around in an open container, or in a puddle in the driveway or on the garage floor. Children and pets are attracted by its sweet smell, but antifreeze can be fatal if ingested.**

⚠ **Warning: If the engine is hot, the electric cooling fan may start rotating even if the engine is not running. Be careful to keep your hands, hair, and any loose clothing well clear when working in the engine compartment.**

⚠ **Warning: Refer to Section 11 for precautions to be observed when working on models equipped with air conditioning.**

2 Cooling system hoses – disconnection and renewal

Note: Refer to the warnings given in Section 1 of this Chapter before proceeding. Hoses should only be disconnected once the engine has cooled sufficiently to avoid scalding.

Conventional hose connections – general instructions

1 The number, routing and pattern of hoses will vary according to model, but the same basic procedure applies. Before commencing work, make sure that the new hoses are to hand, along with new hose clips if needed. It is good practice to renew the hose clips at the same time as the hoses.

2 Drain the cooling system, as described in Chapter 1A or 1B (as applicable), saving the coolant if it is fit for re-use. Squirt a little penetrating oil onto the hose clips if they are corroded.

3 Release the hose clips from the hose concerned. Three types of clip are used; worm-drive, spring and 'sardine-can'. The worm-drive clip is released by turning its screw anti-clockwise. The spring clip is released by squeezing its tags together with pliers, at the same time working the clip away from the hose stub **(see illustration)**. The 'sardine-can' clip is not re-usable, and is best cut off with snips or side cutters.

4 Unclip any wires, cables or other hoses which may be attached to the hose being removed. Make notes for reference when refitting if necessary.

2.3 Releasing a radiator top hose spring clip

5 Release the hose from its stubs, using a gentle twisting motion. Be careful not to damage the stubs on delicate components such as the radiator. If the hose is stuck fast, try carefully prising the end of the hose with a screwdriver or similar, taking care not to use excessive force. The best course is often to cut off a stubborn hose using a sharp knife, but again be careful not to damage the stubs.

6 Before fitting the new hose, smear the stubs with washing-up liquid or a suitable rubber lubricant to aid fitting. Do not use oil or grease, which may attack the rubber.

7 Fit the hose clips over the ends of the hose, then fit the hose over its stubs. Work the hose into position. When satisfied, locate and tighten the hose clips.

8 Refill the cooling system as described in Chapter 1A or 1B. Run the engine, and check that there are no leaks.

9 Recheck the tightness of the hose clips on any new hoses after a few hundred miles.

10 Top-up the coolant level if necessary.

Radiator hose(s) – bayonet-type connection

Note: A new O-ring should be used when reconnecting the hose.

Removal

11 On certain models, the radiator bottom and/or top hose(s) may be connected to the radiator using a plastic bayonet-type

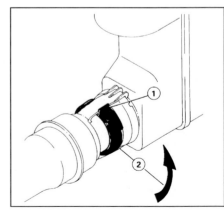

2.13 To release the bayonet-type radiator hose connection, turn the locking ring (2) until it contacts the stop (1)

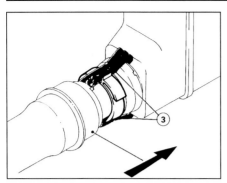

2.14 Press the connector away from the hose to ensure that the two retaining lugs (3) are free

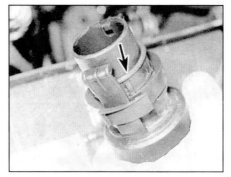

2.18 On refitting, fit a new O-ring (arrowed) to the hose union

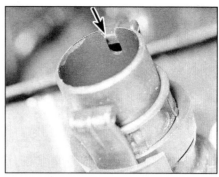

2.20 Offer the hose to the stub on the radiator, with the cut-out (arrowed) at the bottom

connection. To disconnect this type of connector, proceed as follows.

12 Drain the cooling system, as described in Chapter 1A or 1B, saving the coolant if it is fit for re-use.

13 Turn the locking ring (2) anti-clockwise until it contacts the stop (1) **(see illustration)**.

14 Press the connector away from the hose, to ensure that the two retaining lugs (3) are free **(see illustration)**.

15 Pull the hose, complete with the connector, from the radiator.

16 Recover the O-ring from the connector, and discard it; a new one must be used on refitting.

Refitting

17 Wipe the connector and the stub on the radiator thoroughly with a clean, lint-free cloth.

18 Fit a new O-ring to the male half of the connector, ensuring that it is correctly seated **(see illustration)**.

19 Turn the locking ring clockwise until it clicks.

20 Offer the hose to the stub on the radiator, with the locating cut-out in the male part of the connector located at the bottom **(see illustration)**.

21 Push the connector into the stub until both the retaining lugs click into position. Make sure that the O-ring is not trapped.

22 Pull the connector rearwards (away from the stub) to adjust the position of the retaining lugs if necessary.

23 Refill the cooling system as described in Chapter 1A or 1B.

24 Check thoroughly for leaks as soon as possible after disturbing any part of the cooling system.

Radiator hose(s) – spring clip connection

Note: *A new O-ring should be used when reconnecting the hose.*

Removal

25 On certain models, the radiator bottom and/or top hose(s) may be connected to the radiator using a wire spring clip. To disconnect this type of connector, proceed as follows.

26 Drain the cooling system, as described in Chapter 1A or 1B, saving the coolant if it is fit for re-use.

27 Using a small screwdriver, extract the retaining spring clip from the radiator outlet **(see illustration)**.

28 Pull the hose from the radiator and recover the O-ring from the end of the hose **(see illustration)**. Discard the O-ring; a new one must be used on refitting.

Refitting

29 Wipe the hose end and the outlet on the radiator thoroughly with a clean, lint-free cloth.

30 Fit a new O-ring to the hose, ensuring that it is correctly seated.

31 Refit the retaining spring clip to the radiator, then push on the hose until it locks in position.

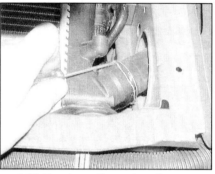

2.27 To release the spring-clip type radiator hose connection, extract the clip with a small screwdriver . . .

32 Refill the cooling system as described in Chapter 1A or 1B.

33 Check thoroughly for leaks as soon as possible after disturbing any part of the cooling system.

Heater matrix hose connections

Note: *New O-rings should be used when reconnecting the hoses.*

Removal

34 The two hoses are connected to the matrix by means of a single connector.

35 Prise the metal retaining clip from the top of the connector **(see illustration)**.

36 Release the plastic retaining clip by pushing it towards the left-hand hose connection **(see illustration)**.

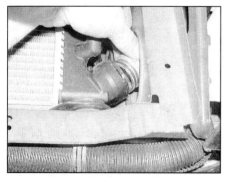

2.28 . . . then withdraw the hose from the radiator

2.35 Remove the metal clip from the top of the heater matrix connector on the engine compartment bulkhead . . .

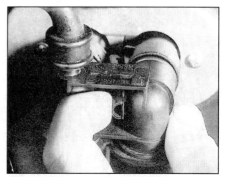

2.36 . . . then release the plastic retaining clip . . .

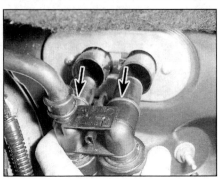

2.37 . . . and pull the connector away from the bulkhead – recover the O-rings (arrowed)

3.11 On diesel engine models, where applicable, remove the air cleaner support bracket from the front body panel

3.12 Disconnect the upper hose at the coolant expansion tank

37 Pull the connector assembly from the heater matrix. Recover the O-ring seals from the connector, and discard them; new ones should be used on refitting **(see illustration)**.

Refitting

38 Refitting is a reversal of the removal procedure, using new O-rings.
39 Refill the cooling system as described in Chapter 1A or 1B. Run the engine, and check that there are no leaks.

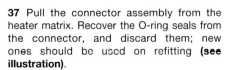
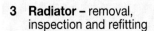

3 Radiator – removal, inspection and refitting

Note: *If leakage is the reason for removing the radiator, bear in mind that minor leaks can often be cured using a radiator sealant with the radiator in situ.*

Removal

Petrol engine models

1 Disconnect the battery negative terminal (refer to *Disconnecting the battery* in the Reference Section of this manual).
2 Drain the cooling system as described in Chapter 1A.
3 Referring to Chapter 4A if necessary, on

1.4, 1.6 and 1.8 litre (8-valve) engines, remove the air inlet duct from the air cleaner and front body panel. On 1.8 and 2.0 litre (16-valve) engines, remove the complete air cleaner assembly and air inlet duct.
4 Where applicable, remove the radiator grille as described in Chapter 11, Section 22, then undo the two bolts and remove the air cleaner support bracket from the front body panel.
5 On models where the electric cooling fan assembly is mounted behind the radiator (ie, between the radiator and the engine), disconnect the cooling fan wiring connector, and release the fan mounting bracket from the radiator clips. Remove the cooling fan assembly from the engine compartment.
6 On models without air conditioning, where applicable, disconnect the wiring connector from the cooling fan switch or temperature sensor located on the left-hand side of the radiator.
7 Disconnect all the coolant hoses from the radiator with reference to Section 2.
8 Working at the top of the radiator, lift the ends of the radiator retaining clips (one each side) and move the top of the radiator toward the engine. Lift the radiator upward to disengage the lower locating lugs and remove the radiator from the engine compartment. Take care not to damage the radiator fins on surrounding components as it is lifted out.

Diesel engine models

9 Disconnect the battery negative terminal (refer to *Disconnecting the battery* in the Reference Section of this manual).
10 Drain the cooling system as described in Chapter 1B.
11 Remove the complete air cleaner assembly and air inlet duct as described in Chapter 4B. Where applicable, remove the radiator grille as described in Chapter 11, Section 22, then undo the two bolts and remove the air cleaner support bracket from the front body panel **(see illustration)**.
12 Slacken the clip and disconnect the upper hose at the coolant expansion tank **(see illustration)**.
13 Where applicable, disconnect the wiring connector from the coolant level sensor on the rear of the expansion tank **(see illustration)**.
14 Lift the right-hand side of the expansion tank upward to disengage the rubber mounting grommets, then slide the tank sideways to disengage the left-hand mounting pegs **(see illustration)**.
15 Extract the wire spring clip and disconnect the lower right-hand hose from the expansion tank **(see illustration)**.
16 Extract the lower left-hand hose retaining clip, disconnect the hose and remove the

3.13 Disconnect the wiring connector from the coolant level sensor

3.14 Disengage the expansion tank from its rubber mountings

3.15 Extract the wire spring clip and disconnect the lower right-hand hose from the expansion tank

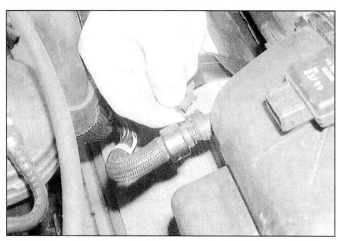

3.16 Extract the lower left-hand expansion tank hose retaining clip and disconnect the hose

3.17 Remove the expansion tank mounting bracket from the front body panel

expansion tank from the engine compartment **(see illustration)**.

17 Undo the three bolts and remove the expansion tank mounting bracket from the front body panel **(see illustration)**.

18 Where applicable, disconnect the wiring connector from the cooling fan switch or temperature sensor located on the left-hand side of the radiator.

19 Disconnect all the coolant hoses from the radiator with reference to Section 2.

20 Working at the top of the radiator, lift the ends of the radiator retaining clips (one each side) and move the top of the radiator toward the engine. Lift the radiator upward to disengage the lower locating lugs and remove the radiator from the engine compartment **(see illustrations)**. Take care not to damage the radiator fins on surrounding components as it is lifted out.

Inspection

21 If the radiator has been removed due to suspected blockage, reverse-flush it as described in Chapter 1A or 1B. Clean dirt and debris from the radiator fins, using an air line (in which case, wear eye protection) or a soft brush. Be careful, as the fins are sharp, and easily damaged.

22 If necessary, a radiator specialist can perform a 'flow test' on the radiator, to establish whether an internal blockage exists.

23 A leaking radiator must be referred to a specialist for permanent repair. Do not attempt to weld or solder a leaking radiator, as damage to the plastic components may result.

24 In an emergency, minor leaks from the radiator can be cured by using a suitable radiator sealant, in accordance with its manufacturer's instructions, with the radiator *in situ*.

25 If the radiator is to be sent for repair or renewed, remove all hoses and the cooling fan switch or temperature sensor (where fitted).

26 Inspect the condition of the radiator mounting rubbers, and renew them if necessary.

Refitting

27 Refitting is a reversal of removal, bearing in mind the following points:

a) *Ensure that the lower lugs on the radiator are correctly engaged with the mounting rubbers in the body panel.*

b) *Reconnect the hoses with reference to*

Section 2, using new O-rings where applicable.

c) *On completion, refill the cooling system as described in Chapter 1A or 1B.*

4 Thermostat – removal, testing and refitting

Removal

1 Disconnect the battery negative terminal (refer to *Disconnecting the battery* in the Reference Section of this manual).

2 Drain the cooling system as described in Chapter 1A or 1B.

3 Where necessary, release any relevant wiring and hoses from the retaining clips, and position clear of the thermostat housing to improve access. On most models, it will also be necessary to remove the air cleaner air inlet duct or the complete air cleaner assembly as described in Chapter 4A or 4B.

4 Release the clip and disconnect the coolant hose from the thermostat housing cover.

5 Unscrew the retaining bolts, and carefully withdraw the thermostat housing cover to expose the thermostat **(see illustrations)**.

3.20a Lift the ends of the radiator retaining clips on each side . . .

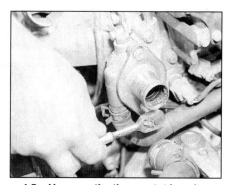

3.20b . . . and lift the radiator out of the engine compartment

4.5a Unscrew the thermostat housing retaining bolts . . .

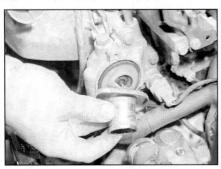

4.5b . . . then withdraw the cover to expose the thermostat – 1.4 litre petrol engine models

4.6a Lift the thermostat from the housing . . .

4.6b . . . and recover the sealing ring – 1.4 litre petrol engine models

Note that the design of the thermostat housing varies between engine types, but the thermostat removal procedure for each type is similar.

6 Lift the thermostat from the housing, noting which way round the thermostat is fitted, and recover the sealing ring(s) **(see illustrations)**.

Testing

7 A rough test of the thermostat may be made by suspending it with a piece of string in a container full of water. Heat the water to bring it to the boil – the thermostat must open by the time the water boils. If not, renew it.

8 If a thermometer is available, the precise opening temperature of the thermostat may be determined; compare with the figures given in the Specifications. The opening temperature is also marked on the thermostat.

9 A thermostat which fails to close as the water cools must also be renewed.

Refitting

10 Refitting is a reversal of removal, bearing in mind the following points:

a) Examine the sealing ring(s) for damage or deterioration, and if necessary, renew.

b) Ensure that the thermostat is fitted the correct way round as noted during removal.

c) On completion, refill the cooling system as described in Chapter 1A or 1B.

5 Electric cooling fan(s) – removal and refitting

General information

1 On models without air conditioning, the current supply to the cooling fan(s) is via the battery and a fuse (see Chapter 12). The circuit is completed by the cooling fan thermostatic switch, which (on most models) is mounted in the left-hand side of the radiator. On models with air conditioning, the cooling fans are controlled by the air conditioning system control unit in conjunction with a temperature sensor located in the thermostat housing.

2 Either a single, or twin fan arrangement may be fitted, according to model. The fan and shroud assembly is located in front of the radiator on most models, although on certain 1.4, 1.6 and 1.8 litre (8-valve) petrol engine models, the assembly is located between the radiator and engine.

Removal

3 Disconnect the battery negative terminal (refer to *Disconnecting the battery* in the Reference Section of this manual).

4 On models where the cooling fan assembly is mounted between the radiator and engine, disconnect the cooling fan wiring connector, and release the fan mounting bracket from the radiator clips. Remove the cooling fan assembly from the engine compartment.

5 On models where the cooling fan assembly is mounted in front of the radiator, remove the radiator as described in Section 3.

6 Unscrew the locking ring and disconnect the round wiring connector from the lower left-hand corner of the fan shroud **(see illustration)**. Where individual connectors are used, trace the wiring back from the fan and disconnect the relevant connectors.

7 Lift the ends of the fan shroud retaining clips (one each side) and move the top of the shroud toward the engine. Lift the assembly upward to disengage the lower locating lugs and remove it from the engine compartment **(see illustrations)**.

8 To remove the fan motor(s) from the shroud, undo the three nuts and bolts securing the relevant motor to the shroud **(see illustration)**.

5.6 Disconnect the wiring connector from the lower left-hand corner of the fan shroud

5.7a Lift the ends of the fan shroud retaining clips on each side . . .

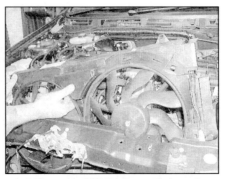

5.7b . . . and lift the fan and shroud assembly out of the engine compartment

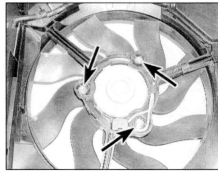

5.8 Fan motor retaining nuts (arrowed)

Withdraw the motor and fan assembly and disconnect the wiring connector. The fan can be removed from the motor spindle after extracting the retaining clip, or undoing the retaining bolt, as applicable.

9 To gain access to the motor relays, unclip and lift off the cover over the relay box located in the centre of the fan shroud (see illustration). Note that on some models the relay box cover may be secured by a screw.

10 Lift the relay mounting plate from the shroud, disconnect the wiring connector and remove the relevant relay (see illustration).

Refitting

11 Refitting is a reversal of removal. With the fan assembly in place, refit the radiator (where applicable) as described in Section 3.

6 Cooling system electrical switches and sensors – removal and refitting

Switch/sensor location and description – petrol engine models

Cooling fan switch

1 On models without air conditioning, the cooling fan switch has a blue wiring connector with either a red or yellow ring, and is located in the top left-hand corner of the radiator.

2 On models with air conditioning, the cooling fans are controlled by the air conditioning system control unit in conjunction with a temperature sensor located in the top of the thermostat housing. The sensor can be identified by its brown wiring connector (see illustration).

Temperature warning light switch/temperature gauge sensor

3 The coolant temperature warning light switch/temperature gauge sensor has a blue wiring connector with either a grey or violet ring and is located at the left-hand end of the cylinder head, or in the thermostat housing.

Engine management system coolant temperature sensor

4 The engine management system coolant temperature sensor has a green wiring connector with a yellow ring and is mounted in the thermostat housing.

Switch/sensor location and description – 1.9 litre diesel engine models

Cooling fan switch

5 On models without air conditioning, the cooling fan switch has a blue wiring connector with a yellow ring and is mounted on the left-hand side of the radiator.

6 On models with air conditioning, the cooling fans are controlled by the air conditioning system control unit in conjunction with a

5.9 To remove the fan motor relays, lift off the cover over the relay box in the centre of the fan shroud

temperature sensor located in the thermostat housing. The sensor can be identified by its brown wiring connector.

Temperature warning light switch/temperature gauge sensor

7 The coolant temperature warning light switch/temperature gauge sensor has a blue wiring connector (with a grey ring on models without air conditioning) and is located in the thermostat housing.

Preheating/EGR system coolant temperature switch/sensor

8 The coolant temperature switch or sensor used for control of the preheating and EGR systems has a green wiring connector with a pink or green ring and is mounted in the thermostat housing.

Switch/sensor location and description – 2.0 litre diesel engine models

9 On 2.0 litre diesel engines the coolant temperature sensor has a blue wiring connector and is mounted in the thermostat/water outlet housing (see illustration). The temperature signal from this sensor is used by the engine management electronic control unit to control the operation of the cooling fans, preheating control unit, air conditioning system and temperature warning light/gauge.

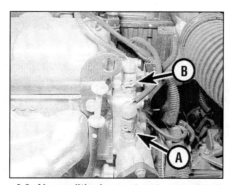

6.2 Air conditioning system temperature sensor (A) and engine management coolant temperature sensor (B) – 1.6 litre petrol engine models

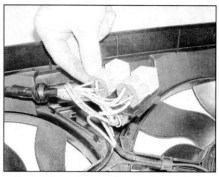

5.10 Lift out the relay mounting plate, disconnect the wiring and remove the relevant relay

Removal

⚠ **Warning: The engine and radiator should be cold before removing a cooling system switch or sensor.**

10 Disconnect the battery negative terminal (refer to *Disconnecting the battery* in the Reference Section of this manual).

11 Partially drain the cooling system to just below the level of the switch/sensor (as described in Chapter 1A or 1B). Alternatively, have ready a suitable bung to plug the switch aperture in the radiator or housing when the switch is removed. If this method is used, take great care not to damage the radiator, and do not use anything which will allow foreign matter to enter the cooling system.

12 Where necessary, refer to Chapter 4A or 4B and remove the air cleaner and air inlet ducts for access to the switches/sensors located in the thermostat housing or cylinder head.

13 Unplug the wiring connector from the relevant switch/sensor.

14 Carefully unscrew the switch/sensor from its mounting and recover the sealing ring (where applicable). If the system has not been drained, plug the switch/sensor aperture to prevent further coolant loss.

Refitting

15 If the switch/sensor was originally fitted using sealing compound, clean the switch/sensor threads thoroughly, and coat

6.9 Coolant temperature sensor (arrowed) – 2.0 litre diesel engine models

7.4a Undo the securing bolts (arrowed) . . .

7.4b . . . and withdraw the coolant pump impeller assembly from the housing – 1.4 litre petrol engine models

them with fresh sealing compound. If the switch was originally fitted using a sealing ring, use a new sealing ring on refitting.

16 Fit the switch/sensor to its location, tighten it securely and reconnect the wiring connector.

17 Refill and bleed the cooling system as described in Chapter 1A or 1B. Follow the bleeding instructions carefully, to ensure that all air is expelled from the cooling system.

18 On completion, refit any components removed for access, then start the engine and run it until it reaches normal operating temperature. Continue to run the engine, and check that the component(s) controlled by the switch/sensor operate correctly.

7 Coolant pump – removal and refitting

Aluminium cylinder block engines

Note: *A new impeller assembly O-ring, and where applicable, a new impeller housing O-ring, will be required on refitting.*

Removal

1 The coolant pump is driven by the timing belt, and is located in a housing at the timing belt end of the engine.

2 Drain the cooling system as described in Chapter 1A or 1B.

3 Remove the timing belt as described in the relevant Part of Chapter 2.

4 Remove the securing bolts, and withdraw the pump impeller assembly from the pump housing (access is most easily obtained from under the wheelarch). Recover the O-ring **(see illustrations)**.

5 If desired, the pump impeller housing can be removed from the rear of the coolant pump housing. Access is most easily obtained from underneath the vehicle (it may be necessary to remove the exhaust heat shield). Disconnect the coolant hoses from the impeller housing (be prepared for coolant spillage), then remove the securing bolts and withdraw the impeller housing. Again, recover the O-ring.

Refitting

6 Ensure that all mating faces are clean.

7 Where applicable, refit the impeller housing to the rear of the coolant pump housing, using a new O-ring. Reconnect the coolant hoses securely.

8 Refit the impeller assembly to the pump housing, using a new O-ring.

9 Refit the timing belt as described in the relevant Part of Chapter 2.

10 Refill the cooling system as described in Chapter 1A or 1B.

Cast-iron cylinder block engines

Note: *A new pump O-ring must be used on refitting.*

11 The pump is driven by the timing belt, and is located directly in the cylinder block.

12 Proceed as described previously for engines with an aluminium cylinder block, but note that there is no separate impeller housing.

8 Thermostat/fuel filter housing (1.9 litre diesel engine models) – removal and refitting

Removal

Note: *A new gasket must be used when refitting the main housing.*

1 Disconnect the battery negative terminal (refer to *Disconnecting the battery* in the Reference Section of this manual).

2 Drain the cooling system as described in Chapter 1B.

3 Place a plastic sheet over the transmission bellhousing and the starter motor, to prevent any fuel spilled during the following procedure from causing damage.

4 Remove the fuel filter as described in Chapter 1B.

5 Disconnect the wiring plugs from the coolant sensors mounted in the top of the housing.

6 Disconnect the coolant hoses from the plastic thermostat housing.

7 Disconnect the coolant hose from the stub at the rear of the housing.

8 Unscrew the bolt securing the plastic fuel filter housing to the main housing, then withdraw the plastic housing and move it clear of the main housing. Recover the O-ring from the base of the plastic housing **(see illustrations)**.

9 Unscrew the three securing bolts, and withdraw the main housing from the cylinder head **(see illustrations)**. Recover the gasket.

10 Disconnect the coolant hose from the base of the housing, and remove the housing.

Refitting

11 Refitting is a reversal of removal, bearing in mind the following points:

a) *Examine the condition of the O-ring on the base of the plastic housing, and renew if necessary.*

b) *Use a new gasket when refitting the main housing.*

8.8a Unscrew the securing bolt (arrowed) . . .

8.8b . . . withdraw the plastic housing . . .

8.8c . . . and recover the O-ring

8.9a Unscrew the three securing bolts (arrowed) . . .

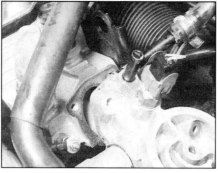

8.9b . . . and withdraw the main thermostat housing

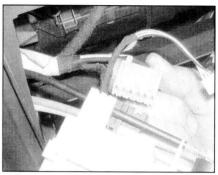

10.3 Disconnect the wiring plugs at the rear of the heater/ventilation control unit

c) *Ensure that all hoses, pipes and wires are correctly reconnected.*
d) *Refill the cooling system as described in Chapter 1B.*
e) *On completion, prime the fuel system as described in Chapter 4B.*

9 Heating and ventilation system – general information

The heating/ventilation system consists of a four-speed blower motor (housed behind the facia), face level vents in the centre and at each end of the facia, and air ducts to the front footwells.

The control unit is located in the facia, and the controls operate flap valves to deflect and mix the air flowing through the various parts of the heating/ventilation system. The flap valves are contained in the air distribution housing, which acts as a central distribution unit, passing air to the various ducts and vents.

Cold air enters the system through the grille at the rear of the engine compartment. If required, the airflow is boosted by the blower, and then flows through the various ducts, according to the settings of the controls. Stale air is expelled through ducts at the rear of the vehicle. If warm air is required, the cold air is passed over the heater matrix, which is heated by the engine coolant.

On models fitted with air conditioning, a recirculation switch enables the outside air

supply to be closed off, while the air inside the vehicle is recirculated. This can be useful to prevent unpleasant odours entering from outside the vehicle, but should only be used briefly, as the recirculated air inside the vehicle will soon become stale.

10 Heater/ventilation components – removal and refitting

Heater/ventilation control unit

Removal

1 Disconnect the battery negative terminal (refer to *Disconnecting the battery* in the Reference Section of this manual).
2 Remove the facia centre panel as described in Chapter 11.
3 Working at the rear of the control unit, disconnect the two wiring plugs **(see illustration)**.
4 Note the locations and correct fitted positions of the three control cables at the rear of the control unit. Using a small screwdriver, release the outer cables from the support brackets, then disengage the inner cables from the operating levers **(see illustrations)**.
5 Withdraw the control unit from the car.

Refitting

6 Refitting is a reversal of removal, but ensure

that the control cables are securely reconnected to their original locations.

Heater/ventilation control cables

Removal

7 Disconnect the cables from the heater/ventilation control unit, as described previously in this Section during the control unit removal procedure.
8 Working through the facia aperture or under the facia (it may be necessary to remove certain facia panels for access – see Chapter 11 – depending on which cable is to be removed), release the clips and disconnect the relevant cable from the heater assembly. Note the routing of the cable to ensure correct refitting.

Refitting

9 Refitting is a reversal of removal, ensuring that the cables are correctly routed, and securely reconnected.

Heater matrix

Note: *New heater hose connector O-rings must be used on refitting.*

Removal

10 Drain the cooling system as described in Chapter 1A or 1B.
11 Remove the complete facia assembly as described in Chapter 11.
12 Working inside the car, unclip and withdraw the ventilation duct on the driver's side **(see illustration)**.

10.4a Using a small screwdriver, release the control outer cables from the support brackets . . .

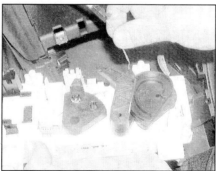

10.4b . . . then disengage the inner cables from the operating levers

10.12 Unclip and withdraw the ventilation duct on the driver's side

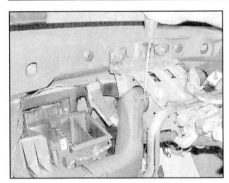

10.13a Undo the screw securing the passenger's side ventilation duct to the steering column support bracket

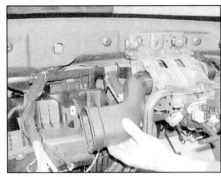

10.13b Release the duct from the heater unit and withdraw it from the steering column support bracket

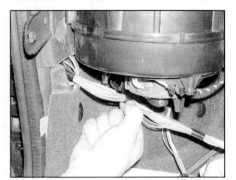

10.14a Release the wiring harness from the cable ties and clips on the blower motor . . .

10.14b . . . and around the heater unit

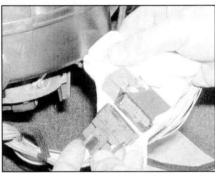
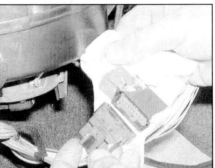
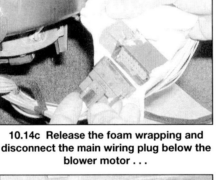

10.14c Release the foam wrapping and disconnect the main wiring plug below the blower motor . . .

13 Undo the screw securing the passenger's side ventilation duct to the steering column support bracket. Release the duct from the heater unit and withdraw it from the centre of the steering column support bracket **(see illustrations)**.

14 Release the wiring harness from the cable ties and retaining clips on the blower motor and around the heater unit. Disconnect the main wiring plug (located below the blower motor and wrapped in foam) and the second wiring plug adjacent to the centre footwell vent housing **(see illustrations)**.

15 Undo the two screws securing the wiring harness support to the bulkhead above the heater unit **(see illustration)**.

16 Disconnect the water drain tube from the base of the blower motor housing.

17 Working in the engine compartment, disconnect the heater hoses from the matrix pipes with reference to Section 2.

18 Undo the two screws securing the cover plate over the matrix pipes bulkhead seal. Lift off the cover plate, noting the orientation of the D-shaped cut-out **(see illustrations)**.

19 Withdraw the rubber bulkhead seal from the matrix pipes **(see illustration)**.

20 Undo the two bolts securing the steering column support bracket to the engine compartment bulkhead **(see illustration)**.

21 From inside the car, undo the bolt securing each end of the steering column support bracket brace to the bracket on the

10.14d . . . and the second wiring plug adjacent to the footwell vent housing

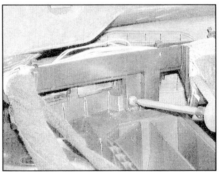
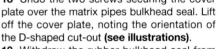

10.15 Undo the screws securing the wiring harness support to the bulkhead above the heater unit

10.18a Undo the screws and lift off the cover plate over the matrix pipes bulkhead seal . . .

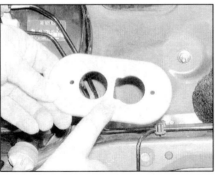

10.18b . . . noting the orientation of the D-shaped cut-out

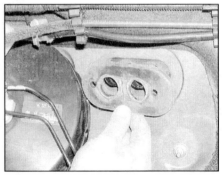

10.19 Withdraw the rubber bulkhead seal from the matrix pipes

10.20 Undo the two bolts securing the steering column support bracket to the engine compartment bulkhead

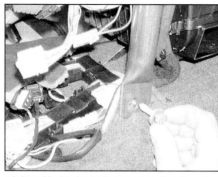

10.21a Undo the bolt securing the steering column support bracket brace to the centre bracket on the floor . . .

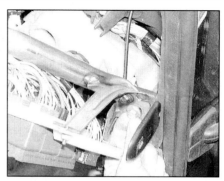

10.21b . . . and to the bracket adjacent to the door aperture

floor and adjacent to the door aperture **(see illustrations)**. Carefully withdraw the steering column and support bracket from the bulkhead slightly and support it on blocks if necessary to avoid straining the column and wiring.

22 Again working in the engine compartment, unscrew the two nuts and recover the washers securing the heater assembly to the bulkhead. Unscrew the remaining securing bolt located below the air intake grille **(see illustrations)**.

23 Working inside the car, unscrew the bolt securing the bottom of the heater to the bracket on the floor **(see illustration)**.

24 With the aid of an assistant working in the engine compartment, ease the matrix pipes from the bulkhead, and carefully pull the heater assembly into the vehicle interior **(see illustration)**.

25 With the heater assembly removed, release the four securing clips (using four small screwdrivers to hold the clips open), then withdraw the matrix from the heater casing **(see illustrations)**.

Refitting

26 Refitting is a reversal of removal bearing in mind the following points.

a) Offer the heater assembly into position, pushing the heater matrix pipes through the bulkhead as the assembly is refitted

(an assistant working in the engine compartment will ease the task).

b) Ensure that the lug on the heater base engages with the centre of the drain tube grommet as the assembly is offered into position.

c) When reconnecting the heater hoses to the pipes, fit new O-rings to the matrix pipes, then reconnect the hose connector to the pipes.

Heater blower motor

Removal

27 The blower motor assembly is located on the passenger side of the vehicle.

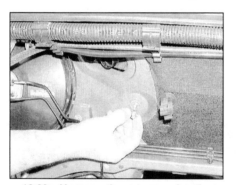

10.22a Unscrew the nuts securing the heater assembly to the bulkhead . . .

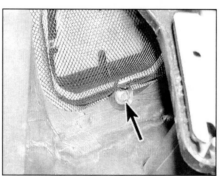

10.22b . . . and unscrew the remaining bolt (arrowed) below the air intake grille

10.23 From inside the car, unscrew the bolt (arrowed) securing the heater to the floor bracket

10.24 Ease the matrix pipes from the bulkhead, and carefully pull the heater assembly into the vehicle interior

10.25a Using four small screwdrivers, release the securing clips . . .

10.25b . . . then withdraw the matrix from the heater casing

10.31 Undo the screws and withdraw the blower motor from the heater unit

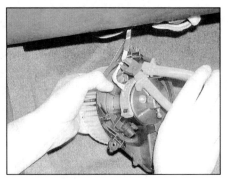

10.32a Cut the cable tie securing the wiring to the motor cover . . .

10.32b . . . pull the rubber wiring grommet away . . .

28 Disconnect the battery negative terminal (refer to *Disconnecting the battery* in the Reference Section of this manual).

29 Working inside the vehicle, unclip the lower facia trim panel from the floor and the bottom of the facia, and withdraw the panel.

30 Disconnect the water drain tube from the base of the blower motor housing.

31 Unscrew the four screws securing the motor assembly to the heater unit and lower the motor from its location **(see illustration)**.

32 Cut the cable tie securing the wiring to the motor cover then pull the rubber wiring grommet away, and disconnect the wiring plugs **(see illustrations)**.

Refitting

33 Refitting is a reversal of removal.

Heater blower motor resistor

Removal

34 Disconnect the battery negative terminal (refer to *Disconnecting the battery* in the Reference Section of this manual).

35 Remove the glovebox as described in Chapter 11, Section 28.

36 Working through the glovebox aperture, disconnect the wiring connector from the resistor **(see illustration)**.

37 Using a small screwdriver, carefully release the resistor cover retaining tabs and withdraw the unit from the heater assembly **(see illustrations)**.

Refitting

38 Refitting is a reversal of removal.

11 Air conditioning system – general information and precautions

General information

An air conditioning system is available on certain models. It enables the temperature of incoming air to be lowered, and also dehumidifies the air, which makes for rapid demisting and increased comfort.

The cooling side of the system works in the same way as a domestic refrigerator. Refrigerant gas is drawn into a belt-driven compressor, and passes into a condenser mounted on the front of the radiator, where it loses heat and becomes liquid. The liquid passes through an expansion valve to an evaporator, where it changes from liquid under high pressure to gas under low pressure. This change is accompanied by a drop in temperature, which cools the evaporator. The refrigerant returns to the compressor, and the cycle begins again.

Air blown through the evaporator passes to the air distribution unit, where it is mixed with hot air blown through the heater matrix to achieve the desired temperature in the passenger compartment.

The heating side of the system works in the same way as on models without air conditioning (see Section 9).

The operation of the system is controlled by an electronic control unit, which controls the electric cooling fan(s), the compressor and the facia-mounted warning light. Any problems with the system should be referred to a Citroën dealer.

Precautions

When an air conditioning system is fitted, it is necessary to observe special precautions whenever dealing with any part of the system, or its associated components. If for any reason the system must be disconnected, entrust this task to your Citroën dealer or a refrigeration engineer.

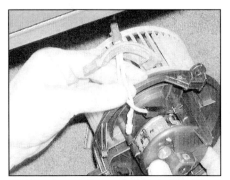

10.32c . . . and disconnect the wiring plugs

10.36 Disconnect the wiring connector from the blower motor resistor . . .

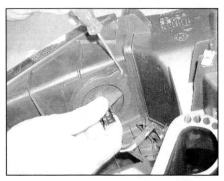

10.37a . . . release the retaining tabs . . .

10.37b . . . and withdraw the resistor from the heater unit

Warning: The air conditioning system contains a liquid refrigerant, and it is therefore dangerous to disconnect any part of the system without specialised knowledge and equipment.

The refrigerant is potentially dangerous, and should only be handled by qualified persons. If it is splashed onto the skin, it can cause frostbite. It is not itself poisonous, but in the presence of a naked flame (including a cigarette) it forms a poisonous gas. Uncontrolled discharging of the refrigerant is dangerous, and potentially damaging to the environment.

12 Air conditioning system components – removal and refitting

Note: *Do not operate the air conditioning system if it is known to be short of refrigerant, as this may damage the compressor.*

1 The only operation which can be carried out easily without discharging the refrigerant is the renewal of the auxiliary (compressor) drivebelt. This is described in the relevant Part of Chapter 1. All other operations must be referred to a Citroën dealer or an air conditioning specialist.

2 If necessary, the compressor can be unbolted and moved aside, without disconnecting its flexible hoses, after removing the drivebelt.

Warning: Do not attempt to open the refrigerant circuit. Refer to the precautions given in Section 11.

Chapter 4 Part A:
Fuel/exhaust systems – petrol engines

Contents

Accelerator cable – removal, refitting and adjustment 3
Accelerator pedal – removal and refitting 4
Air cleaner assembly and inlet ducts – removal and refitting 2
Air cleaner filter element renewal . . . . .See Chapter 1A
Bosch Motronic and Sagem Lucas system components –
  removal and refitting 13
Exhaust manifold – removal and refitting 16
Exhaust system – general information, removal and refitting 17
Fuel filter – renewal . . . . .See Chapter 1A
Fuel gauge sender unit – removal and refitting 9
Fuel injection system – depressurisation 7
Fuel injection system – testing and adjustment 11
Fuel injection systems – general information 6
Fuel pump – removal and refitting 8
Fuel tank – removal and refitting 10
General information and precautions 1
Inlet manifold – removal and refitting 15
Magneti Marelli system components – removal and refitting 14
Throttle housing – removal and refitting 12
Unleaded petrol – general information and usage 5

Degrees of difficulty

Easy, suitable for novice with little experience	**Fairly easy,** suitable for beginner with some experience	**Fairly difficult,** suitable for competent DIY mechanic	**Difficult,** suitable for experienced DIY mechanic	**Very difficult,** suitable for expert DIY or professional 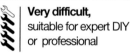

Specifications

System type

1.4 litre engines:	
Pre-1999 models	Magneti Marelli 1 AP
1999 models onward:	
To emission standard L3	Sagem Lucas SL96
To emission standard L4	Bosch Motronic MP7.3
1.6 litre engines:	
Pre-1999 models	Bosch Motronic MP5.2
1999 models onward	Bosch Motronic MP7.2
1.8 litre (8-valve) engines:	
Manual transmission models	Magneti Marelli 1 AP
Automatic transmission models	Magneti Marelli 8P
1.8 litre (16-valve) engines	Sagem Lucas SL96
2.0 litre engines	Bosch Motronic MP5.2

Fuel system data

Fuel pump type	Electric, immersed in tank
Idle speed*:	
1.4 litre engines:	
Without air conditioning	850 rpm
With air conditioning	950 ± 50 rpm
1.6 litre engines:	
Without air conditioning	850 ± 50 rpm
With air conditioning	900 ± 50 rpm
1.8 litre (8-valve) engines	
Without air conditioning	800 ± 50 rpm
With air conditioning	900 ± 50 rpm
1.8 and 2.0 litre (16-valve) engines	850 ± 50 rpm
Idle mixture CO content*	Less than 0.5%

*Not adjustable – controlled by ECU

Recommended fuel

Minimum octane rating . . . .   95 RON unleaded

Torque wrench settings

	Nm	lbf ft
Engine/transmission rear mounting link nut	50	37
Exhaust manifold nuts:		
1.4 and 1.6 litre engines	16	12
1.8 and 2.0 litre engines	35	26
Exhaust system fasteners:		
1.4 and 1.6 litre engines:		
Front pipe-to-manifold nuts	30	22
Front pipe mounting bolt	35	26
Front pipe-to-catalytic converter nuts	10	7
Clamping ring nuts	20	15
1.8 and 2.0 litre engines:		
Front pipe-to-manifold nuts	10	7
Clamping ring nuts	20	15
Inlet manifold nuts:		
1.4 and 1.6 litre engines	8	6
1.8 and 2.0 litre engines	20	15

1 General information and precautions

The fuel supply system consists of a fuel tank (which is mounted under the rear of the car, with an electric fuel pump immersed in it), a fuel filter, fuel feed and return lines. The fuel pump supplies fuel to the fuel rail, which acts as a reservoir for the four fuel injectors which inject fuel into the inlet tracts. The fuel filter incorporated in the feed line from the pump to the fuel rail ensures that the fuel supplied to the injectors is clean.

 Warning: Many of the procedures in this Chapter require the removal of fuel lines and connections, which may result in some fuel spillage. Before carrying out any operation on the fuel system, refer to the precautions given in 'Safety first!' at the beginning of this manual, and follow them implicitly. Petrol is a highly dangerous and volatile liquid, and the precautions necessary when handling it cannot be overstressed.

Refer to Section 6 for further information on the operation of each fuel injection system,

and to Section 17 for information on the exhaust system.

Note: *Residual pressure will remain in the fuel lines long after the vehicle was last used. When disconnecting any fuel line, first depressurise the fuel system as described in Section 7.*

2 Air cleaner assembly and inlet ducts – removal and refitting

Removal

Note: *Where crimped-type hose clips or ties are fitted, cut and discard them and use standard worm-drive hose clips, or new cable ties on refitting.*

1.4 litre engines

1 Slacken the retaining clip securing the air inlet duct to the front of the air cleaner lid and the clip securing the lid to the throttle housing **(see illustration)**.
2 Disconnect the breather hose at the front of the air cleaner lid by slackening the retaining clip (where fitted) or disconnecting the quick-release connection.
3 Undo the screws securing the lid to the air

cleaner housing. Release the lid from the air cleaner housing, air inlet duct and throttle housing, then lift out the air filter element.
4 Release the air cleaner housing from the support bracket and remove it from the engine compartment.
5 To remove the air inlet duct, undo the bolts securing the front of the duct to the front body panel and to the support bracket on the side of the engine.
6 If the air cleaner housing is still in position, slacken the clip securing the inlet duct to the front of the air cleaner lid and remove the duct assembly from the engine compartment.

1.6 litre engines

7 Slacken the retaining clips (where fitted) and disconnect the vacuum hose and breather hose from the air cleaner lid. Where fitted, disconnect the wiring connector from the inlet air temperature sensor **(see illustration)**.
8 Slacken the retaining clip and free the air cleaner lid from the throttle housing **(see illustration)**. Similarly, disconnect the air inlet duct from the side of the air cleaner housing.
9 Lift the air cleaner housing assembly out of the engine compartment.
10 To remove the air inlet duct assembly, undo the bolt securing the front of the duct to

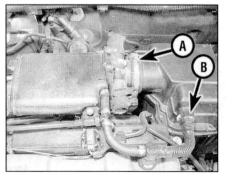

2.1 Air cleaner lid-to-throttle housing retaining clip (A) and breather hose quick-release connection (B) – 1.4 litre engines

2.7 Disconnect the wiring connector from the inlet air temperature sensor – 1.6 litre engines

2.8 Slacken the clip securing the air cleaner to the throttle housing – 1.6 litre engines

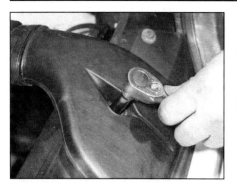

2.10a Unscrew the bolt securing the inlet duct to the front body panel . . .

2.10b . . . then release the fastener securing it to the cylinder head . . .

2.10c . . . and remove the duct assembly from the engine compartment – 1.6 litre engines

the front body panel, then release the fastener securing the rear of the duct to the cylinder head. Remove the complete duct assembly from the engine compartment **(see illustrations)**.

1.8 litre (8-valve) engines

11 Slacken the retaining clip(s) and disconnect the breather hose(s) from the side of the air cleaner-to-throttle housing duct. Slacken the duct retaining clips, then disconnect it from the air cleaner and throttle housing, and remove it from the vehicle. Where necessary, recover the rubber sealing ring from the throttle housing.

12 Release the two retaining clips, then slacken and remove the two retaining screws from the front of the cylinder head cover, and remove the air cleaner element cover from the head. Withdraw the air cleaner element.

13 To remove the air inlet duct, undo the bolt (or nut) securing the rear section of the duct to the end of the cylinder head, then slacken the retaining clip and disconnect the duct from the cylinder head cover. Undo the bolt securing the front of the duct to the front body panel and manoeuvre the duct out of the engine compartment.

1.8 and 2.0 litre (16-valve) engines

14 Slacken the retaining clip and disconnect the air cleaner-to-throttle housing duct from the throttle housing.

15 Undo the screws securing the lid to the air cleaner housing. Disconnect the crankcase ventilation hose, then lift off the lid and take out the filter element.

16 Undo the nut securing the rear of the air cleaner housing to the support bracket. Lift the housing upward to disengage it from the lower front locating lugs. On some models, as the housing is lifted up, it will be necessary to disengage a small plastic retaining tag at the front securing the housing to the air inlet duct underneath.

17 To remove the air inlet duct, undo the bolt securing the front section of the duct to the front body panel.

18 Undo the two intermediate section support bracket nuts (where fitted), and the two bolts securing the air cleaner mounting

bracket to the front body panel. Lift the duct, complete with air cleaner mounting bracket, from the car.

Refitting

19 Refitting is a reversal of the removal procedure, ensuring that all hoses are properly reconnected, and that all ducts are correctly seated and securely held by their retaining clips.

---

3 Accelerator cable – removal, refitting and adjustment

Removal

Note: *On models fitted with the AL4 automatic transmission, it will be necessary for the transmission ECU to be initialised and matched electronically to the engine management ECU on completion, as adjustment of the accelerator cable will affect the throttle potentiometer signal – the initialisation work must be referred to a Citroën dealer.*

1 Working in the engine compartment, free the accelerator inner cable from the throttle housing cam, then pull the outer cable out from its mounting bracket rubber grommet. Slide the flat washer off the end of the cable, and remove the spring clip **(see illustration)**.

2 Working back along the length of the cable, free it from any retaining clips or ties, noting its correct routing.

3 Reach up under the fascia, depress the ends of the cable end fitting, and detach the inner cable from the top of the accelerator pedal.

4 Release the outer cable grommet from the pedal mounting bracket, then tie a length of string to the end of the cable.

5 Return to the engine compartment, release the cable grommet from the bulkhead and withdraw the cable. When the end of the cable appears, untie the string and leave it in position – it can then be used to draw the cable back into position on refitting.

Refitting

6 Tie the string to the end of the cable, then use the string to draw the cable into position through the bulkhead. Once the cable end is visible, untie the string, then fit the outer cable grommet into the pedal bracket, and push the inner cable end fitting into position in the pedal.

7 From within the engine compartment, ensure the outer cable is correctly seated in the bulkhead grommet, then work along the cable, securing it in position with the retaining clips and ties, and ensuring that the cable is correctly routed.

8 Slide the flat washer onto the cable end and refit the spring clip.

9 Pass the outer cable through its throttle housing mounting bracket grommet, and reconnect the inner cable to the throttle cam. Adjust the cable as described below.

Adjustment

10 Remove the spring clip from the accelerator outer cable. Ensuring that the throttle cam is fully against its stop, gently pull the cable out of its grommet until all free play is removed from the inner cable.

11 With the cable held in this position, refit the spring clip to the last exposed outer cable groove in front of the rubber grommet and

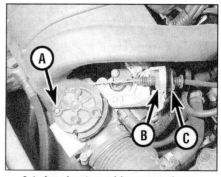

3.1 Accelerator cable connections – 1.8 litre (16-valve) engines

A *Inner cable attachment at throttle housing cam*
B *Mounting bracket rubber grommet*
C *Flat washer and spring clip*

washer. When the clip is refitted and the outer cable is released, there should be only a small amount of free play in the inner cable.

12 Have an assistant depress the accelerator pedal, and check that the throttle cam opens fully and returns smoothly to its stop.

4 Accelerator pedal – removal and refitting

Removal

1 Reach up under the facia, depress the ends of the cable end fitting, and detach the inner cable from the top of the accelerator pedal.

Right-hand drive models

2 Unscrew the nut from the end of the pedal pivot shaft, whilst retaining the pivot shaft with an open-ended spanner on the flats provided.
3 Withdraw the pedal and pivot shaft assembly from the pedal bracket.
4 Examine the pivot shaft for signs of wear or damage and, if necessary, renew it. The pivot shaft is a screw fit in the pedal.

Left-hand drive models

5 On left-hand drive models, unscrew the two nuts and lift off the pedal pivot housing cover and upper bearing.
6 Withdraw the pedal from the lower bearing.
7 Examine the pivot bushes and shaft for signs of wear, and renew as necessary.

Refitting

8 Refitting is a reversal of the removal procedure, applying a little multi-purpose grease to the pedal pivot point. On completion, adjust the accelerator cable as described in Section 3.

5 Unleaded petrol – general information and usage

Note: *The information given in this Chapter is correct at the time of writing. If updated information is thought to be required, check with a Citroën dealer. If travelling abroad, consult one of the motoring organisations (or a similar authority) for advice on the fuel available.*

1 All Citroën Xsara petrol engines are designed to run on unleaded fuel with a minimum octane rating of 95 (RON). All engines have a catalytic converter, and so must be run on unleaded fuel **only**. Under no circumstances should leaded fuel, or lead replacement petrol (LRP) be used, as this will damage the converter.
2 RON and MON are different testing standards; RON stands for Research Octane Number (also written as RM), while MON stands for Motor Octane Number (also written as MN).

6 Fuel injection systems – general information

Note: *The fuel injection ECU is of the 'self-learning' type, meaning that as it operates, it also monitors and stores the settings which give optimum engine performance under all operating conditions. When the battery is disconnected, these settings are lost and the ECU reverts to the base settings programmed into its memory at the factory. On restarting, this may lead to the engine running/idling roughly for a short while, until the ECU has re-learned the optimum settings. This process is best accomplished by taking the vehicle on a road test (for approximately 15 minutes), covering all engine speeds and loads, concentrating mainly in the 2500 to 3500 rpm region.*

On all engines, the fuel injection and ignition functions are combined into a single engine management system. The systems fitted are manufactured by Bosch, Sagem Lucas and Magneti Marelli, and are very similar to each other in most respects, the only significant differences being within the system ECUs. Each system incorporates a closed-loop catalytic converter and an evaporative emission control system, and complies with the latest emission control standards. Refer to Chapter 5B for information on the ignition side of each system; the fuel side of the system operates as follows.

The fuel pump supplies fuel from the tank to the fuel rail, via a replaceable cartridge filter mounted underneath the rear of the vehicle. The pump itself is mounted inside the fuel tank, the pump motor is permanently immersed in fuel, to keep it cool. The fuel rail is mounted directly above the fuel injectors and acts as a fuel reservoir.

Fuel rail supply pressure is controlled by the pressure regulator, mounted at the end of the fuel rail or, on later Bosch systems, in front of the fuel tank. The regulator contains a spring-loaded valve, which lifts to allow excess fuel to return to the tank when the optimum operating pressure of the fuel system is exceeded (eg, during low speed, light load cruising). The regulator also contains a diaphragm which is supplied with vacuum from the inlet manifold. This allows the regulator to reduce the fuel supply pressure during light load, high manifold depression conditions (eg, during idling or deceleration) to prevent excess fuel being 'sucked' through the open injectors.

The fuel injectors are electromagnetic pintle valves, which spray atomised fuel into the combustion chambers under the control of the engine management system ECU. There are four injectors, one per cylinder, mounted in the inlet manifold close to the cylinder head. Each injector is mounted at an angle that allows it to spray fuel directly onto the

back of the inlet valve(s). The ECU controls the volume of fuel injected by varying the length of time for which each injector is held open.

The fuel injection systems are typically of the simultaneous injection type, whereby all four injectors open at the same time and fuel is injected into each cylinder's inlet tract twice per engine cycle; once during the power stroke and once during the induction stroke. On later Bosch systems, however, sequential fuel injection is used whereby each injector operates individually in cylinder sequence.

The electrical control system consists of the ECU, along with the following sensors:
a) *Throttle potentiometer – informs the ECU of the throttle valve position, and the rate of throttle opening/closing.*
b) *Coolant temperature sensor – informs the ECU of engine temperature.*
c) *Inlet air temperature sensor – informs the ECU of the temperature of the air passing through the throttle housing.*
d) *Lambda sensor – informs the ECU of the oxygen content of the exhaust gases (explained in greater detail in Part D of this Chapter).*
e) *Manifold pressure sensor – informs the ECU of the load on the engine (expressed in terms of inlet manifold vacuum).*
f) *Crankshaft sensor – informs the ECU of engine speed and crankshaft angular position.*
g) *Vehicle speed sensor – informs the ECU of the vehicle speed.*
h) *Knock sensor – informs the ECU of pre-ignition (detonation) within the cylinders. Not all systems utilise this sensor.*
i) *Camshaft sensor – informs the ECU of which cylinder is on the firing stroke on later systems with sequential injection.*

Signals from each of the sensors are compared by the ECU and, based on this information, the ECU selects the response appropriate to those values, and controls the fuel injectors (varying the pulse width – the length of time the injectors are held open – to provide a richer or weaker air/fuel mixture, as appropriate). The air/fuel mixture is constantly varied by the ECU, to provide the best settings for cranking, starting (with either a hot or cold engine) and engine warm-up, idle, cruising and acceleration.

The ECU also has full control over the engine idle speed, typically via a stepper motor fitted to the throttle housing. The stepper motor pushrod controls the amount of air passing through a bypass drilling at the side of the throttle. When the throttle valve is closed (accelerator pedal released), the ECU uses the motor to alter the position of the pushrod, controlling the amount of air bypassing the throttle valve and so controlling the idle speed. The ECU also carries out 'fine tuning' of the idle speed by varying the ignition timing to increase or reduce the torque of the engine as it is idling. This helps to stabilise the idle speed when electrical or mechanical loads (such as headlights, air conditioning, etc) are switched on and off.

On certain Bosch systems, ECU control of the engine idle speed is by means of an auxiliary air valve which bypasses the throttle valve. When the throttle valve is closed, the ECU controls the opening of the air valve, which in turn regulates the amount of air entering the manifold, and so controls the idle speed.

The throttle housing on most engines is fitted with an electric heating element. The heater is supplied with current by the ECU, warming the throttle housing on cold starts to help prevent icing of the throttle valve.

The exhaust and evaporative loss emission control systems are described in more detail in Chapter 4D.

If there is any abnormality in any of the readings obtained from the coolant temperature sensor, the inlet air temperature sensor or the lambda sensor, the ECU enters its 'back-up' mode. If this happens, the erroneous sensor signal is overridden, and the ECU assumes a pre-programmed 'back-up' value, which will allow the engine to continue running, albeit at reduced efficiency. If the ECU enters this mode, the warning lamp on the instrument panel will be illuminated, and the relevant fault code will be stored in the ECU memory.

If the warning light illuminates, the vehicle should be taken to a Citroën dealer at the earliest opportunity. Once there, a complete test of the engine management system can be carried out, using a special electronic diagnostic test unit, which is plugged into the system's diagnostic connector.

7 Fuel injection system – depressurisation

Note: *Refer to the warning note in Section 1 before proceeding.*

 Warning: The following procedure will merely relieve the pressure in the fuel system – remember that fuel will still be present in the system components and take precautions accordingly before disconnecting any of them.

1 The fuel system referred to in this Section is defined as the tank-mounted fuel pump, the fuel filter, the fuel injectors, the fuel rail and the pressure regulator, and the metal pipes and flexible hoses of the fuel lines between these components. All these contain fuel which will be under pressure while the engine is running, and/or while the ignition is switched on. The pressure will remain for some time after the ignition has been switched off, and must be relieved in a controlled fashion when any of these components are disturbed for servicing work.

2 Disconnect the battery negative terminal (refer to *Disconnecting the battery* in the Reference Section of this manual).

3 Place a container beneath the connection/union to be disconnected, and have a large rag ready to soak up any escaping fuel not being caught by the container.

4 Slowly loosen the connection or union nut to avoid a sudden release of pressure, and position the rag around the connection, to catch any fuel spray which may be expelled. Once the pressure is released, disconnect the fuel line. Plug the pipe ends, to minimise fuel loss and prevent the entry of dirt into the fuel system.

8 Fuel pump – removal and refitting

Note: *Refer to the warning note in Section 1 before proceeding.*

Removal

1 Disconnect the battery negative terminal (refer to *Disconnecting the battery* in the Reference Section of this manual).

2 For access to the fuel pump, tilt or remove the rear seat as described in Chapter 11. The pump is located in the fuel tank on the right-hand side and is accessible through an opening in the floor beneath the rear seat.

3 Lift up the cut-out section of carpet then, using a screwdriver, carefully prise the plastic access cover from the floor to expose the fuel pump **(see illustrations)**.

4 Disconnect the wiring connector from the fuel pump, and tape the connector to the vehicle body to prevent it from disappearing behind the tank **(see illustration)**.

5 Mark the hoses for identification purposes, then disconnect the quick-release fittings using a small screwdriver to release the locking clip **(see illustration)**. Disconnect both hoses from the top of the pump, and plug the hose ends.

6 Noting the alignment marks on the pump cover and the locking ring, unscrew the ring and remove it from the tank. This is best accomplished by making up a simple tool from two strips of metal, suitably drilled and joined together with two lengths of threaded bar and locknuts. Engage the tool with the raised ribs of the locking ring, and turn the ring anti-clockwise until it can be unscrewed by hand **(see illustrations)**.

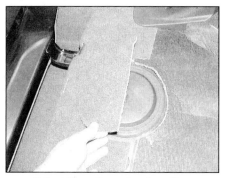

8.3a Lift up the cut-out section of carpet . . .

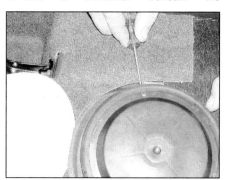

8.3b . . . then carefully prise the fuel pump access cover from the floor

8.4 Disconnect the wiring connector from the fuel pump

8.5 Disconnect the fuel hose quick-release fittings using a small screwdriver to release the locking clip

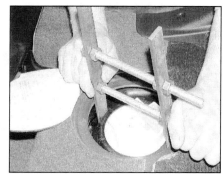

8.6a Using a home made tool, slacken the fuel pump locking ring . . .

8.6b . . . then unscrew the locking ring
from the tank

8.7a Lift the fuel pump and sender unit
assembly out of the fuel tank . . .

8.7b . . . and recover the sealing O-ring

7 Lift the fuel pump and sender unit assembly out of the fuel tank, taking great care not to damage the float arm, or to spill fuel onto the interior of the vehicle. Recover the sealing O-ring and discard it – a new one must be used on refitting **(see illustrations)**.

8 Note that the fuel pump and sender unit is only available as a complete assembly – no components are available separately.

Refitting

9 Ensure the fuel pump pick-up filter is clean and free of debris, then locate the new sealing O-ring on the top of the fuel tank.

10 Carefully manoeuvre the pump and sender unit assembly into the fuel tank, aligning the notch on the pump body with the cut-out in the tank **(see illustration)**. Take

care not to displace the O-ring as the pump is fitted.

11 Refit the locking ring and securely tighten it until the small raised arrow on the ring is aligned with the arrow on the top of the pump **(see illustration)**.

12 Reconnect the feed and return hoses to the top of the fuel pump, using the marks made on removal to ensure that they are correctly reconnected.

13 Reconnect the pump wiring connector.

14 Reconnect the battery negative terminal and start the engine. Check the fuel pump feed and return hoses unions for signs of leakage.

15 If all is well, refit the plastic access cover. Tilt or refit the rear seat as described in Chapter 11 (as applicable).

9 Fuel gauge sender unit –
removal and refitting

The fuel gauge sender unit is integral with the fuel pump. Refer to the procedures contained in Section 8.

10 Fuel tank –
removal and refitting

Note: Refer to the warning note in Section 1 before proceeding.

Removal

1 Before removing the fuel tank, all fuel must be drained from the tank. Since a fuel tank drain plug is not provided, it is therefore preferable to carry out the removal operation when the tank is nearly empty. Before proceeding, disconnect the battery negative terminal (refer to Disconnecting the battery in the Reference Section of this manual) and syphon or hand-pump the remaining fuel from the tank.

2 Carry out the operations described in Section 8, paragraphs 1 to 5 to disconnect the fuel hoses and wiring connector from the fuel pump.

3 Remove the exhaust system and relevant heat shield(s) as described in Section 17.

4 Disconnect the two handbrake cables from the handbrake lever as described in Chapter 9.

5 From underneath the vehicle, remove the retaining clips, and release each handbrake cable from its guides on the underside of the fuel tank **(see illustration)**. Position both cables clear of the tank, so that they will not hinder the removal procedure.

6 Working at the right-hand side of the fuel tank, release the retaining clips then disconnect the filler neck vent pipe and main filler neck hose from the fuel tank/filler neck. Similarly, disconnect the breather and vent hoses at their connections on the right-hand side of the tank. Some breather hoses are joined to the tank with quick-release fittings; to disconnect these fittings, slide the cover along the hose then depress the centre ring and pull the hose out of its fitting **(see illustrations)**.

8.10 When refitting, align the notch on the pump body with the cut-out (arrowed) in the tank

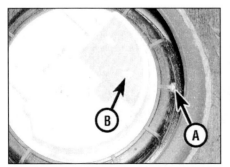

8.11 Refit and tighten the locking ring until the raised arrow (A) on the ring is aligned with the arrow (B) on the pump

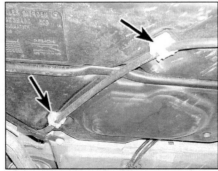

10.5 Release the handbrake cables from the fuel tank guides (arrowed)

10.6a Disconnect the main breather hose (arrowed) from the filler neck . . .

7 Release the fuel filter and, on later 1.4 and 1.6 litre engines, the fuel pressure regulator from their mountings and move them to one side.

8 Place a trolley jack with an interposed block of wood beneath the tank, then raise the jack until it is supporting the weight of the tank.

9 Slacken and remove the retaining nut and bolts, then remove the two support rods from the underside of the tank.

10 Undo the additional retaining bolt at the front left-hand side of the tank.

11 Slowly lower the fuel tank out of position, disconnecting any other relevant vent pipes as they become accessible (where necessary), and remove the tank from underneath the vehicle.

12 If the tank is contaminated with sediment or water, remove the fuel pump as described in Section 8, and swill the tank out with clean fuel. The tank is injection-moulded from a synthetic material – if seriously damaged, it should be renewed. However, in certain cases, it may be possible to have small leaks or minor damage repaired. Seek the advice of a specialist before attempting to repair the fuel tank.

Refitting

13 Refitting is the reverse of the removal procedure, noting the following points:
  a) *When lifting the tank back into position, take care to ensure that none of the hoses become trapped between the tank and vehicle body.*
  b) *Ensure all pipes and hoses are correctly routed, and securely held in position with their retaining clips.*
  c) *Reconnect the handbrake cables and adjust the handbrake as described in Chapter 9.*
  d) *On completion, refill the tank with a small amount of fuel, and check for signs of leakage prior to taking the vehicle out on the road.*

11 Fuel injection system – testing and adjustment

Testing

1 If a fault appears in the fuel injection/engine management system, first ensure that all the system wiring connectors are securely connected and free of corrosion. Ensure that the fault is not due to poor maintenance; ie, check that the air cleaner filter element is clean, the spark plugs are in good condition and correctly gapped, the cylinder compression pressures are correct, and that the engine breather hoses are clear and undamaged, referring to the relevant Parts of Chapters 1, 2 and 5 for further information.

2 If these checks fail to reveal the cause of the problem, the vehicle should be taken to a Citroën dealer or suitably-equipped garage for testing. A diagnostic socket is located adjacent to the passenger compartment fusebox in which a fault code reader or other suitable test equipment can

10.6b ... and the main filler hose (arrowed) from the tank

be connected. By using the code reader or test equipment, the engine management ECU (and the various other vehicle system ECUs) can be interrogated, and any stored fault codes can be retrieved. This will allow the fault to be quickly and simply traced, alleviating the need to test all the system components individually, which is a time-consuming operation that carries a risk of damaging the ECU.

Adjustment

3 Experienced home mechanics with a considerable amount of skill and equipment (including a tachometer and an accurately calibrated exhaust gas analyser) may be able to *check* the exhaust CO level and the idle speed. However, if these are found to be outside the specified tolerance, the car must be taken to a suitably-equipped garage for further testing. Neither the mixture adjustment (exhaust gas CO level) nor the idle speed are adjustable, and should either be incorrect, a fault may be present in the engine management system.

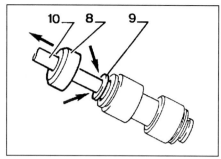

10.6c Fuel tank breather hose quick-release connector

  8 *Cover*   9 *Centre ring*   10 *Hose*

12 Throttle housing – removal and refitting

Removal

1 Disconnect the battery negative terminal (refer to *Disconnecting the battery* in the Reference Section of this manual).

1.4 and 1.6 litre engines

2 Remove the air cleaner assembly as described in Section 2.

3 Disconnect the accelerator inner cable from the throttle cam, then withdraw the outer cable from the mounting bracket, along with its rubber washer and spring clip.

4 Depress the retaining clip and disconnect the wiring connector(s) from the throttle potentiometer, and, where necessary, from the electric heating element, and/or the stepper motor (as applicable) **(see illustration)**.

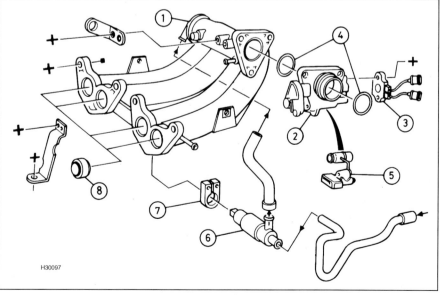

12.4 Throttle housing and inlet manifold components – early 1.6 litre engines

  1 *Inlet manifold*
  2 *Throttle housing*
  3 *Throttle potentiometer*
  4 *O-ring seals*
  5 *Electric heating element*
  6 *Idle speed auxiliary air valve*
  7 *Mounting bracket*
  8 *Sealing rings*

H30097

5 Slacken and remove the retaining screws, and remove the throttle housing from the inlet manifold. Recover the O-ring from manifold (where fitted) and discard it; a new one must be used when refitting.

1.8 and 2.0 litre engines

6 Remove the air cleaner-to-throttle housing duct as described in Section 2.

7 On 1.8 litre (8-valve) engines with automatic transmission, carefully lever the accelerator linkage rod off its throttle housing balljoint.

8 On all other engines, disconnect the accelerator inner cable from the throttle cam, then withdraw the outer cable from the mounting bracket along with its flat washer and spring clip. Where necessary, also disconnect the kickdown cable as described in Chapter 7B.

9 Depress the retaining clips, and disconnect the wiring connectors from the throttle potentiometer, the electric heating element, the inlet air temperature sensor and idle speed stepper motor (as applicable).

10 Release the retaining clips (where fitted), and disconnect all the relevant vacuum and breather hoses from the throttle housing. Make identification marks on the hoses, to ensure they are connected correctly on refitting.

11 Where necessary, undo the bolts or screws and release the accelerator cable bracket and housing support bracket.

13.4a On early 1.6 litre engines, undo the retaining nut and bolt . . .

12 Slacken and remove the retaining screws, and remove the throttle housing from the inlet manifold. Remove the O-ring from the manifold, and discard it – a new one must be used on refitting.

Refitting

13 Refitting is a reversal of the removal procedure, noting the following points:
  a) Fit a new O-ring to the manifold, then refit the throttle housing and securely tighten its retaining nuts or screws (as applicable).
  b) Ensure all hoses are correctly reconnected and, where necessary, are securely held in position by the retaining clips.

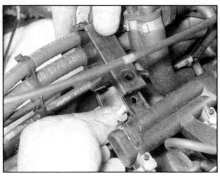

13.4b . . . and release the wiring/hose support clip from the fuel rail

  c) Ensure all wiring is correctly routed, and that the connectors are securely reconnected.
  d) On completion, adjust the accelerator cable as described in Section 3 and, where necessary, the kickdown cable as described in Chapter 7B.

13 Bosch Motronic and Sagem Lucas system components – removal and refitting

1.4 and 1.6 litre engines

Fuel rail and injectors

Note: *Refer to the warning note in Section 1 before proceeding. If a faulty injector is suspected, before condemning the injector, it is worth trying the effect of one of the proprietary injector-cleaning treatments which are available from car accessory shops.*

1 Disconnect the battery negative terminal (refer to *Disconnecting the battery* in the Reference Section of this manual).

2 Remove the air cleaner assembly as described in Section 2.

3 On later engines with the ignition HT coil module mounted above the fuel rail, remove the coil module as described in Chapter 5B.

4 On early engines, disconnect the vacuum pipe from the fuel pressure regulator. On early 1.6 litre engines, undo the retaining nut and bolt and release the wiring/hose support clip from the end of the fuel rail **(see illustrations)**.

5 Bearing in mind the information given in Section 7, disconnect the fuel feed and, on early engines, the return hose quick-release fittings, using a small screwdriver to release the locking clip.

6 Depress the retaining tangs and disconnect the wiring connectors from the four injectors.

7 Slacken and remove the fuel rail retaining bolts and nuts, then carefully ease the fuel rail and injector assembly out from the inlet manifold and remove it from the engine. Remove the O-rings from the end of each injector and discard them; they must be renewed whenever they are disturbed.

8 Slide out the retaining clip(s) and remove the relevant injector(s) from the fuel rail **(see illustration)**. Remove the upper O-ring from

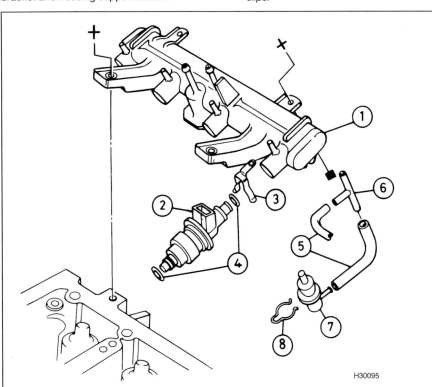

13.8 Fuel rail and injector components – early 1.6 litre engines

1 Fuel rail	4 O-ring seals	7 Fuel pressure regulator
2 Injector	5 Fuel hoses	8 Retaining clip
3 Retaining clip	6 T-piece	

13.15 Disconnect the throttle potentiometer wiring connector – 1.6 litre engines

13.20a Lift the retaining clip . . .

13.20b . . . and disconnect the wiring connector from the ECU

each disturbed injector and discard; all disturbed O-rings must be renewed.

9 Refitting is a reversal of the removal procedure, noting the following points.

a) Fit new O-rings to all disturbed injector unions.

b) Apply a smear of engine oil to the O-rings to aid installation, then ease the injectors and fuel rail into position ensuring that none of the O-rings are displaced.

c) On later engines, refit the ignition coil module as described in Chapter 5B.

d) On completion, start the engine and check for fuel leaks.

Fuel pressure regulator

Note 1: *The following procedure applies to models with the fuel pressure regulator mounted on the fuel rail. On later models, the regulator is mounted on the fuel tank – at the time of writing, information on the later installation was not available.*

Note 2: *Refer to the warning note in Section 1 before proceeding.*

10 Disconnect the battery negative terminal (refer to *Disconnecting the battery* in the Reference Section of this manual).

11 Disconnect the vacuum pipe from the regulator. Note that on early engines, access to the regulator is poor with the fuel rail in position, if necessary, remove the fuel rail as described earlier, then remove the regulator.

12 Bearing in mind the information given in Section 7, place a wad of rag over the regulator, to catch any fuel spray which may be released, then remove the retaining clip and ease the regulator out from the fuel rail.

13 Refitting is a reversal of the removal procedure. Examine the regulator seal for signs of damage or deterioration and renew if necessary.

Throttle potentiometer

14 Disconnect the battery negative terminal (refer to *Disconnecting the battery* in the Reference Section of this manual).

15 Depress the retaining clip and disconnect the wiring connector from the throttle potentiometer **(see illustration)**.

16 Slacken and remove the two retaining screws, then disengage the potentiometer

from the throttle valve spindle and remove it from the engine.

17 Refit in the reverse order of removal. Ensure that the potentiometer is correctly engaged with the throttle valve spindle.

Electronic control unit (ECU)

Note: *If a new ECU is to be fitted, this work must be entrusted to a Citroën dealer. It is necessary to initialise the new ECU after installation which requires the use of dedicated Citroën diagnostic equipment.*

18 The ECU is located in the plastic box which forms part of the rear of the battery mounting tray. On some engines, access to the ECU retaining nuts/bolts is poor and it is beneficial to remove the battery mounting tray as described in Chapter 5A, then remove the ECU with the tray on the bench.

19 Disconnect the battery negative terminal (refer to *Disconnecting the battery* in the Reference Section of this manual).

20 Unclip the cover over the ECU, then lift the retaining clip and disconnect the ECU wiring connector **(see illustrations)**.

21 Undo the retaining nuts or bolts and lift the ECU from the battery tray **(see illustration)**.

22 Refitting is a reverse of the removal procedure ensuring the wiring connector is securely reconnected.

Idle speed auxiliary air valve

23 The auxiliary air valve is only fitted to

1.6 litre engines and is mounted on the underside of the inlet manifold (early engines) or on the right-hand end of the inlet manifold casting (later engines). On 1.4 litre engines, idle speed regulation is via a stepper motor as described in the next sub-Section.

24 Disconnect the battery negative terminal (refer to *Disconnecting the battery* in the Reference Section of this manual).

25 Depress the retaining clip and disconnect the wiring connector.

26 Slacken the retaining clips and disconnect the air hose(s) from the end of the auxiliary air valve.

27 On early engines, slide the valve out from its mounting bracket, and remove it from the engine compartment. On later engines, undo the securing screw and withdraw the valve from the manifold **(see illustration)**.

28 Refitting is a reversal of the removal procedure. Examine the mounting rubber for signs of deterioration and renew it if necessary.

Idle speed stepper motor

29 The idle speed stepper motor, fitted to 1.4 litre engines, is located on the side of the throttle housing assembly.

30 Disconnect the battery negative terminal (refer to *Disconnecting the battery* in the Reference Section of this manual).

31 Release the retaining clip and disconnect the wiring connector from the motor.

32 Slacken and remove the two retaining

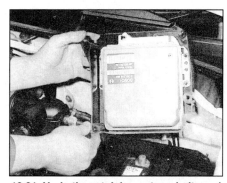

13.21 Undo the retaining nuts or bolts and lift the ECU from the battery tray

13.27 Idle speed auxiliary air valve securing screw (arrowed) – later 1.6 litre engines

13.37 Manifold pressure sensor securing screw (arrowed) – later 1.6 litre engines

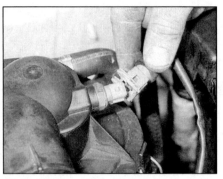

13.42 Disconnect the inlet air temperature sensor wiring connector – early 1.6 litre engines

13.53 Disconnect the fuel feed and return hoses from the fuel rail and fuel pressure regulator – 1.8 litre (16-valve) engines

screws, and withdraw the motor from the throttle housing.

33 Refitting is a reversal of the removal procedure.

Manifold pressure sensor

34 On 1.4 litre engines, the pressure sensor is mounted on the right-hand side of the inlet manifold. On early 1.6 litre engines, the pressure sensor is situated remotely on the right-hand side of the engine compartment where it is mounted on the wing valance. On later 1.6 litre engines, the sensor is mounted directly on the front of the inlet manifold.

35 Disconnect the battery negative terminal (refer to *Disconnecting the battery* in the Reference Section of this manual).

36 On early 1.6 litre engines, undo the retaining nut, and free the sensor from its mounting bracket. Disconnect the wiring connector and vacuum hose and remove the sensor from the engine compartment.

37 On later engines, remove the securing screw and withdraw the sensor from the manifold **(see illustration)**. Disconnect the wiring connector, and remove the sensor from the engine.

38 Refitting is the reverse of the removal procedure.

Coolant temperature sensor

39 Refer to Chapter 3, Section 6.

Inlet air temperature sensor

40 On early engines, the inlet air temperature sensor is screwed into the air cleaner housing

lid. On later engines it is located on the underside of the throttle housing.

41 Disconnect the battery negative terminal (refer to *Disconnecting the battery* in the Reference Section of this manual).

42 Disconnect the wiring connector, then unscrew the sensor and remove it from the vehicle **(see illustration)**.

43 Refitting is the reverse of removal.

Crankshaft sensor

44 The crankshaft sensor is situated on the front face of the transmission clutch housing.

45 Disconnect the battery negative terminal (refer to *Disconnecting the battery* in the Reference Section of this manual).

46 Trace the wiring back from the sensor to the wiring connector and disconnect it from the main harness.

47 Prise out the rubber grommet, then undo the retaining bolt and withdraw the sensor from the transmission unit.

48 Refitting is reverse of the removal procedure ensuring the sensor retaining bolt is securely tightened and the grommet is correctly seated in the transmission housing.

Knock sensor

49 Refer to Chapter 5B.

Vehicle speed sensor

50 The vehicle speed sensor is an integral part of the speedometer drive housing. Refer to Chapter 7A or 7B, as applicable, for removal and refitting details.

1.8 and 2.0 litre (16-valve) engines

Fuel rail and injectors

Note: *Refer to the warning note in Section 1 before proceeding. If a faulty injector is suspected, before condemning the injector, it is worth trying the effect of one of the proprietary injector-cleaning treatments which are available from car accessory shops.*

51 Disconnect the battery negative terminal (refer to *Disconnecting the battery* in the Reference Section of this manual).

52 Disconnect the vacuum pipe from the fuel pressure regulator.

53 Bearing in mind the information given in Section 7, slacken the retaining clips and disconnect the fuel feed and return hoses from the fuel rail and fuel pressure regulator **(see illustration)**. Where the original crimped-type Citroën hose clips are still fitted, cut them and discard; replace them with standard worm-type hose clips on refitting.

54 Disconnect the wiring harness connector along the front of the fuel rail then depress the retaining tangs and disconnect the wiring connectors from the four injectors **(see illustration)**.

55 Slacken and remove the fuel rail retaining bolts, then carefully ease the fuel rail and injector assembly out from the inlet manifold and remove it from the engine **(see illustrations)**. Remove the O-rings from the

13.54 Disconnect the wiring connectors from the fuel injectors – 1.8 litre (16-valve) engines

13.55a Slacken and remove the fuel rail retaining bolts . . .

13.55b . . . then carefully ease the fuel rail and injector assembly from the inlet manifold – 1.8 litre (16-valve) engines

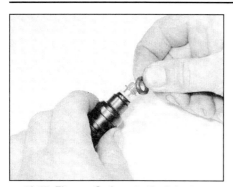

13.57 Fit new O-rings to the injectors before refitting – 1.8 litre (16-valve) engines

end of each injector and discard them; they must be renewed whenever they are disturbed.

56 Slide out the retaining clip(s) and remove the relevant injector(s) from the fuel rail. Remove the upper O-ring from each disturbed injector and discard; all disturbed O-rings must be renewed.

57 Refitting is a reversal of the removal procedure, noting the following points.
  a) *Fit new O-rings to all disturbed injector unions (see illustration).*
  b) *Apply a smear of engine oil to the O-rings to aid installation, then ease the injectors and fuel rail into position ensuring that none of the O-rings are displaced.*
  c) *On completion, start the engine and check for fuel leaks.*

Fuel pressure regulator

Note: *Refer to the warning note in Section 1 before proceeding.*

58 Disconnect the battery negative terminal (refer to *Disconnecting the battery* in the Reference Section of this manual).

59 Bearing in mind the information given in Section 7, slacken the retaining clips and disconnect the fuel feed and return hoses from the fuel rail and pressure regulator.

60 Disconnect the vacuum pipe from the regulator **(see illustration)**.

61 Place some rags under the regulator, to catch any spilt fuel. Remove the retaining clip and ease the regulator out from the fuel rail **(see illustrations)**.

62 Refitting is a reversal of the removal procedure. Examine the regulator seal for

13.61a Remove the retaining clip . . .

13.60 Disconnect the vacuum pipe from the regulator – 1.8 litre (16-valve) engines

signs of damage or deterioration and renew if necessary.

Throttle potentiometer

63 Disconnect the battery negative terminal (refer to *Disconnecting the battery* in the Reference Section of this manual).

64 Depress the retaining clip and disconnect the wiring connector from the throttle potentiometer located beneath the throttle housing.

65 Slacken and remove the two retaining screws, then disengage the potentiometer from the throttle valve spindle and remove it from the vehicle.

66 Refit in the reverse order of removal. Ensure that the potentiometer is correctly engaged with the throttle valve spindle.

Electronic control unit (ECU)

67 Refer to paragraphs 18 to 22.

Idle speed stepper motor

68 The idle speed control stepper motor is located on the side of the throttle housing assembly.

69 Disconnect the battery negative terminal (refer to *Disconnecting the battery* in the Reference Section of this manual).

70 Release the retaining clip, and disconnect the wiring connector from the motor.

71 Slacken and remove the two retaining screws, and withdraw the motor from the throttle housing.

72 Refitting is a reversal of the removal procedure.

13.61b ... and ease the regulator from the fuel rail. Check the sealing ring condition (arrowed) before refitting – 1.8 litre (16-valve) engines

Manifold pressure sensor

73 The pressure sensor is situated on the underside of the inlet manifold.

74 Disconnect the battery negative terminal (refer to *Disconnecting the battery* in the Reference Section of this manual).

75 Disconnect the wiring connector from the sensor.

76 Undo the securing screw, then pull the sensor out of the manifold.

77 Refitting is the reverse of the removal procedure.

Coolant temperature sensor

78 Refer to Chapter 3, Section 6.

Inlet air temperature sensor

79 The inlet air temperature sensor is located in the throttle housing.

80 Disconnect the battery negative terminal (refer to *Disconnecting the battery* in the Reference Section of this manual).

81 Loosen the retaining clip, and release the air inlet duct from the throttle housing. The inlet air temperature sensor is visible in the top of the housing.

82 Trace the wiring back from the sensor to its wiring connector on the throttle housing, and unplug the connector.

83 The sensor itself can be pressed out of the throttle housing. Note that it is sealed in place with sealant, to prevent air leaks; a suitable sealant will be required for refitting.

84 Refitting is the reverse of removal.

Crankshaft sensor

85 The crankshaft sensor is situated on the upper face of the transmission clutch housing.

86 Disconnect the battery negative terminal (refer to *Disconnecting the battery* in the Reference Section of this manual).

87 Trace the wiring back from the sensor to the wiring connector and disconnect it from the main harness.

88 Undo the retaining bolt and withdraw the sensor from the transmission.

89 Refitting is reverse of the removal procedure.

Knock sensor

90 Refer to Chapter 5B.

Vehicle speed sensor

91 The vehicle speed sensor is an integral part of the speedometer drive housing. Refer to Chapter 7A or 7B, as applicable, for removal and refitting details.

14 Magneti Marelli system components – removal and refitting

1.4 litre engines

Fuel rail and injectors

1 Refer to the information given in Section 13, paragraphs 1 to 9.

Fuel pressure regulator

2 Refer to the information given in Section 13, paragraphs 10 to 13.

Throttle potentiometer

3 Refer to the information given in Section 13, paragraphs 14 to 17.

Electronic control unit (ECU)

4 Refer to the information given in Section 13, paragraphs 18 to 22.

Idle speed stepper motor

5 The idle speed stepper motor is located on the side of the throttle housing assembly.
6 Disconnect the battery negative terminal (refer to *Disconnecting the battery* in the Reference Section of this manual).
7 Release the retaining clip, and disconnect the wiring connector from the motor **(see illustration)**.
8 Slacken and remove the two retaining screws, and withdraw the motor from the throttle housing.
9 Refitting is a reversal of the removal procedure.

Manifold pressure sensor

10 The manifold pressure sensor is mounted on the right-hand end of the inlet manifold casting.
11 Disconnect the battery negative terminal (refer to *Disconnecting the battery* in the Reference Section of this manual).
12 Release the locking tab and unplug the wiring from the sensor connector.
13 Undo the securing screw and withdraw the sensor from the manifold, recovering the sealing ring.
14 Refitting is a reversal of removal.

Coolant temperature sensor

15 Refer to Chapter 3, Section 6.

Inlet air temperature sensor

16 The sensor is threaded into the underside of the throttle housing.
17 Disconnect the battery negative terminal (refer to *Disconnecting the battery* in the Reference Section of this manual).
18 Disconnect the sensor wiring connector, then unscrew the sensor and remove it from the throttle housing. Recover the sealing ring, where applicable.

19 Refitting is the reverse of removal.

Crankshaft sensor

20 Refer to the information given in Section 13, paragraphs 44 to 48.

Knock sensor

21 Refer to Chapter 5B.

Vehicle speed sensor

22 The vehicle speed sensor is an integral part of the speedometer drive housing. Refer to Chapter 7A for removal and refitting details.

1.8 litre (8-valve) engines with manual transmission

Fuel rail and injectors

Note: *Refer to the warning note in Section 1 before proceeding. If a faulty injector is suspected, before condemning the injector, it is worth trying the effect of one of the proprietary injector-cleaning treatments.*
23 Disconnect the battery negative terminal (refer to *Disconnecting the battery* in the Reference Section of this manual).
24 Remove the air cleaner-to-throttle housing duct, referring to Section 2.
25 Disconnect the vacuum pipe from the fuel pressure regulator.
26 Release the retaining clips, and disconnect the ventilation hoses located above the fuel rail.
27 Bearing in mind the information given in Section 7, disconnect the fuel feed and return hose quick-release fittings, using a small screwdriver to release the locking clips.
28 Depress the retaining clips, and unplug the wiring connectors from the four injectors.
29 Slacken and remove the three fuel rail retaining bolts, then carefully ease the fuel rail and injector assembly out from the inlet manifold, and remove it from the vehicle. Remove the O-rings from the end of each injector, and discard them; these must be renewed whenever they are disturbed.
30 Slide out the retaining clip(s), and remove the relevant injector(s) from the fuel rail. Remove the upper O-ring from each injector as it is removed, and discard it; all O-rings must be renewed once they have been disturbed.

31 Refitting is a reversal of the removal procedure, noting the following points:
  a) *Fit new O-rings to all disturbed injectors.*
  b) *Apply a smear of engine oil to the O-rings to aid installation, then ease the injectors and fuel rail into position, ensuring that none of the O-rings are displaced.*
  c) *On completion, start the engine and check for fuel leaks.*

Fuel pressure regulator

Note: *Refer to the warning note in Section 1 before proceeding.*
32 Disconnect the battery negative terminal (refer to *Disconnecting the battery* in the Reference Section of this manual).
33 Remove the air cleaner-to-throttle housing duct, referring to Section 2.
34 Disconnect the vacuum pipe from the fuel pressure regulator.
35 Bearing in mind the information given in Section 7, disconnect the fuel return hose quick-release fitting, using a small screwdriver to release the locking clip.
36 Place some rags under the regulator, to catch any spilt fuel. Remove the retaining clip and ease the regulator out from the fuel rail.
37 Refitting is a reversal of the removal procedure. Examine the regulator seal for signs of damage or deterioration and renew if necessary.

Throttle potentiometer

38 Disconnect the battery negative terminal (refer to *Disconnecting the battery* in the Reference Section of this manual).
39 Depress the retaining clip and disconnect the wiring connector from the throttle potentiometer.
40 Slacken and remove the two retaining screws, then disengage the potentiometer from the throttle valve spindle and remove it from the vehicle.
41 Refit in the reverse order of removal. Ensure that the potentiometer is correctly engaged with the throttle valve spindle.

Electronic control unit (ECU)

42 Refer to the information given in Section 13, paragraphs 18 to 22.

Idle speed stepper motor

43 Refer to the information given in paragraphs 5 to 9 of this Section.

Manifold pressure sensor

44 The manifold pressure sensor is mounted on the left-hand end of the inlet manifold, next to the throttle housing.
45 Disconnect the battery negative terminal (refer to *Disconnecting the battery* in the Reference Section of this manual).
46 Release the retaining clip, and disconnect the wiring connector from the sensor.
47 Undo the securing screw and withdraw the sensor from the manifold, recovering the sealing ring.
48 Refitting is a reversal of removal.

Coolant temperature sensor

49 Refer to Chapter 3, Section 6.

14.7 Disconnect the wiring connector from the idle speed stepper motor . . .

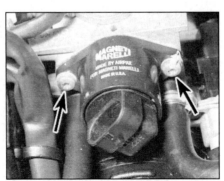

14.8 . . . then remove the two screws and withdraw the motor from the throttle housing – 1.4 litre engines

Inlet air temperature sensor

50 The inlet air temperature sensor is located at the front of the throttle housing.

51 Disconnect the battery negative terminal (refer to *Disconnecting the battery* in the Reference Section of this manual).

52 Trace the wiring back from the sensor to its wiring connector, and remove the screw securing the connector to the throttle housing.

53 Carefully ease the sensor out of position, and remove it from the throttle housing. Examine the sensor O-ring for damage or deterioration, and renew if necessary.

54 Refitting is a reversal of removal, using a new O-ring where necessary.

Crankshaft sensor

55 Refer to the information given in Section 13, paragraphs 85 to 89.

Vehicle speed sensor

56 The vehicle speed sensor is an integral part of the transmission speedometer drive assembly. Refer to Chapter 7A for removal and refitting details.

Knock sensor

57 Refer to Chapter 5B.

1.8 litre (8-valve) engines with automatic transmission

Fuel injectors

Note: *Refer to the warning note in Section 1 before proceeding. If a faulty injector is suspected, before condemning the injector, it is worth trying the effect of one of the proprietary injector-cleaning treatments.*

58 Disconnect the battery negative terminal (refer to *Disconnecting the battery* in the Reference Section of this manual).

59 Remove the air cleaner-to-throttle housing duct as described in Section 2.

60 Undo the two bolts securing the wiring tray to the top of the manifold, and position the tray clear of the injectors.

61 Depress the retaining clip(s) and disconnect the wiring connector(s) from the injector(s).

62 Slacken the retaining screw and remove the injector retaining plate; Nos 1 and 2 injectors are retained by one plate, Nos 3 and 4 by another.

63 Bearing in mind the information given in Section 7, place a wad of clean rag over the injector, to catch any fuel spray which may be released, then carefully ease the relevant injector(s) out of the manifold. Remove the O-rings from the end of each disturbed injector, and discard them – these must be renewed whenever they are disturbed.

64 On refitting the injectors, fit new O-rings to the end of each injector. Apply a smear of engine oil to the O-ring, to aid installation, then ease the injector(s) back into position in the manifold.

65 Ensure each injector connector is correctly positioned, then refit the retaining plate and securely tighten its retaining screw. Reconnect the wiring connector(s) to the injector(s).

66 Refit the wiring tray to the top of the manifold and securely tighten its retaining bolts.

67 Refit the air cleaner-to-throttle body duct and reconnect the battery. Start the engine and check the injectors for signs of leakage.

Fuel pressure regulator

Note: *Refer to the warning note in Section 1 before proceeding.*

68 Disconnect the battery negative terminal (refer to *Disconnecting the battery* in the Reference Section of this manual).

69 Remove the air cleaner-to-throttle housing duct, referring to Section 2.

70 Disconnect the vacuum pipe from the fuel pressure regulator.

71 Bearing in mind the information given in Section 7, place some rags under the regulator, to catch any spilt fuel. Remove the retaining clip and ease the regulator out from the fuel rail.

72 Refitting is a reversal of the removal procedure. Examine the regulator seal for signs of damage or deterioration and renew if necessary.

Throttle potentiometer

73 The throttle potentiometer is fitted to the right-hand side of the throttle housing.

74 Disconnect the battery negative terminal (refer to *Disconnecting the battery* in the Reference Section of this manual).

75 Depress the retaining clip and disconnect the potentiometer wiring connector. Slacken and remove the two retaining screws, and remove the potentiometer from the throttle housing.

76 Refitting is the reverse of removal, ensuring that the potentiometer is correctly engaged with the throttle valve spindle.

Electronic control unit (ECU)

77 Refer to the information given in Section 13, paragraphs 18 to 22.

Idle speed control stepper motor

78 The idle speed control stepper motor is located on the front of the throttle housing assembly.

79 Disconnect the battery negative terminal (refer to *Disconnecting the battery* in the Reference Section of this manual).

80 Release the retaining clip and disconnect the wiring connector from the motor. Slacken and remove the two retaining screws, and withdraw the motor from the throttle housing.

81 Refitting is a reversal of the removal procedure.

Manifold pressure sensor

82 The manifold pressure sensor is situated remotely on the right-hand side of the engine compartment.

83 Disconnect the battery negative terminal (refer to *Disconnecting the battery* in the Reference Section of this manual).

84 Disconnect the wiring plug and the vacuum hose from the sensor.

85 Undo the sensor mounting bracket retaining nut and bolt and withdraw the sensor and bracket. Undo the three nuts and remove the sensor from the mounting bracket.

86 Refitting is the reverse of the removal procedure.

Coolant temperature sensor

87 Refer to Chapter 3, Section 6.

Inlet air temperature sensor

88 The inlet air temperature sensor is located in the throttle housing.

89 To remove the sensor, first remove the throttle potentiometer as described in paragraphs 73 to 76.

90 Depress the retaining clip and disconnect the wiring connector from the air temperature sensor.

91 Remove the screw securing the sensor connector to the top of the throttle housing, then carefully ease the sensor out of position and remove it from the throttle housing. Examine the sensor O-ring for signs of damage or deterioration, and renew if necessary.

92 Refitting is a reversal of the removal procedure, using a new O-ring where necessary, and ensuring that the throttle potentiometer is correctly engaged with the throttle valve spindle.

Crankshaft sensor

93 Refer to the information given in Section 13, paragraphs 85 to 89.

Vehicle speed sensor

94 The vehicle speed sensor is an integral part of the transmission speedometer drive assembly. Refer to Chapter 7B for removal and refitting details.

15 Inlet manifold – removal and refitting

Removal

Note: *Refer to the warning note in Section 1 before proceeding.*

1 Disconnect the battery negative terminal (refer to *Disconnecting the battery* in the Reference Section of this manual) then proceed as described under the relevant sub-heading.

1.4 and 1.6 litre engines

2 Remove the air cleaner assembly as described in Section 2.

3 On later engines with the ignition HT coil module mounted above the fuel rail, remove the coil module as described in Chapter 5B.

4 Disconnect the accelerator inner cable from the throttle cam, then withdraw the outer cable from the mounting bracket, along with its flat washer and spring clip.

5 Depress the retaining clip and disconnect the wiring connector(s) from the throttle potentiometer, and, where necessary, from the electric heating element, air temperature sensor, auxiliary air valve or stepper motor (as applicable).

6 Release the retaining clips (where fitted) and disconnect all the relevant vacuum and breather hoses from the manifold. Make identification marks on the hoses to ensure they are connected correctly on refitting.

7 Bearing in mind the information given in Section 7, disconnect the fuel feed and, on early engines, the return hose quick-release fittings, using a small screwdriver to release the locking clip.

8 Depress the retaining tangs and disconnect the wiring connectors from the four injectors. Free the wiring from any relevant retaining clips and position it clear of the manifold.

9 Where necessary, undo the retaining bolt and remove the support bracket from the manifold.

10 Undo the manifold retaining nuts and withdraw the manifold from the engine compartment. Recover the four manifold seals and discard them; new ones must be used on refitting.

1.8 litre (8-valve) engines with manual transmission

11 Remove the air cleaner-to-throttle housing duct as described in Section 2.

12 Disconnect the accelerator inner cable from the throttle cam, then withdraw the outer cable from the mounting bracket along with its flat washer and spring clip.

13 Depress the retaining clips and disconnect the wiring connectors from the four fuel injectors.

14 Disconnect the wiring connectors from the throttle potentiometer, stepper motor, manifold pressure sensor and inlet air temperature sensor.

15 Bearing in mind the information given in Section 7, disconnect the fuel feed and return hose quick-release fittings, using a small screwdriver to release the locking clips.

16 Slacken the retaining clip(s) and disconnect the braking system vacuum servo unit hose, and all the relevant vacuum/breather hoses, from the manifold. Where necessary, make identification marks on the hoses, to ensure they are correctly reconnected on refitting.

17 Release the retaining clip and free all the disconnected hoses from the clip on the top of the fuel rail.

18 Slacken and remove the bolt securing the dipstick tube to the side of the manifold.

19 Undo the six nuts and bolts securing the manifold to the cylinder head, and remove the

15.29 Disconnecting the inlet manifold breather hoses from the cylinder head cover – 1.8 litre (16-valve) engines

manifold from the engine compartment. Recover the manifold seals and discard them – new ones must be used on refitting.

1.8 litre (8-valve) engines with automatic transmission

20 Remove the air cleaner-to-throttle housing duct as described in Section 2.

21 Disconnect the accelerator inner cable from the throttle cam, then withdraw the outer cable from the mounting bracket along with its flat washer and spring clip. Disconnect the kickdown cable as described in Chapter 7B.

22 Undo the two bolts securing the wiring tray to the top of the manifold, and position the tray, and its associated wiring and hoses, clear of the manifold so that it does not hinder removal.

23 Depress the retaining clips and disconnect the wiring connectors from the four fuel injectors.

24 Disconnect the wiring connectors from the throttle potentiometer, stepper motor, and inlet air temperature sensor.

25 Bearing in mind the information given in Section 7, slacken the retaining clips and disconnect the fuel feed and return hoses from either side of the manifold. Where the original crimped-type Citroën hose clips are still fitted, cut them off and discard them; use standard worm-drive hose clips on refitting.

26 Slacken the retaining clip(s) and disconnect the braking system vacuum servo unit hose, and all the relevant

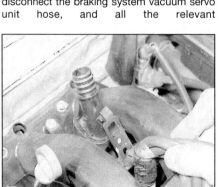

15.31a Unclip the wiring harness from the bracket at the rear of the manifold . . .

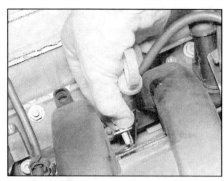

15.30 Slacken and remove the bolt securing the dipstick tube to the rear of the manifold – 1.8 litre (16-valve) engines

vacuum/breather hoses, from the top of the manifold. Where necessary, make identification marks on the hoses, to ensure they are correctly reconnected on refitting.

27 Undo the manifold retaining nuts and withdraw the manifold from the engine compartment. Recover the two manifold seals and discard them – new ones must be used on refitting.

1.8 and 2.0 litre (16-valve) engines

28 Remove the throttle housing as described in Section 12 and the fuel rail and injectors as described in Section 13.

29 Slacken the retaining clip(s), and disconnect the braking system vacuum servo unit hose, and all the relevant vacuum/breather hoses, from the manifold **(see illustration)**. Where necessary, make identification marks on the hoses, to ensure that they are correctly reconnected on refitting.

30 Slacken and remove the bolt securing the dipstick tube to the rear of the manifold **(see illustration)**.

31 Release the wiring loom from the retaining clips and brackets at the rear, and at the timing belt end of the engine **(see illustrations)**.

32 Undo the nuts and bolts securing the manifold to the cylinder head, and move the manifold away from the engine. As it is withdrawn, disconnect the wiring connector from the pressure sensor on the base of the

15.31b . . . and from the timing belt end of the manifold – 1.8 litre (16-valve) engines

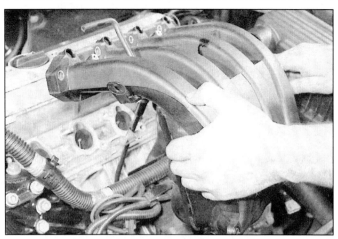

15.32a Withdraw the inlet manifold . . .

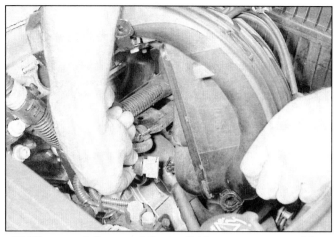

15.32b . . . and disconnect the manifold pressure sensor wiring connector – 1.8 litre (16-valve) engines

manifold **(see illustrations)**. Remove the manifold from the engine compartment.

33 Recover the manifold seals, and discard them – new ones must be used on refitting **(see illustration)**.

Refitting

34 Refitting is a reverse of the relevant removal procedure, noting the following points:

a) *Ensure that the manifold and cylinder head mating surfaces are clean and dry, then locate the new seals in their recesses in the manifold. Refit the manifold and tighten its retaining nuts and bolts to the specified torque.*

b) *Ensure that all relevant hoses are reconnected to their original positions and are securely held (where necessary) by the retaining clips.*

c) *Adjust the accelerator cable as described in Section 3 then, where necessary, adjust the kickdown cable as described in Chapter 7B.*

---

16 Exhaust manifold –
removal and refitting

Removal

1.4 and 1.6 litre engines

1 Disconnect the hot-air intake hose from the manifold shroud and remove it from the vehicle.

2 Slacken and remove the retaining screws, and remove the shroud from the top of the exhaust manifold.

3 Where fitted, remove the secondary air injection valve as described in Chapter 4D, Section 2.

4 Firmly apply the handbrake, then jack up the front of the car and support it securely on axle stands (see *Jacking and vehicle support*).

5 Undo the nuts securing the exhaust front pipe to the manifold, then remove the bolt securing the front pipe to its mounting bracket. Disconnect the front pipe from the manifold, and recover the gasket. Support the front pipe on a block of wood to avoid straining the lambda sensor wiring.

6 Undo the eight retaining nuts securing the manifold to the head. Manoeuvre the manifold out of the engine compartment, and discard the manifold gaskets.

1.8 litre (8-valve) engines

7 Firmly apply the handbrake, then jack up the front of the vehicle and support it on axle stands (see *Jacking and vehicle support*).

8 Undo the two nuts securing the front pipe to the manifold. Recover the springs and spring cups, and withdraw the bolts, then disconnect the front pipe from the manifold, and recover the gasket.

9 Undo the eight retaining nuts securing the manifold to the head. Manoeuvre the manifold out of the engine compartment, complete with the gasket.

10 Undo the two retaining bolts and separate the manifold, intermediate heat shield and gasket, noting the spacers which are fitted between the gasket, heat shield and manifold.

1.8 and 2.0 litre (16-valve) engines

11 Firmly apply the handbrake, then jack up the front of the car and support it securely on axle stands (see *Jacking and vehicle support*).

12 Disconnect the wiring from the lambda sensor or, alternatively, support the exhaust front pipe after disconnection, to avoid any strain being placed on the sensor wiring.

13 Undo the nuts securing the exhaust front pipe to the manifold and recover the springs. Disconnect the front pipe from the manifold, and recover the gasket.

14 Unscrew the nut and remove the bolt securing the engine/transmission rear mounting link to the mounting on the rear of the cylinder block.

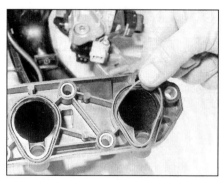

15.33 Recover the seals from the recesses in the manifold – 1.8 litre (16-valve) engines

15 Tilt the engine forward slightly for access to the rear of the cylinder head and support it in this position with a block of wood. Take care not to strain any hoses or wiring.

16 Slacken and remove the five retaining bolts, and remove the shroud from the top of the exhaust manifold.

17 Undo the retaining nuts securing the manifold to the cylinder head. Manoeuvre the manifold upwards out of the engine compartment, and discard the manifold gaskets.

Refitting

18 Refitting is the reverse of the removal procedure, noting the following points:

a) *Examine all the exhaust manifold studs for signs of damage and corrosion; remove all traces of corrosion, and repair or renew any damaged studs.*

b) *Ensure that the manifold and cylinder head sealing faces are clean and flat, and fit the new manifold gasket(s). Tighten the manifold retaining nuts to the specified torque.*

c) *Reconnect the front pipe to the manifold, using the information given in Section 17.*

d) *On 16-valve engines, tighten the engine/transmission rear mounting link nut and bolt to the specified torque.*

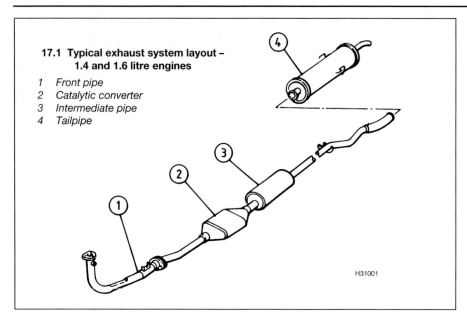

**17.1 Typical exhaust system layout –
1.4 and 1.6 litre engines**

1 Front pipe
2 Catalytic converter
3 Intermediate pipe
4 Tailpipe

H31001

17 Exhaust system – general information, removal and refitting

General information

1 On 1.4 and 1.6 litre engines, the exhaust system consists of four sections: the front pipe, the catalytic converter, the intermediate pipe and centre silencer, and the tailpipe and main silencer **(see illustration)**. All exhaust sections are joined by a flanged joint. The front pipe joints are secured by nuts and bolts, the catalytic converter joint being of the spring-loaded ball type, to allow for movement in the exhaust system. The catalytic converter-to-intermediate pipe joint and the intermediate pipe-to-silencer joint are secured by a clamping ring.

2 On 1.8 and 2.0 litre engines, the exhaust system consists of three sections; the front pipe/catalytic converter, the intermediate pipe and centre silencer, and the tailpipe and main silencer. The front pipe to manifold joint is of the spring-loaded ball type, to allow for movement in the exhaust system and all other joints are secured by a clamping ring.

3 The system is suspended throughout its entire length by rubber mountings.

Removal – 1.4 and 1.6 litre engines

4 Each exhaust section can be removed individually, or alternatively, the complete system can be removed as a unit. Even if only one part of the system needs attention, it is often easier to remove the whole system and separate the sections on the bench.

5 To remove the system or part of the system, first jack up the front or rear of the car and support it on axle stands (see *Jacking and vehicle support*). Alternatively, position the car over an inspection pit or on car ramps.

Front pipe

6 Trace the wiring back from the lambda sensor to its wiring connectors, which are clipped to the transmission housing, and disconnect them from the main harness.

7 Undo the nuts securing the front pipe flange joint to the manifold, and the single bolt securing the front pipe to its mounting bracket. Separate the flange joint and collect the gasket.

8 Slacken and remove the two nuts securing the front pipe flange joint to the catalytic converter, and recover the spring cups and springs. Remove the bolts, then withdraw the front pipe from underneath the vehicle, and recover the wire-mesh gasket **(see illustrations)**.

Catalytic converter

9 Later 1.4 litre engines have a second lambda sensor located 'downstream' of the catalytic converter. On models so equipped, trace the wiring back from the lambda sensor to its wiring connectors, and disconnect them from the main harness

10 Undo the two nuts securing the front pipe flange joint to the catalytic converter. Recover

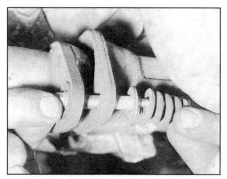

17.8a Remove the fasteners securing the exhaust front pipe to the catalytic converter . . .

the springs and spring cups, and withdraw the bolts.

11 Slacken the catalytic converter clamping ring bolts and disengage the clamp from the flange joint.

12 Free the converter, then withdraw it from underneath the vehicle, and recover the wire-mesh gasket from the front pipe joint.

Intermediate pipe

13 Slacken the clamping ring bolts and disengage the clamps from the front and rear flange joints.

14 Unhook the intermediate pipe from its mounting rubber and remove it from underneath the vehicle.

Tailpipe

15 Slacken the tailpipe clamping ring bolts and disengage the clamp from the flange joint.

16 Unhook the tailpipe from its mounting rubbers and remove it from the vehicle.

Complete system

17 Disconnect the lambda sensor wiring connectors from the main wiring harness.

18 Undo the nuts securing the front pipe flange joint to the manifold, and the single bolt securing the front pipe to its mounting bracket. Separate the flange joint and collect the gasket. Free the system from all its mounting rubbers and lower it from under the vehicle.

Heat shield(s)

19 The heat shields are secured to the underside of the body by various nuts and bolts. Each shield can be removed once the relevant exhaust section has been removed. If a shield is being removed to gain access to a component located behind it, it may prove sufficient in some cases to remove the retaining nuts and/or bolts, and simply lower the shield, without disturbing the exhaust system.

Removal – 1.8 and 2.0 litre engines

20 Each exhaust section can be removed individually, or alternatively, the complete system can be removed as a unit. Even if only

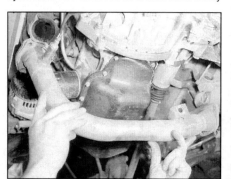

17.8b . . . then withdraw the front pipe from under the vehicle – 1.4 and 1.6 litre engines

one part of the system needs attention, it is often easier to remove the whole system and separate the sections on the bench.

21 To remove the system or part of the system, first jack up the front or rear of the car and support it on axle stands (see *Jacking and vehicle support*). Alternatively, position the car over an inspection pit or on car ramps.

Front pipe/catalytic converter

22 Trace the wiring back from the lambda sensor to its wiring connectors, which are clipped to the transmission housing, and disconnect them from the main harness.

23 Slacken and remove the two nuts securing the front pipe flange joint to the manifold, and recover the spring cups and springs. Remove the bolts, separate the joint and recover the sealing ring.

24 Slacken the catalytic converter clamping ring bolts and disengage the clamp from the flange joint. Withdraw the front pipe/catalytic converter from underneath the vehicle.

Intermediate pipe

25 Slacken the clamping ring bolts and disengage the clamps from the front and rear flange joints.

26 Unhook the intermediate pipe from its mounting rubber and remove it from underneath the vehicle.

Tailpipe

27 Slacken the tailpipe clamping ring bolts and disengage the clamp from the flange joint.

28 Unhook the tailpipe from its mounting rubbers and remove it from the vehicle.

Complete system

29 Disconnect the lambda sensor wiring connectors from the main wiring harness.

30 Slacken and remove the two nuts securing the front pipe flange joint to the manifold, and recover the spring cups and springs. Remove the bolts, separate the joint and recover the sealing ring.

31 Free the system from all its mounting rubbers and lower it from under the vehicle.

Heat shield(s)

32 Refer to paragraph 19.

Refitting – all engines

33 Each section is refitted by reversing the removal sequence, noting the following points:

a) *Ensure that all traces of corrosion have been removed from the flanges and renew all necessary gaskets.*

b) *Inspect the rubber mountings for signs of damage or deterioration, and renew as necessary.*

c) *Prior to assembling the spring-loaded joint, a smear of high-temperature grease should be applied to the joint mating surfaces.*

d) *Where joints are secured together by a clamping ring, apply a smear of exhaust system jointing paste to the flange joint, to ensure a gas-tight seal. Tighten the clamping ring nuts evenly and progressively to the specified torque setting, so that the clearance between the clamp halves remains equal on either side.*

e) *Prior to tightening the exhaust system fasteners, ensure that all rubber mountings are correctly located, and that there is adequate clearance between the exhaust system and vehicle underbody.*

f) *Ensure that the lambda sensor wiring is reconnected correctly and secured to the underbody by the relevant retaining clips.*

Notes

Chapter 4 Part B:
Fuel/exhaust systems – 1.9 litre diesel engines

Contents

Accelerator cable – removal, refitting and adjustment 11
Accelerator pedal – removal and refitting 12
Air cleaner assembly and inlet ducts – removal and refitting 3
Air cleaner filter element renewal . . . . .See Chapter 1B
Electronic control system components –
    testing, removal and refitting 22
Exhaust manifold – removal and refitting 16
Exhaust system – general information and component renewal . . . 21
Fast idle thermostatic sensor – removal, refitting and adjustment . . 4
Fuel filter renewal . . . . .See Chapter 1B
Fuel filter water draining . . . . .See Chapter 1B
Fuel gauge sender and pick-up unit – removal and refitting 13
Fuel injection pump – adjustment 9

Fuel injection pump (DW series engines) – removal and refitting . . . 6
Fuel injection pump (XUD series engines) – removal and refitting . . 5
Fuel injectors – testing, removal and refitting 10
Fuel system – priming and bleeding 2
Fuel tank – removal and refitting 14
General information and precautions 1
Injection timing – checking methods and adjustment 7
Injection timing (XUD series engines) – checking and adjustment . . 8
Inlet manifold – removal and refitting 15
Intercooler – removal and refitting 20
Turbocharger – description and precautions 17
Turbocharger – examination and renovation 19
Turbocharger – removal and refitting 18

Degrees of difficulty

Easy, suitable for novice with little experience	Fairly easy, suitable for beginner with some experience	Fairly difficult, suitable for competent DIY mechanic	Difficult, suitable for experienced DIY mechanic	Very difficult, suitable for expert DIY or professional 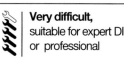

Specifications

General

System type:
  XUD series engines:
    Engine code DJY (XUD9A) . . . . Mechanical fuel injection pump, indirect injection
    Engine code DHY (XUD9TE) . . . . Mechanical fuel injection pump, indirect injection, turbocharger and intercooler
    Engine code DHV (XUD9BSD) . . . . Mechanical fuel injection pump with partial electronic control, indirect injection, 'soft-blown' turbocharger
  DW series engines:
    Engine code WJZ (DW8) . . . . Mechanical fuel injection pump, indirect injection
Firing order . . . . 1-3-4-2 (No 1 at flywheel end)

Injection pump

Type:
  XUD series engines:
    Engine code DJY (XUD9A) . . . . Bosch XUD 211 or Lucas XUD LP05
    Engine code DHY (XUD9TE) . . . . Lucas XUD 110
    Engine code DHV (XUD9BSD) . . . . Bosch VE 4/8
  DW series engines . . . . Bosch VE 4/9 or Lucas DPC
Direction of rotation . . . . Clockwise, viewed from sprocket end
Pump timing:
  Bosch pump – engine code DJY (XUD9A):
    Static timing:
      Engine position . . . . No 4 piston at TDC
      Pump timing measurement . . . . 0.90 ± 0.02 mm
  Bosch pump – engine code DHV (XUD9BSD):
    Static timing:
      Engine position . . . . No 4 piston at TDC
      Pump timing measurement . . . . 0.74 ± 0.02 mm
  Bosch pump – engine code WJZ (DW8):
    Static timing:
      Engine position . . . . No 4 piston at TDC
      Pump timing measurement . . . . 0.58 ± 0.04 mm
  Lucas pump – engine codes DJY (XUD9A), DHY (XUD9TE) and WJZ (DW8):
    Static timing:
      Engine position . . . . No 4 piston at TDC
      Pump position . . . . Value shown on pump – see text
Idle speed:
  XUD series engines:
    Engine codes DJY (XUD9A) and DHY (XUD9TE):
      Without air conditioning . . . . 800 +0 –50 rpm
      With air conditioning . . . . 850 +0 –50 rpm
    Engine code DHV (XUD9BSD) . . . . 875 ± 25 rpm
  DW series engines:
    Bosch fuel injection pump:
      Without air conditioning . . . . 800 ± 25 rpm
      With air conditioning . . . . 875 ± 25 rpm
    Lucas fuel injection pump:
      Without air conditioning . . . . 820 ± 25 rpm
      With air conditioning . . . . 875 ± 25 rpm
Anti-stall speed:
  XUD series engines:
    Engine codes DJY (XUD9A) and DHY (XUD9TE) . . . . 1500 ± 100 rpm
    Engine code DHV (XUD9BSD) . . . . 875 +20 +50 rpm
  DW series engines:
    Bosch fuel injection pump:
      Without air conditioning . . . . 800 +20 +50 rpm
      With air conditioning . . . . 875 +20 +50 rpm
    Lucas fuel injection pump . . . . 1500 rpm
Anti-stall shim thickness:
  XUD series engines:
    Engine codes DJY (XUD9A) and DHY (XUD9TE):
      Bosch fuel injection pump . . . . 3.0 mm
      Lucas fuel injection pump . . . . 4.0 mm
    Engine code DHV (XUD9BSD) . . . . 1.0 mm
  DW series engines:
    Bosch fuel injection pump . . . . 1.0 mm
    Lucas fuel injection pump . . . . 3.0 mm
Fast idle speed:
  XUD series engines:
    Engine codes DJY (XUD9A) and DHY (XUD9TE) . . . . 950 ± 50 rpm
    Engine code DHV (XUD9BSD) . . . . 950 ± 125 rpm
  DW series engines . . . . 950 ± 25 rpm
Maximum speed:
  XUD series engines:
    Engine code DJY (XUD9A) . . . . 5100 ± 80 rpm
    Engine code DHY (XUD9TE) . . . . 5150 ± 125 rpm
    Engine code DHV (XUD9BSD) . . . . 5250 ± 100 rpm
  DW series engines . . . . 5350 ± 125 rpm

Injectors

Type . . . . Pintle
Opening pressure:
    Bosch fuel injection pump:
        Engine code DJY (XUD9A) . . . . 130 ± 10 bars
        Engine code DHV (XUD9BSD) . . . . 165 ± 5 bars
        Engine code WJZ (DW8) . . . . 120 ± 8 bars
    Lucas fuel injection pump:
        Engine code DJY (XUD9A) . . . . 140 bars
        Engine code DHY (XUD9TE) . . . . 150 bars
        Engine code WJZ (DW8) . . . . 142 to 149 bars

Turbocharger

Type . . . . KKK K03, or Garrett GT15
Boost pressure (approximate):
    Engine code DHY (XUD9TE) . . . . 1 bar at 3000 rpm
    Engine code DHV (XUD9BSD) . . . . 0.3 to 0.4 bars at 2000 rpm

Torque wrench settings

	Nm	lbf ft
Exhaust manifold nuts/bolts:		
XUD series engines	25	18
DW series engines	30	22
Fuel pipe union nuts	20	15
Injection pump mounting nuts/bolts	25	18
Injection pump sprocket nut (XUD series engines)	50	37
Injection pump sprocket bolts (DW series engines)	23	17
Injection pump timing hole blanking plug:		
Lucas pump	6	4
Bosch pump	15	11
Injectors to cylinder head	90	66
Turbocharger mounting bolts:		
DHY (XUD9TE engine) models	55	41
DHV (XUD9BSD engine) models	35	26
Turbocharger oil pipe unions	20	15

1 General information and precautions

General information

The fuel system consists of a rear-mounted fuel tank, a fuel filter with integral water separator, a fuel injection pump, injectors and associated components. A turbocharger is fitted to DHY (XUD9TE) and DHV (XUD9BSD) engines, together with an intercooler on the DHY unit.

The exhaust system is conventional, but to meet the latest emission levels an unregulated catalytic converter and an exhaust gas recirculation system are fitted to all models.

Fuel is drawn from the fuel tank to the fuel injection pump by a vane-type transfer pump incorporated in the fuel injection pump. Before reaching the pump, the fuel is heated by coolant flowing through the base of the thermostat/fuel filter housing. The fuel then passes through a fuel filter, where foreign matter and water are removed. Excess fuel lubricates the moving components of the pump, and is then returned to the tank.

The fuel injection pump is driven at half-crankshaft speed by the timing belt. The high pressure required to inject the fuel into the compressed air in the swirl chambers is achieved by a cam plate acting on a single piston on the Bosch pump, or by two opposed pistons forced together by rollers running in a cam ring on the Lucas pump. The fuel passes through a central rotor with a single outlet drilling which aligns with ports leading to the injector pipes.

Fuel metering is controlled by a centrifugal governor, which reacts to accelerator pedal position and engine speed. The governor is linked to a metering valve, which increases or decreases the amount of fuel delivered at each pumping stroke. On turbocharged models, a separate device also increases fuel delivery with increasing boost pressure.

Basic injection timing is determined when the pump is fitted. When the engine is running, it is varied automatically to suit the prevailing engine speed by a mechanism which turns the cam plate or ring.

The four fuel injectors produce a homogeneous spray of fuel into the swirl chambers located in the cylinder head. The injectors are calibrated to open and close at critical pressures to provide efficient and even combustion. Each injector needle is lubricated by fuel, which accumulates in the spring chamber and is channelled to the injection pump return hose by leak-off pipes.

Bosch or Lucas fuel system components may be fitted, depending on engine type. Components from the latter manufacturer are marked either 'Lucas', 'CAV', 'Roto-Diesel' or 'Con-Diesel', depending on their date and place of manufacture. With the exception of the fuel filter assembly, replacement components must be of the same make as those originally fitted.

Cold starting is assisted by preheater or 'glow' plugs fitted to each swirl chamber. Additionally, a thermostatic sensor in the cooling system operates a fast idle lever on the injection pump to increase the idling speed when the engine is cold.

A stop solenoid cuts the fuel supply to the injection pump rotor when the ignition is switched off, and there is also a hand-operated stop lever for use in an emergency.

Provided that the specified maintenance is carried out, the fuel injection equipment will give long and trouble-free service. The injection pump itself may well outlast the engine. The main potential cause of damage to the injection pump and injectors is dirt or water in the fuel.

Servicing of the injection pump and injectors is very limited for the home mechanic, and any dismantling or adjustment other than that described in this Chapter must be entrusted to a Citroën dealer or fuel injection specialist.

Diesel electronic control systems

Primarily to comply with increasingly stringent emission regulations, and to allow an engine immobiliser facility to be incorporated into the vehicle anti-theft system, all Xsara diesel engines utilise electronic control of certain functions. The extent of the electronic control employed depends on the engine type and the territory of export, which largely governs the emission level of the particular engine.

The primary areas where electronic control is used are as follows.

a) *Vehicle anti-theft system.*
b) *Exhaust gas recirculation system.*
c) *Preheating system.*

On all engines, the fuel injection pump stop solenoid is integral with an anti-theft module mounted on the side, or rear, of the injection pump. When the ignition key is removed from the lock, the stop solenoid is permanently de-activated by the anti-theft module, thus immobilising the engine. The engine will remain immobilised until the anti-theft system recognises the insertion of a correctly-coded ignition key in the lock. Further information on the operation of the anti-theft system is contained in Chapter 12.

An exhaust gas recirculation (EGR) system is also fitted to all diesel engines. The EGR system reduces the level of nitrogen oxides produced during combustion by recirculating a proportion of the exhaust gases back into the inlet manifold under certain operating conditions. The operating conditions necessary for exhaust gas recirculation and the sensors supplying the necessary information are as follows.

a) *Engine at normal operating temperature – coolant temperature switch/sensor signal.*
b) *Engine operating under no load or part-load conditions – throttle position switch/sensor signal.*
c) *Engine speed above a specified value – crankshaft sensor signal (certain engines only).*

Details of the EGR system operation are contained in Chapter 4D, Section 3.

The sensors listed above are also used for control of the preheating system, and supply information on engine temperature, and engine speed and load. Details of the preheating system operation are contained in Chapter 5C.

On DHV (XUD9BSD engine) models an electronic control unit (ECU) is used to control the EGR system, the preheating system, and the injection timing of the fuel injection pump. The ECU uses the coolant temperature sensor signal to determine engine temperature, and the crankshaft sensor signal to determine engine speed and position. In addition, information on fuel injector operation is provided by a needle lift sensor incorporated into No 3 fuel injector, and information on throttle position and engine load is provided by a throttle position sensor fitted to the injection pump control lever.

Further information on the various sensors will be found in Section 22.

Precautions

⚠ *Warning: It is necessary to take certain precautions when working on the fuel system components, particularly the fuel injectors. Before carrying out any operations on the fuel system, refer to the precautions given in 'Safety first!' at the beginning of this manual, and to any additional warning notes at the start of the relevant Sections.*

2 Fuel system – priming and bleeding

1 After disconnecting part of the fuel supply system or running out of fuel, it is necessary to prime the system and bleed off any air which may have entered the system components.

2 All engines are fitted with a hand-operated priming pump, consisting of a rubber bulb, or pump plunger. On XUD series engines, the priming pump rubber bulb is located on the right-hand side of the engine compartment **(see illustration)**. On DW series engines, the priming pump plunger is located on the side of the fuel filter assembly at the front of the engine. To gain access, release the clip in the centre of the engine cover and undo the retaining screw on the right-hand side. Remove the engine oil dipstick then lift the cover off the engine.

3 An automatic bleed valve is fitted to certain engines, which bleeds the air from the low pressure circuit when it is primed. On engines without an automatic bleed valve, a bleed screw is fitted to the injection pump fuel inlet pipe union bolt **(see illustration)**. Where a bleed screw is fitted, slacken the screw half a turn.

4 Pump the priming pump bulb or plunger until fuel free from air bubbles emerges from the bleed screw (where fitted), or until resistance is felt. Retighten the bleed screw.

5 Switch on the ignition (to activate the stop solenoid) and continue pumping the priming pump until firm resistance is felt, then pump a few more times.

6 If a large amount of air has entered the pump, place a wad of rag around the fuel return union on the pump (to absorb spilt fuel), then slacken the union. Operate the priming pump (with the ignition switched on to activate the stop solenoid), or crank the engine on the starter motor in 10 second bursts, until fuel free from air bubbles emerges from the fuel union. Tighten the union and mop up split fuel.

⚠ *Warning: Be prepared to stop the engine if it should fire, to avoid excessive fuel spray and spillage.*

7 If air has entered the injector pipes, place wads of rag around the injector pipe unions at the injectors (to absorb spilt fuel), then slacken the unions. Crank the engine on the starter motor until fuel emerges from the unions, then stop cranking the engine and retighten the unions. Mop up spilt fuel. *Refer to the warning given in the previous paragraph.*

8 Start the engine with the accelerator pedal depressed slightly. Additional cranking may be necessary to finally bleed the system before the engine starts.

9 On completion, refit the engine cover and dipstick on DW series engines.

3 Air cleaner assembly and inlet ducts – removal and refitting

General

1 On most models, the air cleaner assembly and air inlet ducting is a complex arrangement of flexible hoses and rigid ducts connecting the air cleaner housing, intercooler and turbocharger, as applicable. The exact arrangement of the ducts and their attachments varies considerably according to ancillary equipment fitted, territory of export, and whether the vehicle is left-hand or right-hand drive.

2 Cold air enters the base of the air cleaner through an inlet duct attached to the front body panel. On non-turbo models, the filtered air then passes to the air distribution housing and/or inlet manifold. On turbo models, the filtered air passes to the turbocharger, where it is compressed, and the compressed air is

2.2 Hand-operated fuel system priming pump on XUD engine models

2.3 Injection pump bleed screw (arrowed) located in the fuel inlet pipe union bolt

3.7 Air cleaner and inlet duct components – DJY (XUD9A engine) models

1 Air cleaner-to-air distribution housing duct
2 Air cleaner housing
3 Air inlet duct
4 Air distribution housing
5 EGR pipe connection
6 EGR vacuum valve
7 EGR solenoid valve

H32230

then fed into the inlet manifold. On DHY (XUD9TE engine) models, the compressed air from the turbocharger passes through an intercooler before being fed into the inlet manifold.

3 The ducts pass over the top and rear of the engine to the inlet and outlet connections on the turbocharger, air distribution housing or inlet manifold. To gain access to the turbocharger connections it will be necessary to jack up the front of the car and support it securely on axle stands (see *Jacking and vehicle support*), and remove the engine undertray.

4 When removing a section of ducting, note the arrangement of any additional cable and hose clips which are often attached to the duct retaining bolts or nuts. In most instances it will also be necessary to disconnect and move aside additional hoses or wiring to allow access to the duct attachments, and to enable the relevant duct to be manipulated from its location. Make notes of any additional components removed or disconnected, as a guide for refitting.

5 When any section of ducting is removed, suitably plug or cover the remaining sections or components, using clean rag, to prevent

any dirt or foreign material from entering. This is particularly important on turbo models, and especially so when the ducts at the turbocharger itself have been disconnected.

6 Where crimped-type hose clips or ties are fitted, cut and discard them and use standard worm-drive hose clips, or new cable ties on refitting.

Air cleaner and inlet ducts – DJY (XUD9A engine) models

Removal

7 Slacken the retaining clips securing the air cleaner to air distribution housing duct in position and undo the duct mounting nut and bolt **(see illustration)**. Disconnect the duct and remove it from the engine. Recover the seal from the air distribution housing.

8 Undo the bolt securing the front of the air inlet duct to the front body panel.

9 Undo the nut securing the base of the air cleaner housing to the support bracket. Lift up the housing and disengage the front locating pegs from the body panel mounting bracket. Withdraw the air cleaner housing and air inlet duct from the engine compartment as an assembly.

Refitting

10 Refitting is a reverse of the removal procedure. Examine the condition of the seals and retaining clips and renew if necessary.

Air distribution housing – DJY (XUD9A engine) models

Removal

11 Slacken the retaining clips and disconnect the air duct and the crankcase breather hose from the front of the air distribution housing.

12 Remove the clip securing the flexible portion of the EGR pipe to the rear of the air distribution housing. If the original crimped clip is still in place, cut it off; new clips are supplied by Citroën parts stockists with a screw clamp fixing. If a screw clamp type clip is fitted, undo the screw and manipulate the clip off the pipe.

13 Unscrew the two bolts securing the housing to the front mounting brackets **(see illustration)**. Recover the spacer plates.

14 Unscrew the four bolts securing the rear of the housing to the inlet manifold. Recover the washers **(see illustration)**.

3.13 Front air distribution housing securing bolt (arrowed) . . .

3.14 . . . and air distribution housing-to-inlet manifold bolts (arrowed) – DJY (XUD9A engine) models

15 Lift the housing from the inlet manifold, and recover the seals.

Refitting

16 Refitting is a reverse of the removal procedure, bearing in mind the following points:
 a) *Check the condition of the four rubber seals and renew as a set if any one shows signs of deterioration.*
 b) *Secure the EGR pipe with a new screw clamp type clip, if a crimped type was initially fitted.*

Air cleaner – DHY (XUD9TE engine) models

Removal

17 Slacken the retaining clip securing the air cleaner-to-turbocharger duct to the top of the air cleaner **(see illustration)**.
18 Undo the retaining nut securing the duct to the battery carrier and release the duct from the top of the air cleaner. Recover the seal from the end of the duct.
19 Undo the nuts securing the air cleaner housing to the support brackets and recover the washers.
20 Firmly apply the handbrake, then jack up the front of the car and support it securely on axle stands (see *Jacking and vehicle support*). Remove the engine undertray.
21 From under the car, slacken the retaining clip and disconnect the air inlet duct from the side of the air cleaner housing, then withdraw the housing from under the car.

Refitting

22 Refitting is a reverse of the removal procedure. Examine the condition of the seals and retaining clips and renew if necessary.

Inlet ducts – DHY (XUD9TE engine) models

Removal

23 To remove the air cleaner air inlet duct, undo the bolt securing the front of the duct to the front body panel.
24 Undo the nuts securing the duct to the support brackets along the side of the air cleaner housing.
25 Firmly apply the handbrake, then jack up the front of the car and support it securely on axle stands (see *Jacking and vehicle support*). Remove the engine undertray.
26 From under the car, slacken the retaining clip and disconnect the air inlet duct from the side of the air cleaner housing, then withdraw the duct upwards from the engine compartment.
27 To remove the air cleaner-to-turbocharger air duct, remove the intercooler as described in Section 20 for improved access.
28 Slacken the retaining clip securing the duct to the top of the air cleaner.
29 Undo the retaining nut securing the duct to the battery carrier and release the duct from the top of the air cleaner. Recover the seal from the end of the duct.
30 Undo the two stud bolts securing the duct at the rear of the cylinder head.
31 From under the car, slacken the retaining

clip securing the lower end of the duct to the turbocharger.
32 Release the lower end of the duct, then work it upwards from its location.
33 When access permits, slacken the retaining clip and disconnect the ventilation hose, then remove the duct as an assembly from the engine compartment.
34 To remove the turbocharger-to-intercooler air duct, slacken the clips securing the ends of the duct to the turbocharger and intercooler.
35 Manipulate the duct upwards and out of the engine compartment.

Refitting

36 Refitting is a reverse of the removal procedure. Examine the condition of the seals and retaining clips and renew if necessary.

Air cleaner – DHV (XUD9BSD engine) models

Removal

37 Slacken the retaining clip and disconnect the flexible air duct from the air cleaner housing lid.
38 Undo the bolt securing the front of the air inlet duct to the front body panel.
39 Undo the nut securing the base of the air cleaner housing to the support bracket. Lift up the housing and disengage the front locating pegs from the body panel mounting bracket. Withdraw the air cleaner housing and air inlet duct from the engine compartment as an assembly.

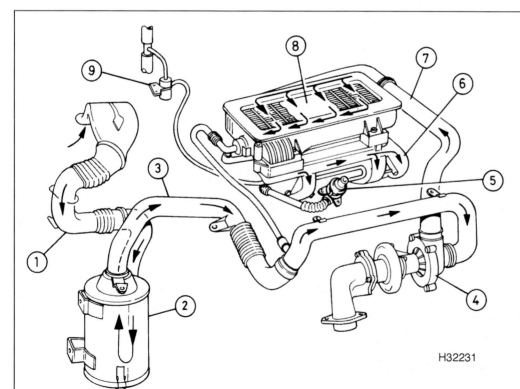

3.17 Air cleaner and inlet duct components – DHY (XUD9TE engine) models

1 Air inlet duct
2 Air cleaner housing
3 Air cleaner-to-turbocharger duct
4 Turbocharger
5 EGR vacuum valve
6 Inlet manifold
7 Turbocharger-to-intercooler duct
8 Intercooler
9 EGR solenoid valve

Arrows indicate direction of air flow

H32231

Refitting

40 Refitting is a reverse of the removal procedure. Examine the condition of the retaining clips and renew if necessary.

Inlet ducts – DHV (XUD9BSD engine) models

Removal

41 To remove the air cleaner-to-turbocharger inlet duct, slacken the retaining clip and disconnect the flexible air duct from the air cleaner housing lid **(see illustration)**.
42 Slacken the retaining clip and disconnect the crankcase ventilation hose from the oil separator on the right-hand side of the rigid upper duct.
43 Undo the two bolts securing the rigid upper duct to the inlet manifold.
44 Firmly apply the handbrake, then jack up the front of the car and support it securely on axle stands (see *Jacking and vehicle support*). Remove the engine undertray.
45 From under the car, slacken the retaining clip securing the lower end of the duct to the turbocharger.
46 Release the lower end of the duct, then work it upwards from its location and remove the duct as an assembly from the engine compartment.
47 To remove the turbocharger-to-inlet manifold duct at the rear of the engine, first remove the air cleaner to turbocharger inlet duct as described previously.
48 Slacken the retaining clips securing the upper end of the duct to the throttle valve housing, and the lower end to the turbocharger.
49 Undo the bolts securing the rear of the duct to the manifold and support bracket.
50 Release the upper and lower ends of the

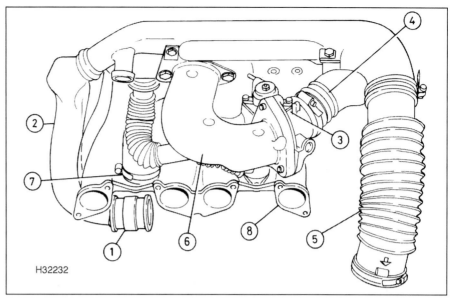

3.41 Air inlet duct components – DHV (XUD9BSD engine) models

1   Air duct turbocharger connection
2   Air cleaner-to-turbocharger rigid duct
3   Throttle valve housing
4   Turbocharger-to-inlet manifold duct upper connection
5   Air cleaner-to-turbocharger flexible duct
6   Air inlet elbow
7   Turbocharger-to-inlet manifold duct lower connection
8   Inlet manifold

duct, then work it upwards from its location and remove the duct as an assembly from the engine compartment.
51 To remove the throttle valve housing and air inlet elbow, slacken the retaining clip and remove the air duct from the throttle valve housing.
52 Disconnect the vacuum hose from the throttle valve actuator.

53 Undo the bolts securing the air inlet elbow to the inlet manifold and lift off the elbow and throttle valve housing as an assembly.

Refitting

54 Refitting is a reverse of the removal procedure. Examine the condition of any applicable seals and retaining clips and renew if necessary.

Air cleaner – WJZ (DW8 engine) models

Removal

55 Slacken the retaining clip and disconnect the flexible air duct from the air cleaner housing lid **(see illustration)**.
56 Undo the bolt securing the front of the air inlet duct to the front body panel.
57 Undo the nut securing the base of the air cleaner housing to the support bracket. Lift up the housing and disengage the front locating pegs from the body panel mounting bracket. Withdraw the air cleaner housing and air inlet duct from the engine compartment as an assembly.

Refitting

58 Refitting is a reverse of the removal procedure. Examine the condition of the retaining clips and renew if necessary.

Inlet duct and resonator – WJZ (DW8 engine) models

Removal

59 Release the clip in the centre of the engine cover and undo the retaining screw on the right-hand side. Remove the engine oil dipstick then lift the cover off the engine.

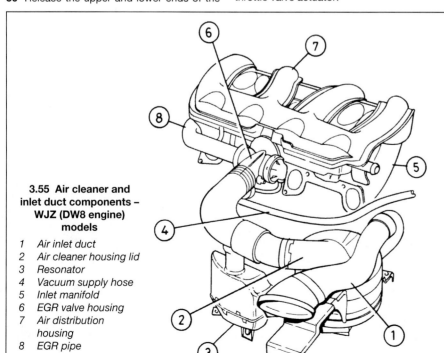

3.55 Air cleaner and inlet duct components – WJZ (DW8 engine) models

1   Air inlet duct
2   Air cleaner housing lid
3   Resonator
4   Vacuum supply hose
5   Inlet manifold
6   EGR valve housing
7   Air distribution housing
8   EGR pipe

60 Slacken the retaining clips and disconnect the inlet duct from the air cleaner housing lid, and from the EGR valve housing. Undo the retaining bolt at the base of the resonator and withdraw the inlet duct and resonator from the engine as an assembly.

Refitting

61 Refitting is a reverse of the removal procedure. Examine the condition of the retaining clips and renew if necessary.

Air distribution housing – WJZ (DW8 engine) models

Removal

62 Release the clip in the centre of the engine cover and undo the retaining screw on the right-hand side. Remove the engine oil dipstick then lift the cover off the engine.
63 Slacken the retaining clip and disconnect the inlet duct from the EGR valve housing. Disconnect the wiring connector and vacuum hose from the EGR valve.
64 Remove the clip securing the flexible portion of the EGR pipe to the side of the EGR valve housing. If the original crimped clip is still in place, cut it off; new clips are supplied by Citroën parts stockists with a screw clamp fixing. If a screw clamp type clip is fitted, undo the screw and manipulate the clip off the pipe.
65 Slacken the retaining clip and disconnect the crankcase ventilation hose from the left-hand side of the air distribution housing.
66 Unscrew the two bolts securing the front of the air distribution housing to the mounting brackets. Recover the washers.
67 Unscrew the two bolts securing the rear of the housing to the inlet manifold. Recover the washers.
68 Lift the housing from the inlet manifold, and recover the four O-ring seals.

Refitting

69 Refitting is a reverse of the removal procedure, bearing in mind the following points:
  a) Check the condition of the four O-ring seals and renew as a set if any one shows signs of deterioration.
  b) Secure the EGR pipe with a new screw clamp type clip, if a crimped type was initially fitted.

4 Fast idle thermostatic sensor – removal, refitting and adjustment

Removal

Note: *A new sealing washer (where applicable) must be used when refitting the sensor.*

1 The thermostatic sensor is located in the side of the thermostat/fuel filter housing.
2 On DHY (XUD9TE engine) turbo models remove the intercooler, on DJY (XUD9A engine) models, remove the air distribution housing, and on WJZ (DW8 engine) models, remove the engine cover and the air cleaner assembly and air inlet ducts. On all other models, depending on equipment fitted, remove the air inlet ducts and/or breather hoses as necessary for access. Refer to the relevant Sections of this Chapter for further information.
3 Drain the cooling system as described in Chapter 1B.
4 Loosen the clamp screw or nut (as applicable), and disconnect the fast idle cable end fitting from the inner cable at the fuel injection pump fast idle lever **(see illustration)**.
5 Slide the cable from the adjustment screw located in the bracket on the fuel injection pump **(see illustration)**.
6 Using a suitable open-ended spanner, unscrew the thermostatic sensor from the thermostat/fuel filter housing, and withdraw the sensor complete with the cable **(see illustration)**. Recover the sealing washer, where applicable.

Refitting

7 If sealing compound was originally used to fit the sensor in place of a washer, thoroughly clean all traces of old sealing compound from the sensor and housing. Ensure that no traces of sealant are left in the internal coolant passages of the housing.
8 Fit the sensor, using suitable sealing compound or a new washer as applicable, and tighten it securely.
9 Insert the adjustment screw into the bracket on the fuel injection pump, and screw on the locknut finger-tight.

10 Insert the inner cable through the fast idle lever, and position the end fitting on the cable, but do not tighten the clamp screw or nut (as applicable).
11 Adjust the cable as described in the following paragraphs.

Adjustment

12 With the engine cold, push the fast idle lever fully towards the flywheel end of the engine. Tighten the clamp screw or nut with the cable end fitting touching the lever.
13 Adjust the screw to ensure that the fast idle lever is touching its stop, then tighten the locknut.
14 Measure the exposed length of the inner cable.
15 Refit the components removed for access to the sensor, with reference to the relevant Sections of this Chapter.
16 Refill the cooling system as described in Chapter 1B, and run the engine to its normal operating temperature.
17 Check that the fast idle cable is slack. If not, it is likely that the sensor is faulty.
18 With the engine hot, check that there is approximately 6.0 mm of free play in the cable; This indicates that the thermostatic sensor is functioning correctly.
19 Check that the engine speed increases when the fast idle lever is pushed towards the flywheel end of the engine. With the lever against its stop, the fast idle speed should be as specified (See Section 9 for fast idle adjustment details).
20 Stop the engine.

5 Fuel injection pump (XUD series engines) – removal and refitting

Caution: Be careful not to allow dirt into the injection pump or injector pipes during this procedure. New sealing rings should be used on the fuel pipe banjo unions when refitting.

Removal

1 Prior to removing the injection pump, the engine immobiliser function of the vehicle anti-theft system must be deactivated. This

4.4 Fast idle cable end fitting clamp nut (arrowed) – Lucas pump

4.5 Sliding the fast idle cable from the adjustment screw – Bosch pump

4.6 Fast idle thermostatic sensor (arrowed)

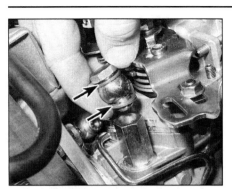

5.9a Disconnecting the fuel pump fuel supply banjo union. Note sealing washers (arrowed) – Bosch pump

5.9b Refitting the fuel supply banjo bolt with a small section of fuel hose (arrowed) to prevent dirt entry – Bosch pump

5.10 Injection pump fuel return pipe banjo union (arrowed) – Bosch pump

will allow the pump to be serviced or bench-tested if required. To deactivate the system, proceed as follows:

a) *Open the bonnet.*

b) *Lower the driver's window then switch off the ignition (where applicable) and leave the car.*

c) *Close the driver's door then reach through the open window and switch on the ignition.*

d) *Wait for the electronic immobiliser warning lamp on the instrument panel to extinguish, then switch off the ignition.*

e) *Disconnect the electronic immobiliser unit wiring connector at the rear of the injection pump. Note that this must be done within five minutes of switching off the ignition.*

2 Disconnect the battery negative terminal (refer to *Disconnecting the battery* in the Reference Section of this manual).

3 Cover the components below the injection pump with a plastic bag, or plastic sheets as a precaution against spillage of diesel fuel.

4 On DHY (XUD9TE engine) turbo models remove the intercooler, and on DJY (XUD9A engine) models, remove the air distribution housing. On all models, depending on equipment fitted, remove the air inlet ducts and/or breather hoses as necessary for access. Refer to the relevant Sections of this Chapter for further information.

5 Chock the rear wheels and release the handbrake. Jack up the front right-hand corner of the vehicle until the wheel is just clear of the ground. Support the vehicle on an axle stand

(see Jacking and vehicle support) and engage the 4th or 5th gear. This will enable the engine to be turned easily by turning the right-hand wheel.

6 Remove the upper timing belt covers with reference to Chapter 2C.

7 Disconnect the accelerator cable from the fuel injection pump, with reference to Section 11.

8 Disconnect the fast idle cable from the fuel injection pump, with reference to Section 4.

9 Loosen the clip, or undo the banjo union, and disconnect the fuel supply hose. Recover the sealing washers from the banjo union, where applicable. Cover the open end of the hose, and refit and cover the banjo bolt to keep dirt out **(see illustrations)**.

10 Disconnect the main fuel return pipe and the injector leak-off return pipe banjo union **(see illustration)**. Recover the sealing washers from the banjo union. Again, cover

the open end of the hose and the banjo bolt to keep dirt out. Take care not to get the inlet and outlet banjo unions mixed up.

11 Disconnect all relevant wiring from the pump. Note that on certain pumps, this can be achieved by simply disconnecting the wiring connectors at the brackets on the pump **(see illustration)**. On some pumps, it will be necessary to disconnect the wiring from the individual components (some connections may be protected by rubber covers).

12 Unscrew the union nuts securing the injector pipes to the fuel injection pump and injectors. Counterhold the unions on the pump, while unscrewing the pipe-to-pump union nuts. Remove the pipes as a set. Cover open unions to keep dirt out, using small plastic bags, or fingers cut from clean rubber gloves **(see illustrations)**.

5.11 Disconnecting a fuel injection pump wiring plug – Bosch pump

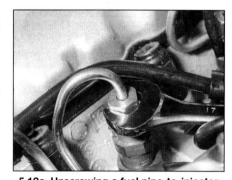

5.12a Unscrewing a fuel pipe-to-injector union

5.12b Cover the open end of the injector to prevent dirt entry

5.12c Unscrewing a fuel pipe-to-pump union – Bosch pump

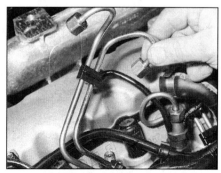

5.12d Removing a fuel pipe assembly

5.14 Bolts inserted through timing holes in injection pump sprocket

5.15 Mark the injection pump in relation to the mounting bracket (arrowed)

13 Turn the crankshaft until the two bolt holes in the fuel injection pump sprocket are aligned with the corresponding holes in the engine front plate.

14 Insert two M8 bolts through the holes, and hand-tighten them. Note that the bolts retain the sprocket while the fuel injection pump is removed, thereby making it unnecessary to remove the timing belt **(see illustration)**.

15 Mark the fuel injection pump in relation to the mounting bracket, using a scriber or felt tip pen **(see illustration)**. This will ensure the correct pump timing is retained when refitting.

16 Unscrew the three front mounting nuts, and recover the washers. Unscrew and remove the rear mounting nut and bolt, noting the locations of the washers, and support the injection pump on a block of wood **(see illustrations)**.

17 Release the injection pump sprocket from the pump shaft, as described in Chapter 2C, Section 8. Note that the sprocket can be left engaged with the timing belt as the pump is withdrawn from its mounting bracket. Refit the M8 bolts to retain the sprocket in position while the pump is removed.

18 Carefully withdraw the pump. Recover the Woodruff key from the end of the pump shaft if it is loose, and similarly recover the bush from the rear of the mounting bracket.

Refitting

19 Commence refitting the injection pump by fitting the Woodruff key to the shaft groove (if removed).

20 Offer the pump to the mounting bracket,

5.16a Unscrewing an injection pump front mounting nut – Bosch pump

and support it on a block of wood, as during removal.

21 Engage the pump shaft with the sprocket, and refit the sprocket as described in Chapter 2C, Section 8. Ensure that the Woodruff key does not fall out of the shaft as the sprocket is engaged.

22 Align the marks made on the pump and mounting bracket before removal. If a new pump is being fitted, transfer the mark from the old pump to give an approximate setting.

23 Refit and lightly tighten the pump mounting nuts and bolt.

24 Set up the injection timing, as described in Sections 7 and 8.

25 Refit and reconnect the injector fuel pipes.

26 Reconnect all relevant wiring to the pump.

27 Reconnect the fuel supply and return hoses, and tighten the unions, as applicable. Use new sealing washers on the banjo unions.

28 Reconnect the fast idle cable as described in Section 4, but wait until the injection pump refitting procedure is completed before carrying out the cable adjustment procedure.

29 Reconnect and adjust the accelerator cable with reference to Section 11.

30 Refit the upper timing belt covers.

31 Lower the vehicle to the ground.

32 Refit the intercooler, air distribution housing, air cleaner and air inlet ducts as applicable.

33 Remove the plastic bag or cover placed below the pump to protect against fuel spillage.

34 Reconnect the battery negative terminal.

5.16b Unscrewing an injection pump rear mounting nut (arrowed) – Bosch pump

35 Bleed the fuel system as described in Section 2.

36 Adjust the fast idle cable as described in Section 4, then start the engine, and check the fuel injection pump adjustments as described in Section 9.

6 Fuel injection pump (DW series engines) – removal and refitting

Caution: Be careful not to allow dirt into the injection pump or injector pipes during this procedure. New sealing rings should be used on the fuel pipe banjo unions when refitting.

Removal

1 Release the clip in the centre of the engine cover and undo the retaining screw on the right-hand side. Remove the engine oil dipstick then lift the cover off the engine.

2 Prior to removing the injection pump, the engine immobiliser function of the vehicle anti-theft system must be deactivated. This will allow the pump to be serviced or bench-tested if required. To deactivate the system, proceed as follows:

a) *Lower the driver's window then switch off the ignition (where applicable) and leave the car.*

b) *Close the driver's door then reach through the open window and switch on the ignition.*

c) *Wait for the electronic immobiliser warning lamp on the instrument panel to extinguish, then switch off the ignition.*

d) *Disconnect the electronic immobiliser unit wiring connector at the rear of the injection pump. Note that this must be done within five minutes of switching off the ignition.*

3 Disconnect the battery negative terminal (refer to *Disconnecting the battery* in the Reference Section of this manual).

4 Remove the air inlet ducts and the air distribution housing as described in Section 3.

5 Cover the components below the injection pump with a plastic bag, or plastic sheets as a precaution against spillage of diesel fuel.

6 Disconnect the fuel supply and return hose quick-release fittings using a small screwdriver to release the locking clip. Cover the open unions to prevent dirt entry, using small plastic bags, or fingers cut from clean rubber gloves.

7 Remove the timing belt as described in Chapter 2D. After removal of the timing belt, temporarily refit the right-hand engine mounting.

8 Unscrew and remove the three bolts securing the injection pump sprocket to the pump hub and remove the sprocket.

9 Disconnect the wiring connectors at the rear of the injection pump.

10 Disconnect the accelerator cable from the fuel injection pump, with reference to Section 11.

11 Disconnect the fast idle cable from the fuel injection pump, with reference to Section 4.

12 Where applicable, undo the banjo union and disconnect the remaining fuel hose from the injection pump. Recover the sealing washers from the banjo union. Suitably cover the open union, and refit and cover the banjo bolt to prevent dirt entry.

13 Unscrew the union nuts securing the injector pipes to the fuel injection pump and injectors. Counterhold the unions on the pump, while unscrewing the pipe-to-pump union nuts. Remove the pipes as a set and suitably cover the open unions to prevent dirt entry.

14 Unscrew the three front mounting bolts, and recover the washers. Unscrew and remove the rear mounting nut and bolt, noting the locations of the washers, and carefully withdraw the pump. Recover the bush from the rear of the mounting bracket

Refitting

15 Locate the pump on the mounting bracket, and refit the rear mounting bolt washers and nut. Refit the three front mounting bolts and washers then tighten all the mountings to the specified torque.

16 Refit and reconnect the injector fuel pipes.

17 Reconnect all relevant wiring to the pump.

18 Reconnect the fast idle cable as described in Section 4, but wait until the injection pump refitting procedure is completed before carrying out the cable adjustment procedure.

19 Reconnect and adjust the accelerator cable with reference to Section 11.

20 Position the injection pump sprocket on the hub and refit the three retaining bolts. Tighten the bolts hand tight only at this stage.

21 Refit the timing belt as described in Chapter 2D.

22 Reconnect the fuel supply and return hoses, and tighten the unions, as applicable. Use new sealing washers on the banjo unions.

23 Remove the plastic bag or cover placed below the pump to protect against fuel spillage.

24 Refit the air distribution housing and air inlet ducts as described in Section 3.

25 Lower the vehicle to the ground.

26 Reconnect the battery negative terminal.

8.3 Removing the injection pump timing inspection plug – Lucas pump

27 Bleed the fuel system as described in Section 2.

28 Adjust the fast idle cable as described in Section 4, then start the engine, and check the fuel injection pump adjustments as described in Section 9.

29 Refit the engine cover on completion.

7 Injection timing – checking methods and adjustment

XUD series engines

1 Checking the injection timing is not a routine operation, and should only be necessary after the injection pump has been disturbed.

2 The static timing procedure described in this Chapter must be carried out carefully to be accurate. A dial test indicator will be needed, with probes and adaptors appropriate to the type of injection pump. Read through the procedures before starting work, to find out what is involved.

DW series engines

3 Both types of fuel injection pump (Bosch and Lucas) are fitted to the DW engine by means of non-adjustable mountings. This means that the static injection timing is fixed and cannot be adjusted by rotating the pump body with respect to the engine. The only way of checking that the timing is correct is to set the engine to TDC, as described in Chapter 2D, Section 3. In this position, the timing hole in the injection pump sprocket hub should line up with a corresponding hole in the injection pump body, allowing the fitment of a sprocket locking tool. Misalignment of the timing holes means that the timing belt has been incorrectly fitted.

4 If you suspect that the injection timing is

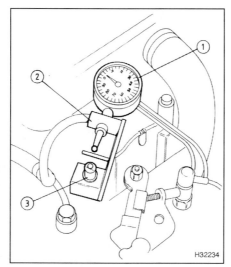

8.4 Citroën injection pump timing dial gauge (1), mounting bracket (2) and timing probe (3) in position on the injection pump

incorrect (because of excessive smoke, noisy combustion, poor performance or heavy fuel consumption, for example) there may be a fault with the injection pump. Have the car inspected by a Citroën dealer or diesel injection specialist, who will have the equipment needed to check the injection pump timing dynamically (ie, whilst the engine is running).

8 Injection timing (XUD series engines) – checking and adjustment

Caution: The maximum engine speed and transfer pressure settings, together with timing access plugs, are sealed by the manufacturers at the factory using locking wire and lead seals. Do not disturb the wire if the vehicle is still within the warranty period otherwise the warranty will be invalidated. Also do not attempt the timing procedure unless accurate instrumentation is available. Suitable special tools for carrying out pump timing should be available from larger motor factors or your Citroën dealer. Refer to the precautions given in Section 1 of this Chapter before proceeding.

Lucas injection pump

Note: *To check the injection pump timing a special timing probe and mounting bracket (Citroën tool No 4093-TJ) is required. Without access to this piece of equipment, injection pump timing should be entrusted to a Citroën dealer or other suitably-equipped specialist.*

1 If the injection timing is being checked with the pump in position on the engine unit, rather than as part of the pump refitting procedure, disconnect the battery negative terminal (refer to *Disconnecting the battery* in the Reference Section of this manual), and cover the alternator with a clean cloth or plastic bag to prevent the possibility of fuel being spilt onto it. Remove the injector pipes as described in Sections 5 or 6 as applicable.

2 Referring to Chapter 2C, Section 3, align the engine assembly/valve timing holes to lock the crankshaft in position. Remove the crankshaft locking tool, then turn the crankshaft **backwards** (anti-clockwise) approximately a quarter of a turn.

3 Unscrew the access plug from the guide on the top of the pump body and recover the sealing washer **(see illustration)**. Insert the special timing probe (Citroën tool No 4093-TJ) into the guide, making sure it is correctly seated against the guide sealing washer surface. **Note:** *The timing probe must be seated against the guide sealing washer surface and not the upper lip of the guide for the measurement to be accurate.*

4 Mount the bracket on the pump guide (Citroën tool No 4093-TJ) and securely mount the dial gauge (dial test indicator) in the bracket so that its tip is in contact with the bracket linkage **(see illustration)**. Position the

8.6 Pump timing values marked on label (1) and tag (2) – Lucas pump

dial gauge so that its plunger is at the mid-point of its travel and zero the gauge.

5 Rotate the crankshaft slowly in the correct direction of rotation (clockwise) until the crankshaft locking tool can be re-inserted.

6 With the crankshaft locked in position read the dial gauge; the reading should correspond to the value marked on the pump (there is a tolerance of ± 0.04 mm). The timing value may be marked on a label on the top of the pump, or alternatively on a tag attached to the pump control lever **(see illustration)**.

7 If adjustment is necessary, slacken the front pump mounting nuts and the rear mounting bolt, then slowly rotate the pump body until the point is found where the specified reading is obtained on the dial gauge. When the pump is correctly positioned, tighten both its front mounting nuts and the rear bolt to their specified torque settings.

8 Withdraw the timing probe slightly, so that it is positioned clear of the pump rotor dowel, and remove the crankshaft locking pin. Rotate the crankshaft through one and three quarter rotations in the normal direction of rotation.

9 Slide the timing probe back into position ensuring that it is correctly seated against the guide sealing washer surface, not the upper lip, then zero the dial gauge.

10 Rotate the crankshaft slowly in the correct direction of rotation until the crankshaft locking tool can be re-inserted. Recheck the timing measurement.

11 If adjustment is necessary, slacken the pump mounting nuts and bolt and repeat the operations in paragraphs 7 to 10.

12 When the pump timing is correctly set, remove the dial gauge and mounting bracket and withdraw the timing probe.

13 Refit the screw and sealing washer to the guide and tighten it securely.

14 If the procedure is being carried out as part of the pump refitting sequence, proceed as described in Section 5.

15 If the procedure is being carried out with the pump fitted to the engine, refit the injector pipes tightening their union nuts to the specified torque setting. Reconnect the battery, then bleed the fuel system – see Section 2. Start the engine and adjust the idle speed and anti-stall speeds as described in Section 9.

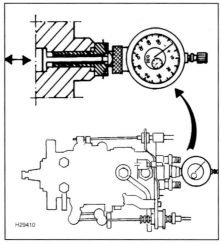

8.23 Dial test indicator and timing probe for use with Bosch pump

Bosch injection pump

Note: *A dial test indicator, a probe and an adaptor will be required for this procedure. If the Citroën tools cannot be obtained, suitable alternatives to fit a range of Bosch fuel injection pumps can be purchased from most motor factors or diesel injection specialists.*

16 If the injection timing is being checked with the pump in position on the engine unit, rather than as part of the pump refitting procedure, disconnect the battery negative terminal (refer to *Disconnecting the battery* in the Reference Section of this manual), and cover the alternator with a clean cloth or plastic bag to prevent the possibility of fuel being spilt onto it.

17 On non-turbo models, remove the air inlet duct between the air distribution housing and the air cleaner assembly as described in Section 3.

18 Remove the injector pipes as described in Section 5 or 6 as applicable.

19 Disconnect the wiring connectors at the rear of the injection pump.

20 Slacken the clamp screw and/or nut (as applicable) and slide the fast idle cable end fitting arrangement along the cable so that it is no longer in contact with the pump fast idle lever (ie, so the fast idle lever returns to its stop) (see Section 4).

21 Referring to Chapter 2C, Section 3, align the engine assembly/valve timing holes to lock the crankshaft in position. Remove the crankshaft locking tool, then turn the crankshaft **backwards** (anti-clockwise) approximately a quarter of a turn.

22 Unscrew the access screw, situated in the centre of the four injector pipe unions, from the rear of the injection pump. As the screw is removed, position a suitable container beneath the pump to catch any escaping fuel. Mop up any spilt fuel with a clean cloth.

23 Screw the adaptor (Citroën tool No 7010-T) into the rear of the pump and attach the probe (Citroën tool No 5003-TD) to the dial gauge. Mount the dial gauge and probe in

the adaptor **(see illustration)**. If access to the special Citroën tools cannot be gained, suitable alternatives can be purchased from most good motor factors. Position the dial gauge so that its plunger is at the mid-point of its travel and securely tighten the adaptor locknut.

24 Slowly rotate the crankshaft back and forth whilst observing the dial gauge, to determine when the injection pump piston is at the bottom of its travel (BDC). When the piston is correctly positioned, zero the dial gauge.

25 Rotate the crankshaft slowly in the correct direction of rotation until the crankshaft locking tool can be re-inserted.

26 The reading obtained on the dial gauge should be equal to the specified pump timing measurement given in the Specifications at the start of this Chapter. If adjustment is necessary, slacken the front and rear pump mounting nuts and bolts and slowly rotate the pump body until the point is found where the specified reading is obtained. When the pump is correctly positioned, tighten both its front and rear mounting nuts and bolts securely.

27 Rotate the crankshaft through one and three quarter rotations in the normal direction of rotation. Find the injection pump piston BDC as described in paragraph 24 and zero the dial gauge.

28 Rotate the crankshaft slowly in the correct direction of rotation until the crankshaft locking tool can be re-inserted (bringing the engine back to TDC). Recheck the timing measurement.

29 If adjustment is necessary, slacken the pump mounting nuts and bolts and repeat the operations in paragraphs 26 to 28.

30 When the pump timing is correctly set, unscrew the adaptor and remove the dial gauge and probe.

31 Refit the screw and sealing washer to the pump and tighten it securely.

32 If the procedure is being carried out as part of the pump refitting sequence, proceed as described in Section 5.

33 If the procedure is being carried out with the pump fitted to the engine, refit the injector pipes tightening their union nuts to the specified torque setting. Where applicable, refit the air inlet duct, then reconnect the battery and bleed the fuel system as described in Section 2.

34 Start the engine and adjust the idle speed and anti-stall speeds as described in Section 9. Also adjust the fast idle cable as described in Section 4.

9 Fuel injection pump – adjustment

1 The usual type of tachometer (rev counter), which works from ignition system pulses, cannot be used on diesel engines. A diagnostic socket is provided for the use of

Citroën test equipment, but this will not normally be available to the home mechanic. For the following adjustments to be accurately carried out, it will be necessary to purchase or hire an appropriate tachometer, or entrust the work to a Citroën dealer or other suitably-equipped specialist.

2 Before making adjustments, warm up the engine to normal operating temperature. Make sure that the accelerator cable and fast idle cables are correctly adjusted as described in Sections 11 and 4 respectively.

3 On WJZ (DW8 engine) models, release the clip in the centre of the engine cover and undo the retaining screw on the right-hand side. Remove the engine oil dipstick then lift the cover off the engine.

Lucas fuel injection pump

4 With the engine idling, place a shim of the correct thickness (see *Specifications*), between the pump control lever and the anti-stall adjustment screw **(see illustration)**.

5 Push the manual stop lever back against its stop, and hold it in position by inserting a 3.0 mm diameter rod/drill through the hole in the fast idle lever.

6 The engine speed should be as specified for the anti-stall speed.

7 If adjustment is necessary, loosen the locknut, turn the anti-stall adjustment screw as required, then tighten the locknut.

8 Remove the rod/drill and the shim, and check that the engine is idling at the specified idle speed.

9 If adjustment is necessary, loosen the locknut on the idle speed adjustment screw. Turn the screw as required, and retighten the locknut.

10 Move the pump control lever to increase the engine speed to approximately 3000 rpm, then quickly release the lever. The deceleration period should be between 2.5 and 3.5 seconds, and the engine speed should drop to approximately 50 rpm below idle.

11 If the deceleration is too fast and the engine stalls, unscrew the anti-stall adjustment screw a quarter-turn towards the control lever. If the deceleration is too slow, resulting in poor engine braking, turn the screw a quarter-turn away from the lever.

12 Retighten the locknut after making an

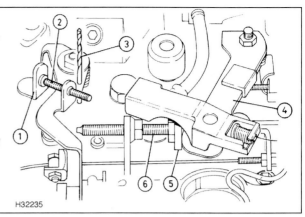

9.4 Lucas fuel injection pump adjustment details

1   Manual stop lever
2   Idle speed adjustment screw
3   Drill bit inserted in fast idle lever
4   Pump control lever
5   Shim inserted between pump control lever and anti-stall adjustment screw
6   Anti-stall adjustment screw

adjustment. Recheck the idle speed, and adjust if necessary as described previously.

13 With the engine idling, check the operation of the manual stop control by turning the stop lever clockwise **(see illustration 9.4)**. The engine must stop instantly.

14 Where applicable, disconnect the tachometer on completion.

15 With all the previously described adjustments completed, check the adjustment of the throttle position switch located on the pump control lever as follows.

16 Working at the fuel injection pump end of the accelerator cable, make a mark on the inner cable, 11.0 mm from the end of the outer cable **(see illustration 9.21)**.

17 Have an assistant depress the accelerator pedal until the mark on the inner cable is

aligned with the end of the outer cable. With the cable in this position, the throttle position switch contacts should just open.

18 If adjustment is necessary, check that the mark on the inner cable is still aligned with the outer cable end, then slacken the screw securing the plastic operating cam to the pump control lever **(see illustration)**.

19 Move the operating cam until the switch contacts open, then tighten the securing screw.

20 Disconnect the tachometer and where applicable, refit the engine cover on completion.

Bosch fuel injection pump

21 Loosen the locknut, and unscrew the anti-stall adjustment screw until it is clear of the pump control lever **(see illustration)**.

22 Start the engine and allow it to idle. If the

9.18 Throttle position switch operating cam retaining screw (arrowed) – Lucas pump

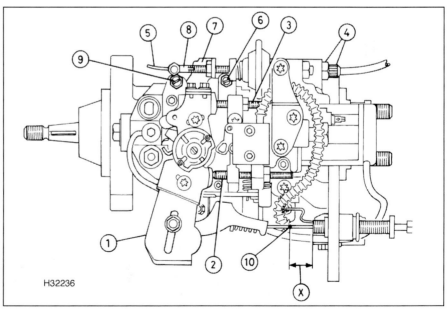

9.21 Bosch fuel injection pump adjustment details

1	Pump control lever	7	Fast idle lever
2	Maximum speed adjustment screw	8	Fast idle cable end fitting
3	Anti-stall adjustment screw	9	Fast idle adjustment screw
4	Fast idle cable adjustment screw and locknut	10	Mark to be made on accelerator cable for throttle position switch adjustment
5	Fast idle cable		$X = 11.0$ mm
6	Idle speed adjustment screw		

idle speed is incorrect, loosen the locknut and turn the idle speed adjustment screw as required, then retighten the locknut.

23 Insert a shim or feeler blade of the correct thickness between the pump control lever and the anti-stall adjustment screw.

24 The engine speed should be as specified for the anti-stall speed.

25 If adjustment is necessary, loosen the locknut and turn the anti-stall adjustment screw as required. Retighten the locknut.

26 Remove the shim or feeler blade and allow the engine to idle.

27 Slacken the locknut and unscrew the control lever damper adjustment screw, located on the rear of the lever, and insert a 2.0 mm shim or feeler blade between the damper rod and adjustment screw. Make sure the pump control lever is in the idle position then turn the adjustment screw so that the feeler blade/shim is a light, sliding fit between the screw and damper rod. Hold the screw in this position, and tighten its locknut.

28 Move the fast idle lever fully towards the flywheel end of the engine, and check that the engine speed increases to the specified fast idle speed. If necessary, loosen the locknut and turn the fast idle adjusting screw as required, then retighten the locknut.

29 With the engine idling, check the operation of the manual stop control by turning the stop lever. The engine must stop instantly.

30 Disconnect the tachometer on completion.

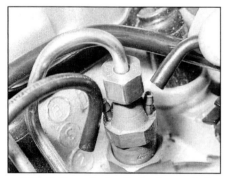

10.5 Pulling a leak-off pipe from a fuel injector

31 With all the previously described adjustments completed, check the adjustment of the throttle position switch located on the pump control lever as follows.

32 Working at the fuel injection pump end of the accelerator cable, make a mark on the inner cable, 11.0 mm from the end of the outer cable.

33 Have an assistant depress the accelerator pedal until the mark on the inner cable is aligned with the end of the outer cable. With the cable in this position, the throttle position switch contacts should just open.

34 If adjustment is necessary, check that the mark on the inner cable is still aligned with the outer cable end, then slacken the two switch retaining screws.

35 Turn the switch body until the contacts open and tighten the retaining screws.

36 Where applicable, refit the engine cover on completion.

10 Fuel injectors – testing, removal and refitting

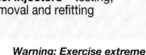

⚠ **Warning: Exercise extreme caution when working on the fuel injectors. Never expose the hands or any part of the body to injector spray, as the high working pressure can cause the fuel to penetrate the skin, with possibly fatal results. You are strongly advised to have any work which involves testing the injectors under pressure carried out by a dealer or fuel injection specialist.**

Testing

1 Injectors do deteriorate with prolonged use, and it is reasonable to expect them to need reconditioning or renewal after 60 000 miles (100 000 km) or so. Accurate testing, overhaul and calibration of the injectors must be left to a specialist. A defective injector which is causing knocking or smoking can be located without dismantling as follows.

2 Run the engine at a fast idle. Slacken each injector union in turn, placing rag around the union to catch spilt fuel, and being careful not

to expose the skin to any spray. When the union on the defective injector is slackened, the knocking or smoking will stop.

Removal

Note: *To remove the injector fitted with the needle lift sensor on DHV (XUD9BSD engine) models, a suitable slotted socket will be required to allow clearance for the sensor wire. These sockets are available from Citroën dealers (as a special tool) or from diesel injection specialists.*

3 On DHY (XUD9TE engine) turbo models, remove the intercooler, on DJY (XUD9A engine) models, remove the air distribution housing, and on WJZ (DW8 engine) models, remove the air inlet ducts and the air distribution housing. On all other models, depending on equipment fitted, remove the air inlet ducts and/or breather hoses as necessary for access. Refer to the relevant Sections of this Chapter for further information.

4 Carefully clean around the injectors and injector pipe union nuts.

5 Pull the leak-off pipes from the injectors **(see illustration)**. Where applicable, disconnect the injector needle lift sensor wiring connector.

6 Unscrew the union nuts securing the injector pipes to the fuel injection pump. Counterhold the unions on the pump when unscrewing the nuts. Cover open unions to prevent dirt entry, using small plastic bags, or fingers cut from clean rubber gloves.

7 Unscrew the union nuts and disconnect the pipes from the injectors **(see illustration)**. If necessary, the injector pipes may be completely removed. Note carefully the locations of the pipe clamps, for use when refitting. Cover the ends of the injectors, to prevent dirt entry.

8 Unscrew the injectors using a deep socket or box spanner, and remove them from the cylinder head **(see illustration)**.

9 On XUD series engines, recover the copper washers and fire seal washers from the cylinder head. Also recover the sleeves if they are loose **(see illustrations)**. On DW series engines, recover the copper washers.

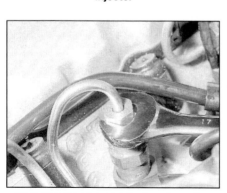

10.7 Unscrewing an injector pipe union nut

10.8 Unscrew the injectors, and remove them from the cylinder head

10.9a Removing a fuel injector copper washer . . .

10.9b . . . fire seal washer . . .

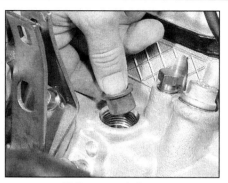

10.9c . . . and sleeve

Refitting

10 Obtain new copper washers and, where applicable, fire seal washers. Also renew the sleeves, if they are damaged.

11 Take care not to drop the injectors, or allow the needles at their tips to become damaged. The injectors are precision-made to fine limits, and must not be handled roughly. In particular, never mount them in a bench vice.

12 Commence refitting by inserting the sleeves (if removed) into the cylinder head, followed by the fire seal washers (convex face uppermost), and copper washers, as applicable.

13 Insert the injectors and tighten them to the specified torque.

14 Refit the injector pipes and tighten the union nuts. Make sure the pipe clamps are in their previously-noted positions. If the clamps are wrongly positioned or missing, problems may be experienced with pipes breaking or splitting.

15 Reconnect the leak-off pipes and, where applicable, the injector needle lift sensor wiring connector.

16 Refit the components removed for access with reference to the relevant Sections of this Chapter..

17 Start the engine. If difficulty is experienced, bleed the fuel system as described in Section 2.

11 Accelerator cable – removal, refitting and adjustment

Removal

1 On WJZ (DW8 engine) models, release the clip in the centre of the engine cover and undo the retaining screw on the right-hand side. Remove the engine oil dipstick then lift the cover off the engine.

2 Operate the pump control lever on the fuel injection pump, and release the inner cable from the lever **(see illustration)**.

3 Pull the outer cable from the grommet in the fuel injection pump bracket **(see illustration)**. Slide the flat washer off the end of the cable, and remove the spring clip.

4 Release the cable from the remaining clips and brackets in the engine compartment, noting its routing.

5 Working in the passenger compartment, reach up under the facia, depress the ends of the cable end fitting, and detach the inner cable from the top of the accelerator pedal.

6 Release the outer cable grommet from the pedal mounting bracket, then tie a length of string to the end of the cable.

7 Return to the engine compartment, release the cable grommet from the bulkhead and withdraw the cable. When the end of the cable appears, untie the string and leave it in position – it can then be used to draw the cable back into position on refitting.

Refitting

8 Tie the string to the end of the cable, then use the string to draw the cable into position through the bulkhead. Once the cable end is visible, untie the string, then fit the outer cable grommet into the pedal bracket, and push the inner cable end fitting into position in the pedal.

9 From within the engine compartment, ensure the outer cable is correctly seated in the bulkhead grommet, then work along the cable, securing it in position with the retaining clips and ties, and ensuring that the cable is correctly routed.

10 Slide the flat washer onto the cable end and refit the spring clip.

11 Pass the outer cable through its injection pump mounting bracket grommet, and

reconnect the inner cable to the pump control lever. Adjust the cable as described below.

Adjustment

12 Remove the spring clip from the accelerator outer cable. Ensuring that the control lever is against its stop, gently pull the cable out of its grommet until all free play is removed from the inner cable.

13 With the cable held in this position, refit the spring clip to the last exposed outer cable groove in front of the rubber grommet and washer. When the clip is refitted and the outer cable is released, there should be only a small amount of free play in the inner cable.

14 Have an assistant depress the accelerator pedal, and check that the control lever opens fully and returns smoothly to its stop.

15 Where applicable, refit the engine cover.

12 Accelerator pedal – removal and refitting

Refer to Chapter 4A, Section 4, but adjust the accelerator cable as described above.

13 Fuel gauge sender and pick-up unit – removal and refitting

1 The fuel gauge sender and pick-up unit is located in the same position as the fuel pump on petrol models and the removal and refitting procedures are virtually identical. Refer to Chapter 4A, Section 8.

2 On completion, bleed the fuel system as described in Section 2.

14 Fuel tank – removal and refitting

Refer to Chapter 4A, Section 10.

11.2 Releasing the accelerator inner cable from the lever on the injection pump

11.3 Pulling the accelerator outer cable from the bracket

15.14 Withdrawing the inlet manifold from the cylinder head – DHY (XUD9TE engine) models

16.6 Exhaust manifold securing nuts (arrowed) on turbo engines – viewed with engine removed for clarity

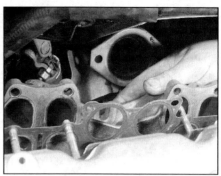

16.7 Lifting the exhaust manifold and gasket from the cylinder head

15 Inlet manifold – removal and refitting

Removal

Note: *Renew the manifold gaskets when refitting.*

DJY (XUD9A engine) and WJZ (DW8 engine) models

1 Disconnect the battery negative terminal (refer to *Disconnecting the battery* in the Reference Section of this manual).
2 Remove the air inlet duct and air distribution housing as described in Section 3.
3 Undo the six nuts securing the manifold flanges to the cylinder head, and the single hexagonal bolt from the centre flange. Recover the washers from the manifold studs, where fitted.
4 Withdraw the manifold from the cylinder head and collect the three gaskets.

DHV (XUD9BSD engine) models

5 Disconnect the battery negative terminal (refer to *Disconnecting the battery* in the Reference Section of this manual).
6 Refer to Chapter 4D, Section 3, and remove the exhaust gas recirculation (EGR) valve from the exhaust manifold.
7 Undo the six nuts securing the manifold flanges to the cylinder head, and the single hexagonal bolt from the centre flange. Recover the washers from the manifold studs, where fitted.
8 Withdraw the manifold from the cylinder head and collect the three gaskets.

DHY (XUD9TE engine) models

9 Disconnect the battery negative terminal (refer to *Disconnecting the battery* in the Reference Section of this manual).
10 Remove the intercooler as described in Section 20.
11 Release the hose clips and disconnect the air inlet hoses from the air duct connecting the turbocharger to the air cleaner housing. Manipulate the air duct from the inlet manifold, and remove it from the engine compartment. Place a wad of clean rag into

the open end of the turbocharger air hose (or the turbocharger itself, if the hose has been removed completely), to prevent the possibility of dirt entry. Also release the securing clip, and remove the intercooler air hose from the turbocharger.
12 Refer to Chapter 4D, Section 3, and remove the exhaust gas recirculation (EGR) valve from the exhaust manifold.
13 Undo the six nuts securing the manifold flanges to the cylinder head, and the single hexagonal bolt from the centre flange. Recover the washers from the manifold studs, where fitted.
14 Withdraw the manifold from the cylinder head and collect the three gaskets **(see illustration)**.

Refitting

15 Refitting is a reversal of removal, bearing in mind the following points.
a) *Renew the gaskets when refitting the manifold.*
b) *Ensure that all fixings and attachments are securely tightened.*
c) *Ensure that all relevant hoses and pipes are correctly reconnected and routed.*

16 Exhaust manifold – removal and refitting

Removal

Note: *Renew the manifold gaskets when refitting.*

1 Remove the inlet manifold as described in Section 15.
2 On non-turbo models, disconnect the catalytic converter from the manifold, with reference to Section 21.
3 On turbo models, remove the turbocharger as described in Section 18. Note that on DHV (XUD9BSD engine) models the exhaust manifold is removed as part of the turbocharger removal procedure.
4 On certain models, it may be necessary to unbolt the resonator chamber from the manifold, to allow sufficient clearance for the manifold to be removed.

5 On DJY (XUD9A engine) models, remove the exhaust gas recirculation (EGR) valve from the exhaust manifold. On WJZ (DW8 engine) models, undo the two bolts and release the EGR supply pipe from the exhaust manifold.
6 Unscrew the six exhaust manifold securing nuts, and recover the spacers (where fitted) from the studs **(see illustration)**.
7 Lift the exhaust manifold from the cylinder head, and recover the gaskets **(see illustration)**.
8 It is possible that some of the manifold studs may be unscrewed from the cylinder head when the manifold securing nuts are unscrewed. In this event, the studs should be screwed back into the cylinder head once the manifolds have been removed, using two manifold nuts locked together.

Refitting

9 Refitting is a reversal of removal, bearing in mind the following points.
a) *Renew the manifold gaskets on refitting.*
b) *Refit the turbocharger as described in Section 18 or reconnect the catalytic converter to the manifold as described in Section 21, as appropriate.*
c) *Refit the inlet manifold as described in Section 15.*
d) *Tighten all fixings to the specified torque, where applicable.*
e) *Ensure that all relevant hoses and pipes are correctly reconnected and routed.*

17 Turbocharger – description and precautions

Description

1 A turbocharger is fitted to some engines. It increases engine efficiency by raising the pressure in the inlet manifold above atmospheric pressure. Instead of the air simply being sucked into the cylinders, it is forced in. Additional fuel is supplied by the injection pump in proportion to the increased air intake.
2 Energy for the operation of the turbocharger comes from the exhaust gas.

The gas flows through a specially-shaped housing (the turbine housing) and in so doing, spins the turbine wheel. The turbine wheel is attached to a shaft, at the end of which is another vaned wheel known as the compressor wheel. The compressor wheel spins in its own housing, and compresses the inlet air on the way to the inlet manifold.

3 On DHY (XUD9TE engine) models, between the turbocharger and the inlet manifold, the compressed air passes through an intercooler. This is an air-to-air heat exchanger, mounted over the engine, and supplied with cooling air ducted through the bonnet insulation. The purpose of the intercooler is to remove some of the heat gained in being compressed from the inlet air. Because cooler air is denser, removal of this heat further increases engine efficiency.

4 Boost pressure (the pressure in the inlet manifold) is limited by a wastegate, which diverts the exhaust gas away from the turbine wheel in response to a pressure-sensitive actuator.

5 The turbo shaft is pressure-lubricated by an oil feed pipe from the main oil gallery. The shaft 'floats' on a cushion of oil. A drain pipe returns the oil to the sump.

Precautions

6 The turbocharger operates at extremely high speeds and temperatures. Certain precautions must be observed to avoid premature failure of the turbo, or injury to the operator.

7 Do not operate the turbo with any of its parts exposed, or with any of its hoses removed. Foreign objects falling onto the rotating vanes could cause excessive damage, and (if ejected) personal injury.

8 Do not race the engine immediately after start-up, especially if it is cold. Give the oil a few seconds to circulate.

9 Always allow the engine to return to idle speed before switching it off – do not blip the throttle and switch off, as this will leave the turbo spinning without lubrication.

10 Allow the engine to idle for several minutes before switching off after a high-speed run.

11 Observe the recommended intervals for oil and filter changing, and use a reputable oil of the specified quality. Neglect of oil changing, or use of inferior oil, can cause carbon formation on the turbo shaft, leading to subsequent failure.

18 Turbocharger – removal and refitting

Removal

DHY (XUD9TE engine) models

1 Remove the inlet manifold as described in Section 15.

18.2 Disconnecting the oil feed pipe from the turbocharger – DHY (XUD9TE engine) models

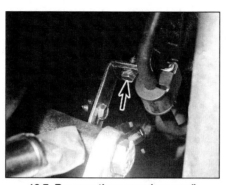

18.7 Remove the screw (arrowed) securing the oil feed pipe – DHY (XUD9TE engine) models

2 Unscrew the union nut, and disconnect the oil feed pipe from the top of the turbocharger (see illustration).

3 Apply the handbrake, then jack up the front of the vehicle and support securely on axle stands (see Jacking and vehicle support).

4 Carefully prise the three gearchange selector link rod balljoints off the two transmission levers and the fixed bracket.

5 Disconnect the catalytic converter from the turbocharger, with reference to Section 21.

6 Loosen the securing clips, and remove the hose connecting the turbocharger oil return

18.8b . . . and withdraw the oil feed pipe – DHY (XUD9TE engine) models

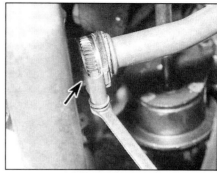

18.6 Remove the turbocharger oil return hose (arrowed) from the pipe on the cylinder block – DHY (XUD9TE engine) models

18.8a Unscrew the union nut . . .

pipe to the pipe on the cylinder block (see illustration).

7 Remove the screw securing the oil feed pipe to the support bracket at the rear of the cylinder block (see illustration).

8 Unscrew the union nut securing the oil feed pipe to the cylinder block, then withdraw the oil feed pipe from above the engine (see illustrations).

9 Remove the filter from the cylinder block end of the oil feed pipe (where fitted), and examine it for contamination (see illustration). Clean or renew if necessary.

10 Working under the vehicle, unscrew and

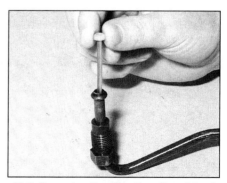

18.9 Removing the filter from the oil feed pipe – DHY (XUD9TE engine) models

18.10 Turbocharger lower securing bolts (arrowed) – viewed from underneath – DHY (XUD9TE engine) models

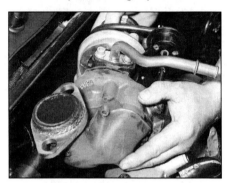

18.12 Withdrawing the turbocharger – DHY (XUD9TE engine) models

remove the two lower turbocharger securing bolts **(see illustration)**.

11 Support the turbocharger, then remove the upper turbocharger securing bolt, and recover the spacer **(see illustration)**.

12 Carefully manipulate the turbocharger out through the top of the engine compartment **(see illustration)**. If it is to be refitted, store the turbocharger carefully, and plug its openings to prevent dirt entry.

DHV (XUD9BSD engine) models

13 Remove the inlet manifold as described in Section 15.

14 Unscrew the union nut, and disconnect the oil feed pipe from the top of the turbocharger.

15 Apply the handbrake, then jack up the front of the vehicle and support securely on

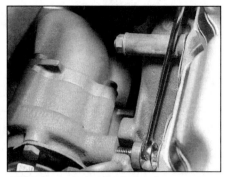

18.11 Unscrewing the turbocharger upper securing bolt DHY – (XUD9TE engine) models

axle stands (see *Jacking and vehicle support*).

16 Disconnect the catalytic converter from the turbocharger, with reference to Section 21.

17 Remove the screw securing the oil feed pipe to the support bracket at the rear of the cylinder block.

18 Unscrew the union nut securing the oil feed pipe to the cylinder block, then withdraw the oil feed pipe from above the engine.

19 Undo the two bolts and separate the oil return pipe flange from the turbocharger. Recover the flange gasket.

20 Undo the upper retaining bolt and lower nut securing the support bracket to the turbocharger and cylinder block. Remove the washers and withdraw the bracket.

21 Undo the two turbocharger lower mounting bolts.

22 Slacken the turbocharger upper mounting bolt and manipulate the turbocharger away from the exhaust manifold. Temporarily support the turbocharger in this position.

23 Unscrew the six exhaust manifold securing nuts, and recover the spacers, where fitted, from the studs.

24 Working from above, withdraw the exhaust manifold from the studs and lift it up and out of the engine compartment. Collect the manifold gaskets from the studs.

25 The turbocharger can now be lifted out from behind the engine, through the top of the engine compartment. If it is to be refitted, store the turbocharger carefully, and plug its openings to prevent dirt entry.

Refitting

26 Refitting is a reversal of removal, bearing in mind the following points:
  a) If a new turbocharger is being fitted, change the engine oil and filter. Also renew the filter in the oil feed pipe.
  b) Prime the turbocharger with clean engine oil through the oil feed pipe union before reconnecting the union.
  c) Do not fully tighten the oil feed pipe unions until both ends of the pipe are in place. When tightening the oil return pipe union, position it so that the return hose is not strained.

19 Turbocharger – examination and renovation

1 With the turbocharger removed, inspect the housing for cracks or other visible damage.

2 Spin the turbine or the compressor wheel, to verify that the shaft is intact and to feel for excessive shake or roughness. Some play is normal, since in use the shaft is 'floating' on a film of oil. Check that the wheel vanes are undamaged.

3 If the exhaust or induction passages are oil-contaminated, the turbo shaft oil seals have probably failed. (On the induction side, this will also have contaminated the intercooler – where fitted, which should if necessary be flushed with solvent.)

4 No DIY repair of the turbo is possible. A new unit may be available on an exchange basis.

20 Intercooler – removal and refitting

Removal

1 Slacken the retaining clip and disconnect the hose from the front edge of the intercooler **(see illustration)**.

2 Slacken the retaining clips and disconnect the hoses from the valve on the left-hand side of the intercooler. Similarly, disconnect the air inlet duct on the right-hand side **(see illustrations)**.

20.1 Disconnect the hose (arrowed) from the front edge of the intercooler

20.2a Detach the hoses (arrowed) from the valve on the left-hand side of the intercooler . . .

20.2b . . . and the air inlet duct from the right-hand end of the intercooler

20.3 Lift the upper seal from the top of the intercooler

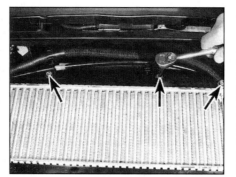

20.4a Unscrew the three upper securing bolts (arrowed) . . .

20.4b . . . and the two front securing bolts . . .

3 Lift off the intercooler upper seal for access to the retaining bolts **(see illustration)**.
4 Unscrew the three rear, and two front retaining bolts and lift the intercooler off the engine **(see illustrations)**. Recover the seal between the intercooler outlet and the inlet manifold.

Refitting

5 Refitting is a reversal of removal.

21 Exhaust system – general information and component renewal

General information

1 According to model, the exhaust system consists of either two or three sections. Three section systems consist of a catalytic converter, an intermediate pipe, and a tailpipe. On two section systems, the catalytic converter and intermediate pipe are combined to form a single section.
2 On all models, the catalytic converter-to-manifold joint is of the spring-loaded ball type, to allow for movement in the exhaust system, and the other joints are secured by clamping rings.
3 The system is suspended throughout its entire length by rubber mountings.

Removal

4 Each exhaust section can be removed individually, or alternatively, the complete system can be removed as a unit. Even if only one part of the system needs attention, it is often easier to remove the whole system and separate the sections on the bench.
5 To remove the system or part of the system, first jack up the front or rear of the car, and support it on axle stands (see *Jacking and vehicle support*). Alternatively, position the car over an inspection pit, or on car ramps.

Catalytic converter

6 Slacken the catalytic converter clamping ring bolts, and disengage the clamp from the flange joint.
7 Slacken and remove the two nuts securing

the catalytic converter to the manifold, and recover the spring cups and springs **(see illustrations)**. Withdraw the bolts and remove the catalytic converter from underneath the vehicle. Recover the wire-mesh gasket from the manifold joint.

Intermediate pipe

8 Slacken the clamping ring bolts, and disengage both clamps from the flange joints.
9 Release the pipe from its mounting rubber and remove it from underneath the vehicle.

Tailpipe

10 Slacken the tailpipe clamping ring bolts, and disengage the clamp from the flange joint.
11 Unhook the tailpipe from its mounting rubbers, and remove it from the vehicle.

Complete system

12 Slacken and remove the two nuts securing the catalytic converter flange joint to the manifold, and recover the spring cups and springs. Remove the bolts, then free the system from its mounting rubbers and remove it from underneath the vehicle. Recover the wire-mesh gasket from the manifold joint.

Heat shield(s)

13 The heat shields are secured to the underside of the body by various nuts and bolts. Each shield can be removed once the relevant exhaust section has been removed. If a shield is being removed to gain access to a component located behind it, it may prove

20.4c . . . and remove the intercooler

sufficient in some cases to remove the retaining nuts and/or bolts, and simply lower the shield, without disturbing the exhaust system.

Refitting

14 Each section is refitted by reversing the removal sequence, noting the following points:
a) *Ensure that all traces of corrosion have been removed from the flanges, and renew all necessary gaskets.*
b) *Inspect the rubber mountings for signs of damage or deterioration, and renew as necessary.*
c) *Prior to assembling the spring-loaded joint, a smear of high-temperature grease should be applied to the joint mating surfaces.*
d) *On joints secured together by a clamping*

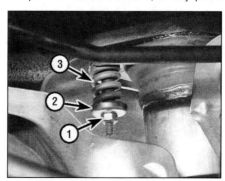

21.7a Catalytic converter-to-turbocharger securing nut (1), spring seat (2) and spring (3) – viewed from underneath vehicle

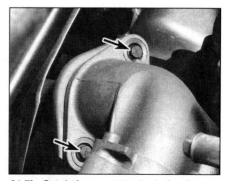

21.7b Catalytic converter-to-turbocharger securing bolts (arrowed) – viewed from engine compartment

ring, apply a smear of exhaust system jointing paste to the flange joint, to ensure a gas-tight seal. Tighten the clamping ring nuts evenly and progressively, so that the clearance between the clamp halves remains equal on either side.

e) Prior to tightening the exhaust system fasteners, ensure that all rubber mountings are correctly located, and that there is adequate clearance between the exhaust system and vehicle underbody.

22 Electronic control system components – testing, removal and refitting

General information

1 All diesel engines covered in this Chapter utilise electronic control of certain functions. The number and type of sensors, actuators and associated components used on a particular engine depends on the engine type, territory of export and emission level. The following information is therefore provided as a general guide to the components that may be encountered, according to engine type.

Electronic Control Unit (ECU)

2 An ECU is used on DHV (XUD9BSD engine) models to control the injection timing, preheater glow plug operation and the exhaust gas recirculation system. The ECU receives signals from sensors, which monitor engine coolant temperature, engine speed, fuel injector operation and engine load. These signals are used by the ECU to control the previously mentioned system functions.

Crankshaft sensor

3 This is an inductive pulse generator bolted to the transmission bellhousing, to scan a reference ridge on the flywheel. As the ridge passes the sensor tip, a signal is generated, which is used by the ECU, or the EGR system, to determine engine speed. The crankshaft sensor is used on all engines.

Coolant temperature sensor/switch

4 The coolant temperature sensor is an NTC (Negative Temperature Coefficient) thermistor – that is, a semi-conductor whose electrical resistance decreases as its temperature increases. The sensor supplies a constantly-varying (analogue) voltage signal, corresponding to the temperature of the engine coolant. The sensor is used for control of the EGR system and preheating system and, on DHV (XUD9BSD engine) models, is also used to refine the calculations made by the ECU when determining fuel metering. On some models, the sensor consists simply of a switch whose internal contacts close once a predetermined coolant temperature has been attained.

Throttle position switch

5 The throttle position switch is fitted to all except DHV (XUD9BSD engine) models, and is located on the top of the injection pump,

attached to the pump control lever. The switch contacts close when the pump control lever has moved through a set distance, thus providing an engine load signal for the EGR and preheating systems.

Throttle position sensor

6 The throttle position sensor is used on DHV (XUD9BSD engine) models, and is located on the top of the injection pump, attached to the pump control lever. The unit consists of a potentiometer whose resistance varies according to accelerator position. From this information, the ECU can regulate the fuel injection timing according to driver input and engine load.

Injector needle lift sensor

7 The needle lift sensor, used on DHV (XUD9BSD engine) models, is an integral part of No 3 fuel injector, and sends a signal to the ECU whenever the injector opens.

Preheating system control unit

8 This unit is fitted to all models and operates the preheating system glow plugs during cold starting conditions. On DHV (XUD9BSD engine) models, the unit is controlled by the ECU.

EGR valves

9 Introduction of part of the exhaust gas back into the inlet manifold is controlled by an EGR solenoid valve and EGR vacuum valve. Vacuum from the engine vacuum pump is directed to the EGR solenoid valve. When the solenoid valve is actuated (depending on coolant temperature and engine load or speed) the vacuum is diverted to the vacuum valve, thus opening the valve.

Testing

10 If a fault appears in the system, first ensure all the system wiring connectors are securely connected and free of corrosion. Ensure the fault is not due to poor maintenance; ie, check that the air cleaner filter element is clean, the cylinder compression pressures are correct, and that the engine breather hoses are clear and undamaged, referring to Chapters 1B, 2C and 2D for further information.

11 If these checks fail to reveal the cause of the problem, the vehicle should be taken to a suitably-equipped Citroën dealer for testing. A wiring block connector is incorporated in the engine management circuit, into which a special electronic diagnostic tester can be plugged. The tester will locate the fault quickly and simply, alleviating the need to test all the system components individually, which is a time-consuming operation that also carries a risk of damaging the ECU (where fitted).

Removal and refitting

General

12 Before disconnecting any of these components, disconnect the battery negative terminal (refer to *Disconnecting the battery* in the Reference Section of this manual).

ECU

Note 1: *The ECU is fragile. Take care not to drop it or subject it to any other kind of*

impact, and do not subject it to extremes of temperature, or allow it to get wet.
Note 2: *If a new ECU is to be fitted, this work must be entrusted to a Citroën dealer. It is necessary to initialise the new ECU after installation, which requires the use of dedicated Citroën diagnostic equipment.*

13 The ECU is located in the plastic box which forms part of the rear of the battery mounting tray.

14 Unclip the cover over the ECU, then lift the retaining clip and disconnect the ECU wiring connector.

15 Undo the retaining nuts or bolts and lift the ECU from the battery tray.

16 Refitting is a reversal of removal ensuring the wiring connector is securely reconnected.

Crankshaft sensor

17 The crankshaft sensor is situated on the front face of the transmission clutch housing.

18 Trace the wiring back from the sensor to the wiring connector, and disconnect it from the main harness.

19 Prise out the rubber grommet then undo the retaining bolt and withdraw the sensor from the transmission.

20 Refitting is reversal of removal, ensuring that the sensor retaining bolt is securely tightened and the grommet is correctly seated in the transmission housing.

Coolant temperature sensor/switch

21 Refer to Chapter 3, Section 6.

Throttle position switch

22 The throttle position switch is fitted to the top of the fuel injection pump. To gain access to the switch on WJZ (DW8 engine) models, release the clip in the centre of the engine cover and undo the retaining screw on the right-hand side. Remove the engine oil dipstick then lift the cover off the engine.

23 Disconnect the switch wiring connector at the rear of the injection pump and release the connector and wiring from the clips and bracket on the pump.

24 Undo the two screws and remove the switch from the top of the pump.

25 Refitting is reversal of removal, but before tightening the retaining screws, adjust the switch position as described in Section 9.

Throttle position sensor

26 The throttle position sensor is fitted to the top of the fuel injection pump. Although it can be individually removed, Citroën test equipment is required to adjust the sensor position when refitting. Any removal and refitting of this component should therefore be entrusted to a Citroën dealer.

Injector needle lift sensor

27 The needle lift sensor is an integral part of No 3 fuel injector. Fuel injector removal and refitting procedures are contained in Section 10.

Preheating system control unit

28 Refer to Chapter 5C.

EGR valves

29 Refer to Chapter 4D, Section 3.

Chapter 4 Part C:
Fuel/exhaust systems – 2.0 litre diesel engines

Contents

Accelerator cable – removal, refitting and adjustment 5
Accelerator pedal – removal and refitting 6
Accumulator rail – removal and refitting 11
Air cleaner assembly and inlet ducts – removal and refitting 4
Air cleaner filter element renewal . . . . .See Chapter 1B
Electronic control system components – testing,
   removal and refitting 13
Exhaust manifold – removal and refitting 15
Exhaust system – general information and component renewal . . . 18
Fuel filter renewal . . . . .See Chapter 1B
Fuel filter water draining . . . . .See Chapter 1B

Fuel gauge sender unit – removal and refitting 8
Fuel injectors – removal and refitting 12
Fuel lift pump – removal and refitting 7
Fuel system – priming and bleeding 3
Fuel tank – removal and refitting 9
General information and system operation 1
High pressure Diesel injection system – special information 2
High pressure fuel pump – removal and refitting 10
Inlet manifold – removal and refitting 14
Turbocharger – description and precautions 16
Turbocharger – removal, inspection and refitting 17

Degrees of difficulty

Easy, suitable for novice with little experience	**Fairly easy,** suitable for beginner with some experience 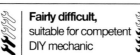	**Fairly difficult,** suitable for competent DIY mechanic	**Difficult,** suitable for experienced DIY mechanic	**Very difficult,** suitable for expert DIY or professional

Specifications

General

System type	HDi (High pressure Diesel injection) with full electronic control, direct injection and turbocharger
Designation	Bosch EDC 15
Firing order	1-3-4-2 (No 1 at flywheel end)
Fuel system operating pressure	1350 bars

High pressure fuel pump

Type	Bosch CP 1
Direction of rotation	Clockwise, viewed from sprocket end

Injectors

Type	Electromagnetic

Turbocharger

Type	Garrett GT15 or KKK K03
Boost pressure (approximate)	1 bar at 3000 rpm

Torque wrench settings

	Nm	lbf ft
Accumulator rail mounting bolts	23	17
Exhaust manifold nuts	20	15
Exhaust system fasteners:		
Catalytic converter-to-manifold nuts	10	7
Clamping ring nuts	20	15
Fuel injector clamp nuts	30	22
Fuel pressure sensor-to-accumulator rail	45	33
High pressure fuel pipe union nuts*:		
Fuel pump-to-accumulator rail fuel pipe unions	20	15
Accumulator rail-to-fuel injector fuel pipe unions	25	18
High pressure fuel pump front mounting bolts and nut	20	15
High pressure fuel pump rear mounting bolt and nut	22	16
High pressure fuel pump sprocket nut	50	37

These torque settings are using Citroën crow's-foot adaptors - see Section 2

1 General information and system operation

General information

The fuel system consists of a rear-mounted fuel tank and fuel lift pump, a fuel cooler mounted under the car, a fuel filter with integral water separator, and a turbocharged, electronically-controlled High pressure Diesel injection (HDi) system.

The exhaust system is conventional, but to meet the latest emission levels an unregulated catalytic converter and an exhaust gas recirculation system are fitted to all models.

The HDi system (generally known as a 'common rail' system) derives its name from the fact that a common rail (referred to as an accumulator rail), or fuel reservoir, is used to supply fuel to all the fuel injectors. Instead of an in-line or distributor type injection pump, which distributes the fuel directly to each injector, a high pressure pump is used, which generates a very high fuel pressure (approximately 1350 bars) in the accumulator rail. The accumulator rail stores fuel, and maintains a constant fuel pressure, with the aid of a pressure control valve. Each injector is supplied with high pressure fuel from the accumulator rail, and the injectors are individually controlled via signals from the system electronic control unit (ECU). The injectors are electromagnetically-operated.

In addition to the various sensors used on models with a conventional fuel injection pump, common rail systems also have a fuel pressure sensor. The fuel pressure sensor allows the ECU to maintain the required fuel pressure, via the pressure control valve.

System operation

For the purposes of describing the operation of a common rail injection system, the components can be divided into three sub-systems; the low-pressure fuel system, the high pressure fuel system and the electronic control system.

Low-pressure fuel system

The low-pressure fuel system consists of the following components:
a) Fuel tank.
b) Fuel lift pump.
c) Fuel cooler.
d) Fuel filter/water trap.
e) Low-pressure fuel lines.

The low-pressure system (fuel supply system) is responsible for supplying clean fuel to the high pressure fuel system.

High pressure fuel system

The high pressure fuel system consists of the following components:
a) High pressure fuel pump with pressure control valve.
b) High pressure accumulator rail.
c) Fuel injectors.

d) High pressure fuel lines.

After passing through the fuel filter, the fuel reaches the high pressure pump, which forces it into the accumulator rail, generating a pressure of 1350 bars. As diesel fuel has a certain elasticity, the pressure in the accumulator rail remains constant, even though fuel leaves the rail each time one of the injectors operates. Additionally, a pressure control valve mounted on the high pressure pump ensures that the fuel pressure is maintained within pre-set limits.

The pressure control valve is operated by the ECU. When the valve is opened, fuel is returned from the high pressure pump to the tank, via the fuel return lines, and the pressure in the accumulator rail falls. To enable the ECU to trigger the pressure control valve correctly, the pressure in the accumulator rail is measured by a fuel pressure sensor.

The electromagnetically-controlled fuel injectors are operated individually, via signals from the ECU, and each injector injects fuel directly into the relevant combustion chamber. The fact that high fuel pressure is always available allows very precise and highly flexible injection in comparison to a conventional injection pump: for example combustion during the main injection process can be improved considerably by the pre-injection of a very small quantity of fuel.

Electronic control system

The electronic control system consists of the following components:
a) Electronic control unit (ECU).
b) Crankshaft speed/position sensor.
c) Camshaft position sensor.
d) Accelerator pedal position sensor.
e) Coolant temperature sensor.
f) Fuel temperature sensor.
g) Air mass meter.
h) Fuel pressure sensor.
i) Fuel injectors.
j) Fuel pressure control valve.
k) Preheating control unit.
l) EGR solenoid valve.

The information from the various sensors is passed to the ECU, which evaluates the signals. The ECU contains electronic 'maps' which enable it to calculate the optimum quantity of fuel to inject, the appropriate start of injection, and even pre- and post-injection fuel quantities, for each individual engine cylinder under any given condition of engine operation.

Additionally, the ECU carries out monitoring and self-diagnostic functions. Any faults in the system are stored in the ECU memory, which enables quick and accurate fault diagnosis using appropriate diagnostic equipment (such as a suitable fault code reader).

System Components

Fuel lift pump

The fuel lift pump and integral fuel gauge sender unit is electrically-operated, and is mounted in the fuel tank.

High pressure pump

The high pressure pump is mounted on the engine in the position normally occupied by the conventional distributor fuel injection pump. The pump is driven at half engine speed by the timing belt, and is lubricated by the fuel which it pumps.

The fuel lift pump forces the fuel into the high pressure pump chamber, via a safety valve.

The high pressure pump consists of three radially-mounted pistons and cylinders. The pistons are operated by an eccentric cam mounted on the pump drive spindle. As a piston moves down, fuel enters the cylinder through an inlet valve. When the piston reaches bottom dead centre (BDC), the inlet valve closes, and as the piston moves back up the cylinder, the fuel is compressed. When the pressure in the cylinder reaches the pressure in the accumulator rail, an outlet valve opens, and fuel is forced into the accumulator rail. When the piston reaches top dead centre (TDC), the outlet valve closes, due to the pressure drop, and the pumping cycle is repeated. The use of multiple cylinders provides a steady flow of fuel, minimising pulses and pressure fluctuations.

As the pump needs to be able to supply sufficient fuel under full-load conditions, it will supply excess fuel during idle and part-load conditions. This excess fuel is returned from the high pressure circuit to the low-pressure circuit (to the tank) via the pressure control valve.

The pump incorporates a facility to effectively switch off one of the cylinders to improve efficiency and reduce fuel consumption when maximum pumping capacity is not required. When this facility is operated, a solenoid-operated needle holds the inlet valve in the relevant cylinder open during the delivery stroke, preventing the fuel from being compressed.

Accumulator rail

As its name suggests, the accumulator rail acts as an accumulator, storing fuel and preventing pressure fluctuations. Fuel enters the rail from the high pressure pump, and each injector has its own connection to the rail. The fuel pressure sensor is mounted in the rail, and the rail also has a connection to the fuel pressure control valve on the pump.

Pressure control valve

The pressure control valve is operated by the ECU, and controls the system pressure. The valve is integral with the high pressure pump and cannot be separated.

If the fuel pressure is excessive, the valve opens, and fuel flows back to the tank. If the pressure is too low, the valve closes, enabling the high pressure pump to increase the pressure.

The valve is an electromagnetically-operated ball valve. The ball is forced against its seat, against the fuel pressure, by a powerful spring, and also by the force provided by the electromagnet. The force generated by the electromagnet is directly proportional to the current applied to it by the ECU. The desired pressure can therefore be set by varying the current applied to the electromagnet. Any pressure fluctuations are damped by the spring.

Fuel pressure sensor

The fuel pressure sensor is mounted in the accumulator rail, and provides very precise information on the fuel pressure to the ECU.

Fuel injector

The injectors are mounted on the engine in a similar manner to conventional diesel fuel injectors. The injectors are electro-magnetically-operated via signals from the ECU, and fuel is injected at the pressure existing in the accumulator rail. The injectors are high-precision instruments and are manufactured to very high tolerances.

Fuel flows into the injector from the accumulator rail, via an inlet valve and an inlet throttle, and an electromagnet causes the injector nozzle to lift from its seat, allowing injection. Excess fuel is returned from the injectors to the tank via a return line. The injector operates on a hydraulic servo principle: the forces resulting inside the injector due to the fuel pressure effectively amplify the effects of the electromagnet, which does not provide sufficient force to open the injector nozzle directly. The injector functions as follows.

Five separate forces are essential to the operation of the injector.

a) A nozzle spring forces the nozzle needle against the nozzle seat at the bottom of the injector, preventing fuel from entering the combustion chamber.

b) In the valve at the top of the injector, the valve spring forces the valve ball against the opening to the valve control chamber. The fuel in the chamber is unable to escape through the fuel return.

c) When triggered, the electromagnet exerts a force which overcomes the valve spring force, and moves the valve ball away from its seat. This is the triggering force for the start of injection. When the valve ball moves off its seat, fuel enters the valve control chamber.

d) The pressure of the fuel in the valve control chamber exerts a force on the valve control plunger, which is added to the nozzle spring force.

e) A slight chamfer towards the lower end of the nozzle needle causes the fuel in the control chamber to exert a force on the nozzle needle.

When these forces are in equilibrium, the injector is in its rest (idle) state, but when a voltage is applied to the electromagnet, the forces work to lift the nozzle needle, injecting fuel into the combustion chamber. There are four phases of injector operation as follows:

a) Rest (idle) state – all forces are in equilibrium. The nozzle needle closes off the nozzle opening, and the valve spring forces the valve ball against its seat.

b) Opening – the electromagnet is triggered which opens the nozzle and triggers the injection process. The force from the electromagnet allows the valve ball to leave its seat. The fuel from the valve control chamber flows back to the tank via the fuel return line. When the valve opens, the pressure in the valve control chamber drops, and the force on the valve plunger is reduced. However, due to the effect of the input throttle, the pressure on the nozzle needle remains unchanged. The resulting force in the valve control chamber is sufficient to lift the nozzle from its seat, and the injection process begins.

c) Injection – within a few milliseconds, the triggering current in the electromagnet is reduced to a lower holding current. The nozzle is now fully open, and fuel is injected into the combustion chamber at the pressure present in the accumulator rail.

d) Closing – the electromagnet is switched off, at which point the valve spring forces the valve ball firmly against its seat, and in the valve control chamber, the pressure is the same as that at the nozzle needle. The force at the valve plunger increases, and the nozzle needle closes the nozzle opening. The forces are now in equilibrium once more, and the injector is once more in the idle state, awaiting the next injection sequence.

ECU and sensors

The ECU and sensors are described earlier in this Section – see *Electronic control system*.

---

2 High pressure Diesel injection system – special information

Warnings and precautions

1 It is essential to observe strict precautions when working on the fuel system components, particularly the high pressure side of the system. Before carrying out any operations on the fuel system, refer to the precautions given in *Safety first!* at the beginning of this manual, and to the following additional information.

Do not carry out any repair work on the high pressure fuel system unless you are competent to do so, have all the necessary tools and equipment required, and are aware of the safety implications involved.

Before starting any repair work on the fuel system, wait at least 30 seconds after switching off the engine to allow the fuel circuit to return to atmospheric pressure.

Never work on the high pressure fuel system with the engine running.

Keep well clear of any possible source of fuel leakage, particularly when starting the engine after carrying out repair work. A leak in the system could cause an extremely high pressure jet of fuel to escape, which could result in severe personal injury.

Never place your hands or any part of your body near to a leak in the high pressure fuel system.

Do not use steam cleaning equipment or compressed air to clean the engine or any of the fuel system components.

Repair procedures and general information

2 Strict cleanliness must be observed at all times when working on any part of the fuel system. This applies to the working area in general, the person doing the work, and the components being worked on.

3 Before working on the fuel system components, they must be thoroughly cleaned with a suitable degreasing fluid. Citroën recommend the use of a specific product (SODIMAC degreasing fluid – available from Citroën dealers). Alternatively, a suitable brake cleaning fluid may be used. Cleanliness is particularly important when working on the fuel system connections at the following components:

a) Fuel filter.
b) High pressure fuel pump.
c) Accumulator rail.
d) Fuel injectors.
e) High pressure fuel pipes.

4 After disconnecting any fuel pipes or components, the open union or orifice must be immediately sealed to prevent the entry of dirt or foreign material. Plastic plugs and caps in various sizes are available in packs from motor factors and accessory outlets, and are particularly suitable for this application **(see illustration)**. Fingers cut from disposable rubber gloves should be used to protect components such as fuel pipes, fuel injectors and wiring connectors, and can be secured in place using elastic bands. Suitable gloves of this type are available at no cost from most petrol station forecourts.

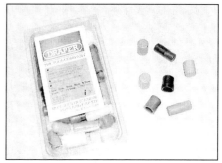

2.4 Typical plastic plug and cap set for sealing disconnected fuel pipes and components

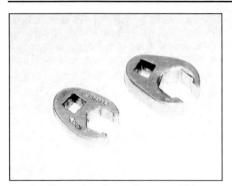

2.7 Two crow-foot adaptors will be necessary for tightening the fuel pipe unions

4.2 Undo the four plastic nuts and lift off the engine cover

4.3 Disconnect the flexible air inlet duct from the air mass meter and turbocharger rigid inlet duct

5 Whenever any of the high pressure fuel pipes are disconnected or removed, a new pipes must be obtained for refitting.

6 On the completion of any repair on the high pressure fuel system, Citroën recommend the use of ARDROX 9D1 BRENT leak-detecting compound. This is a powder which is applied to the fuel pipe unions and connections and turns white when dry. Any leak in the system will cause the product to darken indicating the source of the leak.

7 The torque wrench settings given in the Specifications must be strictly observed when tightening component mountings and connections. This is particularly important when tightening the high pressure fuel pipe

unions. To enable a torque wrench to be used on the fuel pipe unions, two crow-foot adaptors are required (Citroën special tools - 4220-T.D. and -4220-T.C.). Suitable alternatives are available from motor factors and accessory outlets **(see illustration)**.

3 Fuel system – priming and bleeding

1 The fuel system is entirely self-bleeding because the fuel lift pump supplies fuel to the high pressure pump whenever the ignition is switched on.

2 In the case of running out of fuel, or after disconnecting any part of the fuel supply system, ensure that there is fuel in the tank, then start the engine in the normal way.

4 Air cleaner assembly and inlets ducts – removal and refitting

Removal

Air cleaner assembly and front air inlet ducts

1 Disconnect the battery negative terminal (refer to *Disconnecting the battery* in the Reference Section of this manual).

2 Undo the four plastic nuts and lift off the engine cover **(see illustration)**.

3 Slacken the retaining clips and disconnect the flexible air inlet duct from the air mass meter and turbocharger rigid inlet duct **(see illustration)**. Suitably plug or cover the turbocharger rigid inlet duct, using clean rag to prevent any dirt or foreign material from entering.

4 Disconnect the wiring plug from the accelerator pedal position sensor, adjacent to the air cleaner housing **(see illustration)**.

5 Rotate the accelerator pedal position sensor quadrant, and release the inner cable from the quadrant **(see illustration)**.

6 Withdraw the outer cable from the grommet in the pedal position sensor body, and recover the flat washer from the end of the cable.

7 Disconnect the wiring connector from the air mass meter on the side of the air cleaner lid **(see illustration)**.

8 Undo the nuts securing the base of the air cleaner housing to the front and rear support brackets **(see illustration)**.

9 Undo the bolt securing the wiring harness retaining clip to the air cleaner bracket.

10 Lift the air cleaner housing upwards at the rear, disengage the two front locating lugs

4.4 Disconnect the wiring plug from the accelerator pedal position sensor

4.5 Rotate the pedal position sensor quadrant, and release the accelerator inner cable

4.7 Disconnect the wiring connector from the air mass meter

4.8 Undo the nuts securing the base of the air cleaner housing to the front and rear support brackets

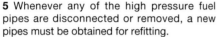

4.10 Lift the air cleaner housing upwards at the rear and disengage the two front locating lugs

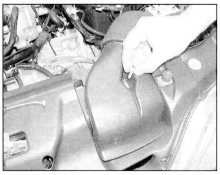

4.11 Undo the bolt securing the front of the air inlet duct to the front body panel

4.12 Undo the two bolts and remove the flexible tube from the engine compartment

and remove the assembly from the engine compartment **(see illustration)**.

11 To remove the air cleaner air inlet duct, undo the bolt securing the front of the inlet duct to the front body panel **(see illustration)**. Detach and remove the duct from the flexible tube.

12 Undo the two bolts securing the flexible tube to the air cleaner support bracket and remove the tube from the engine compartment **(see illustration)**.

Turbocharger rear inlet and outlet ducts

13 The rigid ducts at the rear of the engine, connecting the turbocharger to the flexible air inlet duct and to the inlet manifold are inaccessible with the engine in the car. To gain access it will be necessary to either remove the engine/transmission unit as described in Chapter 2F, or remove the front suspension subframe as described in Chapter 10.

14 Once access has been gained, begin removal of the turbocharger rigid inlet duct by disconnecting the crankcase ventilation hose at the top of the duct **(see illustration)**.

15 Undo the bolt securing the duct to the inlet manifold elbow **(see illustration)**.

16 At the lower end, undo the bolt securing the duct to the turbocharger **(see illustration)**. Lift off the duct and recover the seal from the lower end.

17 To remove the turbocharger-to-inlet

manifold rigid plastic duct, slacken the retaining clip and release the connecting hose from the inlet manifold elbow **(see illustration)**.

18 Slacken the clip securing the connecting hose at the lower end of the duct to the turbocharger. Release the attachment strap from the lug on the turbocharger and withdraw the duct from the engine **(see illustration)**.

Refitting

19 Refitting is a reverse of the removal procedure. Examine the condition of the seals and retaining clips and renew if necessary.

20 Where applicable, refit the

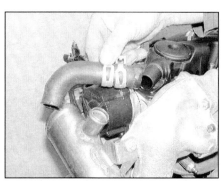

4.14 Disconnect the crankcase ventilation hose at the top of the turbocharger rigid inlet duct

engine/transmission as described in Chapter 2F, or the front suspension subframe as described in Chapter 10.

21 Reconnect and adjust the accelerator cable as described in Section 5.

5 Accelerator cable – removal, refitting and adjustment

Removal

1 Undo the four plastic nuts and lift off the engine cover.

2 Rotate the accelerator pedal position

4.15 Undo the bolt (arrowed) securing the rigid inlet duct to the inlet manifold elbow

4.16 Undo the bolt securing the rigid inlet duct to the turbocharger and remove the duct

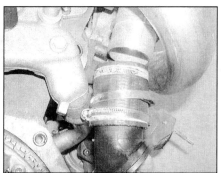

4.17 Slacken the clip and release the plastic duct connecting hose from the inlet manifold elbow

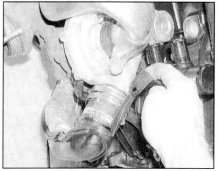

4.18 Slacken the connecting hose clip, release the attachment strap and withdraw the plastic duct from the engine

sensor quadrant, and release the inner cable from the quadrant.

3 Withdraw the outer cable from the grommet in the pedal position sensor body, recover the flat washer from the end of the cable and remove the spring clip.

4 Release the cable from the remaining clips and brackets in the engine compartment, noting its routing.

5 Working in the passenger compartment, reach up under the facia, depress the ends of the cable end fitting, and detach the inner cable from the top of the accelerator pedal.

6 Release the outer cable grommet from the pedal mounting bracket, then tie a length of string to the end of the cable.

7 Return to the engine compartment, release the cable grommet from the bulkhead and withdraw the cable. When the end of the cable appears, untie the string and leave it in position – it can then be used to draw the cable back into position on refitting.

Refitting

8 Refitting is a reversal of removal, but ensure that the cable is routed as noted before removal and, on completion, adjust the cable as follows.

Adjustment

9 Remove the spring clip from the accelerator outer cable. Ensuring that the pedal position sensor quadrant is against its stop, gently pull the cable out of its grommet until all free play is removed from the inner cable.

10 With the cable held in this position, refit the spring clip to the last exposed outer cable groove in front of the rubber grommet and washer. When the clip is refitted and the outer cable is released, there should be only a small amount of free play in the inner cable.

11 Have an assistant depress the accelerator pedal, and check that the pedal position sensor quadrant opens fully and returns smoothly to its stop.

12 Refit the engine cover on completion.

6 Accelerator pedal – removal and refitting

Refer to Chapter 4A, Section 4, but adjust the accelerator cable as described above.

7 Fuel lift pump – removal and refitting

The diesel fuel lift pump is located in the same position as the conventional fuel pump on petrol models, and the removal and refitting procedures are virtually identical. Refer to Chapter 4A, Section 8.

8 Fuel gauge sender unit – removal and refitting

The fuel gauge sender unit is integral with the fuel lift pump. Refer to Chapter 4A, Section 8.

9 Fuel tank – removal and refitting

Refer to Chapter 4A, Section 10.

10 High pressure fuel pump – removal and refitting

Removal

⚠ **Warning: Refer to the information contained in Section 2 before proceeding.**

Note: *A new fuel pump-to-accumulator rail high pressure fuel pipe will be required for refitting.*

1 Remove the timing belt as described in Chapter 2D. After removal of the timing belt, temporarily refit the right-hand engine mounting.

2 At the connections above the fuel pump, disconnect the fuel supply and return hose quick-release fittings using a small screwdriver to release the locking clip **(see illustration)**. Suitably plug or cover the open unions to prevent dirt entry.

3 Similarly disconnect the supply and return hose quick-release fittings at the fuel filter and plug or cover the open unions. Release the fuel hoses from the relevant retaining clips.

4 Lift the fuel filter out of its mounting bracket and move it slightly to one side, away from the pump.

5 Undo the bolts and remove the filter mounting bracket from the engine.

6 Undo the bolts securing the plastic wiring harness guide to the front of the engine **(see illustration)**. It will be necessary to lift up the wiring harness as far as possible for access to the rear of the fuel pump. If necessary, disconnect the relevant wiring connectors to enable the harness and guide assembly to be moved further for additional access.

7 Disconnect the wiring connector at the pressure control valve on the rear of the fuel pump, and at the piston de-activator switch on the top of the pump.

8 Thoroughly clean the high pressure fuel pipe unions on the fuel pump and accumulator rail. Using an open-ended spanner, unscrew the union nuts securing the high pressure fuel pipe to the fuel pump and accumulator rail. Counterhold the unions on the pump and accumulator rail with a second spanner, while unscrewing the union nuts. Withdraw the high pressure fuel pipe and plug or cover the open unions to prevent dirt entry **(see illustration)**. Note that a new high pressure fuel pipe will be required for refitting.

9 Undo the nut and bolt securing the fuel

10.2 Disconnect the fuel supply and return hose quick-release fittings at the connections above the fuel pump

10.6 Undo the bolt (arrowed) to release the plastic wiring harness guide

10.8 Unscrew the unions and remove the high pressure fuel pipe

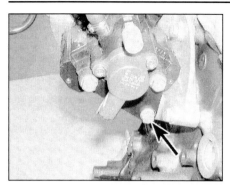

10.9 Undo the nut and bolt (arrowed) securing the fuel pump rear mounting to the mounting bracket

Tool Tip 1: A sprocket holding tool can be made from two lengths of steel strip bolted together to form a forked end. Bend the ends of the strip through 90° to form the fork 'prongs'.

Tool Tip 2: Make a sprocket releasing tool from a short strip of steel. Drill two holes in the strip to correspond with the two holes in the sprocket. Drill a third hole just large enough to accept the flats of the sprocket retaining nut.

pump rear mounting to the mounting bracket **(see illustration)**.

10 Using a suitable socket, undo the fuel pump sprocket retaining nut. The sprocket can be held stationary as the nut is slackened using a suitable forked tool engaged with the holes in the sprocket **(see Tool Tip 1)**.

11 The fuel pump sprocket is a taper fit on the pump shaft and it will be necessary to make up another tool to release it from the taper **(see Tool Tip 2)**.

12 Partially unscrew the sprocket retaining nut, fit the home-made tool, and secure it to the sprocket with two suitable bolts. Prevent the sprocket from rotating as before, and unscrew the sprocket retaining nut **(see illustration)**. The nut will bear against the tool as it is undone, forcing the sprocket off the shaft taper. Once the taper is released, remove the tool, unscrew the nut fully, and remove the sprocket from the pump shaft.

13 Undo the nut and two bolts securing the front of the fuel pump to the mounting bracket **(see illustrations)**. Withdraw the pump, complete with fuel supply and return hoses, rearwards, and lift it off the engine.

Caution: The high pressure fuel pump is manufactured to extremely close tolerances and must not be dismantled in any way. Do not unscrew the fuel pipe male union on the rear of the pump, or attempt to remove the pressure control valve, piston de-activator switch, or the seal on the pump shaft. No parts for the pump are available separately and if the unit is in any way suspect, it must be renewed.

Refitting

14 Locate the pump on the mounting bracket, and refit the front retaining nut and the two bolts. Refit the nut and bolt securing the fuel pump rear mounting to the mounting bracket, then tighten all the mountings to the specified torque.

15 Refit the pump sprocket and retaining nut and tighten the nut to the specified torque. Prevent the sprocket rotating as the nut is tightened using the sprocket holding tool.

16 Remove the blanking plugs from the fuel pipe unions on the pump and accumulator rail. Locate a new high pressure fuel pipe over

the unions and screw on the union nuts finger tight at this stage.

17 Using a torque wrench and crow-foot adaptor, tighten the fuel pipe union nuts to the specified torque. Counterhold the unions on the pump and accumulator rail with an open-ended spanner, while tightening the union nuts **(see illustration)**.

18 Reconnect the wiring connector at the pressure control valve on the rear of the fuel pump.

19 Reposition and secure the plastic wiring harness guide to the front of the engine, and reconnect any additional wiring disconnected for access.

10.12 Using the home-made tools to remove the fuel pump sprocket

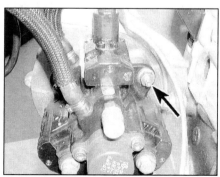

10.13b ... and mounting nut (arrowed)

20 Refit the filter mounting bracket to the engine and securely tighten the retaining bolts. Locate the fuel filter back in position in the mounting bracket.

21 Remove the blanking plugs and reconnect the supply and return hose quick-release fittings at the fuel filter, and at the connections above the fuel pump. Secure the hoses with their respective retaining clips.

22 Refit the timing belt as described in Chapter 2D.

23 With everything reassembled and reconnected, and observing the precautions listed in Section 2, start the engine and allow it to idle. Check for leaks at the high pressure

10.13a Fuel pump front mounting bolts (arrowed) ...

10.17 Tighten the fuel pipe union nuts using a torque wrench and crow-foot adaptor

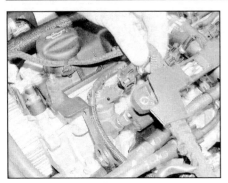

11.3a Disconnect the wiring connectors at the fuel injectors . . .

11.3b . . . and at the piston de-activator switch on top of the fuel pump

11.4 Undo the two nuts and lift off the plastic wiring harness guide

fuel pipe unions with the engine idling. If satisfactory, increase the engine speed to 4000 rpm and check again for leaks. Take the car for a short road test and check for leaks once again on return. If any leaks are detected, obtain and fit another new high pressure fuel pipe. **Do not** attempt to cure even the slightest leak by further tightening of the pipe unions.
24 Refit the engine cover on completion.

11 Accumulator rail – removal and refitting

Removal

Warning: Refer to the information contained in Section 2 before proceeding.

Note: *A complete new set of high pressure fuel pipes will be required for refitting.*
1 Disconnect the battery negative terminal (refer to *Disconnecting the battery* in the Reference Section of this manual).
2 Undo the four plastic nuts and lift off the engine cover.
3 Disconnect the wiring connectors at the fuel injectors and at the piston de-activator switch on the top of the fuel pump **(see illustrations)**.
4 Undo the two nuts securing the plastic wiring harness guide to the cylinder head. Lift the guide off the two mounting studs and move it clear of the accumulator rail **(see illustration)**. Disconnect any additional wiring connectors as necessary to enable the harness and guide assembly to be moved further for increased access.
5 Release the retaining clip and disconnect

the crankcase ventilation hose from the cylinder head cover.
6 At the connections above the fuel pump, disconnect the fuel supply and return hose quick-release fittings using a small screwdriver to release the locking clip. Suitably plug or cover the open unions to prevent dirt entry.
7 Similarly disconnect the supply and return hose quick-release fittings at the fuel filter and plug or cover the open unions. Release the fuel hoses from the relevant retaining clips.
8 Thoroughly clean all the high pressure fuel pipe unions on the accumulator rail, fuel pump and injectors. Using an open-ended spanner, unscrew the union nuts securing the high pressure fuel pipe to the fuel pump and accumulator rail. Counterhold the unions on the pump and accumulator rail with a second spanner, while unscrewing the union nuts. Withdraw the high pressure fuel pipe and plug or cover the open unions to prevent dirt entry.
9 Again using two spanners, hold the unions and unscrew the union nuts securing the high pressure fuel pipes to the fuel injectors and accumulator rail **(see illustrations)**. Withdraw the high pressure fuel pipes and plug or cover the open unions to prevent dirt entry.
10 Disconnect the wiring connectors at the fuel temperature sensor and fuel pressure sensor on the accumulator rail **(see illustration)**.
11 Undo the three bolts securing the accumulator rail to the cylinder head and withdraw the rail from its location **(see illustrations)**.

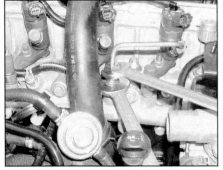

11.9a Using two spanners, unscrew the fuel pipe unions at the accumulator rail . . .

11.9b . . . and at each injector

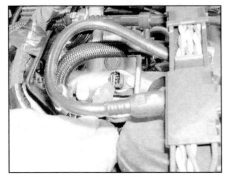

11.10 Disconnect the wiring connector at the fuel temperature sensor

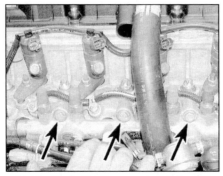

11.11a Undo the three accumulator rail retaining bolts (arrowed) . . .

11.11b . . . and withdraw the accumulator rail from the engine

Caution: Do not attempt to remove the four high pressure fuel pipe male unions from the accumulator rail. These parts are not available separately and if disturbed are likely to result in fuel leakage on reassembly.

12 Obtain a complete new set of high pressure fuel pipes for refitting.

Refitting

13 Locate the accumulator rail in position, refit the three securing bolts and tighten to the specified torque.

14 Working on one fuel injector at a time, remove the blanking plugs from the fuel pipe unions on the accumulator rail and the relevant injector. Locate a new high pressure fuel pipe over the unions and screw on the union nuts finger tight at this stage.

15 When all four fuel pipes are in place, hold the unions with a spanner and tighten the union nuts to the specified torque using a torque wrench and crow-foot adaptor **(see illustration)**.

16 Similarly, fit a new high pressure fuel pipe to the fuel pump and accumulator rail, and tighten the union nuts to the specified torque.

17 Reconnect the fuel temperature sensor and fuel pressure sensor wiring connectors.

18 Remove the blanking plugs and reconnect the supply and return hose quick-release fittings at the fuel filter, and at the connections above the fuel pump. Secure the hoses with their respective retaining clips.

19 Reconnect the crankcase ventilation hose to the cylinder head cover.

20 Reposition the plastic wiring harness guide over the two mounting studs and secure with the retaining nuts.

21 Reconnect the fuel injector and pump piston de-activator switch wiring connectors, and reconnect any additional wiring disconnected for access.

22 Check that everything has been reconnected and secured with the relevant retaining clips then reconnect the battery negative terminal.

23 Observing the precautions listed in Section 2, start the engine and allow to idle. Check for leaks at the high pressure fuel pipe unions with the engine idling. If satisfactory,

11.15 Using a torque wrench and crow-foot adaptor, tighten the fuel pipe union nuts

increase the engine speed to 4000 rpm and check again for leaks. Take the car for a short road test and check for leaks once again on return. If any leaks are detected, obtain and fit additional new high pressure fuel pipes as required. **Do not** attempt to cure even the slightest leak by further tightening of the pipe unions.

24 Refit the engine cover on completion.

12 Fuel injectors – removal and refitting

Removal

⚠️ *Warning: Refer to the information contained in Section 2 before proceeding.*

Note: *The following procedure describes the removal and refitting of the injectors as a complete set, however each injector may be removed individually if required. New copper washers, upper seals, injector clamp retaining nuts and a high pressure fuel pipe will be required for each disturbed injector when refitting.*

1 Carry out the operations described in Section 11, paragraphs 1 to 4.

2 At the connections above the fuel pump, disconnect the fuel supply and return hose quick-release fittings using a small screwdriver to release the locking clip.

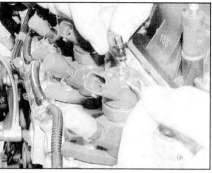

12.4 Extract the circlip and disconnect the injector leak-off pipes

Suitably plug or cover the open unions to prevent dirt entry, then release the fuel hoses from the relevant retaining clips.

3 Thoroughly clean all the high pressure fuel pipe unions on the fuel injectors and accumulator rail. Using two open-ended spanners, unscrew the union nuts securing the high pressure fuel pipes to the fuel injectors and accumulator rail. Withdraw the high pressure fuel pipes and plug or cover the open unions on the injectors and accumulator rail to prevent dirt entry. Note that a new high pressure fuel pipe will be required for each removed injector when refitting.

4 Extract the retaining circlip and disconnect the leak-off pipe from each fuel injector **(see illustration)**.

5 Unscrew the nut and remove the washer securing each injector clamp to its cylinder head stud **(see illustrations)**. Note that new clamp nuts will be required for refitting.

6 Withdraw the injectors, together with their clamps, from the cylinder head **(see illustration)**. Slide the clamp off the injector once it is clear of the mounting stud. If the injectors are a tight fit in the cylinder head and cannot be released, unscrew the mounting stud using a stud extractor and slide off the injector clamp. Using an open-ended spanner engaged with the clamp locating slot on the injector body, free the injector by twisting it and at the same time lifting it upwards.

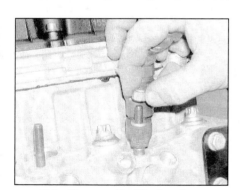

12.5a Unscrew the injector clamp retaining nut . . .

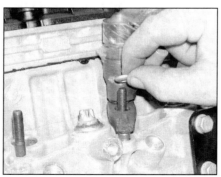

12.5b . . . and remove the washer

12.6 Withdraw the injectors, together with their clamps, from the cylinder head

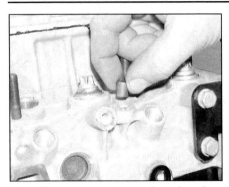

12.7 Recover the injector clamp locating dowel from the cylinder head

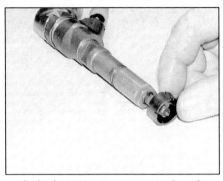

12.12a Locate a new upper seal on the body of each injector . . .

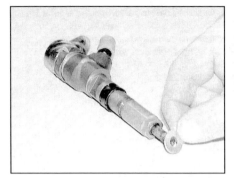

12.12b . . . and place a new copper washer on the injector nozzle

7 Recover the injector clamp locating dowel from the cylinder head **(see illustration)**.

8 Remove the copper washer and the upper seal from each injector, or from the cylinder head if they remained in place during injector removal. New copper washers and upper seals will be required for refitting.

9 Examine each injector visually for any signs of obvious damage or deterioration. If any defects are apparent, renew the injector(s).
Caution: The injectors are manufactured to extremely close tolerances and must not be dismantled in any way. Do not unscrew the fuel pipe union on the side of the injector, or separate any parts of the injector body. Do not attempt to clean carbon deposits from the injector nozzle or carry out any form of ultra-sonic or pressure testing.

10 If the injectors are in a satisfactory condition, plug the fuel pipe union (if not already done) and suitably cover the electrical element and the injector nozzle.

11 Prior to refitting, obtain new copper washers, upper seals, injector clamp retaining nuts and high pressure fuel pipes for each removed injector.

Refitting

12 Locate a new upper seal on the body of each injector, and place a new copper washer on the injector nozzle **(see illustrations)**.

13 Refit the injector clamp locating dowels to the cylinder head.

14 Place the injector clamp in the slot on each injector body and refit the injectors to the cylinder head. Guide the clamp over the mounting stud and onto the locating dowel as each injector is inserted.

15 Fit the washer and a new injector clamp retaining nut to each mounting stud. Tighten the nuts finger tight only at this stage.

16 Working on one fuel injector at a time, remove the blanking plugs from the fuel pipe unions on the accumulator rail and the relevant injector. Locate a new high pressure fuel pipe over the unions and screw on the union nuts. Take care not to cross-thread the nuts or strain the fuel pipes as they are fitted. Once the union nut threads have started,

tighten the nuts moderately tight only at this stage.

17 When all the fuel pipes are in place, tighten the injector clamp retaining nuts to the specified torque.

18 Using an open-ended spanner, hold each fuel pipe union in turn and tighten the union nut to the specified torque using a torque wrench and crow-foot adaptor. Tighten all the disturbed union nuts in the same way.

19 Connect the leak-off pipes to each fuel injector and secure with the retaining circlips.

20 Remove the blanking plugs and reconnect the supply and return hose quick-release fittings at the connections above the fuel pump. Secure the hoses with their respective retaining clips.

21 Reposition the plastic wiring harness guide over the two mounting studs and secure with the retaining nuts.

22 Reconnect the fuel injector and pump piston de-activator switch wiring connectors, and reconnect any additional wiring disconnected for access.

23 Check that everything has been reconnected and secured with the relevant retaining clips then reconnect the battery negative terminal.

24 Observing the precautions listed in Section 2, start the engine and allow it to idle. Check for leaks at the high pressure fuel pipe unions with the engine idling. If satisfactory, increase the engine speed to 4000 rpm and check again for leaks. Take the car for a short road test and check for leaks once again on return. If any leaks are detected, obtain and fit additional new high pressure fuel pipes as required. **Do not** attempt to cure even the slightest leak by further tightening of the pipe unions.

25 Refit the engine cover on completion.

13 Electronic control system components – testing, removal and refitting

Testing

1 If a fault is suspected in the electronic

control side of the system, first ensure that all the wiring connectors are securely connected and free of corrosion. Ensure that the suspected problem is not of a mechanical nature, or due to poor maintenance; ie, check that the air cleaner filter element is clean, the engine breather hoses are clear and undamaged, and that the cylinder compression pressures are correct, referring to Chapters 1B and 2D for further information.

2 If these checks fail to reveal the cause of the problem, the vehicle should be taken to a Citroën dealer or suitably-equipped garage for testing. A diagnostic socket is located adjacent to the passenger compartment fusebox in which a fault code reader or other suitable test equipment can be connected. By using the code reader or test equipment, the engine management ECU (and the various other vehicle system ECUs) can be interrogated, and any stored fault codes can be retrieved. This will allow the fault to be quickly and simply traced, alleviating the need to test all the system components individually, which is a time-consuming operation that carries a risk of damaging the ECU.

Removal and refitting

3 Before carrying out any of the following procedures, disconnect the battery negative terminal (refer to *Disconnecting the battery* in the Reference Section of this manual). Reconnect the battery on completion of refitting.

Electronic control unit (ECU)

Note: *If a new ECU is to be fitted, this work must be entrusted to a Citroën dealer. It is necessary to initialise the new ECU after installation, which requires the use of dedicated Citroën diagnostic equipment.*

4 The ECU is located in the plastic box which forms part of the rear of the battery mounting tray. To gain access, first remove the air cleaner assembly as described in Section 4.

5 Remove the battery and mounting tray as described in Chapter 5A.

6 With the battery mounting tray removed, undo the retaining nuts and bolts and lift

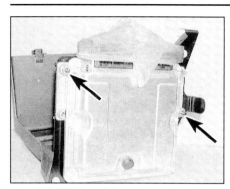

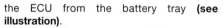

13.6 ECU retaining nuts and bolts (arrowed)

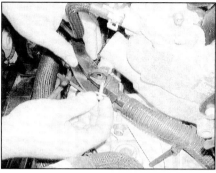

13.9 Release the plastic wiring harness guide for access to the crankshaft speed/position sensor

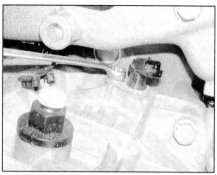

13.11 Slacken the bolt securing the sensor to the bellhousing

the ECU from the battery tray **(see illustration)**.

7 Refitting is a reverse of the removal procedure ensuring the wiring connector is securely reconnected.

Crankshaft speed/position sensor

8 The crankshaft speed/position sensor is located at the top of the transmission bellhousing, directly above the engine flywheel. To gain access, remove the air cleaner assembly as described in Section 4, then remove the battery and battery tray as described in Chapter 5A.

9 Undo the retaining nuts and bolts and release the plastic wiring harness guide from its mountings **(see illustration)**.

10 Working below the thermostat housing, disconnect the wiring connector from the crankshaft speed/position sensor.

11 Slacken the bolt securing the sensor to the bellhousing **(see illustration)**. It is not necessary to remove the bolt completely as the sensor mounting flange is slotted.

12 Turn the sensor body to clear the mounting bolt, then withdraw the sensor from the bellhousing **(see illustration)**.

13 Refitting is reverse of the removal procedure ensuring the sensor retaining bolt is securely tightened.

Camshaft position sensor

14 The camshaft position sensor is mounted on the right-hand end of the cylinder

head cover, directly behind the camshaft sprocket.

15 Remove the timing belt upper and intermediate covers as described in Chapter 2D.

16 Disconnect the sensor wiring connector **(see illustration)**.

17 Undo the retaining bolt and lift the sensor off the cylinder head cover.

18 To refit and adjust the sensor position, locate the sensor on the cylinder head cover and loosely refit the retaining bolt.

19 The air gap between the tip of the sensor and the target plate at the rear of the camshaft sprocket hub must be set to 1.2 mm, using feeler blades. Clearance for the feeler blades is limited with the timing belt and camshaft sprocket in place, but it is just possible if the feeler blades are bent through 90° so they can be inserted through the holes in the sprocket, to rest against the inner face of the target plate.

20 With the feeler blades placed against the target plate, move the sensor toward the sprocket until it just contacts the feeler blades. Hold the sensor in this position and tighten the retaining bolt **(see illustration)**.

21 With the gap correctly adjusted, reconnect the sensor wiring connector, then refit the timing belt upper and intermediate covers as described in Chapter 2D.

Accelerator pedal position sensor

22 The accelerator pedal position sensor is

located at the front of the engine, adjacent to the air cleaner housing **(see illustration)**.

23 Remove the air cleaner assembly as described in Section 4.

24 Undo the two nuts and bolts and remove the sensor assembly from the mounting bracket on the side of the air cleaner housing.

25 Refitting is reverse of the removal procedure.

Coolant temperature sensor

26 Refer to Chapter 3, Section 6.

Fuel temperature sensor

⚠️ **Warning: Refer to the information contained in Section 2 before proceeding.**

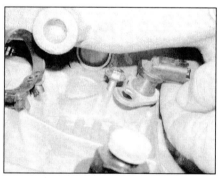

13.12 Turn the sensor body to clear the bolt and withdraw it from the bellhousing

13.16 Disconnect the camshaft position sensor wiring connector

13.20 Insert feeler blades bent through 90° through the sprocket to measure the camshaft position sensor air gap

13.22 Accelerator pedal position sensor location (arrowed) adjacent to the air cleaner housing

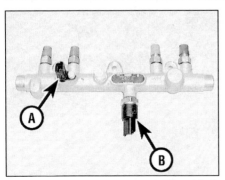

13.27 Fuel temperature sensor (A) and fuel pressure sensor (B) locations on the accumulator rail (shown removed for clarity)

Note: *Do not remove the sensor from the accumulator rail unless there is a valid reason to do so. At the time of writing there was no information as to the availability of the sensor seal as a separate item. Consult a Citroën parts stockist for the latest information before proceeding.*

27 The fuel temperature sensor is located towards the right-hand end of the accumulator rail **(see illustration)**.

28 Undo the four plastic nuts and lift off the engine cover.

29 Disconnect the fuel temperature sensor wiring connector.

30 Thoroughly clean the area around the sensor and its location on the accumulator rail.

31 Suitably protect the components below the sensor and have plenty of clean rags handy. Be prepared for considerable fuel spillage.

32 Undo the retaining bolt and withdraw the sensor from the accumulator rail. Plug the opening in the accumulator rail as soon as the sensor is withdrawn.

33 Prior to refitting, if the original sensor is to be refitted, renew the sensor seal, where applicable (see the note at the start of this sub-Section).

34 Locate the sensor in the accumulator rail and refit the retaining bolt, tightened securely.

35 Refit the sensor wiring connector.

36 Observing the precautions listed in Section 2, start the engine and allow it to idle. Check for leaks at the fuel temperature sensor

with the engine idling. If satisfactory, increase the engine speed to 4000 rpm and check again for leaks. Take the car for a short road test and check for leaks once again on return. If any leaks are detected, obtain and fit a new sensor.

37 Refit the engine cover on completion.

Air mass meter

38 The air mass meter is attached to the lid of the air cleaner housing.

39 Undo the four plastic nuts and lift off the engine cover.

40 Slacken the retaining clips and disconnect the flexible air inlet duct from the air mass meter and turbocharger rigid inlet duct. Suitably plug or cover the turbocharger rigid inlet duct, using clean rag to prevent any dirt or foreign material from entering.

41 Disconnect the wiring connector from the air mass meter.

42 Undo the screws securing the lid to the air cleaner housing and lift off the lid, complete with air mass meter.

43 Undo the two screws and withdraw the air mass meter from the air cleaner lid.

44 Refitting is reverse of the removal procedure.

Fuel pressure sensor

 Warning: Refer to the information contained in Section 2 before proceeding.

Note: *Citroën special tool (-).4220 TH (27 mm forked adaptor) or suitable equivalent will be required for this operation.*

45 The fuel pressure sensor is located centrally on the underside of the accumulator rail **(see illustration 13.27)**.

46 Undo the four plastic nuts and lift off the engine cover.

47 Release the retaining clip and disconnect the crankcase ventilation hose from the cylinder head cover.

48 Disconnect the fuel supply and return hose quick-release fittings at the fuel filter, using a small screwdriver to release the locking clip. Suitably plug or cover the open unions to prevent dirt entry. Release the fuel hoses from the relevant retaining clips.

49 Disconnect the fuel pressure sensor wiring connector.

50 Thoroughly clean the area around the sensor and its location on the accumulator rail.

51 Suitably protect the components below the sensor and have plenty of clean rags handy. Be prepared for considerable fuel spillage.

52 Using the Citroën special tool (or suitable alternative 27 mm forked adaptor) and a socket bar, unscrew the fuel pressure sensor from the base of the accumulator rail.

53 Obtain and fit a new sealing ring to the sensor prior to refitting.

54 Locate the sensor in the accumulator rail and tighten it to the specified torque using the special tool (or alternative) and a torque wrench.

55 Refit the sensor wiring connector.

56 Observing the precautions listed in Section 2, start the engine and allow it to idle. Check for leaks at the fuel pressure sensor with the engine idling. If satisfactory, increase the engine speed to 4000 rpm and check again for leaks. Take the car for a short road test and check for leaks once again on return. If any leaks are detected, obtain and fit another new sensor sealing ring.

57 Refit the engine cover on completion.

Fuel pressure control valve

58 The fuel pressure control valve is integral with the high pressure fuel pump and cannot be separated.

Preheating system control unit

59 Refer to Chapter 5C.

EGR solenoid valve

60 Refer to Chapter 4D, Section 3.

14 Inlet manifold –
removal and refitting

Removal

Note: *Renew the manifold gasket when refitting.*

1 Remove the exhaust manifold as described in Section 15.

2 Undo the four bolts and four nuts securing the inlet manifolds flanges to the cylinder head **(see illustration)**. Recover the washers.

3 Lift the manifold off the cylinder head studs and recover the gasket **(see illustrations)**.

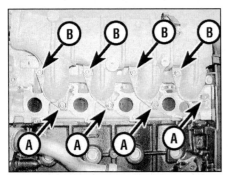

14.2 Inlet manifold retaining nuts (A) and bolts (B)

14.3a Lift the manifold off the cylinder head studs . . .

14.3b . . . and recover the gasket

15.5 Unscrew the turbocharger oil feed pipe union nut

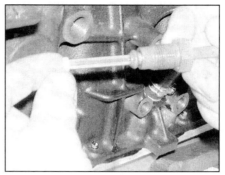

15.6 Withdraw the oil feed pipe and remove the filter

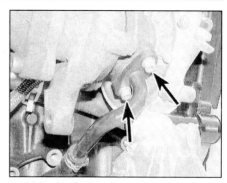

15.7a Undo the oil return pipe flange securing bolts (arrowed) . . .

Refitting

4 Refitting is reverse of the removal procedure, bearing in mind the following points.
  a) Ensure that the manifold and cylinder head mating faces are clean, with all traces of old gasket removed.
  b) Use a new gasket when refitting the manifold.
  c) Ensure that all fixings and attachments are securely tightened.
  d) Refit the exhaust manifold as described in Section 15.

15 Exhaust manifold – removal and refitting

Note: *The exhaust manifold is removed complete with the turbocharger and there is insufficient clearance to gain access to all the relevant attachments from either above or below with the engine in the car. Two alternatives are possible; either remove the complete engine/transmission unit from the car as described in Chapter 2F, or remove the front suspension subframe as described in Chapter 10. Both are involved operations and the course of action taken is largely dependent on the tools, equipment, skill and patience available.*

1 The following procedure is based on the assumption that the engine/transmission unit has been removed from the car. If the front suspension subframe has been removed instead, the operations are basically the same, but it may be necessary to disconnect and move aside certain additional items, and to be prepared for considerable manipulation to withdraw the components from the engine compartment.

2 If not already done, disconnect the battery negative terminal (refer to *Disconnecting the battery* in the Reference Section of this manual).

3 If the engine is in the car, remove the catalytic converter as described in Section 18.

4 Remove the turbocharger rear inlet and outlet ducts as described in Section 4.

5 Unscrew the union nut securing the turbocharger oil feed pipe to the cylinder block, then withdraw the pipe from its location **(see illustration)**.

6 Remove the filter from the end of the oil feed

15.7b . . . separate the flange and recover the gasket

pipe, and examine it for contamination **(see illustration)**. Clean or renew if necessary.

7 Undo the two bolts securing the oil return pipe flange to the turbocharger. Separate the flange and recover the gasket **(see illustrations)**.

8 Remove the exhaust gas recirculation (EGR) valve and connecting pipe from the exhaust manifold as described in Chapter 4D, Section 3.

9 Undo the eight exhaust manifold retaining nuts and recover the spacers from the studs **(see illustrations)**.

10 Undo the nut and bolt securing the base of the turbocharger to the support bracket on the cylinder block.

11 Withdraw the turbocharger and exhaust manifold off the mounting studs and remove the assembly from the engine. Recover the manifold gasket **(see illustrations)**.

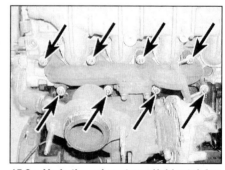

15.9a Undo the exhaust manifold retaining nuts (arrowed)

15.9b . . . and recover the spacers from the studs

15.11a Withdraw the turbocharger and exhaust manifold off the mounting studs . . .

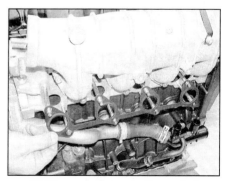

15.11b . . . and recover the gasket

Refitting

12 Refitting is a reverse of the removal procedure, bearing in mind the following points:

a) *Ensure that the manifold and cylinder head mating faces are clean, with all traces of old gasket removed.*

b) *Use new gaskets when refitting the manifold to the cylinder head and the oil return pipe flange to the turbocharger.*

c) *Tighten the exhaust manifold retaining nuts to the specified torque.*

d) *Refit the EGR valve and connecting pipe as described in Chapter 4D, Section 3.*

e) *Refit the turbocharger rear inlet and outlet ducts as described in Section 4.*

f) *If the engine is in the car, refit the catalytic converter as described in Section 18.*

g) *Refit the engine/transmission unit or the front suspension subframe with reference to Chapter 2F or 10 as applicable.*

16 Turbocharger – description and precautions

Description

1 A turbocharger is fitted to all 2.0 litre diesel engines. It increases engine efficiency by raising the pressure in the inlet manifold above atmospheric pressure. Instead of the air simply being sucked into the cylinders, it is forced in.

2 Energy for the operation of the turbocharger comes from the exhaust gas. The gas flows through a specially-shaped housing (the turbine housing) and, in so doing, spins the turbine wheel. The turbine wheel is attached to a shaft, at the end of which is another vaned wheel known as the compressor wheel. The compressor wheel spins in its own housing, and compresses the inlet air on the way to the inlet manifold.

3 Boost pressure (the pressure in the inlet manifold) is limited by a wastegate, which diverts the exhaust gas away from the turbine wheel in response to a pressure-sensitive actuator.

4 The turbo shaft is pressure-lubricated by an oil feed pipe from the main oil gallery. The shaft 'floats' on a cushion of oil. A drain pipe returns the oil to the sump.

Precautions

5 The turbocharger operates at extremely

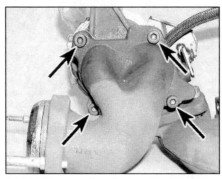

17.2 Exhaust outlet elbow-to-turbocharger retaining bolts (arrowed)

high speeds and temperatures. Certain precautions must be observed, to avoid premature failure of the turbo, or injury to the operator.

6 Do not operate the turbo with any of its parts exposed, or with any of its hoses removed. Foreign objects falling onto the rotating vanes could cause excessive damage, and (if ejected) personal injury.

7 Do not race the engine immediately after start-up, especially if it is cold. Give the oil a few seconds to circulate.

8 Always allow the engine to return to idle speed before switching it off – do not blip the throttle and switch off, as this will leave the turbo spinning without lubrication.

9 Allow the engine to idle for several minutes before switching off after a high-speed run.

10 Observe the recommended intervals for oil and filter changing, and use a reputable oil of the specified quality. Neglect of oil changing, or use of inferior oil, can cause carbon formation on the turbo shaft, leading to subsequent failure.

17 Turbocharger – removal, inspection and refitting

Removal

1 Remove the exhaust manifold as described in Section 15. The turbocharger and exhaust manifold are removed from the engine as a complete assembly. The turbocharger can then be separated from the manifold on the bench as follows.

2 Undo the four bolts securing the exhaust outlet elbow to the turbocharger body and

17.3 Turbocharger-to-exhaust manifold retaining nuts (arrowed)

separate the elbow from the turbocharger **(see illustration)**.

3 Undo the three retaining nuts and lift the turbocharger off the manifold studs **(see illustration)**.

Inspection

4 With the turbocharger removed, inspect the housing for cracks or other visible damage.

5 Spin the turbine or the compressor wheel, to verify that the shaft is intact and to feel for excessive shake or roughness. Some play is normal, since in use, the shaft is 'floating' on a film of oil. Check that the wheel vanes are undamaged.

6 If oil contamination of the exhaust or induction passages is apparent, it is likely that turbo shaft oil seals have failed.

7 No DIY repair of the turbo is possible and none of the internal or external parts are available separately. If the turbocharger is suspect in any way a complete new unit must be obtained.

Refitting

8 Refitting is a reverse of the removal procedure, bearing in mind the following points:

a) *If a new turbocharger is being fitted, change the engine oil and filter. Also renew the filter in the oil feed pipe.*

b) *Prime the turbocharger by injecting clean engine oil through the oil feed pipe union before reconnecting the union.*

18 Exhaust system – general information and component renewal

Refer to Chapter 4B, Section 21.

Chapter 4 Part D:
Emission control systems

Contents

Catalytic converter – general information and precautions 4
Emission control systems (diesel engines) –
   testing and component renewal 3
Emission control systems (petrol engines) –
   testing and component renewal 2
General information 1

Degrees of difficulty

Easy, suitable for novice with little experience	Fairly easy, suitable for beginner with some experience	Fairly difficult, suitable for competent DIY mechanic	Difficult, suitable for experienced DIY mechanic	Very difficult, suitable for expert DIY or professional

---

1 General information

All petrol engines use unleaded petrol and also have various other features built into the fuel system to help minimise harmful emissions. In addition, all engines are equipped with the crankcase emission control system described below. All engines are also equipped with a catalytic converter and an evaporative emission control system. 1.4 litre engines to emission standard L4, also utilise a secondary air injection system to quickly bring the catalytic converter up to normal working temperature.

All diesel engines are also designed to meet the strict emission requirements and are equipped with a crankcase emission control system and a catalytic converter. To further reduce exhaust emissions, all diesel engines are also fitted with an exhaust gas recirculation (EGR) system.

The emission control systems function as follows.

Petrol engines

Crankcase emission control

To reduce the emission of unburned hydrocarbons from the crankcase into the atmosphere, the engine is sealed and the blow-by gases and oil vapour are drawn from inside the crankcase, through a wire mesh oil separator, into the inlet tract to be burned by the engine during normal combustion.

Under all conditions the gases are forced out of the crankcase by the (relatively) higher crankcase pressure; if the engine is worn, the raised crankcase pressure (due to increased blow-by) will cause some of the flow to return under all manifold conditions.

Exhaust emission control

To minimise the amount of pollutants which escape into the atmosphere, all models are fitted with a catalytic converter in the exhaust system. The system is of the closed-loop type, in which one or two lambda sensors in the exhaust system provides the engine management ECU with constant feedback, enabling the ECU to adjust the air/fuel mixture ratio to provide the best possible conditions for the converter to operate.

The lambda sensor has a heating element built-in that is controlled by the ECU through the lambda sensor relay to quickly bring the sensor's tip to an efficient operating temperature. The sensor's tip is sensitive to oxygen and sends the ECU a varying voltage depending on the amount of oxygen in the exhaust gases; if the intake air/fuel mixture is too rich, the exhaust gases are low in oxygen so the sensor sends a low-voltage signal, the voltage rising as the mixture weakens and the amount of oxygen rises in the exhaust gases. Peak conversion efficiency of all major pollutants occurs if the intake air/fuel mixture is maintained at the chemically-correct ratio for the complete combustion of petrol of 14.7 parts (by weight) of air to 1 part of fuel (the 'stoichiometric' ratio). The sensor output voltage alters in a large step at this point, the ECU using the signal change as a reference point and correcting the intake air/fuel mixture accordingly by altering the fuel injector pulse width.

Evaporative emission control

To minimise the escape into the atmosphere of unburned hydrocarbons, an evaporative emission control system is fitted to all models. The fuel tank filler cap is sealed and a charcoal canister is mounted underneath the right-hand wing to collect the petrol vapours generated in the tank when the car is parked. It stores them until they can be cleared from the canister (under the control of the engine management ECU) via the purge valve into the inlet tract to be burned by the engine during normal combustion.

To ensure that the engine runs correctly when it is cold and/or idling and to protect the catalytic converter from the effects of an over-rich mixture, the purge control valve(s) is/are not opened by the ECU until the engine has warmed up, and the engine is under load; the valve solenoid is then modulated on and off to allow the stored vapour to pass into the inlet tract.

Secondary air injection

Later 1.4 litre engines to emission standard L4 are also equipped with a secondary air injection system. This system is designed to reduce exhaust emissions in the period between first starting the engine, and until the catalytic converter reaches operating (functioning) temperature. Introduction of air into the exhaust system during the initial start-up period, creates an 'afterburner' effect which quickly increases the temperature in the exhaust system front pipe, thus bringing the catalytic converter up to normal operating temperatures very quickly.

The system consists of an air pump, mounted at the front left-hand side of the car, an air injection valve, mounted on a bracket at the front of the cylinder head, a connecting pipe linking the valve to the exhaust manifold, and interconnecting air hoses.

The system operates for between 10 and 45 seconds after engine start-up, dependant on coolant temperature.

Diesel engines

Crankcase emission control

To reduce the emission of unburned hydrocarbons from the crankcase into the atmosphere, the engine is sealed and the blow-by gases and oil vapour are drawn from inside the crankcase, through a wire mesh oil separator, into the inlet tract to be burned by the engine during normal combustion.

Under all conditions the gases are forced out of the crankcase by the (relatively) higher crankcase pressure; if the engine is worn, the raised crankcase pressure (due to increased blow-by) will cause some of the flow to return under all manifold conditions.

Exhaust emission control

To minimise the level of exhaust pollutants released into the atmosphere, a catalytic converter is fitted in the exhaust system of all models.

The catalytic converter consists of a canister containing a fine mesh impregnated with a catalyst material, over which the hot exhaust gases pass. The catalyst speeds up the oxidation of harmful carbon monoxide, unburnt hydrocarbons and soot, effectively reducing the quantity of harmful products released into the atmosphere via the exhaust gases.

Exhaust gas recirculation system

This system is designed to recirculate small quantities of exhaust gas into the inlet tract, and therefore into the combustion process. This process reduces the level of oxides of nitrogen present in the final exhaust gas which is released into the atmosphere.

The volume of exhaust gas recirculated is controlled by vacuum supplied from the brake servo vacuum pump, via a solenoid valve controlled by the glow plug preheating system, or by an electronic control unit.

A vacuum-operated valve is fitted to the exhaust manifold, to regulate the quantity of exhaust gas recirculated. The valve is operated by the vacuum supplied via the solenoid valve.

Additionally, on certain models, a butterfly valve mounted on the inlet manifold allows the ratio of air-to-recirculated exhaust gas to be controlled. The butterfly valve also enables the exhaust gases to be drawn into the inlet manifold at idle or under light load, when the valve on the exhaust manifold is fully open.

The system is controlled by an electronic control unit, which receives information on coolant temperature, engine load, and engine speed, via the coolant temperature switch/sensor, throttle position switch/sensor and crankshaft sensor respectively.

2 Emission control systems (petrol engines) – testing and component renewal

Crankcase emission control

1 The components of this system require no attention other than to check that the hose(s) are clear and undamaged at regular intervals.

Evaporative emission control system

Testing

2 If the system is thought to be faulty, disconnect the hoses from the charcoal canister and purge control valve and check that they are clear by blowing through them. If the purge control valve(s) or charcoal canister are thought to be faulty, they must be renewed.

Charcoal canister – renewal

3 The charcoal canister is located behind the right-hand front wing. To gain access to the canister, firmly apply the handbrake, then jack up the front of the car and support it securely on axle stands (see Jacking and vehicle support). Undo the retaining screw from the base of the wheelarch liner then prise out the retaining clips and remove the liner from underneath the wing.

4 Slacken and remove the retaining bolt then free the canister from its mounting clamp and lower it out from underneath the wing. Mark the hoses for identification purposes.

5 Slacken the retaining clips then disconnect

2.7 Evaporative emission control system purge valve (arrowed) on 1.4 litre petrol engines

both hoses and remove the canister from the vehicle. Where the crimped-type hose clips are fitted, cut the clips and discard them, replace them with standard worm-drive hose clips on refitting. Where the hoses are equipped with quick-release fittings depress the centre collar of the fitting with a small flat-bladed screwdriver then detach the hose from the canister.

6 Refitting is a reverse of the removal procedure ensuring the hoses are correctly reconnected.

Purge valve(s) – renewal

7 The purge valve is located in the right-hand rear corner of the engine compartment **(see illustration)**.

8 Disconnect the battery negative terminal (refer to Disconnecting the battery in the Reference Section of this manual).

9 Depress the retaining clip and disconnect the wiring connector from the valve. Disconnect the hoses from either end of the valve then release the valve from its retaining clip or strap and remove it from the engine compartment, noting which way around it is fitted.

10 Refitting is a reversal of the removal procedure, ensuring the valve is fitted the correct way around and the hoses are securely connected.

Exhaust emission control

Testing

11 The performance of the catalytic converter can only be checked by measuring the exhaust gases using a good-quality, carefully-calibrated exhaust gas analyser. If access to such equipment can be gained, it should be connected and used according with the maker's instructions.

12 If the CO level at the tailpipe is too high, the vehicle should be taken to a Citroën dealer so that the complete engine management system can be thoroughly checked using the special diagnostic equipment. Once these have been checked and are known to be free from faults, the fault must be in the catalytic converter, which must be renewed.

Catalytic converter – renewal

13 Refer to Chapter 4A.

Lambda sensor(s) – renewal

Note 1: The lambda sensor is delicate and will not work if it is dropped or knocked, if its power supply is disrupted, or if any cleaning materials are used on it.

Note 2: Later 1.4 litre engines to emission standard L4 are fitted with a 'downstream' lambda sensor located after the catalytic converter. Removal and refitting procedures are the same for both sensors.

14 Trace the wiring back from the lambda sensor, which is screwed into the top of the exhaust front pipe, to the top of the transmission unit. Disconnect both wiring

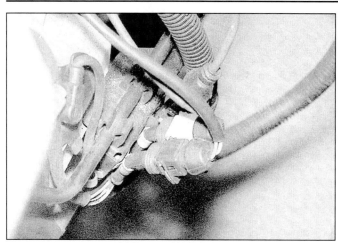

2.14 On 1.4 and 1.6 litre petrol engines the lambda sensor wiring connectors are clipped onto the front of the transmission . . .

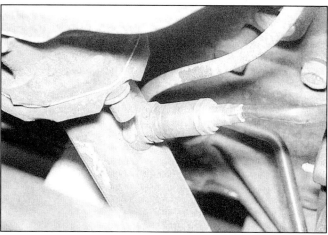

2.15 . . . and the sensor is screwed into the top of the exhaust front pipe

connectors and free the wiring from any relevant retaining clips or ties **(see illustration)**.

15 Unscrew the sensor from the exhaust system front pipe and remove it, along with its sealing washer **(see illustration)**.

16 Refitting is a reverse of the removal procedure, using a new sealing washer. Prior to installing the sensor apply a smear of high temperature grease to the sensor threads. Ensure the sensor is securely tightened and that the wiring is correctly routed and in no danger of contacting either the exhaust system or engine.

Secondary air injection

Testing

17 The components of this system require no attention other than to check that the hose(s) are clear and undamaged at regular intervals.

18 Accurate testing of the system operation entails the use of diagnostic test equipment and should be entrusted to a Citroën dealer.

Air pump – renewal

19 The air pump is located at the front left-hand side of the engine compartment.

20 Disconnect the battery negative terminal (refer to *Disconnecting the battery* in the Reference Section of this manual).

21 Slacken and remove the three nuts and withdraw the pump from the mounting bracket.

22 Disconnect the air hoses and wiring connector and remove the pump.

23 Refitting is a reverse of the removal procedure, ensuring that the hoses are correctly reconnected.

Air injection valve

24 Disconnect the battery negative terminal (refer to *Disconnecting the battery* in the Reference Section of this manual).

25 Slacken and remove the retaining screws, and remove the shroud from the top of the exhaust manifold.

26 Undo the two bolts securing the connecting pipe flange to the exhaust manifold.

27 Undo the two bolts securing the valve mounting bracket to the cylinder head.

28 Withdraw the valve and connecting pipe, disconnect the air hose and remove the air injection valve and connecting pipe as an assembly.

29 If necessary, the air pipe can be removed from the valve and the valve removed from the mounting bracket after undoing the two retaining nuts. Collect the flange gasket after removal.

30 Refitting is a reverse of the removal procedure, but use a new gasket between the valve and mounting bracket.

---

3 Emission control systems (diesel engines) – testing and component renewal

Crankcase emission control

1 The components of this system require no attention other than to check that the hose(s) are clear and undamaged at regular intervals.

Exhaust emission control

Testing

2 The performance of the catalytic converter can only be checked by measuring the exhaust gases using a good-quality, carefully-calibrated exhaust gas analyser. If access to such equipment can be gained, it should be connected and used according with the maker's instructions.

3 If the exhaust emissions are excessive, before assuming the catalytic converter is faulty, it is worth checking the problem is not due to a faulty injector(s), or other diesel fuel system fault. Refer to your Citroën dealer for further information.

Catalytic converter – renewal

4 Refer to Chapter 4B or 4C.

Exhaust gas recirculation system

Testing

5 Testing of the system should be entrusted to a Citroën dealer.

Component renewal

1.9 litre – DJY (XUD9A engine) models

6 Disconnect the battery negative terminal (refer to *Disconnecting the battery* in the Reference Section of this manual).

7 Remove the air inlet duct and air distribution housing as described in Chapter 4B, Section 3.

8 Remove the cylinder head cover as described in Chapter 2C.

9 Remove the clip securing the lower flexible portion of the EGR pipe to the EGR valve. If the original crimped clip is still in place, cut it off; new clips are supplied by Citroën parts stockists with a screw clamp fixing. If a screw clamp type clip is fitted, undo the screw and manipulate the clip off the pipe.

10 Disconnect the vacuum hose from the top of the EGR valve.

11 Undo the two bolts securing the EGR valve to the exhaust manifold. Lift off the valve and recover the gasket.

12 To remove the EGR solenoid valve, disconnect the two vacuum hoses and the wiring connector. Undo the mounting nuts and remove the valve from the mounting bracket.

13 Refitting is a reverse of the removal procedure, bearing in mind the following points:

a) *Ensure that the EGR valve and exhaust manifold mating faces are clean and use a new gasket.*

b) *Secure the EGR pipe with new screw clamp type clips, if crimped type clips were initially fitted.*

c) *Refit the cylinder head cover as described in Chapter 2C.*

d) Refit the air inlet duct and air distribution housing as described in Chapter 4B.

1.9 litre – DHY (XUD9TE engine) models

14 Disconnect the battery negative terminal (refer to *Disconnecting the battery* in the Reference Section of this manual).

15 Remove the intercooler as described in Chapter 4B, Section 20.

16 Remove the air inlet ducts as described in Chapter 4B, Section 3.

17 Remove the cylinder head cover as described in Chapter 2C.

18 Remove the clips securing the flexible portion of the EGR pipe to the EGR valve and inlet manifold. If the original crimped clips are still in place, cut them off; new clips are supplied by Citroën parts stockists with a screw clamp fixing. If screw clamp type clips are fitted, undo the screws and manipulate the clips off the pipe.

19 Disconnect the vacuum hose from the top of the EGR valve.

20 Undo the two bolts securing the EGR valve to the exhaust manifold. Lift off the valve and recover the gasket.

21 To remove the EGR solenoid valve, disconnect the two vacuum hoses and the wiring connector. Undo the mounting nuts and remove the valve from the mounting bracket.

22 Refitting is a reverse of the removal procedure, bearing in mind the following points:

a) *Ensure that the EGR valve and exhaust manifold mating faces are clean and use a new gasket.*

b) *Secure the EGR pipe with new screw clamp type clips, if crimped type clips were initially fitted.*

c) *Refit the cylinder head cover as described in Chapter 2C.*

d) *Refit the air inlet ducts and intercooler as described in Chapter 4B.*

1.9 litre – DHV (XUD9BSD engine) models

23 Disconnect the battery negative terminal (refer to *Disconnecting the battery* in the Reference Section of this manual).

24 Remove the air inlet ducts throttle valve housing and air inlet elbow as described in Chapter 4B, Section 3.

25 Remove the cylinder head cover as described in Chapter 2C.

26 Disconnect the vacuum hose from the top of the EGR valve.

27 Remove the clip securing the upper flexible portion of the EGR pipe to the inlet manifold. If the original crimped clip is still in place, cut it off; new clips are supplied by Citroën parts stockists with a screw clamp fixing. If a screw clamp type clip is fitted, undo the screw and manipulate the clip off the pipe.

28 Undo the two bolts securing the EGR valve to the exhaust manifold.

29 Lift and swivel the valve until sufficient clearance exists to enable the remaining EGR pipe securing clip to be removed.

30 Remove the EGR pipe then withdraw the valve and recover the gasket.

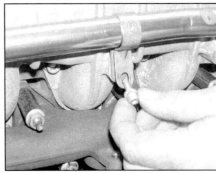

3.39 On 2.0 litre diesel engines, undo the bolts securing the EGR pipe support clips to the inlet manifold . . .

31 To remove the EGR solenoid valve, disconnect the two vacuum hoses and the wiring connector. Undo the mounting bracket bolts and remove the valve from the engine compartment.

32 Refitting is a reverse of the removal procedure, bearing in mind the following points:

a) *Ensure that the EGR valve and exhaust manifold mating faces are clean and use a new gasket.*

b) *Secure the EGR pipe with new screw clamp type clips, if crimped type clips were initially fitted.*

c) *Refit the cylinder head cover as described in Chapter 2C.*

d) *Refit the air inlet elbow, throttle valve housing and inlet ducts as described in Chapter 4B.*

1.9 litre – WJZ (DW8 engine) models

33 Disconnect the battery negative terminal (refer to *Disconnecting the battery* in the Reference Section of this manual).

34 Remove the air distribution housing as described in Chapter 4B, Section 3.

35 Unscrew the EGR valve housing from the air distribution housing and recover the O-ring seal.

36 To remove the EGR pipe, undo the two bolts securing the pipe to the exhaust manifold and release the pipe side support strap.

37 Remove the inlet manifold as described in Chapter 4B, and lift out the EGR pipe.

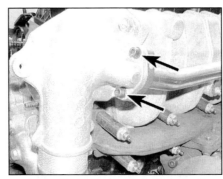

3.41a Undo the two bolts (arrowed) securing the EGR pipe to the inlet manifold elbow . . .

3.40 . . . and the two nuts securing the EGR valve to the exhaust manifold

38 Refitting is a reverse of the removal procedure, bearing in mind the following points:

a) *Ensure that the EGR valve and exhaust manifold mating faces are clean.*

b) *Refit the inlet manifold and air distribution housing as described in Chapter 4B.*

2.0 litre – RHY (DW10TD engine) models

Note: *There is insufficient clearance to gain access to all the relevant EGR valve attachments from either above or below with the engine in the car. Two alternatives are possible; either remove the complete engine/transmission unit from the car as described in Chapter 2F, or remove the front suspension subframe as described in Chapter 10. Both are involved operations and the course of action taken is largely dependent on the tools, equipment, skill and patience available.*

39 Undo the bolts securing the EGR pipe support clips to the inlet manifold **(see illustration)**.

40 Disconnect the vacuum hose, then undo the two nuts securing the EGR valve to the exhaust manifold **(see illustration)**.

41 Undo the two bolts securing the EGR pipe to the inlet manifold elbow. Withdraw the EGR valve and pipe assembly from the manifold and recover the gasket at the EGR pipe-to-inlet manifold flange **(see illustrations)**.

42 To separate the EGR pipe from the valve, remove the clip securing the upper flexible portion of the pipe to the valve. If the original crimped clip is still in place, cut it off; new

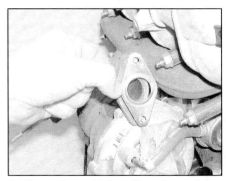

3.41b . . . then withdraw the valve and pipe assembly and recover the gasket at the EGR pipe flange

clips are supplied by Citroën parts stockists with a screw clamp fixing. If a screw clamp type clip is fitted, undo the screw and manipulate the clip off the pipe.

43 To remove the EGR solenoid valve, disconnect the two vacuum hoses and the wiring connector. Undo the mounting bracket bolts and remove the valve from the engine compartment.

44 Refitting is a reverse of the removal procedure, bearing in mind the following points:

a) *Ensure that the EGR valve and exhaust manifold mating faces are clean.*

b) *Secure the EGR pipe with new screw clamp type clips, if crimped type clips were initially fitted.*

c) *Refit the engine/transmission unit or the front suspension subframe as described in Chapter 2F or 10, as applicable.*

4 Catalytic converter – general information and precautions

1 The catalytic converter is a reliable and simple device which needs no maintenance in itself, but there are some facts of which an owner should be aware if the converter is to function properly for its full service life.

Petrol engines

a) *DO NOT use leaded petrol in a car equipped with a catalytic converter – the lead will coat the precious metals, reducing their converting efficiency and will eventually destroy the converter.*

b) *Always keep the ignition and fuel systems well-maintained in accordance with the manufacturer's schedule.*

c) *If the engine develops a misfire, do not drive the car at all (or at least as little as possible) until the fault is cured.*

d) *DO NOT push- or tow-start the car – this will soak the catalytic converter in unburned fuel, causing it to overheat when the engine does start.*

e) *DO NOT switch off the ignition at high engine speeds.*

f) *DO NOT use fuel or engine oil additives – these may contain substances harmful to the catalytic converter.*

g) *DO NOT continue to use the car if the engine burns oil to the extent of leaving a visible trail of blue smoke.*

h) *Remember that the catalytic converter operates at very high temperatures. DO NOT, therefore, park the car in dry undergrowth, over long grass or piles of dead leaves after a long run.*

i) *Remember that the catalytic converter is FRAGILE – do not strike it with tools during servicing work.*

j) *In some cases a sulphurous smell (like that of rotten eggs) may be noticed from the exhaust. This is common to many catalytic converter-equipped cars and once the car has covered a few thousand miles the problem should disappear.*

k) *The catalytic converter, used on a well-maintained and well-driven car, should last for between 50 000 and 100 000 miles – if the converter is no longer effective it must be renewed.*

Diesel engines

2 Refer to parts f, g, h and i of the petrol engine information given above.

Chapter 5 Part A:
Starting and charging systems

Contents

Alternator – removal and refitting 8
Alternator – testing and overhaul 9
Alternator drivebelt – removal, refitting and tensioning 7
Battery – removal and refitting 4
Battery – testing and charging 3
Battery check . . . . .See *Weekly checks*
Battery tray and mounting plate – removal and refitting 5
Charging system – testing 6
Electrical fault finding – general information 2

Electrical system check . . . . .See *Weekly checks*
General information and precautions 1
Ignition switch – removal and refitting 13
Oil level sensor – removal and refitting 15
Oil pressure warning light switch – removal and refitting 14
Starter motor – removal and refitting 11
Starter motor – testing and overhaul 12
Starting system – testing 10

Degrees of difficulty

Easy, suitable for novice with little experience		**Fairly easy,** suitable for beginner with some experience		**Fairly difficult,** suitable for competent DIY mechanic		**Difficult,** suitable for experienced DIY mechanic	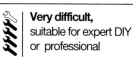	**Very difficult,** suitable for expert DIY or professional

Specifications

System type . . . .   12-volt, negative earth

Battery

Type . . . .   Fulmen, Delco or Steco
Charge condition:
   Poor . . . .   12.5 volts
   Normal . . . .   12.6 volts
   Good . . . .   12.7 volts

Alternator

Type . . . .   Valeo or Bosch (depending on model)

Starter motor

Type . . . .   Valeo or Bosch (depending on model)

Torque wrench setting	Nm	lbf ft
Battery mounting plate retaining bolts	45	33

1 General information and precautions

General information

The engine electrical system consists mainly of the charging and starting systems. Because of their engine-related functions, these components are covered separately from the body electrical devices such as the lights, instruments, etc (which are covered in Chapter 12). On petrol models refer to Part B for information on the ignition system, and on diesel models refer to Part C for information on the preheating system.

The electrical system is of the 12-volt negative earth type.

The battery is of the low maintenance or 'maintenance-free' (sealed for life) type and is charged by the alternator, which is belt-driven from the crankshaft pulley.

The starter motor is of the pre-engaged type incorporating an integral solenoid. On starting, the solenoid moves the drive pinion into engagement with the flywheel ring gear before the starter motor is energised. Once the engine has started, a one-way clutch prevents the motor armature being driven by the engine until the pinion disengages from the flywheel.

Precautions

Further details of the various systems are given in the relevant Sections of this Chapter. While some repair procedures are given, the usual course of action is to renew the component concerned. The owner whose interest extends beyond mere component renewal should obtain a copy of the *Automobile Electrical & Electronic Systems Manual*, available from the publishers of this manual.

It is necessary to take extra care when working on the electrical system to avoid damage to semi-conductor devices (diodes and transistors), and to avoid the risk of personal injury. In addition to the precautions given in *Safety first!* at the beginning of this manual, observe the following when working on the system:

Always remove rings, watches, etc, before working on the electrical system. Even with the battery disconnected, capacitive discharge could occur if a component's live terminal is earthed through a metal object. This could cause a shock or nasty burn.

Do not reverse the battery connections. Components such as the alternator, electronic control units, or any other components having semi-conductor circuitry could be irreparably damaged.

If the engine is being started using jump leads and a slave battery, connect the batteries positive-to-positive and negative-to-negative (see 'Jump starting'). This also applies when connecting a battery charger.

Never disconnect the battery terminals, the alternator, any electrical wiring or any test instruments when the engine is running.

Do not allow the engine to turn the alternator when the alternator is not connected.

Never 'test' for alternator output by 'flashing' the output lead to earth.

Never use an ohmmeter of the type incorporating a hand-cranked generator for circuit or continuity testing.

Always ensure that the battery negative terminal is disconnected when working on the electrical system.

Before using electric-arc welding equipment on the car, disconnect the battery, alternator and components such as the engine management and the ABS electronic control units to protect them from the risk of damage.

Several systems fitted to the vehicle require battery power to be available at all times, either to ensure their continued operation (such as the clock) or to maintain control unit memories or security codes which would be wiped if the battery were to be disconnected. To ensure that there are no unforeseen consequences of this action, Refer to 'Disconnecting the battery' in the Reference Section of this manual for further information.

2 Electrical fault finding – general information

Refer to Chapter 12.

3 Battery – testing and charging

Standard and low maintenance battery – testing

1 If the vehicle covers a small annual mileage, it is worthwhile checking the specific gravity of the electrolyte every three months to determine the state of charge of the battery. Use a hydrometer to make the check and compare the results with the following table. Note that the specific gravity readings assume an electrolyte temperature of 15°C (60°F); for every 10°C (18°F) below 15°C (60°F) subtract 0.007. For every 10°C (18°F) above 15°C (60°F) add 0.007.

	Above 25°C (77°F)	Below 25°C (77°F)
Fully-charged	1.210 to 1.230	1.270 to 1.290
70% charged	1.170 to 1.190	1.230 to 1.250
Discharged	1.050 to 1.070	1.110 to 1.130

2 If the battery condition is suspect, first check the specific gravity of electrolyte in each cell. A variation of 0.040 or more between any cells indicates loss of electrolyte or deterioration of the internal plates.

3 If the specific gravity variation is 0.040 or more, the battery should be renewed. If the cell variation is satisfactory but the battery is discharged, it should be charged as described later in this Section.

Maintenance-free battery – testing

4 In cases where a 'sealed for life' maintenance-free battery is fitted, topping-up and testing of the electrolyte in each cell is not possible. The condition of the battery can therefore only be tested using a battery condition indicator or a voltmeter.

5 Certain models may be fitted with a 'Delco' type maintenance-free battery, with a built-in charge condition indicator. The indicator is located in the top of the battery casing, and indicates the condition of the battery from its colour. If the indicator shows green, then the battery is in a good state of charge. If the indicator turns darker, eventually to black, then the battery requires charging, as described later in this Section. If the indicator shows clear/yellow, then the electrolyte level in the battery is too low to allow further use, and the battery should be renewed.

Caution: Do not attempt to charge, load or jump start a battery when the indicator shows clear/yellow.

6 If testing the battery using a voltmeter, connect the voltmeter across the battery and compare the result with those given in the Specifications under 'charge condition'. The test is only accurate if the battery has not been subjected to any kind of charge for the previous six hours. If this is not the case, switch on the headlights for 30 seconds, then wait four to five minutes before testing the battery after switching off the headlights. All other electrical circuits must be switched off, so check that the doors and tailgate are fully shut when making the test.

7 If the voltage reading is less than 12.2 volts, then the battery is discharged, whilst a reading of 12.2 to 12.4 volts indicates a partially discharged condition.

8 If the battery is to be charged, remove it from the vehicle (see Section 4) and charge it as described later in this Section.

Standard and low maintenance battery – charging

Note: *The following is intended as a guide only. Always refer to the manufacturer's recommendations (often printed on a label attached to the battery) before charging a battery.*

9 Charge the battery at a rate of 3.5 to 4.0 amps and continue to charge the battery at this rate until no further rise in specific gravity is noted over a four hour period.

10 Alternatively, a trickle charger charging at the rate of 1.5 amps can safely be used overnight.

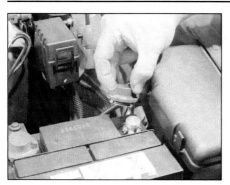

4.2a Unscrew the plastic-capped nut . . .

4.2b . . . or slacken the clamp bolt nut to release the battery negative terminal

4.3 With the quick-release type of battery positive terminal fixing, lift the cover to release the clamp

11 Specially rapid 'boost' charges which are claimed to restore the power of the battery in 1 to 2 hours are not recommended, as they can cause serious damage to the battery plates through overheating.

12 While charging the battery, note that the temperature of the electrolyte should never exceed 37.8°C (100°F).

Maintenance-free battery – charging

Note: *The following is intended as a guide only. Always refer to the manufacturer's recommendations (often printed on a label attached to the battery) before charging a battery.*

13 This battery type takes considerably longer to fully recharge than the standard type, the time taken being dependent on the extent of discharge, but it can take anything up to three days.

14 A constant voltage type charger is required, to be set, when connected, to 13.9 to 14.9 volts with a charger current below 25 amps. Using this method, the battery should be usable within three hours, giving a voltage reading of 12.5 volts, but this is for a partially discharged battery and, as mentioned, full charging can take considerably longer.

15 If the battery is to be charged from a fully discharged state (condition reading less than 12.2 volts), have it recharged by your Citroën dealer or local automotive electrician, as the

charge rate is higher and constant supervision during charging is necessary.

4 Battery – removal and refitting

Note: *Refer to 'Disconnecting the battery' in the Reference Section of this manual before proceeding.*

Removal

1 The battery is located on the left-hand side of the engine compartment.

2 Disconnect the lead(s) at the battery negative (earth) terminal. Two possible types of battery negative terminal fixings may be encountered. With the first type, the leads are secured to a stud on the top of the terminal by means of a plastic-capped nut. On the second type a conventional fitting is used, secured in position by a clamp bolt and nut **(see illustrations)**.

3 Remove the insulation cover (where fitted) and disconnect the positive terminal lead(s). The positive terminal fixings will either be one of the types described in paragraph 2, or of the quick release type, whereby lifting the plastic insulation cover automatically releases the terminal clamp **(see illustration)**.

4 Unscrew the battery clamp retaining bolt and slacken the nut on the retaining stud.

Release the clamp stud from its lower location and remove the clamp.

5 Lift the battery out of the engine compartment.

Refitting

7 Refitting is a reversal of removal, but smear petroleum jelly on the terminals when reconnecting the leads, and always reconnect the positive lead first, and the negative lead last.

5 Battery tray and mounting plate – removal and refitting

Removal

1 Remove the battery as described in Section 4.

2 Referring to the relevant Part of Chapter 4, remove the air cleaner and air inlet duct components as necessary for access to the battery tray.

3 On models where the engine management electronic control unit (ECU) is housed in the end of the battery tray, lift off the cover or peel back the protective sleeve, and disconnect the wiring connector from the ECU **(see illustration)**.

4 Release all the relevant clips securing the wiring to the tray and remove the battery tray from the engine compartment **(see illustrations)**.

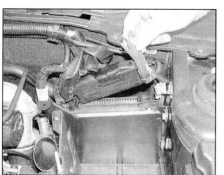

5.3 Disconnect the ECU wiring connector . . .

5.4a . . . release the wiring from the retaining clips . . .

5.4b . . . and lift out the battery tray

5.5 Undo the four battery mounting plate retaining bolts (arrowed) . . .

5.6 . . . then withdraw the mounting plate after releasing any additional wiring retaining clips

8.3a Lift off the rubber covers . . .

5 To remove the mounting plate, undo the four bolts securing the mounting plate to the top of the left-hand engine/transmission mounting **(see illustration)**.

6 Release any additional wiring retaining clips and withdraw the mounting plate from the engine compartment **(see illustration)**.

Refitting

7 Refitting is a reversal of removal, ensuring that the mounting plate retaining bolts are tightened to the specified torque.

6 Charging system – testing

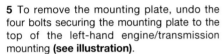

Note: *Refer to the warnings given in 'Safety first!' and in Section 1 of this Chapter before starting work.*

1 If the ignition warning light fails to illuminate when the ignition is switched on, first check the alternator wiring connections for security. If satisfactory, check that the warning light bulb has not blown, and that the bulbholder is secure in its location in the instrument panel. If the light still fails to illuminate, check the continuity of the warning light feed wire from the alternator to the bulbholder. If all is satisfactory, the alternator is at fault and should be renewed or taken to an auto-electrician for testing and repair.

2 If the ignition warning light illuminates when the engine is running, stop the engine and

check that the drivebelt is correctly tensioned (see Chapter 1A or 1B) and that the alternator connections are secure. If all is so far satisfactory, have the alternator checked by an auto-electrician for testing and repair.

3 If the alternator output is suspect even though the warning light works correctly, the regulated voltage may be checked as follows.

4 Connect a voltmeter across the battery terminals and start the engine.

5 Increase the engine speed until the voltmeter reading remains steady; the reading should be approximately 12 to 13 volts, and no more than 14 volts.

6 Switch on as many electrical accessories (eg, the headlights, heated rear window and heater blower) as possible, and check that the alternator maintains the regulated voltage at around 13 to 14 volts.

7 If the regulated voltage is not as stated, the fault may be due to worn brushes, weak brush springs, a faulty voltage regulator, a faulty diode, a severed phase winding or worn or damaged slip rings. The alternator should be renewed or taken to an auto-electrician for testing and repair.

7 Alternator drivebelt – removal, refitting and tensioning

Refer to the procedure given for the auxiliary drivebelt in Chapter 1A or 1B.

8 Alternator – removal and refitting

Removal

1 Disconnect the battery negative terminal (refer to *Disconnecting the battery* in the Reference Section of this manual).

2 Remove the auxiliary drivebelt as described in Chapter 1A or 1B.

3 Remove the rubber covers (where fitted) from the alternator terminals, then unscrew the retaining nuts and disconnect the wiring from the rear of the alternator **(see illustrations)**.

4 Unscrew the nut(s) and/or bolt(s) securing the alternator to the upper mounting bracket **(see illustration)**.

5 Unscrew the lower nut(s) and/or mounting bolt(s), or undo the nut securing the adjuster bolt bracket to the alternator (as applicable). Note that, where a long through-bolt is used to secure the alternator in position, the bolt does not need to be fully removed; the alternator can be disengaged from the bolt once it has been slackened sufficiently. On some models, it may be necessary to remove the drivebelt idler/tensioner pulley to gain access to the alternator mounting nuts and bolts (depending on specification). On 2.0 litre diesel models, the lower front mounting bolt also carries the auxiliary drivebelt idler pulley which can be left in position on the bolt as it is removed **(see illustrations)**.

8.3b . . . then undo the nuts (arrowed) and disconnect the wiring from the alternator

8.4 Slacken and remove the alternator upper mounting bolt . . .

8.5a . . . and lower bolt (arrowed), and remove the alternator – 1.8 litre petrol engine model

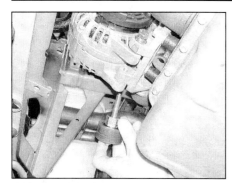

8.5b On 2.0 litre diesel engine models, the lower front mounting bolt also carries the auxiliary drivebelt idler pulley

6 Manoeuvre the alternator away from its mounting brackets and out of the engine bay.

Refitting

7 Refitting is a reversal of removal, tensioning the auxiliary drivebelt with reference to Chapter 1A or 1B, and ensuring that the alternator mountings are securely tightened.

9 Alternator – testing and overhaul

If the alternator is thought to be suspect, it should be removed from the vehicle and taken to an auto-electrician for testing. Most auto-electricians will be able to supply and fit brushes at a reasonable cost. However, check on the cost of repairs before proceeding as it may prove more economical to obtain a new or exchange alternator.

10 Starting system – testing

Note: *Refer to the precautions given in 'Safety first!' and in Section 1 of this Chapter before starting work.*

1 If the starter motor fails to operate when the ignition key is turned to the appropriate position, the following possible causes may be to blame.
 a) *The battery is faulty.*
 b) *The electrical connections between the switch, solenoid, battery and starter motor are somewhere failing to pass the necessary current from the battery through the starter to earth.*
 c) *The solenoid is faulty.*
 d) *The starter motor is mechanically or electrically defective.*

2 To check the battery, switch on the headlights. If they dim after a few seconds, this indicates that the battery is discharged – recharge (see Section 3) or renew the battery.

If the headlights glow brightly, operate the ignition switch and observe the lights. If they dim, then this indicates that current is reaching the starter motor, therefore the fault must lie in the starter motor. If the lights continue to glow brightly (and no clicking sound can be heard from the starter motor solenoid), this indicates that there is a fault in the circuit or solenoid – see following paragraphs. If the starter motor turns slowly when operated, but the battery is in good condition, then this shows that either the starter motor is faulty, or there is considerable resistance in the circuit.

3 If a fault in the circuit is suspected, disconnect the battery leads (including the earth connection to the body), the starter/solenoid wiring and the engine/transmission earth strap. Thoroughly clean the connections, and reconnect the leads and wiring, then use a voltmeter or test lamp to check that full battery voltage is available at the battery positive lead connection to the solenoid, and that the earth is sound. Smear petroleum jelly around the battery terminals to prevent corrosion – corroded connections are amongst the most frequent causes of electrical system faults.

4 If the battery and all connections are in good condition, check the circuit by disconnecting the ignition switch feed wire from the solenoid terminal. Connect a voltmeter or test lamp between the wire end and a good earth (such as the battery negative terminal), and check that the wire is live when the ignition switch is turned to the 'start' position. If it is, then the circuit is sound – if not the circuit wiring can be checked as described in Chapter 12.

5 The solenoid contacts can be checked by connecting a voltmeter or test lamp between the battery positive feed connection on the starter side of the solenoid, and earth. When the ignition switch is turned to the 'start' position, there should be a reading or lighted bulb, as applicable. If there is no reading or lighted bulb, the solenoid is faulty and should be renewed.

6 If the circuit and solenoid are proved sound, the fault must lie in the starter

motor. In this event, it may be possible to have the starter motor overhauled by a specialist, but check on the cost of spares before proceeding, as it may prove more economical to obtain a new or exchange motor.

11 Starter motor – removal and refitting

Removal

1 Disconnect the battery negative terminal (refer to *Disconnecting the battery* in the Reference Section of this manual).

2 So that access to the motor can be gained both from above and below, firmly apply the handbrake then jack up the front of the vehicle and support it on axle stands (see *Jacking and vehicle support*).

2 On 1.4 and 1.6 litre petrol engine models, remove the air cleaner and air inlet duct(s) as necessary for access to the starter motor.

3 Slacken and remove the two retaining nuts and disconnect the wiring from the starter motor solenoid. Recover the washers under the nuts **(see illustration)**.

4 Undo the three mounting bolts (two at the rear of the motor, and one which comes through from the top of the transmission housing), supporting the motor as the bolts are withdrawn **(see illustration)**. Recover the washers from under the bolt heads and note the locations of any wiring or hose brackets secured by the bolts.

5 Manoeuvre the starter motor out from underneath the engine and recover the locating dowel(s) from the starter motor/transmission (as applicable).

Refitting

6 Refitting is a reversal of removal, ensuring that the locating dowel(s) are correctly positioned. Also make sure that any wiring or hose brackets are in place under the bolt heads as noted prior to removal.

11.3 Unscrew the two nuts (arrowed) and disconnect the wiring from the rear of the starter motor – 1.8 litre petrol engine model

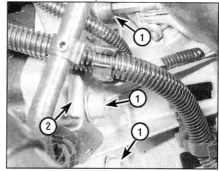

11.4 Unscrew the starter motor securing bolts (1). Note the location of the bracket (2) – 1.8 litre petrol engine model

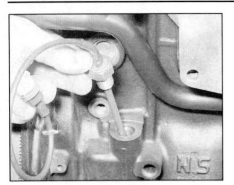

15.2 Removing the oil level sensor from the cylinder block

12 Starter motor –
testing and overhaul

If the starter motor is thought to be suspect, it should be removed from the vehicle and taken to an auto-electrician for testing. Most auto-electricians will be able to supply and fit brushes at a reasonable cost. However, check on the cost of repairs before proceeding as it may prove more economical to obtain a new or exchange motor.

13 Ignition switch –
removal and refitting

The ignition switch is integral with the steering column lock, and can be removed as described in Chapter 10.

14 Oil pressure warning light
switch – removal and refitting

Removal

1 The switch is located at the front of the cylinder block, above the oil filter mounting. Note that on some models access to the switch may be improved if the vehicle is jacked up and supported on axle stands so that the switch can be reached from underneath (see *Jacking and vehicle support*).
2 Disconnect the battery negative terminal (refer to *Disconnecting the battery* in the Reference Section of this manual).
3 Remove the protective sleeve from the wiring plug (where applicable), then disconnect the wiring from the switch.

4 Unscrew the switch from the cylinder block, and recover the sealing washer. Be prepared for oil spillage, and if the switch is to be left removed from the engine for any length of time, plug the hole in the cylinder block.

Refitting

5 Examine the sealing washer for signs of damage or deterioration and if necessary renew.
6 Refit the switch, complete with washer, and tighten it securely. Reconnect the wiring connector.
7 Lower the vehicle to the ground then check and, if necessary, top up the engine oil as described in *Weekly checks*.

15 Oil level sensor –
removal and refitting

1 The sensor is located on the front side of the cylinder block, just to the right of the oil filter.
2 The removal and refitting procedure is as described for the oil pressure switch in Section 14. Access is most easily obtained from underneath the vehicle **(see illustration)**.

Chapter 5 Part B:
Ignition system (petrol engines)

Contents

Ignition HT coil – removal, testing and refitting 3
Ignition system – general information 1
Ignition system – testing 2
Ignition system check . . . . See Chapter 1A
Ignition timing – checking and adjustment 4
Knock sensor – removal and refitting 5
Spark plugs . . . . See Chapter 1A

Degrees of difficulty

Easy, suitable for novice with little experience	**Fairly easy,** suitable for beginner with some experience	**Fairly difficult,** suitable for competent DIY mechanic	**Difficult,** suitable for experienced DIY mechanic	**Very difficult,** suitable for expert DIY or professional

Specifications

General

System type	Static (distributorless) ignition system controlled by engine management ECU
Firing order	1-3-4-2 (No 1 cylinder at transmission end)
Spark plugs	See Chapter 1A Specifications
Ignition timing	Controlled by engine management ECU

Ignition HT coil

Resistances*:
  8-valve engines:

Primary windings	0.5 to 0.8 ohms
Secondary windings – Bosch coil	14.0 k ohms
Secondary windings – Sagem Lucas coil	7.1 k ohms

  16-valve engines:

Primary windings	0.8 ohms
Secondary windings	10.0 k ohms

*The above results are approximate values and are accurate only when the coil is at 20°C. See text for further information

Torque wrench setting

	Nm	lbf ft
Knock sensor securing bolt	20	15

1 Ignition system – general information

Early 1.4 and 1.6 litre engines, and all 1.8 litre (8-valve) engines

The ignition system is integrated with the fuel injection system to form a combined engine management system under the control of one ECU (See Chapter 4A for further information). The ignition side of the system is of the static (distributorless) type, consisting only of two twin-output ignition coils. The ignition coils are housed in a single unit, mounted on the left-hand end of the cylinder head; four HT leads connect the coil output terminals to the spark plugs.

Each ignition coil serves two cylinders (one coil supplies cylinders 1 and 4, and the other cylinders 2 and 3).

Under the control of the ECU, the ignition coil operates on the 'wasted spark' principle, ie, each spark plug sparks twice for every cycle of the engine, once during the compression stroke and once during the exhaust stroke. The spark voltage is greatest in the cylinder which is under compression; in the cylinder on its exhaust stroke, the compression is low and this produces a very weak spark which has no effect on the exhaust gases.

The ECU uses its inputs from the various sensors to calculate the required ignition advance setting and coil charging time, depending on engine temperature, load and speed. At idle speeds, the ECU varies the ignition timing to alter the torque characteristic of the engine, enabling the idle speed to be controlled. This system operates in conjunction with the idle speed stepper motor/idle actuator valve – see Chapter 4A for additional details.

According to engine management system type, a knock sensor may also incorporated into the ignition system. Mounted onto the cylinder block, the sensor detects the high-frequency vibrations caused when the engine starts to pre-ignite, or 'pink'. Under these conditions, the knock sensor sends an electrical signal to the ECU which in turn retards the ignition advance setting in small steps until the 'pinking' ceases.

Later 1.4 and 1.6 litre engines, and all 1.8 and 2.0 litre (16-valve) engines

On these models, the ignition side of the system is also of the static (distributorless) type and operates as described previously. The primary difference is that the ignition coils are housed in a single unit mounted directly above the spark plugs. The coils are integral with the spark plug caps and are pushed directly onto the spark plugs, one for each plug. This removes the need for any HT leads connecting the coils to the plugs.

2 Ignition system – testing

> **Warning: Voltages produced by an electronic ignition system are considerably higher than those produced by conventional ignition systems. Extreme care must be taken when working on the system with the ignition switched on. Persons with surgically-implanted cardiac pacemaker devices should keep well clear of the ignition circuits, components and test equipment.**

If a fault appears in the engine management (fuel injection/ignition) system, first ensure that the fault is not due to a poor electrical connection or poor maintenance; ie, check that the air cleaner filter element is clean, the spark plugs are in good condition and correctly gapped, that the engine breather hoses are clear and undamaged, referring to Chapter 1A for further information. Also check that the accelerator cable is correctly adjusted as described in Chapter 4A. If the engine is running very roughly, check the compression pressures and the valve clearances as described in Chapter 2A or 2B.

If these checks fail to reveal the cause of the problem the vehicle should be taken to a suitably-equipped Citroën dealer for testing. A wiring block connector is incorporated in the engine management circuit into which a special electronic diagnostic tester can be plugged. The tester will locate the fault quickly and simply alleviating the need to test all the system components individually which is a time consuming operation that carries a high risk of damaging the ECU.

The only ignition system checks which can be carried out by the home mechanic are those described in Chapter 1A relating to the spark plugs and, on certain models, the ignition coil test described in this Chapter. If necessary, the system wiring and wiring connectors can be checked as described in Chapter 12 ensuring that the ECU wiring connector(s) have first been disconnected.

3 Ignition HT coil – removal, testing and refitting

Removal

Early 1.4 and 1.6 litre engines, and all 1.8 litre (8-valve) engines

1 The ignition HT coil is mounted on the left-hand end of the cylinder head.

2 Disconnect the battery negative terminal (refer to *Disconnecting the battery* in the Reference Section of this manual).

3 Depress the retaining clip and unplug the wiring connector from the HT coil **(see illustration)**.

4 Make a note of the correct fitted positions of the HT leads then disconnect them from the coil terminals **(see illustration)**. Alternatively, the leads can be disconnected from the spark plugs (see Chapter 1A) and removed with the coil module.

5 Undo the four retaining screws securing the coil to its mounting bracket and remove it from the engine compartment **(see illustration)**.

Later 1.4 and 1.6 litre engines

6 Disconnect the battery negative terminal (refer to *Disconnecting the battery* in the Reference Section of this manual).

3.3 Unplug the wiring connector from the HT ignition coil

3.4 Disconnect the HT leads from the coil terminals

3.5 Undo the four retaining screws and remove the HT ignition coil from its mounting bracket

3.7 Unplug the wiring connector from the top of the ignition coil module

3.8a Remove radio suppresser from the right-hand end of the coil module . . .

3.8b . . . together with its mounting bracket

7 Unplug the wiring connector from the top of the ignition coil module **(see illustration)**.

8 Where applicable, unscrew the securing nut and remove radio suppresser from the right-hand end of the coil module, together with its mounting bracket **(see illustrations)**.

9 Undo the securing nut and remove the hose clip support bracket from the left-hand end of the coil module **(see illustration)**.

10 Remove the securing nuts and free the ignition coil module from its mounting studs. Carefully ease the HT extension pillars away from the tops of the spark plugs and remove the module from the engine compartment **(see illustrations)**.

1.8 and 2.0 litre (16-valve) engines

11 Disconnect the battery negative terminal (refer to *Disconnecting the battery* in the Reference Section of this manual).

12 There are four separate ignition HT coils, one on the top of each spark plug. To gain access to the coils, disconnect the wiring connectors at the left-hand end of the coil unit, then undo the six retaining bolts and lift the coil unit upwards, off the spark plugs and from its location in the cylinder head cover. The individual coils can now be removed as required.

Testing

Early 1.4 and 1.6 litre engines, and all 1.8 litre (8-valve) engines

13 Testing of the coil consists of using a multimeter set to its resistance function, to check the primary (LT '+' to '−' terminals) and secondary (LT '+' to HT lead terminal) windings for continuity, bearing in mind that on the static type HT coil there are two sets of each windings. Compare the results obtained to those given in the Specifications at the start of this Chapter. Note the resistance of the coil windings will vary slightly according to the coil temperature, the results in the Specifications are approximate values for when the coil is at 20°C.

14 Check that there is no continuity between the HT lead terminal and the coil body/mounting bracket.

15 If the coil is thought to be faulty, have your findings confirmed by a Citroën dealer before renewing the coil.

Later 1.4 and 1.6 litre engines, and all 1.8 and 2.0 litre (16-valve) engines

16 The circuitry arrangement of the ignition coils and the coil unit on these engines is such that testing of an individual coil in isolation from the remainder of the engine management

3.9 Remove the hose clip support bracket from the left-hand end of the coil module

system is unlikely to prove effective in diagnosing a particular fault. Should there be any reason to suspect a faulty individual coil, the engine management system should be tested by a Citroën dealer using diagnostic test equipment (see Section 2).

Refitting

17 Refitting is a reversal of the relevant removal procedure ensuring the wiring connectors are securely reconnected and, where necessary, the HT leads are correctly connected.

3.10a Remove the securing nuts . . .

3.10b . . . and lift the ignition coil module from its mounting studs

4 Ignition timing – checking and adjustment

1 There are no timing marks on the flywheel or crankshaft pulley. The timing is constantly being monitored and adjusted by the engine management ECU, and nominal values cannot be given. Therefore, it is not possible for the home mechanic to check the ignition timing.

2 The only way in which the ignition timing can be checked is using special electronic test equipment, connected to the engine management system diagnostic connector (refer to Chapter 4A for further information).

5 Knock sensor – removal and refitting

Removal

1 On 1.4 litre engines, the knock sensor is screwed into the front face of the cylinder block, and on all other engines, into the rear face.

2 Disconnect the battery negative terminal (refer to *Disconnecting the battery* in the Reference Section of this manual).

3 To gain access to the rear-mounted sensor, chock the rear wheels then jack up the front of the vehicle and support it on axle stands (see *Jacking and vehicle support*).

4 Trace the wiring back from the sensor to its wiring connector, and disconnect it from the main loom.

5 Undo the sensor securing bolt and remove the sensor from the cylinder block.

Refitting

6 Refitting is a reversal of the removal procedure, ensuring that the sensor securing bolt is tightened to the specified torque.

Chapter 5 Part C:
Preheating system (diesel engines)

Contents

Glow plugs – removal, inspection and refitting 2
Preheating system – description and testing 1
Preheating system control unit – removal and refitting 3

Degrees of difficulty

Easy, suitable for novice with little experience	Fairly easy, suitable for beginner with some experience	Fairly difficult, suitable for competent DIY mechanic	Difficult, suitable for experienced DIY mechanic	Very difficult, suitable for expert DIY or professional 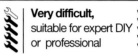

Specifications

Glow plugs

Resistance (typical) . . . .   Less than 1 ohm

Torque wrench setting	Nm	lbf ft
Glow plugs	22	16

1 Preheating system – description and testing

Description

1 To assist cold starting, diesel engines are fitted with a preheating system, which consists of a number of glow plugs (one per cylinder), a glow plug control unit, a facia-mounted warning lamp, a coolant temperature sensor mounted on the cylinder head, an ambient air temperature sensor mounted inside the glow plug control unit, and the associated electrical wiring.

2 The glow plugs are miniature electric heating elements, encapsulated in a metal case with a probe at one end and electrical connection at the other. Each combustion chamber has one glow plug threaded into it, with the tip of the glow plug probe positioned directly in line with incoming spray of fuel from the injectors. When the glow plug is energised, it heats up rapidly, causing the fuel passing over the glow plug probe to be heated to its optimum combustion temperature, ready for combustion. In addition, some of the fuel passing over the glow plugs is ignited and this helps to trigger the combustion process.

3 The pre-heating system begins to operate as soon as the ignition key is switched to the second position, but only if the engine coolant temperature is below 60°C. A facia-mounted warning lamp informs the driver that preheating is taking place. The lamp extinguishes when sufficient preheating has taken place to allow the engine to be started, but power will still be supplied to the glow plugs for a further period until the engine is started. If no attempt is made to start the engine, the power supply to the glow plugs is switched off after a period of time, to prevent battery drain and glow plug burn-out.

4 On 1.9 litre engines with conventional diesel injection systems, the duration of the preheating period is governed by the glow plug control unit. This device monitors the temperature of the air in the engine bay via a built-in ambient air temperature sensor, then alters the preheating time (the length for which the glow plugs are supplied with current) to suit the conditions. On 1.9 and 2.0 litre engines with electronically-controlled diesel injection systems, the glow plug control unit is operated by the injection system ECU, which determines the necessary preheating time based on inputs from the various system sensors.

5 Post-heating takes place after the ignition key has been released from the 'Start' position; the glow plugs continue to operate for at least a further 15 seconds, helping to improve fuel combustion whilst the engine is warming up, resulting in quieter, smoother running and reduced exhaust emissions. The overall duration of the post-heating period is dependent on the coolant temperature, which is measured by a sensor mounted in the thermostat housing, and by engine speed which is determined by a switch, or a potentiometer on the injection pump control lever.

Testing

6 If the system malfunctions, testing is ultimately by substitution of known good units, but some preliminary checks may be made as follows.

7 Connect a voltmeter or 12-volt test lamp between the glow plug supply cable and earth (engine or vehicle metal). Make sure that the live connection is kept clear of the engine and bodywork.

8 Have an assistant switch on the ignition, and check that voltage is applied to the glow plugs. Note the time for which the warning light is lit, and the total time for which voltage is applied before the system cuts out. Switch off the ignition.

9 At an under-bonnet temperature of 20°C, typical times noted should be 5 or 6 seconds for warning light operation, followed by a further 10 seconds supply after the light goes out. Warning light time will increase with lower temperatures and decrease with higher temperatures.

10 If there is no supply at all, the control unit or associated wiring is at fault.

11 To gain access to the glow plugs for further testing, refer to Chapter 4B, where necessary, and remove the following components, according to model:

1.9 litre (XUD9 non-turbo engines) – Remove the air distribution housing.

1.9 litre (XUD9 turbo engines) – Remove the intercooler (where fitted).

1.9 litre (DW8 engines) – Release the clip in the centre of the engine cover and undo the retaining screw on the right-hand side. Remove the engine oil dipstick then lift the cover off the engine.

2.0 litre engines – Release the four plastic fasteners and remove the engine cover from the top of the engine. It may also be necessary to move the wiring harness tray to one side after undoing the two retaining nuts, for access to No 4 glow plug.

12 Disconnect the main supply cable and the interconnecting wire or strap from the top of the glow plugs. Be careful not to drop the nuts and washers.

2.2a Unscrew the nut . . .

2.2b . . . and disconnect the main supply cable (where necessary) . . .

2.2c . . . and the interconnecting wire from the glow plug

13 Use a continuity tester, or a 12-volt test lamp connected to the battery positive terminal, to check for continuity between each glow plug terminal and earth. The resistance of a glow plug in good condition is very low (less than 1 ohm), so if the test lamp does not light or the continuity tester shows a high resistance, the glow plug is certainly defective.
14 If an ammeter is available, the current draw of each glow plug can be checked. After an initial surge of 15 to 20 amps, each plug should draw 12 amps. Any plug which draws much more or less than this is probably defective.
15 As a final check, the glow plugs can be removed and inspected as described in the following Section. On completion, refit any components removed for access with reference to Chapter 4B.

2 Glow plugs – removal, inspection and refitting

Removal

Caution: If the preheating system has just been energised, or if the engine has been running, the glow plugs will be very hot.
1 Disconnect the battery negative terminal (refer to *Disconnecting the battery* in the Reference Section of this manual). To gain access to the glow plugs, remove the components described in Section 1, paragraph 11, according to model.
2 Unscrew the nut from the relevant glow plug terminal(s), and recover the washer(s).

Note that the main supply cable is connected to Number 1 cylinder glow plug and an interconnecting wire is fitted between the four plugs **(see illustrations)**.
3 Where applicable, carefully move any obstructing pipes or wires to one side to enable access to the relevant glow plug(s).
4 Unscrew the glow plug(s) and remove from the cylinder head **(see illustration)**.

Inspection

5 Inspect each glow plug for physical damage. Burnt or eroded glow plug tips can be caused by a bad injector spray pattern. Have the injectors checked if this sort of damage is found.
6 If the glow plugs are in good physical condition, check them electrically using a 12-volt test lamp or continuity tester as described in the previous Section.
7 The glow plugs can be energised by applying 12 volts to them to verify that they heat up evenly and in the required time. Observe the following precautions.
  a) *Support the glow plug by clamping it carefully in a vice or self-locking pliers. Remember it will become red-hot.*
  b) *Make sure that the power supply or test lead incorporates a fuse or overload trip to protect against damage from a short-circuit.*
  c) *After testing, allow the glow plug to cool for several minutes before attempting to handle it.*
8 A glow plug in good condition will start to glow red at the tip after drawing current for 5 seconds or so. Any plug which takes much longer to start glowing, or which starts

glowing in the middle instead of at the tip, is defective.

Refitting

9 Refit by reversing the removal operations. Apply a smear of copper-based anti-seize compound to the plug threads and tighten the glow plugs to the specified torque. Do not overtighten, as this can damage the glow plug element.
10 Refit any components removed for access with reference to Chapter 4B.

3 Preheating system control unit – removal and refitting

Removal

1 The unit is located on the left-hand side of the engine compartment where it is mounted on a bracket just in front of the fuse/relay box.
2 Disconnect the battery negative terminal (refer to *Disconnecting the battery* in the Reference Section of this manual).
3 Unscrew the retaining nut securing the unit to the mounting bracket **(see illustration)**.
4 Unscrew the two retaining nuts and free the main feed and supply wires from the base of the unit, then disconnect the wiring connector **(see illustration)**. Remove the unit from the engine compartment.

Refitting

5 Refitting is a reversal of removal, ensuring that the wiring connectors are correctly connected.

2.4 Unscrew the glow plug and remove it from the cylinder head

3.3 Unscrew the preheating system control unit retaining nut (arrowed) . . .

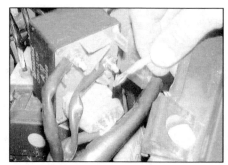

3.4 . . . then disconnect the main feed and supply wires and the wiring connector

Chapter 6
Clutch

Contents

Clutch assembly – removal, inspection and refitting 4
Clutch cable – removal and refitting 2
Clutch pedal – removal and refitting 3
Clutch release mechanism – removal, inspection and refitting 5
General checks . . . . .See Chapter 1A or 1B
General information 1

Degrees of difficulty

| Easy, suitable for novice with little experience | | Fairly easy, suitable for beginner with some experience | | Fairly difficult, suitable for competent DIY mechanic | | Difficult, suitable for experienced DIY mechanic | | Very difficult, suitable for expert DIY or professional | |

Specifications

Type	Single dry plate with diaphragm spring, cable-operated

Friction plate diameter
Petrol engines:
1.4 litre engines	180 mm
1.6 and 1.8 litre engines	200 mm
2.0 litre engines	215 mm

Diesel engines:
Turbo models	215 mm
Non-turbo models	200 mm

Clutch release mechanism
Petrol engines:
All except 2.0 engines	'Push-type'
2.0 litre engines	'Pull-type'

Diesel engines:
All except 1.9 litre, DHY (XUD9TE) turbo engines	'Push-type'
1.9 litre, DHY (XUD9TE) turbo engines	'Pull-Type'

Torque wrench settings	**Nm**	**lbf ft**
Pressure plate retaining bolts:		
1.4 and 1.6 litre engines	15	11
1.8, 1.9 litre and 2.0 engines	20	15

1 General information

The clutch consists of a friction plate, a pressure plate assembly, a release bearing and the release mechanism; all of these components are contained in the large cast-aluminium alloy bellhousing, sandwiched between the engine and the transmission. The release mechanism is mechanical, being operated by a cable.

The friction plate is fitted between the engine flywheel and the clutch pressure plate, and is allowed to slide on the transmission input shaft splines.

The pressure plate assembly is bolted to the engine flywheel. When the engine is running, drive is transmitted from the crankshaft, via the flywheel, to the friction plate (these components being clamped securely together by the pressure plate assembly) and from the friction plate to the transmission input shaft.

To interrupt the drive, the spring pressure must be relaxed. On the models covered in this manual, two different types of clutch release mechanism are used. The first is a conventional 'push-type' mechanism, where an independent clutch release bearing, fitted concentrically around the transmission input shaft, is pushed onto the pressure plate assembly. The second is a 'pull-type' mechanism, where the clutch release bearing is an integral part of the pressure plate assembly, and is lifted away from the friction plate.

At the transmission end of the clutch cable on models with the conventional 'push-type' mechanism, the outer cable is retained by a fixed mounting bracket, and the inner cable is attached to the release fork lever. Depressing the clutch pedal pulls the control cable inner wire, and this rotates the release fork by acting on the lever at the fork's upper end. The release fork then presses the release bearing against the pressure plate spring fingers. This causes the springs to deform and releases the clamping force on the pressure plate.

At the transmission end of the clutch cable on models with the 'pull-type' mechanism, the inner cable is attached to a fixed mounting bracket, and the outer cable acts against the release fork lever. Depressing the clutch pedal rotates the release fork. The release fork then lifts the release bearing, which is attached to the pressure plate springs, away from the friction plate, and releases the clamping force exerted at the pressure plate periphery.

On all models the clutch cable has an automatic adjuster built into the cable, and no manual adjustment is required.

2 Clutch cable – removal and refitting

Removal

1 Remove the battery, battery tray and mounting plate as described in Chapter 5A. Depending on model and clearance available, remove any remaining air cleaner and air inlet duct components as described in the relevant Part of Chapter 4, to gain access to the cable run over the top of the transmission.

2 Working in the engine compartment, release the inner cable end fitting from the support bracket or clutch release lever. Depress the retaining tabs and release the outer cable from the transmission **(see illustrations)**.

3 It is just possible to reach the cable after removing the carpet trim panel, however, access to the clutch pedal inside the car is very limited and it is recommended that the facia be removed first, although this is a major operation.

4 Reach up and release the retaining clip then unhook the inner cable from the upper end of the clutch pedal.

5 Return to the engine compartment, then release the cable guide from the bulkhead and withdraw the cable forwards, releasing it from any relevant retaining clips and guides.

6 Firmly apply the handbrake, then jack up the front of the car and support it securely on axle stands (see *Jacking and vehicle support*). Remove the engine undertray.

7 Release the cable from the retaining clips on the subframe and remove it from the car, noting its correct routing.

8 Examine the cable, looking for worn end fittings or a damaged outer casing, and for signs of fraying of the inner cable. Check the cable's operation; the inner cable should move smoothly and easily through the outer casing. Remember that a cable that appears serviceable when tested off the car may well be much heavier in operation when in its working position. Renew the cable if it shows signs of excessive wear or any damage.

Refitting

9 Apply a thin smear of multi-purpose grease to the cable end fittings, then pass the cable through the engine compartment bulkhead.

10 Hold the clutch pedal in its raised position by wedging a suitable tool beneath it.

11 Guide the end of the cable onto the pedal and secure with the retaining clip.

12 From within the engine compartment, lubricate the cable guide and locate it into position on the bulkhead.

13 Ensuring that the cable is correctly routed, secure the cable to the subframe, and engine compartment retaining clips then lay the cable over the transmission.

14 Attach the outer cable to the transmission and connect the inner cable to the clutch release lever or support bracket. Ensure that the cable spacers and washers are correctly positioned against the lever/support bracket.

15 Depress the clutch pedal two or three times to settle the cable and operate the automatic adjuster.

16 Refit the battery mounting plate, battery tray and battery, referring to Chapter 5A if necessary.

17 Refit the air cleaner and air inlet duct components as described in the relevant Part of Chapter 4.

18 Refit the carpet trim panel, and the engine undertray then lower the car to the ground.

3 Clutch pedal – removal and refitting

Removal

1 Depending on model and clearance available, remove the air cleaner and air inlet duct components as described in the relevant Part of Chapter 4, to gain access to the clutch cable attachment on the transmission.

2 Working in the engine compartment, release the clutch inner cable end fitting from the support bracket or clutch release lever.

3 It is just possible to reach the pedal and cable after removing the carpet trim panel, however, access to the clutch pedal inside the car is very limited and it is recommended that the facia be removed first, although this is a major operation.

4 Reach up and release the retaining clip then unhook the clutch inner cable from the upper end of the clutch pedal.

5 Detach the pedal helper spring end pieces and remove the helper spring from the pedal and pedal bracket.

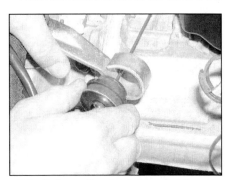

2.2a Release the clutch inner cable end fitting from the support bracket or release lever . . .

2.2b . . . then depress the retaining tabs and release the outer cable from the transmission

6 Undo the nut from the clutch pedal pivot bolt and withdraw the bolt **(see illustration)**.
7 Remove the clutch pedal from the pedal bracket and stop-plate. Recover the bush from the pedal pivot.
8 Check the condition of the pedal, pivot bush and helper spring assembly and renew any components as necessary.

Refitting

9 Lubricate the pedal pivot bolt with multi-purpose grease, then locate the pedal in the bracket and insert the pivot bolt. Refit the pivot bolt nut but do not fully tighten it at this stage.
10 Reconnect the helper spring to the pedal and pedal bracket.
11 Raise the pedal fully and guide the end of the cable onto the pedal. Secure the cable with the retaining clip.
12 Reconnect the clutch inner cable end fitting to the transmission support bracket or clutch release lever.
13 Slacken the nut and bolt securing the pedal stop-plate to the pedal bracket.
14 Using a lever, raise the stop-plate fully so that there is a considerable amount of free play at the pedal.
15 Lower the stop-plate until there is between 1.0 and 3.0 mm free play at the pedal. Hold the stop-plate in this position and tighten the retaining nut and bolt and the pedal pivot bolt nut.
16 Depress the pedal two or three times and check the operation of the cable and clutch release mechanism.
17 Refit the remaining components removed for access.

---

4 Clutch assembly – removal, inspection and refitting

Note: *Although most friction materials no longer contain asbestos, it is safest to assume that some still do, and to take precautions accordingly.*

Removal

 Warning: Dust created by clutch wear and deposited on the clutch components may contain asbestos, which is a health hazard. DON'T blow it out with compressed air, nor inhale any of it. DO NOT use petrol or petroleum-based solvents to clean off the dust. Brake system cleaner or methylated spirit should be used to flush the dust into a suitable receptacle. After the clutch components are wiped clean with rags, dispose of the contaminated rags and cleaner in a sealed, marked container.

1 Unless the complete engine/transmission unit is to be removed from the car and separated for major overhaul (see Chapter 2E or 2F), the clutch can be reached by removing the transmission as described in Chapter 7A.
2 Before disturbing the clutch, use chalk or a

3.6 Clutch pedal pivot bolt retaining nut (arrowed)

marker pen to mark the relationship of the pressure plate assembly to the flywheel.
3 Working in a diagonal sequence, slacken the pressure plate bolts by half a turn at a time, until spring pressure is released and the bolts can be unscrewed by hand.
4 Prise the pressure plate assembly off its locating dowels, and collect the friction plate, noting which way round the plate is fitted.

Inspection

Note: *Due to the amount of work necessary to remove and refit clutch components, it is considered good practice to renew the clutch friction plate, pressure plate assembly and release bearing as a matched set, even if only one of these is worn enough to require renewal. It is worth considering the renewal of the clutch components on a preventative basis if the engine and/or transmission have been removed for some other reason.*

5 When cleaning clutch components, read first the warning at the beginning of this Section; remove dust using a clean, dry cloth, and working in a well-ventilated atmosphere.
6 Check the friction plate facings for signs of wear, damage or oil contamination. If the friction material is cracked, burnt, scored or damaged, or if it is contaminated with oil or grease (shown by shiny black patches), the friction plate must be renewed.
7 If the friction material is still serviceable, check that the centre boss splines are unworn, that the torsion springs are in good condition and securely fastened, and that all the rivets are tight. If any wear or damage is found, the friction plate must be renewed.

4.13 Fit the friction plate so that its spring hub assembly faces away from the flywheel

8 If the friction material is fouled with oil, this must be due to an oil leak from the crankshaft left-hand oil seal, from the sump-to-cylinder block joint, or from the transmission input shaft. Renew the seal or repair the joint, as appropriate, as described in the relevant Part of Chapter 2 or 7, before installing the new friction plate.
9 Check the pressure plate assembly for obvious signs of wear or damage; shake it to check for loose rivets or worn or damaged fulcrum rings, and check that the drive straps securing the pressure plate to the cover do not show signs (such as a deep yellow or blue discoloration) of overheating. If the diaphragm spring is worn or damaged, or if its pressure is in any way suspect, the pressure plate assembly should be renewed.
10 Examine the machined bearing surfaces of the pressure plate and of the flywheel; they should be clean, completely flat, and free from scratches or scoring. If either is discoloured from excessive heat, or shows signs of cracks, it should be renewed – although minor damage of this nature can sometimes be polished away using emery paper.
11 Check that the release bearing contact surface rotates smoothly and easily, with no sign of noise or roughness. Also check that the surface itself is smooth and unworn, with no signs of cracks, pitting or scoring. If there is any doubt about its condition, the bearing must be renewed. On clutches with a 'pull-type' release mechanism, this means that the complete pressure plate assembly must also be renewed.

Refitting

12 On reassembly, ensure that the bearing surfaces of the flywheel and pressure plate are completely clean, smooth, and free from oil or grease. Use solvent to remove any protective grease from new components.
13 Fit the friction plate so that its spring hub assembly faces away from the flywheel; there may be a marking showing which way round the plate is to be refitted **(see illustration)**.
14 Refit the pressure plate assembly, aligning the marks made on dismantling (if the original pressure plate is re-used), and locating the pressure plate on its three locating dowels **(see illustration)**. Fit the

4.14 Refit the pressure plate assembly, locating it on the three dowels

4.16 Using a clutch-aligning tool to centralise the friction plate

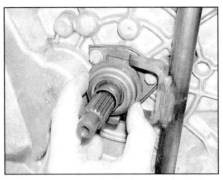

5.2 Unhook the release bearing from the fork, and slide it off the input shaft

5.3a Draw out the release fork retaining pin using a nut screwed onto the threaded end . . .

pressure plate bolts, but tighten them only finger-tight, so that the friction plate can still be moved.

15 The friction plate must now be centralised, so that when the transmission is refitted, its input shaft will pass through the splines at the centre of the friction plate.

16 Centralisation can be achieved by passing a screwdriver or other long bar through the friction plate and into the hole in the crankshaft; the friction plate can then be moved around until it is centred on the crankshaft hole. Alternatively, a clutch-aligning-tool can be used to eliminate the guesswork; these can be obtained from most accessory shops **(see illustration)**.

> **HAYNES HINT** A home-made aligning tool can be fabricated from a length of metal rod or wooden dowel which fits closely inside the crankshaft hole, and has insulating tape wound around it to match the diameter of the friction plate splined hole.

17 When the friction plate is centralised, tighten the pressure plate bolts evenly and in

a diagonal sequence to the specified torque setting.

18 Apply a **thin** smear of molybdenum disulphide grease (Citroën recommend the use of Molykote BR2 Plus – available from your Citroën dealer) to the splines of the friction plate and the transmission input shaft, and also to the release bearing bore and release fork shaft.

19 Refit the transmission as described in Chapter 7A.

5 Clutch release mechanism – removal, inspection and refitting

Note: *Refer to the warning concerning the dangers of asbestos dust at the beginning of Section 4.*

Removal

1 Unless the complete engine/transmission unit is to be removed from the car and separated for major overhaul (see Chapter 2E or 2F), the clutch release mechanism can be reached by removing the transmission only, as described in Chapter 7A.

2 On models with a conventional 'push-type'

release mechanism, unhook the release bearing from the fork, and slide it off the input shaft **(see illustration)**.

3 The release lever must now be removed from the top of the release fork shaft. This is done in one of three ways, depending on engine and transmission type as follows:

a) *On 1.4 and 1.6 litre petrol engines, drive out the roll pin, and remove the release lever from the top of the release fork shaft. Discard the roll pin – a new one must be used on refitting.*

b) *On 2.0 litre petrol engines and 1.9 litre turbo diesel engines, lift up the retaining clip and pull out the retaining pin. Remove the release lever from the top of the release fork shaft.*

c) *On all other engines, screw a nut onto the threaded end of the release lever retaining pin. Tighten the nut to draw the pin from the lever then remove the release lever from the top of the release fork shaft (see illustrations). Discard the retaining pin – a new one must be used on refitting.*

4 With the release lever removed, lift the release shaft up to disengage it from the lower bush, and manoeuvre it out from the transmission **(see illustration)**.

5 Depress the retaining tabs, and remove the

5.3b . . . then remove the retaining pin from the fork

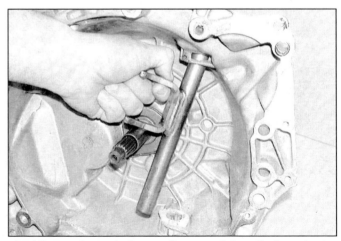

5.4 Lift the release shaft up to disengage it from the lower bush, and manoeuvre it from the transmission

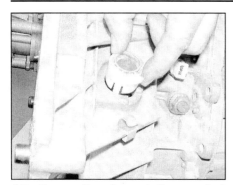

5.5a Remove the release shaft upper pivot bush . . .

5.5b . . . and lower pivot bush from the transmission

5.10 Secure the release lever to the shaft by tapping in a new roll pin or retaining pin

upper and lower pivot bushes from the transmission housing **(see illustrations)**.

Inspection

6 Check the release mechanism, renewing any component which is worn or damaged. Carefully check all bearing surfaces and points of contact.

7 Check that the release bearing contact surface rotates smoothly and easily, with no sign of noise or roughness, and that the surface itself is smooth and unworn, with no signs of cracks, pitting or scoring. If there is

any doubt about its condition, the bearing must be renewed. On models with a 'pull-type' release mechanism, this means that the complete pressure plate assembly must be renewed, as described in Section 4.

Refitting

8 Apply a smear of molybdenum disulphide grease to the shaft pivot bushes and the contact surfaces of the release fork.

9 Locate the lower pivot bush in the transmission, ensuring it is securely retained by its locating tangs, and refit the release fork.

Slide the upper bush down the release fork shaft, and clip it into position in the transmission housing.

10 On models with a conventional 'push-type' release mechanism, refit the release lever to the shaft. Align the lever with the shaft hole, and secure it to the shaft by tapping a new roll pin or retaining pin fully into position **(see illustration)**. Slide the release bearing onto the input shaft, and engage it with the release fork.

11 Refit the transmission as described in Chapter 7A.

Notes

Chapter 7 Part A:
Manual transmission

Contents

Gearchange linkage – removal and refitting 3
General information 1
Manual transmission – draining and refilling 2
Manual transmission – removal and refitting 7
Manual transmission oil level check . . . . .See Chapter 1A or 1B

Manual transmission overhaul – general information 8
Oil seals – renewal 4
Reversing light switch – testing, removal and refitting 5
Vehicle speed sensor – removal and refitting 6

Degrees of difficulty

| Easy, suitable for novice with little experience | | Fairly easy, suitable for beginner with some experience | | Fairly difficult, suitable for competent DIY mechanic | | Difficult, suitable for experienced DIY mechanic | | Very difficult, suitable for expert DIY or professional | |

Specifications

General

Type	Manual, five forward speeds and reverse. Synchromesh on all forward speeds

Designation:
1.4 and 1.6 litre engine models	MA
1.8 litre and larger-engine models	BE3

Lubrication

Recommended oil type	Refer to *Lubricants and fluids*
Capacity	2.0 litres

Torque wrench settings

	Nm	lbf ft
MA transmission		
Clutch release bearing guide sleeve bolts	12	9
Engine-to-transmission bolts	35	26
Engine/transmission left-hand mounting:		
Mounting bracket-to-transmission nuts	25	18
Mounting bracket-to-body bolts	25	18
Rubber mounting-to-bracket nuts	25	18
Rubber mounting centre nut	65	48
Lower suspension arm balljoint clamp bolt nut*	40	30
Oil drain plug	25	18
Oil filler/level plug	25	18
Reversing light switch	25	18
Right-hand driveshaft intermediate bearing retaining bolt nuts	17	13
Roadwheel bolts	85	63

New nuts must be used.

	Nm	lbf ft
BE3 transmission		
Clutch cable bracket retaining bolts ('pull-type' clutch only)	18	13
Clutch release bearing guide sleeve bolts	12	9
Engine-to-transmission bolts	35	26
Engine/transmission left-hand mounting:		
Mounting bracket-to-transmission nuts	25	18
Mounting bracket-to-body bolts	25	18
Rubber mounting-to-bracket nuts	25	18
Rubber mounting centre nut	65	48
Lower suspension arm balljoint clamp bolt nut*	40	30
Oil drain plug	35	26
Oil filler/level plug	20	15
Reversing light switch	25	18
Right-hand driveshaft intermediate bearing retaining bolt nuts	17	13
Roadwheel bolts	85	63

New nuts must be used.

1 General information

The transmission is contained in a cast-aluminium alloy casing bolted to the engine's left-hand end, and consists of the gearbox and final drive differential – often called a transaxle.

Drive is transmitted from the crankshaft via the clutch to the input shaft, which has a splined extension to accept the clutch friction plate, and rotates in sealed ball-bearings. From the input shaft, drive is transmitted to the output shaft, which rotates in a roller bearing at its right-hand end, and a sealed ball-bearing at its left-hand end. From the output shaft, the drive is transmitted to the differential crownwheel, which rotates with the differential case and planetary gears, thus driving the sun gears and driveshafts. The rotation of the planetary gears on their shaft allows the inner roadwheel to rotate at a slower speed than the outer roadwheel when the car is cornering.

The input and output shafts are arranged side-by-side, parallel to the crankshaft and driveshafts, so that their gear pinion teeth are in constant mesh. In the neutral position, the output shaft gear pinions rotate freely, so that drive cannot be transmitted to the crownwheel.

Gear selection is via a floor-mounted lever and selector shaft mechanism. The selector shaft causes the appropriate selector fork to move its respective synchro-sleeve along the shaft, to lock the gear pinion to the synchro-hub. Since the synchro-hubs are splined to the output shaft, this locks the pinion to the shaft, so that drive can be transmitted. To ensure that gear-changing can be made quickly and quietly, a synchro-mesh system is fitted to all forward gears, consisting of baulk rings and spring-loaded fingers, as well as the gear pinions and synchro-hubs. The synchro-mesh cones are formed on the mating faces of the baulk rings and gear pinions.

Two different manual transmissions are used on the models covered in this manual; 1.4 and 1.6 litre models have the MA transmission, whereas 1.8 litre and larger-engined models are fitted with the BE3 unit.

2 Manual transmission – draining and refilling

Note: *A suitable square section wrench may be required to undo the transmission filler/level and drain plugs. These wrenches can be obtained from most motor factors or your Citroën dealer.*

HAYNES HiNT *It may be possible to use the square end fitting on a ratchet handle (as found in a typical socket set) to undo the plug.*

1 This operation is much quicker and more efficient if the car is first taken on a journey of sufficient length to warm the engine/transmission up to normal operating temperature.

2 Park the car on level ground, switch off the ignition and apply the handbrake firmly. To gain access to the filler/level plug, jack up the front and rear of the car and support it securely on axle stands (see *Jacking and vehicle support*). Note that the car must be level, to ensure accuracy, when refilling and checking the oil level.

3 Remove the engine undertray, the left-hand front wheel, and the plastic wheelarch liner. The liner is secured by various screws and clips under the wheelarch. Release all the fasteners, and remove liner from under the front wing.

4 Wipe clean the area around the filler/level plug, which is situated on the left-hand end of the transmission, next to the end cover. Unscrew the filler/level plug from the

2.4a Unscrew the filler/level plug . . .

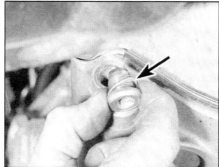

2.4b . . . and recover the sealing washer (arrowed) – MA transmission

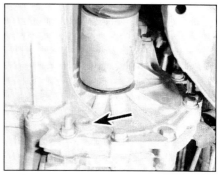

2.5a Drain plug location (arrowed) – MA transmission

transmission and recover the sealing washer **(see illustrations)**.

5 Position a suitable container under the drain plug (situated at the rear of the transmission) and unscrew the plug. On the MA transmission, the plug is on the left-hand side of the differential housing; on the BE3 transmission, it is on the base of the differential housing **(see illustrations)**.

6 Allow the oil to drain completely into the container. If the oil is hot, take precautions against scalding. Clean both the filler/level and the drain plugs, being especially careful to wipe any metallic particles off the magnetic inserts. Discard the original sealing washers; they should be renewed whenever they are disturbed.

7 When the oil has finished draining, clean the drain plug threads and those of the transmission casing, fit a new sealing washer and refit the drain plug, tightening it to the specified torque.

8 Refill the transmission slowly, through the filler/level plug orifice, until the oil begins to trickle out of the orifice **(see illustration)**. Use only good-quality oil of the specified type (refer to *Lubricants and fluids*). To ensure that a correct level is established, wait until the initial trickle has stopped and allow the oil to settle within the transmission. Add a little more oil until a new trickle emerges; the level will be correct when the new flow ceases.

9 When the level is correct, fit a new sealing

washer to the filler/level plug, refit the plug and tighten it to the specified torque.

10 Refit the wheelarch liner, engine undertray and roadwheel, then lower the car to the ground. Tighten the roadwheel bolts to the specified torque.

3 Gearchange linkage – removal and refitting

Note: *The gearchange linkage is not adjustable. If difficulty is experienced in gear selection, or if there is excess free play at the gearchange lever, dismantle the linkage and check the condition of the link rod balljoints and pivot bushes as described below.*

Removal

1 Firmly apply the handbrake, then jack up the front of the vehicle and support it on axle stands (see *Jacking and vehicle support*).

2 Remove the engine undertray, then remove the air cleaner and air inlet duct(s) as described in Chapter 4A or 4B.

MA transmission

3 With the transmission in neutral, slacken and remove the nut, and withdraw the pivot bolt securing the selector rod to the base of the gearchange lever.

4 Using a flat-bladed screwdriver, carefully prise the two selector link rod balljoints off the

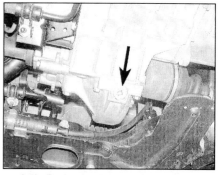

2.5b Drain plug location (arrowed) – BE3 transmission

transmission lever and fixed bracket on the transmission **(see illustration)**. Disengage the selector rod from the bellcrank pivot ball and remove it, complete with the two link rods, from underneath the vehicle.

5 Prise off the protective cap, then slacken and remove the bellcrank pivot bolt and washer. Carefully prise the bellcrank link rod balljoint off the transmission lever and remove the bellcrank and link rod assembly **(see illustration)**.

6 Inspect all the linkage components for signs of wear or damage, paying particular attention to the pivot bushes and link rod balljoints, and renew worn components as necessary.

7 To remove the gearchange lever, remove the centre console as described in Chap-

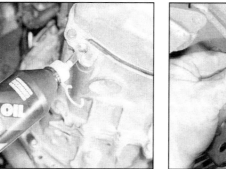

2.8 Refill the transmission slowly until the oil begins to trickle out of the orifice

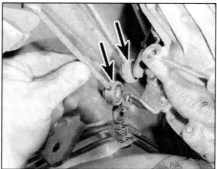

3.4 Carefully prise the two selector link rod balljoints (arrowed) off the transmission lever and fixed bracket – MA transmission

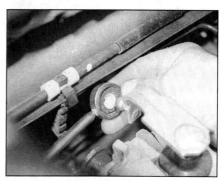

3.5 Carefully prise the bellcrank link rod balljoint off the transmission lever – MA transmission

3.8a Peel back the lower gaiter . . .

3.8b . . . then disengage the mounting plate . . .

3.8c . . . and peel the upper gaiter away from the lever baseplate

ter 11, then undo the four retaining nuts and remove the gearchange lever, complete with rubber mounting plate, from the vehicle.

8 Peel back the lower gaiter from the base of the gearchange lever, then disengage the lever mounting plate. Slide the upper gaiter up the lever to gain access to the gearchange lever pivot ball. Examine the lever components for signs of wear or damage, paying particular attention to the rubber gaiters, and renew components as necessary. The lever can be separated from its baseplate after the retaining ring has been unclipped **(see illustrations)**.

3.8d The lever and baseplate can be separated once the retaining ring has been unclipped

3.10 Carefully prise the three selector link rod balljoints (arrowed) off the transmission levers and fixed bracket – BE3 transmission

BE3 transmission

9 With the transmission in neutral, slacken and remove the nut, and withdraw the pivot bolt securing the selector rod to the base of the gearchange lever.

10 Using a flat-bladed screwdriver, carefully prise the three selector link rod balljoints off the two transmission levers and the fixed bracket **(see illustration)**. Disengage the selector rod from the bellcrank pivot ball and remove it, with the two link rods, from underneath the vehicle.

11 Where fitted, carefully prise the plastic cap off the pivot bolt securing the gearchange linkage bellcrank to the subframe.

12 Slacken and remove the bellcrank pivot bolt and washer, then manoeuvre the bellcrank and the remaining link rod out from under the vehicle. Recover the spacer and pivot bushes from the centre of the bellcrank.

13 Inspect all the linkage components for signs of wear or damage, paying particular attention to the pivot bushes and link rod balljoints. Renew any worn components as necessary. If required, the gearchange lever can be removed and inspected as described above in paragraphs 7 and 8.

Refitting

14 Refitting is a reversal of the removal procedure, noting the following points:

 a) *Prior to refitting the linkage, check that*

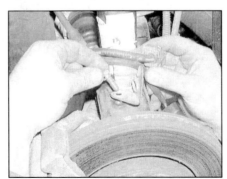

4.2 Unbolt the flexible brake hose support bracket from the top of the swivel hub

 the gearchange lever is still in the neutral position.

 b) *Apply a smear of multi-purpose grease to the bellcrank pivot ball. Do not grease the link rod balljoints or the pivot bushes.*

 c) *Ensure that all link rods are securely pressed onto their balljoints.*

 d) *Where applicable, refit the air cleaner components as described in Chapter 4A or 4B, and the centre console as described in Chapter 11.*

4 Oil seals – renewal

Driveshaft oil seals

1 Drain the transmission oil as described in Section 2.

2 Unbolt the flexible brake hose support bracket from the top of the swivel hub, so as not to strain the brake hose during subsequent operations **(see illustration)**. Similarly, on models equipped with ABS, release the wheel sensor wiring harness from the bracket and from the support clip under the wheelarch.

3 Slacken and remove the nut, then withdraw the lower suspension arm balljoint clamp bolt from the swivel hub **(see illustration)**. Discard the nut – a new one must be used on refitting.

4.3 Undo the nut and withdraw the lower suspension arm balljoint clamp bolt from the swivel hub

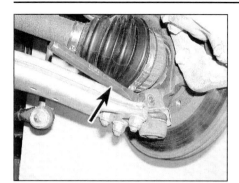

4.4a Spread the swivel hub by tapping a small chisel (arrowed) into the split . . .

4.4b . . . then pull the lower suspension arm downwards using a bar and chain or similar arrangement, pivoting on the subframe

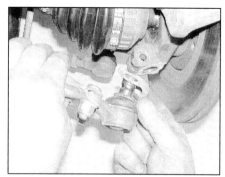

4.5 When the balljoint is released, remove the protector plate from the balljoint shank

4 Tap a small chisel into the split on the swivel hub, to spread the hub slightly and allow the balljoint shank to be withdrawn. Pull the lower suspension arm downwards to release the balljoint shank from the swivel hub. To do this it will be necessary to use a long bar and block of wood which will engage under the front subframe. Attach the bar to the suspension arm, preferably with a chain, or alternatively with a stout strap or rope **(see illustrations)**. Lever down on the bar to release the balljoint from the swivel hub.

5 Once the balljoint is free, remove the protector plate which is fitted to the balljoint shank, then proceed as described under the relevant sub-heading **(see illustration)**.

Right-hand seal

6 Loosen the two intermediate bearing retaining bolt nuts, then rotate the bolts through 90° so that their offset heads are clear of the bearing outer race **(see illustrations)**.

7 Carefully pull the swivel hub assembly outwards, and pull on the inner end of the driveshaft to free the intermediate bearing from its mounting bracket.

8 Once the driveshaft end is free from the transmission, slide the dust seal off the inner end of the shaft, noting which way around it is fitted, and support the inner end of the driveshaft to avoid damaging the constant velocity joints or gaiters.

9 Carefully prise the oil seal out of the

transmission, using a large flat-bladed screwdriver **(see illustration)**.

10 Remove all traces of dirt from the area around the oil seal aperture, then apply a smear of grease to the outer lip of the new oil seal. Fit the new seal into its aperture, and drive it squarely into position using a suitable tubular drift (such as a socket) which bears only on the hard outer edge of the seal, until it abuts its locating shoulder. If the seal was supplied with a plastic protector sleeve, leave this in position until the driveshaft has been refitted **(see illustrations)**.

11 Thoroughly clean the driveshaft splines, then apply a thin film of grease to the oil seal lips and to the driveshaft inner end splines.

12 Slide the dust seal into position on the

4.6a On the right-hand driveshaft, slacken the intermediate bearing retaining bolt nuts . . .

end of the shaft, ensuring that its flat surface is facing the transmission.

13 Carefully locate the inner driveshaft splines with those of the differential sun gear, taking care not to damage the oil seal, then align the intermediate bearing with its mounting bracket, and push the driveshaft fully into position. If necessary, use a soft-faced mallet to tap the outer race of the bearing into position in the mounting bracket.

14 Ensure that the intermediate bearing is correctly seated, then rotate its retaining bolts back through 90° so that their offset heads are resting against the bearing outer race, and tighten the retaining nuts to the specified torque. Remove the plastic seal protector

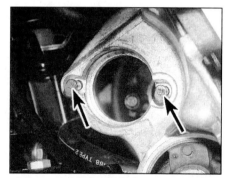

4.6b . . . then turn the bolts through 90° to disengage their offset heads (arrowed) from the bearing (driveshaft removed for clarity)

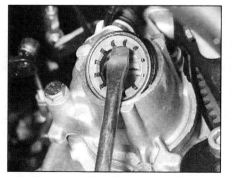

4.9 Use a large flat-bladed screwdriver to prise the driveshaft oil seals out of position

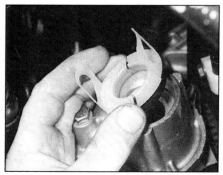

4.10a Fit the new seal to the transmission, noting the plastic seal protector . . .

4.10b . . . and tap it into position using a tubular drift

4.23a Undo the three release bearing guide sleeve retaining bolts . . .

4.23b . . . and withdraw the guide sleeve from the input shaft

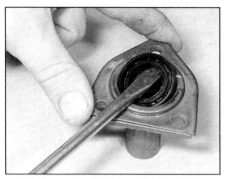

4.24 Removing the input shaft seal from the guide sleeve

(where supplied), and slide the dust seal tight up against the oil seal.

15 Engage the balljoint shank with the lower suspension arm, making sure the balljoint protector is correctly seated in the hub. Refit the clamp bolt and a new nut and tighten the nut to the specified torque.

16 Refit the flexible brake hose support bracket to the swivel hub and, where applicable, secure the ABS wheel sensor wiring to the bracket and clip.

17 Refill the transmission with the specified type and quantity of oil as described in Section 2.

Left-hand seal

18 Pull the swivel hub assembly outwards and withdraw the driveshaft inner constant velocity joint from the transmission. Support the driveshaft, to avoid damaging the constant velocity joints or gaiters.

19 Renew the oil seal as described above in paragraphs 9 to 11.

20 Carefully locate the inner constant velocity joint splines with those of the differential sun gear, taking care not to damage the oil seal, and push the driveshaft fully into position. Where fitted, remove the plastic protector from the oil seal.

21 Carry out the operations described above in paragraphs 15 to 17.

Input shaft oil seal

22 Remove the transmission as described in Section 7.

23 Undo the three bolts securing the clutch release bearing guide sleeve in position, and slide the guide sleeve off the input shaft, along with its O-ring or gasket, as applicable **(see illustrations)**. Recover any shims or thrustwashers which have stuck to the rear of the guide sleeve, and refit them to the input shaft.

24 Carefully lever the oil seal out of the guide sleeve using a suitable flat-bladed screwdriver **(see illustration)**.

25 Before fitting a new seal, check the input shaft's seal rubbing surface for signs of burrs, scratches or other damage, which may have caused the seal to fail in the first place. It may be possible to polish away minor faults of this sort using fine abrasive paper; however, more serious defects will require the renewal of the input shaft. Ensure that the input shaft is clean and greased, to protect the seal lips on refitting.

26 Dip the new seal in clean oil, and fit it to the guide sleeve.

27 Fit a new O-ring or gasket (as applicable) to the rear of the guide sleeve, then carefully slide the sleeve into position over the input shaft **(see illustration)**. Refit the retaining bolts and tighten them to the specified torque setting.

28 Take the opportunity to inspect the clutch components if not already done (see Chapter 6). Finally, refit the transmission as described in Section 7.

Selector shaft oil seal

MA transmission

29 On these models, to renew the selector shaft seal, the transmission must be dismantled. This task should therefore be entrusted to a Citroën dealer or transmission specialist.

BE3 transmission

30 Firmly apply the handbrake, then jack up the front of the car and support it securely on axle stands (see *Jacking and vehicle support*).

31 Remove the engine undertray, the left-hand front wheel, and the plastic wheelarch liner. The liner is secured by various screws and clips under the wheelarch. Release all the fasteners, and remove liner from under the front wing.

32 Using a large flat-bladed screwdriver, lever the link rod balljoint off the transmission selector shaft, and disconnect the link rod.

33 Using a large flat-bladed screwdriver, carefully prise the selector shaft seal out of the housing, and slide it off the end of the shaft **(see illustrations)**.

34 Before fitting a new seal, check the selector shaft's seal rubbing surface for signs of burrs, scratches or other damage, which may have caused the seal to fail in the first place. It may be possible to polish away minor faults of this sort using fine abrasive paper; however, more serious defects will require the renewal of the selector shaft.

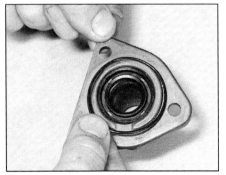

4.27 Fit a new O-ring/gasket (as applicable) to the rear of the guide sleeve

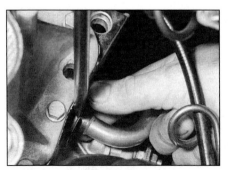

4.33a On the BE3 transmission, use a screwdriver to prise the selector shaft seal out of position . . .

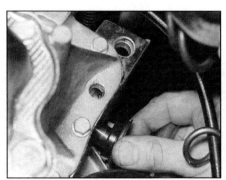

4.33b . . . then slide the seal off the shaft

5.4 Disconnecting the wiring connector from the reversing light switch (arrowed)

35 Apply a smear of grease to the new seal's outer edge and sealing lip, then carefully slide the seal along the selector shaft. Press the seal fully into position in the transmission housing.

36 Refit the link rod to the selector shaft, ensuring that its balljoint is pressed firmly onto the shaft.

37 Refit the wheelarch liner, engine undertray and roadwheel, then lower the car to the ground. Tighten the roadwheel bolts to the specified torque.

5 Reversing light switch – testing, removal and refitting

Testing

1 The reversing light circuit is controlled by a plunger-type switch screwed into the top of the transmission casing. If a fault develops, first ensure that the circuit fuse has not blown.

2 To test the switch, disconnect the wiring connector, and use a multimeter (set to the resistance function) or a battery-and-bulb test circuit to check that there is continuity between the switch terminals only when reverse gear is selected. If this is not the case, and there are no obvious breaks or other damage to the wires, the switch is faulty, and must be renewed.

Removal

3 Where necessary, to improve access to the switch, remove the air cleaner and air inlet duct(s) as described in the relevant Part of Chapter 4. If necessary, also remove the battery and battery tray as described in Chapter 5A.

4 Disconnect the wiring connector, then unscrew the switch from the transmission casing along with its sealing washer **(see illustration)**.

Refitting

5 Fit a new sealing washer to the switch, then screw it back into position in the top of the transmission housing and tighten it to the specified torque. Refit the wiring plug, and test the operation of the circuit. Refit any components removed for access.

6 Vehicle speed sensor – removal and refitting

Removal

1 Firmly apply the handbrake, then jack up the front of the car and support it on axle stands (see *Jacking and vehicle support*). The vehicle speed sensor is on the rear of the transmission housing, next to the inner end of the right-hand driveshaft.

2 Remove the engine undertray, then disconnect the wiring connector from the speed sensor.

3 Slacken and remove the retaining bolt, along with the heat shield (where fitted), and withdraw the speed sensor and driven pinion assembly from the transmission housing, along with its O-ring.

4 Examine the driven pinion for signs of damage, and if evident, renew the speed sensor assembly. Renew the sealing O-ring as a matter of course.

5 If the driven pinion is worn or damaged, also examine the drive pinion in the transmission housing for similar signs.

6 On the MA transmission, to renew the drive pinion, the transmission must be dismantled and the differential gear removed. This task should therefore be entrusted to a Citroën dealer or a transmission specialist.

7 On the BE3 transmission, to renew the drive pinion, first disengage the right-hand driveshaft from the transmission, as described in paragraphs 1 to 8 of Section 4. Undo the three retaining bolts, and remove the speed sensor extension housing from the transmission, along with its O-ring. Remove the drive pinion from the differential gear, and recover any adjustment shims from the gear **(see illustrations)**.

Refitting

8 On the BE3 transmission, where the drive pinion has been removed, refit the adjustment shims to the differential gear, then locate the drive pinion on the gear, ensuring it is correctly engaged in the gear slots **(see illustration)**. Fit a new O-ring to the rear of the extension housing, then refit the housing to the transmission and securely tighten its retaining bolts. Inspect the driveshaft oil seal for signs of wear, and renew if necessary. Refit the driveshaft to the transmission, with reference to Section 4.

9 Fit a new O-ring to the speed sensor assembly and refit it to the transmission, ensuring that the drive and driven pinions are correctly engaged.

10 Refit the retaining bolt and the heat shield (where fitted), and tighten the bolt. Reconnect the wiring connector to the speed sensor.

11 Refit the engine undertray and lower the vehicle to the ground.

7 Manual transmission – removal and refitting

Removal

1 Drain the transmission oil as described in Section 2, then refit the drain and filler plugs, tightening them to the specified torque.

6.7a On the BE3 transmission, undo the three bolts . . .

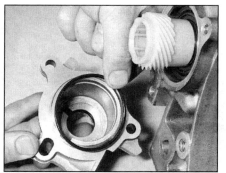

6.7b . . . and remove the speed sensor extension housing, O-ring and drive pinion from the transmission (transmission removed for clarity)

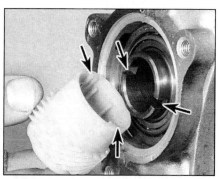

6.8 On refitting, ensure the drive pinion dogs are correctly engaged with the gear slots (arrowed)

7.6a Release the inner clutch cable end fitting from the clutch release lever . . .

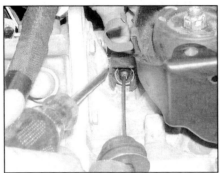

7.6b . . . then depress the retaining tabs and release the outer cable from the transmission

7.10a Undo the nuts and release the power steering pipe retaining clips from the front . . .

2 Remove the battery, battery tray and mounting plate as described in Chapter 5A.
3 Remove the air cleaner and air inlet duct(s) as described in the relevant Part of Chapter 4. On XUD9 turbo diesel models, also remove the intercooler.
4 Remove both driveshafts as described in Chapter 8.
5 Remove the starter motor as described in Chapter 5A.
6 Release the inner clutch cable end fitting from the support bracket or clutch release lever. Depress the retaining tabs and release

7.10b . . . and from the underside of the transmission

the outer cable from the transmission **(see illustrations)**.
7 Disconnect the wiring connector from the reversing light switch, TDC sensor and vehicle speed sensor. Undo the retaining nut(s), and disconnect the earth straps from the transmission housing. Disconnect the wiring from any additional switches/sensors as necessary, free the wiring loom from the retaining clips, and position it clear of the transmission.
8 On the MA transmission, undo the bolt securing the exhaust front pipe to its transmission mounting bracket.
9 Using a flat-bladed screwdriver, carefully prise the gearchange mechanism link rod balljoints off their respective levers on the transmission. Position the rods clear of the transmission.
10 Undo the retaining nuts and release the retaining clips securing the power steering pipe to the transmission **(see illustrations)**. Position the pipe clear of the unit so that it will not be damaged during the removal procedure.
11 Undo the retaining bolt(s), and remove the flywheel lower cover plate (where fitted) from the transmission **(see illustration)**.
12 On the BE3 transmission, remove the

vehicle speed sensor drive gear extension housing from the transmission as described in Section 6.
13 Place a jack with a block of wood beneath the engine, to take the weight of the engine. Alternatively, attach a couple of lifting eyes to the engine, and fit a hoist or support bar to take the engine weight.
14 Place a jack and block of wood beneath the transmission, and raise the jack to take the weight of the transmission.
15 Undo the bolt securing the engine/transmission rear mounting link to the bracket on the subframe.
16 Slacken and remove the centre nut and washer from the left-hand engine/transmission mounting. Undo the two bolts securing the mounting to the support bracket, and remove the rubber mounting **(see illustration)**.
17 On the MA transmission, undo the three retaining nuts and remove the mounting plate from the top of the transmission.
18 On the BE3 transmission, remove the washer and spacer from the mounting stud, then unscrew the stud from the top of the transmission housing. Collect the large spacer plate from the mounting stud.
19 On models with a 'pull-type' clutch release

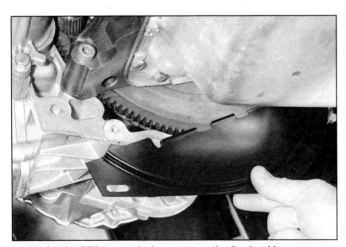

7.11 On the BE3 transmission, remove the flywheel lower cover plate

7.16 Undo the two retaining bolts and remove the left-hand engine/transmission mounting

7.19a On models with a 'pull-type' clutch, withdraw the retaining pin . . .

7.19b . . . then remove the clutch release lever . . .

7.19c . . . and make an alignment mark between the release fork shaft and transmission housing (arrowed)

mechanism (see Chapter 6), withdraw the retaining pin and remove the clutch release lever from the top of the release fork shaft. This is necessary to allow the fork shaft to rotate freely to disengage from the release bearing as the transmission is pulled away from the engine. Make an alignment mark across the centre of the clutch release fork shaft using a scriber, paint or similar, and mark its position relative to the transmission housing **(see illustrations)**. Undo the retaining bolts, and remove the clutch cable bracket from the top of the transmission housing.

20 With the jack positioned beneath the transmission taking the weight, slacken and remove the remaining bolts securing the transmission housing to the engine. Note the correct fitted positions of each bolt, and the necessary brackets, as they are removed, to use as a reference on refitting. Make a final check that all components have been disconnected, and are positioned clear of the transmission so that they will not hinder the removal procedure.

21 With the bolts removed, move the trolley jack and transmission to the left, to free it from its locating dowels then pivot the differential end of the transmission upwards (to disengage it from the subframe).

22 Once the transmission is free, lower the jack and manoeuvre the unit out from under the car. Remove the locating dowels from the transmission or engine if they are loose, and keep them in a safe place.

23 On models with a 'pull-type' clutch, make a second alignment mark on the transmission housing, marking the relative position of the release fork mark after removal, noting the angle at which the release fork is positioned **(see illustration 7.24)**. This mark can then be used to position the release fork before refitting, to ensure that the fork correctly engages with the clutch release bearing as the transmission is installed.

Refitting

24 The transmission is refitted by a reversal of the removal procedure, bearing in mind the following points:
a) Apply a little high-melting-point grease (Citroën recommend the use of Molykote

BR2 plus – available from your Citroën dealer) to the splines of the transmission input shaft. Do not apply too much, otherwise there is a possibility of the grease contaminating the clutch friction plate.
b) Ensure that the locating dowels are correctly positioned prior to installation.
c) On models with a 'pull-type' clutch, before refitting, position the clutch release bearing so that its arrow mark is pointing upwards (bearing fork slots facing towards the front of the engine), and align the release fork shaft mark with the second mark made on the transmission housing (release fork positioned at approximately 60° to clutch housing face) **(see illustration)**. This will ensure that the release fork and bearing will engage correctly as the transmission is refitted to the engine. If the bearing and fork are correctly engaged, the mark on the shaft should be aligned with the original mark made on the transmission housing. Ensure that the release fork and bearing are correctly engaged before bolting the transmission to the engine.
d) On the BE3 transmission, apply thread-locking fluid to the left-hand engine/transmission mounting stud threads, prior to refitting it to the transmission. Tighten the stud to the specified torque.

7.24 On models with a 'pull-type' clutch, prior to refitting the transmission, align the release fork mark with the second mark made on removal

e) Tighten all nuts and bolts to the specified torque (where given).
f) Renew the driveshaft oil seals (Section 5), then refit the driveshafts (see Chapter 8).
g) On completion, refill the transmission with the specified type and quantity of lubricant, as described in Section 2.

8 Manual transmission overhaul – general information

Overhauling a manual transmission is a difficult and involved job for the DIY home mechanic. In addition to dismantling and reassembling many small parts, clearances must be precisely measured and, if necessary, changed by selecting shims and spacers. Internal transmission components are also often difficult to obtain, and in many instances, extremely expensive. Because of this, if the transmission develops a fault or becomes noisy, the best course of action is to have the unit overhauled by a specialist repairer, or to obtain an exchange reconditioned unit.

Nevertheless, it is not impossible for the more experienced mechanic to overhaul the transmission, provided the special tools are available, and the job is done in a deliberate step-by-step manner, so that nothing is overlooked.

The tools necessary for an overhaul include internal and external circlip pliers, bearing pullers, a slide hammer, a set of pin punches, a dial test indicator, and possibly a hydraulic press. In addition, a large, sturdy workbench and a vice will be required.

During dismantling of the transmission, make careful notes of how each component is fitted, to make reassembly easier and more accurate.

Before dismantling the transmission, it will help if you have some idea what area is malfunctioning. Certain problems can be closely related to specific areas in the transmission, which can make component examination and replacement easier. Refer to the *Fault finding* Section in the Reference Section for more information.

Notes

Chapter 7 Part B:
Automatic transmission

Contents

AL4 transmission electronic system components – removal and
  refitting 11
Automatic transmission – removal and refitting 12
Automatic transmission fluid level check . . . . .See Chapter 1A
Automatic transmission fluid – draining and refilling 13
Automatic transmission overhaul – general information 14
Fluid cooler – removal and refitting 9
General information 1
Kickdown cable (4 HP 14 transmission) – adjustment 5

Kickdown cable (4 HP 14 transmission) – renewal 6
Oil seals – renewal 8
Selector cable (4 HP 14 transmission) – adjustment 2
Selector cable – removal and refitting 3
Selector lever assembly (4 HP 14 transmission) –
  removal and refitting 4
Starter inhibitor/reversing light switch (4 HP 14 transmission) –
  removal, testing and refitting 10
Vehicle speed sensor – removal and refitting 7

Degrees of difficulty

Easy, suitable for novice with little experience	**Fairly easy,** suitable for beginner with some experience	**Fairly difficult,** suitable for competent DIY mechanic	**Difficult,** suitable for experienced DIY mechanic 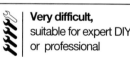	**Very difficult,** suitable for expert DIY or professional 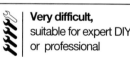

Specifications

General

Type . . . . Automatic, four forward speeds and reverse
Designation:
  1.8 and 2.0 litre petrol engine models . . . . 4 HP 14
  1.6 litre petrol engine models AL4

Lubrication

Recommended fluid . . . . Refer to *Lubricants and fluids*
Capacities:
  4 HP 14 transmission:
    From dry . . . . 6.2 litres
    Drain and refill . . . . 2.4 litres
  AL4 transmission:
    From dry . . . . 5.8 litres
    Drain and refill . . . . 3.0 litres

Torque wrench settings

	Nm	lbf ft
4 HP 14 transmission		
Dipstick tube-to-sump union nut	45	33
Engine-to-transmission securing bolts	40	30
Engine/transmission left-hand mounting:		
Rubber mounting-to-body bolts	21	15
Mounting stud to transmission	50	37
Rubber mounting centre nut	65	48
Fluid cooler centre bolt	50	37
Selector cable fixings:		
Outer cable locknuts	10	7
Mounting bracket-to-transmission bolts	20	15
Cable-to-mounting bracket screws	10	7
Selector lever retaining nuts	7	5
Starter inhibitor/reversing light switch		
Torque converter-to-driveplate bolts	35	26
Transmission selector lever retaining nut	30	22
AL4 transmission		
Engine-to-transmission securing bolts	52	38
Engine/transmission left-hand mounting:		
Rubber mounting-to-body bolts	27	20
Mounting stud to transmission	50	37
Rubber mounting centre nut	65	48
Fluid cooler centre bolt	50	37
Input speed sensor	10	7
Oil drain plug	33	24
Oil filler and level plugs	24	18
Output speed sensor	10	7
Selector lever position switch bolts	15	11
Torque converter-to-driveplate bolts:		
Stage 1	10	7
Stage 2	30	22
Transmission selector shaft lever clamp bolt and nut	15	11

1 General information

4 HP 14 transmission

1.8 and 2.0 litre petrol engine models are optionally available with a four-speed fully-automatic transmission, consisting of a torque converter, an epicyclic geartrain, and hydraulically-operated clutches and brakes (see illustration).

The torque converter provides a fluid coupling between engine and transmission, which acts as an automatic clutch, and also provides a degree of torque multiplication when accelerating.

The epicyclic geartrain provides one of the four forward or one reverse gear ratios, according to which of its component parts are held stationary or allowed to turn. The components of the geartrain are held or released by brakes and clutches which are activated by a hydraulic control unit. A fluid pump within the transmission provides the necessary hydraulic pressure to operate the brakes and clutches.

Driver control of the transmission is by a seven-position selector lever. The transmission has a 'drive' position, and a 'hold' facility on the first three gear ratios. The 'drive' position D provides automatic changing throughout the range of all four gear ratios, and is the one to select for normal driving. An automatic kickdown facility shifts the transmission down a gear if the accelerator pedal is fully depressed. The 'hold' facility is very similar, but limits the number of gear ratios available – ie, when the selector lever is in the 3 position, only the first three ratios can be selected; in the 2 position, only the first two can be selected, and so on. The lower ratio 'hold' is useful for providing engine braking when travelling down steep gradients, or for preventing unwanted selection of top gear on twisty roads. Note, however, that the transmission should *never* be shifted down a position if the engine speed exceeds 4000 rpm.

AL4 type transmission

The AL4 transmission, optionally available on later 1.6 litre petrol engine models, is a development of the earlier 4 HP 14 unit, and incorporates electronic control; the automatic gearchanges are electronically-controlled, rather than hydraulically as with the 4 HP 14 type. The advantage of electronic management is to provide a faster gearchange response. A kickdown facility is also provided, to enable a faster acceleration response when required.

The torque converter incorporates an automatic lock-up feature which eliminates any possibility of converter slip in the top two gears; this aids performance and economy. In addition to the normal alternative of manual change, the three-position mode switch on the centre console (adjacent to the selector lever) provides 'normal', 'sport' or 'snow' settings, as required. In 'sport' mode, upshifts are delayed longer, to make full use of engine power. In 'snow' mode, either 2nd or 3rd gear is used to pull away from rest, maximising traction in slippery conditions.

Another feature of this transmission is the Park Lock, which is partly a safety, and partly a security, feature. Moving the lever out of the P position requires the ignition to be on, and the brake pedal must also be depressed.

The gear selector cable has an automatic adjuster mechanism, meaning that cable adjustment should not be required. The AL4 transmission is also regarded as being 'lubricated for life', with routine fluid changes not featuring in the manufacturer's maintenance schedule.

In the event of a problem developing with the transmission, the transmission ECU may

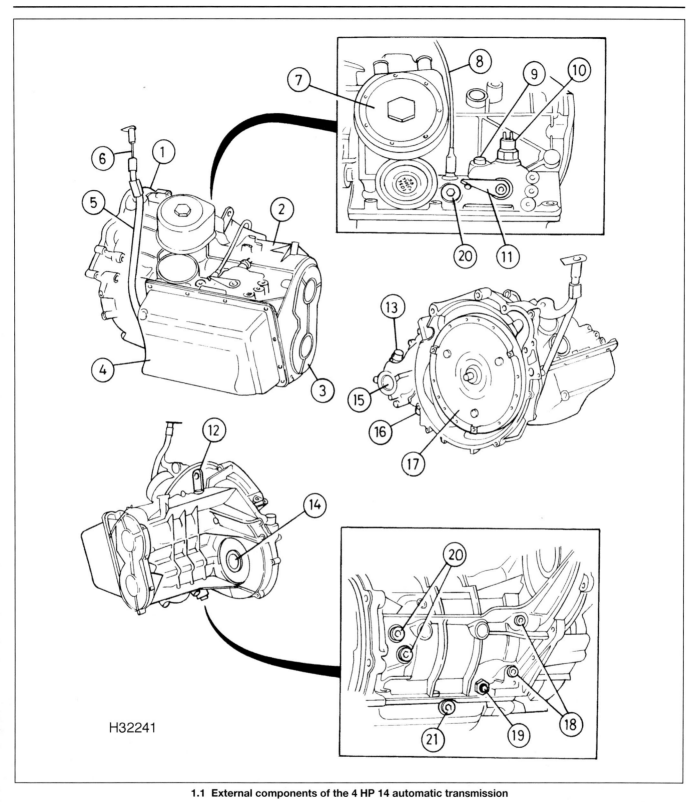

H32241

1.1 External components of the 4 HP 14 automatic transmission

1	Torque converter housing	7	Fluid cooler
2	Main casing	8	Kickdown cable
3	End cover	9	Breather
4	Sump	10	Starter inhibitor/reversing
5	Dipstick tube		light switch
6	Dipstick		

11	Selector lever	16	Final drive drain plug
12	Lifting eye	17	Torque converter
13	Vehicle speed sensor drive	18	Output shaft bearing bolts
14	Final drive left-hand output	19	Brake band adjuster
15	Final drive right-hand	20	Pressure test points
	output	21	Sump drain plug

select one of two emergency back-up modes, to enable the car to continue being driven. When operating in this back-up mode, shifting out of N or R will become more jerky, or the transmission will only select 3rd gear (no gearchanges). If a fault is suspected, your Citroën dealer will be able to download fault codes from the transmission ECU memory, to speed up diagnosis.

All transmission types

Due to the complexity of the automatic transmission, any repair or overhaul work must be left to a Citroën dealer with the necessary special equipment for fault diagnosis and repair. The contents of the following Sections are therefore confined to supplying general information, and any service information and instructions that can be used by the owner.

2 Selector cable (4 HP 14 transmission) – adjustment

1 Position the selector lever firmly against its detent in the N (neutral) position.
2 Remove the battery, battery tray and mounting plate as described in Chapter 5A, then remove the air inlet duct as described in Chapter 4A.
3 Using a large flat-bladed screwdriver, carefully lever the selector cable end fitting off the transmission selector lever balljoint, whilst ensuring that the lever does not move.
4 First ensure that the cable end fitting is screwed at least 5.0 mm onto the end of the inner cable thread.
5 With both the selector levers in the N position, the selector cable end fitting should

be correctly aligned with the transmission lever balljoint, so that the cable can be connected to the lever without the balljoint moving. If necessary, adjust the position of the end fitting by screwing or unscrewing it (as applicable) on the cable thread, bearing in mind the point made above in paragraph 4. If this proves impossible, further adjustments can be made by slackening the locknuts securing the outer cable to its mounting bracket **(see illustration)**. Reposition the nuts as required until the end fitting and balljoint are correctly aligned, then tighten the nuts.
6 Once the end fitting is correctly positioned, press it firmly onto the balljoint, and check that it is securely retained.
7 Refit any parts removed to improve access using a reverse of the removal procedure.

3 Selector cable – removal and refitting

Removal

4 HP 14 transmission

1 Firmly apply the handbrake, then jack up the front of the vehicle and support it on axle stands (see *Jacking and vehicle support*). Position the selector lever in the N position.
2 Remove the battery, battery tray and mounting plate as described in Chapter 5A, then remove the air inlet duct as described in Chapter 4A.
3 Remove the exhaust system heat shield(s) to gain access to the base of the selector lever assembly (see Chapter 4A).
4 Working on the transmission end of the cable, undo the two screws securing the outer

cable to its retaining bracket, and carefully lever the inner cable end fitting off its balljoint on the transmission selector lever. Note that the transmission selector lever must not be disturbed until the cable is refitted. As a precaution, mark the position of the lever in relation to the transmission housing.
5 Work back along the selector cable, releasing it from any relevant retaining clips, noting its correct routing.
6 Working inside the vehicle, carefully prise the selector lever trim panel out from the centre console.
7 Slacken and remove the screws securing the handle to the shaft of the selector lever. Depress the selector lever handle detent knob, then rotate the handle through 90° anti-clockwise, lift the assembly up, and rotate it back 90° clockwise to release the detent button from the selector lever pushrod. With the handle removed, withdraw the detent button and spring from the handle.
8 Undo the four nuts securing the selector lever to the floor.
9 Working underneath the vehicle, disengage the selector lever assembly from the body, and remove the lever and cable assembly, noting the correct routing of the cable.
10 With the assembly on the bench, prise the rubber dust cover from the base of the lever, and slide it along the cable.
11 Slacken the outer cable retaining nut, then remove the retaining clip. Carefully prise the selector cable end fitting off its balljoint on the base of the selector lever, and separate cable and lever assembly.
12 Examine the cable, looking for worn end fittings or a damaged outer casing, and for signs of fraying of the inner cable. Check the cable's operation; the inner cable should move smoothly and easily through the outer casing. Remember – a cable that appears serviceable when tested off the car may well be much heavier in operation when compressed into its working position. Renew the cable if it shows any signs of excessive wear or any damage.

AL4 transmission

13 Release the Park Lock by switching on the ignition and pressing the brake pedal. Position the selector lever in the 2nd gear position, then switch off the ignition.
14 Remove the air cleaner assembly and air inlet ducting as described in Chapter 4A.
15 Remove the battery, battery tray and mounting plate as described in Chapter 5A.
16 Using a suitable forked tool (a fork type balljoint splitter could be used, or failing that, a large flat-bladed screwdriver), carefully prise the selector cable balljoint off the selector lever **(see illustration)**.
17 Extract the retaining C-clip and release the outer cable and cable grommet from the transmission bracket.
18 Firmly apply the handbrake, then jack up the front of the car and support it securely on axle stands (see *Jacking and vehicle support*).

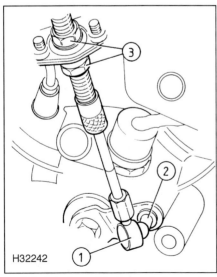

2.5 Selector cable transmission end fixings – 4 HP 14 transmission

1 *Cable end fitting*
2 *Selector lever balljoint*
3 *Outer cable locknuts*

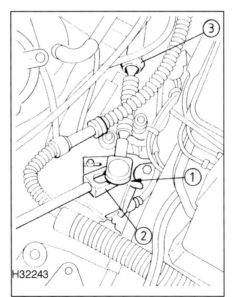

3.16 Prise off the selector cable balljoint (1) using a forked tool (2), then remove the cable from the bracket (3) – AL4 transmission

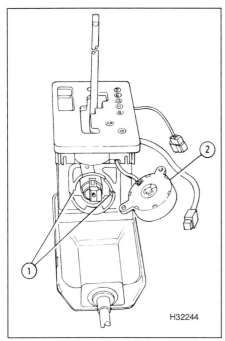

3.21 Park Lock solenoid valve attachment on the selector lever upper housing – AL4 transmission

1 Retaining screws
2 Park Lock solenoid valve

19 Detach and lower the exhaust system in the area below the passenger compartment selector lever, and remove the heatshield in order to release the selector cable retaining clamp.

20 Remove the centre console as described in Chapter 11.

21 Undo the two screws and withdraw the Park Lock solenoid valve from the front of the selector lever upper housing **(see illustration)**.

22 Pull the selector lever knob upwards off the lever, without twisting it.

23 Undo the two nuts securing the selector lever upper housing to the lower housing and lift off the upper housing. On later models, there may be two additional upper housing retaining screws which are accessible through the selector lever gate.

24 Undo the remaining nuts and bolts securing the selector lever lower housing to the floor, then withdraw the lower housing and cable from the car.

Refitting

4 HP 14 transmission

25 Apply a smear of molybdenum disulphide grease to the exposed sections of the inner cable and balljoints, and to the detent mechanism of the selector lever.

26 Insert the selector cable into the selector lever housing, ensuring that the outer cable flange holes are correctly located on the pegs on the housing. Secure the cable in position with the retaining clip, ensuring that the outer

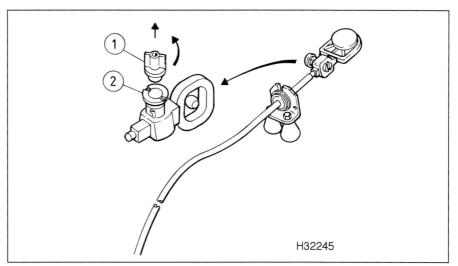

3.40 When fitting a new selector cable, remove the locking key (1) from the cable adjuster boss (2) – AL4 transmission

ends of the clip are correctly located in the slots in the lever housing, and the inner ends are correctly hooked over the base of the housing. Tighten the outer cable retaining nut.

27 Press the inner cable end fitting firmly onto the lever balljoint. Check that the balljoint connection is securely made, then slide the rubber dust cover back into position over the selector lever base.

28 Ensuring that the cable is correctly routed, manoeuvre the lever and cable assembly back into position from underneath the vehicle.

29 From inside the vehicle, pull the lever up into position, and tighten all four selector lever retaining nuts.

30 Refit the spring and detent button to the selector lever handle, and press the button fully into the handle. Keeping the button depressed, slide the handle assembly onto the lever then, exerting light downward pressure on the handle, rotate the handle through 90° clockwise, then back 90° anti-clockwise to engage the detent button with the lever pushrod. Release the detent button, then refit the four handle retaining screws and tighten them securely. Check the operation of the selector lever detent button before proceeding.

31 From underneath the vehicle, work along the length of the selector cable, ensuring that it is retained by all the relevant clips. Align the outer cable bracket with its mounting bracket on the transmission, then refit and tighten its retaining bolts.

32 Ensure that the selector lever is in the N position and the transmission selector lever is still in the neutral position, then adjust the cable and connect it to the transmission lever as described in paragraphs 4 to 6 of Section 2.

33 Refit the heat shield(s) as described in Chapter 4A, then lower the vehicle to the ground.

34 Refit all components removed for access using a reverse of the removal procedure.

AL4 transmission

35 Refit the selector lever upper and lower housing, the Park Lock solenoid and centre console, using the reverse of the removal procedure.

36 Move the gear selection lever in the passenger compartment to the P position.

37 Under the car, fit the selector cable retaining clamp, exhaust heatshield and other disturbed exhaust system components as necessary.

38 In the engine compartment, move the transmission selector lever to the P position (fully towards the engine compartment bulkhead).

39 Fit the cable and grommet to the transmission bracket and secure with the C-clip. Reconnect the selector cable balljoint to the transmission selector lever, pressing it firmly into place.

40 If a new selector cable has been fitted, remove the locking key from the automatic adjuster mechanism **(see illustration)**.

41 If the selector cable adjustment is suspect, press the adjuster boss without deflecting or bending the cable, and then release it **(refer to illustration 3.40)**.

42 Final refitting is now a reversal of removal. Check for satisfactory operation of the selector cable on completion.

4 Selector lever assembly (4 HP 14 transmission) – removal and refitting

Note: *This procedure does not apply to the AL4 transmission. At the time of writing, it appears that the selector lever housing and selector cable for the AL4 unit are not available separately. To remove the selector lever housing on the AL4 transmission, refer to Section 3.*

Removal

1 Firmly apply the handbrake, then jack up the front of the vehicle and support it on axle stands (see *Jacking and vehicle support*). Position the selector lever in the N position.

2 Remove the exhaust system heat shield(s) to gain access to the base of the selector lever assembly (see Chapter 4A).

3 Carry out the procedures described in paragraphs 6 to 8 of Section 3.

4 Working again from underneath the vehicle, disengage the selector lever assembly from the body, and lower it out of position.

5 Prise the rubber dust cover from the base of the lever, and slide it along the cable.

6 Slacken the outer cable retaining nut, then remove the retaining clip. Carefully prise the selector cable end fitting off its balljoint on the base of the selector lever, and remove the lever assembly from underneath the vehicle.

Refitting

7 Carry out the operations described in paragraphs 25 to 30 of Section 3.

8 Refit the heat shield(s) and exhaust system as described in Chapter 4A, then lower the vehicle to the ground.

9 On completion, check the selector cable adjustment as described in Section 2.

5 Kickdown cable (4 HP 14 transmission) – adjustment

Note: *This Section does not apply to the AL4 transmission, as the kickdown function is controlled electronically.*

1 Remove the air inlet duct as described in Chapter 4A for access to the throttle housing.

2 Detach the kickdown inner cable from the throttle housing cam then, referring to Chapter 4A, check that the accelerator cable is correctly adjusted **(see illustration)**.

3 Pull the kickdown inner cable fully out of its outer cable until resistance is felt. Hold the cable in this position and measure the distance between the end of the crimped lug

5.2 Kickdown cable connection to the throttle housing cam – 4 HP 14 transmission

on the inner cable and the threaded end of the outer cable **(see illustration)**. This should be approximately 39.0 mm. If necessary, slacken the two outer cable locknuts, and position the nuts as required so that the distance is as specified.

4 Reconnect the kickdown cable to the throttle housing cam and close the throttle. Ensuring that the throttle housing cam is fully against its stop, there should now be a gap of 0.5 to 1.0 mm between the inner cable crimped lug and the threaded end of the outer cable **(see illustration)**. If not, adjust the gap by repositioning the outer cable locknuts as required. Once the outer cable is correctly positioned and the gap is as specified, securely tighten the cable locknuts.

5 Refit the air inlet duct as described in Chapter 4A on completion.

6 Kickdown cable (4 HP 14 transmission) – renewal

Renewal of the kickdown cable is a complex task, which should be entrusted to a Citroën dealer. To detach the cable at the transmission end requires removal of the hydraulic valve block, which is a task that should not be undertaken by the home mechanic.

7 Vehicle speed sensor – removal and refitting

Refer to Chapter 7A.

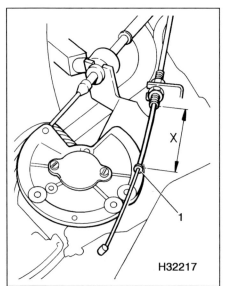

5.3 Extend the kickdown cable, and measure distance (X) between the cable lug (1) and the outer cable end – 4 HP 14 transmission

8 Oil seals – renewal

Driveshaft oil seals

1 Refer to Chapter 7A, Section 4.

Selector shaft oil seal

4 HP 14 transmission

2 Position the selector lever firmly against its detent mechanism in the N position.

3 To improve access to the transmission end of the selector cable, remove the battery, battery tray and mounting plate as described in Chapter 5A, then remove the air inlet duct as described in Chapter 4A.

4 Undo the two screws securing the outer cable to its retaining bracket, and carefully lever the inner cable end fitting off its balljoint on the transmission selector lever. Note the transmission selector shaft must not be disturbed until the cable is refitted. As a precaution, mark the position of the lever in relation to the transmission housing.

5 Undo the retaining nut, and remove the lever from the transmission selector shaft.

6 Punch or drill two small holes opposite each other in the seal. Screw a self-tapping screw into each, and pull on the screws with pliers to extract the seal.

7 Clean the seal housing, and polish off any burrs or raised edges, which may have caused the seal to fail in the first place. Small imperfections can be removed using emery paper, but larger defects will require the renewal of the selector shaft.

8 Lubricate the lips of the new seal with clean engine oil, and carefully ease the seal into

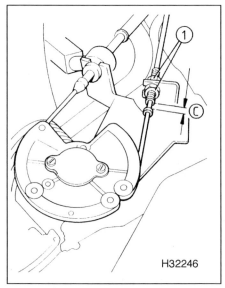

5.4 Reconnect the cable, and check that clearance (c) is as given in the text. Adjust by repositioning the locknuts (1) – 4 HP 14 transmission

position over the end of the shaft, taking great care not to damage its sealing lip. Tap the seal into position until it is flush with the transmission casing, using a suitable tubular drift (such as a socket) which bears only on the hard outer edge of the seal. Note that the seal lips should face inwards.

9 Refit the selector lever to the shaft and tighten its retaining nut.

10 Align the outer cable bracket with its mounting bracket on the transmission, then refit and tighten its retaining bolts.

11 Ensure that the selector lever is in the N position and the transmission selector lever is still in the neutral position, then adjust the cable and connect it to the transmission lever as described in paragraphs 4 to 6 of Section 2.

AL4 transmission

12 Remove the selector lever position switch as described in Section 11 for access to the oil seal.

13 Renew the seal as described above in paragraphs 6 to 8.

14 Refit the selector lever position switch as described in Section 11.

9 Fluid cooler – removal and refitting

Removal

1 The fluid cooler is mounted on the front (4 HP 14) or rear (AL4) of the transmission housing. To gain access to the fluid cooler, remove the air inlet duct(s) as described in Chapter 4A (depending on model). Slacken and remove the bolts securing the hose retaining bracket in position, and position the bracket clear of the fluid cooler.

2 Using a hose clamp or similar, clamp both the fluid cooler coolant hoses to minimise coolant loss during subsequent operations **(see illustration)**.

3 Slacken the retaining clips, and disconnect both coolant hoses from the fluid cooler – be prepared for some coolant spillage. Wash off

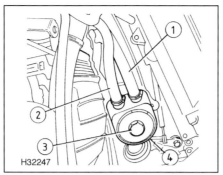

9.2 Transmission fluid cooler details – 4 HP 14 transmission

1 Coolant hose   3 Centre bolt
2 Coolant hose   4 Fluid cooler

any spilt coolant immediately with cold water, and dry the surrounding area before proceeding further.

4 Slacken and remove the fluid cooler centre bolt, and remove the cooler from the transmission. Remove the seal from the centre bolt, and the two seals fitted to the base of the cooler, and discard them; new ones must be used on refitting.

Refitting

5 Lubricate the new seals with clean automatic transmission fluid, then fit the two new seals to the base of the fluid cooler, and a new seal to the centre bolt **(see illustrations)**.

6 Locate the fluid cooler on the transmission housing, ensuring its flat edge is parallel to the mating surface of the housing. Refit the centre bolt, and tighten it to the specified torque setting.

7 Reconnect the coolant hoses to the fluid cooler, and securely tighten their retaining clips. Remove the hose clamp.

8 Refit the disturbed inlet duct/air cleaner housing components (as applicable) as described in Chapter 4A.

9 On completion, top-up and bleed the cooling system, and check the automatic transmission fluid level, as described in Chapter 1A.

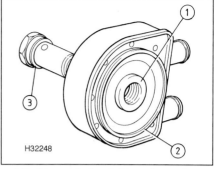

9.5a Transmission fluid cooler seals – 4 HP 14 transmission

1 Cooler inner seal   3 Centre bolt
2 Cooler outer seal   seal

10 Starter inhibitor/reversing light switch (4 HP 14 transmission) – removal, testing and refitting

General information

1 The starter inhibitor/reversing light switch is a dual-function switch which is screwed into the top of the transmission housing. The inhibitor function of the switch ensures that the engine can only be started with the selector lever in either the N or P positions, therefore preventing the engine being started with the transmission in gear. This is achieved by the switch cutting the supply to the starter motor solenoid. If at any time it is noted that the engine can be started with the selector lever in any position other than P or N, then it is likely that the inhibitor function of the switch is suspect. The switch also performs the function of the reversing light switch, illuminating the reversing lights whenever the selector lever is in the R position.

Removal

2 To improve access to the switch, remove the battery, battery tray and mounting plate as described in Chapter 5A, then remove the air inlet duct(s) as described in Chapter 4A.

3 Trace the wiring back from the switch, and disconnect it at the wiring connector.

4 Unscrew the switch, and remove it from the top of the transmission housing, along with its washer.

Testing

> ⚠ **Warning: Ensure that the transmission selector lever is in the N or P position during the following tests.**

5 Temporarily refit and reconnect the battery, and reconnect the switch wiring.

6 With the ignition switched on and the starter inhibitor/reversing light switch plunger pressed fully in, check that the reversing lights are illuminated.

7 With the switch plunger released, check that it is possible to start the engine.

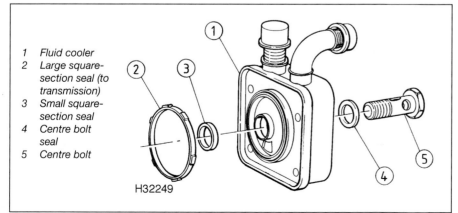

1 Fluid cooler
2 Large square-section seal (to transmission)
3 Small square-section seal
4 Centre bolt seal
5 Centre bolt

9.5b Transmission fluid cooler details – AL4 transmission

8 With the switch plunger in the mid-position check that it is not possible to start the engine and that the reversing lights are not illuminated.

9 If the switch does not operate as described, check the security and continuity of the switch wiring connections. If the wiring is satisfactory, the switch should be renewed.

Refitting

10 Fit a new washer to the switch, screw it back into the transmission, and tighten it to the specified torque. Note that washers of various thicknesses are available in the form of a shim kit from Citroën dealers. If the original switch is being refitted, a washer 0.2 mm thicker than the original should be used. If a new switch is being fitted, a washer at least 1.6 mm thick should be used.

11 Temporarily refit and reconnect the battery, then reconnect the switch wiring and carry out the following tests.

12 Firmly apply the handbrake and footbrake and check that it is possible to start the engine with the selector lever in the P and N positions, but not in any other positions.

13 Check that it is not possible to start the engine with the selector lever moved half way between the N and R positions and N and D positions.

14 Check that the reversing lights are only illuminated with the selector lever in the R position.

15 If the switch does not operate as described, fit a slightly thicker washer and repeat the procedure until the correct operation is achieved.

16 On completion, refit the mounting plate, battery tray and battery as described in Chapter 5A, then refit the air inlet duct(s).

11 AL4 transmission electronic system components – removal and refitting

Electronic control unit

Note: *If a new electronic control unit is being fitted, it will be necessary for the transmission ECU to be initialised and matched electronically to the engine management ECU on completion – the initialisation must be referred to a Citroën dealer.*

1 The transmission ECU is located behind the battery. To gain access, first remove the battery and battery tray as described in Chapter 5A, then remove the air inlet ducts as described in Chapter 4A.

2 Disconnect the ECU wiring connector, then undo the three ECU mounting bracket screws.

3 Lift out the ECU and its mounting bracket, then undo the bolts and separate the ECU from the bracket.

4 Refitting is a reversal of removal, ensuring that the ECU wiring connector is securely connected.

Input speed sensor

5 The input speed sensor is located on the left-hand end of the transmission, in front of the driveshaft.

6 Remove the battery, battery tray and mounting plate as described in Chapter 5A, then remove the air cleaner and air inlet ducts as described in Chapter 4A.

7 Remove the two securing screws from the modular connector located at the rear of the transmission, and disconnect the wiring as it is removed.

8 Extract the yellow three-way wiring connector from the modular connector.

9 Detach the wiring harness from the transmission as necessary for access to the sensor. Unscrew and remove the sensor retaining bolt, then withdraw the sensor from the transmission **(see illustration)**. Recover the sensor O-ring seal, and discard it.

10 Refitting is a reversal of removal. Use a new O-ring seal when refitting the sensor, and tighten its retaining bolt to the specified torque. Ensure that all wiring connections are securely re-made.

Output speed sensor

11 The output speed sensor is fitted to the rear of the transmission, just below the selector cable bracket **(refer to illustration 11.9)**.

12 Disconnect the battery negative terminal

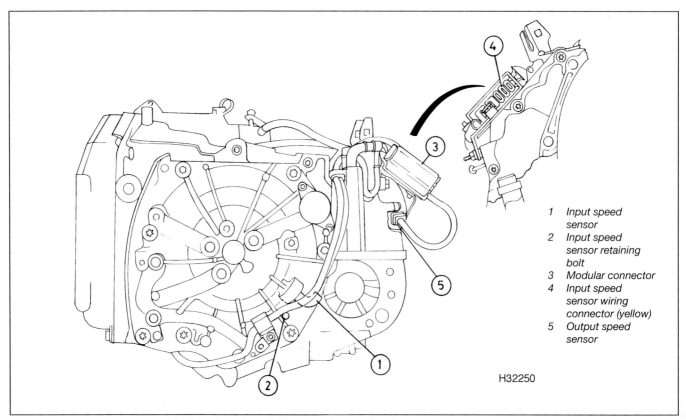

1 Input speed sensor
2 Input speed sensor retaining bolt
3 Modular connector
4 Input speed sensor wiring connector (yellow)
5 Output speed sensor

H32250

11.9 End-on view of AL4 transmission, showing speed sensor details

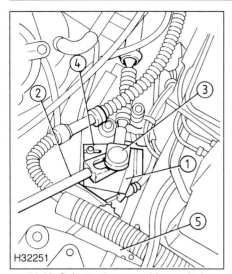

11.19 Selector lever position switch details – AL4 transmission

1 Selector lever position switch
2 Forked tool
3 Selector cable balljoint
4 Transmission selector lever clamp bolt and nut
5 Wiring harness support bracket

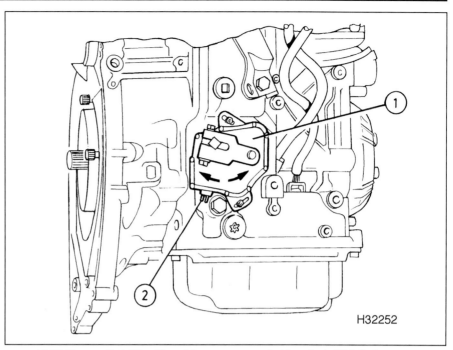

11.30 Turn switch (1) until resistance measured at terminals (2) falls to zero – AL4 transmission

(refer to *Disconnecting the battery* in the Reference Section of this manual).

13 Disconnect the speed sensor wiring plug located behind the modular connector.

14 Unscrew and remove the sensor retaining bolt, then withdraw the sensor from the transmission. Recover the sensor O-ring seal, and discard it.

15 Refitting is a reversal of removal. Use a new O-ring seal when refitting the sensor, and tighten its retaining bolt to the specified torque. Ensure that the wiring connection is securely re-made.

Selector lever position switch

16 The selector lever position switch is situated on top of the transmission, attached to the selector cable.

17 Remove the battery, battery tray and mounting plate as described in Chapter 5A, then remove the air inlet duct as described in Chapter 4A.

18 From inside the car, move the selector lever to the N position.

19 Using a suitable forked tool (a fork type balljoint splitter could be used, or failing that, a large flat-bladed screwdriver), carefully prise the selector cable balljoint off the transmission selector lever **(see illustration)**. Take care not to bend the transmission selector lever during this operation.

20 Mark the position of the transmission selector lever in relation to the splined shaft of the switch, for use when refitting. Unscrew and remove the clamp bolt and nut from the selector lever, and remove the lever from the shaft splines.

21 Detach the wiring harness and its support bracket from in front of the switch.

22 If the original switch is to be refitted, mark the position of the two switch retaining bolts in the slotted holes of the switch. If the switch is refitted in exactly the same position, there should be no need to check the switch resistance on refitting.

23 Unscrew the switch retaining bolts, disconnect the two switch wiring, and remove the switch from the engine compartment.

24 With the switch removed, check the condition of the selector shaft oil seal. If signs of leakage are evident, renew the seal as described in Section 8.

25 Refitting is a reversal of removal, but the switch position must be set to ensure correct operation.

26 If the original switch is being refitted, the switch bolts can be aligned in the switch slots as marked on removal.

27 If a new switch is being fitted, or the marks have been lost, connect an ohmmeter between the two pins provided on the front of the switch (do not use a test light, or any multi-meter which supplies more than 100 mA, or the switch will be damaged). Fit the switch retaining bolts loosely at this stage.

28 Refit the transmission selector lever to the splined shaft of the switch and tighten the clamp bolt and nut to the specified torque.

29 Ensure that the transmission selector lever is in the neutral N position.

30 Turn the switch body until the resistance measured on the ohmmeter falls to zero **(see illustration)**.

31 When the switch position is correct,

tighten the retaining bolts to the specified torque.

32 Refit all remaining components removed for access, and check for satisfactory operation on completion.

Park Lock solenoid

33 The Park Lock solenoid is located on the front of the gear selector lever housing in the passenger compartment.

34 To gain access to the solenoid, remove the centre console as described in Chapter 11.

35 Unscrew the two retaining bolts, disconnect the wiring plug, and remove the solenoid.

36 Refitting is a reversal of removal.

37 In the event of a fault in the system, such that the selector lever cannot be moved out of P with the ignition on and the brake pedal depressed, the system can be disabled manually, as follows.

38 Carefully prise out the trim panel around the selector lever, and remove it.

39 Using a suitable flat-bladed screwdriver, carefully ease the central plunger away from the switch body to release the locking mechanism. Move the selector lever to the N position and it should now be possible to start the engine and drive the car.

12 Automatic transmission – removal and refitting

Removal

4 HP 14 transmission

1 Chock the rear wheels, apply the handbrake, and place the selector lever in the

N (neutral) position. Jack up the front of the vehicle, and securely support it on axle stands (see *Jacking and vehicle support*). Remove both front roadwheels.

2 Drain the transmission fluid as described in Chapter 1A, then refit the drain plugs, tightening them securely.

3 Remove the battery, battery tray and mounting plate as described in Chapter 5A.

4 Remove the air inlet duct(s) as described in Chapter 4A.

5 Detach the kickdown inner cable from the throttle housing cam, then slacken the outer cable locknuts and free the cable from its mounting bracket. Release the kickdown cable from any relevant retaining clips, so that it is free to be removed with the transmission.

6 Undo the two screws securing the outer selector cable to its retaining bracket, and carefully lever the inner cable end fitting off its balljoint on the transmission selector lever. Note that the transmission selector lever must not be disturbed until the cable is refitted. As a precaution, mark the position of the lever in relation to the transmission housing. Work back along the selector cable, releasing it from any relevant retaining clips, and position it clear of the transmission.

7 Remove the starter motor as described in Chapter 5A.

8 Undo the union nut securing the dipstick tube to the transmission sump, then undo the bolt securing the tube to the transmission housing, and remove the dipstick from the transmission.

9 Disconnect the wiring connectors from the starter inhibitor/reversing light switch and vehicle speed sensor housing. Undo the retaining nut/bolt(s) and disconnect the earth strap(s) from the top of the transmission housing.

10 Disconnect and release the wiring connectors situated on the support bracket in front of the transmission fluid cooler. Undo the retaining nuts and bolts and remove the support bracket from the transmission.

11 Using a hose clamp or similar, clamp both the fluid cooler coolant hoses to minimise coolant loss. Slacken the retaining clips and disconnect both coolant hoses from the fluid cooler – be prepared for some coolant spillage. Wash off any spilt coolant immediately with cold water.

12 Unbolt and remove any additional securing brackets for coolant hoses or hydraulic pipes from the front or the base of the transmission, noting their locations.

13 From under the car, release the retaining clips (as necessary) and free the power steering pipe from the transmission.

14 Undo the retaining bolts and remove the lower driveplate cover plate from the transmission, to gain access to the torque converter retaining bolts. Slacken and remove the visible bolt then, using a socket and extension bar to rotate the crankshaft pulley, undo the remaining bolts securing the torque converter to the driveplate as they become accessible. There are three bolts in total.

15 To ensure that the torque converter does not fall out as the transmission is removed, secure it in position using a length of metal strip bolted to one of the starter motor bolt holes.

16 Remove the driveshafts as described in Chapter 8.

17 Place a jack with a block of wood beneath the engine, to take the weight of the engine. Alternatively, attach a couple of lifting eyes to the engine, and fit a hoist or support bar to take the weight of the engine.

18 Place a jack and block of wood beneath the transmission, and raise the jack to take the weight of the transmission.

19 Slacken and remove the centre nut and washer from the left-hand engine/transmission mounting. Undo the two nuts and washers securing the mounting rubber in position and remove it from the engine compartment.

20 Slide the spacer (where fitted) off the mounting stud, then unscrew the stud from the top of the transmission housing and remove it along with its washer. If the mounting stud is tight, a universal stud extractor can be used to unscrew it.

21 With the jack positioned beneath the transmission taking the weight, slacken and remove the remaining bolts securing the transmission housing to the engine. Note the correct fitted positions of each bolt as it is removed, to use as a reference on refitting. Make a final check that all necessary components have been disconnected, and positioned clear of the transmission so that they will not hinder the removal procedure.

22 With the bolts removed, move the trolley jack and transmission to the left, to free it from its locating dowels.

23 Once the transmission is free, lower the jack and manoeuvre the unit out from under the car. If they are loose, remove the locating dowels from the transmission or engine, and keep them in a safe place.

AL4 transmission

Note: *If a new transmission unit is being fitted, it will be necessary for the transmission ECU to be initialised and matched electronically to the engine management ECU on completion – the initialisation must be referred to a Citroën dealer.*

24 Chock the rear wheels, apply the handbrake, and place the selector lever in the N (neutral) position. Jack up the front of the vehicle, and securely support it on axle stands (see *Jacking and vehicle support*). Remove both front roadwheels.

25 Remove the battery, battery tray and mounting plate as described in Chapter 5A, then remove the air cleaner and air inlet duct as described in Chapter 4A.

26 Slacken the locking rings and disconnect the two circular main wiring loom connectors – one located behind the transmission ECU, and one located forward of the battery tray location.

27 Disconnect the transmission ECU wiring connector, then undo the three ECU mounting bracket screws. Lift out the mounting bracket and ECU as an assembly.

28 Disconnect the wiring harness from the modular connector located at the rear of the transmission.

29 Disconnect the output speed sensor wiring plug located behind the modular connector.

30 Disconnect the vehicle speed sensor wiring plug located directly above the inner end of the right-hand driveshaft.

31 Using a hose clamp or similar, clamp both the fluid cooler coolant hoses to minimise coolant loss during subsequent operations.

32 Slacken the retaining clips, and disconnect both coolant hoses from the fluid cooler – be prepared for some coolant spillage. Wash off any spilt coolant immediately with cold water, and dry the surrounding area before proceeding further.

33 Undo the retaining bolt(s and disconnect the earth straps from the top of the transmission housing.

34 Using a suitable forked tool (a fork type balljoint splitter could be used, or failing that, a large flat-bladed screwdriver), carefully prise the selector cable balljoint off the selector lever.

35 Extract the retaining C-clip and release the selector outer cable and cable grommet from the transmission bracket.

36 Disconnect and release the wiring connectors and relevant support brackets running along the top of the transmission.

37 Disconnect the wiring connectors at the engine speed sensor and oxygen sensor located below the thermostat housing and radiator top hose.

38 Remove the exhaust system front pipe as described in Chapter 4A.

39 Remove the starter motor as described in Chapter 5A.

40 Undo the retaining bolts and remove the lower driveplate cover plate from the transmission, to gain access to the torque converter retaining nuts. Slacken and remove the visible nut then, using a socket and extension bar to rotate the crankshaft pulley, undo the remaining nuts securing the torque converter to the driveplate as they become accessible. There are three nuts in total.

41 To ensure that the torque converter does not fall out as the transmission is removed, secure it in position using a length of metal strip bolted to one of the starter motor bolt holes.

42 Remove the driveshafts as described in Chapter 8.

43 Place a jack with a block of wood beneath the engine, to take the weight of the engine. Alternatively, attach a couple of lifting eyes to the engine, and fit a hoist or support bar to take the weight of the engine.

44 Place a jack and block of wood beneath the transmission, and raise the jack to take the weight of the transmission.

45 Slacken and remove the centre nut and washer from the left-hand engine/transmission mounting. Undo the two nuts and washers securing the mounting rubber in position and remove it from the engine compartment.

46 Slide the spacer (where fitted) off the mounting stud, then unscrew the stud from the top of the transmission housing and remove it along with its washer. If the mounting stud is tight, a universal stud extractor can be used to unscrew it.

47 With the jack positioned beneath the transmission taking the weight, slacken and remove the remaining bolts securing the transmission housing to the engine. Note the correct fitted positions of each bolt as it is removed, to use as a reference on refitting. Make a final check that all necessary components have been disconnected, and positioned clear of the transmission so that they will not hinder the removal procedure.

48 With the bolts removed, move the trolley jack and transmission to the left, to free it from its locating dowels.

49 Once the transmission is free, lower the jack and manoeuvre the unit out from under the car. If they are loose, remove the locating dowels from the transmission or engine, and keep them in a safe place.

Refitting

50 Both transmission types are refitted using a reversal of the removal procedure, bearing in mind the following points:

a) Ensure that the bush fitted to the centre of the crankshaft is in good condition, and apply a little Molykote G1 grease to the torque converter centring pin. Do not apply too much, otherwise there is a possibility of the grease contaminating the torque converter.

b) On the AL4 transmission, turn the torque converter so that one of the mounting studs is positioned opposite the right-hand driveshaft output shaft (approximately the 9 o'clock position). Turn the engine crankshaft so that the corresponding mounting hole in the driveplate is in the same position. The torque converter mounting studs and the corresponding holes in the driveplate should then be in alignment when the transmission is fitted.

c) Ensure that the engine/transmission locating dowels are correctly positioned prior to installation.

d) Once the transmission and engine are correctly joined, refit the securing bolts, tightening them to the specified torque setting, then remove the metal strip used to retain the torque converter.

e) Apply thread-locking fluid to the left-hand engine/transmission mounting stud threads prior to refitting it to the transmission. Tighten the stud to the specified torque.

f) Tighten all nuts and bolts to the specified torque (where given).

g) On the 4 HP 14 transmission, renew the driveshaft oil seals as described in Chapter 7A, Section 4.

h) Refit the driveshafts to the transmission as described in Chapter 8.

i) On the 4 HP 14 transmission, adjust the selector cable and kickdown cable as described in Sections 2 and 5.

j) On completion, top-up the cooling system, then refill the transmission with the specified type and quantity of fluid/oil as described in Chapter 1A (4 HP 14 transmission) or Section 13 (AL4 transmission).

13 Automatic transmission fluid – draining and refilling

4 HP 14 transmission

1 Refer to Chapter 1A.

AL4 transmission

2 Routine oil renewal is not required by the manufacturers, nor is it necessary for any of the operations described in this Manual. If you wish to renew the transmission oil because the car has covered a large mileage, or because the transmission is being removed for internal repairs, the procedure is as follows.

3 The oil must be drained when it is hot, so take the car on a moderate journey (at least 30 minutes), to warm the transmission up to normal operating temperature.

4 To improve access to the oil drain and level plugs on the base of the housing, it may be preferable to jack up the front and rear of the car, and support it on axle stands (see *Jacking and vehicle support*). Note that it will be essential that the car is level when checking the oil level after refilling.

5 Remove the engine undertray then place a container of sufficient capacity under the transmission. Unscrew and remove the oil level plug, then the drain plug, from the base of the transmission **(see illustration)**.

> **Warning: Take precautions against scalding as the oil will be very hot.**

6 Allow the oil to drain, then refit the drain plug and tighten to the specified torque. Do not refit the level plug in the centre of the drain plug at this stage.

7 Make sure that the car is level (front-to-rear and side-to-side). Using a square-section wrench, remove the oil filler plug from the top of the transmission housing **(see illustration)**.

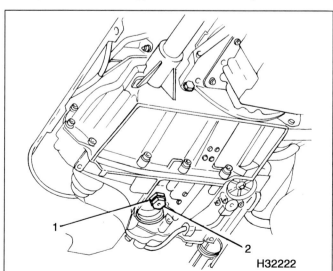

13.5 Transmission oil drain plug (1) and oil level plug (2), inside drain plug – AL4 transmission

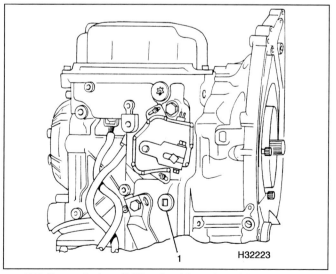

13.7 Transmission oil filler plug (1) as viewed from above – AL4 transmission

8 Add the specified oil (3 litres may be required) until it runs out of the level plug in the base of the transmission. As access to the filler plug is limited, Citroën mechanics use a filling bottle with a length of small-bore hose attached. The end of the hose is inserted into the filler orifice and the bottle (filled with the specified oil) is then suspended from the bonnet. A suitable alternative could easily be made up from, for example, a clean plastic drinks bottle with the base cut off, and with a hose attached to the cap.

9 Fit and tighten the level plug and filler plug to the specified torque, then refit the undertray and lower the car to the ground.

10 Final level checking must be done with the transmission oil at normal operating temperature, so once again take the car on a moderate journey (at least 30 minutes), to warm up the transmission.

11 With the transmission oil hot, carry out the level checking procedure described in Chapter 1A, Section 15.

14 Automatic transmission overhaul – general information

In the event of a fault occurring with the transmission, it is first necessary to determine whether it is of an electrical, mechanical or hydraulic nature, and to do this, special test equipment is required. It is therefore essential to have the work carried out by a Citroën dealer if a transmission fault is suspected.

Do not remove the transmission from the car for possible repair before professional fault diagnosis has been carried out, since most tests require the transmission to be in the vehicle.

Chapter 8
Driveshafts

Contents

Driveshaft overhaul – general information 4
Driveshaft rubber gaiter and constant
   velocity (CV) joint check . . . . .See Chapter 1A or 1B
Driveshaft rubber gaiters – renewal 3

Driveshafts – removal and refitting 2
General information 1
Right-hand driveshaft intermediate bearing – renewal 5

Degrees of difficulty

Easy, suitable for novice with little experience	Fairly easy, suitable for beginner with some experience	Fairly difficult, suitable for competent DIY mechanic 	Difficult, suitable for experienced DIY mechanic	Very difficult, suitable for expert DIY or professional

Specifications

Lubrication (overhaul only – see text)

Lubricant type/specification . . . .   Use only special grease supplied in sachets with gaiter kits – joints are otherwise pre-packed with grease and sealed

Torque wrench settings	Nm	lbf ft
Driveshaft retaining nut:		
M20x150 nut	250	185
M24x150 nut	320	236
Lower suspension arm balljoint retaining nuts	40	30
Right-hand driveshaft intermediate bearing retaining bolt nuts	17	13
Roadwheel bolts	85	63

1 General information

Drive is transmitted from the differential to the front wheels by means of two tubular driveshafts of unequal length.

Both driveshafts are splined at their outer ends, to accept the wheel hubs, and are threaded so that each hub can be fastened by a large nut. The inner end of each driveshaft is splined, to accept the differential sun gear.

Constant velocity (CV) joints are fitted to each end of the driveshafts, to ensure the smooth and efficient transmission of power at all suspension and steering angles. On 1.4 and 1.6 litre engine models, the outer constant velocity joints are of the spider-and-yoke type; on all other models, they are of the ball-and-cage type. The inner constant velocity joints are of the tripod type on all models.

On the right-hand side, due to the length of the driveshaft, the inner constant velocity joint is situated approximately halfway along the shaft's length, and an intermediate support bearing is mounted in the engine/transmission rear mounting bracket. The inner end of the driveshaft passes through the bearing (which prevents any lateral movement of the driveshaft inner end) and the inner constant velocity joint outer member.

2 Driveshafts – removal and refitting

Removal

Note: *Do not allow the vehicle to rest on its wheels with one or both driveshafts removed, as damage to the wheel bearing(s) may result. If moving the vehicle is unavoidable, temporarily insert the outer end of the driveshaft(s) in the hub(s) and tighten the hub nut(s): in this case, the inner end(s) of the driveshaft(s) must be supported, for example by suspending with string from the vehicle underbody. Do not allow the driveshaft to hang down under its own weight. On models with a staked driveshaft nut, a new nut must be used on refitting. New lower arm balljoint clamp bolt nuts must be used on refitting.*

1 Firmly apply the handbrake, then jack up the front of the car and support it securely on axle stands (see *Jacking and vehicle support*). Remove the appropriate front roadwheel.

2 Drain the transmission oil or fluid as described in the relevant Part of Chapter 1 or 7 as applicable. **Note:** *On models with the AL4 automatic transmission, this is not necessary.*

3 On models equipped with ABS, trace the wiring connector back from the wheel sensor, freeing it from its retaining clips, and disconnect it at its wiring connector.

4 On models where the driveshaft nut is

2.4 On models with a staked driveshaft retaining nut, relieve the staking with a suitable chisel-nosed tool

staked, using a hammer and a chisel or similar tool, tap up the staking securing the driveshaft retaining nut in position **(see illustration)**. Note that a new retaining nut must be used on refitting.

5 On models where the driveshaft nut is secured by an R-clip, withdraw the R-clip and remove the locking cap from the driveshaft retaining nut.

6 Refit at least two roadwheel bolts to the front hub, and tighten them securely. Have an assistant firmly depress the brake pedal to prevent the front hub from rotating, then using a socket and a long extension bar, slacken and remove the driveshaft retaining nut. Alternatively, a tool can be fabricated from two lengths of steel strip (one long, one short)

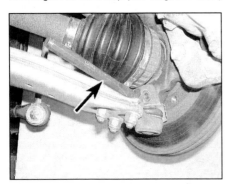

2.8a Spread the swivel hub by tapping a small chisel (arrowed) into the split . . .

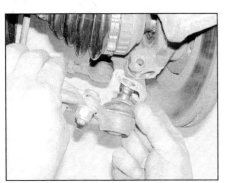

2.9 When the balljoint is released, remove the protector plate from the balljoint shank

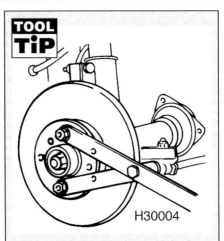

Using a fabricated tool to hold the front hub stationary whilst the driveshaft retaining nut is slackened.

and a nut and bolt; the nut and bolt forming the pivot of a forked tool. Bolt the tool to the hub using two wheel bolts, and hold the tool to prevent the hub from rotating as the driveshaft retaining nut is undone **(see Tool Tip)**. This nut is very tight; make sure that there is no risk of pulling the car off the axle stands (see *Jacking and vehicle support*). (If the roadwheel trim allows access to the driveshaft nut, the initial slackening can be

2.8b . . . then pull the lower suspension arm downwards using a bar and chain or similar arrangement, pivoting on the subframe

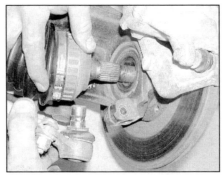

2.10 Pull the swivel hub outwards, and withdraw the driveshaft outer constant velocity joint from the hub

2.7 Undo the nut and withdraw the lower suspension arm balljoint clamp bolt from the swivel hub

done with the wheels chocked and on the ground.)

7 Slacken and remove the nut, then withdraw the lower suspension arm balljoint clamp bolt from the swivel hub. Discard the nut – a new one must be used on refitting **(see illustration)**.

8 Tap a small chisel into the split on the swivel hub, to spread the hub slightly and allow the balljoint shank to be withdrawn **(see illustration)**. Pull the lower suspension arm downwards to release the balljoint shank from the swivel hub. To do this it will be necessary to use a long bar and block of wood which will engage under the front subframe. Attach the bar to the suspension arm, preferably with a chain, or alternatively with a stout strap or rope. Lever down on the bar to release the balljoint from the swivel hub **(see illustration)**.

9 Once the balljoint is free, remove the protector plate which is fitted to the balljoint shank **(see illustration)**.

Left-hand driveshaft

10 Carefully pull the swivel hub assembly outwards, and withdraw the driveshaft outer constant velocity joint from the hub assembly **(see illustration)**. If necessary, the shaft can be tapped out of the hub using a soft-faced mallet.

11 Support the driveshaft, then withdraw the inner constant velocity joint from the transmission, taking care not to damage the driveshaft oil seal **(see illustration)**. Remove the driveshaft from the vehicle.

2.11 Support the driveshaft, then withdraw the inner constant velocity joint from the transmission

2.12a On the right-hand driveshaft, slacken the two intermediate bearing retaining bolt nuts . . .

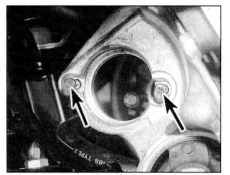

2.12b . . . then turn the bolts through 90° to disengage their offset heads (arrowed) from the bearing (driveshaft removed for clarity)

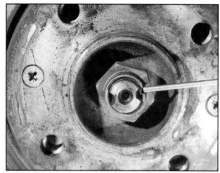

2.22 On models with a staked driveshaft retaining nut, tighten the nut and stake it firmly into the driveshaft groove

Right-hand driveshaft

12 Loosen the two intermediate bearing retaining bolt nuts, then rotate the bolts through 90°, so that their offset heads are clear of the bearing outer race **(see illustrations)**.

13 Carefully pull the swivel hub assembly outwards, and withdraw the driveshaft outer constant velocity joint from the hub assembly. If necessary, the shaft can be tapped out of the hub using a soft-faced mallet.

14 Support the outer end of the driveshaft, then pull on the inner end of the shaft to free the shaft from the transmission, and the intermediate bearing from its mounting bracket.

15 Once the driveshaft end is free from the transmission, slide the dust seal off the inner end of the shaft, noting which way around it is fitted, and remove the driveshaft.

Refitting

16 Before installing the driveshaft, examine the driveshaft oil seal in the transmission for signs of damage or deterioration and, if necessary, renew it, referring to Chapter 7A or 7B for further information. (Having got this far it is worth renewing the seal as a matter of course.)

17 Thoroughly clean the driveshaft splines, and the apertures in the transmission and hub assembly. Apply a thin film of grease to the oil seal lips, and to the driveshaft splines and

shoulders. Check that all gaiter clips are securely fastened.

Left-hand driveshaft

18 Offer up the driveshaft, and locate the joint splines with those of the differential sun gear, taking great care not to damage the oil seal. Push the joint fully into position.

19 Locate the outer constant velocity joint splines with those of the swivel hub, and slide the joint back into position in the hub.

20 Refit the protector plate to the lower arm balljoint then, using the method employed on removal, locate the balljoint shank in the swivel hub, ensuring that the lug on the protector plate is correctly located in the clamp split. Insert the balljoint clamp bolt (from the rear of the swivel hub), then fit the new retaining nut and tighten it to the specified torque.

21 Lubricate the inner face and threads of the driveshaft retaining nut with clean engine oil, and refit it to the end of the driveshaft. Use the method employed on removal to prevent the hub from rotating, and tighten the driveshaft retaining nut to the specified torque. Check that the hub rotates freely.

22 On models where the driveshaft nut is staked, stake the new nut into the driveshaft grooves using a hammer and punch **(see illustration)**.

23 On models where the driveshaft nut is secured by an R-clip, engage the locking cap

with the driveshaft nut so that one of its cutouts is aligned with the driveshaft hole. Secure the cap in position with the R-clip **(see illustrations)**.

24 Where necessary, reconnect the ABS wheel sensor wiring connector, ensuring that the wiring is correctly routed and retained by all the necessary clips and ties.

25 Refit the roadwheel, then lower the vehicle to the ground and tighten the roadwheel bolts to the specified torque.

26 Refill the transmission with the specified type and amount of fluid/oil, and check the level using the information given in the relevant Parts of Chapter 1 and 7.

Right-hand driveshaft

27 Check that the intermediate bearing rotates smoothly, without any sign of roughness or undue free play between its inner and outer races. If necessary, renew the bearing as described in Section 5. Examine the dust seal for signs of damage or deterioration, and renew if necessary.

28 Apply a smear of grease to the outer race of the intermediate bearing, and to the inner lip of the dust seal.

29 Pass the inner end of the shaft through the bearing mounting bracket, then carefully slide the dust seal into position on the driveshaft, ensuring that its flat surface is facing the transmission **(see illustration)**.

30 Carefully locate the inner driveshaft splines with those of the differential sun gear,

2.23a On models where the driveshaft nut is secured by an R-clip, refit the locking cap . . .

2.23b . . . and secure it in position with the R-clip

2.29 Locate the dust seal on the inner end of the right-hand driveshaft, ensuring it is fitted the correct way round

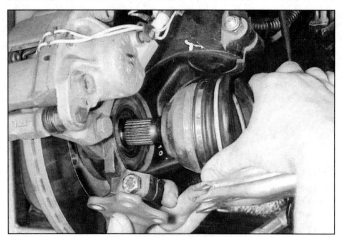

2.31 Pull out the swivel hub assembly, and locate the outer constant velocity joint splines with those of the swivel hub

2.32 Secure the intermediate bearing in position, then slide the dust seal up tight against the driveshaft oil seal

taking care not to damage the oil seal. Align the intermediate bearing with its mounting bracket, and push the driveshaft fully into position. If necessary, use a soft-faced mallet to tap the outer race of the bearing into position in the mounting bracket.

31 Locate the outer constant velocity joint splines with those of the swivel hub, and slide the joint back into position in the hub **(see illustration)**.

32 Ensure that the intermediate bearing is correctly seated, then rotate its retaining bolts back through 90°, so that their offset heads are resting against the bearing outer race. Tighten the retaining nuts to the specified torque. Ensure that the dust seal is tight against the driveshaft oil seal **(see illustration)**.

33 Carry out the operations described above in paragraphs 20 to 26.

3 Driveshaft rubber gaiters – renewal

Outer joint

1 Remove the driveshaft from the car as described in Section 2.

1.4 and 1.6 litre engine models

2 Remove the inner constant velocity joint and gaiter as described below in paragraphs 24 to 29. It is recommended that the inner gaiter is also renewed, regardless of its apparent condition.

3 Release the two outer gaiter retaining clips, then slide the gaiter off the inner end of the driveshaft.

4 Thoroughly clean the outer constant velocity joint using paraffin, or a suitable solvent, and dry it thoroughly. Carry out a visual inspection of the joint.

5 Check the driveshaft spider and outer member yoke for signs of wear, pitting or

scuffing on their bearing surfaces. Also check that the outer member pivots smoothly and easily, with no traces of roughness.

6 If the spider or outer member reveals signs of wear or damage, it will be necessary to renew the complete driveshaft as an assembly, since no components are available separately. If the joint components are in satisfactory condition, obtain a repair kit from your Citroën dealer, consisting of a new gaiter, retaining clips, and the correct type and quantity of grease.

7 Tape over the splines on the inner end of the driveshaft, then carefully slide the outer gaiter onto the shaft.

8 Pack the joint with the grease supplied in the repair kit. Work the grease well into the bearing tracks whilst twisting the joint, and fill the rubber gaiter with any excess.

9 Ease the gaiter over the joint, and ensure that the gaiter lips are correctly located in the grooves on both the driveshaft and constant velocity joint. Lift the outer sealing lip of the gaiter, to equalise the air pressure in the gaiter.

10 Fit the large metal retaining clip to the gaiter. Remove any slack in the gaiter retaining clip by carefully compressing the raised section of the clip. In the absence of the special tool, a pair of side cutters may be used. Secure the small retaining clip using the same procedure. Check that the constant velocity joint moves freely in all directions before proceeding further.

11 Refit the inner constant velocity joint as described in paragraphs 32 to 39.

All except 1.4 and 1.6 litre engine models

12 Secure the driveshaft in a vice equipped with soft jaws, and release the two rubber gaiter retaining clips. If necessary, the gaiter retaining clips can be cut to release them.

13 Slide the rubber gaiter down the shaft, to

expose the outer constant velocity joint. Scoop out the excess grease.

14 Using a hammer and suitable soft metal drift, sharply strike the inner member of the outer joint to drive it off the end of the shaft. The joint is retained on the driveshaft by a circlip, and striking the joint in this manner forces the circlip into its groove, so allowing the joint to slide off.

15 Once the joint assembly has been removed, remove the circlip from the groove in the driveshaft splines, and discard it. A new circlip must be fitted on reassembly.

16 Withdraw the rubber gaiter from the driveshaft, and slide off the gaiter inner end plastic bush.

17 With the constant velocity joint removed from the driveshaft, thoroughly clean the joint using paraffin, or a suitable solvent, and dry it thoroughly. Carry out a visual inspection of the joint.

18 Move the inner splined driving member from side-to-side, to expose each ball in turn at the top of its track. Examine the balls for cracks, flat spots, or signs of surface pitting.

19 Inspect the ball tracks on the inner and outer members. If the tracks have widened, the balls will no longer be a tight fit. At the same time, check the ball cage windows for wear or cracking between the windows.

20 If any of the constant velocity joint components are found to be worn or damaged, it will be necessary to renew the complete joint assembly (where available), or even the complete driveshaft (where no joint components are available separately). Refer to your Citroën dealer for further information on parts availability. If the joint is in satisfactory condition, obtain a repair kit consisting of a new gaiter, circlip, retaining clips, and the correct type and quantity of grease.

21 To install the new gaiter, refer to the accompanying illustrations, and perform the

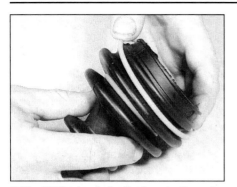

3.21a Fit the hard plastic rings to the outer CV joint gaiter . . .

3.21b . . . then slide on the new plastic bush (arrowed), and seat it in its recess in the shaft. Slide the gaiter onto the shaft . . .

3.21c . . . and seat the gaiter inner end on top of the plastic bush

operations shown (see illustrations). Be sure to stay in order, and follow the captions carefully. Note that the hard plastic rings are not fitted to all gaiters, and the gaiter retaining clips supplied with the repair kit may be different to those shown in the sequence. To secure this other type of clip in position, lock the ends of the clip together, then remove any slack in the clip by carefully compressing the raised section of the clip using a pair of side cutters.

22 Check that the constant velocity joint moves freely in all directions, then refit the driveshaft to the car as described in Section 2.

3.21d Fit the new circlip to its groove in the driveshaft splines . . .

3.21e . . . then locate the joint outer member on the splines, and slide into position over the circlip. Ensure that the joint is firmly retained by the circlip before proceeding

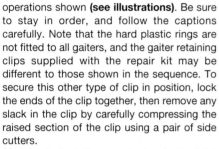

3.21f Pack the joint with the grease supplied, working it well into the ball tracks while twisting the joint, then locate the gaiter outer lip in its groove on the outer member

3.21g Fit the outer gaiter retaining clip and, using a hook fabricated out of welding rod and a pair of pliers, pull the clip tightly to remove all slack

3.21h Bend the clip end back over the buckle, then cut off the excess clip

3.21i Fold the clip end underneath the buckle . . .

3.21j . . . then fold the buckle firmly down onto the clip to secure the clip in position

3.21k Carefully lift the gaiter inner end to equalise air pressure in the gaiter, then secure the inner gaiter retaining clip in position using the same method

Inner joint

23 Remove the driveshaft from the vehicle as described in Section 2.

1.4 and 1.6 litre engine models

24 Secure the driveshaft in a vice equipped with soft jaws then, using a suitable pair of pliers, carefully peel back the lip of the constant velocity joint outer member cover.

25 Once the lip of the cover is fully released, pull the joint outer member out from the cover, and recover the spring and thrust cap from the end of the shaft. Remove the O-ring from the outside of the outer member, and discard it.

26 Fold the gaiter back, and wipe away the excess grease from the tripod joint. If the rollers are not secured to the joint with circlips, wrap adhesive tape around the joint to hold them in position.

27 Using a dab of paint, or a hammer and punch, mark the relative position of the tripod joint in relation to the driveshaft. Using circlip pliers, extract the circlip securing the joint to the driveshaft.

28 The tripod joint can now be removed. If it is tight, draw the joint off the driveshaft end, using a two- or three-legged bearing puller. Ensure that the legs of the puller are located behind the joint inner member, and do not contact the joint rollers. Alternatively, support the inner member of the tripod joint, and press the shaft out of the joint using a hydraulic press, ensuring that no load is applied to the joint rollers.

29 With the tripod joint removed, slide the gaiter and inner retaining collar off the end of the driveshaft.

30 Thoroughly clean all the constant velocity joint components using paraffin, or a suitable solvent, and dry them thoroughly – take great care not to remove the alignment marks made on dismantling, especially if paint was used. Carry out a visual inspection of the joint.

31 Examine the tripod joint, rollers and outer member for any signs of scoring or wear, and for smoothness of movement of the rollers on the tripod stems. If any component is worn, the complete driveshaft assembly must be renewed; no joint components are available separately. If the joint components

are in good condition, obtain a repair kit from your Citroën dealer, consisting of a new rubber gaiter and outer cover, circlip, thrust cap, spring, O-ring, and the correct quantity of the special grease.

32 Slide the gaiter into position inside the metal outer cover, then tape over the splines on the end of the driveshaft, and carefully slide the inner retaining collar and gaiter/cover assembly onto the shaft.

33 Remove the tape then, aligning the marks made on dismantling, engage the tripod joint with the driveshaft splines. Use a hammer and soft metal drift to tap the joint onto the shaft, taking great care not to damage the driveshaft splines or joint rollers.

34 Secure the tripod joint in position with the new circlip, ensuring that it is correctly located in the driveshaft groove.

35 Remove the tape (where fitted), and evenly distribute the special grease contained in the repair kit around the tripod joint and outer member. Pack the gaiter/cover with the remainder, then draw the cover over the tripod joint.

36 Fit the new O-ring, spring and thrust cap to the joint outer member.

37 Position the outer member assembly over the tripod joint, and locate the thrust cap against the end of the driveshaft. Push the outer member onto the shaft, compressing the spring, and locate it inside the outer cover. Secure the outer member in position by peening the end of the cover evenly over the joint outer edge.

38 Briefly lift the inner gaiter lip, using a blunt instrument such as a knitting needle, to equalise the air pressure within the gaiter. Secure the inner clip in position.

39 Check that the constant velocity joint moves freely in all directions, then refit the driveshaft to the car as described in Section 2.

All except 1.4 and 1.6 litre engine models

40 Remove the outer constant velocity joint as described above in paragraphs 1 to 5.

41 Tape over the splines on the driveshaft, and carefully remove the outer constant velocity joint rubber gaiter, and the gaiter inner end plastic bush. It is recommended

that the outer joint gaiter is also renewed, regardless of its apparent condition.

42 Release the retaining clips, then slide the gaiter off the shaft, and remove its plastic bush. As the gaiter is released, the joint outer member will also be freed from the end of the shaft **(see illustrations)**.

43 Thoroughly clean the joint using paraffin, or a suitable solvent, and dry it thoroughly. Check the tripod joint bearings and joint outer member for signs of wear, pitting or scuffing on their bearing surfaces. Check that the bearing rollers rotate smoothly and easily around the tripod joint, with no traces of roughness.

44 If the tripod joint or outer member reveal signs of wear or damage, it will be necessary to renew the complete driveshaft assembly, since the joint is not available separately. If the joint is in satisfactory condition, obtain a repair kit consisting of a new gaiter, retaining clips, and the correct type and quantity of grease. Although not strictly necessary, it is also recommended that the outer constant velocity joint gaiter is renewed, regardless of its apparent condition.

45 On reassembly, pack the inner joint with the grease supplied in the gaiter kit. Work the grease well into the bearing tracks and rollers, while twisting the joint.

46 Clean the shaft, using emery cloth to remove any rust or sharp edges which may damage the gaiter, then slide the plastic bush and inner joint gaiter along the driveshaft. Locate the plastic bush in its recess on the shaft, and seat the inner end of the gaiter on top of the bush.

47 Fit the outer member over the end of the shaft, and locate the gaiter in the groove on the joint outer member. Push the outer member onto the joint, so that its spring-loaded plunger is compressed, then lift the outer edge of the gaiter to equalise air pressure in the gaiter. Fit both the inner and outer retaining clips, securing them in position using the information given in paragraph 21. Ensure that the gaiter retaining clips are securely tightened, then check that the joint moves freely in all directions.

48 Refit the outer constant velocity joint components using the information given in paragraph 21.

3.42a Release the inner gaiter retaining clips, and remove the joint outer member

3.42b Slide the gaiter off the end of the driveshaft . . .

3.42c . . . and remove the plastic bush

4 Driveshaft overhaul – general information

1 If any of the checks described in *Road test* in Chapter 1A or 1B reveal wear in any driveshaft joint, firmly apply the handbrake, then jack up the front of the car and support it securely on axle stands (see *Jacking and vehicle support*). Remove the appropriate front roadwheel.

2 On models with a staked driveshaft nut, if the staking is still effective, the driveshaft nut should be correctly tightened; if in doubt, relieve the staking, then tighten the nut to the specified torque and restake it into the driveshaft grooves. Refit the roadwheel trim or centre cap (as applicable), and repeat the check on the remaining driveshaft nut.

3 On models where the driveshaft nut is secured by an R-clip, if the R-clip is fitted, the driveshaft nut should be correctly tightened; if in doubt, remove the R-clip and locking cap, and use a torque wrench to check that the nut is securely fastened. Once tightened, refit the locking cap and R-clip, then refit the centre cap or trim. Repeat this check on the remaining driveshaft nut.

4 Road test the vehicle, and listen for a metallic clicking from the front as the vehicle is driven slowly in a circle on full-lock. If a clicking noise is heard, this indicates wear in the outer constant velocity joint. This means that the joint must be renewed; reconditioning is not possible.

5 If vibration, consistent with road speed, is felt through the car when accelerating, there is a possibility of wear in the inner constant velocity joints.

6 To check the joints for wear, remove the driveshafts, then dismantle them as described in Section 3; if any wear or free play is found, the affected joint must be renewed. In the case of the inner joints (and on some models, the outer joints), this means that the complete driveshaft assembly must be renewed, as the joints are not available separately. Refer to your Citroën dealer for information on the availability of driveshaft components.

5 Right-hand driveshaft intermediate bearing – renewal

Note: *A suitable bearing puller will be required, to draw the bearing and collar off the driveshaft end.*

1 Remove the right-hand driveshaft as described in Section 2 of this Chapter.

2 Check that the bearing outer race rotates smoothly and easily, without any signs of roughness or undue free play between the

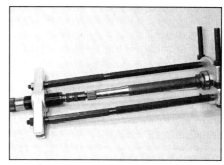

5.3 Using a long-reach bearing puller to remove the intermediate bearing from the right-hand driveshaft

inner and outer races. If necessary, renew the bearing as follows.

3 Using a long-reach universal bearing puller, carefully draw the collar and intermediate bearing off the driveshaft inner end **(see illustration)**. Apply a smear of grease to the inner race of the new bearing, then fit the bearing over the end of the driveshaft. Using a hammer and suitable piece of tubing which bears only on the bearing inner race, tap the new bearing into position on the driveshaft, until it abuts the constant velocity joint outer member. Once the bearing is correctly positioned, tap the bearing collar onto the shaft until it contacts the bearing inner race.

4 Check that the bearing rotates freely, then refit the driveshaft as described in Section 2.

Chapter 9
Braking system

Contents

Anti-lock braking system (ABS) – general information 23	Hydraulic system – bleeding 2
Anti-lock braking system (ABS) components – removal and refitting 24	Master cylinder – removal and refitting 13
Brake fluid level check . . . . .See *Weekly checks*	Rear brake caliper – removal, overhaul and refitting 11
Brake fluid renewal . . . . .See Chapter 1A or 1B	Rear brake disc – inspection, removal and refitting 8
Brake pedal – removal and refitting 14	Rear brake drum – removal, inspection and refitting 9
Front brake caliper – removal, overhaul and refitting 10	Rear brake pad wear check . . . . .See Chapter 1A or 1B
Front brake disc – inspection, removal and refitting 7	Rear brake pads – renewal 5
Front brake pad wear check . . . . .See Chapter 1A or 1B	Rear brake pressure-regulating valve – removal and refitting 20
Front brake pads – renewal 4	Rear brake shoe wear check . . . . .See Chapter 1A or 1B
General information 1	Rear brake shoes – renewal 6
Handbrake – adjustment 17	Rear wheel cylinder – removal and refitting 12
Handbrake 'on' warning light switch – removal and refitting 22	Stop-light switch – removal, refitting and adjustment 21
Handbrake cables – removal and refitting 19	Vacuum pump (diesel models) – removal and refitting 25
Handbrake lever – removal and refitting 18	Vacuum pump (diesel models) – testing and overhaul 26
Hydraulic pipes and hoses – renewal 3	Vacuum servo unit – testing, removal and refitting 15
	Vacuum servo unit check valve – removal, testing and refitting 16

Degrees of difficulty

Easy, suitable for novice with little experience	**Fairly easy,** suitable for beginner with some experience	**Fairly difficult,** suitable for competent DIY mechanic 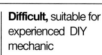	**Difficult,** suitable for experienced DIY mechanic	**Very difficult,** suitable for expert DIY or professional

Specifications

Rear drum brakes

Drum internal diameter (new):
  Hatchback and Coupé models:

1.4, 1.6 and 1.8 litre (8-valve) petrol models without ABS	180.0 mm
1.9 litre non-turbo diesel models without ABS	180.0 mm
1.9 litre turbo diesel models without ABS	203.0 mm
All models with ABS	203.0 mm
Estate models	228.6 mm

Maximum drum diameter after machining:

180.0 mm diameter drum	182.0 mm
203.0 mm diameter drum	205.0 mm
228.6 mm diameter drum	230.6 mm
Brake shoe minimum thickness	1.5 mm

Rear disc brakes

Disc diameter	247.0 mm

Disc thickness:

New	8.0 mm
Minimum thickness	6.0 mm
Maximum disc run-out	0.05 mm
Brake pad minimum thickness	2.0 mm

Front brakes

Type	Disc, with single-piston sliding caliper
Caliper type:	
Petrol models:	
With solid discs	Bendix VZO
With ventilated discs:	
.Except for 1.8 and 2.0 litre (16-valve) models	ATE/Teves FN 48
.1.8 and 2.0 litre (16-valve) models	Lucas C54
Diesel models:	
1.9 litre models	ATE/Teves FN 48
2.0 litre models	Lucas C54
Disc diameter:	
Hatchback and Coupé models:	
1.8 and 2.0 litre (16-valve) petrol models	266.0 mm
2.0 litre diesel models	266.0 mm
All other models	247.0 mm
Estate models:	
1.4 and 1.6 litre petrol models without ABS	247.0 mm
1.8 and 2.0 litre petrol models without ABS	266.0 mm
Non-turbo diesel models without ABS	247.0 mm
Turbo diesel models without ABS	266.0 mm
All models with ABS	266.0 mm
Disc thickness:	
New:	
247.0 mm diameter solid disc	13.0 mm
247.0 mm diameter ventilated disc	20.4 mm
266.0 mm diameter disc	20.0 mm
Minimum thickness:	
247.0 mm diameter solid disc	11.0 mm
247.0 mm diameter ventilated disc	18.4 mm
266.0 mm diameter disc	18.0 mm
Maximum disc run-out	0.1 mm
Brake pad minimum thickness	2.0 mm

Torque wrench settings

	Nm	lbf ft
ABS hydraulic modulator retaining nuts	15	11
ABS wheel sensor retaining bolts*	8	6
Brake pedal through bolt nut	20	15
Front brake caliper guide pin bolts	27	20
Front brake caliper mounting bracket-to-swivel hub bolts*	105	77
Master cylinder-to-servo unit nuts	20	15
Rear brake caliper mounting bolts	120	89
Rear brake pressure-regulating valve mounting bracket bolts	20	15
Rear hub nut	190	140
Roadwheel bolts	85	63
Vacuum pump retaining nuts/bolts (diesel models)	25	18
Vacuum servo unit mounting nuts	23	17

Use thread-locking compound.

1 General information

The braking system is of the servo-assisted, dual-circuit hydraulic type. The arrangement of the hydraulic system is such that each circuit operates one front and one rear brake from a tandem master cylinder. Under normal circumstances, both circuits operate in unison. However, in the event of hydraulic failure in one circuit, full braking force will still be available at two wheels.

Some large-capacity engine models have disc brakes all round as standard; all other models are fitted with front disc brakes and rear drum brakes. An Anti-lock Braking System (ABS) is fitted as standard to certain models, and is offered as an option on all other models (refer to Section 23 for further information on ABS operation).

The front disc brakes are actuated by single-piston sliding type calipers, which ensure that equal pressure is applied to each disc pad.

On models with rear drum brakes, the rear brakes incorporate leading and trailing shoes, which are actuated by twin-piston wheel cylinders. The wheel cylinders incorporate integral pressure-regulating valves, which control the hydraulic pressure applied to the rear brakes. The regulating valves help to prevent rear wheel lock-up during emergency braking. A self-adjust mechanism is incorporated, to automatically compensate for brake shoe wear. As the brake shoe linings wear, the footbrake operation automatically operates the adjuster mechanism, which effectively lengthens the shoe strut and repositions the brake shoes, to reduce the lining-to-drum clearance.

On models with rear disc brakes, the brakes are actuated by single-piston sliding calipers which incorporate mechanical handbrake mechanisms. To prevent rear wheel lock-up during emergency braking, a load-sensitive pressure regulating valve assembly is fitted into the hydraulic circuit to each rear brake. The valve is mounted on the underside of the vehicle at the rear and is attached to the rear suspension by means of an operating rod and spring. The valve measures the load on the rear of the vehicle via the movement of the rear suspension and regulates the hydraulic pressure applied to the rear brakes accordingly. On later models equipped with ABS, the hydraulic pressure applied to the rear brakes is regulated by the ABS hydraulic modulator under all braking conditions. On these models, the separate mechanical pressure regulating valve assembly is not used.

On all models, the handbrake provides an independent mechanical means of rear brake application.

On diesel models, there is insufficient vacuum in the inlet manifold to operate the braking system servo effectively at all times. To overcome this problem, a vacuum pump is fitted to the engine, to provide sufficient vacuum to operate the servo unit. The vacuum pump is mounted on the end of the cylinder head, and driven directly off the end of the camshaft.

Note: *When servicing any part of the system, work carefully and methodically; also observe scrupulous cleanliness when overhauling any part of the hydraulic system. Always renew components (in axle sets, where applicable) if in doubt about their condition, and use only genuine Citroën replacement parts, or at least those of known good quality. Note the warnings given in 'Safety first!' and at relevant points in this Chapter concerning the dangers of asbestos dust and brake hydraulic fluid.*

2 Hydraulic system – bleeding

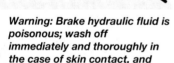

⚠ *Warning: Brake hydraulic fluid is poisonous; wash off immediately and thoroughly in the case of skin contact, and seek immediate medical advice if any fluid is swallowed or gets into the eyes. Certain types of hydraulic fluid are inflammable, and may ignite when allowed into contact with hot components; when servicing any hydraulic system, it is safest to assume that the fluid is inflammable, and to take precautions against the risk of fire as though it is petrol that is being handled. Hydraulic fluid is also an effective paint stripper, and will attack plastics; if any is spilt, it should be washed off immediately, using copious quantities of fresh water. Finally, it is hygroscopic (it absorbs moisture from the air) – old fluid may be contaminated and unfit for further use. When topping-up or renewing the fluid, always use the recommended type, and ensure that it comes from a freshly-opened sealed container.*

Non-ABS models

General

1 The correct operation of any hydraulic system is only possible after removing all air from the components and circuit; this is achieved by bleeding the system.

2 During the bleeding procedure, add only clean, unused hydraulic fluid of the recommended type (see *Lubricants and fluids*); never re-use fluid that has already been bled from the system. Ensure that sufficient fluid is available before starting work.

3 If there is any possibility of incorrect fluid being already in the system, the brake components and circuit must be flushed completely with uncontaminated, correct fluid, and new seals should be fitted to the various components.

4 If hydraulic fluid has been lost from the system, or air has entered because of a leak, ensure that the fault is cured before proceeding further.

5 Park the vehicle on level ground, switch off the engine and select first or reverse gear, then chock the wheels and release the handbrake.

6 Check that all pipes and hoses are secure, unions tight and bleed screws closed. Clean any dirt from around the bleed screws.

7 Unscrew the master cylinder reservoir cap, and top the master cylinder reservoir up to the MAX level line; refit the cap loosely, and remember to maintain the fluid level at least above the MIN level line throughout the procedure, or there is a risk of further air entering the system.

8 There are a number of one-man, do-it-yourself brake bleeding kits currently available from motor accessory shops. It is recommended that one of these kits is used whenever possible, as they greatly simplify the bleeding operation, and also reduce the risk of expelled air and fluid being drawn back into the system. If such a kit is not available, the basic (two-man) method must be used, which is described in detail below.

9 If a kit is to be used, prepare the vehicle as described previously, and follow the kit manufacturer's instructions, as the procedure may vary slightly according to the type being used; generally, they are as outlined below in the relevant sub-section.

10 Whichever method is used, the same sequence must be followed (paragraphs 11 and 12) to ensure the removal of all air from the system.

Bleeding sequence

11 If the system has been only partially disconnected, and suitable precautions were taken to minimise fluid loss, it should be necessary only to bleed that part of the system (ie, the primary or secondary circuit).

12 If the complete system is to be bled, then it should be done working in the following sequence:

  a) Right-hand rear brake.
  b) Left-hand front brake.
  c) Left-hand rear brake.
  d) Right-hand front brake.

Bleeding – basic (two-man) method

13 Collect a clean glass jar, a suitable length of plastic or rubber tubing which is a tight fit

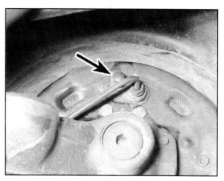

2.14 Rear brake wheel cylinder dust cap (arrowed) – model with rear drum brakes

over the bleed screw, and a ring spanner to fit the screw. The help of an assistant will also be required.

14 Remove the dust cap from the first screw in the sequence **(see illustration)**. Fit the spanner and tube to the screw, place the other end of the tube in the jar, and pour in sufficient fluid to cover the end of the tube.

15 Ensure that the master cylinder reservoir fluid level is maintained at least above the MIN level line throughout the procedure.

16 Have the assistant fully depress the brake pedal several times to build up pressure, then maintain it on the final downstroke.

17 While pedal pressure is maintained, unscrew the bleed screw (approximately one turn) and allow the compressed fluid and air to flow into the jar. The assistant should maintain pedal pressure, following it down to the floor if necessary, and should not release it until instructed to do so. When the flow stops, tighten the bleed screw again, have the assistant release the pedal slowly, and recheck the reservoir fluid level.

18 Repeat the steps given in paragraphs 16 and 17 until the fluid emerging from the bleed screw is free from air bubbles. If the master cylinder has been drained and refilled, and air is being bled from the first screw in the sequence, allow approximately five seconds between cycles for the master cylinder passages to refill.

19 When no more air bubbles appear, tighten the bleed screw securely, remove the tube and spanner, and refit the dust cap. Do not overtighten the bleed screw.

20 Repeat the procedure on the remaining screws in the sequence, until all air is removed from the system and the brake pedal feels firm again.

Bleeding – using a one-way valve kit

21 As their name implies, these kits consist of a length of tubing with a one-way valve fitted, to prevent expelled air and fluid being drawn back into the system; some kits include a translucent container, which can be positioned so that the air bubbles can be more easily seen flowing from the end of the tube.

22 The kit is connected to the bleed screw, which is then opened. The user returns to the driver's seat, depresses the brake pedal with a smooth, steady stroke, and slowly releases it; this is repeated until the expelled fluid is clear of air bubbles **(see illustration)**.

23 Note that these kits simplify work so much that it is easy to forget the master cylinder reservoir fluid level; ensure that this is maintained at least above the MIN level line at all times.

Bleeding – using a pressure-bleeding kit

24 These kits are usually operated by the reservoir of pressurised air contained in the spare tyre. However, note that it will probably be necessary to reduce the pressure to a lower level than normal; refer to the instructions supplied with the kit.

25 By connecting a pressurised, fluid-filled container to the master cylinder reservoir, bleeding can be carried out simply by opening each screw in turn (in the specified sequence), and allowing the fluid to flow out until no more air bubbles can be seen in the expelled fluid.

26 This method has the advantage that the large reservoir of fluid provides an additional safeguard against air being drawn into the system during bleeding.

27 Pressure-bleeding is particularly effective when bleeding 'difficult' systems, or when bleeding the complete system at the time of routine fluid renewal.

All methods

28 When bleeding is complete, and firm pedal feel is restored, wash off any spilt fluid, tighten the bleed screws, and refit their dust caps.

29 Check the hydraulic fluid level in the master cylinder reservoir, and top-up if necessary (see *Weekly checks*).

30 Discard any fluid that has been bled from the system; it will not be fit for re-use.

31 Check the feel of the brake pedal. If it feels at all spongy, air must still be present in the system, and further bleeding is required. Failure to bleed properly after a reasonable repetition of the bleeding procedure may be due to worn master cylinder seals.

ABS models

Warning: On ABS models, ensure that the ignition is switched off before starting the bleeding procedure, to avoid any possibility of voltage being applied to the hydraulic modulator before the bleeding procedure is completed. Ideally, the battery should be disconnected. If voltage is applied to the modulator before the bleeding procedure is complete, this will effectively drain the hydraulic fluid in the modulator, rendering the unit unserviceable. Do not, therefore, attempt to 'run' the modulator in order to bleed the brakes.

32 A pressure-bleeding kit must be used for bleeding the hydraulic system on ABS models – see paragraphs 24 to 27.

33 Following the sequence given in paragraph 12, bleed each brake in turn until clean fluid, free of air bubbles, is seen to

2.22 Bleeding a rear brake caliper using a one-way valve kit

emerge. Pause between bleeding each brake to ensure that the fluid level in the reservoir is above the MIN level.

34 On completion of bleeding, proceed as described in paragraphs 28 to 31 inclusive.

3 Hydraulic pipes and hoses – renewal

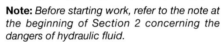

Note: *Before starting work, refer to the note at the beginning of Section 2 concerning the dangers of hydraulic fluid.*

1 If any pipe or hose is to be renewed, minimise fluid loss by first removing the master cylinder reservoir cap, then tightening it down onto a piece of polythene to obtain an airtight seal. Alternatively, flexible hoses can be sealed, if required, using a proprietary brake hose clamp; metal brake pipe unions can be plugged (if care is taken not to allow dirt into the system) or capped immediately they are disconnected. Place a wad of rag under any union that is to be disconnected, to catch any spilt fluid.

2 If a flexible hose is to be disconnected, unscrew the brake pipe union nut before removing the spring clip which secures the hose to its mounting bracket **(see illustration)**.

3 To unscrew the union nuts, it is preferable to obtain a brake pipe spanner of the correct size; these are available from most large motor accessory shops. Failing this, a close-fitting open-ended spanner will be required, though if the nuts are tight or corroded, their flats may be rounded-off if the spanner slips. In such a case, a self-locking wrench is often the only way to unscrew a stubborn union, but it follows that the pipe and the damaged nuts must be

renewed on reassembly. Always clean a union and surrounding area before disconnecting it. If disconnecting a component with more than one union, make a careful note of the connections before disturbing any of them.

4 If a brake pipe is to be renewed, it can be obtained, cut to length and with the union nuts and end flares in place, from Citroën dealers. All that is then necessary is to bend it to shape, following the line of the original, before fitting it to the car. Alternatively, most motor accessory shops can make up brake pipes from kits, but this requires very careful measurement of the original, to ensure that the replacement is of the correct length. The safest answer is usually to take the original to the shop as a pattern.

5 On refitting, do not overtighten the union nuts. It is not necessary to exercise brute force to obtain a sound joint.

6 Ensure that the pipes and hoses are correctly routed, with no kinks, and that they are secured in the clips or brackets provided. After fitting, remove the polythene from the reservoir, and bleed the hydraulic system as described in Section 2. Wash off any spilt fluid, and check carefully for fluid leaks.

4 Front brake pads – renewal

Warning: Renew BOTH sets of front brake pads at the same time – NEVER renew the pads on only one wheel, as uneven braking may result. Note that the dust created by wear of the pads may contain asbestos, which is a health hazard. Never blow it out with compressed air, and don't inhale any of it. An approved filtering mask should be worn when working on the brakes. DO NOT use petrol or petroleum-based solvents to clean brake parts; use brake cleaner or methylated spirit only.

1 Apply the handbrake, then jack up the front of the vehicle and support it on axle stands (see *Jacking and vehicle support*). Remove the front roadwheels.

2 Where fitted, trace the brake pad wear sensor wiring back from the pads, and disconnect it from the wiring connector. Note the routing of the wiring, and free it from any relevant retaining clips.

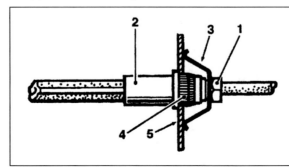

3.2 Hydraulic pipe-to-flexible hose connection

1 *Union nut*
2 *Flexible hose*
3 *Spring clip support*
4 *Splined end fitting*
5 *Mounting bracket*

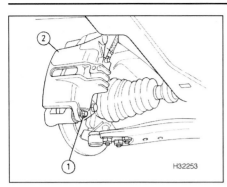

4.5 Unscrew the guide pin bolt (1), and pivot the caliper (2) upwards off the brake pads – Bendix caliper

4.7 Measuring brake pad friction material thickness

4.17 Carefully prise out the pad retaining spring from the caliper – ATE/Teves caliper

3 Push the piston into its bore by pulling the caliper outwards.

4 There are three different types of front brake caliper fitted to the models covered in this manual. Identify the relevant caliper by referring to the Specifications at the start of this Chapter, and to the accompanying illustrations. Note that the various calipers listed in the Specifications may be fitted to models additional to those indicated, however the manufacturer's name is usually stamped on the caliper body.

Bendix caliper

5 Unscrew and remove the guide pin bolt at the base of the caliper, and pivot the caliper upwards off the brake pads **(see illustration)**. Tie the caliper to the suspension strut to hold it in this position.

6 Withdraw the two brake pads from the caliper mounting bracket, noting their correct fitted positions if they are to be re-used (ie, inner and outer).

7 First measure the thickness of each brake pad's friction material. If either pad is worn at any point to the specified minimum thickness or less, all four pads must be renewed **(see illustration)**. Also, the pads should be renewed if any are fouled with oil or grease; there is no satisfactory way of degreasing friction material, once contaminated. If any of the brake pads are worn unevenly, or are fouled with oil or grease, trace and rectify the cause before reassembly. New brake pads and repair kits are available from Citroën dealers.

8 If the brake pads are still serviceable,

carefully clean them using a clean, fine wire brush or similar, paying particular attention to the sides and back of the metal backing. Clean out the grooves in the friction material, and pick out any large embedded particles of dirt or debris. Carefully clean the pad locations in the caliper mounting bracket.

9 Prior to fitting the pads, check that the guide pins are free to slide easily in the caliper body/mounting bracket, and check that the rubber guide pin gaiters are undamaged. Brush the dust and dirt from the caliper and piston, but do not inhale it, as it is injurious to health. Inspect the dust seal around the piston for damage, and the piston for evidence of fluid leaks, corrosion or damage. If attention to any of these components is necessary, refer to Section 10.

10 If new brake pads are to be fitted, the caliper piston must be pushed back into the cylinder to make room for them; either use a G-clamp or similar tool, or use suitable pieces of wood as levers. Provided that the master cylinder reservoir has not been overfilled with hydraulic fluid, there should be no spillage, but keep a careful watch on the fluid level while retracting the piston. If the fluid level rises above the MAX level line at any time, the surplus should be siphoned off or ejected via a plastic tube connected to the bleed screw (see Section 2).

 Warning: Do not syphon the fluid by mouth, as it is poisonous; use a syringe or an old poultry baster.

11 Locate the pads in the caliper mounting bracket, with the friction material of each pad against the brake disc. If the original pads are being refitted, ensure that they are positioned in their correct locations as noted during removal.

12 Swing the caliper back down over the brake pads and refit the guide pin bolt. Tighten the bolt to the specified torque.

13 Depress the brake pedal repeatedly, until the pads are pressed into firm contact with the brake disc, and normal (non-assisted) pedal pressure is restored.

14 Repeat the above procedure on the remaining front brake caliper.

15 Refit the roadwheels, then lower the vehicle to the ground and tighten the roadwheel bolts to the specified torque.

16 Check the hydraulic fluid level in the master cylinder reservoir as described in *Weekly checks*.

ATE/Teves caliper

17 Using a screwdriver, prise the pad retaining spring from the outer edge of the caliper, noting its correct fitted position **(see illustration)**.

18 Prise out the two guide pin bolt dust caps from the inner edge of the caliper **(see illustration)**.

19 Unscrew the guide pin bolts from the caliper, and lift the caliper and inner pad away from the mounting bracket **(see illustrations)**. Tie the caliper to the suspension strut using a suitable piece of wire.

4.18 Remove the guide pin bolt dust caps . . .

4.19a . . . then unscrew the guide pin bolts . . .

4.19b . . . and slide off the caliper and inner pad assembly – ATE/Teves caliper

4.22 Clip the inner pad securely into the caliper piston . . .

4.23 . . . and fit the outer pad to the caliper mounting bracket – ATE/Teves caliper

4.25 Slide the caliper into position, fit the guide pin bolts, and tighten to the specified torque – ATE/Teves caliper

Caution: Do not allow the caliper to hang unsupported on the flexible brake hose.

20 Remove the inner pad from the caliper piston, noting that it is retained by a clip attached to the pad backing plate, and recover the outer pad from the mounting bracket.

21 Proceed as described in paragraphs 7 to 10.

22 Fit the inner pad to the caliper, ensuring that its clip is correctly located in the caliper piston **(see illustration)**.

23 Fit the outer pad to the caliper mounting bracket, ensuring that its friction material is facing the brake disc **(see illustration)**.

24 Slide the caliper and inner pad into

position over the outer pad, and locate it in the mounting bracket.

25 Install the caliper guide pin bolts, and tighten them to the specified torque **(see illustration)**.

26 Refit the guide pin bolt dust caps to the caliper.

27 Refit the pad retaining spring to the caliper, ensuring that its ends are correctly located in the caliper holes **(see illustration)**.

28 Depress the brake pedal repeatedly, until normal (non-assisted) pedal pressure is restored, and the pads are pressed into firm contact with the brake disc.

29 Repeat the above procedure on the remaining front brake caliper.

30 Reconnect the brake pad wear sensor wiring connectors (where fitted), ensuring that the wiring is correctly routed, as noted before removal.

31 Refit the roadwheels, then lower the vehicle to the ground and tighten the roadwheel bolts to the specified torque setting.

32 Check the hydraulic fluid level in the master cylinder reservoir as described in *Weekly checks*.

Lucas caliper

Note: *New guide pin bolts must be used on refitting.*

33 Where applicable, prise off the dust covers, then undo and remove the lower caliper guide pin bolt, using a slim open-ended spanner to prevent the guide pin itself from rotating **(see illustration)**. Discard the guide pin bolt – new bolts must be used on refitting.

34 Slacken the upper guide pin bolt, while holding the guide pin with the open-ended spanner as before. Pivot the caliper upwards off the brake pads, and tie the caliper to the suspension strut to hold it in this position **(see illustration)**.

35 Withdraw the two brake pads from the caliper mounting bracket noting their fitted positions if they are to be re-used (ie, inner and outer). Where fitted, recover the shim from the caliper piston, noting its correct fitted position **(see illustrations)**. Examine the pads as described above in paragraphs 7 to 10.

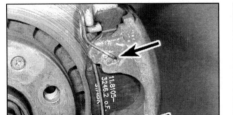

4.27 Ensure that the pad retaining spring ends are correctly located in the caliper holes (arrowed) – ATE/Teves caliper

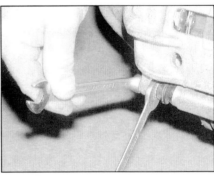

4.33 Retain the guide pin with a spanner while undoing the lower guide pin bolt – Lucas caliper

4.34 Slacken the upper guide pin bolt, and pivot the caliper upwards off the brake pads – Lucas caliper

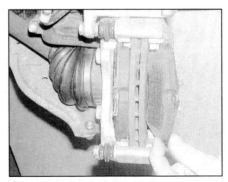

4.35a Withdraw the two brake pads from the caliper mounting bracket . . .

4.35b . . . and, where fitted, recover the shim from the caliper piston – Lucas caliper

36 Install the pads in the caliper mounting bracket, ensuring that the friction material of each pad is against the brake disc, and that the pads are in their correct locations if the original pads are being re-used. Where fitted, locate the shim in place on the caliper piston.

37 Pivot the caliper down over the pads, and pass the pad warning sensor wiring (where applicable) through the caliper aperture and underneath the retaining clip.

38 If not already pre-coated, apply suitable thread locking compound to the threads of the two new guide pin bolts. Insert the lower bolt and tighten it to the specified torque. Hold the guide pin with the open-ended spanner as the guide pin bolt is tightened.

39 Remove the original upper guide pin bolt and fit the new bolt, tightening it to the specified torque. Where applicable, refit the dust covers to the guide pins.

40 Reconnect the brake pad wear sensor wiring connectors (where applicable), ensuring that the wiring is correctly routed through the loop of the caliper bleed screw cap.

41 Depress the brake pedal repeatedly, until the pads are pressed into firm contact with the brake disc, and normal (non-assisted) pedal pressure is restored.

42 Repeat the above procedure on the remaining front brake caliper.

43 Refit the roadwheels, then lower the vehicle to the ground and tighten the roadwheel bolts to the specified torque.

44 Finally, check the hydraulic fluid level in the master cylinder reservoir as described in *Weekly checks*.

All calipers

45 New pads will not give full braking efficiency until they have bedded-in. Be prepared for this, and avoid hard braking as far as possible for the first hundred miles or so after pad renewal.

5 Rear brake pads – renewal

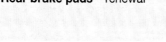

Warning: Renew BOTH sets of rear brake pads at the same time – NEVER renew the pads on only one wheel, as uneven braking may result. Dust created by wear of the pads may contain asbestos, which is a health hazard. Never blow it out with compressed air, and don't inhale any of it. An approved filtering mask should be worn when working on the brakes. DO NOT use petrol or petroleum-based solvents to clean brake parts; use brake cleaner or methylated spirit only.

1 Chock the front wheels, then jack up the rear of the vehicle and support it on axle stands (see *Jacking and vehicle support*). Remove the rear wheels.

2 Extract the small spring clip from the pad

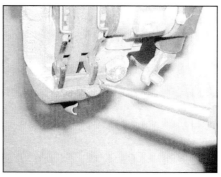

5.2a Extract the spring clip . . .

retaining plate, and then slide the plate out of the caliper **(see illustrations)**. Discard the spring clip – a new one must be used on refitting.

3 Using pliers if necessary, withdraw the two brake pads from the caliper **(see illustration)**. Make a note of the correct fitted position of the anti-rattle springs, and remove the springs from each pad.

4 First measure the thickness of the friction material of each brake pad. If either pad is worn at any point to the specified minimum thickness or less, all four pads must be renewed. Also, the pads should be renewed if any are fouled with oil or grease; there is no satisfactory way of degreasing friction material, once contaminated. If any of the brake pads are worn unevenly, or fouled with oil or grease, trace and rectify the cause before reassembly. New brake pads and spring kits are available from Citroën dealers.

5 If the brake pads are still serviceable, carefully clean them using a clean, fine wire brush or similar, paying particular attention to the sides and back of the metal backing. Clean out the grooves in the friction material, and pick out any large embedded particles of dirt or debris. Carefully clean the pad locations in the caliper body/mounting bracket.

6 Prior to fitting the pads, check that the guide sleeves are free to slide easily in the caliper body, and check that the rubber guide sleeve gaiters are undamaged. Brush the dust

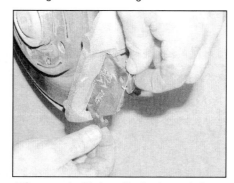

5.3 . . . and withdraw the brake pads from the caliper

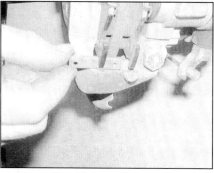

5.2b . . . then slide out the pad retaining plate . . .

and dirt from the caliper and piston, but **do not** inhale it, as it is injurious to health. Inspect the dust seal around the piston for damage, and the piston for evidence of fluid leaks, corrosion or damage. If attention to any of these components is necessary, refer to Section 11.

7 If new brake pads are to be fitted, it will be necessary to retract the piston fully into the caliper bore, by rotating it in a clockwise direction. This can be achieved using a suitable square-section bar, such as the shaft of a screwdriver, which locates snugly in the caliper piston slots **(see illustration)**. Provided that the master cylinder reservoir has not been overfilled with hydraulic fluid, there should be no spillage, but keep a careful watch on the fluid level while retracting the piston. If the fluid level rises above the MAX level line at any time, the surplus should be siphoned off, or ejected via a plastic tube connected to the bleed screw (see Section 2).

Warning: Do not syphon the fluid by mouth, as it is poisonous; use a syringe or an old poultry baster.

8 Position the caliper piston so that the piston groove is horizontal. This is necessary to ensure that the lug on the inner pad will locate with the caliper piston slot on installation.

9 Refit the anti-rattle springs to the pads, then locate the outer brake pad in the caliper body, ensuring that its friction material is against the brake disc. Slide the inner pad into position in the caliper, ensuring that the lug on

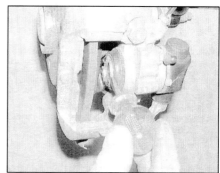

5.7 Retract the piston by turning it clockwise with a screwdriver or square-section bar

5.9 Install the inner pad, ensuring its locating lug is correctly engaged in the piston slot

its backing plate is aligned with the slot in the caliper piston **(see illustration)**.

10 Ensure that the anti-rattle spring ends on both pads are correctly positioned, then slide the retaining plate into place, and secure it in position with a new spring clip. It may be necessary to file an entry chamfer on the edge of the retaining plate, to enable it to be fitted without difficulty.

11 Depress the brake pedal repeatedly until the pads are pressed into firm contact with the brake disc, and normal (non-assisted) pedal pressure is restored. Check that the inner pad lug is correctly engaged with one of the caliper piston slots.

12 Repeat the above procedure on the remaining rear brake caliper.

13 Check the handbrake cable adjustment as described in Section 17, then refit the roadwheels and lower the vehicle to the

ground. Tighten the roadwheel bolts to the specified torque setting.

14 Check the hydraulic fluid level in the master cylinder as described in *Weekly checks*.

15 New pads will not give full braking efficiency until they have bedded-in. Be prepared for this, and avoid hard braking as far as possible for the first hundred miles or so after pad renewal.

6 Rear brake shoes – renewal

⚠️ **Warning: Brake shoes must be renewed on BOTH rear wheels at the same time – NEVER renew the shoes on only one wheel, as uneven braking may result. Also, the dust created by wear of the shoes may contain asbestos, which is a health hazard. Never blow it out with compressed air, and don't inhale any of it. An approved filtering mask should be worn when working on the brakes. DO NOT use petrol or petroleum-based solvents to clean brake parts; use brake cleaner or methylated spirit only.**

1 Remove the brake drum as described in Section 9.

2 Working carefully, and taking the necessary precautions, remove all traces of brake dust from the brake drum, backplate and shoes.

3 Measure the thickness of the friction material of each brake shoe at several points; if either shoe is worn at any point to the specified minimum thickness or less, all four shoes must be renewed as a set. The shoes should also be renewed if any are fouled with oil or grease; there is no satisfactory way of degreasing friction material, once contaminated.

4 If any of the brake shoes are worn unevenly, or fouled with oil or grease, trace and rectify the cause before reassembly.

5 To renew the brake shoes, proceed as described under the relevant sub-heading.

Bendix brake shoes

Note: *The components encountered may vary in detail, but the principles described in the*

following paragraphs are equally applicable to all models. Make a careful note of the fitted positions of all components before dismantling.

6 Using a pair of pliers, remove the shoe retainer spring cups by depressing and turning them through 90° **(see illustrations)**. With the cups removed, lift off the springs and withdraw the retainer pins.

7 Ease the shoes out one at a time from the lower pivot point, to release the tension of the return spring, then disconnect the lower return spring from both shoes **(see illustration)**.

8 Ease the upper end of both shoes out from their wheel cylinder locations, taking care not to damage the wheel cylinder seals, and disconnect the handbrake cable from the trailing shoe. The brake shoe and adjuster strut assembly can then be manoeuvred out of position and away from the backplate. Do not depress the brake pedal until the brakes are reassembled; wrap an elastic band around the wheel cylinder pistons to retain them.

9 With the shoe and adjuster strut assembly on a bench, make a note of the correct fitted positions of the springs and adjuster strut, to use as a guide on reassembly. Release the handbrake lever stop-peg (if not already done), then carefully detach the adjuster strut bolt retaining spring from the leading shoe. Disconnect the upper return spring, then detach the leading shoe and return spring from the trailing shoe and strut assembly. Unhook the spring securing the adjuster strut to the trailing shoe, and separate the two.

10 If genuine Citroën brake shoes are being installed, in some instances it will be necessary to remove the handbrake lever from the original trailing shoe, and install it on the new shoe. Secure the lever in position with a new retaining clip. All return springs should be renewed, regardless of their apparent condition; spring kits are also available from Citroën dealers.

11 Withdraw the adjuster bolt from the strut, and carefully examine the assembly for signs of wear or damage. Pay particular attention to the threads of the adjuster bolt and the knurled adjuster wheel, and renew if necessary. Note that left-hand and right-hand

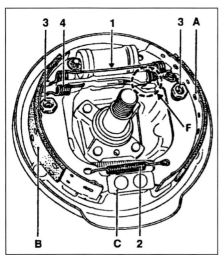

6.6a Correct fitted positions of the Bendix rear brake components

A Leading shoe
B Trailing shoe
C Lower pivot point
F Adjuster strut mechanism
1 Upper return spring
2 Lower return spring
3 Retaining pin, spring and spring cup
4 Adjuster strut-to-trailing shoe spring

6.6b Removing a shoe retainer spring cup

6.7 On Bendix rear brake shoes, ease the shoes out of the lower pivot point, and disconnect the lower return spring

struts are not interchangeable – they are marked G (gauche) and D (droit) respectively. Also note that the strut adjuster bolts are not interchangeable; the left-hand strut bolt has a left-handed thread, and the right-hand bolt a right-handed thread.

12 Ensure that the components on the end of the strut are correctly positioned, then apply a little high-melting-point grease to the threads of the adjuster bolt **(see illustration)**. Screw the adjuster wheel onto the bolt until only a small gap exists between the wheel and the head of the bolt, then fit the bolt in the strut.

13 Fit the adjuster strut retaining spring to the trailing shoe, ensuring that the shorter hook of the spring is engaged with the shoe. Attach the adjuster strut to the spring end, then ease the strut into its slot in the trailing shoe.

14 Engage the upper return spring with the trailing shoe, then hook the leading shoe onto the other end of the spring, and lever the leading shoe down until the adjuster bolt head is correctly located in its groove. Once the bolt is correctly located, hook its retaining spring into the slot on the leading shoe.

15 Peel back the rubber protective caps, and check the wheel cylinder for fluid leaks or other damage; check that both cylinder pistons are free to move easily. Refer to Section 12, if necessary, for information on wheel cylinder renewal.

16 Prior to installation, clean the backplate, and apply a thin smear of high-temperature brake grease or anti-seize compound to all those surfaces of the backplate which bear on the shoes, particularly the wheel cylinder pistons and lower pivot point **(see illustration)**. Do not allow the lubricant to foul the friction material.

17 Ensure that the handbrake lever stop-peg is correctly located against the edge of the trailing shoe, and remove the elastic band fitted to the wheel cylinder.

18 Manoeuvre the shoe and strut assembly into position on the vehicle, and locate the upper end of both shoes with the wheel cylinder pistons. Attach the handbrake cable to the trailing shoe lever. Fit the lower return spring to both shoes, and ease the shoes into position on the lower pivot point.

19 Tap the shoes to centralise them with the backplate, then refit the shoe retainer pins and springs, and secure them in position with the spring cups.

20 Using a screwdriver, turn the strut adjuster wheel to expand the shoes until the brake drum just slides over the shoes.

21 Refit the brake drum (see Section 9).

22 Repeat the above procedure on the remaining rear brake.

23 Once both sets of rear shoes have been renewed, adjust the lining-to-drum clearance by repeatedly depressing the brake pedal. Whilst depressing the pedal, have an assistant listen to the rear drums, to check that the adjuster strut is functioning correctly;

6.12 Correct fitted position of Bendix adjuster strut components

if so, a clicking sound will be emitted by the strut as the pedal is depressed.

24 Check and, if necessary, adjust the handbrake as described in Section 17.

25 On completion, check the hydraulic fluid level in the master cylinder as described in *Weekly checks*.

Lucas/Girling brake shoes

Note: *The components encountered may vary in detail, but the principles described in the following paragraphs are equally applicable to all models. Make a careful note of the fitted positions of all components before dismantling.*

26 Make a note of the correct fitted positions of the springs and adjuster strut, to use as a guide on reassembly **(see illustration)**.

27 Carefully unhook both the upper and lower return springs, and remove them from the brake shoes.

28 Using a pair of pliers, remove the leading shoe retainer spring cup by depressing it and turning through 90°. With the cup removed, lift off the spring, then withdraw the retainer pin and remove the shoe from the backplate. Unhook the adjusting lever spring, and remove it from the leading shoe.

29 Detach the adjuster strut, and remove it from the trailing shoe.

30 Remove the trailing shoe retainer spring cup, spring and pin by depressing and turning them through 90°, then detach the handbrake cable and remove the shoe from the vehicle. Do not depress the brake pedal until the brakes are reassembled; wrap a strong elastic band around the wheel cylinder pistons to retain them.

31 If genuine Citroën brake shoes are being installed, in some instances it will be necessary to remove the adjusting lever from the original leading shoe, and install it on the new shoe. All return springs should be renewed, regardless of their apparent condition; spring kits are also available from Citroën dealers.

32 Withdraw the forked end from the strut, and carefully examine the assembly for signs of wear or damage. Pay particular attention to the threads and the knurled adjuster wheel, and renew if necessary. Note that left-hand

6.16 Apply a little high-melting-point grease to the shoe contact points on the backplate

and right-hand struts are not interchangeable.

33 Peel back the rubber protective caps, and check the wheel cylinder for fluid leaks or other damage; check that both cylinder pistons are free to move easily. Refer to Section 12, if necessary, for information on wheel cylinder renewal.

34 Prior to installation, clean the backplate, and apply a thin smear of high-temperature brake grease or anti-seize compound to all those surfaces of the backplate which bear on the shoes, particularly the wheel cylinder pistons and lower pivot point. Do not allow the lubricant to foul the friction material.

35 Ensure that the handbrake lever stop-peg is correctly located against the edge of the trailing shoe, and remove the elastic band fitted to the wheel cylinder.

36 Locate the upper end of the trailing shoe in the wheel cylinder piston, then refit the retainer pin and spring, and secure it in position with the spring cup. Connect the handbrake cable to the lever.

37 Screw in the adjuster wheel until the minimum strut length is obtained, then hook the strut into position on the trailing shoe. Rotate the adjuster strut forked end, so that the cut-out of the fork will engage with the

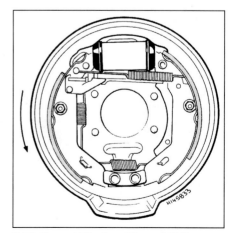

6.26 Correct fitted positions of Girling rear brake components

Arrow indicates direction of wheel rotation

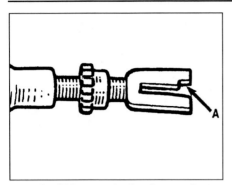

6.37 On Girling rear brake shoes, adjuster strut fork cut-out (A) must engage with leading shoe adjusting lever on refitting

7.3 Using a micrometer to measure disc thickness

leading shoe adjusting lever once the shoe is installed **(see illustration)**.

38 Fit the spring to the leading shoe adjusting lever, so that the shorter hook of the spring engages with the lever.

39 Slide the leading shoe assembly into position, ensuring that it is correctly engaged with the adjuster strut fork, and that the fork cut-out is engaged with the adjusting lever. Ensure that the upper end of the shoe is located in the wheel cylinder piston, then secure the shoe in position with the retainer pin, spring and spring cup.

40 Install the upper and lower return springs, then tap the shoes to centralise them with the backplate.

41 Using a screwdriver, turn the strut adjuster wheel to expand the shoes until the brake drum just slides over the shoes.

42 Refit the brake drum as described in Section 9.

43 Repeat the above procedure on the remaining rear brake.

44 Once both sets of rear shoes have been renewed, adjust the lining-to-drum clearance by repeatedly depressing the brake pedal. Whilst depressing the pedal, have an assistant listen to the rear drums, to check that the adjuster strut is functioning correctly; if so, a clicking sound will be emitted by the strut as the pedal is depressed.

45 Check and, if necessary, adjust the handbrake as described in Section 17.

46 On completion, check the hydraulic fluid

level in the master cylinder as described in *Weekly checks*.

All shoes

47 New shoes will not give full braking efficiency until they have bedded-in. Be prepared for this, and avoid hard braking as far as possible for the first hundred miles or so after shoe renewal.

---

7 Front brake disc – inspection, removal and refitting

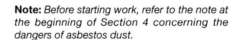

Note: *Before starting work, refer to the note at the beginning of Section 4 concerning the dangers of asbestos dust.*

Inspection

Note: *If either disc requires renewal, BOTH should be renewed at the same time, to ensure even and consistent braking. New brake pads should also be fitted.*

1 Apply the handbrake, then jack up the front of the car and support it on axle stands (see *Jacking and vehicle support*). Remove the appropriate front roadwheel.

2 Slowly rotate the brake disc so that the full area of both sides can be checked; remove the brake pads if better access is required to the inboard surface. Light scoring is normal in the area swept by the brake pads, but if

heavy scoring or cracks are found, the disc must be renewed.

3 It is normal to find a lip of rust and brake dust around the disc's perimeter; this can be scraped off if required. If, however, a lip has formed due to excessive wear of the brake pad swept area, then the disc's thickness must be measured using a micrometer **(see illustration)**. Take measurements at several places around the disc, at the inside and outside of the pad swept area; if the disc has worn at any point to the specified minimum thickness or less, the disc must be renewed.

4 If the disc is thought to be warped, it can be checked for run-out. Either use a dial gauge mounted on any convenient fixed point while the disc is slowly rotated, or use feeler blades to measure (at several points all around the disc) the clearance between the disc and a fixed point, such as the caliper mounting bracket **(see illustration)**. If the measurements obtained are at the specified maximum or beyond, the disc is excessively warped, and must be renewed; however, it is worth checking first that the hub bearing is in good condition (Chapter 1A or 1B and/or 10). Also try the effect of removing the disc and turning it through 180° to reposition it on the hub; if the run-out is still excessive, the disc must be renewed.

5 Check the disc for cracks, especially around the wheel bolt holes, and any other wear or damage, and renew if necessary.

Removal

6 Remove the brake pads as described in Section 4.

7 Undo the two bolts securing the caliper mounting bracket to the swivel hub **(see illustration)**. Withdraw the mounting bracket, complete with caliper (where applicable) from the disc and swivel hub, and tie it to the front suspension coil spring, to avoid placing any strain on the fluid hose.

8 Use chalk or paint to mark the relationship of the disc to the hub, then remove the screws securing the brake disc to the hub, and remove the disc **(see illustrations)**. If it is tight, lightly tap its rear face with a hide or plastic mallet.

7.4 Checking disc run-out using a dial gauge

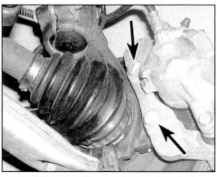

7.7 Front caliper mounting bracket retaining bolts (arrowed) – Lucas caliper

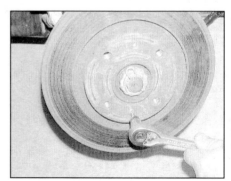

7.8a Undo the two retaining screws . . .

7.8b . . . and remove the front brake disc

8.4 Removing a rear brake disc

Refitting

9 Refitting is the reverse of the removal procedure, noting the following points:

a) Ensure that the mating surfaces of the disc and hub are clean and flat.

b) Align (if applicable) the marks made on removal, and securely tighten the disc retaining screws.

c) If a new disc has been fitted, use a suitable solvent to wipe any preservative coating from the disc before refitting the caliper.

d) Apply suitable thread locking compound to the threads of the caliper mounting bracket retaining bolts and tighten the bolts to the specified torque.

e) Refit the brake pads as described in Section 4.

f) Refit the roadwheel, then lower the vehicle to the ground and tighten the roadwheel bolts to the specified torque. On completion, repeatedly depress the brake pedal until normal (non-assisted) pedal pressure returns.

8 Rear brake disc – inspection, removal and refitting

Note: Before starting work, refer to the note at the beginning of Section 5 concerning the dangers of asbestos dust.

Inspection

Note: If either disc requires renewal, BOTH should be renewed at the same time, to ensure even and consistent braking. New brake pads should also be fitted.

1 Firmly chock the front wheels, then jack up the rear of the car and support it on axle stands (see Jacking and vehicle support). Remove the appropriate rear roadwheel.

2 Inspect the disc as described in Section 7.

Removal

3 Remove the brake pads as described in Section 5.

4 Use chalk or paint to mark the relationship of the disc to the hub, then remove the screw securing the brake disc to the hub, and

remove the disc **(see illustration)**. If it is tight, lightly tap its rear face with a hide or plastic mallet.

Refitting

5 Refitting is the reverse of the removal procedure, noting the following points:

a) Ensure that the mating surfaces of the disc and hub are clean and flat.

b) Align (if applicable) the marks made on removal, and securely tighten the disc retaining screws.

c) If a new disc has been fitted, use a suitable solvent to wipe any preservative coating from the disc, before refitting the caliper.

d) Refit the brake pads as described in Section 5.

e) Refit the roadwheel, then lower the vehicle to the ground and tighten the roadwheel bolts to the specified torque.

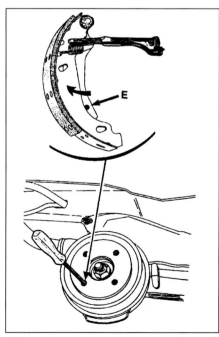

9.6a Using a screwdriver inserted through the brake drum to release the handbrake operating lever

E Handbrake operating lever stop-peg location

9 Rear brake drum – removal, inspection and refitting

Note: Before starting work, refer to the note at the beginning of Section 6 concerning the dangers of asbestos dust.

Hatchback and Coupé models

Removal

Note: A new rear hub nut, hub cap and oil seal must be used on refitting.

1 Chock the front wheels, then jack up the rear of the vehicle and support it on axle stands (see Jacking and vehicle support). Remove the appropriate rear wheel.

2 Using a hammer and a large flat-bladed screwdriver, carefully tap and prise the cap out of the centre of the brake drum. Discard the cap – a new one must be used on refitting. Using a hammer and chisel, tap up the staking securing the hub retaining nut to the groove in the stub axle.

3 Using a socket and long bar, slacken and remove the rear hub nut, and withdraw the thrustwasher. Discard the hub nut – a new nut must used on refitting.

4 It should now be possible to withdraw the brake drum and hub bearing assembly from the stub axle by hand. It may be difficult to remove the drum due to the tightness of the hub bearing on the stub axle, or due to the brake shoes binding on the inner circumference of the drum. If the bearing is tight, tap the periphery of the drum using a hide or plastic mallet, or use a universal puller, secured to the drum with the wheel bolts, to pull it off. If the brake shoes are binding, first check that the handbrake is fully released, then proceed as follows.

5 Referring to Section 17 for further information, fully slacken the handbrake cable adjuster nut, to obtain maximum free play in the cable.

6 Insert a screwdriver through one of the wheel bolt holes in the brake drum, so that it contacts the handbrake operating lever on the trailing brake shoe. Push the lever until the stop-peg slips behind the brake shoe web, allowing the brake shoes to retract fully **(see illustrations)**. The brake drum can now be

9.6b Releasing the handbrake operating lever

9.14 Check that the handbrake lever stop-peg is positioned against the shoe edge

withdrawn. With the drum removed, prise the oil seal off the stub axle; the seal must be renewed as a matter of course.

Inspection

Note: *If either drum requires renewal, BOTH should be renewed at the same time, to ensure even and consistent braking. New brake shoes should also be fitted.*

7 Working carefully, remove all traces of brake dust from the drum, but *avoid inhaling the dust, as it is injurious to health.*

8 Clean the outside of the drum, and check it for obvious signs of wear or damage, such as cracks around the roadwheel bolt holes; renew the drum if necessary.

9 Examine carefully the inside of the drum. Light scoring of the friction surface is normal, but if heavy scoring is found, the drum must be renewed. It is usual to find a lip on the drum's inboard edge which consists of a mixture of rust and brake dust; this should be scraped away, to leave a smooth surface which can be polished with fine (120- to 150-grade) emery paper. If, however, the lip is due to the friction surface being recessed by excessive wear, then the drum must be renewed.

10 If the drum is thought to be excessively worn, or oval, its internal diameter must be measured at several points using an internal micrometer. Take measurements in pairs, the second at right-angles to the first, and compare the two, to check for signs of ovality. Provided that it does not enlarge the drum to beyond the specified maximum diameter, it may be possible to have the drum refinished by skimming or grinding; if this is not possible, the drums on both sides must be renewed. Note that if the drum is to be skimmed, BOTH drums must be refinished, to maintain a consistent internal diameter on both sides.

11 Check the condition of the oil seal seating ring in the rear of the brake drum, and the spacer on the stub axle. If any signs of wear or damage are present, renew these components as necessary.

Refitting

12 Apply a smear of clean engine oil to the stub axle, and slide on the oil seal until it is seated on the spacer.

13 If a new brake drum is to be installed, use a suitable solvent to remove any preservative coating that may have been applied to its interior. Note that it may also be necessary to shorten the adjuster strut length, by rotating the strut wheel, to allow the drum to pass over the brake shoes.

14 Ensure that the handbrake lever stop-peg is correctly repositioned against the edge of the brake shoe web **(see illustration)**, then locate the brake drum on the stub axle.

15 Fit the thrustwasher and new hub nut, and tighten the hub nut to the specified torque. Stake the nut firmly into the groove on the stub axle, to secure it in position, then tap the new hub cap into place in the centre of the brake drum.

16 Depress the footbrake several times to operate the self-adjusting mechanism.

17 Repeat the above procedure on the remaining rear brake assembly (where necessary), then check and, if necessary, adjust the handbrake cable as described in Section 17.

18 On completion, refit the roadwheel(s), then lower the vehicle to the ground and tighten the wheel bolts to the specified torque.

Estate models

Removal

19 Chock the front wheels, then jack up the rear of the vehicle and support it on axle stands (see *Jacking and vehicle support*). Remove the appropriate rear roadwheel.

20 Remove the drum retaining screws.

21 It should now be possible to withdraw the brake drum by hand. It may be difficult to remove the drum due to the brake shoes binding on the inner circumference of the drum. If the brake shoes are binding, first check that the handbrake is fully released, then proceed as described in paragraphs 5 and 6, ignoring the reference to the oil seal.

Inspection

22 Refer to paragraphs 7 to 10 inclusive.

Refitting

23 Proceed as described in paragraphs 13 and 14.

24 Refit and tighten the drum retaining screws.

25 Proceed as described in paragraphs 16 to 18 inclusive.

---

10 Front brake caliper – removal, overhaul and refitting

Note: *Before starting work, refer to the note at the beginning of Section 2 concerning the dangers of hydraulic fluid, and to the warning at the beginning of Section 4 concerning the dangers of asbestos dust.*

Removal

1 Apply the handbrake, then jack up the front of the vehicle and support it on axle stands (see *Jacking and vehicle support*). Remove the appropriate roadwheel.

2 Minimise fluid loss by first removing the master cylinder reservoir cap, and then tightening it down onto a piece of polythene, to obtain an airtight seal. Alternatively, use a brake hose clamp, a G-clamp or a similar tool to clamp the flexible hose.

Bendix caliper

3 Remove the brake pads as described in Section 4.

4 Clean the area around the hydraulic fluid hose union on the caliper, then loosen the fluid hose union nut by half a turn.

5 Unscrew and remove the two bolts securing the caliper mounting bracket to the swivel hub. Lift the caliper and mounting bracket assembly away from the brake disc and swivel hub, and unscrew the caliper from the end of the fluid hose.

ATE/Teves caliper

6 Where applicable, disconnect the brake pad wear sensor wiring, and free it from any retaining clips.

7 Clean the area around the hydraulic fluid hose union on the caliper, then loosen the fluid hose union nut by half a turn.

8 Using a screwdriver, prise the pad retaining spring from the outer edge of the caliper, noting its correct fitted position.

9 Prise out the two guide pin bolt dust caps from the inner edge of the caliper.

10 Unscrew the guide pin bolts from the caliper, and lift the caliper and inner pad away from the mounting bracket. Unscrew caliper from the end of the fluid hose. The outer pad can be left in the caliper mounting bracket.

11 Remove the inner pad from the caliper piston, noting that it is retained by a clip attached to the pad backing plate.

Lucas caliper

Note: *New guide pin bolts must be used on refitting.*

12 Clean the area around the hydraulic fluid hose union on the caliper, then loosen the fluid hose union nut by half a turn. Where applicable, disconnect the pad wear warning sensor wiring connector, and free it from any relevant retaining clips.

13 Slacken and remove the upper and lower caliper guide pin bolts, using a slim open-ended spanner to prevent the guide pin itself from rotating. Discard the guide pin bolts – new bolts must be used on refitting. With the guide pin bolts removed, lift the caliper away from the brake disc, then unscrew the caliper from the end of the brake hose. Note that the brake pads need not be disturbed, and can be left in position in the caliper mounting bracket.

Overhaul

14 The caliper can be overhauled after

obtaining the relevant repair kit from a Citroën dealer. Ensure that the correct repair kit is obtained for the caliper being worked on. Note the locations of all components to ensure correct refitting, and lubricate the new seals using clean brake fluid. Follow the assembly instructions supplied with the repair kit.

Refitting

Bendix caliper

15 Screw the caliper fully onto the flexible hydraulic fluid hose union, then position the caliper and mounting bracket assembly over the brake disc.

16 Apply a suitable locking compound to the threads of the caliper mounting bracket retaining bolts and refit the bolts. Tighten the bolts to the specified torque.

17 Securely tighten the hydraulic fluid hose union, then refit the brake pads as described in Section 4.

18 Remove the brake hose clamp or polythene, as applicable, and bleed the hydraulic system as described in Section 2. Providing the precautions described were taken to minimise brake fluid loss, it should only be necessary to bleed the relevant front brake.

19 Refit the roadwheel, then lower the vehicle to the ground and tighten the roadwheel bolts to the specified torque.

ATE/Teves caliper

20 Refit the inner brake pad to the caliper, ensuring that the clip engages correctly with the piston.

21 Screw the caliper fully onto the flexible hydraulic fluid hose union, then position the caliper over the brake disc. Ensure that the outer pad is in position in the caliper mounting bracket.

22 Slide the caliper and inner pad into position over the outer pad, and locate the caliper in the mounting bracket.

23 Fit the caliper guide pin bolts, and tighten them to the specified torque setting.

24 Refit the guide pin bolt dust caps.

25 Refit the pad retaining spring to the caliper, ensuring that its ends are correctly located in the caliper holes.

26 Where applicable, reconnect the pad wear sensor wiring, ensuring that it is correctly routed as noted before removal.

27 Tighten the hydraulic fluid hose union securely, then remove the brake hose clamp or polythene, where fitted, and bleed the hydraulic system as described in Section 2. Providing the precautions described were taken to minimise brake fluid loss, it should only be necessary to bleed the relevant front brake.

28 Depress the brake pedal repeatedly, until normal (non-assisted) pedal pressure is restored, and the pads are pressed into firm contact with the brake disc.

29 Refit the roadwheel, then lower the vehicle to the ground and tighten the roadwheel bolts to the specified torque.

Lucas caliper

30 Screw the caliper body fully onto the flexible hydraulic fluid hose union, then check that the brake pads are still correctly fitted in the caliper mounting bracket.

31 Position the caliper over the pads and, where applicable, pass the pad wear warning sensor wiring through the caliper aperture. If the threads of the new guide pin bolts are not already pre-coated with locking compound, apply a suitable locking compound to them. Fit the new lower guide pin bolt, then press the caliper into position and fit the new upper guide pin bolt. Tighten both the guide pin bolts to the specified torque, while retaining the guide pin with an open-ended spanner.

32 Reconnect the brake pad wear sensor wiring connectors, ensuring that the wiring is correctly routed through the loop of the caliper bleed screw cap.

33 Tighten the hydraulic fluid hose union securely, then remove the brake hose clamp or polythene, where fitted, and bleed the hydraulic system as described in Section 2. Providing the precautions described were

taken to minimise brake fluid loss, it should only be necessary to bleed the relevant front brake.

34 Depress the brake pedal repeatedly, until the pads are pressed into firm contact with the brake disc, and normal (non-assisted) pedal pressure is restored.

35 Refit the roadwheel, then lower the vehicle to the ground and tighten the roadwheel bolts to the specified torque.

11 Rear brake caliper – removal, overhaul and refitting

Note: *Before starting work, refer to the note at the beginning of Section 2 concerning the dangers of hydraulic fluid, and to the warning at the beginning of Section 5 concerning the dangers of asbestos dust.*

Removal

Note: *New caliper mounting bolts must be used on refitting.*

1 Chock the front wheels, then jack up the rear of the vehicle and support on axle stands (see *Jacking and vehicle support*). Remove the relevant rear wheel.

2 Remove the brake pads as described in Section 5.

3 Ensure that the handbrake is fully released, then free the handbrake inner cable from the caliper handbrake operating lever. Tap the outer cable out of its bracket on the caliper body **(see illustrations)**.

4 Minimise fluid loss by first removing the master cylinder reservoir cap, and then tightening it down onto a piece of polythene, to obtain an airtight seal. Alternatively, use a brake hose clamp, a G-clamp or a similar tool to clamp the rear flexible hose at the nearest convenient point to the brake caliper.

5 Wipe away all traces of dirt around the brake pipe union on the caliper, and unscrew the union nut. Carefully ease the pipe out of the caliper, and plug or tape over its end to

11.3a Disconnect the handbrake inner cable from the caliper lever . . .

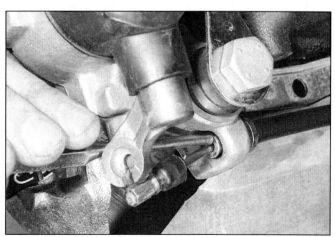

11.3b . . . then tap the outer cable out from the caliper body

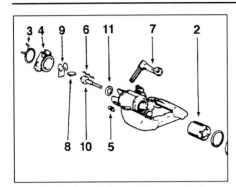

11.7 Exploded view of the rear brake caliper

1	Dust seal	6	Spring washers
2	Piston	7	Handbrake
3	Retaining clip		operating lever
4	Handbrake	8	Plunger cam
	mechanism dust	9	Return spring
	cover	10	Adjusting screw
5	Circlip	11	Thrustwasher

12.3 To minimise fluid loss, fit a brake hose clamp to the flexible hose

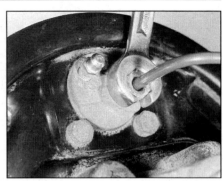

12.4 Using a brake pipe spanner to unscrew the wheel cylinder union nut

prevent dirt entry. Wipe off any spilt fluid immediately.

6 Slacken the two bolts securing the caliper assembly to the trailing arm, and remove them, along with the mounting plate, noting which way around the plate is fitted. Lift the caliper assembly away from the brake disc, and remove it from the vehicle.

Overhaul

7 The caliper can be overhauled after obtaining the relevant repair kit from a Citroën dealer. Note the locations of all components (this applies particularly if the handbrake mechanism is dismantled) to ensure correct refitting, and lubricate the new seals using brake fluid **(see illustration)**. Follow the assembly instructions supplied with the repair kit.

Refitting

8 Apply a suitable locking compound to the threads of the caliper mounting bolts. Position the caliper over the brake disc and install the caliper mounting bolts and the mounting plate. With the plate correctly positioned, tighten the caliper bolts to the specified torque.

9 Engage the brake pipe with the caliper and screw in the union nut. Tighten the union nut securely, then remove the clamp from the flexible brake hose, or the polythene from the master cylinder reservoir (as applicable).

10 Insert the handbrake cable through its bracket on the caliper, and tap the outer cable into position using a hammer and suitable pin punch. Reconnect the inner cable to the caliper operating lever.

11 Refit the brake pads as described in Section 5.

12 Bleed the hydraulic system as described in Section 2. Note that, providing the precautions described were taken to minimise

brake fluid loss, it should only be necessary to bleed the relevant rear brake.

13 Repeatedly apply the brake pedal until normal (non-assisted) pedal pressure returns. Check and if necessary adjust the handbrake cable as described in Section 17.

14 Refit the roadwheel, then lower the vehicle to the ground and tighten the wheel bolts to the specified torque.

12 Rear wheel cylinder – removal and refitting

Note: *Before starting work, refer to the note at the beginning of Section 2 concerning the dangers of hydraulic fluid, and to the warning at the beginning of Section 6 concerning the dangers of asbestos dust.*

Removal

1 Remove the brake drum as described in Section 9.

2 Using pliers, carefully unhook the upper brake shoe return spring, and remove it from both brake shoes. Pull the upper ends of the shoes away from the wheel cylinder to disengage them from the pistons.

3 Minimise fluid loss by first removing the master cylinder reservoir cap, and then tightening it down onto a piece of polythene, to obtain an airtight seal. Alternatively, use a brake hose clamp, a G-clamp or a similar tool to clamp the flexible hose at the nearest convenient point to the wheel cylinder **(see illustration)**.

4 Wipe away all traces of dirt around the brake pipe union at the rear of the wheel cylinder, and unscrew the union nut **(see illustration)**. Carefully ease the pipe out of the wheel cylinder, and plug or tape over its end to prevent dirt entry. Wipe off any spilt fluid immediately.

5 Unscrew the two wheel cylinder retaining bolts from the rear of the backplate, and remove the cylinder, taking great care not to allow surplus hydraulic fluid to contaminate the brake shoe linings.

6 Note that it is not possible to overhaul the cylinder, since no components are available separately. If faulty, the complete wheel cylinder assembly must be renewed.

Refitting

7 Ensure that the backplate and wheel cylinder mating surfaces are clean, then spread the brake shoes and manoeuvre the wheel cylinder into position.

8 Engage the brake pipe, and screw in the union nut two or three turns to ensure that the thread has started.

9 Insert the two wheel cylinder retaining bolts, and tighten them securely. Now fully tighten the brake pipe union nut.

10 Remove the clamp from the flexible brake hose, or the polythene from the master cylinder reservoir (as applicable).

11 Ensure that the brake shoes are correctly located in the cylinder pistons, then carefully refit the brake shoe upper return spring. Use a screwdriver to stretch the spring into position.

12 Refit the brake drum as described in Section 9.

13 Bleed the brake hydraulic system as described in Section 2. Providing suitable precautions were taken to minimise loss of fluid, it should only be necessary to bleed the relevant rear brake.

13 Master cylinder – removal and refitting

Note: *Before starting, refer to the warning in Section 2 on the dangers of hydraulic fluid.*

Removal

1 On left-hand-drive models, to provide improved access, remove the battery and battery tray as described in Chapter 5A.

2 On all models, remove the master cylinder reservoir cap, and drain the hydraulic fluid from the reservoir. Alternatively, open any convenient bleed screw in the system, and gently pump the brake pedal to expel the fluid through a plastic tube connected to the screw (see Section 2). Disconnect the wiring

13.2 Disconnecting the wiring connector from the master cylinder fluid level sender

13.3 Using a brake pipe spanner to unscrew the master cylinder union nut

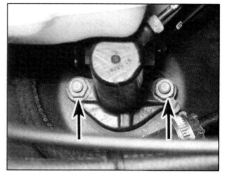

13.4 Master cylinder retaining nuts (arrowed)

connector from the brake fluid level sender unit **(see illustration)**.

 Warning: Do not syphon the fluid by mouth, as it is poisonous; use a syringe or an old poultry baster.

3 Wipe clean the area around the brake hydraulic pipe unions on the side of the master cylinder, and place absorbent rags beneath the pipe unions to catch any surplus fluid. Make a note of the correct fitted positions of the unions, then unscrew the union nuts/bolts and carefully withdraw the pipes **(see illustration)**. Where banjo unions are fitted, recover the copper washer located on each side of the union, and obtain new washers for refitting. Plug or tape over the pipe ends and master cylinder orifices, to minimise the loss of brake fluid, and to prevent the entry of dirt into the system. Wash off any spilt fluid immediately with cold water.

4 Slacken and remove the two nuts securing the master cylinder to the vacuum servo unit, then withdraw the unit from the engine compartment **(see illustration)**.

5 If necessary the reservoir can be separated from the cylinder body after extracting the small clip and withdrawing the retaining pin. The reservoir can then be pulled up and off the two seals in the cylinder body.

6 Note that it is not possible to overhaul the master cylinder itself, since no internal components are available separately. If faulty, the complete cylinder assembly must be renewed.

Refitting

7 If the reservoir has been removed, check the condition of the two reservoir seals in the master cylinder and obtain new seals if necessary. Similarly, check, and if necessary renew, the O-ring on the end of the cylinder body. Lubricate the ports on the reservoir with clean brake fluid and locate the reservoir in position. Refit the retaining pin and secure with the clip.

8 Fit the master cylinder to the servo unit, ensuring that the servo unit pushrod enters the master cylinder bore centrally. Refit the master cylinder mounting nuts, and tighten them to the specified torque.

9 Wipe clean the brake pipe unions, refit them to the master cylinder ports and tighten them securely. Where banjo unions are used, ensure that a new copper washer is fitted on each side of the union.

10 On left-hand-drive models, refit the battery tray and battery.

11 On all models, refill the master cylinder reservoir with new fluid, and bleed the complete hydraulic system as described in Section 2.

14 Brake pedal – removal and refitting

Removal

1 Access to the brake pedal is very limited and it is recommended that the facia be removed first, although this is a major operation. However, it is just possible to reach the pedal attachments after removing the carpet trim panel.

2 Prise off the securing clip, and withdraw the clevis pin securing the servo pushrod to the pedal. Note that a new spring clip will be required for refitting.

3 Unscrew the nut from the end of the pedal through-bolt (counterhold the through-bolt if necessary).

4 Withdraw the through-bolt from the pedal, and recover the spacer bush if it is loose. Withdraw the pedal.

Refitting

5 Refitting is a reversal of removal, using a new spring clip to secure the servo pushrod clevis pin.

15 Vacuum servo unit – testing, removal and refitting

Testing

1 To test the operation of the servo unit, depress the footbrake several times to exhaust the vacuum, then start the engine whilst keeping the pedal firmly depressed. As

the engine starts, there should be a noticeable 'give' in the brake pedal as the vacuum builds up. Allow the engine to run for at least two minutes, then switch it off. If the brake pedal is now depressed it should feel normal, but further applications should result in the pedal feeling firmer, with the pedal stroke decreasing with each application.

2 If the servo does not operate as described, first inspect the servo unit check valve as described in Section 16. On diesel engine models, also check the operation of the vacuum pump as described in Section 26.

3 If the servo unit still fails to operate satisfactorily, the fault lies within the unit itself. Repairs to the unit are not possible – if faulty, the servo unit must be renewed.

Removal

Note: *On certain right-hand-drive models, to gain the clearance required to remove the servo unit, it may prove necessary to unbolt the right-hand engine/transmission mounting and move the engine forwards slightly; this is due to the lack of clearance between the servo unit and the rear of the engine. If this proves necessary, refer to the relevant Part of Chapter 2 for further information on supporting the engine and dismantling the mounting. Additionally, on some models, it may be necessary to remove the inlet manifold (refer to the relevant Part of Chapter 4) and/or the camshaft cover and surrounding components – refer to the relevant Chapter for details. A new servo mounting gasket will be required on refitting.*

4 Remove the master cylinder as described in Section 13.

5 Slacken the retaining clip (where fitted) and disconnect the vacuum hose from the servo unit check valve.

6 On left-hand drive models, unbolt the support plate located in front of the servo.

7 From inside the car, prise off the spring clip, then withdraw the clevis pin securing the servo unit pushrod to the brake pedal. Note that a new spring clip will be required for refitting.

8 Prise back the sound insulation from the centre of the pedal mounting bracket for access to the servo mounting nuts.

9 Undo the four retaining nuts securing the servo unit to the bulkhead, then return to the engine compartment and manoeuvre the servo unit out of position, noting the gasket which is fitted to the rear of the unit.

Refitting

10 Check the servo unit check valve sealing grommet for signs of damage or deterioration, and renew if necessary.

11 Fit a new gasket to the rear of the servo unit, and reposition the unit in the engine compartment.

12 From inside the car, refit the servo unit mounting nuts and tighten them to the specified torque.

13 Refit the servo unit pushrod-to-brake pedal clevis pin, and secure it in position with a new spring clip.

14 Reconnect the vacuum hose to the servo unit check valve and, where necessary, securely tighten its retaining clip.

15 Refit the master cylinder as described in Section 13.

16 Where applicable, reconnect the engine/transmission mounting, and/or refit any components removed to provide access.

17 On completion, start the engine, check for air leaks at the vacuum hose-to-servo unit connection, and check the operation of the braking system.

16 Vacuum servo unit check valve – removal, testing and refitting

Removal

1 On certain models, the check valve is obscured by the master cylinder fluid reservoir. Where this is the case, the reservoir must be removed for access to the valve as follows.

a) *Disconnect the battery negative terminal (refer to 'Disconnecting the battery' in the Reference Section of this manual), then disconnect the wiring plug from the brake fluid level sensor.*

b) *Remove the master cylinder reservoir cap, and drain the hydraulic fluid from the reservoir.*

⚠️ **Warning: Do not syphon the fluid by mouth, as it is poisonous; use a syringe or an old poultry baster. Alternatively, open any convenient bleed screw in the system, and gently pump the brake pedal to expel the fluid through a plastic tube connected to the screw (see Section 2).**

c) *Remove the spring clip, then withdraw the reservoir securing pin, and lift the reservoir from the master cylinder. Plug the openings in the master cylinder to prevent dirt ingress.*

2 Slacken the retaining clip (where fitted), and disconnect the vacuum hose from the servo unit check valve.

3 Withdraw the valve from its rubber sealing grommet, using a pulling and twisting motion. Remove the grommet from the servo.

Testing

4 Examine the check valve for signs of damage, and renew if necessary. The valve may be tested by blowing through it in both directions. Air should flow through the valve in one direction only – when blown through from the servo unit end of the valve. Renew the valve if this is not the case.

5 Examine the rubber sealing grommet and flexible vacuum hose for signs of damage or deterioration, and renew as necessary.

Refitting

6 Fit the sealing grommet into the servo unit.

7 Ease the check valve into position, taking care not to displace or damage the grommet. Reconnect the vacuum hose to the valve, and tighten its retaining clip (as applicable).

8 If the master cylinder fluid reservoir has been removed, proceed as follows.

a) *Refit the reservoir, using new seals if necessary, then refit the securing pin and the spring clip.*

b) *Reconnect the fluid level sensor wiring, then reconnect the battery negative terminal.*

c) *Fill the reservoir with fluid, then bleed the complete hydraulic system as described in Section 2.*

9 On completion, start the engine and check the check valve-to-servo unit connection for signs of air leaks.

17 Handbrake – adjustment

1 To check the handbrake adjustment, first apply the footbrake firmly several times to establish correct shoe-to-drum/pad-to-disc clearance, then apply and release the handbrake several times to ensure that the self-adjust mechanism is fully adjusted. Applying normal moderate pressure, pull the handbrake lever to the fully-applied position, counting the number of clicks emitted from the handbrake ratchet mechanism. If adjustment is correct, there should be 3 to 5

clicks before the handbrake is fully applied. If this is not the case, adjust as follows.

2 For access to the handbrake adjuster nut, remove the centre console as described in Chapter 11.

3 Chock the front wheels, then jack up the rear of the vehicle and support it on axle stands (see *Jacking and vehicle support*).

4 Apply and release the handbrake ten times.

5 With the handbrake set on the first notch of the ratchet mechanism, lift the carpet flap over the adjusting nut and turn the adjusting nut until only a slight drag can be felt when the rear wheels/hubs are turned **(see illustration)**. Once this is so, fully release the handbrake lever, and check that the wheels/hubs rotate freely. Check the adjustment by applying the handbrake fully, counting the clicks from the handbrake ratchet and, if necessary, re-adjust.

6 Refit the centre console, then lower the vehicle to the ground.

18 Handbrake lever – removal and refitting

Removal

1 Remove the centre console as described in Chapter 11.

2 Slacken the handbrake lever adjusting nut to obtain maximum free play in the cables, and disengage the inner cables from the handbrake lever equaliser plate.

3 Slacken and remove the three handbrake lever retaining nuts, and remove the lever from the vehicle **(see illustration)**.

Refitting

4 Refitting is a reversal of removal. Prior to refitting the centre console, adjust the handbrake as described in Section 17.

19 Handbrake cables – removal and refitting

Removal

1 Remove the centre console as described in Chapter 11. The handbrake cable consists of

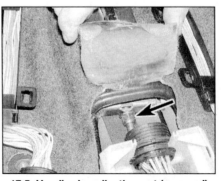

17.5 Handbrake adjusting nut (arrowed)

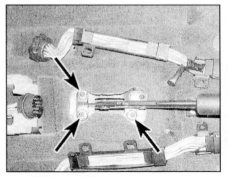

18.3 Handbrake lever retaining nuts (arrowed)

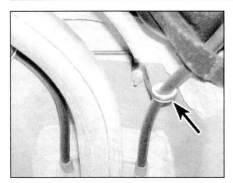

19.4 Withdraw the relevant handbrake cable from its support guide (arrowed) . . .

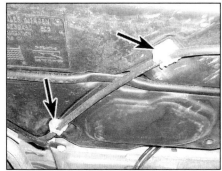

19.5a . . . then release the cable from the fuel tank clips (arrowed) . . .

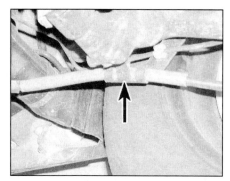

19.5b . . . and from the trailing arm bracket (arrowed)

two sections, a right- and a left-hand section, which are linked to the lever by an equaliser plate. Each section can be removed individually.

2 Slacken the handbrake lever adjusting nut to obtain maximum free play in the cable(s), and disengage the inner cables from the handbrake lever equaliser plate.

3 Firmly chock the front wheels, then jack up the rear of the vehicle and support it on axle stands (see *Jacking and vehicle support*).

4 Where necessary, slacken and remove the retaining nuts, then release the exhaust system heat shield(s) from the vehicle underbody, to gain access to the front of the relevant handbrake cable. Free the front end of the outer cable from the body, and withdraw the cable from its support guide **(see illustration)**.

5 Working back along the length of the cable, prise off the retaining clips and free it from fuel tank, then depress the retaining tangs and free the cable from its trailing arm bracket **(see illustrations)**.

6 On models with rear drum brakes, remove the rear brake shoes from the relevant side as described in Section 6. Using a hammer and pin punch, carefully tap the outer cable out

19.6 On drum brake models, drive the outer cable from the brake backplate

from the brake backplate, and remove it from underneath the vehicle **(see illustration)**.

7 On models with rear disc brakes, disengage the inner cable from the caliper handbrake lever then, using a hammer and pin punch, tap the outer cable out of its mounting bracket on the caliper, and remove the cable from underneath the vehicle **(see illustration)**.

Refitting

8 Refitting is a reversal of the removal procedure, adjusting the handbrake as described in Section 17.

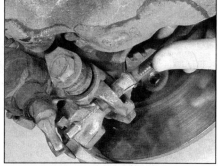

19.7 On disc brake models, disconnect the cable from the brake caliper

20 Rear brake pressure-regulating valve – removal and refitting

Removal

Note: *Before starting work, refer to the warning at the beginning of Section 2 concerning the dangers of hydraulic fluid.*

1 Firmly chock the front wheels, then jack up the rear of the vehicle and support it on axle stands (see *Jacking and vehicle support*).

2 Minimise fluid loss by first removing the master cylinder reservoir cap, and then tightening it down onto a piece of polythene, to obtain an airtight seal.

3 Release the retaining clip and disconnect the lower end of the regulating valve operating rod from the bracket on the rear suspension.

4 Wipe clean the area around the brake pipe unions on the valve, and place absorbent rags beneath the pipe unions to catch any surplus fluid.

5 Unscrew the union nuts and carefully withdraw the brake pipes from the pressure-regulating valve **(see illustration)**. Plug or tape over the pipe ends and valve orifices, to minimise the loss of brake fluid, and to prevent the entry of dirt into the system.

6 Undo the two bolts securing the valve mounting bracket to the underbody and remove the assembly from under the car.

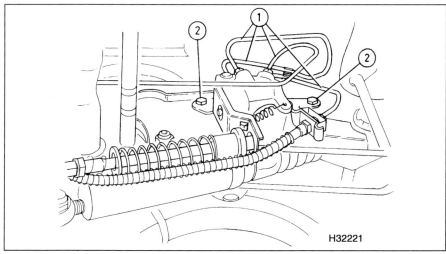

H32221

20.5 Rear brake pressure-regulating valve brake pipe unions (1) and mounting bracket retaining bolts (2)

Refitting

7 Refitting is a reverse of the removal procedure, ensuring that the brake pipe union nuts are securely tightened. On completion, bleed the complete braking system as described in Section 2. If a new valve has been fitted, or if the adjusting nuts on the operating rod have been disturbed, the vehicle should be taken to a Citroën dealer for adjustment of the valve pressure settings.

21 Stop-light switch – removal, refitting and adjustment

Removal

1 The stop-light switch is located on the brake pedal bracket under the facia.
2 Remove the carpet trim panel, then reach up and disconnect the switch wiring connector.
3 Loosen the locking ring and unscrew the switch from the pedal bracket.

Refitting and adjustment

4 Screw the switch back into position in the mounting bracket, until the gap between the end of the main body of the switch and the lug on the brake pedal is 2.0 to 3.0 mm.
5 Once the stop-light switch is correctly positioned, reconnect the wiring connector, and check the operation of the stop-lights. The stop-lights should illuminate after the brake pedal has travelled approximately 5.0 mm.
6 When the adjustment is correct, secure the switch with the locking ring and refit the carpet trim panel.

22 Handbrake 'on' warning light switch – removal and refitting

Removal

1 Remove the centre console as described in Chapter 11.
2 Undo the retaining screw and withdraw the switch from the handbrake lever base **(see illustration)**.

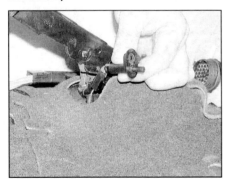

22.2 Removing the handbrake 'on' warning light switch

3 Disconnect the wiring connector and remove the switch.

Refitting

4 Refitting is a reverse of the removal procedure.

23 Anti-lock braking system (ABS) – general information

ABS is available as an option on certain models covered by this manual, and is fitted as standard equipment on others. The purpose of the system is to prevent the wheels locking during heavy braking. This is achieved by automatic release of the brake on the relevant wheel, followed by re-application of the brake. The system comprises an electronic control unit, a hydraulic modulator block, hydraulic solenoid valves (located in the modulator block), an electrically-driven fluid return pump, and four roadwheel sensors.

Models with ABS may be fitted with rear drum or rear disc brakes.

The solenoids (which control the fluid pressure to the calipers/wheel cylinders) are controlled by the electronic control unit, which itself receives signals from the wheel sensors. The wheel sensors monitor the speed of rotation of each wheel. By comparing these speed signals from the four wheels, the control unit can determine when a wheel is decelerating at an abnormal rate, compared to the speed of the vehicle. Using this information, the control unit can predict when a wheel is about to lock, and is able to reduce the fluid pressure to the brake on the relevant wheel to prevent it locking.

During normal operation, the system functions in the same way as a conventional non-ABS braking system.

24 Anti-lock braking system (ABS) components – removal and refitting

Modulator assembly

Note: *Before starting, refer to the note in Section 2 on the dangers of hydraulic fluid.*

Removal

1 Disconnect the battery negative terminal (refer to *Disconnecting the battery* in the Reference Section of this manual).
2 If necessary to improve access, remove the air inlet ducts from the vicinity of the modulator assembly as described in the relevant Part of Chapter 4.
3 Slacken the locking ring and disconnect the main wiring harness connector located above the modulator assembly.
4 Minimise hydraulic fluid loss by first

removing the master cylinder reservoir cap, and then tightening it down onto a piece of polythene, to obtain an airtight seal.
5 Disconnect the wiring connector from the front of the modulator assembly.
6 Wipe clean the area around the brake pipe unions on the side of the modulator, and place absorbent rags beneath the pipe unions to catch any surplus fluid. Make a note of the correct fitted positions of the unions, then unscrew the union nuts and carefully withdraw the pipes. Plug or tape over the pipe ends and modulator orifices to minimise the loss of fluid, and to prevent the entry of dirt into the system.
7 Undo the two retaining nuts, one on each side of the modulator, and remove the unit from the engine compartment.

Refitting

8 If a new modulator assembly is being fitted, it will be supplied pre-filled with hydraulic fluid, and sealed with blanking plugs. Leave the plugs in position until just before connecting the brake pipes.
9 Locate the modulator in position and refit the two retaining nuts. Tighten the nuts to the specified torque.
10 Reconnect the brake pipes to their correct locations as noted during removal and tighten the union nuts securely.
11 Reconnect the modulator wiring connector and the main wiring harness connector.
12 Where applicable, refit the air inlet duct then reconnect the battery.
13 Remove the polythene from the master cylinder reservoir and bleed the complete hydraulic system as described in Section 2.

Electronic control unit

14 The electronic control unit is removed with the modulator assembly as described previously. The ECU is an integral part of the modulator and the two components cannot be separated.

Front wheel sensor

Removal

Note: *Thread locking compound must be applied to the sensor securing stud on refitting.*
15 Disconnect the battery negative terminal (refer to *Disconnecting the battery* in the Reference Section of this manual).
16 Firmly apply the handbrake, then jack up the front of the car and support it securely on axle stands (see *Jacking and vehicle support*). Remove the relevant front roadwheel.
17 Unclip the wheel sensor wiring from the brackets on the suspension strut and inner wheelarch.
18 Trace the wiring back from the sensor, and separate the two halves of the wiring connector. Note the routing of the wiring to aid correct refitting.
19 Unscrew the retaining nut and lift off the wheel sensor protective cover **(see illustration)**.

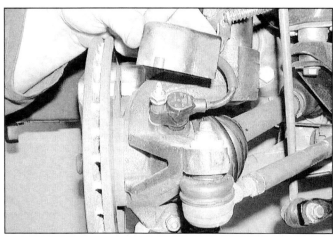

24.19 Unscrew the nut and lift off the wheel sensor protective cover

24.20a Unscrew the securing stud . . .

20 Unscrew the securing stud, and withdraw the sensor from the swivel hub **(see illustrations)**.

Refitting

21 Refitting is a reversal of removal, noting the following points:
a) *Ensure that the mating faces of the sensor and the swivel hub are clean, and apply a smear of high melting point brake grease to the sensor location in the swivel hub before refitting.*
b) *Ensure that the end face of the sensor is clean.*
c) *Coat the threads of the sensor securing stud with thread-locking compound and tighten the stud to the specified torque.*
d) *Route the wiring as noted before removal.*

Rear wheel sensor

Note: *Thread-locking compound must be applied to the sensor securing stud on refitting.*

Removal

22 Chock the front wheels, then jack up the rear of the vehicle and support it on axle stands (see *Jacking and vehicle support*). Remove the appropriate roadwheel.
23 Trace the wiring back from the sensor to its wiring connector, then free the connector from its retaining clip, and disconnect the wiring from the main wiring loom.
24 Work back along the sensor wiring, and free it from the retaining clips. Note the routing of the wiring to aid correct refitting.
25 Slacken and remove the bolt securing the sensor unit to the trailing arm, and remove the sensor and lead assembly **(see illustration)**.

Refitting

26 Refitting is a reversal of removal, bearing in mind the following points:
a) *Ensure that the mating faces of the sensor and the trailing arm are clean, and apply a smear of high melting point brake grease to the sensor location in the trailing arm before refitting.*
b) *Ensure that the end face of the sensor is clean.*
c) *Coat the threads of the sensor securing bolt with thread-locking compound and tighten the stud to the specified torque.*
d) *Route the wiring as noted before removal.*

25 Vacuum pump (diesel models) – removal and refitting

Removal

Note: *New O-rings must be used on refitting.*
1 On 1.9 litre models, to improve access, remove the intercooler (where fitted) and the air inlet ducts as described in Chapter 4B. On 2.0 litre models, refer to Chapter 4C and disconnect both ends of the rigid duct at the rear of the engine connecting the turbocharger to the flexible air inlet duct. Note that there is insufficient clearance to remove the duct completely, but it can be moved aside sufficiently to gain access to the vacuum pump.
2 Release the retaining clip and disconnect the vacuum hose from the pump.
3 Slacken and remove the three bolts/nuts and washers securing the pump to the left-hand end of the cylinder head, then remove the pump, along with its two O-rings. Discard the O-rings – new ones must be used

24.20b . . . and withdraw the front wheel sensor from the swivel hub

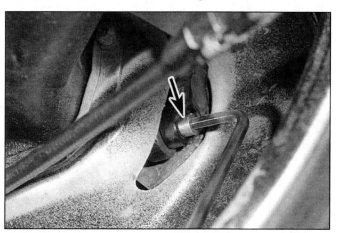

24.25 Undo the securing bolt and remove the rear wheel sensor from the trailing arm

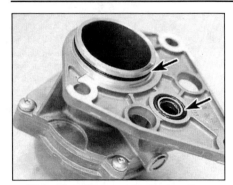

25.4a Vacuum pump O-ring locations (arrowed) on 1.9 litre models

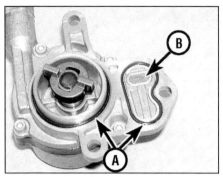

25.4b Vacuum pump O-ring locations (A) and gauze filter (B) on 2.0 litre models

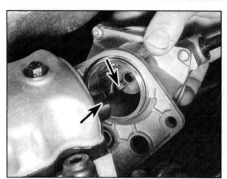

25.4c Ensure the drive dog is correctly aligned with the camshaft slot (arrowed) when refitting the vacuum pump

on refitting. On 2.0 litre models, check the condition of the gauze filter at the rear of the pump and renew if necessary.

Refitting

4 Fit new O-rings to the pump recesses, then align the drive dog with the slot in the end of the camshaft, and refit the pump to the cylinder head, ensuring that the O-rings remain correctly seated **(see illustrations)**.
5 Refit the pump mounting bolts/nuts and washers, and tighten them to the specified torque.
6 Reconnect the vacuum hose to the pump, and tighten its securing clip.

7 Where applicable, refit the intercooler and air inlet ducts as described in Chapter 4B or 4C.

26 Vacuum pump (diesel models) – testing and overhaul

Testing

1 The operation of the braking system vacuum pump can be checked using a vacuum gauge.
2 Disconnect the vacuum pipe from the pump, and connect the gauge to the pump union using a suitable length of hose.
3 Start the engine and allow it to idle, then measure the vacuum created by the pump. As a guide, after one minute, a minimum of approximately 500 mm Hg should be recorded. If the vacuum registered is significantly less than this, it is likely that the pump is faulty. However, seek the advice of a Citroën dealer before condemning the pump.

Overhaul

4 Overhaul of the vacuum pump is not possible, since no components are available separately for it. If faulty, the complete pump assembly must be renewed.

Chapter 10
Suspension and steering

Contents

Front hub bearings – renewal 3
Front suspension and steering check . . . .
   See Chapter 1A or 1B
Front suspension anti-roll bar – removal and refitting 8
Front suspension anti-roll bar connecting link –
   removal and refitting 9
Front suspension lower arm – removal, overhaul and refitting 6
Front suspension lower arm balljoint – removal and refitting 7
Front suspension strut – overhaul 5
Front suspension strut – removal and refitting 4
Front suspension subframe – removal and refitting 10
Front swivel hub assembly – removal and refitting 2
General information 1
Ignition switch/steering column lock – removal and refitting 19
Power steering fluid level check . . . . .See Weekly checks

Power steering pump – removal and refitting 22
Power steering system – bleeding 21
Rear axle assembly – removal and refitting 15
Rear hub assembly – removal and refitting 11
Rear hub bearings – renewal 12
Rear shock absorber – removal, testing and refitting 14
Rear suspension components – general 13
Steering column – removal, inspection and refitting 18
Steering gear assembly – removal, overhaul and refitting 20
Steering wheel – removal and refitting 17
Track rod balljoint – removal and refitting 23
Vehicle ride height – checking 16
Wheel alignment and steering angles – general information 24
Wheel and tyre maintenance and tyre pressure
   checks . . . . .See Weekly checks

Degrees of difficulty

Easy, suitable for novice with little experience	**Fairly easy,** suitable for beginner with some experience	**Fairly difficult,** suitable for competent DIY mechanic	**Difficult,** suitable for experienced DIY mechanic	**Very difficult,** suitable for expert DIY or professional

Specifications

Steering
Power steering fluid type . . . .   See Lubricants and fluids

Front wheel alignment and steering angles
Front wheel toe setting . . . .   1.5 ± 1.0 mm (0°15' ± 10') toe-in
Front wheel castor (not adjustable) . . . .   0°30' ± 40'
Front wheel camber (not adjustable) . . . .   0° ± 1°
King pin inclination (not adjustable) . . . .   10°50' ± 1°

Rear wheel alignment
Rear wheel toe setting (not adjustable) . . . .   0.3 ± 1.5 mm toe-in
Rear wheel camber (not adjustable) . . . .   1°20' ± 40' negative

Roadwheels
Type . . . .   Pressed-steel or aluminium alloy (depending on model)
Size . . . .   5.5J x 14 or 6J x 15 (depending on model)
Maximum run-out at rim . . . .   1.2 mm
Maximum eccentricity on tyre bead locating surface . . . .   0.8 mm

Tyre pressures . . . .   See end of Weekly checks

Torque wrench settings

	Nm	lbf ft
Front suspension		
Anti-roll bar:		
Mounting clamp bolts	65	48
Connecting link securing nuts	40	30
Lower arm balljoint clamp bolt nut	40	30
Lower arm balljoint retaining nuts	50	37
Lower arm front pivot bolt	85	63
Lower arm rear pivot bush mounting bolts:		
8 mm bolt	30	22
10 mm bolt	65	48
Strut upper mounting bolts	25	18
Strut piston rod retaining nut	45	33
Strut-to-swivel hub bolt:		
Hexagon head type bolt	55	41
Torx type bolt	45	33
Subframe mounting bolts	80	59
Rear suspension		
Rear axle mountings:		
Front mounting-to-body nuts	55	41
Rear mounting nuts	45	33
Rear hub nut	190	140
Shock absorber lower mounting nut	96	71
Shock absorber upper mounting bolt	75	55
Steering		
Steering column mounting nuts/bolts	25	18
Steering column shaft-to-intermediate shaft universal joint pinch-bolt	25	18
Steering gear mounting bolts	50	37
Steering intermediate shaft-to-steering gear pinion universal joint pinch-bolt nut	23	17
Steering wheel nut	33	24
Track rod balljoint-to-swivel hub nut	40	30
Roadwheels		
Wheel bolts	85	63

1 General information

The independent front suspension is of the MacPherson strut type, incorporating coil springs and integral telescopic shock absorbers. The MacPherson struts are located by transverse lower suspension arms, which utilise rubber inner mounting bushes, and incorporate a balljoint at the outer ends. The front swivel hubs, which carry the wheel bearings, brake calipers and the hub/disc assemblies, are clamped to the MacPherson struts, and connected to the lower arms via the balljoints. A front anti-roll bar is fitted to all models. The anti-roll bar is rubber-mounted onto the subframe, and is attached to the front suspension struts by a connecting link on each side.

The rear suspension is of the independent trailing arm type, which consists of two trailing arms, linked by a tubular crossmember. Torsion bars linking the trailing arms are situated in front of and behind the crossmember, and a stabilizer bar linking the arms passes through the centre of the crossmember.

The complete rear axle assembly is mounted onto the vehicle underbody by four 'self-steering' rubber mountings. These mountings are designed to move slightly under extreme cornering forces. This movement of the rear axle assembly has the effect of actually turning the rear wheels slightly, to help steer the vehicle in the required direction. This improves the handling of the vehicle when cornering at high speeds.

The steering column has a universal joint fitted in the centre of its length, which is connected to an intermediate shaft having a second universal joint at its lower end. The lower universal joint is clamped to the steering gear pinion by means of a pinch-bolt.

The steering gear is mounted onto the front subframe, and is connected by two track rods, with balljoints at their outer ends, to the steering arms projecting rearwards from the swivel hubs. The track rods and balljoints are threaded, to facilitate toe setting adjustment.

Power-assisted steering is fitted as standard on all models. Hydraulic power for the steering system is provided by a pump, which is driven off the crankshaft pulley by the auxiliary drivebelt.

2 Front swivel hub assembly – removal and refitting

Removal

Note: *All Nyloc nuts disturbed on removal must be renewed as a matter of course. These nuts have threads which are pre-coated with locking compound (this is only effective once), and include the track rod balljoint nut, lower suspension arm balljoint clamp bolt nut, and the swivel hub clamp bolt nut. Suitable thread-locking compound will also be required for the brake caliper mounting bracket bolts.*

Caution: Do not allow the vehicle to rest on its wheels with one or both driveshafts disconnected from the swivel hubs, as damage to the wheel bearing(s) may result. If moving the vehicle is unavoidable, temporarily insert the outer end of the driveshaft(s) in the hub(s) and tighten the hub nut(s).

1 Chock the rear wheels, then firmly apply the handbrake. Jack up the front of the vehicle, and support it on axle stands (see *Jacking and*

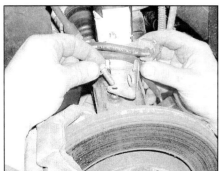

2.5 Remove the bolt securing the wiring retaining bracket to the swivel hub

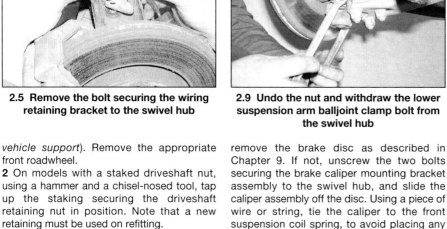

2.9 Undo the nut and withdraw the lower suspension arm balljoint clamp bolt from the swivel hub

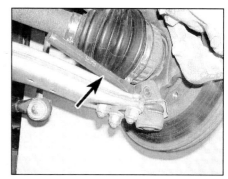

2.10a Spread the swivel hub by tapping a small chisel (arrowed) into the split . . .

vehicle support). Remove the appropriate front roadwheel.

2 On models with a staked driveshaft nut, using a hammer and a chisel-nosed tool, tap up the staking securing the driveshaft retaining nut in position. Note that a new retaining must be used on refitting.

3 On models where the driveshaft nut is secured by an R-clip, withdraw the R-clip, and remove the locking cap from the driveshaft retaining nut.

4 Refit at least two roadwheel bolts to the front hub, and tighten them securely. Have an assistant firmly depress the brake pedal, to prevent the front hub from rotating, then using a socket and extension bar, slacken and remove the driveshaft retaining nut. Alternatively, a tool can be fabricated from two lengths of steel strip (one long, one short) and a nut and bolt; the nut and bolt forming the pivot of a forked tool. Bolt the tool to the hub using two wheel bolts, and hold the tool to prevent the hub from rotating as the driveshaft nut is undone (see Chapter 8, Section 2).

5 Slacken and remove the bolt securing the wiring retaining bracket to the top of the swivel hub **(see illustration)**.

6 On models with ABS, remove the wheel sensor from the swivel hub as described in Chapter 9.

7 If the hub bearings are to be disturbed,

remove the brake disc as described in Chapter 9. If not, unscrew the two bolts securing the brake caliper mounting bracket assembly to the swivel hub, and slide the caliper assembly off the disc. Using a piece of wire or string, tie the caliper to the front suspension coil spring, to avoid placing any strain on the hydraulic brake hose.

8 On all models, slacken and remove the nut securing the steering gear track rod balljoint to the swivel hub, and release the balljoint tapered shank using a balljoint separator.

9 Slacken and remove the nut, then withdraw the lower suspension arm balljoint clamp bolt from the swivel hub **(see illustration)**. Discard the nut – a new one must be used on refitting.

10 Tap a small chisel into the split on the swivel hub to spread the hub slightly, and allow the balljoint shank to be withdrawn **(see illustration)**. Pull the lower suspension arm downwards to release the balljoint shank from the swivel hub. To do this it will be necessary to use a long bar and block of wood which will engage under the front subframe. Attach the bar to the suspension arm, preferably with a chain, or alternatively with a stout strap or rope. Lever down on the bar to release the balljoint from the swivel hub **(see illustration)**.

11 Once the balljoint is free, remove the protector plate which is fitted to the balljoint shank **(see illustration)**.

12 Undo the nut and withdraw the swivel

hub-to-suspension strut clamp bolt, noting that the bolt fits from the rear of the vehicle.

13 Tap a small chisel into the split on the swivel hub to spread the hub slightly. Free the swivel hub assembly from the end of the strut, then release it from the outer constant velocity joint splines, and remove it from the vehicle.

Refitting

14 Note that all Nyloc nuts disturbed on removal must be renewed as a matter of course. These nuts have threads which are pre-coated with locking compound (this is only effective once), and include the track rod balljoint nut, lower suspension arm balljoint clamp bolt nut, and the swivel hub clamp bolt nut.

15 Ensure that the driveshaft outer constant velocity joint and hub splines are clean, then slide the hub fully onto the driveshaft splines.

16 Slide the hub assembly fully onto the suspension strut, aligning the split in the hub clamp with the lug on the base of the strut. Also ensure that the stop bosses on the strut are in contact with the top surface of the swivel hub. Insert the swivel hub-to-suspension strut clamp bolt from the rear side of the strut, then fit a new nut to the clamp bolt, and tighten it to the specified torque **(see illustration)**.

17 Refit the protector plate to the lower arm balljoint then, using the method employed on

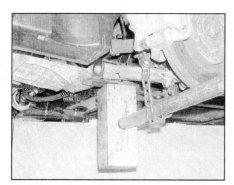

2.10b . . . then pull the lower suspension arm downwards using a bar and chain or similar arrangement, pivoting on the subframe

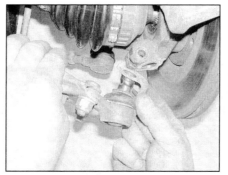

2.11 When the balljoint is released, remove the protector plate from the balljoint shank

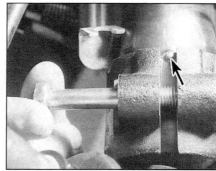

2.16 Ensure the swivel hub clamp is aligned with the lug (arrowed) on the strut prior to inserting the clamp bolt

removal, locate the balljoint shank in the swivel hub, ensuring that the lug on the protector plate is correctly located in the clamp split. Insert the balljoint clamp bolt (from the rear of the swivel hub), then fit the new retaining nut and tighten it to the specified torque.

18 Engage the track rod balljoint in the swivel hub, then fit a new retaining nut and tighten it to the specified torque.

19 Where necessary, refit the brake disc to the hub, referring to Chapter 9 for further information. Apply a suitable locking compound to the threads of the caliper mounting bracket bolts. Slide the caliper assembly into position over the disc, then fit the mounting bolts and tighten them to the specified torque (see Chapter 9).

20 Where applicable, refit the ABS wheel sensor as described in Chapter 9.

21 Refit the wiring retaining bracket to the top of the swivel hub, and tighten its retaining bolt securely.

22 Lubricate the inner face and threads of the driveshaft retaining nut with clean engine oil (a new nut must be used on models with a staked nut), and refit it to the end of the driveshaft. Use the method employed on removal to prevent the hub from rotating, and tighten the driveshaft retaining nut to the specified torque (see Chapter 8). Check that the hub rotates freely.

23 On models with a staked driveshaft nut, stake the nut firmly into the driveshaft grooves using a hammer and punch.

24 On models where the driveshaft nut is secured with an R-clip, engage the locking cap with the driveshaft nut so that one of its cut-outs is aligned with the driveshaft hole. Secure the cap with the R-clip.

25 Refit the roadwheel, then lower the vehicle to the ground and tighten the roadwheel bolts to the specified torque.

3 Front hub bearings – renewal

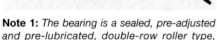

Note 1: *The bearing is a sealed, pre-adjusted and pre-lubricated, double-row roller type,* *and is intended to last the car's entire service life without maintenance or attention. Never overtighten the driveshaft nut beyond the specified torque wrench setting in an attempt to 'adjust' the bearing.*

Note 2: *A press will be required to dismantle and rebuild the assembly; if such a tool is not available, a large bench vice and spacers (such as large sockets) will serve as an adequate substitute. The bearing's inner races are an interference fit on the hub; if the inner race remains on the hub when it is pressed out of the hub carrier, a knife-edged bearing puller will be required to remove it. A new bearing retaining circlip must be used on refitting.*

1 Remove the swivel hub assembly as described in Section 2.

2 Support the swivel hub securely on blocks or in a vice. Using a tubular spacer which bears only on the inner end of the hub flange, press the hub flange out of the bearing. If the bearing's outboard inner race remains on the hub, remove it using a bearing puller (see note above).

3 Extract the bearing retaining circlip from the inner end of the swivel hub assembly **(see illustration)**.

4 Where necessary, refit the inner race back in position over the ball cage, and securely support the inner face of the swivel hub. Using a tubular spacer which bears only on the inner race, press the complete bearing assembly out of the swivel hub.

5 Thoroughly clean the hub and swivel hub, removing all traces of dirt and grease, and polish away any burrs or raised edges which might hinder reassembly. Check both for cracks or any other signs of wear or damage, and renew them if necessary. Renew the circlip, regardless of its apparent condition.

6 On reassembly, apply a light film of oil to the bearing outer race and hub flange shaft, to aid installation of the bearing.

7 Securely support the swivel hub, and locate the bearing in the hub. Press the bearing fully into position, ensuring that it enters the hub squarely, using a tubular spacer which bears only on the bearing outer race.

8 Once the bearing is correctly seated, secure the bearing in position with the new circlip, ensuring that it is correctly located in the groove in the swivel hub.

9 Securely support the outer face of the hub flange, and locate the swivel hub bearing inner race over the end of the hub flange. Press the bearing onto the hub, using a tubular spacer which bears only on the inner race of the hub bearing, until it seats against the hub shoulder. Check that the hub flange rotates freely, and wipe off any excess oil or grease.

10 Refit the swivel hub assembly as described in Section 2.

4 Front suspension strut – removal and refitting

Removal

Note: *All Nyloc nuts disturbed on removal must be renewed as a matter of course. These nuts have threads which are pre-coated with locking compound (this is only effective once), and include the swivel hub clamp bolt nut, and the anti-roll bar connecting link nut. Suitable spring compressor tools will be required for this operation.*

1 Chock the rear wheels, apply the handbrake, then jack up the front of the vehicle and support it on axle stands (see *Jacking and vehicle support*). Remove the appropriate roadwheel.

2 Slacken and remove the bolt securing the wiring retaining bracket to the top of the swivel hub.

3 Unclip the brake flexible hydraulic hose and any wiring from the strut.

4 Unscrew the nut (and recover the washer) securing the anti-roll bar connecting link to the strut, and position the link clear of the strut. Counterhold the link with an Allen key to prevent rotation as the nut is undone **(see illustration)**. Discard the nut – a new one must be used on refitting.

5 Undo the nut and withdraw the swivel hub-to-suspension strut clamp bolt, noting that the bolt fits from the rear of the strut. Discard the nut – a new one must be used on refitting **(see illustration)**.

3.3 Front hub bearing retaining circlip (arrowed)

4.4 Unscrew the nut securing the anti-roll bar connecting link to the strut

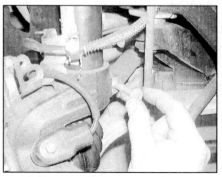

4.5 Unscrew the nut and remove the swivel hub-to-suspension strut clamp bolt

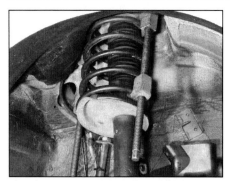

4.6 Coil spring compressors fitted to strut spring

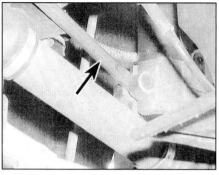

4.7 Tap a small chisel (arrowed) into the split in the swivel hub to spread the hub

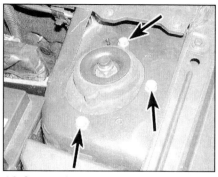

4.8 Suspension strut upper mounting bolts (arrowed)

6 The coil spring must now be compressed to enable the strut to be removed. Working under the wheelarch, fit suitable spring compressors to the spring and compress the spring sufficiently to enable the lower end of the strut to be disconnected from the swivel hub **(see illustration)**. Ensure that the compressors used are of a type that incorporate a method for positively locking them to the spring (usually by a small clamp bolt). Any other type may slip off or slide round the spring as they are tightened.

7 Tap a small chisel into the split on the swivel hub to spread the hub slightly, and allow the end of the strut to be withdrawn **(see illustration)**.

8 Working in the engine compartment, slacken and remove the three suspension strut upper mounting bolts, then withdraw the strut from under the wheelarch **(see illustration)**.

Refitting

9 With the coil spring compressors in place, as during removal, manoeuvre the strut assembly into position, ensuring that the top mounting plate locating pin is correctly located in the corresponding hole in the body. Engage the lower end of the strut with the swivel hub, aligning the split in the hub with the lug on the base of the strut. Also ensure that the stop bosses on the strut are in contact with the top surface of the swivel hub.

10 Insert the strut upper mounting bolts, and tighten them to the specified torque.

5.3 Unscrew the strut piston rod nut while counterholding the piston rod with a suitable Allen key

11 Insert the swivel hub-to-suspension strut clamp bolt from the rear side of the strut. Fit a new nut to the clamp bolt, and tighten it to the specified torque.

12 Carefully slacken and then remove the spring compressors.

13 Reconnect the anti-roll bar connecting link to the strut. Fit a new nut to the connecting link, and tighten it to the specified torque.

14 Refit the wiring retaining bracket to the top of the swivel hub, and clip the flexible hose and wiring to their locations on the strut.

15 Refit the roadwheel, then lower the vehicle to the ground and tighten the roadwheel bolts to the specified torque.

5 Front suspension strut – overhaul

> **Warning: Before attempting to dismantle the suspension strut, a suitable tool to hold the coil spring in compression must be obtained. Adjustable coil spring compressors which can be positively secured to the spring coils are readily available, and are recommended for this operation. Any attempt to dismantle the**

strut without such a tool is likely to result in damage or personal injury.

1 With the strut removed from the car as described in Section 4, clean away all external dirt then mount the unit upright in a vice.

2 If not already in place, fit the spring compressors to the coils of the spring. Ensure that the compressors used are of a type that incorporate a method for positively locking them to the spring (usually by a small clamp bolt). Any other type may slip off or slide round the spring as they are tightened. Tighten the compressors until the load is taken off the spring seats.

3 Remove the protective cap then unscrew the piston rod nut, counterholding the piston rod with a suitable Allen key **(see illustration)**. Note that a new nut will be required for reassembly.

4 Remove the nut and washer, then lift off the collar, mounting plate, bearing, upper spring seat and flat washer. Remove the coil spring, then slide off the piston dust cover and rubber damper stop **(see illustration)**. The spring may remain in the compressed state ready for refitting to the strut. If the spring is to be renewed, release the compressors very gently and evenly until they can be removed and fitted to the new spring.

5 With the strut assembly now completely dismantled, examine all the components for

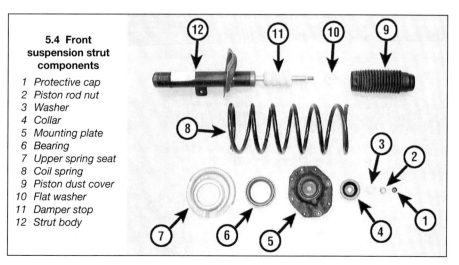

5.4 Front suspension strut components

1 Protective cap
2 Piston rod nut
3 Washer
4 Collar
5 Mounting plate
6 Bearing
7 Upper spring seat
8 Coil spring
9 Piston dust cover
10 Flat washer
11 Damper stop
12 Strut body

5.8a Pull the piston rod out as far as it will go and fit the damper stop

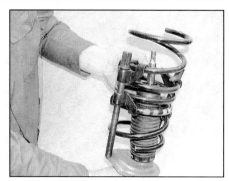

5.8b Fit the piston dust cover . . .

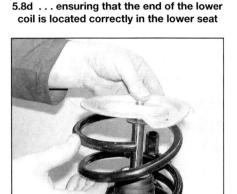

5.8c . . . followed by the compressed spring . . .

wear, damage or deformation, and check the bearing for smoothness of operation. Renew any components as necessary.

6 Examine the strut body for signs of fluid leakage or damage, and the piston for signs of pitting or scoring. Test the operation of the strut, while holding it in an upright position, by moving the piston through a full stroke and then through short strokes of 50 to 100 mm. In both cases, the resistance felt should be smooth and continuous. If the resistance is jerky, or uneven, or if there is any visible sign of wear or damage, renewal is necessary.

7 If any doubt exists about the condition of the coil spring, carefully remove the spring compressors, and check the spring for distortion and signs of cracking. Renew the spring if it is damaged or distorted.

8 To reassemble the strut, follow the accompanying photos. Be sure to stay in order, and carefully read the caption underneath each **(see illustrations)**.

9 Refit the strut to the car as described in Section 4 on completion of reassembly.

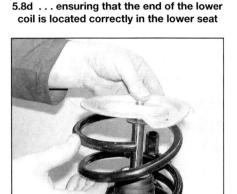

5.8d . . . ensuring that the end of the lower coil is located correctly in the lower seat

5.8e Place the flat washer in position . . .

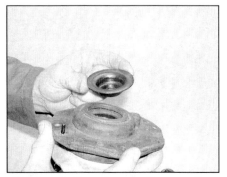

5.8f . . . followed by the upper spring seat . . .

5.8g . . . bearing . . .

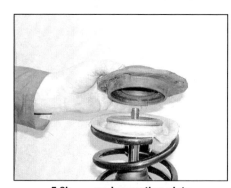

5.8h . . . and mounting plate

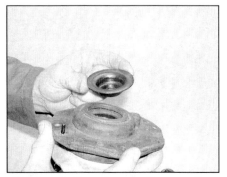

5.8i Locate the collar over the mounting plate . . .

5.8j . . . fit the upper washer . . .

5.8k . . . then fit and tighten the piston rod nut

6.3 Remove the lower arm front pivot bolt . . .

6.4 . . . and the two rear mounting bush bolts (second bolt arrowed) . . .

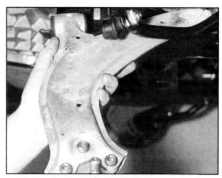

6.6 . . . then remove the lower arm from the vehicle

6 Front suspension lower arm – removal, overhaul and refitting

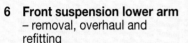

Removal

Note: *All Nyloc nuts disturbed on removal must be renewed as a matter of course. These nuts have threads which are pre-coated with locking compound (this is only effective once), and include the lower arm balljoint clamp bolt nut.*

1 Chock the rear wheels then jack up the front of the vehicle and support it on axle stands (see *Jacking and vehicle support*). Remove the appropriate front roadwheel.

2 Slacken and remove the nut, then withdraw the lower arm balljoint clamp bolt from the swivel hub. Discard the nut – a new one must be used on refitting.

3 Slacken and remove the lower arm front pivot bolt and nut. Recover the nut from its housing if it is loose **(see illustration)**.

4 Unscrew the two bolts securing the lower arm rear mounting bush to the subframe, noting that the larger bolt also secures the anti-roll bar mounting clamp (counterhold the nut if necessary) **(see illustration)**. Recover the nut from the top of the anti-roll bar mounting clamp.

5 Tap a small chisel into the split on the swivel hub to spread the hub slightly, and allow the balljoint shank to be withdrawn. Withdraw the inner end of the arm from the subframe and release the balljoint from the

swivel hub. Remove the protector plate which is fitted to the balljoint shank.

6 Manoeuvre the lower arm assembly out from underneath the vehicle **(see illustration)**.

Overhaul

Note: *If the lower arm balljoint is renewed, new retaining nuts must be used on refitting.*

7 Thoroughly clean the lower arm and the area around the arm mountings, removing all traces of dirt and underseal if necessary, then check carefully for cracks, distortion or any other signs of wear or damage, paying particular attention to the pivot bushes, and renew components as necessary.

8 Check that the lower arm balljoint moves freely, without any sign of roughness; check also that the balljoint dust cover shows no sign of deterioration, and is free from cracks and splits. If renewal is necessary, slacken and remove its retaining bolts, and remove the balljoint from the arm. Fit the new balljoint, and insert its retaining bolts. Fit new nuts to the bolts, and tighten them to the specified torque.

9 Examine the shank of the lower arm pivot bolt for signs of wear or scoring, and renew if necessary.

Refitting

10 Manoeuvre the lower arm assembly into position, refit the protector plate to the lower arm balljoint, then locate the balljoint shank in the swivel hub. Ensure that the lug on the protector plate is correctly located in the clamp split.

11 Insert the balljoint clamp bolt (from the rear

of the swivel hub), then fit the new retaining nut and tighten it to the specified torque.

12 Refit the front pivot bolt, tightening it finger-tight only. Ensure that the nut is located in its housing.

13 Refit the rear pivot bush retaining bolts and nut, ensuring that the bush bracket is located between the subframe and the anti-roll bar clamp. Tighten the fixings to the specified torque.

14 Refit the roadwheel, then lower the vehicle and tighten the roadwheel bolts to the specified torque. Rock the vehicle to settle the disturbed components, then tighten the lower arm front pivot bolt to the specified torque.

7 Front suspension lower arm balljoint – removal and refitting

Removal

Note: *A new balljoint clamp bolt nut, and new balljoint securing nuts must be used on refitting.*

1 Chock the rear wheels then jack up the front of the vehicle and support it on axle stands (see *Jacking and vehicle support*). Remove the appropriate front roadwheel.

2 Slacken and remove the nut, then withdraw the lower suspension arm balljoint clamp bolt from the swivel hub. Discard the nut – a new one must be used on refitting.

3 Tap a small chisel into the split on the swivel hub to spread the hub slightly, and allow the balljoint shank to be withdrawn. Pull the lower suspension arm downwards to release the balljoint shank from the swivel hub. To do this it will be necessary to use a long bar and block of wood which will engage under the front subframe. Attach the bar to the suspension arm, preferably with a chain, or alternatively with a stout strap or rope. Lever down on the bar to release the balljoint from the swivel hub **(see illustration 2.10b)**.

4 Once the balljoint is free, remove the protector plate which is fitted to the balljoint shank.

5 Slacken and remove the three nuts, then withdraw the balljoint retaining bolts and remove the balljoint from the lower arm **(see illustrations)**. Discard the nuts – new ones must be used on refitting.

7.5a Remove the three retaining bolts . . .

7.5b . . . and remove the lower arm balljoint

6 Check that the lower arm balljoint moves freely, without any sign of roughness. Check also that the balljoint dust cover shows no sign of deterioration, and is free from cracks and splits. Renew worn or damaged components as necessary.

Refitting

7 Locate the balljoint in the end of the suspension arm, and insert the three retaining bolts. Fit new nuts to the bolts, and tighten them to the specified torque.

8 Refit the protector plate to the lower arm balljoint then, using the method employed on removal, locate the balljoint shank in the swivel hub, ensuring that the lug on the protector plate is correctly located in the clamp split. Insert the balljoint clamp bolt (from the rear of the swivel hub), then fit the new retaining nut and tighten it to the specified torque.

9 Refit the roadwheel, then lower the vehicle and tighten the roadwheel bolts to the specified torque.

---

8 Front suspension anti-roll bar – removal and refitting

Removal

Note: *All Nyloc nuts disturbed on removal must be renewed as a matter of course. These nuts have threads which are pre-coated with locking compound (this is only effective once), and include the anti-roll bar connecting link nuts, engine/transmission rear mounting bolt nut, and the intermediate shaft pinch-bolt nut (and pinch-bolt).*

1 Firmly apply the handbrake, then jack up the front of the car and support it securely on axle stands (see *Jacking and vehicle support*). Position the roadwheels in the straight-ahead position, then remove both front roadwheels.

2 Undo the nut and washer securing the left-hand connecting link to the anti-roll bar, and position the link clear of the bar **(see illustration)**. Repeat the procedure on the right-hand side.

3 Where applicable, unclip the clutch cable from the brackets on the subframe.

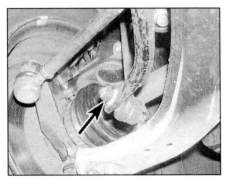

8.2 Undo the nut and washer (arrowed) securing the left-hand connecting link to the anti-roll bar

4 Release the power steering fluid pipe support clips from the engine and transmission.

5 Working in the engine compartment, unscrew the securing nut from the intermediate shaft-to-steering gear pinion pinch-bolt, then carefully tap the pinch-bolt from the universal joint – discard the pinch-bolt and nut, new ones must be used on refitting. Pull off the metal clip securing the intermediate shaft to the pinion.

6 Make alignment marks on the universal joint and the steering gear pinion, then push the universal joint upwards to separate it from the pinion.

7 Unscrew the nut and remove the bolt securing the engine/transmission rear mounting link to the mounting on the rear of the cylinder block.

8 Make a final check to ensure that all relevant pipes, hoses and wiring harnesses have been released and moved clear of the subframe to allow the rear of the subframe to be lowered.

9 Slacken and remove the four subframe rear mounting bolts. Loosen the two subframe front mounting bolts by a few turns, until it is possible to lower the rear edge of the subframe approximately 65.0 mm. Wedge a block of wood between the rear of the subframe and the vehicle underbody to hold the subframe in this position. Where applicable, recover the alignment dowels fitted between the subframe and the body.

10 Slacken the two anti-roll bar mounting clamp retaining bolts, and recover the nuts from the top of the clamps. Remove both clamps from the subframe.

11 Manoeuvre the anti-roll bar out from underneath the vehicle, and remove the mounting bushes from the bar.

12 Carefully examine the anti-roll bar components for signs of wear, damage or deterioration, paying particular attention to the mounting bushes. Renew worn components as necessary.

Refitting

13 Fit the rubber mounting bushes to the anti-roll bar, ensuring that the lugs on the inside of each bush engage with the corresponding cut-outs in the anti-roll bar. The bushes are correctly positioned when the alignment marks on the edges of the bushes are aligned with the paint marks on the anti-roll bar.

14 Offer up the anti-roll bar, and manoeuvre it into position on the subframe. Refit the mounting clamps, ensuring that their ends are correctly located in the hooks on the subframe, and refit the retaining bolts and nuts. Ensure that the bush markings are still aligned with the paint marks on the bar, then tighten the mounting clamp retaining bolts to the specified torque.

15 The remainder of the refitting is a reversal of the removal procedure, noting the following points:

a) All Nyloc nuts disturbed on removal must be renewed as a matter of course. These nuts have threads which are pre-coated with locking compound (this is only effective once), and include the anti-roll bar connecting link nuts, and the engine/transmission rear mounting bolt nut, and the intermediate shaft pinch-bolt nut (and pinch-bolt).

b) Tighten all nuts and bolts to the specified torque settings (where given).

c) Ensure that the metal clip is correctly refitted to the steering intermediate shaft universal joint.

d) Fit a new intermediate shaft pinch-bolt and nut, ensuring that the lugs on the bolt engage with the cut-outs in the universal joint.

e) On completion have the front wheel alignment checked and where necessary adjusted (see Section 24).

---

9 Front suspension anti-roll bar connecting link – removal and refitting

Removal

Note: *New connecting link securing nuts must be used on refitting.*

1 Firmly apply the handbrake, then jack up the front of the car and support it securely on axle stands (see *Jacking and vehicle support*). Remove the appropriate front roadwheel.

2 Slacken and remove the upper and lower connecting link retaining nuts and washers, and remove the link from the vehicle.

3 Examine the connecting link for signs of damage, paying particular attention to the mounting bushes or balljoints (as applicable), and renew the link if necessary. It is not possible to renew the bushes or balljoints separately. Note that the connecting link retaining nuts must be renewed as a matter of course.

Refitting

4 Refitting is a reversal of the removal procedure, using new retaining nuts and tightening them to the specified torque.

---

10 Front suspension subframe – removal and refitting

Removal

Note: *All Nyloc nuts disturbed on removal must be renewed as a matter of course. These nuts have threads which are pre-coated with locking compound (this is only effective once), and include the rear engine/transmission mounting bolt nuts and steering gear bolt nuts.*

1 Firmly apply the handbrake, then jack up the front of the car and support it securely on axle stands (see *Jacking and vehicle support*). Remove both front roadwheels.

2 Unscrew and remove the bolt securing the engine/transmission rear mounting link to the mounting on the rear of the cylinder block. Remove the bolt securing the rear mounting link to the bracket on the subframe and withdraw the link.

3 Undo the bolt(s) securing the power steering fluid pipe(s) to the mounting bracket(s) on the subframe, and free the pipe(s) from any subframe retaining clips.

4 Slacken the steering gear mounting bolts, and recover the nuts. Withdraw the mounting bolts, and recover the spacers from the subframe apertures. Secure the steering gear to the exhaust front pipe using a large cable tie or similar.

5 On models with manual transmission, using a large screwdriver, carefully lever the three gearchange linkage link rods off their balljoints on the transmission. Slacken and remove the pivot bolt securing the selector rod to the gearchange lever.

6 Where applicable, release the clutch cable from the clips on the subframe.

7 Slacken and remove the suspension lower arm front pivot bolt and nut on both sides. Recover the nut from its housing if it is loose.

8 Unscrew the two bolts securing the suspension lower arm rear mounting bush to the subframe on each side, noting that the larger bolt also secures the anti-roll bar mounting clamp (counterhold the nut if necessary). Recover the nut from the top of each anti-roll bar mounting clamp.

9 Release the inner ends of both suspension lower arms from their locations in the subframe.

10 Place a jack and a suitable block of wood under the subframe to support the subframe as it is lowered.

11 Slacken and remove the four rear subframe mounting bolts, and the two front bolts, then carefully lower the subframe assembly out of position and remove it from underneath the vehicle **(see illustrations)**. Where applicable, recover the alignment dowels fitted between the subframe and the body. Ensure that the subframe assembly does not catch the power steering pipes as it is lowered out of position.

10.11a Front subframe left-hand rear mounting bolts (arrowed) . . .

Refitting

12 Refitting is a reversal of the removal procedure, noting the following points:
  a) Where applicable, ensure that the alignment dowels are in position between the subframe and the body.
  b) All Nyloc nuts disturbed on removal must be renewed as a matter of course. These nuts have threads which are pre-coated with locking compound (this is only effective once) and include the rear engine/transmission mounting bolt nuts and steering gear mounting bolt nuts.
  c) Tighten all nuts and bolts to the specified torque settings (where given).
  d) On completion have the front wheel alignment checked and where necessary adjusted (see Section 24).

11 Rear hub assembly – removal and refitting

Rear drum brakes

Hatchback and Coupé models

1 On these models, the rear hub is an integral part of the brake drum. Refer to Chapter 9 for drum removal and refitting details.

Estate models

Note: *Do not remove the hub assembly unless it is absolutely necessary. A puller will be required to draw the hub assembly off the*

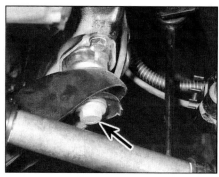

10.11b . . . and front mounting bolt (arrowed)

stub axle, and the hub bearing will almost certainly be damaged by the removal procedure. A new hub nut, and a new hub cap must be used on refitting.

2 Remove the rear brake drum as described in Chapter 9.

3 Proceed as described for disc brake models in paragraphs 6 to 14.

4 On completion, refit the brake drum as described in Chapter 9.

Rear disc brakes

Note: *Do not remove the hub assembly unless it is absolutely necessary. A puller will be required to draw the hub assembly off the stub axle, and the hub bearing will almost certainly be damaged by the removal procedure. A new hub nut, and a new hub cap must be used on refitting.*

Removal

5 Remove the rear brake disc as described in Chapter 9.

6 Using a hammer and a large flat-bladed screwdriver, carefully tap and prise the cap out of the centre of the hub. Discard the cap – a new one must be used on refitting. Using a hammer and a chisel-nosed tool, tap up the staking securing the hub retaining nut to the groove in the stub axle **(see illustrations)**.

7 Using a socket and long bar, slacken and remove the rear hub nut, and withdraw the thrustwasher. Discard the hub nut – a new nut must used on refitting.

8 Using a puller, draw the hub assembly off the stub axle, along with the outer bearing **(see illustration)**. With the hub removed, use

11.6a Tap off the hub centre cap . . .

11.6b . . . then tap up the rear hub staking using a hammer and suitable punch

11.8 Use a two-legged puller to draw the hub assembly off the stub axle

11.14a Fit the thrustwasher and new hub nut, and tighten to the specified torque

11.14b Using a hammer and suitable punch . . .

11.14d . . . then fit the new hub cap

11.14c . . . stake the hub nut firmly into the stub axle groove . . .

stub axle. Fit the outer bearing, and tap it into position using the tubular drift.

14 Fit the thrustwasher and new hub nut, and tighten the hub nut to the specified torque. Stake the nut firmly into the groove on the stub axle to secure it in position, then tap the new hub cap into place in the centre of the hub **(see illustrations)**.

15 Refit the rear brake disc as described in Chapter 9.

12 Rear hub bearings – renewal

Note: *The bearing is intended to last the car's entire service life without maintenance or attention. Never overtighten the hub nut beyond the specified torque setting in an attempt to 'adjust' the bearings.*

Rear drum brakes

Hatchback and Coupé models

1 Remove the rear brake drum as described in Chapter 9.

2 Using circlip pliers, extract the bearing retaining circlip from the centre of the brake drum **(see illustration)**.

3 Prise the oil seal seating ring from the rear of the hub **(see illustration)**.

4 Securely support the drum hub, then press or drive the bearing out of position, using a tubular drift which bears on the bearing inner race. Alternatively, the bearing can be removed using an improvised tool made up from a suitable socket or tube, washers, nut and a suitable long bolt or threaded rod **(see illustration)**.

5 Thoroughly clean the hub, removing all traces of dirt and grease, and polish away any burrs or raised edges which might hinder reassembly. Check the hub for cracks or any other signs of wear or damage, and renew them if necessary. The bearing and its circlip must be renewed whenever they are disturbed. Note that a replacement bearing kit, which consists of the bearing, circlip and

a bearing puller to draw the inner bearing inner race off the stub axle, then remove the flanged hub spacer, noting which way around it is fitted. On later models a plain spacer is used which can be fitted either way round.

9 Refit the races to the hub bearing, and check the hub bearing for signs of roughness. It is recommended that the bearing should be renewed as a matter of course, as it, or its oil seal, will almost certainly have been damaged during removal. This means that the complete hub assembly must be renewed, since it is not possible to obtain the bearing separately.

10 With the hub removed, examine the stub axle shaft for signs of wear or damage. If stub axle shaft is worn, it will be necessary to

renew the complete trailing arm, as the shaft is not available separately. Trailing arm renewal entails the use of numerous special tools and must be entrusted to a Citroën dealer.

Refitting

11 Lubricate the stub axle shaft with clean engine oil, then slide on the spacer, ensuring it is fitted the correct way round on early versions.

12 Fit the inner bearing inner race, and tap it fully onto the stub axle using a hammer and a tubular drift which bears only on the flat inside edge of the race.

13 Ensure that the bearing is packed with grease, then slide the hub assembly onto the

12.2 Extracting the rear hub bearing circlip

12.3 Prising the oil seal seating ring from the rear hub

12.4 Drawing the hub bearing from the hub using improvised tools

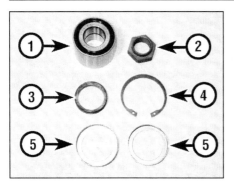

12.5 Rear hub bearing kit

1	Bearing	4	Circlip
2	Hub nut	5	Seal seating rings
3	Oil seal		(alternative sizes)

spacer, is available from Citroën dealers **(see illustration)**.

6 Carefully prise the oil seal from the stub axle, and fit the new seal supplied in the bearing kit. Note the spacer fitted behind the oil seal **(see illustration)**.

7 Examine the stub axle shaft for signs of wear or damage. If stub axle shaft is worn, it will be necessary to renew the complete trailing arm, as the shaft is not available separately. Trailing arm renewal entails the use of numerous special tools and must be entrusted to a Citroën dealer.

8 On reassembly, apply a light film of clean engine oil to the bearing outer race, to aid installation of the bearing.

9 Securely support the drum, and locate the bearing in the hub. Press the bearing fully into position, ensuring it enters the hub squarely, using a tubular spacer which bears only on the bearing outer race. Alternatively, the bearing can be drawn into position with the improvised tool used previously, but note that a different socket or tube will be required, to bear on the bearing outer race **(see illustrations)**.

10 Ensure that the bearing is correctly seated against the hub shoulder, and secure it in position with the new circlip. Ensure that the circlip is correctly seated in its hub groove.

11 Tap the new oil seal seating ring into position in the rear of the hub, taking care not

12.6 Fitting a new oil seal to the stub axle. Note spacer (arrowed)

to damage the oil seal seating surface **(see illustrations)**. Note that two different-sized oil seal seating rings may be supplied in the bearing kit – ensure the correct ring is used.

12 Refit the brake drum as described in Chapter 9.

Estate models

13 On these models, the rear hub bearing is integral with the rear hub, and it is not possible to renew the hub bearing separately. If the bearing is worn, the complete rear hub assembly must be renewed. See Section 11 for hub removal and refitting procedures.

Rear disc brakes

14 On models with rear disc brakes, it is not possible to renew the rear hub bearing separately. If the bearing is worn, the complete rear hub assembly must be renewed. Refer to Section 11 for hub removal and refitting procedures.

13 Rear suspension components – general

Although it is possible to remove the rear suspension torsion bars, trailing arms and stabilizer bar independently of the complete rear axle assembly, it is essential to have certain special tools available to complete the work successfully.

Due to the complexity of the tasks, and the

12.9a Locate the bearing in the hub . . .

requirement for special tools to accurately set the suspension geometry on refitting, the removal and refitting of individual rear suspension components is considered to be beyond the scope of DIY work, and should be entrusted to a Citroën dealer.

Procedures for removal and refitting of the rear shock absorbers, and the complete rear suspension assembly are given in Sections 14 and 15 respectively.

14 Rear shock absorber – removal, testing and refitting

Removal

Note: *New shock absorber mounting nuts must be used on refitting.*

1 Chock the front wheels, then jack up the rear of the vehicle and support it on axle stands (see *Jacking and vehicle support*). Remove the relevant rear roadwheel.

2 If the left-hand shock absorber is to be removed note that, on some models, it will first be necessary to remove the exhaust tailpipe and tailpipe heatshield, in order to allow the shock absorber upper mounting bolt to be withdrawn. If this is the case, refer to the relevant Part of Chapter 4 for information on exhaust system removal. Similarly, if removing the right-hand shock absorber, it may be necessary to remove the spare wheel from its cradle.

12.9b . . . then draw the bearing into position

12.11a Fit the new oil seal seating ring . . .

12.11b . . . and tap it into position

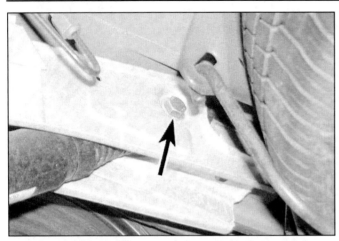

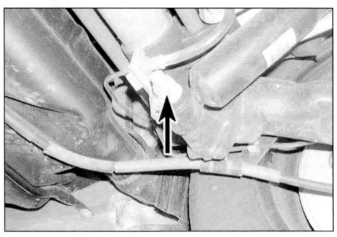

14.5a Rear shock absorber upper mounting bolt (arrowed) . . .

14.5b . . . and lower mounting nut (arrowed)

3 Using a trolley jack, raise the trailing arm until the shock absorber is slightly compressed.

4 Unscrew the securing bolt, and detach the handbrake cable bracket from the trailing arm.

5 Slacken and remove the nuts and washers from both the upper and lower shock absorber mounting bolts **(see illustrations)**. Counterhold the bolts.

6 Withdraw the mounting bolts, noting which way round they are fitted, and manoeuvre the shock absorber out from underneath the vehicle. Recover the washer from the top mounting bolt. Note that the lower mounting bolts also secure the brake pipe/hose mounting brackets and, on certain models, the rear brake pressure-regulating valve operating rod bracket.

Testing

7 Examine the shock absorber for signs of fluid leakage or damage. Test the operation of the shock absorber, while holding it in an upright position, by moving the piston through a full stroke and then through short strokes of 50 to 100 mm. In both cases, the resistance felt should be smooth and continuous. If the resistance is jerky, or uneven, or if there is any visible sign of wear or damage, renewal is necessary. Also check the rubber mounting bushes for damage and deterioration. Renew the complete unit if any damage or excessive wear is evident; the mounting bushes are not available separately. Inspect the shanks of the mounting bolts for signs of wear or damage, and renew as necessary.

Refitting

8 Prior to refitting the shock absorber, mount it upright in the vice, and operate it fully through several strokes in order to prime it. Apply a smear of multi-purpose grease to both the shock absorber mounting bolts.

9 Manoeuvre the shock absorber into position, and insert its mounting bolts; ensure

that the upper bolt is inserted from the inside of the trailing arm (with the washer in position), and the lower bolt from the outside.

10 Fit the brake pipe/hose mounting brackets and, where applicable, rear brake pressure-regulating valve operating rod bracket. Place the washers in position then screw the new nuts onto the mounting bolts, but do not tighten the nuts at this stage.

11 Measure the distance between the shock absorber bolt head centres, and adjust the position of the jack under the trailing arm until a distance of 288.0 mm is obtained between the bolt centres. Tighten the shock absorber mounting nuts and bolts to the specified torque then remove the jack from under the trailing arm.

12 Refit the handbrake cable bracket, apply suitable locking compound to the bolt threads, then refit and tighten the securing bolt.

13 Where necessary, refit the heat shield and tailpipe as described in the relevant Part of Chapter 4. Similarly, where applicable, refit the spare wheel.

14 Refit the roadwheel, then lower the car to the ground and tighten the roadwheel bolts to the specified torque.

15 Rear axle assembly – removal and refitting

Removal

1 Disconnect the battery negative terminal (refer to *Disconnecting the battery* in the Reference Section of this manual).

2 Firmly chock the front wheels, then jack up the rear of the vehicle and support it on axle stands (see *Jacking and vehicle support*). Remove both rear roadwheels, then lower the spare wheel out from underneath the rear of the vehicle, and unhook the wheel carrier.

3 Remove the relevant exhaust system components and heat shield(s) as described in the relevant Part of Chapter 4.

4 Remove the centre console as described in Chapter 11.

5 Referring to Chapter 9 if necessary, slacken the handbrake lever adjusting nut to obtain maximum free play in the handbrake cables, and disengage the inner cables from the handbrake lever equaliser plate.

6 From underneath the vehicle, work along the length of each handbrake cable, and free them from any retaining clips which secure them to the vehicle underbody. Note the routing of the cables to ensure correct refitting.

7 Where necessary, disconnect the ABS wheel sensors at the wiring connectors, and free them from any retaining clips.

8 To minimise brake hydraulic fluid loss, remove the master cylinder reservoir cap, and then tighten it down onto a piece of polythene, to obtain an airtight seal.

9 Trace the brake pipes back from the caliper/backplate to their unions, which are situated either on the brackets attached to the top of the axle mounting brackets, or screwed into the rear brake pressure-regulating valve. Slacken the union nuts, and disconnect the pipes. Plug the pipe ends, to minimise fluid loss and prevent the entry of dirt into the hydraulic system.

10 Make a final check that all necessary components have been disconnected and positioned so that they will not hinder the removal procedure, then position a trolley jack beneath the centre of the rear axle assembly. Raise the jack until it is supporting the weight of the axle.

11 Working in the luggage compartment, lift up the luggage compartment carpet to gain access to the rear axle nuts. Prise the covers from the floor to reveal the retaining nuts.

12 Slacken and remove the two retaining nuts and washers from each front mounting assembly, and the single nut and washer securing each rear mounting assembly to the vehicle **(see illustrations)**.

13 Lower the jack and axle assembly out of position, and remove it from underneath the car.

14 Examine the rear axle mountings for signs of damage or deterioration of the mounting rubber, and renew if necessary. Note that all four mountings should be renewed as a set; do not renew the mountings individually.

Refitting

15 Refitting is a reversal of the removal procedure, bearing in mind the following points:
  a) *Take care not to crush the brake pipes when positioning the axle assembly under the body.*
  b) *Raise the rear axle assembly into position, and tighten the mounting retaining nuts to their specified torque settings.*
  c) *Ensure that the brake pipes, handbrake cables and wiring (as applicable) are correctly routed, and retained by all the necessary retaining clips.*
  d) *Tighten the brake pipe union nuts.*
  e) *Reconnect and adjust the handbrake cables as described in Chapter 9.*
  f) *Bleed the braking system hydraulic circuit as described in Chapter 9.*
  g) *On completion, have the vehicle ride height checked by a Citroën dealer at the earliest opportunity.*

16 Vehicle ride height – checking

Checking of the vehicle ride height requires the use of Citroën special tools to accurately compress the suspension in a suspension checking bay.

The operation should be entrusted to a Citroën dealer, as it not possible to carry out checking accurately without the use of the appropriate tools.

17 Steering wheel – removal and refitting

Note: *Models equipped with an air bag can be identified by the presence of an air bag label on the steering wheel centre pad.*

Models without an air bag

Removal

1 Set the front roadwheels in the straight-ahead position, and release the steering lock by inserting the ignition key.

2 Carefully ease off the steering wheel centre pad, then slacken the steering wheel retaining bolt. Do not fully remove the bolt at this stage.

3 Where applicable, disconnect the wiring connector from the radio/cassette player remote control circuit board located in the slot at the top of the steering wheel.

15.12a Rear axle assembly front mounting nuts (arrowed)

4 Tap the wheel upwards near the centre, using the palm of your hand, or twist it from side-to-side, whilst pulling to release it from the shaft splines.

5 Once the wheel is released, remove the bolt then mark the steering wheel and steering column shaft in relation to each other.

6 Lift the steering wheel off the column splines and where applicable, feed the wiring through the centre of the steering wheel as it is withdrawn.

Refitting

7 Refitting is a reversal of removal, noting the following points:
  a) *On models with remote control switches in the steering wheel, ensure that the roadwheels are in the straight-ahead position then align the two arrows on the face of the steering column rotary connector before fitting the steering wheel.*
  b) *Where applicable, make sure that the wiring is correctly routed through the wheel.*
  c) *Align the marks made on removal, and tighten the retaining bolt to the specified torque.*

Models with an air bag

Removal

8 Remove the air bag unit as described in Chapter 12.

9 Set the front wheels in the straight-ahead position, and release the steering lock by inserting the ignition key.

17.13 Remove the steering wheel retaining bolt and washer . . .

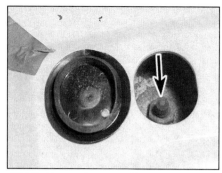

15.12b Rear axle assembly rear mounting nut (arrowed)

10 Slacken the steering wheel retaining bolt. Do not fully remove the bolt at this stage.

11 Where applicable, disconnect the wiring connector from the radio/cassette player remote control circuit board located in the slot at the top of the steering wheel **(see illustration)**.

12 Tap the wheel upwards near the centre, using the palm of your hand, or twist it from side-to-side, whilst pulling to release it from the shaft splines.

13 Once the wheel is released, remove the bolt then mark the steering wheel and steering column shaft in relation to each other **(see illustration)**.

14 Carefully withdraw the steering wheel, feeding the wiring harness for the air bag rotary connector and, where fitted, the radio/cassette player controls through the wheel as it is withdrawn **(see illustration)**.

17.11 Disconnect the wiring connector from the radio/cassette player remote control circuit board

17.14 . . . and feed the wiring harness through the wheel as it is withdrawn

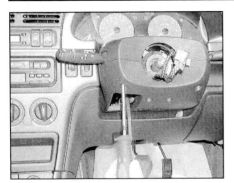

18.3a Unscrew the three lower steering column shroud securing screws . . .

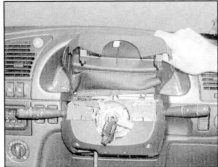

18.3b . . . unclip and lift off the upper shroud . . .

18.3c . . . then remove the lower shroud

Refitting

15 Refitting is a reversal of removal, noting the following points:

a) *Ensure that the roadwheels are in the straight-ahead position then align the two arrows on the face of the steering column rotary connector before fitting the steering wheel.*

b) *Make sure that the wiring is correctly routed through the wheel.*

c) *Align the marks made on removal, and tighten the retaining bolt to the specified torque.*

d) *Refit the air bag unit as described in Chapter 12.*

18 Steering column – removal, inspection and refitting

Removal

Note: *Where applicable, a new intermediate shaft-to-steering gear pinion nut and bolt must be used on refitting.*

1 Disconnect the battery negative terminal (refer to *Disconnecting the battery* in the Reference Section of this manual).

2 Remove the steering wheel as described in Section 17.

3 Unscrew the three lower steering column shroud securing screws. Unclip and lift off the

upper shroud, then remove the lower shroud **(see illustrations)**.

4 Where fitted, disconnect the rotary connector wiring connectors and undo the three securing screws. Withdraw the connector from the steering column and feed the wiring harness through the combination switch housing **(see illustrations)**.

5 Disconnect the wiring connectors from the rear of the steering column combination switches **(see illustration)**.

6 Unscrew the three securing screws, and withdraw the combination switch housing from the steering column **(see illustrations)**.

7 Disconnect the wiring connector from the rear of the ignition switch electronic immobiliser receiver **(see illustration)**.

18.4a Undo the three rotary connector securing screws (arrowed) . . .

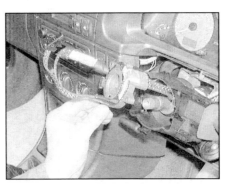

18.4b . . . and withdraw the connector from the steering column

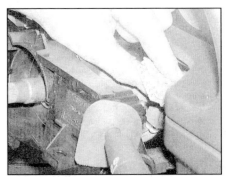

18.5 Disconnect the combination switch wiring connectors . . .

18.6a . . . unscrew the three securing screws . . .

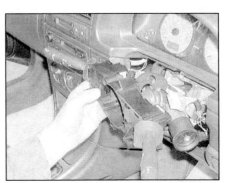

18.6b . . . and withdraw the combination switch housing from the steering column

18.7 Disconnect the wiring connector from the ignition switch electronic immobiliser receiver

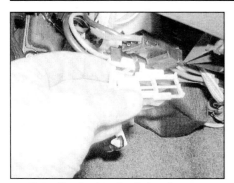

18.8a Unclip the plastic brackets . . .

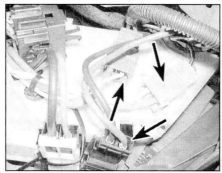

18.8b . . . and disconnect the three wiring connectors (arrowed)

18.9 Unscrew the steering column-to-intermediate shaft pinch-bolt

8 Working under the facia at the side of the steering column, unclip the plastic brackets and disconnect the three wiring connectors **(see illustrations)**.

9 Make alignment marks on the universal joint and the intermediate shaft, then unscrew the column-to-intermediate shaft pinch-bolt **(see illustration)**.

10 Unscrew the two lower steering column securing bolts **(see illustration)**.

11 Unscrew the two upper steering column securing nuts, and carefully withdraw the column from the vehicle **(see illustrations)**.

12 To remove the intermediate shaft, proceed as follows. Note that on certain models, it will be necessary to jack up the front of the vehicle and support on axle stands (see *Jacking and vehicle support*) for access to the intermediate shaft-to-steering gear joint. On some models, the joint can be reached through the engine compartment.

a) *Unscrew the securing nut from the intermediate shaft-to-steering gear pinion pinch-bolt, then carefully tap the pinch-bolt from the universal joint – discard the pinch-bolt and nut, new ones must be used on refitting.*

b) *Pull off the metal clip securing the intermediate shaft to the pinion.*

c) *Make alignment marks on the universal joint and the steering gear pinion, then push the universal joint upwards to separate it from the pinion.*

d) *Release the shaft from the pinion splines, and remove it from the vehicle.*

Inspection

13 The steering column incorporates a telescopic safety feature. In the event of a front-end crash, the shaft collapses and prevents the steering wheel injuring the driver. Before refitting the steering column, examine the column and mountings for signs of damage and deformation, and renew as necessary.

14 Check the steering shaft for signs of free play in the column bushes, and check the universal joints for signs of damage or roughness in the joint bearings. If any damage or wear is found on the steering column universal joints or shaft bushes, the column must be renewed as an assembly.

15 Where disturbed, the intermediate shaft-to-steering gear pinch-bolt and nut must be renewed as a matter of course.

Refitting

16 Where removed, refit the intermediate shaft, engaging the universal joint with the steering gear drive pinion splines (align the marks made on removal). Ensure that the metal clip is correctly refitted to the intermediate shaft-to-steering gear universal joint, then fit a new pinch-bolt and nut, ensuring that the lugs on the bolt engage with the cut-outs in the universal joint. Tighten the nut to the specified torque.

17 Check that the stop plate on the end of the steering shaft is positioned centrally within the groove of the surrounding metal clip **(see illustration)**. Push the shaft in or out of the steering column slightly, if necessary, to centralise the plate in the clip groove.

18 Manoeuvre the steering column assembly into position then, aligning the marks made prior to removal, engage the universal joint with the intermediate shaft splines.

19 Fit the column over its mounting studs, and refit the steering column upper mounting nuts. Fit the lower mounting bolts and tighten the bolts and the nuts to the specified torque.

20 Check that the steering shaft stop plate is still positioned centrally in the metal clip groove, then refit the universal joint pinch-

18.10 Unscrew the two lower steering column securing bolts (arrowed)

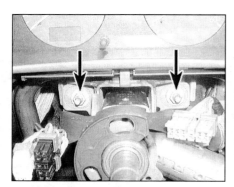

18.11a Unscrew the two upper nuts (arrowed) . . .

18.11b . . . and withdraw the steering column from the vehicle

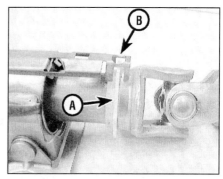

18.17 Before refitting, check that the stop plate (A) is centred in the groove of the metal clip (B)

19.3a Prise off the electronic immobiliser receiver from the steering lock . . .

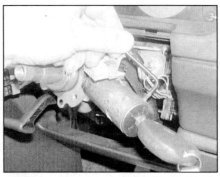

19.3b . . . then remove the lock retaining screw and washer from the side of the lock

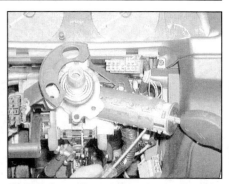

19.5 Depress the retaining lug on the side of the lock . . .

bolt. Tighten the pinch-bolt to the specified torque.

21 Reconnect the wiring connectors under the facia and secure them in position with the plastic brackets.

22 Reconnect the wiring connector to the rear of the ignition switch electronic immobiliser receiver.

23 Locate the combination switch housing on the steering column and secure with the three retaining screws. Reconnect the wiring connectors to the rear of the combination switches.

24 Where applicable, feed the rotary connector wiring harness through the combination switch housing and locate the rotary connector in position. Refit and tighten the three securing screws and reconnect the wiring.

25 Locate the upper and lower steering column shrouds in position and secure with the three screws.

26 Refit the steering wheel as described in Section 17.

19 Ignition switch/steering column lock – removal and refitting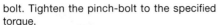

Removal

1 Carry out the operations described in Section 18, paragraphs 1 to 7.

2 Trace the wiring back from the ignition

switch, and disconnect its wiring connectors under the facia.

3 Prise off the electronic immobiliser receiver, then slacken and remove the lock retaining screw and washer from the side of the lock **(see illustrations)**.

4 With the ignition key inserted, turn the key so that is aligned with the mark positioned between the A and S marks on the barrel.

5 Using a small flat-bladed screwdriver, depress the retaining lug on the side of the lock **(see illustration)**.

6 Withdraw the lock assembly from the steering column, and feed the wiring harness through the column tube **(see illustration)**.

Refitting

7 Feed the wiring harness through the column tube and locate the lock assembly in position. Check that the ignition key is still aligned with the mark positioned between the A and S marks, then push the lock firmly into place until the retaining lug engages.

8 Secure the lock with the retaining screw and washer, then refit the electronic immobiliser receiver. Reconnect the wiring connector to the immobiliser receiver.

9 Remove the ignition key and check that the steering lock functions correctly.

10 Reconnect the wiring connectors under the facia.

11 Locate the combination switch housing on the steering column and secure with the three retaining screws. Reconnect the wiring

connectors to the rear of the combination switches.

12 Where applicable, feed the rotary connector wiring harness through the combination switch housing and locate the rotary connector in position. Refit and tighten the three securing screws and reconnect the wiring.

13 Locate the upper and lower steering column shrouds in position and secure with the three screws.

14 Refit the steering wheel as described in Section 17.

20 Steering gear assembly – removal, overhaul and refitting

Removal

Note: *All Nyloc nuts disturbed on removal must be renewed as a matter of course. These nuts have threads which are pre-coated with locking compound (this is only effective once), and include the track rod balljoint nuts, steering gear mounting bolt nuts, and the intermediate shaft pinch-bolt nut.*

1 Firmly apply the handbrake, then jack up the front of the vehicle and support on axle stands (see *Jacking and vehicle support*). Remove both front roadwheels.

2 Slacken and remove the nuts securing the steering gear track rod balljoints to the swivel hubs, and release the balljoint tapered shanks using a universal balljoint separator **(see illustration)**.

3 Unscrew the nut from the intermediate shaft-to-steering gear pinion pinch-bolt, then carefully tap the pinch-bolt from the universal joint – discard the pinch-bolt and nut, new ones must be used on refitting. Pull off the metal clip securing the intermediate shaft to the pinion.

4 Make alignment marks on the universal joint and the steering gear pinion, then push the universal joint upwards to separate it from the pinion.

5 Using brake hose clamps, clamp both the supply and return hoses near the power steering fluid reservoir. This will minimise fluid loss during subsequent operations.

19.6 . . . then withdraw the lock assembly and feed the wiring through the column tube

20.2 Releasing a track rod balljoint using a balljoint separator

6 Unscrew and remove the bolt securing the engine/transmission rear mounting link to the mounting on the rear of the cylinder block.

7 Where applicable, unclip the clutch cable from the brackets on the subframe.

8 Undo the bolt(s) securing the power steering fluid pipe(s) to the mounting bracket(s) on the engine/transmission and subframe.

9 Place a jack and a suitable block of wood under the front subframe to support the subframe as it is lowered.

10 Slacken and remove the four rear subframe mounting bolts, and the two front bolts, then carefully lower the subframe slightly. Where applicable, recover the alignment dowels fitted between the subframe and the body.

11 Mark the unions to ensure that they are correctly positioned on reassembly, then unscrew the feed and return pipe union nuts from the steering gear assembly; be prepared for fluid spillage, and position a suitable container beneath the pipes whilst unscrewing the union nuts. Disconnect both pipes, and plug the pipe ends and steering gear orifices, to prevent fluid leakage and to keep dirt out of the hydraulic system.

12 Undo the two retaining screws (where fitted), then unclip the heat shield and remove it from the top of the steering gear assembly.

13 Undo the steering gear mounting bolts, and recover the nuts **(see illustration)**. Withdraw the mounting bolts, and recover the spacers from the subframe apertures.

14 Manoeuvre the steering gear out from under the right-hand wheelarch (right-hand drive models) or left-hand wheelarch (left-hand drive models).

Overhaul

15 Examine the steering gear assembly for signs of wear or damage, and check that the rack moves freely throughout the full length of its travel, with no signs of roughness or excessive free play between the steering gear pinion and rack. It is possible to overhaul the steering gear assembly housing components, but this task should be entrusted to a Citroën dealer. The only components which can be

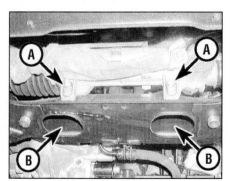

20.13 Undo the steering gear the mounting bolts, and recover the nuts (A) and spacers (B) from the subframe apertures

renewed easily by the home mechanic are the track rod balljoints (see Section 23).

16 Inspect all the steering gear fluid unions for signs of leakage, and check that all union nuts are securely tightened. Also examine the steering gear hydraulic ram for signs of fluid leakage or damage, and if necessary renew it.

Refitting

17 Note that all Nyloc nuts disturbed on removal must be renewed as a matter of course. These nuts have threads which are pre-coated with locking compound (this is only effective once), and include the track rod balljoint nuts, and the steering gear mounting bolt nuts.

18 Manoeuvre the steering gear assembly into position from the right-hand or left-hand side of the vehicle, as applicable.

19 Position the spacers in the subframe apertures, then insert the mounting bolts. Fit the new nuts onto the steering gear, then tighten the mounting bolts to the specified torque.

20 Clip the heat shield onto the top of the steering gear, and securely tighten its two retaining screws (where fitted).

21 Wipe clean the feed and return pipe unions, then refit them to their respective positions on the steering gear, and tighten the union nuts securely.

22 Where applicable, ensure that the alignment dowels are in position between the subframe and body, then raise the jack and locate the subframe in position. Fit the front and rear subframe retaining bolts and tighten to the specified torque.

23 Refit the power steering fluid pipe(s) to the mounting bracket(s) on the engine/transmission and subframe.

24 Where applicable, secure the clutch cable to the brackets on the subframe.

25 Refit the bolt securing the engine/transmission rear mounting link to the cylinder block and tighten to the specified torque (refer to the relevant Part of Chapter 2).

26 Engage the intermediate shaft universal joint with the steering gear pinion splines (align the marks made before removal). Ensure that the metal clip is correctly refitted to the intermediate shaft-to-steering gear universal joint, then fit a new pinch-bolt and nut, ensuring that the lugs on the bolt engage with the cut-outs in the universal joint. Tighten the nut to the specified torque.

27 Engage the track rod balljoints in the swivel hubs, then fit a new retaining nut to each one. Tighten the nuts to the specified torque.

28 Make a final check that all cables, pipes and hoses are correctly routed, and are securely held by all the necessary retaining clips.

29 Refit the roadwheels, then lower the vehicle to the ground and tighten the roadwheel bolts to the specified torque.

30 Remove the hose clamps from the power steering hoses, then top-up the fluid reservoir

and bleed the hydraulic system as described in Section 21.

31 On completion have the front wheel alignment checked and, if necessary, adjusted (see Section 24).

21 Power steering system – bleeding

1 This procedure will only be necessary when any part of the hydraulic system has been disconnected.

2 Referring to *Weekly checks*, remove the fluid reservoir filler cap, and top-up with the specified fluid to the maximum level mark.

3 With the engine stopped, slowly move the steering from lock-to-lock several times to purge out the trapped air, then top-up the level in the fluid reservoir. Repeat this procedure until the fluid level in the reservoir does not drop any further.

4 Start the engine, then slowly move the steering from lock-to-lock several times to purge out any remaining air in the system. Repeat this procedure until bubbles cease to appear in the fluid reservoir.

5 If, when turning the steering, an abnormal noise is heard from the fluid lines, it indicates that there is still air in the system. Check this by turning the wheels to the straight-ahead position and switching off the engine. If the fluid level in the reservoir rises, then air is present in the system, and further bleeding is necessary.

6 Once all traces of air have been removed from the power steering hydraulic system, turn the engine off and allow the system to cool. Once cool, check that the fluid level is up to the maximum mark on the power steering fluid reservoir, topping-up if necessary.

22 Power steering pump – removal and refitting

Removal

Note: *A new fluid feed pipe union O-ring must be used on refitting.*

1 The power steering pump is mounted directly above, or directly below the alternator or air conditioning compressor, depending on the engine type and the specification level of the vehicle (if the pump is mounted in the lower position, access is most easily obtained from underneath the vehicle).

2 Where fitted, remove the retaining bolts from the power steering pump pulley shield, and remove the shield.

3 Remove the auxiliary drivebelt as described in the relevant Part of Chapter 1.

4 Using brake hose clamps, clamp both the supply and return hoses near the power steering fluid reservoir. This will minimise fluid loss during subsequent operations.

5 Undo the retaining nut, and free the fluid hose retaining clip from the rear of the pump, where necessary.

6 Slacken the retaining clip, and disconnect the fluid supply hose from the pump. If the original Citroën clip is still fitted, cut the clip and discard it; replace it with a standard worm-drive hose clip on refitting. Slacken the union nut, and disconnect the feed pipe from the pump, along with its O-ring. Be prepared for some fluid spillage as the pipe and hose are disconnected, and plug the hose/pipe end and pump unions, to minimise fluid loss and prevent the entry of dirt into the system.

7 On 1.4 and 1.6 litre petrol models, undo the two bolts at the rear securing the pump to the mounting bracket, and the two bolts at the front securing the mounting bracket to the cylinder block. Withdraw the pump and mounting bracket from the engine.

8 On all other models, undo the rear mounting bolt or mounting stud, and the two front mounting bolts and withdraw the pump from the engine. Access to the front mounting bolts can be gained through the holes in the pump pulley.

Refitting

9 Manoeuvre the pump into position, then refit its mounting bolts and tighten them securely.

10 Fit a new O-ring to the feed pipe union, then reconnect the pipe to the pump and securely tighten the union nut. Refit the supply pipe to the pump, and securely tighten its retaining clip. Remove the brake hose clamps used to minimise fluid loss.

11 Where applicable, refit the fluid hose retaining clip to the rear of the pump, and securely tighten its retaining nut.

12 Refit and tension the auxiliary drivebelt as described in Chapter 1A or 1B, then, where applicable, refit the pump pulley shield.

13 On completion, bleed the hydraulic system as described in Section 21.

23 Track rod balljoint – removal and refitting

Removal

Note: *A new track rod end-to-swivel hub nut must be used on refitting.*

1 Apply the handbrake, then jack up the front of the vehicle and support it on axle stands (see *Jacking and vehicle support*). Remove the appropriate front roadwheel.

2 If the balljoint is to be re-used, use a straight-edge and a scriber, or similar, to mark its relationship to the track rod.

3 Hold the track rod, and unscrew the balljoint locknut by a quarter of a turn **(see illustration)**. Do not move the locknut from this position, as it will serve as a handy reference mark on refitting.

4 Slacken and remove the nut securing the track rod balljoint to the swivel hub, and release the balljoint tapered shank using a universal balljoint separator. Discard the nut – a new one must be used when refitting.

5 Counting the **exact** number of turns necessary to do so, unscrew the balljoint from the track rod.

6 Count the number of exposed threads between the end of the balljoint and the locknut, and record this figure. If a new balljoint is to be fitted, unscrew the locknut from the old balljoint.

7 Carefully clean the balljoint and the threads. Renew the balljoint if its movement is sloppy or too stiff, if excessively worn, or if damaged in any way; carefully check the stud taper and threads. If the balljoint dust cover is damaged, the complete balljoint assembly must be renewed; it is not possible to obtain the dust cover separately.

Refitting

8 If a new balljoint is to be fitted, screw the locknut onto its threads, and position it so that the same number of exposed threads are visible, as was noted prior to removal.

9 Screw the balljoint into the track rod by the number of turns noted on removal. This should bring the balljoint locknut to within a quarter of a turn from the end face of the track rod, with the alignment marks that were made on removal (if applicable) lined up. Hold the track rod and securely tighten the locknut.

10 Refit the balljoint shank to the swivel hub, then fit a new retaining nut and tighten it to the specified torque.

11 Refit the roadwheel, then lower the vehicle to the ground and tighten the roadwheel bolts to the specified torque.

12 On completion have the front wheel alignment checked, and if necessary, adjusted (see Section 24).

24 Wheel alignment and steering angles – general information

General

1 A car's steering and suspension geometry is defined in four basic settings – all angles

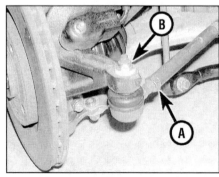

23.3 Track rod balljoint locknut (A) and balljoint-to-swivel hub retaining nut (B)

are expressed in degrees (toe settings are also expressed as a measurement); the relevant settings are camber, castor, steering axis inclination, and toe-setting. With the exception of front wheel toe setting, none of these settings are adjustable, and in all cases, special equipment is necessary to check them. Note that the front wheel toe setting is often referred to as 'tracking' or 'front wheel alignment'.

Front wheel toe setting – checking and adjustment

2 Due to the special measuring equipment necessary to accurately check the front wheel toe setting, and the skill required to use it properly, checking and adjustment is best left to a Citroën dealer or suitably-equipped garage. Note that most tyre-fitting centres now possess sophisticated alignment equipment and will carry out the check and adjustment at minimal cost. The following is therefore provided as a guide to the procedure involved.

3 The front wheel toe setting is checked by measuring the distance between the front and rear inside edges of the roadwheel rims. Proprietary toe measurement gauges are available from larger motor accessory shops, although considering the infrequent use such equipment is likely to have, purchase may not prove cost effective. The toe setting adjustment is made by screwing the balljoints in or out of their track rods, to alter the effective length of the track rod assemblies.

4 For **accurate** checking, the vehicle **must** be at the kerb weight, ie, unladen and with a full tank of fuel.

5 Before starting work, check first that the tyre sizes and types are as specified, then check the tyre pressures and tread wear, the roadwheel run-out, the condition of the hub bearings, the steering wheel free play, and the condition of the front suspension components (Chapters 1A, 1B or 10). Correct any faults found.

6 Park the vehicle on level ground, check that the front roadwheels are in the straight-ahead position, then rock the rear and front ends to settle the suspension. Release the handbrake, and roll the vehicle backwards 1 metre, then forwards again, to relieve any stresses in the steering and suspension components.

7 Measure the distance between the front edges of the wheel rims and the rear edges of the rims. Subtract the rear measurement from the front measurement, and check that the result is within the specified range.

8 If adjustment is necessary, apply the handbrake, then jack up the front of the vehicle and support it securely on axle stands (see *Jacking and vehicle support*). Turn the steering wheel onto full-left lock, and record the number of exposed threads on the right-hand track rod balljoint. Now turn the steering onto full-right lock, and record the number of threads on the left-hand side. If there are the same number of threads visible on both sides,

then subsequent adjustment should be made equally on both sides. If there are more threads visible on one side than the other, it will be necessary to compensate for this during adjustment. **Note:** *It is most important that after adjustment, the same number of threads are visible on each track rod balljoint.*

9 First clean the track rod balljoint threads; if they are corroded, apply penetrating fluid before starting adjustment. Release the rubber gaiter outboard clips (where necessary), and peel back the gaiters; apply a smear of grease to the inside of the gaiters, so that both are free, and will not be twisted or strained as their respective track rods are rotated.

10 Use a straight-edge and a scriber or similar to mark the relationship of each track rod to its balljoint then, holding each track rod in turn, unscrew its locknut slightly.

11 Alter the length of the track rods, bearing in mind the note made in paragraph 8. Screw them into or out of the balljoints, rotating the track rod using an open-ended spanner fitted to the flats provided. Shortening the track rods (screwing them into their balljoints) will reduce toe-in/increase toe-out **(see illustration)**.

12 When the setting is correct, hold the track rods and securely tighten the balljoint locknuts. Check that the balljoints are seated correctly, and count the exposed threads to check the length of both track rods. If they are not the same, then the adjustment has not been made equally, and problems will be encountered with tyre scrubbing in turns; also, the steering wheel spokes will no longer be horizontal when the wheels are in the straight-ahead position.

13 If the track rod lengths are the same, lower the vehicle to the ground and re-check the toe setting; re-adjust if necessary. When the setting is correct, securely tighten

24.11 Adjusting the front wheel toe setting

the track rod balljoint locknuts. Ensure that the rubber gaiters are seated correctly, and are not twisted or strained, and secure them in position with new retaining clips (where necessary).

Chapter 11
Bodywork and fittings

Contents

Body exterior fittings – removal and refitting 22
Bonnet and support struts – removal, refitting and adjustment 8
Bonnet lock – removal and refitting 10
Bonnet release cable – removal and refitting 9
Central locking components – removal and refitting 17
Centre console – removal and refitting 27
Door – removal, refitting and adjustment 11
Door handle and lock components – removal and refitting 13
Door inner trim panel – removal and refitting 12
Door window glass and regulator – removal and refitting 14
Exterior mirrors and mirror glass – removal and refitting 18
Facia panel assembly – removal and refitting 28
Front body panel – removal and refitting 23
Front bumper – removal and refitting 6
General information 1

Interior trim – removal and refitting 26
Maintenance – bodywork and underframe 2
Maintenance – upholstery and carpets 3
Major body damage – repair 5
Minor body damage – repair 4
Rear bumper – removal and refitting 7
Rear quarter window (Coupé models) – removal and refitting 20
Seat belt components – removal and refitting 25
Seats – removal and refitting 24
Sunroof – general information 21
Tailgate and support struts – removal and refitting 15
Tailgate lock components – removal and refitting 16
Windscreen, tailgate and fixed rear quarter window glass -
    general information 19

Degrees of difficulty

Easy, suitable for novice with little experience	Fairly easy, suitable for beginner with some experience	Fairly difficult, suitable for competent DIY mechanic	Difficult, suitable for experienced DIY mechanic	Very difficult, suitable for expert DIY or professional

Specifications

Torque wrench settings	Nm	lbf ft
Seat mounting bolts	20	15
Seat belt mounting bolts	20	15

1 General information

The bodyshell is made of pressed-steel sections, and is available in three-door Coupé, five-door Hatchback, and five-door Estate versions. Most components are welded together, but some use is made of structural adhesives. The front wings are bolted on.

The bonnet, doors and some other vulnerable panels are made of zinc-coated metal, and are further protected by being coated with an anti-chip primer prior to being sprayed.

Extensive use is made of plastic materials, mainly in the interior, but also in exterior components. The front and rear bumpers and the front grille are injection-moulded from a synthetic material which is very strong, yet light. Plastic components such as wheelarch liners are fitted to the underside of the vehicle, to improve the body's resistance to corrosion.

2 Maintenance –
bodywork and underframe

The general condition of a vehicle's bodywork is the one thing that significantly affects its value. Maintenance is easy, but needs to be regular. Neglect, particularly after minor damage, can lead quickly to further deterioration and costly repair bills. It is important also to keep watch on those parts of the vehicle not immediately visible, for instance the underside, inside all the wheelarches, and the lower part of the engine compartment.

The basic maintenance routine for the bodywork is washing – preferably with a lot of water, from a hose. This will remove all the loose solids which may have stuck to the vehicle. It is important to flush these off in such a way as to prevent grit from scratching the finish. The wheelarches and underframe need washing in the same way, to remove any accumulated mud which will retain moisture and tend to encourage rust. Paradoxically enough, the best time to clean the underframe and wheelarches is in wet weather, when the mud is thoroughly wet and soft. In very wet weather, the underframe is usually cleaned of large accumulations automatically, and this is a good time for inspection.

Periodically, except on vehicles with a wax-based underbody protective coating, it is a good idea to have the whole of the underframe of the vehicle steam-cleaned, engine compartment included, so that a thorough inspection can be carried out to see what minor repairs and renovations are necessary. Steam-cleaning is available at many garages, and is necessary for the removal of the accumulation of oily grime, which sometimes is allowed to become thick in certain areas. If steam-cleaning facilities are not available, there are one or two excellent grease solvents available, which can be brush-applied; the dirt can then be simply hosed off. Note that these methods should not be used on vehicles with wax-based underbody protective coating, or the coating will be removed. Such vehicles should be inspected annually, preferably just prior to winter, when the underbody should be washed down, and any damage to the wax coating repaired using underseal. Ideally, a completely fresh coat should be applied. It would also be worth considering the use of wax-based protection for injection into door panels, sills, box sections, etc, as an additional safeguard against rust damage, where such protection is not provided by the vehicle manufacturer.

After washing paintwork, wipe off with a chamois leather to give an unspotted clear finish. A coat of clear protective wax polish will give added protection against chemical pollutants in the air. If the paintwork sheen has dulled or oxidised, use a cleaner/polisher combination to restore the brilliance of the shine. This requires a little effort, but such dulling is usually caused because regular washing has been neglected. Care needs to be taken with metallic paintwork, as a special non-abrasive cleaner/polisher is required to avoid damage to the finish. Always check that the door and ventilator opening drain holes and pipes are completely clear, so that water can be drained out. Brightwork should be treated in the same way as paintwork. Windscreens and windows can be kept clear of the smeary film which often appears, by the use of proprietary glass cleaner. Never use any form of wax or other body or chromium polish on glass.

3 Maintenance – upholstery and carpets

Mats and carpets should be brushed or vacuum-cleaned regularly, to keep them free of grit. If they are badly stained, remove them from the vehicle for scrubbing or sponging, and make quite sure they are dry before refitting. Seats and interior trim panels can be kept clean by wiping with a damp cloth and a proprietary upholstery cleaner. If they do become stained (which can be more apparent on light-coloured upholstery), use a little liquid detergent and a soft nail brush to scour the grime out of the grain of the material. Do not forget to keep the headlining clean in the same way as the upholstery. When using liquid cleaners inside the vehicle, do not over-wet the surfaces being cleaned. Excessive damp could get into the seams and padded interior, causing stains, offensive odours or

even rot. If the inside of the vehicle gets wet accidentally, it is worthwhile taking some trouble to dry it out properly, particularly where carpets are involved.
Caution: Do not leave oil or electric heaters inside the vehicle for this purpose.

4 Minor body damage – repair

Repairs of minor scratches in bodywork

If the scratch is very superficial, and does not penetrate to the metal of the bodywork, repair is very simple. Lightly rub the area of the scratch with a paintwork renovator, or a very fine cutting paste, to remove loose paint from the scratch, and to clear the surrounding bodywork of wax polish. Rinse the area with clean water.

Apply touch-up paint to the scratch using a fine paint brush; continue to apply fine layers of paint until the surface of the paint in the scratch is level with the surrounding paintwork. Allow the new paint at least two weeks to harden, then blend it into the surrounding paintwork by rubbing the scratch area with a paintwork renovator or a very fine cutting paste. Finally apply wax polish.

Where the scratch has penetrated right through to the metal of the bodywork, causing the metal to rust, a different repair technique is required. Remove any loose rust from the bottom of the scratch with a penknife, then apply rust-inhibiting paint, to prevent the formation of rust in the future. Using a rubber or nylon applicator, fill the scratch with bodystopper paste. If required, this paste can be mixed with cellulose thinners, to provide a very thin paste which is ideal for filling narrow scratches. Before the stopper-paste in the scratch hardens, wrap a piece of smooth cotton rag around the top of a finger. Dip the finger in cellulose thinners, and quickly sweep it across the surface of the stopper-paste in the scratch; this will ensure that the surface of the stopper-paste is slightly hollowed. The scratch can now be painted over as described earlier in this Section.

Repairs of dents in bodywork

When deep denting of the vehicle's bodywork has taken place, the first task is to pull the dent out, until the affected bodywork almost attains its original shape. There is little point in trying to restore the original shape completely, as the metal in the damaged area will have stretched on impact, and cannot be reshaped fully to its original contour. It is better to bring the level of the dent up to a point which is about 3 mm below the level of the surrounding bodywork. In cases where the dent is very shallow anyway, it is not worth trying to pull it out at all. If the underside of the dent is accessible, it can be hammered out

gently from behind, using a mallet with a wooden or plastic head. Whilst doing this, hold a suitable block of wood firmly against the outside of the panel, to absorb the impact from the hammer blows and thus prevent a large area of the bodywork from being 'belled-out'.

Should the dent be in a section of the bodywork which has a double skin, or some other factor making it inaccessible from behind, a different technique is called for. Drill several small holes through the metal inside the area – particularly in the deeper section. Then screw long self-tapping screws into the holes, just sufficiently for them to gain a good purchase in the metal. Now the dent can be pulled out by pulling on the protruding heads of the screws with a pair of pliers.

The next stage of the repair is the removal of the paint from the damaged area, and from an inch or so of the surrounding 'sound' bodywork. This is accomplished most easily by using a wire brush or abrasive pad on a power drill, although it can be done just as effectively by hand, using sheets of abrasive paper. To complete the preparation for filling, score the surface of the bare metal with a screwdriver or the tang of a file, or alternatively, drill small holes in the affected area. This will provide a really good 'key' for the filler paste.

To complete the repair, see the Section on filling and respraying.

Repairs of rust holes or gashes in bodywork

Remove all paint from the affected area, and from an inch or so of the surrounding 'sound' bodywork, using an abrasive pad or a wire brush on a power drill. If these are not available, a few sheets of abrasive paper will do the job most effectively. With the paint removed, you will be able to judge the severity of the corrosion, and therefore decide whether to renew the whole panel (if this is possible) or to repair the affected area. New body panels are not as expensive as most people think, and it is often quicker and more satisfactory to fit a new panel than to attempt to repair large areas of corrosion.

Remove all fittings from the affected area, except those which will act as a guide to the original shape of the damaged bodywork (eg headlight shells etc). Then, using tin snips or a hacksaw blade, remove all loose metal and any other metal badly affected by corrosion. Hammer the edges of the hole inwards, in order to create a slight depression for the filler paste.

Wire-brush the affected area to remove the powdery rust from the surface of the remaining metal. Paint the affected area with rust-inhibiting paint; if the back of the rusted area is accessible, treat this also.

Before filling can take place, it will be necessary to block the hole in some way. This can be achieved by the use of aluminium or plastic mesh, or aluminium tape.

Aluminium or plastic mesh, or glass-fibre matting, is probably the best material to use for a large hole. Cut a piece to the approximate size and shape of the hole to be filled, then position it in the hole so that its edges are below the level of the surrounding bodywork. It can be retained in position by several blobs of filler paste around its periphery.

Aluminium tape should be used for small or very narrow holes. Pull a piece off the roll, trim it to the approximate size and shape required, then pull off the backing paper (if used) and stick the tape over the hole; it can be overlapped if the thickness of one piece is insufficient. Burnish down the edges of the tape with the handle of a screwdriver or similar, to ensure that the tape is securely attached to the metal underneath.

Bodywork repairs – filling and respraying

Before using this Section, see the Sections on dent, minor scratch, rust holes and gash repairs.

Many types of bodyfiller are available, but generally speaking, those proprietary kits which contain a tin of filler paste and a tube of resin hardener are best for this type of repair; some can be used directly from the tube. A wide, flexible plastic or nylon applicator will be found invaluable for imparting a smooth and well-contoured finish to the surface of the filler.

Mix up a little filler on a clean piece of card or board – measure the hardener carefully (follow the maker's instructions on the pack), otherwise the filler will set too rapidly or too slowly. Using the applicator, apply the filler paste to the prepared area; draw the applicator across the surface of the filler to achieve the correct contour and to level the surface. As soon as a contour that approximates to the correct one is achieved, stop working the paste – if you carry on too long, the paste will become sticky and begin to 'pick-up' on the applicator. Continue to add thin layers of filler paste at 20-minute intervals, until the level of the filler is just proud of the surrounding bodywork.

Once the filler has hardened, the excess can be removed using a metal plane or file. From then on, progressively-finer grades of abrasive paper should be used, starting with a 40-grade production paper, and finishing with a 400-grade wet-and-dry paper. Always wrap the abrasive paper around a flat rubber, cork, or wooden block – otherwise the surface of the filler will not be completely flat. During the smoothing of the filler surface, the wet-and-dry paper should be periodically rinsed in water. This will ensure that a very smooth finish is imparted to the filler at the final stage.

At this stage, the 'dent' should be surrounded by a ring of bare metal, which in turn should be encircled by the finely 'feathered' edge of the good paintwork. Rinse the repair area with clean water, until all of the dust produced by the rubbing-down operation has gone.

Spray the whole area with a light coat of primer – this will show up any imperfections in the surface of the filler. Repair these imperfections with fresh filler paste or bodystopper, and once more smooth the surface with abrasive paper. If bodystopper is used, it can be mixed with cellulose thinners, to form a really thin paste which is ideal for filling small holes. Repeat this spray-and-repair procedure until you are satisfied that the surface of the filler, and the feathered edge of the paintwork, are perfect. Clean the repair area with clean water, and allow to dry fully.

The repair area is now ready for final spraying. Paint spraying must be carried out in a warm, dry, windless and dust-free atmosphere. This condition can be created artificially if you have access to a large indoor working area, but if you are forced to work in the open, you will have to pick your day very carefully. If you are working indoors, dousing the floor in the work area with water will help to settle the dust which would otherwise be in the atmosphere. If the repair area is confined to one body panel, mask off the surrounding panels; this will help to minimise the effects of a slight mismatch in paint colours. Bodywork fittings (eg chrome strips, door handles etc) will also need to be masked off. Use genuine masking tape, and several thicknesses of newspaper, for the masking operations.

Before commencing to spray, agitate the aerosol can thoroughly, then spray a test area (an old tin, or similar) until the technique is mastered. Cover the repair area with a thick coat of primer; the thickness should be built up using several thin layers of paint, rather than one thick one. Using 400 grade wet-and-dry paper, rub down the surface of the primer until it is really smooth. While doing this, the work area should be thoroughly doused with water, and the wet-and-dry paper periodically rinsed in water. Allow to dry before spraying on more paint.

Spray on the top coat, again building up the thickness by using several thin layers of paint. Start spraying at the top of the repair area, and then, using a side-to-side motion, work downwards until the whole repair area and about 2 inches of the surrounding original paintwork is covered. Remove all masking material 10 to 15 minutes after spraying on the final coat of paint.

Allow the new paint at least two weeks to harden, then, using a paintwork renovator or a very fine cutting paste, blend the edges of the paint into the existing paintwork. Finally, apply wax polish.

Plastic components

With the use of more and more plastic body components by the vehicle manufacturers (eg bumpers. spoilers, and in some cases major body panels), rectification of more serious damage to such items has become a matter of either entrusting repair work to a specialist in this field, or renewing complete components. Repair of such damage by the

DIY owner is not really feasible, owing to the cost of the equipment and materials required for effecting such repairs. The basic technique involves making a groove along the line of the crack in the plastic, using a rotary burr in a power drill. The damaged part is then welded back together, using a hot air gun to heat up and fuse a plastic filler rod into the groove. Any excess plastic is then removed, and the area rubbed down to a smooth finish. It is important that a filler rod of the correct plastic is used, as body components can be made of a variety of different types (eg polycarbonate, ABS, polypropylene).

Damage of a less serious nature (abrasions, minor cracks etc) can be repaired by the DIY owner using a two-part epoxy filler repair material. Once mixed in equal proportions, this is used in similar fashion to the bodywork filler used on metal panels. The filler is usually cured in twenty to thirty minutes, ready for sanding and painting.

If the owner is renewing a complete component himself, or if he has repaired it with epoxy filler, he will be left with the problem of finding a suitable paint for finishing which is compatible with the type of plastic used. At one time, the use of a universal paint was not possible, owing to the complex range of plastics encountered in body component applications. Standard paints, generally speaking, will not bond to plastic or rubber satisfactorily. However, it is now possible to obtain a plastic body parts finishing kit which consists of a pre-primer treatment, a primer and coloured top coat. Full instructions are normally supplied with a kit, but basically, the method of use is to first apply the pre-primer to the component concerned, and allow it to dry for up to 30 minutes. Then the primer is applied, and left to dry for about an hour before finally applying the special-coloured top coat. The result is a correctly-coloured component, where the paint will flex with the plastic or rubber, a property that standard paint does not normally posses.

5 Major body damage – repair

Where serious damage has occurred, or large areas need renewal due to neglect, it means that complete new panels will need welding-in, and this is best left to professionals. If the damage is due to impact, it will also be necessary to check completely the alignment of the bodyshell, and this can only be carried out accurately by a Citroën dealer, or accident repair specialist, using special jigs. If the body is left misaligned, it is primarily dangerous, as the car will not handle properly, and secondly, uneven stresses will be imposed on the steering, suspension and possibly transmission, causing abnormal wear, or complete failure, particularly to such items as the tyres.

6.3 Disconnect the bonnet safety catch cable from the bonnet lock lever

6.6 Undo the screw securing the splash shields and/or the wheelarch liners to the sides of the bumper

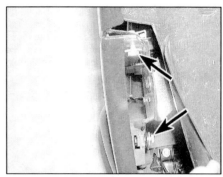

6.8 Unscrew the two bolts each side (arrowed) securing the bumper to the front body panel

6 Front bumper – removal and refitting

Removal

1 For improved access, apply the handbrake, then jack up the front of the vehicle and support securely on axle stands (see *Jacking and vehicle support*).

2 Remove the body-mounted radiator grille as described in Section 22.

3 Disconnect the bonnet safety catch cable from the bonnet lock lever **(see illustration)**.

4 Where fitted, undo the left-hand bonnet lock retaining bolt to release the bumper support cable.

5 Undo the three bolts securing the bumper lower mountings to the cross-member.

6 Working at each side of the bumper, undo the screw securing the splash shields and/or the wheelarch liners to the sides of the bumper **(see illustration)**.

7 On models with foglights, disconnect the foglight wiring connectors.

8 Again working under the bumper, unscrew the four bolts (two on each side) securing the bumper to the front body panel **(see illustration)**. Reach up behind the bumper for access to the bolts.

9 Pull the bumper forward and disengage the plastic catches on each side, then carefully withdraw the bumper from the front of the vehicle **(see illustration)**.

Refitting

10 Refitting is a reversal of removal, ensuring that the bumper correctly engages with the front locating pegs, and side plastic catches, as it is located in position.

7 Rear bumper – removal and refitting

Removal

1 Chock the front wheels, then jack up the rear of the vehicle and support securely on axle stands (see *Jacking and vehicle support*).

2 On Estate models, remove the rear light cluster on both sides as described in Chapter 12, Section 7.

3 Open the tailgate and unscrew the three screws securing the upper edge of the bumper to the body **(see illustration)**. On

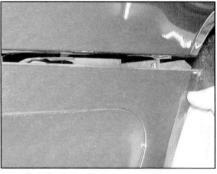

6.9 Pull the bumper forward and disengage the plastic catches on each side

Estate models, undo the additional bolts each side, one at the base of the rear light cluster aperture and one at the lower corner of the tailgate aperture.

4 Working under the bumper, undo the bolt securing the bumper to the bumper bracket each side **(see illustration)**.

5 Working at each side of the bumper, undo the screw securing the splash shields and/or the wheelarch liner to the base of the bumper **(see illustration)**.

6 Ease the wheelarch liner forward for access, then reach up under the wheelarch

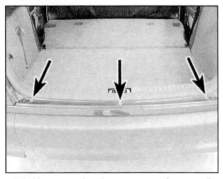

7.3 Unscrew the three screws (arrowed) securing the upper edge of the rear bumper to the body

7.4 Undo the bolt securing the bumper to the bumper bracket each side

7.5 Undo the screw each side securing the splash shields and/or the wheelarch liner to the bumper

and undo the bumper upper mounting bolt each side **(see illustrations)**.

7 Pull the bumper rearward and disengage the plastic catches on each side, then carefully withdraw the bumper from the rear of the vehicle **(see illustrations)**.

Refitting

8 Refitting is a reversal of removal, ensuring that the bumper correctly engages with the side plastic catches as it is located in position.

8 Bonnet and support struts – removal, refitting and adjustment

Bonnet

Removal

1 Open the bonnet and have an assistant support it, then, using a pencil or felt tip pen, mark the outline of each bonnet hinge relative to the bonnet, to use as a guide on refitting.

2 Release the spring clips using a screwdriver and pull the bonnet support struts from the balljoints on the bonnet.

3 Disconnect the windscreen washer fluid pipe from its non-return valve on the left-hand side of the bonnet.

4 Unscrew the bonnet-to-hinge retaining bolts and, with the help of the assistant, carefully lift the bonnet from the vehicle **(see illustration)**. Store the bonnet out of the way in a safe place.

5 Inspect the bonnet hinges for signs of wear and free play at the pivots, and if necessary renew. Each hinge is secured to the body by two bolts. On refitting, apply a smear of multi-purpose grease to the hinges.

Refitting and adjustment

6 With the aid of an assistant, offer up the bonnet and loosely fit the retaining bolts. Align the hinges with the marks made on removal, then tighten the retaining bolts securely, and reconnect the windscreen washer fluid pipe.

7 Reconnect the support struts and secure with the spring clips.

8 Close the bonnet, and check for alignment with the adjacent panels. If necessary, slacken the hinge bolts and re-align the

7.6a Ease the wheelarch liner forward for access . . .

7.6b . . . then reach up and undo the bumper upper mounting bolt each side

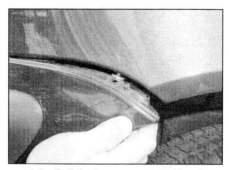

7.7a Pull the bumper rearward and disengage the plastic catches on each side . . .

bonnet to suit. When correctly aligned, tighten the hinge bolts securely.

9 Once the bonnet is correctly aligned, check that the bonnet fastens and releases in a satisfactory manner. If adjustment is necessary, slacken the bonnet lock retaining bolts, and adjust the position of the lock to suit. Once the lock is operating correctly, securely tighten its retaining bolts.

Support struts

Removal

10 Support the bonnet in the open position, with the help of an assistant, or using a stout piece of wood.

11 Using a suitable flat-bladed screwdriver, release the spring clip, and pull the lower end of the support strut from its balljoint on the body **(see illustration)**.

7.7b . . . then withdraw the bumper from the car

12 Similarly, release the strut from the balljoint on the bonnet, and withdraw the strut from the vehicle.

Refitting

13 Refitting is a reversal of removal, but ensure the spring clips are correctly engaged.

9 Bonnet release cable – removal and refitting

Removal

1 Remove the body-mounted radiator grille as described in Section 22.

2 Working under the facia on the driver's side, unscrew the release lever securing nut, and withdraw the lever from the pivot stud **(see illustration)**.

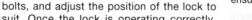

8.4 Unscrewing the bonnet-to-hinge retaining bolts

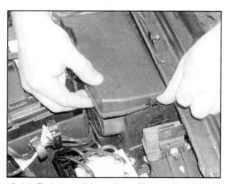

8.11 Release the spring clips and pull the support struts from their balljoints

9.2 Unscrew the bonnet release lever securing nut, and withdraw the lever from the pivot stud

9.3 Disconnect the end of the cable from the bonnet lock lever and lock body

10.2 The bonnet lock assembly left-hand retaining bolt (arrowed) also secures the bumper support cable

3 Working in the engine compartment, disconnect the end of the cable from the lock lever, then unclip the cable outer from the bracket on the lock body **(see illustration)**.

4 Tie a length of string to the end of the cable in the engine compartment, then release the cable from any securing clips in the engine compartment, and carefully pull the cable through into the vehicle interior, noting its routing.

5 Untie the string from the end of the cable, and leave it in position to aid refitting.

Refitting

6 Commence refitting by tying the end of the new cable to the string in the vehicle interior.

7 Use the string to pull the cable through into the engine compartment, routing it as noted before removal.

8 Pull the bulkhead grommet into position, and make sure that it is securely seated in the bulkhead aperture.

9 Further refitting is a reversal of removal.

10 Bonnet lock – removal and refitting

Removal

1 Remove the body-mounted radiator grille as described in Section 22.

2 Unscrew the two bolts securing the lock

assembly to the body front panel, noting that on some models, a bumper support cable is also attached to one of the mounting bolts **(see illustration)**.

3 Withdraw the lock and disconnect the bonnet release cable and safety catch cable from the lock and lock levers.

Refitting

4 Refitting is a reversal of removal. On completion, check the operation of the lock and, if necessary, adjust the position of the lock within the elongated bolt holes to achieve satisfactory operation.

11 Door – removal, refitting and adjustment

Front door

Removal

1 Disconnect the battery negative terminal (refer to *Disconnecting the battery* in the Reference Section of this manual).

2 Open the door, then release the locking ring and disconnect the door wiring connector from the socket in the front door pillar **(see illustration)**.

3 Unscrew the two securing bolts, and disconnect the door check strap from the door pillar **(see illustration)**.

4 Ensure that the door is adequately supported, then unscrew the upper and lower hinge pins. Carefully lift the door from the vehicle.

Refitting

5 Refitting is a reversal of removal, but on completion, check the fit of the door in relation to the surrounding body panels, and if necessary adjust as follows:

a) Jack up the front of the vehicle, and support securely on axle stands (see *Jacking and vehicle support*).

b) Remove the roadwheel and wheelarch liner.

c) Close the door.

d) Using a suitable spanner through the wheelarch, loosen the bolts securing the door hinges to the body, and adjust the position of the door to provide a satisfactory fit. Tighten the bolts on completion.

e) If necessary, the bolts securing the hinges to the door can also be loosened to provide additional adjustment.

Rear door

6 The procedure is as described for the front doors, but the hinge-to-body bolts can be accessed for adjustment with the front door open.

12 Door inner trim panel – removal and refitting

Front door

Removal

1 Using a small screwdriver, carefully prise out the base of the interior handle trim surround and withdraw the surround from the door panel **(see illustration)**.

2 Release the edge of the door mirror interior trim panel, lift it up to disengage the locating lug and withdraw the panel. Where a manual door mirror is fitted, lift the plastic catch and

11.2 Unscrew the locking ring (arrowed) to disconnect the front door wiring connector

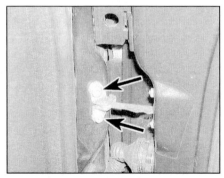

11.3 Front door check strap retaining bolts (arrowed)

12.1 Carefully prise out the base of the front door interior handle trim surround

12.2a Release the edge of the door mirror interior trim panel . . .

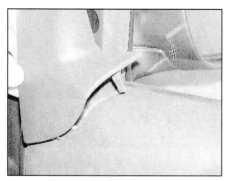

12.2b . . . then lift the panel up to disengage the locating lug

12.2c On manual door mirrors, lift the mirror control stalk plastic catch . . .

remove the trim panel from the mirror control stalk **(see illustrations)**.

3 Carefully prise off the loudspeaker grille from the trim panel **(see illustration)**.

4 Undo the loudspeaker retaining screws, withdraw the speaker and disconnect the wiring **(see illustrations)**.

5 On models with manual windows, pull the winder handle off the spindle, and then remove the spindle trim plate.

6 Undo the door panel upper retaining screw located at the base of the interior handle **(see illustration)**.

7 Undo the door panel centre retaining screw located at the front of the armrest **(see illustration)**.

8 Undo the two screws located in the speaker aperture **(see illustration)**.

9 Using a suitable forked tool, work around the edge of the trim panel, and release the securing clips.

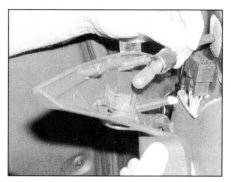

12.2d . . . and remove the trim panel from the control stalk

10 Pull the panel outwards, lift it up and remove it from the door **(see illustration)**.

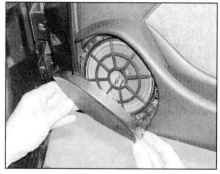

12.3 Carefully prise off the loudspeaker grille from the front door trim panel

12.4a Undo the loudspeaker retaining screws . . .

12.4b . . . then withdraw the speaker and disconnect the wiring

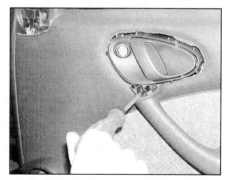

12.6 Undo the trim panel retaining screw from the base of the interior handle . . .

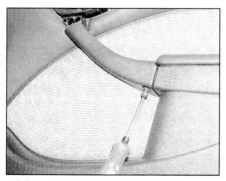

12.7 . . . and from the front of the armrest

12.8 Undo the two trim panel retaining screws located in the loudspeaker speaker aperture

12.10 Pull the trim panel outwards, then lift it up and remove it from the door

12.12 Prise out the rear door upper interior finisher panel at the rear of the door window

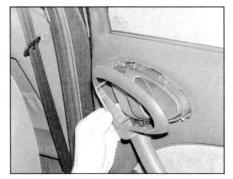

12.13 Prise out the interior handle trim surround

12.14 On models with manual windows, pull the winder handle off the spindle and remove the spindle trim plate

Refitting

11 Before refitting, check whether any of the trim panel retaining studs were broken on removal. Renew the panel retaining studs as necessary, then refit the panel using a reversal of removal.

Rear door

Removal

12 Prise out the upper interior finisher panel at the rear of the door window **(see illustration)**.
13 Carefully prise out the interior handle trim surround and withdraw the surround from the door panel **(see illustration)**.
14 On models with manual windows, pull the

winder handle off the spindle, and then remove the spindle trim plate **(see illustration)**.
15 Carefully prise off the speaker grille from the trim panel **(see illustration)**.
16 Undo the speaker retaining screws, withdraw the speaker and disconnect the wiring **(see illustrations)**.
17 Undo the door panel upper retaining screw located at the base of the interior handle **(see illustration)**.
18 Undo the two centre retaining screw located below the armrest **(see illustration)**.
19 Using a suitable forked tool, work around the edge of the trim panel, and release the securing clips.
20 Pull the panel outwards, lift it up and remove it from the door **(see illustration)**.

Refitting

21 Refitting is a reversal of removal, after first renewing any broken panel retaining studs as necessary.

---

13 Door handle and lock components – removal and refitting

Interior door handle

Removal

1 Remove the door inner trim panel, as described in Section 12.

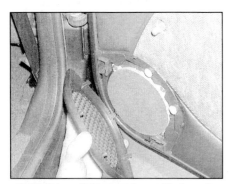

12.15 Prise off the speaker grille from the trim panel

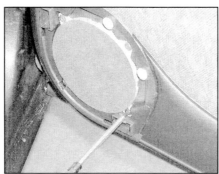

12.16a Undo the speaker retaining screws . . .

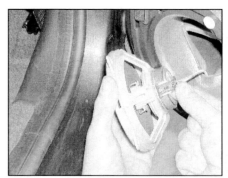

12.16b . . . then withdraw the speaker and disconnect the wiring

12.17 Undo the trim panel retaining screws, one at the base of the interior handle . . .

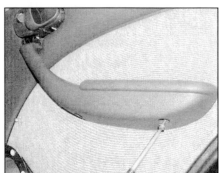

12.18 . . . and two below the armrest

12.20 Pull the trim panel outwards, then lift it up and remove it from the door

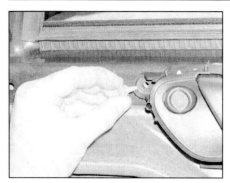

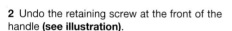

13.2 Undo the retaining screw at the front of the interior door handle

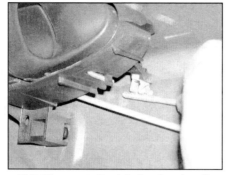

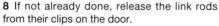

13.3 Disengage the interior door handle locating lug, ease it from the door, and disconnect the link rods

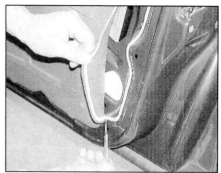

13.6 Carefully release the plastic sealing sheet from the adhesive bead on the front door

2 Undo the retaining screw at the front of the handle **(see illustration)**.

3 Slide the handle assembly towards the front of the door to disengage the locating lug, ease it away from the door and disconnect the link rods (if necessary, release the link rods from the clips on the door) **(see illustration)**.

Refitting

4 Refitting is a reversal of removal, but ensure that the link rods are correctly reconnected, and refit the inner trim panel (see Section 12).

Front door exterior handle

Removal

Note 1: *A new door sealing sheet may be required for refitting.*

Note 2: *On later models, the exterior handle is riveted to the door. Ensure that new rivets of the correct size are available for refitting, or alternatively use suitable nuts and bolts instead.*

5 Remove the interior door handle as described previously.

6 Using a sharp knife, carefully release the plastic sealing sheet from the adhesive bead and remove the sheet from the door. If care is taken, it may just be possible to remove the sheet in one piece and re-use it when refitting **(see illustration)**.

7 Undo the pivot bolt and release the link rod damper from the door **(see illustration)**.

8 If not already done, release the link rods from their clips on the door.

9 Free the wiring harness from the lock plate clip, then release the front edge of the lock plate from the door. Withdraw the lock plate from its location and remove it, together with the link rod **(see illustrations)**.

10 If the exterior door handle is secured by rivets, drill off the rivet heads from the outside and remove the handle from the door **(see illustration)**.

11 If the handle is secured by screws and nuts, working inside the door, unscrew the front handle securing nut then, from the outside, unscrew the rear handle securing screw. Withdraw the handle from the outside of the door.

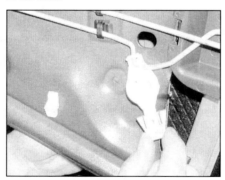

13.7 Undo the pivot bolt and release the link rod damper

Refitting

12 Refitting is a reversal of removal, but fit a new sealing sheet to the door if the original was damaged in any way during removal. On completion, refit the inner trim panel as described in Section 12.

Front door lock cylinder

Removal

Note: *A new door sealing sheet may be required on refitting.*

13 Carry out the operations described in paragraphs 5 to 9 above.

14 Working inside the door, detach the lock cylinder link rod from the door

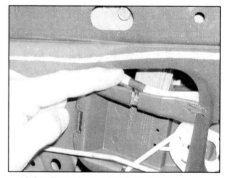

13.9a Free the wiring harness from the clip on the lock plate . . .

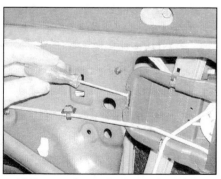

13.9b . . . release the front edge of the lock plate from the door . . .

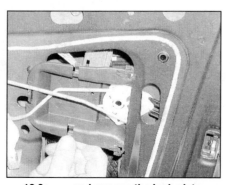

13.9c . . . and remove the lock plate, together with the link rod

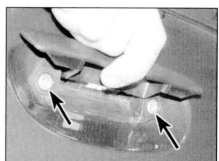

13.10 On later models, the exterior door handle is secured by rivets (arrowed) which must be drilled out for removal

13.14 Detach the front door lock cylinder link rod from the door lock using pointed-nose pliers

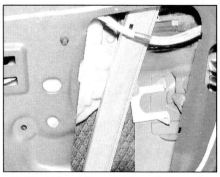

13.15a Extract the retaining clip from the rear of the front door lock cylinder . . .

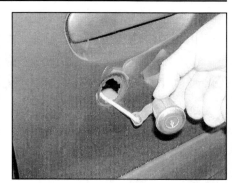

13.15b . . . then remove the lock cylinder and link rod from the outside of the door

lock using pointed-nose pliers **(see illustration)**.

15 Extract the large retaining clip from the rear of the lock cylinder, then remove the lock cylinder and link rod from the outside of the door **(see illustrations)**.

Refitting

16 Refitting is a reversal of removal, but ensure that the lock cylinder retaining clip is securely refitted. Fit a new sealing sheet to the door if the original was damaged in any way during removal. On completion, refit the

door inner trim panel as described in Section 12.

Front door lock

Removal

Note: *A new door sealing sheet may be required on refitting.*

17 Remove the door lock cylinder, as described previously in this Section.

18 Undo the three screws securing the lock assembly to the edge of the door **(see illustration)**.

19 Lower the lock assembly to the bottom of the door and disconnect the link rod **(see illustration)**.

20 Disconnect the central locking motor wiring plug, then manipulate the lock assembly out through the door aperture **(see illustrations)**.

Refitting

21 Refitting is a reversal of removal. Fit a new sealing sheet to the door if the original was damaged in any way during removal. On completion, refit the door inner trim panel as described in Section 12.

Rear door lock

Removal

Note: *A new door sealing sheet may be required on refitting.*

22 Remove the interior door handle as described previously.

23 Using a sharp knife, carefully release the plastic sealing sheet from the adhesive bead and remove the sheet from the door. If care is taken, it may just be possible to remove the sheet in one piece and re-use it when refitting.

24 Prise out the blanking plug, or peel off the circular plastic sheet, then unscrew the

13.18 Undo the three screws securing the front door lock assembly to the edge of the door

13.19 Lower the lock assembly to the bottom of the door and disconnect the link rod

13.20a Disconnect the central locking motor wiring plug . . .

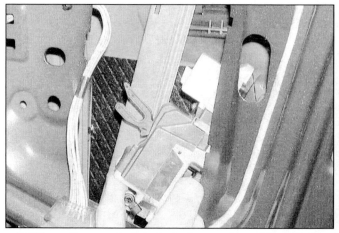

13.20b . . . then manipulate the lock assembly out through the door aperture

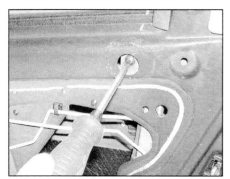

13.24 Unscrew the rear door window glass rear guide channel upper retaining bolt . . .

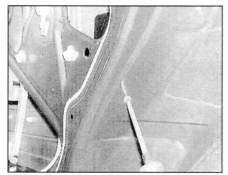

13.25a . . . and lower retaining bolt . . .

13.25b . . . then manipulate the guide out through the door aperture

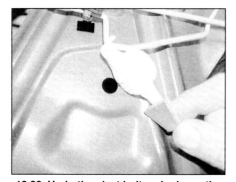

13.26 Undo the pivot bolt and release the link rod damper from the door

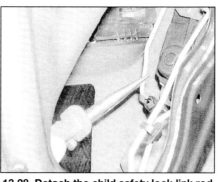

13.28 Detach the child safety lock link rod from the door lock using pointed-nose pliers

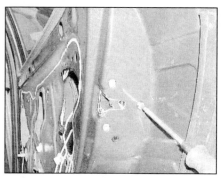

13.29 Undo the three screws securing the rear door lock assembly to the edge of the door

window glass rear guide channel upper retaining bolt **(see illustration)**.

25 Unscrew the rear guide channel lower retaining bolt and manipulate the guide out through the door aperture **(see illustrations)**.

26 Undo the pivot bolt and release the link rod damper from the door **(see illustration)**.

27 If not already done, release the link rods from their clips on the door.

28 Working inside the door, detach the child safety lock link rod from the door lock using pointed-nose pliers **(see illustration)**.

29 Undo the three screws securing the lock assembly to the edge of the door **(see illustration)**.

30 Manipulate the lock assembly and link rods out through the door aperture. Disconnect the central locking motor wiring plug and remove the lock assembly **(see illustrations)**.

31 Lower the lock assembly to the bottom of the door and disconnect the link rod.

32 Disconnect the central locking motor wiring plug, then manipulate the lock assembly out through the door aperture.

Refitting

33 Refitting is a reversal of removal. Fit a new sealing sheet to the door if the original was damaged in any way during removal. On completion, refit the door inner trim panel as described in Section 12.

Rear door exterior door handle

Removal

Note 1: *A new door sealing sheet may be required for refitting.*

Note 2: *On later models, the exterior handle is*

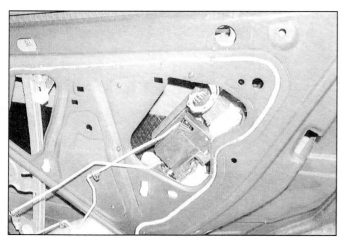

13.30a Manipulate the lock assembly and link rods out through the door aperture . . .

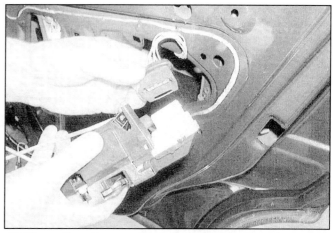

13.30b . . . then disconnect the central locking motor wiring plug and remove the lock assembly

14.4 Release the front door window front attachment lug on the lifting channel bracket from the locating hole in the window glass

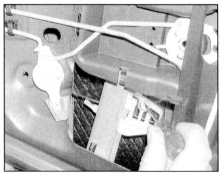

14.5 Release the rear attachment lug on the lifting channel bracket from the locating hole in the glass

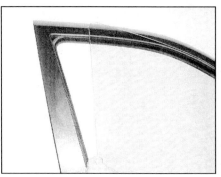

14.6 Lift the front door window glass upwards and remove it from the outside of the door

riveted to the door. Ensure that new rivets of the correct size are available for refitting, or alternatively use suitable nuts and bolts instead.

34 Remove the rear door lock as described previously in this Section.

35 If the exterior door handle is secured by rivets, drill off the rivet heads from the outside and remove the handle from the door.

36 If the handle is secured by screws and nuts, working inside the door, unscrew the front handle securing nut then, from the outside, unscrew the rear handle securing screw. Withdraw the handle from the outside of the door.

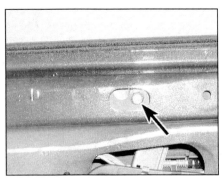

14.9 Unscrew the front door window glass rear lifting channel upper retaining bolt (arrowed)

Refitting

37 Refitting is a reversal of removal, but fit a new sealing sheet to the door If the original was damaged in any way during removal. On completion, refit the inner trim panel as described in Section 12.

---

14 Door window glass and regulator – removal and refitting

Front door window glass

Removal

Note: *A new door sealing sheet may be required on refitting.*

1 Remove the door inner trim panel as described in Section 12.

2 Using a sharp knife, carefully release the plastic sealing sheet from the adhesive bead and remove the sheet from the door. If care is taken, it may just be possible to remove the sheet in one piece and re-use it when refitting.

3 Pull the interior window seal from the lower edge of the window aperture.

4 Position the window so the front attachment to the lifting channel is accessible through the door aperture. Release the attachment lug on the lifting channel bracket from the locating hole in the window glass **(see illustration)**.

5 Reposition the window so that the rear attachment to the lifting channel is accessible through the small door aperture below the door lock. Release the rear lifting channel attachment lug from the glass **(see illustration)**.

6 Lift the window glass upwards and remove it from the outside of the door **(see illustration)**.

Refitting

7 Refitting is a reversal of removal, but fit a new sealing sheet to the door if the original was damaged in any way during removal. On completion, refit the inner trim panel as described in Section 12.

Front door window regulator

Removal

8 Remove the window glass as described previously.

9 Prise out the blanking plug, or peel off the circular plastic sheet, then unscrew the window glass rear lifting channel upper retaining bolt **(see illustration)**.

10 Unscrew the nut securing the lower end of the rear lifting channel to the door **(see illustration)**.

11 Similarly unscrew the front lifting channel upper bolt and lower nut **(see illustrations)**.

12 Where applicable, disconnect the window

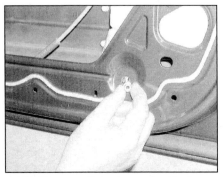

14.10 Unscrew the nut securing the lower end of the rear lifting channel to the door

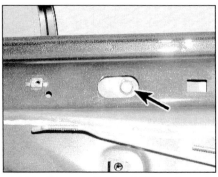

14.11a Unscrew the front lifting channel upper retaining bolt (arrowed) . . .

14.11b . . . and lower nut

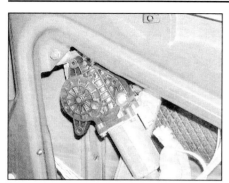

14.12 Where applicable, disconnect the window lift motor wiring plug

14.13a Undo the nut securing the upper edge of the regulator to the door . . .

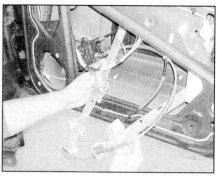

14.13b . . . then manipulate the assembly out through the door aperture

lift motor wiring plug, and release the harness cable clip from the lifting channel **(see illustration)**.

13 Undo the nut securing the upper edge of the regulator to the door, then manipulate the assembly out through the door aperture **(see illustrations)**.

Refitting

14 Refitting is a reversal of removal, but fit new circular sealing sheets to the door if the originals were damaged in any way during removal **(see illustration)**. On completion, refit the inner trim panel as described in Section 12.

Rear door window glass

Removal

Note: *A new door sealing sheet may be required on refitting.*

15 Remove the door inner trim panel as described in Section 12.

16 Using a sharp knife, carefully release the plastic sealing sheet from the adhesive bead and remove the sheet from the door. If care is taken, it may just be possible to remove the sheet in one piece and re-use it when refitting.

17 Pull the interior window seal from the lower edge of the window aperture **(see illustration)**.

18 Prise out the blanking plug, or peel off the circular plastic sheet, then unscrew the window glass rear guide upper retaining bolt.

19 Unscrew the rear guide channel lower retaining bolt and manipulate the guide channel out through the door aperture **(see illustration)**.

20 Undo the two screws securing the plastic exterior trim panel to the door. Pull the panel outwards at the rear to release the plastic clips, and remove the panel **(see illustrations)**.

21 Pull the exterior window seal from the lower edge of the window aperture **(see illustration)**.

22 Release the weatherstrip from the upper corners of the window aperture, then pull the

14.14 Fit new circular plastic sealing sheets to the door if the originals were damaged during removal

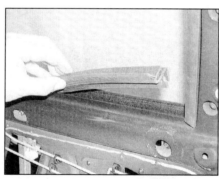

14.17 Pull the rear door interior window seal from the lower edge of the window aperture

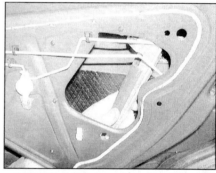

14.19 Unscrew the rear guide channel retaining bolts and manipulate the channel out through the rear door aperture

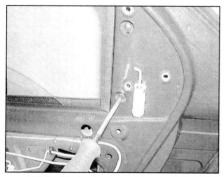

14.20a Undo the exterior trim panel securing screws . . .

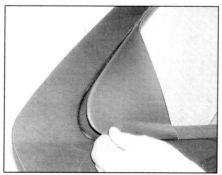

14.20b . . . then pull the panel outwards at the rear to release the plastic clips

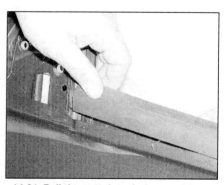

14.21 Pull the exterior window seal from the lower edge of the window aperture

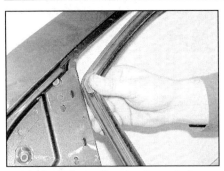

14.22a Release the rear door window glass weatherstrip from the upper corners of the window aperture . . .

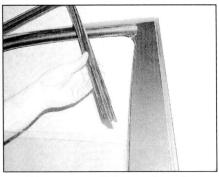

14.22b . . . then pull the weatherstrip out of the window guide channels

14.23a Undo the two screws (arrowed) securing the rear door window glass to the lifting channel bracket . . .

weatherstrip out of the window guide channels **(see illustrations).**
23 Undo the two screws securing the

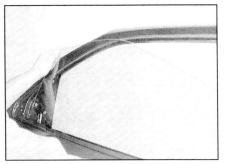

14.23b . . . then remove the glass from the outside of the door, with the rear corner uppermost

window glass to the lifting channel bracket. Lift the window glass upwards and remove it from the outside of the door, with the rear corner uppermost **(see illustrations).**

Refitting

24 Refitting is a reversal of removal, but fit a new main sealing sheet and smaller circular sealing sheets to the door if the originals were damaged in any way during removal. On completion, refit the inner trim panel as described in Section 12.

Rear door window regulator

Removal

Note: *A new door sealing sheet may be required on refitting.*
25 Remove the door inner trim panel as described in Section 12.

26 Using a sharp knife, carefully release the plastic sealing sheet from the adhesive bead and remove the sheet from the door. If care is taken, it may just be possible to remove the sheet in one piece and re-use it when refitting.
27 Lower the window fully and undo the two screws securing the window glass to the lifting channel bracket. Slide the window glass upwards by hand, and tape it to the top of the door frame to secure it in the raised position **(see illustrations).**
28 Undo the bolt securing the base of the lifting channel to the door **(see illustration).**
29 Similarly, unscrew the two upper lifting channel retaining bolts **(see illustration).**
30 Undo the two nuts securing the regulator to the door and manipulate the assembly out through the door aperture **(see illustrations).**

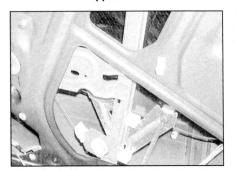

14.27a Undo the two screws securing the rear door window glass to the regulator lifting channel bracket . . .

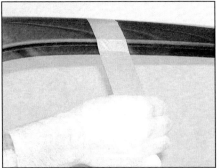

14.27b . . . then slide the glass upwards and tape it to the top of the door frame

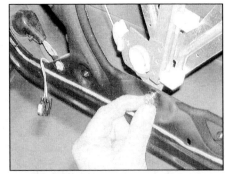

14.28 Undo the bolt securing the base of the lifting channel to the rear door . . .

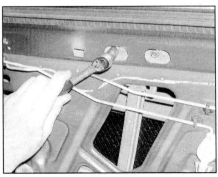

14.29 . . . and the two bolts securing the top of the channel to the door

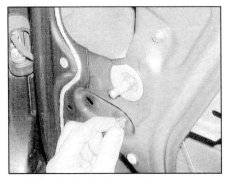

14.30a Undo the two nuts securing the regulator to the door . . .

14.30b . . . and manipulate the assembly out through the door aperture

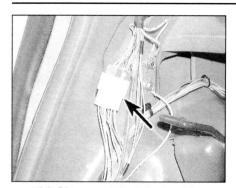

15.3 Disconnect the tailgate wiring harness connector (arrowed)

15.6 Prise out the support strut clips and pull the struts from the balljoints on the tailgate

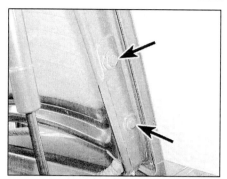

15.7a On Hatchback and Coupé models, unscrew the two bolts (arrowed) securing the hinges to the tailgate . . .

Refitting

31 Refitting is a reversal of removal, but fit a new sealing sheet to the door if the original was damaged in any way during removal. On completion, refit the inner trim panel as described in Section 12.

15 Tailgate and support struts – removal and refitting

Tailgate

Removal

1 Disconnect the battery negative terminal (refer to *Disconnecting the battery* in the Reference Section of this manual).
2 Remove the luggage and passenger compartment trim panels (Coupé models), or the luggage compartment trim panels (Hatchback and Estate models) as described in Section 26.
3 Disconnect the tailgate wiring harness connector located to the rear of the door aperture on the right-hand side **(see illustration)**. Unclip the harness from the retaining clips on the body.
4 Locally release the tailgate weatherstrip from the upper edge of the tailgate aperture,

then detach rear edge of the headlining from the roof panel. Prise out the grommet adjacent to the right-hand tailgate hinge and pull the wiring harness out from the vehicle interior.
5 Disconnect the tailgate washer jet hose and release the hose from the retaining clips so it is free to be removed with the tailgate.
6 With the aid of an assistant, suitably support the tailgate, then prise out the support strut spring clips, and pull the struts from the balljoints on the tailgate **(see illustration)**.
7 On Hatchback and Coupé models, unscrew the two bolts securing the hinges to the tailgate, and the two bolts securing the hinges to the body **(see illustrations)**. On Estate models, unscrew the threaded tailgate hinge pins.
8 Carefully lift the tailgate from the vehicle.

Refitting

9 If a new tailgate is to be fitted, transfer all serviceable components (rubber buffers, lock mechanism, etc) to it.
10 Refitting is a reversal of removal, bearing in mind the following points:
 a) If necessary, adjust the rubber buffers to obtain a good fit when the tailgate is shut.
 b) If necessary, adjust the position of the tailgate lock and/or hinge bolts within their elongated holes to achieve satisfactory lock operation.

Support struts

Removal

11 Support the tailgate in the open position, with the help of an assistant, or using a stout piece of wood.
12 Using a suitable flat-bladed screwdriver, release the spring clip, and pull the support strut from its balljoint on the body.
13 Similarly, release the strut from the balljoint on the tailgate, and withdraw the strut from the vehicle.

Refitting

14 Refitting is a reversal of removal, but ensure the spring clips are correctly engaged.

16 Tailgate lock components – removal and refitting

Tailgate lock

Removal

1 Remove the tailgate trim panel as described in Section 26.
2 Unscrew the two lock securing screws, and withdraw the lock from the tailgate. As the lock is withdrawn, disconnect the operating rod and remove the lock **(see illustrations)**.

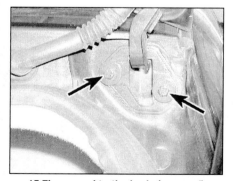

15.7b . . . and to the body (arrowed)

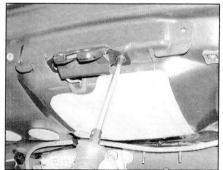

16.2a Unscrew the two lock securing screws, and withdraw the lock from the tailgate . . .

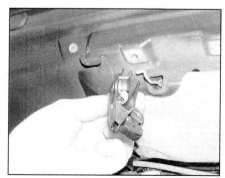

16.2b . . . then disconnect the operating rod and remove the lock

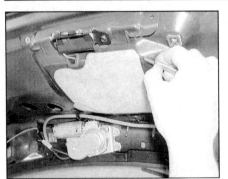

16.5a Release the edges of the foam plastic sealing sheet covering the tailgate centre aperture . . .

16.5b . . . and remove the sealing sheet

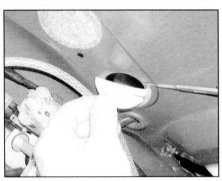

16.6 Remove the circular foam plastic sealing sheets on each side of the tailgate centre aperture

Refitting

3 Refitting is a reversal of removal, but ensure that the lock lever engages correctly as the lock is positioned in the tailgate.

Tailgate lock cylinder

Removal

4 Remove the tailgate trim panel as described in Section 26.

5 Using a sharp knife, carefully release the foam plastic sealing sheet covering the aperture in the centre of the tailgate **(see**

illustrations). It is virtually impossible to remove this sheet without tearing it so be prepared to obtain a new one for refitting.

6 Similarly, remove the four circular foam plastic sealing sheets, two located on each side of the tailgate centre aperture **(see illustration)**.

7 Working through the two previously covered holes, undo the two nuts each side securing the number plate lamp trim moulding to the tailgate **(see illustration)**.

8 Release the retaining clips and remove the plastic cover over the central locking motor

and lock housing assembly **(see illustration)**.

9 Undo the two bolts, securing the lock housing assembly and number plate lamp trim moulding **(see illustration)**.

10 From outside the car, release the number plate lamp trim moulding retaining clips and remove the moulding from the tailgate **(see illustrations)**.

11 Using a small screwdriver, depress the tabs on each side of the lock housing adjacent to the lock cylinder **(see illustration)**.

12 Withdraw the lock housing assembly from inside the tailgate and disconnect the

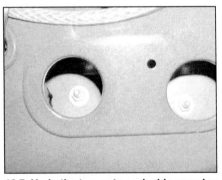

16.7 Undo the two nuts each side securing the number plate lamp trim moulding to the tailgate

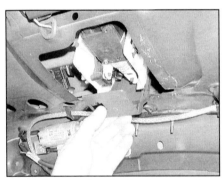

16.8 Remove the plastic cover over the central locking motor and lock housing assembly

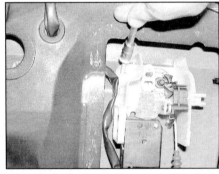

16.9 Undo the two bolts securing the lock housing assembly and number plate lamp trim moulding to the tailgate

16.10a Release the number plate lamp trim moulding retaining clips . . .

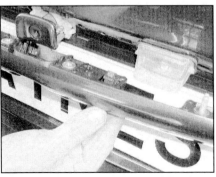

16.10b . . . and remove the moulding from the tailgate

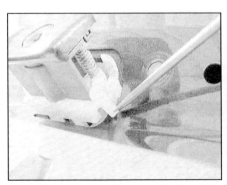

16.11 Depress the tabs on each side of the lock housing

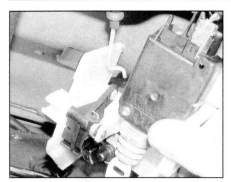

16.12a Withdraw the lock housing assembly from inside the tailgate and disconnect the operating rod . . .

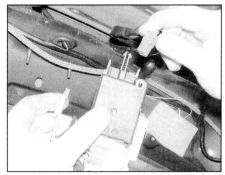

16.12b . . . and the central locking motor wiring connector

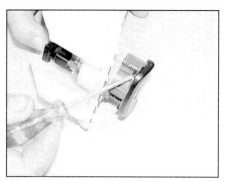

16.13a Depress the retaining tabs . . .

operating rod and central locking motor wiring connector **(see illustrations)**.

13 With the lock housing assembly on the bench, depress the retaining tabs and remove the trim moulding from the lock cylinder **(see illustrations)**.

14 Undo the central locking motor retaining screw, then twist the motor through 90° to release the side attachment lug **(see illustrations)**. Remove the motor from the lock housing.

15 Using pointed-nose pliers, turn the lock cylinder end cap anti-clockwise to release it from the cylinder. Lift off the end cap and recover the seal **(see illustrations)**.

16 Withdraw the lock cylinder from the housing and collect the two springs **(see illustrations)**.

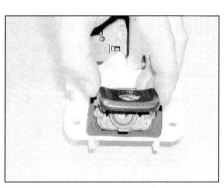

16.13b . . . and remove the trim moulding from the lock cylinder

16.14a Undo the central locking motor retaining screw . . .

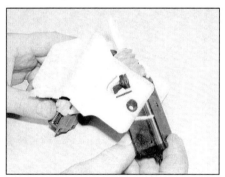

16.14b . . . then twist the motor through 90° to release the side attachment lug

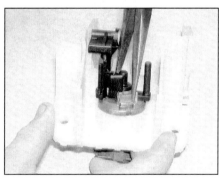

16.15a Turn the lock cylinder end cap anti-clockwise to release it . . .

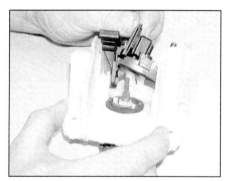

16.15b . . . then lift off the end cap . . .

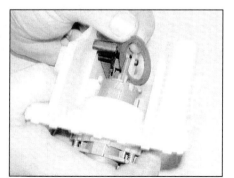

16.15c . . . and recover the seal

16.16a Withdraw the lock cylinder from the housing . . .

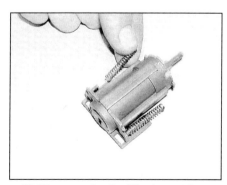

16.16b . . . and collect the two springs

Refitting

17 Refitting is a reversal of removal, bearing in mind the following points:

  a) *Ensure that the slot on the central locking motor operating arm engages with the peg on the lock cylinder end cap when refitting the motor.*

  b) *Reconnect the tailgate lock operating rod to the lever on the lock housing when refitting the housing to the tailgate.*

  c) *Obtain and fit a new foam plastic sealing sheet and circular sealing sheets to the tailgate apertures if the originals were damaged in any way during removal.*

  d) *Check that the lock mechanism operates correctly before refitting the tailgate trim panel.*

Tailgate lock striker

Removal

18 Remove the tailgate aperture lower panel as described in Section 26 for access to the striker plate bolts.

19 Mark the position of the striker on the body, for use when refitting. Unscrew the two securing bolts, and remove the striker from the body.

Refitting

20 Refitting is a reversal of removal. Before tightening the securing bolts, the position of the striker should be altered (the securing bolt holes are elongated) until satisfactory lock operation is obtained. Use the marks made prior to removal, if appropriate.

17 Central locking components – removal and refitting

Control unit

1 The central locking system is controlled by the passenger compartment protection unit (known as the 'body computer') which also controls the operation of the vehicle anti-theft system, engine immobiliser and the interior lamp delay timer. The unit is located under the facia adjacent to the steering column.

2 Should any problems be experienced with the operation of the central locking system or any of the other functions controlled by the body computer, the vehicle should be taken to a Citroën dealer for diagnostic investigation.

Door lock motor

3 The motor is integral with the door lock assembly. Removal and refitting of the lock assembly is described in Section 13.

Tailgate lock motor

4 Removal of the tailgate lock motor is described as part of the tailgate lock cylinder removal procedure in Section 16.

Remote control transmitter battery renewal

5 Using a small screwdriver, carefully prise

the two halves of the transmitter apart, and remove the battery. Note that on early models, it may be necessary to undo a small screw on the side of the unit before the two halves of the transmitter can be separated.

6 Fit the new battery and clip the transmitter back together. Refit the retaining screw, if applicable.

7 To initialise the unit after replacing the battery, switch on the ignition and operate the remote control transmitter.

18 Exterior mirrors and mirror glass – removal and refitting

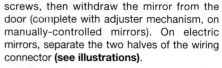

Mirror assembly

Removal

1 On models with electric mirrors, disconnect the battery negative terminal (refer to *Disconnecting the battery* in the Reference Section of this manual).

2 Referring to Section 12, release the edge of the door mirror interior trim panel, lift it up to disengage the locating lug and withdraw the panel. Where a manual door mirror is fitted, lift the plastic catch and remove the trim panel from the mirror control stalk.

3 Place a cloth over the upper edge of the door inner trim panel, to prevent the mirror securing screws falling inside the panel if you drop them. Remove the three mirror securing

screws, then withdraw the mirror from the door (complete with adjuster mechanism, on manually-controlled mirrors). On electric mirrors, separate the two halves of the wiring connector **(see illustrations)**.

Refitting

4 Refitting is a reversal of removal.

Mirror glass

Removal

5 Working at the bottom edge of the mirror glass, locate the ends of the spring clip which secures the glass.

6 Using a suitable screwdriver, spread the ends of the internal spring clip apart to release the glass **(see illustrations)**.

7 Withdraw the glass, and disconnect the wiring, where applicable. Recover the spring clip if it is loose.

Refitting

8 Fit the spring clip to the rear of the mirror glass, ensuring the clip is correctly located in the slots in the rear of the mirror glass.

9 Push the mirror glass into the mirror until the spring clip locks into position in the mirror adjuster groove **(see Haynes Hint)**.

> **HAYNES HINT** *Lightly grease the plastic ring on the mirror adjuster to aid refitting of the spring clip.*

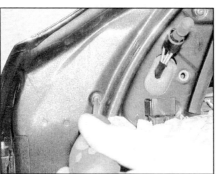

18.3a Undo the three door mirror securing screws . . .

18.3b . . . and withdraw the mirror from the door

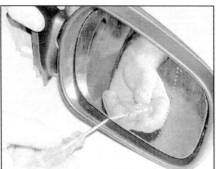

18.6a To remove the mirror glass, spread the ends of the internal spring clip apart to release the glass . . .

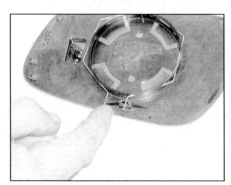

18.6b . . . as shown here with the glass removed

19 Windscreen, tailgate and fixed rear quarter window glass – general information

These areas of glass are secured by the tight fit of the weatherstrip in the body aperture, and are bonded in position with a special adhesive. Renewal of such fixed glass is a difficult, messy and time-consuming task, which is considered beyond the scope of the home mechanic. It is difficult, unless one has plenty of practice, to obtain a secure, waterproof fit. Furthermore, the task carries a high risk of breakage; this applies especially to the laminated glass windscreen. In view of this, owners are strongly advised to have this sort of work carried out by one of the many specialist windscreen fitters.

20 Rear quarter window (Coupé models) – removal and refitting

Removal

1 Open the window.
2 Support the glass, then working inside the vehicle, undo the nut securing the handle to the glass.
3 Using a small screwdriver, depress the centre portion of each hinge then remove the glass from the car.

Refitting

4 Refitting is a reversal of removal.

21 Sunroof – general information

The factory-fitted sunroof is of the electric tilt/slide type.

Due to the complexity of the sunroof mechanism, considerable expertise is required to repair, replace or adjust the sunroof components successfully. Removal of the roof first requires the headlining to be removed, which is a tedious operation, and

23.7 Front body panel retaining bolts (arrowed)

22.2 Undo the bolt securing the air inlet duct to the front body panel

not a task to be undertaken lightly. Any problems with the sunroof should be referred to a Citroën dealer.

For sunroof switch removal, see Chapter 12.

22 Body exterior fittings – removal and refitting

Radiator grille

Removal

1 To remove the bonnet-mounted grille, undo the screws around the periphery of the grille and withdraw the grille from the bonnet.
2 To remove the body-mounted grille, open the bonnet and undo the bolt securing the air inlet duct to the front body panel **(see illustration)**.
3 Undo the three screws along the upper edge of the grille, and the screw on either side of the air intake opening.
4 Lift up the air inlet duct and withdraw the grille from the front body panel **(see illustration)**.

Refitting

5 Refitting is a reversal of removal.

Wheelarch liners and mud shields

6 The wheelarch liners are secured by a combination of self-tapping screws, and push-fit clips. Removal is self-evident, and the clips can be released using a forked-shaped tool.

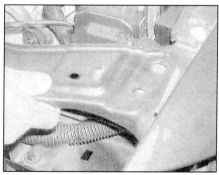

23.9a Lift the front body panel up at the sides to clear the locating studs . . .

22.4 Lift up the air inlet duct and withdraw the grille from the front body panel

7 The mud shields are secured in a similar manner, although certain panels may be secured using pop-rivets. Where applicable, drill out the pop-rivets, and use new rivets on refitting.

Body trim strips and badges

8 The various body trim strips and badges are held in position with a special adhesive tape. Removal requires the trim/badge to be heated, to soften the adhesive, and then cut away from the surface. Due to the high risk of damage to the vehicle paintwork during this operation, it is recommended that this task should be entrusted to a Citroën dealer.

23 Front body panel – removal and refitting

Removal

1 Remove the body-mounted radiator grille as described in Section 22.
2 Remove the front bumper as described in Section 6.
3 Remove the headlights as described in Chapter 12, Section 7.
4 Disconnect the bonnet release cable from the bonnet lock.
5 On diesel engine models, undo the bolts securing the cooling system expansion tank mounting bracket to the front body panel.
6 On models where the air cleaner support bracket is attached to the front body panel, undo the two bolts to release the support bracket.
7 Undo the upper retaining bolt each side securing the front body panel to the front wings **(see illustration)**.
8 Undo the two lower securing bolts each side, located under the headlight apertures.
9 Lift the front body panel up at the sides to clear the locating studs then carefully withdraw the panel from the front of the car **(see illustrations)**.

Refitting

10 Refitting is a reversal of removal.

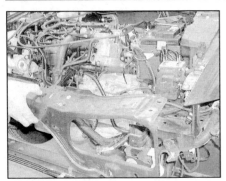

23.9b ... then carefully withdraw the panel from the front of the car

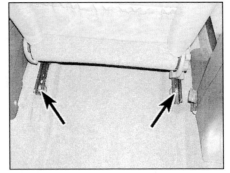

24.3 Undo the rear bolts (arrowed) securing the front seat rails to the floor

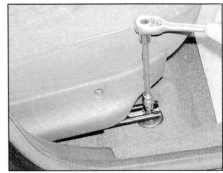

24.5 Move the seat fully rearwards and undo the front bolts securing the seat rails to the floor

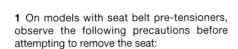

24 Seats – removal and refitting

Front seats

> ⚠ **Warning: Depending on model, the front seats may be equipped with seat belt pre-tensioners, and side air bags may be built into the outer sides of the seats. Where side air bags are fitted, refer to Chapter 12 for the precautions which should be observed when dealing with an air bag system. Do not tamper with the seat belt pre-tensioner unit in any way, and do not attempt to test the unit. Note that the unit is triggered if the mechanism is supplied with an electrical current (including via an ohmmeter), or if the assembly is subjected to a temperature of greater than 100°C.**

1 On models with seat belt pre-tensioners, observe the following precautions before attempting to remove the seat:

 a) Remove the ignition key.
 b) Disconnect the battery negative terminal (refer to 'Disconnecting the battery' in the Reference Section of this manual), and wait for two minutes before carrying out any further work.

Removal

2 Move the seat fully forwards.
3 Remove the bolts (one bolt on each side) securing the rear of the seat rails to the floor **(see illustration)**.
4 Move the seat fully rearwards.
5 Remove the bolts (one bolt on each side) securing the front of the seat rails to the floor **(see illustration)**.
6 Tip the seat backwards and disconnect the wiring connectors on the underside of the seat base **(see illustration)**.
7 Lift the seat from the vehicle and where applicable, recover the washers and the plastic plates from the floor.

Refitting

8 Refitting is a reversal of removal, but ensure that the plastic plates are in position on the floor (where applicable) and tighten the mounting bolts to the specified torque.

Rear seat back

Removal

9 Tilt the rear seat cushion forwards.
10 Unclip the seat belt buckles and undo the seat back hinge front retaining bolts **(see illustration)**.
11 Release the securing catches, and tilt the seat back forwards against the front seats.
12 Working at the rear of the seat back, unscrew the rear bolts securing the hinges to the vehicle floor, then withdraw the seat back.

Refitting

13 Refitting is a reversal of removal, but ensure that the seat belts are not trapped.

Rear seat cushion

Removal

14 Pull the releasing straps, then tilt the rear seat cushion forwards.
15 Undo the nuts securing the hinges to the floor, then lift the seat cushion from the vehicle **(see illustration)**.

Refitting

16 Refitting is a reversal of removal.

25 Seat belt components – removal and refitting

Note: Record the positions of the washers and spacers on the seat belt anchors, and ensure they are refitted in their original positions.

Front seat belt – Coupé models

Removal

1 Remove the rear passenger compartment side trim panel, as described in Section 26.
2 Feed the seat belt and the upper mounting plate through the aperture in the trim panel.
3 Prise off the trim cap from the lower belt

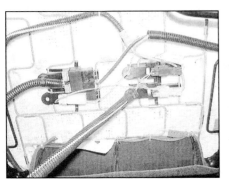

24.6 Tip the front seat backwards and disconnect the wiring connectors on the underside of the seat base

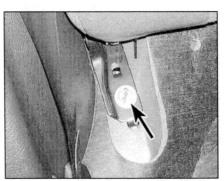

24.10 Rear seat back hinge front retaining bolt (arrowed)

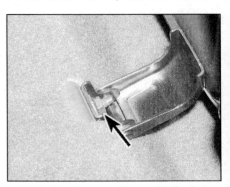

24.15 Rear seat cushion retaining bolt (arrowed)

anchorage bolt. Remove the bolt and washers, then pull out the anchorage bar, and free the seat belt from the bar.

4 Remove the inertia reel securing bolt, and withdraw the seat belt from the vehicle.

Refitting

5 Refitting is a reversal of removal. Ensure that all washers and/or spacers are positioned as noted before removal, and tighten all mounting bolts to the specified torque.

Front seat belt – Hatchback and Estate models

Removal

6 If desired, to improve access, remove the relevant front seat as described in Section 24.

7 Remove the centre pillar trim panels as described in Section 26.

8 Prise off the trim cap, then undo the lower belt and inertia reel anchor bolt, and recover the washer **(see illustrations)**.

9 Withdraw the inertia reel and its mounting plate from the door pillar, then withdraw the seat belt assembly from the vehicle **(see illustration)**.

Refitting

10 Refitting is a reversal of removal. Ensure that all washers and/or spacers are positioned as noted before removal, and tighten all mounting bolts to the specified torque.

Front seat belt stalk – models without front seat belt pre-tensioners

Removal

11 Remove the securing screws or release the clips, as applicable, and remove the trim panel from the side of the seat.

12 Each stalk is secured to the front seat frame by a bolt and washer.

Refitting

13 Tighten the securing bolt to the specified torque.

Front seat belt stalk – models with front seat belt pre-tensioners

 Warning: On models with seat belt pre-tensioners, observe the following precautions before attempting to remove the seat belt stalk assembly:
a) **Remove the ignition key.**
b) **Disconnect the battery negative terminal (refer to 'Disconnecting the battery' in the Reference Section of this manual), and wait for two minutes before carrying out any further work.**
Warning: Do not tamper with the pre-tensioner unit in any way, and do not attempt to test the unit. Note that the unit is triggered if the mechanism is supplied with an electrical current (including via an ohmmeter), or if the assembly is subjected to a temperature of greater than 100°C.

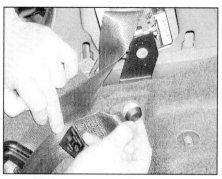

25.8a Prise off the trim cap . . .

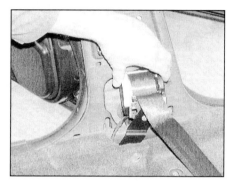

25.9 Withdraw the inertia reel and mounting plate from the door pillar

Removal

14 The seat belt stalk is an integral part of the seat belt pre-tensioner mechanism.

15 Undo the securing screw and remove the protective cover from the pre-tensioner mechanism **(see illustration)**.

16 Disconnect the pre-tensioner wiring connector from the tensioner unit **(see illustration)**.

17 Undo the pre-tensioner securing bolt and withdraw the pre-tensioner and seat belt stalk assembly from the seat.

 Warning: Do not hold the tensioner by the buckle or by the cable – only hold the unit around the tensioner body.

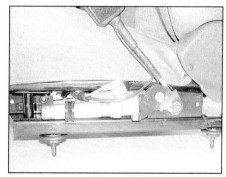

25.16 Seat belt pre-tensioner wiring connector and securing bolt

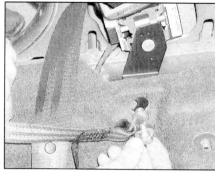

25.8b . . . then undo the front seat belt and inertia reel anchor bolt, and recover the washer

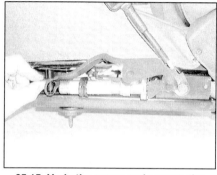

25.15 Undo the screw and remove the protective cover from the seat belt pre-tensioner mechanism

Refitting

18 Refitting is a reversal of removal, but observe the following precautions:
a) *Before refitting, ensure that the battery negative terminal is disconnected, and that the ignition is switched off.*
b) *Do not touch the seat belt buckle when the ignition is first switched on.*

Rear side seat belts

Removal

19 Remove the luggage and passenger compartment trim panels (Coupé models), or the luggage compartment trim panels (Hatchback and Estate models) as described in Section 26.

20 Undo the bolt securing the inertia reel to the body **(see illustration)**. Note the

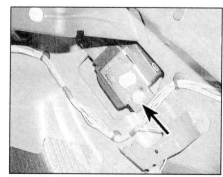

25.20 Rear side seat belt inertia reel retaining bolt (arrowed)

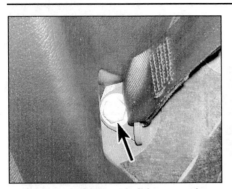

25.21 Rear side seat belt lower anchor bolt (arrowed)

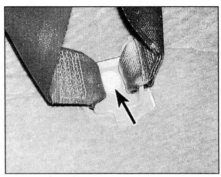

25.23 Rear centre seat belt retaining bolt (arrowed)

locations of any washers and spacers on the bolt.

21 Fold the rear seat cushion forwards for access to the lower seat belt anchor bolt, then unscrew the bolt and withdraw the seat belt assembly from the vehicle **(see illustration)**.

Refitting

22 Refitting is a reversal of removal, but ensure that any washers and spacers are positioned as noted before removal, and tighten the mounting bolts to the specified torque.

Rear centre belt and buckles

Removal

23 The assemblies can simply be unbolted from the floor panel, after folding the rear seat cushion forwards **(see illustration)**. Note the locations of any washers and spacers, to ensure correct refitting.

Refitting

24 Refitting is a reversal of removal. Ensure that all washers and/or spacers are positioned as noted before removal, and tighten all mounting bolts to the specified torque.

Front seat belt pre-tensioner electronic control unit

25 The seat belt pre-tensioners are activated by the air bag system electronic control unit which is located under the centre console. Refer to the air bag system information contained in Chapter 12 for

details of removal and refitting, and precautions to be taken.

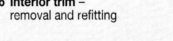

26 Interior trim – removal and refitting

Door inner trim panels

1 Refer to Section 12.

Luggage and passenger compartment trim panels – Coupé models

Removal

2 Disconnect the battery negative terminal (refer to *Disconnecting the battery* in the Reference Section of this manual).

3 Open the tailgate and remove the parcel shelf.

4 Undo the four screws securing the tailgate aperture lower trim panel to the rear sill panel.

5 Pull the panel outward at the sides to release the centre retaining clips, then lift it upwards to disengage the upper lugs. Remove the panel.

6 Unclip the trim cover, then undo the rear seat belt upper anchor bolt, noting the locations of the washers and spacers.

7 Prise the weatherstrip from the edge of the tailgate aperture, and from the rear edge of the door aperture.

8 Undo the two screws in the centre of the

parcel shelf support. Release the parcel shelf support from the side trim panel and remove it from the car.

9 Pull the quarterlight trim panel outwards to release the retaining clips and remove the panel.

10 Unclip the trim cover, then undo the front seat belt upper anchor bolt, noting the locations of the washers and spacers.

11 Remove the loudspeaker grille and undo the passenger compartment side trim panel retaining screw at the rear of the loudspeaker.

12 Undo the passenger compartment side trim panel upper rear retaining screw below the quarterlight window.

13 Starting at the front and working rearwards, release the passenger compartment side trim panel retaining clips and withdraw the panel. Disconnect the loudspeaker wiring and remove the panel from the car.

14 Where fitted, undo the screw at the base of the door pillar upper trim panel. Pull the panel outwards to release the retaining clips and remove the panel.

15 Using a forked tool, prise out the luggage compartment side panel retaining stud.

16 Undo the bolt securing the tie-down strap to the rear of the luggage compartment side panel and remove the strap.

17 Prise up the cover on the tie-down strap hook, undo the screw securing the hook to the side panel and remove the hook.

18 Lift up the luggage compartment floor covering and manipulate the side panel out from its location.

Refitting

19 Refitting is a reversal of removal, but ensure that the panels are correctly interlocked with each other and that all retaining clips are fully engaged. Tighten the seat belt anchor bolt to the specified torque.

Luggage compartment trim panels – Hatchback models

Removal

20 Disconnect the battery negative terminal (refer to *Disconnecting the battery* in the Reference Section of this manual).

21 Open the tailgate and remove the parcel shelf.

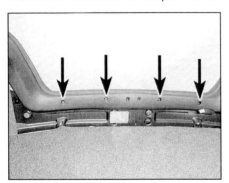

26.22 Undo the four tailgate aperture trim panel securing screws (arrowed) – Hatchback models

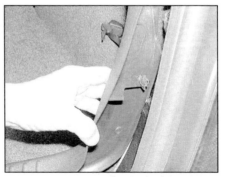

26.23a Pull the tailgate aperture trim panel outward at the sides to release the centre retaining clips . . .

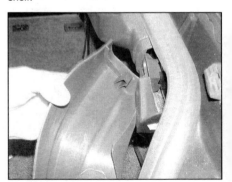

26.23b . . . then lift it upwards to disengage the upper lugs – Hatchback models

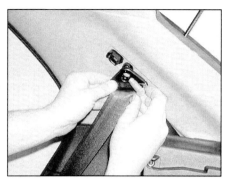

26.24 Undo the rear seat belt upper anchor bolt – Hatchback models

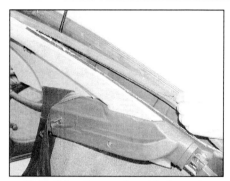

26.25 Prise the weatherstrip from the tailgate and rear door apertures – Hatchback models

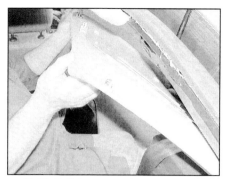

26.26 Pull the quarterlight trim panel outwards to release the clips and remove the panel – Hatchback models

22 Undo the four screws securing the tailgate aperture trim panel to the rear sill panel **(see illustration)**.

23 Pull the panel outward at the sides to release the centre retaining clips, then lift it upwards to disengage the upper lugs **(see illustrations)**. Remove the panel.

24 Unclip the trim cover, then undo the rear seat belt upper anchor bolt, noting the locations of the washers and spacers **(see illustration)**.

25 Prise the weatherstrip from the edge of the tailgate aperture, and from the rear door aperture **(see illustration)**.

26 Pull the quarterlight trim panel outwards to release the retaining clips and remove the panel **(see illustration)**.

27 Undo the wheelarch trim panel upper and lower retaining screws **(see illus-Trations)**.

28 Undo the screw at the rear and at the centre of the parcel shelf support. Release the parcel shelf support from the wheelarch liner and remove it from the car **(see illustrations)**.

29 Release the wheelarch liner retaining clips and remove the liner.

30 Using a small screwdriver, carefully prise the luggage compartment light unit from its location in the side panel. Disconnect the wiring connector and remove the light unit **(see illustrations)**.

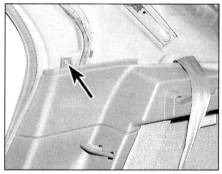

26.27a Undo the wheelarch trim panel upper retaining screw (arrowed) . . .

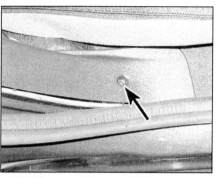

26.27b . . . and lower retaining screw (arrowed) – Hatchback models

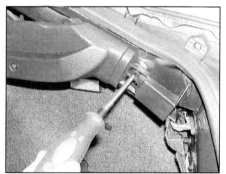

26.28a Undo the retaining screw at the rear of the parcel shelf support . . .

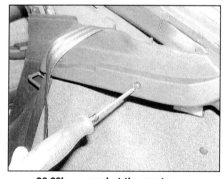

26.28b . . . and at the centre . . .

26.28c . . . then release the parcel shelf support from the wheelarch liner – Hatchback models

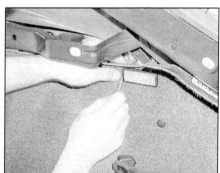

26.30a Carefully prise the luggage compartment light unit from the side panel . . .

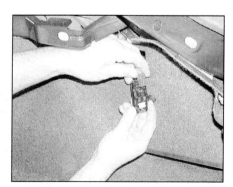

26.30b . . . then disconnect the wiring connector and remove the light unit – Hatchback models

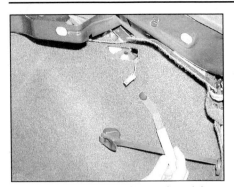

26.31 Prise out the side panel retaining stud – Hatchback models

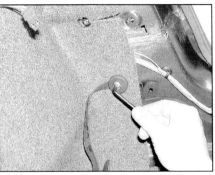

26.32 Undo the bolt securing the tie-down strap to the rear of the side panel – Hatchback models

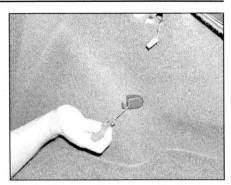

26.33a Prise up the cover on the tie-down strap hook . . .

31 Using a forked tool, prise out the side panel retaining stud **(see illustration)**.
32 Undo the bolt securing the tie-down strap to the rear of the side panel and remove the strap **(see illustration)**.
33 Prise up the cover on the tie-down strap hook, undo the screw securing the hook to the side panel and remove the hook **(see illustrations)**.
34 Lift up the luggage compartment floor covering and manipulate the side panel out from its location **(see illustration)**.

Refitting

35 Refitting is a reversal of removal, but ensure that the panels are correctly interlocked with each other and that

all retaining clips are fully engaged. Tighten the seat belt anchor bolt to the specified torque.

Luggage compartment trim panels – Estate models

Removal

36 Disconnect the battery negative terminal (refer to *Disconnecting the battery* in the Reference Section of this manual).
37 Open the tailgate and remove the parcel shelf. Open the storage compartment and remove any items stored in the compartment.
38 Prise the weatherstrip from around the tailgate aperture, and from the rear door aperture.

39 Undo the four screws securing the tailgate aperture lower trim panel to the rear sill panel and remove the panel **(see illustration)**.
40 Pull the quarterlight trim panel outwards to release the retaining clips and remove the panel **(see illustration)**.
41 Unclip the trim cover, then undo the rear seat belt upper anchor bolt, noting the locations of the washers and spacers **(see illustration)**.
42 Undo the wheelarch trim panel lower retaining screw, and the upper screws, one at each end of the parcel shelf support **(see illustrations)**.
43 Release the wheelarch liner retaining clips and remove the liner.
44 Release the parcel shelf support from its

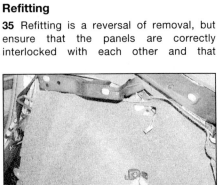

26.33b . . . then undo the screw securing the hook to the side panel – Hatchback models

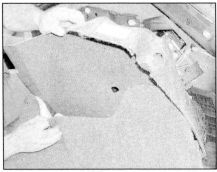

26.34 Lift up the luggage compartment floor covering and manipulate the side panel from its location – Hatchback models

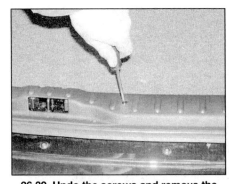

26.39 Undo the screws and remove the tailgate aperture lower trim panel – Estate models

26.40 Pull the quarterlight trim panel outwards to release the clips and remove the panel – Estate models

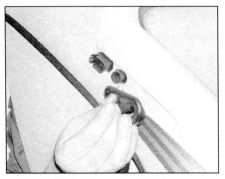

26.41 Undo the rear seat belt upper anchor bolt – Estate models

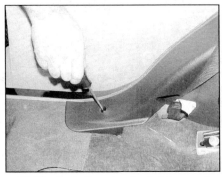

26.42a Undo the wheelarch trim panel lower retaining screw . . .

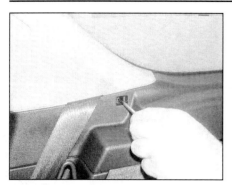

26.42b . . . and the upper screws at the front . . .

26.42c . . . and at the rear of the parcel shelf support – Estate models

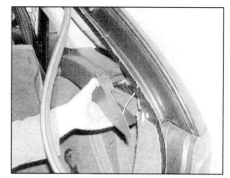

26.44a Release the parcel shelf support from its location . . .

location and, where applicable, reach behind and disconnect the wiring connector at the accessory socket (see illustrations). Release the remaining clips and remove the parcel shelf support from the car.

45 Release the rear door pillar upper trim panel retaining clips and remove the panel (see illustrations).

46 Undo the bolt securing the tie-down strap to the rear of the side panel and remove the strap (see illustration).

47 Prise up the cover on the tie-down strap hook, undo the screw securing the hook to the side panel and remove the hook.

48 Lift up the luggage compartment floor covering and manipulate the side panel out from its location (see illustration).

Refitting

49 Refitting is a reversal of removal, but ensure that the panels are correctly interlocked with each other and that all retaining clips are fully engaged. Tighten the seat belt anchor bolt to the specified torque.

Centre pillar trim panels – Hatchback and Estate models

Removal

50 Open the doors, and prise the weatherstrips from both sides of the centre pillar (see illustration).

51 Unclip the trim plate, then unbolt the upper seat belt anchor bolt (see illustration).

26.44b . . . then, where applicable, disconnect the wiring connector at the accessory socket – Estate models

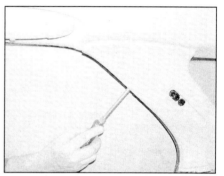

26.45a Release the rear door pillar upper trim panel retaining clips . . .

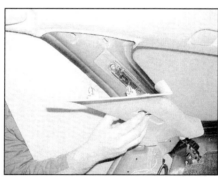

26.45b . . . and remove the panel – Estate models

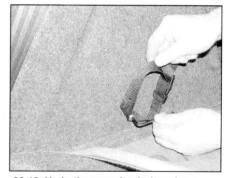

26.46 Undo the securing bolt and remove the tie-down strap – Estate models

26.48 Lift up the floor covering and manipulate the side panel from its location – Estate models

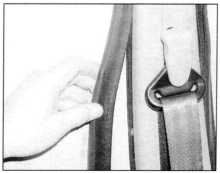

26.50 Prise the weatherstrips from both sides of the centre pillar

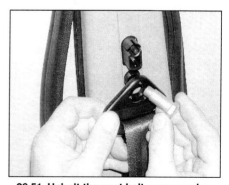

26.51 Unbolt the seat belt upper anchor bolt

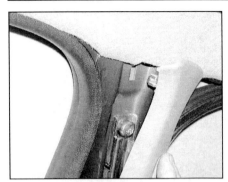

26.52 Release the upper trim panel from the pillar, and disengage it from the lower panel

26.53 Release the lower trim panel upper securing clips

26.54 Lift the lower trim panel upwards to disengage the two lower locating lugs (arrowed)

52 Pull the upper panel from the pillar to release the securing clips, disengage it from the lower panel and remove it from the car **(see illustration)**.

53 Release the two upper securing clips, exposed by removal of the upper panel **(see illustration)**.

54 Lift the panel upwards to disengage the two lower locating lugs **(see illustration)**.

55 Feed the seat belt through the slot in the panel and remove the panel from the car **(see illustration)**.

Refitting

56 Refitting is a reversal of removal. Tighten

the seat belt anchor bolt to the specified torque.

Tailgate trim panel

Removal

Note: *The design of most of the trim panel retaining clips and pegs is such that they will break during removal. Be prepared to obtain new items for refitting.*

57 Open the tailgate and remove the parcel shelf.

58 Remove the fastenings securing the lower trim panel in position. The fastenings consist of a mixture of screws and expanding pegs.

The expanding pegs are removed by unscrewing the centre portion then prising out the peg base **(see illustrations)**.

59 Using a small screwdriver, carefully prise off the interior handle cover. Undo the two screws now exposed, and remove the handle **(see illustrations)**.

60 Disengage the lower panel from the upper panel and remove the lower panel from the tailgate **(see illustration)**.

61 At the top of each side trim panel, tap in the centre pin of the two parcel shelf lifting string pegs. Note that the centre pins will be lost when doing this and two new pegs will be

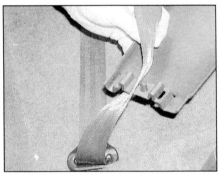

26.55 Feed the seat belt through the slot and remove the trim panel from the car

26.58a Unscrew the centre portion of the tailgate trim panel expanding pegs . . .

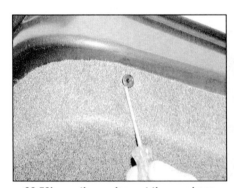

26.58b . . . then prise out the peg base

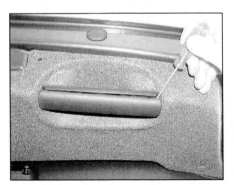

26.59a Prise off the tailgate interior handle cover . . .

26.59b . . . then undo the two screws and remove the handle

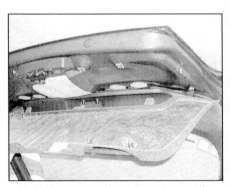

26.60 Disengage the tailgate lower trim panel from the upper panel and remove the lower panel

26.61a Tap in the centre pin of the parcel shelf lifting string pegs . . .

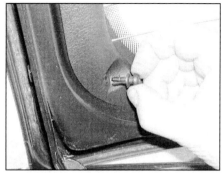

26.61b . . . then remove the lifting string pegs from the tailgate side trim panels

26.62a Release the side trim panels from the tailgate . . .

needed for refitting. Once the centre pin has been tapped in, the peg body can be withdrawn **(see illustrations)**.

62 Release the side trim panels from the tailgate and disengage their lower locating pegs from the intermediate trim panel **(see illustrations)**.

63 Unscrew the two plastic wing nuts in the centre of the intermediate trim panel **(see illustration)**.

64 Release any remaining peg fasteners then sharply pull the intermediate panel from the tailgate to release the internal retaining clips **(see illustrations)**. Be prepared for clip breakage.

65 Remove the intermediate panel from the tailgate **(see illustration)**.

Refitting

66 Refitting is a reversal of removal, ensuring that all broken clips and fastenings are renewed.

Carpets

67 The passenger compartment floor carpet consists of a front and rear section, and is secured at its edges by screws or various types of clips.

68 Carpet removal and refitting is reasonably straightforward, but time-consuming, due to the fact that all adjoining trim panels must be removed first, as must components such as the seats and centre console.

Headlining

Note: *Headlining removal requires considerable skill and experience if it is to be carried out without damage, and is therefore best entrusted to a Citroën dealer or bodywork specialist. A general overview of the procedure is given below for those with the expertise to attempt the operation on a DIY basis.*

69 The headlining is clipped and glued to the roof, and can be withdrawn only once all fittings such as the grab handles, courtesy lights, sun visors, sunroof (if fitted), overhead console (if fitted), front, centre and rear pillar trim panels, and associated additional panels

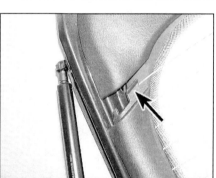

26.62b . . . and disengage their lower locating pegs (arrowed) from the intermediate trim panel

have been removed. The door, tailgate and sunroof aperture weatherstrips will also have to be prised clear and any additional screws and clips removed. Once the headlining attachments are released, the adhesive bonding in the centre panels must be broken using a hot air gun and spatula, starting at the front and working rearwards.

70 When refitting, a coat of neoprene adhesive (available from Citroën dealers) must be applied to the centre panels in the locations noted during removal. Position the headlining carefully and refit all components disturbed during removal. Clean the headlining with soap and water or white spirit on completion.

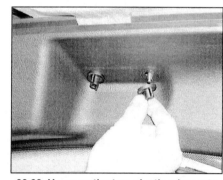

26.63 Unscrew the two plastic wing nuts in the centre of the tailgate intermediate trim panel

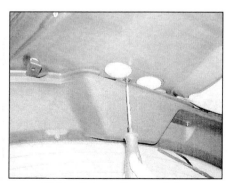

26.64a Release the remaining intermediate trim panel fasteners . . .

26.64b . . . then sharply pull the panel from the tailgate to release the internal clips

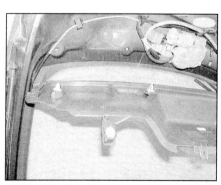

26.65 With the clips released, remove the intermediate trim panel from the tailgate

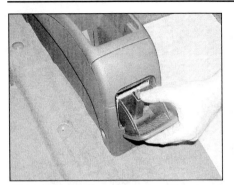

27.2a Remove the ashtray from the rear of the centre console . . .

27.2b . . . then carefully prise off the trim cover or switch surround

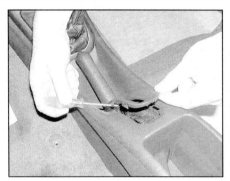

27.3a Prise up the handbrake lever surround . . .

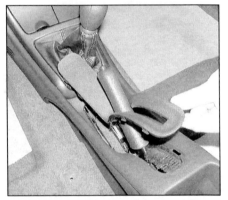

27.3b . . . and withdraw the surround over the handbrake lever

27 Centre console – removal and refitting

Removal

1 Disconnect the battery negative terminal (refer to *Disconnecting the battery* in the Reference Section of this manual).

2 Remove the ashtray from the rear of the centre console then carefully prise off the trim cover or switch surround **(see illustrations)**. On models with rear electric windows, prise the switches from their locations and disconnect the wiring connectors.

3 Prise up the handbrake lever surround and withdraw the surround over the handbrake lever **(see illustrations)**.

4 Remove the ashtray from the front of the centre console, then prise free and remove the oddments tray **(see illustrations)**.

5 On models with manual transmission, unclip the gear lever gaiter from the console, and slide it up the gear lever **(see illustration)**.

6 On models with automatic transmission, unclip the selector lever position indicator trim plate from the console.

7 Release the retaining clips and remove the gear lever gaiter surround **(see illustrations)**.

8 Undo the three upper screws and two lower screws securing the ashtray/cigarette lighter housing to the centre console and facia. Withdraw the housing and disconnect the relevant wiring from the rear **(see illustrations)**.

27.4a Remove the ashtray from the front of the centre console . . .

27.4b . . . then prise free and remove the oddments tray

27.5 On manual transmission models, unclip the gear lever gaiter and slide it up the gear lever

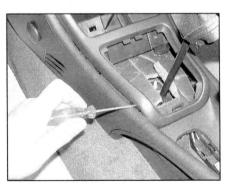

27.7a Release the gear lever gaiter surround retaining clips . . .

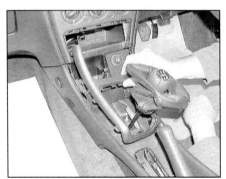

27.7b . . . and remove the surround

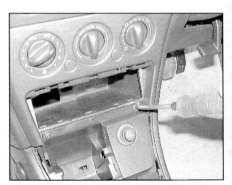

27.8a Undo the three ashtray/cigarette lighter housing upper retaining screws . . .

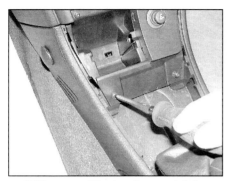

27.8b ... and the two lower retaining screws ...

27.8c ... then withdraw the housing and disconnect the wiring

27.9 Undo the screw each side securing the front of the centre console to the facia

9 Working in the ashtray/cigarette lighter housing aperture, undo the screw each side securing the front of the centre console to the facia **(see illustration)**.

10 Undo the screw each side securing the centre console to the floor mounting bracket **(see illustration)**.

11 Pull the centre console rearward to disengage it from the facia, then lift it up at the rear and over the handbrake lever and gear/selector lever **(see illustration)**. Remove the console from the car.

12 For access to the components under the centre console, lift off the sound insulation padding around the gear/selector lever and over the handbrake lever mountings **(see illustrations)**. The clips securing the

wiring ducts can now be removed and the ducts moved to one side. Remove any additional sound insulation padding as necessary.

Refitting

13 Refitting is a reversal of removal.

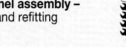

28 Facia panel assembly – removal and refitting

Facia centre panel

Removal

1 Disconnect the battery negative terminal

(refer to *Disconnecting the battery* in the Reference Section of this manual).

2 Remove the ashtray/cigarette lighter housing as described in Section 27, paragraphs 4 to 8.

3 Remove the radio/cassette player as described in Chapter 12.

4 Undo the two screws at the top of the oddments tray aperture, below the heater/ventilation controls **(see illustration)**.

5 Undo the four screws in the radio/cassette player aperture; two at the side and two on the lower edge **(see illustration)**.

6 Withdraw the lower edge of the centre panel from the facia, then disengage

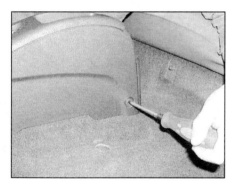

27.10 Undo the screw each side securing the centre console to the floor mounting bracket

27.11 Pull the centre console rearward, then lift it up and over the handbrake lever and gear/selector lever

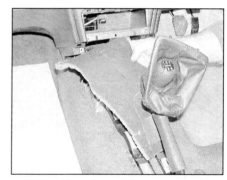

27.12a For access to the components under the facia, remove the sound insulation padding around the gear lever ...

27.12b ... and around the handbrake mountings

28.4 Undo the two facia centre panel retaining screws at the top of the oddments tray aperture ...

28.5 ... and the four screws in the radio/cassette player aperture

28.6a Withdraw the lower edge of the centre panel from the facia . . .

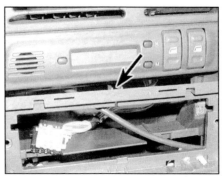

28.6b . . . then disengage the upper centre locating tag (arrowed)

28.8 Release the heater/ventilation control unit from the facia centre panel

the upper centre locating tag **(see illustrations)**.

7 Where applicable, disconnect the wiring connectors from the switches on the right-hand side of the centre panel.

8 Release the heater/ventilation control unit and remove the centre panel from the car **(see illustration)**. Note the locations of the wiring connectors to ensure correct refitting.

Refitting

9 Refitting is a reversal of removal, but ensure that the wiring connectors are reconnected to their correct locations as noted before removal.

Steering column shrouds
Removal

10 Disconnect the battery negative terminal (refer to *Disconnecting the battery* in the Reference Section of this manual).

11 Unscrew the three lower steering column shroud securing screws. Unclip and lift off the upper shroud, then remove the lower shroud **(see illustrations)**.

Refitting

12 Refitting is a reversal of removal.

Instrument panel surround
Removal

13 Remove the steering column shrouds and the facia centre panel as described previously.

14 Carefully prise off the centre trim panel located below the facia centre air vents **(see illustration)**.

15 With the trim panel removed, prise out the electric window lift switches (where fitted) and disconnect the wiring connectors from each switch **(see illustration)**.

16 Carefully prise off the side trim panel located below the facia side air/demister vent **(see illustration)**. Disconnect the wiring connectors from the panel switches and remove the side trim panel.

17 Undo the instrument panel surround securing screws from the following locations:

a) *Two screws along the lower edge of the panel, below the facia centre air vents **(see illustration)**.*

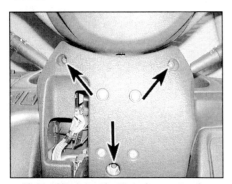

28.11a Unscrew the three lower steering column shroud securing screws (arrowed) . . .

28.11b . . . then unclip and lift off the upper shroud, and remove the lower shroud

28.14 Prise off the centre trim panel located below the facia centre air vents

28.15 Prise out the electric window lift switches (where fitted) and disconnect the wiring connectors

28.16 Remove the side trim panel located below the facia side air/demister vent

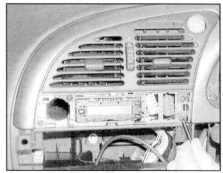

28.17a Undo the instrument panel surround securing screws below the facia centre air vents . . .

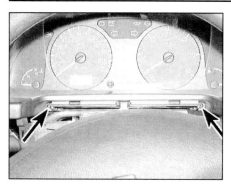

28.17b ... from the lower edge, above the steering column (arrowed) ...

28.17c ... from above the instrument panel ...

28.17d ... and in the side trim panel aperture

b) *Two screws along the lower edge of the panel, above the steering column* **(see illustration)**.
c) *Two screws above the instrument panel* **(see illustration)**.
d) *Two screws in the side trim panel aperture* **(see illustration)**.

18 Withdraw the instrument panel surround from the facia and disconnect the wiring connectors from the hazard warning switch and graphic display (as applicable) **(see illustrations)**. Remove the instrument panel surround from the car.

Refitting

19 Refitting is a reversal of removal, but ensure that all wiring connectors are securely reconnected, and that all the panels are correctly retained by their clips and screws.

Glovebox

Removal

20 Disconnect the battery negative terminal (refer to *Disconnecting the battery* in the Reference Section of this manual).
21 Open the glovebox lid and carefully prise out the glovebox light. Disconnect the wiring connector and remove the light.
22 Undo the three upper screws, three lower screws and two side screws, securing the glovebox to the facia **(see illustrations)**.
23 Withdraw the glovebox (complete with lid) from the facia **(see illustration)**.

Refitting

24 Refitting is a reversal of removal, but feed the wiring for the glovebox light through the glovebox light aperture before locating the glovebox in the facia.

Complete facia assembly

Removal

Note: *This is an involved operation entailing the removal of numerous components and assemblies, and the disconnection of a multitude of wiring connectors. Make notes on the location of all disconnected wiring, or attach labels to the connectors, to avoid confusion when refitting.*

25 Disconnect the battery negative terminal

28.18a Withdraw the instrument panel surround from the facia ...

28.18b ... and disconnect the wiring connectors

28.22a Undo the glovebox upper securing screws ...

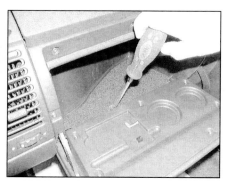

28.22b ... lower securing screws ...

28.22c ... and side securing screws ...

28.23 ... then withdraw the glovebox from the facia

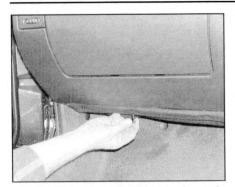

28.33a Release the facia lower trim stud screws . . .

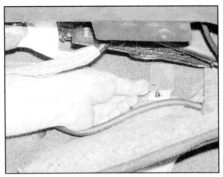

28.33b . . . and push studs, then remove the trim from the floor and underside of the facia

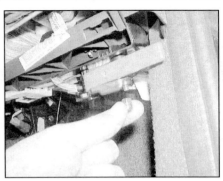

28.34 Undo the nut and withdraw the bonnet release handle from the stud below the facia

(refer to *Disconnecting the battery* in the Reference Section of this manual).

26 Remove the centre console as described in Section 27.

27 Remove the facia centre panel, steering column shrouds, instrument panel surround, and the glovebox as described previously in this Section.

28 Remove the steering wheel as described in Chapter 10.

29 Remove the steering column combination switches as described in Chapter 12, Section 4.

30 Undo the screw located in the upper centre of the instrument panel, and withdraw the panel from the facia. Disconnect the wiring connectors at the rear of the instrument panel and remove the panel from the facia.

31 Remove the windscreen wiper motor assembly, as described in Chapter 12.

32 Where fitted, remove the passenger's air bag as described in Chapter 12.

33 Release the stud screws and the push studs, and remove the lower trim from the floor and from the underside of the facia **(see illustrations)**.

34 Undo the retaining nut and withdraw the bonnet release handle from the stud below the facia **(see illustration)**.

35 Carefully prise up the loudspeaker tweeters from the top of the facia on each side. Disconnect the wiring connectors and remove the tweeters **(see illustration)**.

36 Working through the glovebox aperture, disconnect the wiring connector from the

passenger's air bag override switch (where fitted).

37 Working in the windscreen wiper motor compartment, undo the three nuts securing the facia to the bulkhead **(see illustration)**.

38 Undo the two bolts located above the steering column, in the instrument panel aperture **(see illustration)**.

39 Working through the front centre of the facia, undo the bolt at the rear of the radio/cassette player location, and the bolt at the side of the radio/cassette player aperture **(see illustrations)**.

40 Undo the bolt at the base of the facia above the centre console location, and the two facia side securing screws **(see illustrations)**.

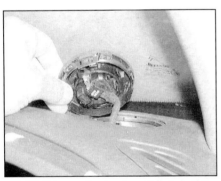

28.35 Prise up the loudspeaker tweeters and disconnect the wiring

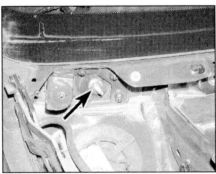

28.37 One of the three facia retaining nuts (arrowed) accessible from inside the windscreen wiper motor compartment

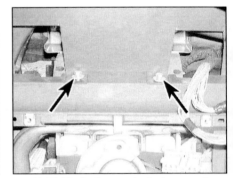

28.38 Undo the two bolts (arrowed) located above the steering column

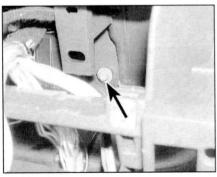

28.39a Undo the bolt (arrowed) at the rear of the radio/cassette player location . . .

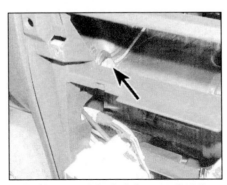

28.39b . . . and the bolt (arrowed) at the side of the radio/cassette player aperture

28.40a Undo the bolt at the base of the facia above the centre console location . . .

28.40b . . . and the screw (arrowed) on each side of the facia

28.41 Ease the facia from the bulkhead and feed the wiring through the various apertures

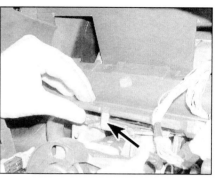

28.43 When refitting check that the facia is located over the tag (arrowed) on the steering column

41 Carefully ease the facia from the bulkhead, ensuring that all wiring is disconnected and fed through the various apertures **(see illustration)**. Withdraw the facia fully from its location and remove it from the car.

Refitting

42 Locate the facia in position, ensuring that all wiring is positioned in the correct apertures ready for reconnection.
43 Check that the facia is located correctly over the tag on the steering column, then refit the retaining screws, nuts and bolts **(see illustration)**.

44 Reconnect the wiring connector to the passenger's air bag override switch (where fitted).
45 Reconnect the wiring connectors and fit the tweeters to their locations in the top of the facia.
46 Refit the bonnet release handle to the stud below the facia and secure with the nut and washer.
47 Refit the lower trim to the floor and underside of the facia.
48 Where applicable, refit the passenger's air bag as described in Chapter 12.
49 Refit the windscreen wiper motor assembly, as described in Chapter 12.

50 Reconnect the instrument panel wiring connectors, locate the panel in the facia and secure with the centre retaining screw.
51 Refit the steering column combination switches as described in Chapter 12, Section 4.
52 Refit the steering wheel as described in Chapter 10.
53 Refit the glovebox, instrument panel surround, steering column shrouds and facia centre panel as described previously in this Section.
54 Refit the centre console as described in Section 27.

Chapter 12
Body electrical systems

Contents

Air bag system – general information, precautions and system de-
   activation 21
Air bag system components – removal and refitting 22
Anti-theft alarm system and engine immobiliser –
   general information 20
Bulbs (exterior lights) – renewal 5
Bulbs (interior lights) – renewal 6
Cigarette lighter – removal and refitting 11
Clock – removal and refitting 10
Electrical fault finding – general information 2
Exterior light units – removal and refitting 7
Fuses and relays – general information 3
General information and precautions 1

Headlight beam alignment – general information 8
Horn – removal and refitting 12
Instrument panel – removal and refitting 9
Loudspeakers – removal and refitting 18
Radio aerial – removal and refitting 19
Radio/cassette player – removal and refitting 17
Rear window wiper motor – removal and refitting 15
Switches – removal and refitting 4
Windscreen/rear window washer system components –
   removal and refitting 16
Windscreen wiper components – removal and refitting 14
Wiper arm – removal and refitting 13

Degrees of difficulty

Easy, suitable for novice with little experience 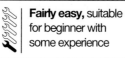	Fairly easy, suitable for beginner with some experience	Fairly difficult, suitable for competent DIY mechanic	Difficult, suitable for experienced DIY mechanic	Very difficult, suitable for expert DIY or professional

Specifications

General

System type . . . . 12-volt negative earth

Bulbs

	Type	Wattage
Headlights:		
Dip/main beam (single optic system)	H4	60/55
Dip/main beam (twin optic system)	H7	55
Front foglight	H1	55
Front sidelights	Push-fit	5
Direction indicator light	Bayonet	21
Direction indicator side repeater	Push-fit	5
Stop/tail light:		
Coupé and Hatchback models	Bayonet	21/5
Estate models	Bayonet	21/4
Rear foglight	Bayonet	21
Reversing light	Bayonet	21
Number plate light	Push-fit	5
High-level stoplight	Push-fit	5
Interior lights	Push fit/festoon	5

Torque wrench setting	Nm	lbf ft
Driver's air bag unit securing screws	8	6

1 General information and precautions

Warning: Before carrying out any work on the electrical system, read through the precautions given in 'Safety first!' at the beginning of this manual, and in Chapter 5A.

The electrical system is of 12-volt negative earth type. Power for the lights and all electrical accessories is supplied by a lead-acid type battery, which is charged by the alternator.

This Chapter covers repair and service procedures for the various electrical components not associated with the engine. Information on the battery, alternator and starter motor can be found in Chapter 5A.

It should be noted that, prior to working on any component in the electrical system, the battery negative terminal should first be disconnected, to prevent the possibility of electrical short-circuits.

Caution: Before proceeding, refer to 'Disconnecting the battery' in the Reference Section of this manual for further information.

2 Electrical fault finding – general information

Note: *Refer to the precautions given in 'Safety first!' and in Section 1 of this Chapter before starting work. The following tests relate to testing of the main electrical circuits, and should not be used to test delicate electronic circuits (such as engine management systems or anti-lock braking systems), particularly where an electronic control unit is used.*

General

1 A typical electrical circuit consists of an electrical component, any switches, relays, motors, fuses, fusible links or circuit breakers related to that component, and the wiring and connectors which link the component to both the battery and the chassis. To help to pinpoint a problem in an electrical circuit, wiring diagrams are included at the end of this Chapter.

2 Before attempting to diagnose an electrical fault, first study the appropriate wiring diagram, to obtain a more complete understanding of the components included in the particular circuit concerned. The possible sources of a fault can be narrowed down by noting whether other components related to the circuit are operating properly. If several components or circuits fail at one time, the problem is likely to be related to a shared fuse or earth connection.

3 Electrical problems usually stem from simple causes, such as loose or corroded connections, a faulty earth connection, a blown fuse, a melted fusible link, or a faulty relay. Visually inspect the condition of all fuses, wires and connections in a problem circuit before testing the components. Use the wiring diagrams to determine which terminal connections will need to be checked, in order to pinpoint the trouble-spot.

4 The basic tools required for electrical fault finding include a circuit tester or voltmeter (a 12-volt bulb with a set of test leads can also be used for certain tests); a self-powered test light (sometimes known as a continuity tester); an ohmmeter (to measure resistance); a battery and set of test leads; and a jumper wire, preferably with a circuit breaker or fuse incorporated, which can be used to bypass suspect wires or electrical components. Before attempting to locate a problem with test instruments, use the wiring diagram to determine where to make the connections.

5 To find the source of an intermittent wiring fault (usually due to a poor or dirty connection, or damaged wiring insulation), a 'wiggle' test can be performed on the wiring. This involves wiggling the wiring by hand, to see if the fault occurs as the wiring is moved. It should be possible to narrow down the source of the fault to a particular section of wiring. This method of testing can be used in conjunction with any of the tests described in the following sub-Sections.

6 Apart from problems due to poor connections, two basic types of fault can occur in an electrical circuit – open-circuit, or short-circuit.

7 Open-circuit faults are caused by a break somewhere in the circuit, which prevents current from flowing. An open-circuit fault will prevent a component from working, but will not cause the relevant circuit fuse to blow.

8 Short-circuit faults are normally caused by a breakdown in wiring insulation, which allows a feed wire to touch either another wire, or an earthed component such as the bodyshell. This allows the current flowing in the circuit to 'escape' along an alternative route, usually to earth. As the circuit does not now follow its original complete path, it is known as a 'short' circuit. A short-circuit fault will normally cause the relevant circuit fuse to blow.

Finding an open-circuit

9 To check for an open-circuit, connect one lead of a circuit tester or voltmeter to either the negative battery terminal or a known good earth.

10 Connect the other lead to a connector in the circuit being tested, preferably nearest to the battery or fuse.

11 Switch on the circuit, bearing in mind that some circuits are live only when the ignition switch is moved to a particular position.

12 If voltage is present (indicated either by the tester bulb lighting or a voltmeter reading, as applicable), this means that the section of the circuit between the relevant connector and the battery is problem-free.

13 Continue to check the remainder of the circuit in the same fashion.

14 When a point is reached at which no voltage is present, the problem must lie between that point and the previous test point with voltage. Most problems can be traced to a broken, corroded or loose connection.

Finding a short-circuit

15 To check for a short-circuit, first disconnect the load(s) from the circuit (loads are the components which draw current from a circuit, such as bulbs, motors, heating elements, etc).

16 Remove the relevant fuse from the circuit, and connect a circuit tester or voltmeter to the fuse connections.

17 Switch on the circuit, bearing in mind that some circuits are live only when the ignition switch is moved to a particular position.

18 If voltage is present (indicated either by the tester bulb lighting or a voltmeter reading, as applicable), this means that there is a short-circuit.

19 If no voltage is present, but the fuse still blows with the load(s) connected, this indicates an internal fault in the load(s).

Finding an earth fault

20 The battery negative terminal is connected to 'earth' – the metal of the engine/transmission and the car body – and most systems are wired so that they only receive a positive feed, the current returning via the metal of the car body. This means that the component mounting and the body form part of that circuit. Loose or corroded mountings can therefore cause a range of electrical faults, ranging from total failure of a circuit, to a puzzling partial fault. In particular, lights may shine dimly (especially when another circuit sharing the same earth point is in operation), motors (eg, wiper motors or the radiator cooling fan motor) may run slowly, and the operation of one circuit may have an apparently-unrelated effect on another. Note that earth straps are used between certain components, such as the engine/transmission and the body, usually where there is no metal-to-metal contact between components, due to flexible rubber mountings, etc.

21 To check whether a component is properly earthed, disconnect the battery, and connect one lead of an ohmmeter to a known good earth point. Connect the other lead to the wire or earth connection being tested. The resistance reading should be zero; if not, check the connection as follows.

22 If an earth connection is thought to be faulty, dismantle the connection, and clean back to bare metal both the bodyshell and the wire terminal or the component earth connection mating surface. Be careful to remove all traces of dirt and corrosion, then use a knife to trim away any paint, so that a clean metal-to-metal joint is made. On reassembly, tighten the joint fasteners securely; if a wire terminal is being refitted,

3.3a For access to the fuses, remove the cover from the interior fuse/relay box . . .

use serrated washers between the terminal and the bodyshell, to ensure a clean and secure connection. When the connection is remade, prevent the onset of corrosion in the future by applying a coat of petroleum jelly or silicone-based grease, or by spraying on (at regular intervals) a proprietary ignition sealer or water-dispersant lubricant.

3 Fuses and relays – general information

Fuses

1 Fuses are designed to break a circuit when a predetermined current is reached, in order to protect the components and wiring which could be damaged by excessive current flow. Any excessive current flow will be due to a fault in the circuit, usually a short-circuit (see Section 2).
2 The main fuses are located in the interior fuse/relay box below the steering column on the driver's side of the facia, and in the engine compartment fuse/relay box on the left-hand side of the engine compartment.
3 For access to the interior fuses, pull the fuse/relay box cover from the facia. For access to the engine compartment fuses, lift off the cover over the fuse/relay box **(see illustrations)**.
4 A blown fuse can be recognised from its melted or broken wire.
5 To remove a fuse, first ensure that the relevant circuit is switched off.

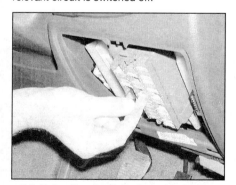

3.6 Using the plastic tool provided in the fuse/relay box to pull a fuse from its location

3.3b . . . and engine compartment fuse/relay box

6 Using the plastic tool provided in the fuse/relay box, pull the fuse from its location **(see illustration)**.
7 Spare fuses are provided in the blank terminal positions in the fuse/relay box.
8 Before renewing a blown fuse, trace and rectify the cause, and always use a fuse of the correct rating. Never substitute a fuse of a higher rating, or make temporary repairs using wire or metal foil; more serious damage, or even fire, could result.
9 Note that the fuses are colour-coded as follows. Refer to the wiring diagrams for details of the fuse ratings and the circuits protected:

Colour	Rating
Orange	5A
Red	10A
Blue	15A
Yellow	20A
Clear or white	25A
Green	30A

10 Additional 'maxi-fuses' are located in the engine compartment fuse/relay box. These are generally known as 'fusible links' and carry a heavy current for the major vehicle circuits. Fusible links do not normally blow, but if they do, this indicates a major circuit failure or short-circuit.

Relays

11 A relay is an electrically-operated switch, which is used for the following reasons:
a) *A relay can switch a heavy current remotely from the circuit in which the current is flowing, allowing the use*

4.3 Disconnect the wiring connector from the steering wheel switches circuit board

of lighter-gauge wiring and switch contacts.
b) *A relay can receive more than one control input, unlike a mechanical switch.*
c) *A relay can have a timer function – for example, the intermittent wiper relay.*

12 Most of the relays are located in the interior fuse/relay box, or in the engine compartment fuse/relay box. Depending on model and equipment fitted, further relays may be located on, or adjacent to, the components they control.
13 If a circuit or system controlled by a relay develops a fault, and the relay is suspect, operate the system. If the relay is functioning, it should be possible to hear it 'click' as it is energised. If this is the case, the fault lies with the components or wiring of the system. If the relay is not being energised, then either the relay is not receiving a main supply or a switching voltage, or the relay itself is faulty. Testing is by the substitution of a known good unit, but be careful – while some relays are identical in appearance and in operation, others look similar but perform different functions.
14 To remove a relay, first ensure that the relevant circuit is switched off. In most cases, the relay can then simply be pulled out from the socket, and pushed back into position. Note, however, that with the ever increasing standardisation of vehicle wiring and electrical system components, many relays are now 'welded' in position in their relevant circuit boards for ease of manufacture. This means that the relays are soldered in place and cannot be individually removed. If faulty, the complete circuit board or relay housing must be renewed as an assembly. Changes of this nature occur regularly during the course of vehicle production and are not normally documented by the vehicle manufacturer. Therefore, if a relay appears reluctant to come free from its location, consider that it may be of the welded type and consult a Citroën dealer for the latest information.

4 Switches – removal and refitting

Note: *Disconnect the battery negative terminal before removing any switch, and reconnect the terminal after refitting the switch. Refer to 'Disconnecting the battery' in the Reference Section of this manual.*

Ignition switch/steering column lock

1 Refer to Chapter 10.

Steering wheel switches

2 Remove the air bag unit as described in Section 22.
3 Disconnect the wiring connector from the steering wheel switches circuit board located in the slot at the top of the steering wheel **(see illustration)**.

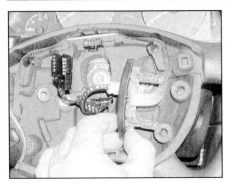

4.4a Withdraw the switches from their locations in the steering wheel . . .

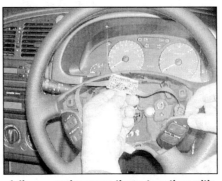

4.4b . . . and remove them, together with the wiring harness

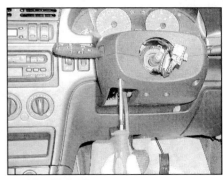

4.7a Undo the two upper screws . . .

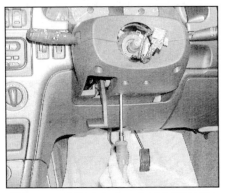

4.7b . . . and the lower screw securing the steering column shrouds to the steering column

4 Withdraw the switches from their locations in the steering wheel, and remove them, together with the wiring harness from the wheel (see illustrations)

5 Refit the switch assembly using a reversal of removal, then refit the air bag unit as described in Section 22.

Steering column combination switches

6 Remove the steering wheel as described in Chapter 10.

7 Undo the three screws securing the steering column shrouds to the steering column (see illustrations).

8 Unclip and lift off the upper shroud, then remove the lower shroud (see illustrations).

9 On models equipped with an air bag,

remove the air bag clock spring as described in Section 22.

10 Disconnect the wiring connectors at the rear of the steering column switches (see illustration).

11 Undo the three screws securing the switch housing to the steering column and remove the housing from the column (see illustrations).

12 The relevant switch can now be removed from the housing after unscrewing the two retaining screws.

13 Refitting is a reversal of removal.

Facia-mounted switches

Centre facia-mounted upper switches

14 Carefully prise the trim panel surround from the switches (see illustrations).

4.8a Unclip and lift off the upper shroud . . .

4.8b . . . then remove the lower shroud

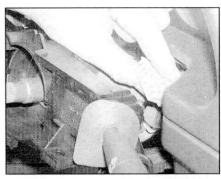

4.10 Disconnect the wiring connectors at the rear of the steering column switches

4.11a Undo the three screws (arrowed) securing the switch housing to the steering column . . .

4.11b . . . and remove the housing from the column

4.14a Carefully prise free the trim panel surround . . .

4.14b . . . and remove the surround from the facia upper switches

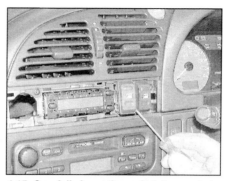

4.15 Carefully lever the switch forwards to release the retaining clips

4.16 Pull the switch out and disconnect the wiring plug

15 Using a small screwdriver, carefully lever the switch forwards to release the retaining clips **(see illustration)**.

16 Pull the switch out, then disconnect the wiring plug and remove the switch **(see illustration)**.

17 Refitting is a reversal of removal.

Centre facia-mounted lower switches

18 Remove the facia centre panel as described in Chapter 11.

19 With the panel removed, depress the retaining catches at the rear of the switch and remove the switch from the panel **(see illustrations)**.

20 Refitting is a reversal of removal.

Driver's side facia-mounted switches

21 Carefully prise the switch panel from its location in the facia, then withdraw the panel and disconnect the switch wiring connectors **(see illustrations)**.

22 Depress the retaining catches at the rear of the switch(es) and remove the switch(es) from the panel **(see illustrations)**.

23 Refitting is a reversal of removal.

Hazard warning switch

24 Remove the instrument panel surround as described in Chapter 11, Section 28.

25 Depress the retaining catches at the rear of the switch and remove the switch from the panel **(see illustration)**.

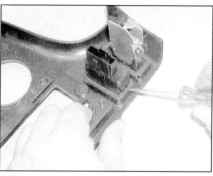

4.19a Depress the retaining catches at the rear of the facia lower switches . . .

4.19b . . . and remove the relevant switch from the centre panel

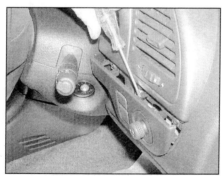

4.21a Carefully prise the driver's side switch panel from the facia . . .

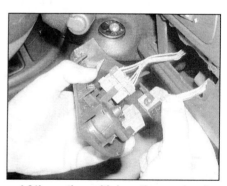

4.21b . . . then withdraw the panel and disconnect the switch wiring connectors

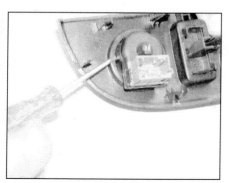

4.22a Depress the retaining catches at the rear of the relevant switch . . .

4.22b . . . and remove the switch from the panel

4.25 Depress the rear retaining catches and remove the hazard warning switch from the instrument panel surround

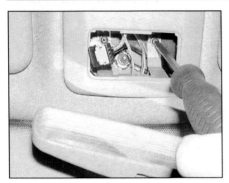

4.34a Remove the two roof console securing screws . . .

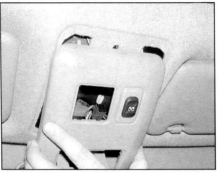

4.34b . . . then lower the console from the roof . . .

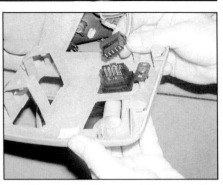

4.34c . . . and disconnect the sunroof switch wiring plug

26 Refitting is a reversal of removal.

Centre console-mounted switches

27 Remove the ashtray from the rear of the centre console then carefully prise off the switch surround.
28 Prise the switches from their locations and disconnect the wiring connectors.
29 Refitting is a reversal of removal.

Courtesy light switches

Note: *On later models, the door-pillar mounted switches are deleted, the switch function being incorporated into the door lock assemblies. The courtesy light delay function is controlled by the body computer located under the facia, adjacent to the steering column.*
30 Open the door, then prise the rubber gaiter from the switch.
31 Remove the securing screw, then withdraw the switch from the door pillar. Disconnect the wiring connector as it becomes accessible.

HAYNES HiNT *Tape the wiring to the door pillar to prevent it falling back into the door pillar. Alternatively, tie a piece of string to the wiring to retrieve it.*

32 Refitting is a reversal of removal, but ensure that the rubber gaiter is correctly seated on the switch.

Electric sunroof switch

33 Carefully prise the interior light and map reading light from the roof console. Disconnect the wiring connectors and remove the light units.
34 Remove the two securing screws, then lower the console from the roof, and disconnect the wiring plugs **(see illustrations)**.
35 Carefully prise the sunroof switch from the roof console.
36 Refitting is a reversal of removal.

5 Bulbs (exterior lights) – renewal

General

1 Whenever a bulb is renewed, note the following points:
a) *Disconnect the battery negative terminal before starting work. Refer to 'Disconnecting the battery' in the Reference Section of this manual.*
b) *Remember that, if the light has just been in use, the bulb may be extremely hot.*
c) *Always check the bulb contacts and holder, ensuring that there is clean metal to metal contact between the bulb and its live(s) and earth. Clean off any corrosion or dirt before fitting a new bulb.*
d) *Wherever bayonet-type bulbs are fitted (see Specifications), ensure that the live*

contact(s) bear firmly against the bulb contact.
e) *Always ensure that the new bulb is of the correct rating, and that it is completely clean before fitting it; this applies particularly to headlight/foglight bulbs (see below).*

Headlight

2 Working in the engine compartment, depress the retaining tag and remove the plastic cover from the rear of the headlight unit **(see illustration)**.
3 Disconnect the wiring plug from the rear of the headlight bulb **(see illustration)**.
4 Release the spring clip and withdraw the bulb **(see illustrations)**.

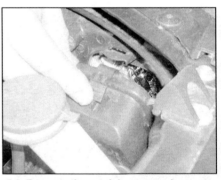

5.2 Depress the retaining tag and remove the plastic cover from the rear of the headlight unit

5.3 Disconnect the wiring plug from the rear of the headlight bulb

5.4a Release the spring clip . . .

5.4b . . . and withdraw the headlight bulb

5.9 Twist the sidelight bulbholder anti-clockwise and withdraw it from the headlight unit

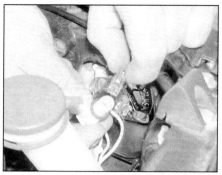

5.10 The sidelight bulb is a push-fit in the bulbholder

5.12 Twist the direction indicator bulbholder anti-clockwise to release it from the rear of the headlight unit

5 When handling the new bulb, use a tissue or clean cloth to avoid touching the glass with the fingers; moisture and grease from the skin can cause blackening and rapid failure of this type of bulb. If the glass is accidentally touched, wipe it clean using methylated spirit.

6 Install the new bulb, ensuring that its locating tabs are correctly seated in the light cut-outs. Secure the bulb in position with the spring clip, and reconnect the wiring plug.

7 Refit the plastic cover, ensuring that it is correctly seated on the headlight unit.

Front sidelight

8 Working in the engine compartment, depress the retaining tag and remove the plastic cover from the rear of the headlight unit.

9 Twist the sidelight bulbholder anti-clockwise, then withdraw it from the headlight unit **(see illustration)**.

10 The bulb is a push-fit in the bulbholder **(see illustration)**.

11 Refitting is the reverse of the removal procedure, ensuring that the bulbholder seal is in good condition.

Front direction indicator

12 Working in the engine compartment, twist the bulbholder anti-clockwise to release it from the rear of the headlight unit **(see illustration)**.

13 The bulb is a bayonet fit in the bulbholder **(see illustration)**.

14 Refitting is a reversal of the removal procedure.

Front direction indicator side repeater

15 Push the light unit towards the front of the car, release the rear of the unit from the front wing, and withdraw the light unit **(see illustrations)**.

16 Withdraw the bulbholder from the light unit and remove the bulb from the bulbholder **(see illustrations)**.

17 Refitting is a reversal of the removal procedure.

5.13 The bulb is a bayonet fit in the bulbholder

Front foglight

18 Reach up under the front bumper and disconnect the foglight wiring connector.

19 Turn the bulbholder a quarter turn and withdraw it from the light unit.

20 Release the spring clip, and remove the bulb from the bulbholder.

21 When handling the new bulb, use a tissue or clean cloth to avoid touching the glass with the fingers; moisture and grease from the skin can cause blackening and rapid failure of this type of bulb. If the glass is accidentally touched, wipe it clean using methylated spirit.

22 Install the new bulb, ensuring that its locating tabs are correctly located. Secure the

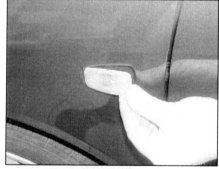

5.15a Push the direction indicator side repeater light unit towards the front of the car . . .

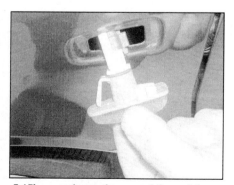

5.15b . . . release the rear of the unit from the front wing and withdraw the light unit

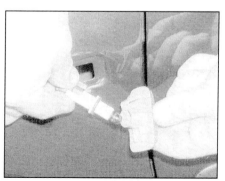

5.16a Withdraw the bulbholder from the light unit . . .

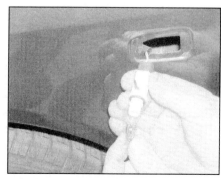

5.16b . . . and remove the bulb from the bulbholder

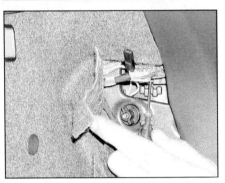

5.25a Using a small screwdriver, release the rear light cluster wiring connector retaining clip . . .

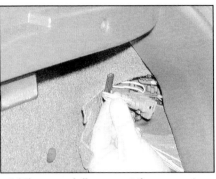

5.25b . . . and disconnect the connector

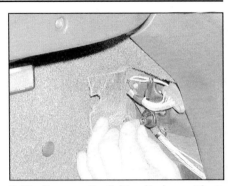

5.26a Unscrew the light unit wing nut from the inside . . .

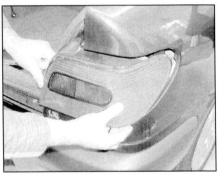

5.26b . . . and withdraw the light unit from the car

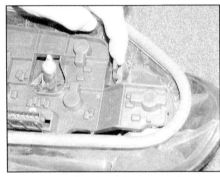

5.27 Depress the retaining tag and remove the bulbholder from the light unit

bulb in position with the clip, and refit the bulbholder.

23 Reconnect the foglight wiring connector.

Rear light cluster

24 Working in the luggage compartment, lift up the carpet flap for access to the rear of the light unit.

25 Using a small screwdriver, release the wiring connector lower retaining clip and disconnect the connector **(see illustrations)**.

26 Support the light unit from the outside, then unscrew the retaining wing nut from the inside. Withdraw the light unit from the car **(see illustrations)**.

27 Depress the retaining tag and remove the bulbholder from the light unit **(see illustration)**.

28 Turn the relevant bayonet fit bulb a quarter turn and remove it from the bulbholder **(see illustration)**.

29 Refitting is a reversal of the removal procedure.

High-level stoplight

30 Open the tailgate and unscrew the two plastic wing nuts at the rear of the stoplight unit **(see illustration)**.

31 Withdraw the stoplight unit from the outside and disconnect the wiring connector **(see illustrations)**. In practice it was found that the stoplight unit was reluctant to release from the tailgate due to the bond of the rubber seal. It may be necessary to carefully tap the

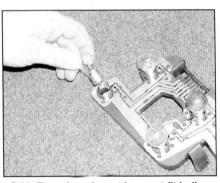

5.28 Turn the relevant bayonet fit bulb a quarter turn and remove it from the bulbholder

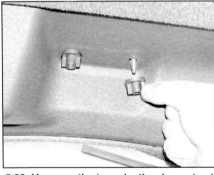

5.30 Unscrew the two plastic wing nuts at the rear of the high-level stoplight unit

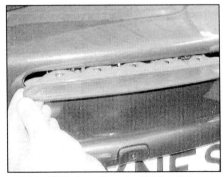

5.31a Withdraw the stoplight unit from outside the tailgate . . .

5.31b . . . and disconnect the wiring connector

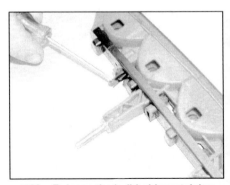

5.32a Release the bulbholder retaining tags . . .

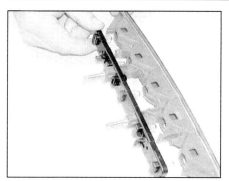

5.32b . . . and withdraw the bulbholder from the rear of the unit

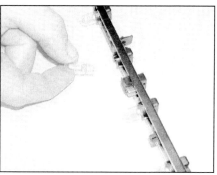

5.33 The bulbs are a push-fit in the bulbholder

5.35a Prise the number plate light unit from the tailgate . . .

retaining studs from the inside, using a hammer handle or similar item.

32 With the stoplight unit removed, release the retaining tags and withdraw the bulbholder from the rear of the unit **(see illustrations)**.

33 The bulbs are a push-fit in the bulbholder **(see illustration)**.

34 Refitting is a reversal of the removal procedure.

Number plate light

35 Using a suitable screwdriver, carefully prise the light unit from the tailgate and disconnect the wiring connector **(see illustrations)**.

36 Release the tag on the side of the lens and lift the lens off the light unit **(see illustration)**.

37 Withdraw the push-fit bulb from the light unit **(see illustration)**.

38 Refitting is a reversal of removal.

6 Bulbs (interior lights) – renewal

General

1 Refer to Section 5, paragraph 1.

Courtesy light

2 Carefully prise the courtesy light from its location and disconnect the wiring connector **(see illustrations)**.

3 Depress the tags on each side of the bulbholder and withdraw the bulbholder from the light unit **(see illustration)**.

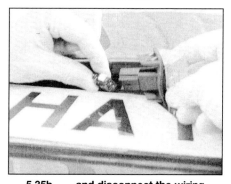

5.35b . . . and disconnect the wiring connector

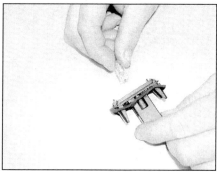

5.37 Withdraw the push-fit bulb from the light unit

4 Withdraw the push-fit bulb from the bulbholder **(see illustration)**.

5 Refitting is a reversal of removal.

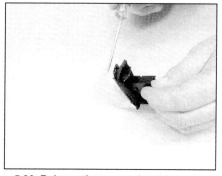

5.36 Release the tag on the side of the lens and lift the lens off the light unit

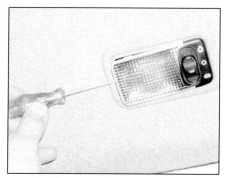

6.2a Carefully prise the courtesy light from its location . . .

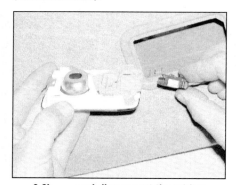

6.2b . . . and disconnect the wiring connector

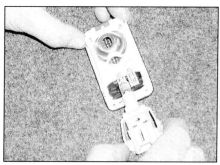

6.3 Depress the tags on each side of the bulbholder and withdraw the bulbholder from the light unit

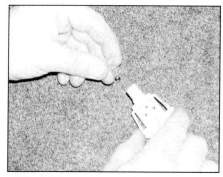

6.4 Withdraw the push-fit bulb from the bulbholder

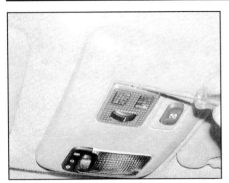

6.6a Prise the map reading light from the roof console . . .

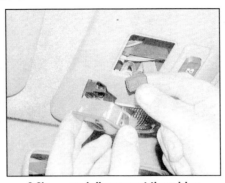

6.6b . . . and disconnect the wiring connector

6.7a Depress the bulbholder retaining tag . . .

6.7b . . . and manipulate the bulbholder from the light unit

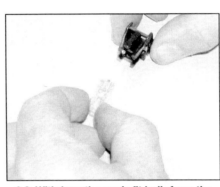

6.8 Withdraw the push-fit bulb from the bulbholder

Map reading light

6 Carefully prise the map reading light from the roof console and disconnect the wiring connector **(see illustrations)**.

7 Using a small screwdriver, depress the tag and manipulate the bulbholder from the light unit **(see illustrations)**.

8 Withdraw the push-fit bulb from the bulbholder **(see illustration)**.

9 Refitting is a reversal of removal.

Glovebox light

10 Open the glovebox, then carefully prise out the light unit, and disconnect the wiring connector **(see illustrations)**.

11 Withdraw the push-fit bulb from the light unit **(see illustration)**.

12 Refitting is a reversal of removal.

6.10a Prise out the glovebox light unit . . .

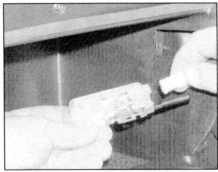

6.10b . . . and disconnect the wiring connector

Luggage compartment light

13 Carefully prise the light unit from its location in the luggage compartment **(see illustration)**.

14 Twist the bulbholder anti-clockwise and remove it from the rear of the light unit **(see illustration)**.

15 Withdraw the push-fit bulb from the bulbholder **(see illustration)**.

16 Refitting is a reversal of removal.

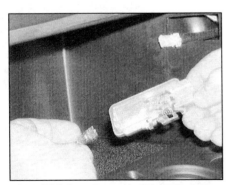

6.11 Withdraw the push-fit bulb from the light unit

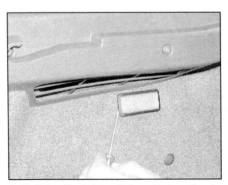

6.13 Prise the light unit from its location in the luggage compartment

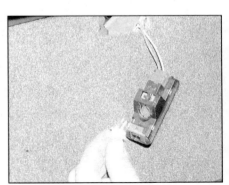

6.14 Twist the bulbholder anti-clockwise and remove it from the rear of the light unit

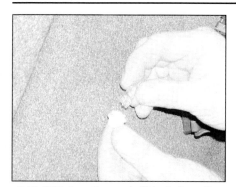

6.15 Withdraw the push-fit bulb from the bulbholder

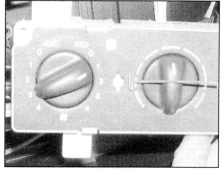

6.18a Using a hook shaped tool inserted in the slots of the heater/ventilation control unit front panel . . .

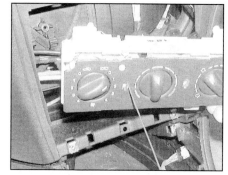

6.18b . . . withdraw the front panel from the control unit

Heater/ventilation control unit illumination bulbs

17 Remove the facia centre panel as described in Chapter 11.

18 Make up a hook-shaped tool such as a length of welding rod with its end bent through 90°. Insert the tool alternately into the two slots on the front panel and pull on the tool to release the front panel from the control unit (see illustrations).

19 Carefully pull the relevant bulb from the circuit board (see illustration).

20 Refitting is a reversal of removal.

Digital clock illumination bulb

21 Carefully prise the trim panel surround from the clock and facia switches.

22 Depress the tag on the side of the clock unit and withdraw the clock from the facia (see illustration). Disconnect the wiring connector and remove the clock.

23 Twist the bulbholder anti-clockwise and remove it from the rear of the clock (see illustration).

24 Withdraw the push-fit bulb from the bulbholder.

25 Refitting is a reversal of removal.

Instrument panel illumination and warning light bulbs

26 Remove the instrument panel as described in Section 9.

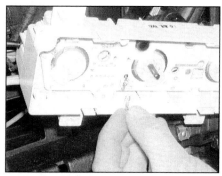

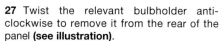

6.19 Carefully pull the relevant bulb from the circuit board

27 Twist the relevant bulbholder anti-clockwise to remove it from the rear of the panel (see illustration).

28 The bulbs are integral with the bulbholders.

29 On completion, refit the instrument panel with reference to Section 9.

7 Exterior light units – removal and refitting

Note: Disconnect the battery negative

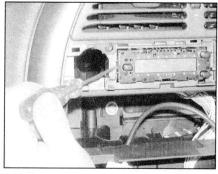

6.22 Depress the tag on the side of the clock unit and withdraw the clock from the facia

terminal before removing any light unit, and reconnect the terminal after refitting the unit. Refer to 'Disconnecting the battery' in the Reference Section of this manual.

Headlight

Removal

1 Remove the front bumper as described in Chapter 11.

2 Disconnect the headlight wiring plug and the wiring plug for the headlight adjuster motor (see illustration).

3 Undo the bolt securing the headlight lower

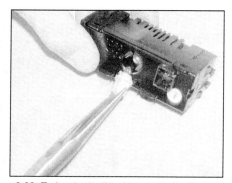

6.23 Twist the bulbholder anti-clockwise and remove it from the rear of the clock

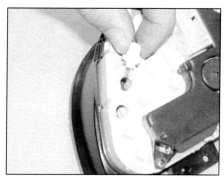

6.27 Twist the relevant bulbholder anti-clockwise to remove it from the rear of the instrument panel

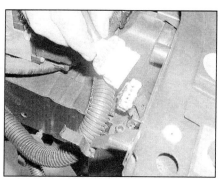

7.2 Disconnect the headlight wiring plug and the wiring plug for the headlight adjuster motor

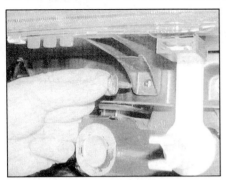

7.3 Undo the bolt securing the headlight lower mounting bracket to the front body panel

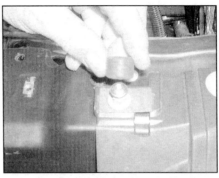

7.4 Lift off the bonnet rubber buffer from the headlight upper inner mounting bolt

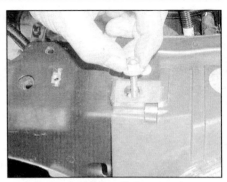

7.5a Undo the headlight upper inner mounting bolt . . .

mounting bracket to the front body panel **(see illustration)**.

4 Lift off the bonnet rubber buffer from the headlight upper inner mounting bolt **(see illustration)**

5 Undo the two headlight upper mounting bolts **(see illustrations)**.

6 Carefully prise the top of the headlight frame over the stud on the front body panel and remove the headlight from its location **(see illustrations)**.

7 If desired, the electric adjuster motor can be removed from the light unit after lifting the tag and turning the adjuster motor through 90° to release it. Once the motor is released, pull the adjuster rod balljoint from the socket in the rear of the headlight **(see illustrations)**.

7.5b . . . and upper outer mounting bolt

7.6a Prise the top of the headlight frame over the stud on the front body panel . . .

Refitting

8 To refit the electric adjuster motor, turn the manual height control adjuster using an Allen key to fully extend the adjuster rod **(see illustration)**. To enable the initial position to be reset after refitting, count the number of turns of the adjuster needed to fully extend the adjuster rod. Engage the balljoint with the socket on the headlight, then fit and secure the adjuster motor. Reset the manual height adjuster to the position noted before removal.

9 Locate the headlight unit on the front body panel, ensuring that the slot on the base of the headlight frame engages with the plastic lug on the front body panel **(see illustration)**. Refit the headlight mounting bolts and tighten securely.

7.6b . . . and remove the headlight from its location

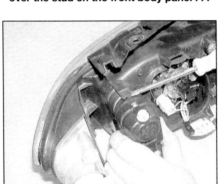
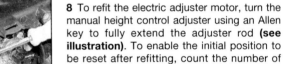

7.7a To remove the headlight electric adjuster motor, lift the tag and turn the adjuster motor through 90° . . .

7.7b . . . then pull the adjuster rod balljoint from the socket in the rear of the headlight

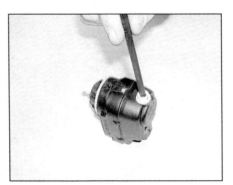

7.8 Before refitting the adjuster motor, turn the height control adjuster using an Allen key to fully extend the adjuster rod

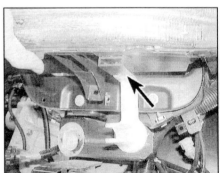

7.9 When refitting the headlight, engage the slot (arrowed) on the base of the headlight with the plastic lug on the body panel

10 The remainder of refitting is a reversal of removal, but on completion have the headlight beam alignment checked at the earliest opportunity.

Front direction indicator side repeater light

11 The procedure is described as part of the bulb renewal procedure in Section 5.

Front foglight

Removal

12 Firmly apply the handbrake, then jack up the front of the car and support it securely on axle stands (see *Jacking and vehicle support*).
13 Release the splash shield and wheelarch liner as necessary for access to the rear of the foglight.
14 Disconnect the foglight wiring connector.
15 Undo the three foglight retaining bolts and remove the unit from the front bumper.

Refitting

16 Refitting is a reversal of removal.

Rear light cluster

17 The procedure is described as part of the bulb renewal procedure in Section 5.

High-level stoplight

18 The procedure is described as part of the bulb renewal procedure in Section 5.

Number plate light

19 The procedure is described as part of the bulb renewal procedure in Section 5.

8 Headlight beam alignment – general information

1 Accurate adjustment of the headlight beam is only possible using optical beam-setting equipment, and this work should therefore be carried out by a Citroën dealer or suitably-equipped workshop.
2 Each headlight unit is equipped with a five-position vertical beam adjuster unit – this can be used to adjust the headlight beam to compensate for the relevant load which the

9.2a Undo the screw located in the upper centre of the instrument panel . . .

vehicle is carrying. The adjuster units are operated by a switch on the facia. The adjusters should be positioned as follows according to the load being carried in the vehicle:

Position 0	Front seats occupied (1 or 2 people)
Position -	Front or rear seats occupied (3 people)
Position 1	Front and rear seats occupied (5 people)
Position 2	Front and rear seats occupied and luggage compartment fully-loaded
Position 3	Driver's seat occupied and luggage compartment fully-loaded

3 Be sure to reset the adjustment if the vehicle load is altered.

9 Instrument panel – removal and refitting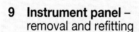

Removal

1 Remove the instrument panel surround as described in Chapter 11, Section 28.
2 Undo the screw located in the upper centre of the instrument panel, and withdraw the panel slightly from the facia **(see illustrations)**.
3 Lift the locking catches and disconnect the wiring connectors from the rear of the

9.2b . . . and withdraw the panel slightly from the facia

instrument panel **(see illustration)**. Remove the instrument panel from the facia.
4 With the instrument panel removed, the lens hood can be removed, if required, by lifting the two retaining tags and separating the panel from the lens hood **(see illustrations)**.
5 Renewal of the illumination and warning light bulbs is described in Section 6. None of the other instrument panel components are available separately and no further dismantling of the panel is possible.

Refitting

6 Refitting is a reversal of removal.

10 Clock – removal and refitting

Removal

1 Disconnect the battery negative terminal (refer to *Disconnecting the battery* in the Reference Section of this manual).
2 Carefully prise the trim panel surround from the clock and facia switches.
3 Depress the tag on the side of the clock unit and withdraw the clock from the facia. Disconnect the wiring connector and remove the clock.

Refitting

4 Refitting is a reversal of removal.

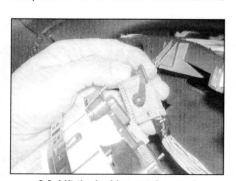

9.3 Lift the locking catches and disconnect the wiring connectors from the rear of the instrument panel

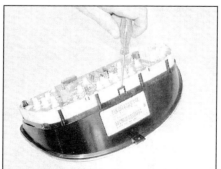

9.4a To remove the instrument panel lens hood, lift the two retaining tags . . .

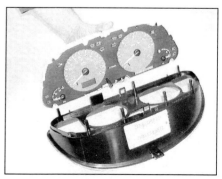

9.4b . . . and separate the panel from the lens hood

11.7a Release the cigarette lighter internal tangs . . .

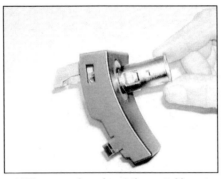

11.7b . . . and push out the metal insert

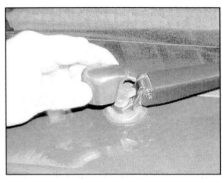

13.3a Lift up the wiper arm spindle nut cover . . .

11 Cigarette lighter –
removal and refitting

Removal

1 Disconnect the battery negative terminal (refer to *Disconnecting the battery* in the Reference Section of this manual).

2 Remove the ashtray from the front of the centre console, then prise free and remove the oddments tray.

3 On models with manual transmission, unclip the gear lever gaiter from the console, and slide it up the gear lever.

4 On models with automatic transmission, unclip the selector lever position indicator trim plate from the console.

5 Release the retaining clips and remove the gear lever gaiter surround.

6 Undo the three upper screws and two lower screws securing the ashtray/cigarette lighter housing to the centre console and facia. Withdraw the housing and disconnect the wiring from the rear.

7 Pull out the lighter element, release the internal tangs and push out the metal insert **(see illustrations)**.

Refitting

8 Refitting is a reversal of removal.

12 Horn –
removal and refitting

Removal

1 Disconnect the battery negative terminal (refer to *Disconnecting the battery* in the Reference Section of this manual).

2 For improved access, apply the handbrake, then jack up the front of the vehicle and support it securely on axle stands (see *Jacking and vehicle support*).

3 Reach up under the front bumper on the left-hand side, and disconnect the wiring plug from the horn.

4 Unscrew the securing nut, and withdraw the horn from its bracket.

Refitting

5 Refitting is a reversal of removal.

13 Wiper arm –
removal and refitting

Removal

1 Operate the wiper motor, then switch it off so that the wiper arm returns to the at-rest position.

2 Stick a piece of masking tape to the window, along the edge of the wiper blade, to use as an alignment aid on refitting.

3 Lift up the wiper arm spindle nut cover, then slacken and remove the spindle nut. Lift the blade off the glass, and pull the wiper arm off its spindle. If necessary, the arm can be levered off the spindle using a suitable flat-bladed screwdriver **(see illustrations)**.

Refitting

4 Ensure that the wiper arm and spindle splines are clean and dry, then refit the arm to the spindle, aligning the wiper blade with the tape fitted on removal.

5 Refit the spindle nut, tightening it securely, and clip the nut cover back into position.

14 Windscreen wiper components –
removal and refitting

Wiper motor and linkage

Removal

1 Disconnect the battery negative terminal (refer to *Disconnecting the battery* in the Reference Section of this manual).

2 Remove the wiper arms (see Section 13).

3 Open the bonnet and undo the screws securing the scuttle cover panel at each side **(see illustration)**.

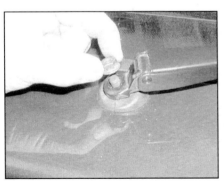

13.3b . . . remove the spindle nut . . .

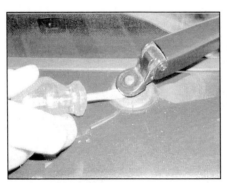

13.3c . . . and pull the arm off its spindle, using a screwdriver if necessary

14.3 Undo the scuttle cover panel retaining screws

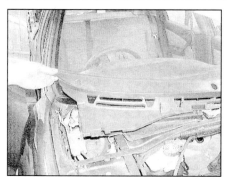

14.4 Prise the scuttle panel upwards to release the plastic retaining clips and remove the panel

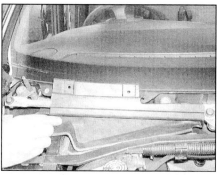

14.5 Undo the securing screws and remove the wiper motor cover panel

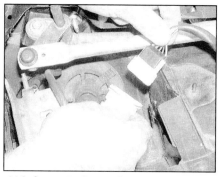

14.6 Separate the two halves of the wiper motor wiring connector

4 Pull or prise the scuttle panel upward from its location to release the plastic retaining clips and remove the scuttle panel **(see illustration)**. Note that these clips are very tight and are not very strong; be prepared for breakage.

5 Undo the securing screws and remove the wiper motor cover panel **(see illustration)**.

6 Separate the two halves of the wiper motor wiring connector **(see illustration)**.

7 Unscrew the four securing bolts, and manipulate the motor/linkage assembly from the scuttle **(see illustrations)**.

Refitting

8 Refitting is a reversal of removal.

Rain sensor

General

9 Certain models are equipped with windscreen wipers actuated by a rain sensor mounted on the windscreen. When the wiper switch is set to position 1, the wipers operate automatically and adapt to an appropriate speed depending on the amount of rain detected by the sensor.

Removal

10 Remove the interior mirror and mirror base by pulling downward.

11 Disconnect the rain sensor wiring plug from the top of the unit.

12 Pull out the green locking bar on each side of the sensor body and withdraw the unit from the mounting on the windscreen.

Caution: Do not touch the rain sensor lens or the detection window on the windscreen once the sensor is removed.

Refitting

13 Locate the sensor on the windscreen mounting, maintain pressure to compress the seal and push in the green locking bars.

14 Reconnect the sensor wiring plug, then refit the interior mirror and base.

15 To check the operation of the sensor, spray water on the outside of the windscreen over the sensor detection window, with the windscreen wipers set to intermittent wipe.

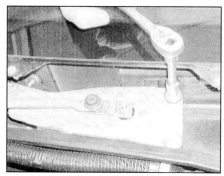

14.7a Unscrew the four securing bolts . . .

15 Rear window wiper motor – removal and refitting

Removal

Note: *New wiper motor securing rivets will be required for refitting.*

1 Disconnect the battery negative terminal (refer to *Disconnecting the battery* in the Reference Section of this manual).

2 Remove the wiper arm (see Section 13).

3 Remove the tailgate trim panel as described in Chapter 11, Section 26.

4 Disconnect the tailgate washer fluid hose and the wiring connector from the wiper motor **(see illustration)**.

5 Drill out the rivets securing the motor, or

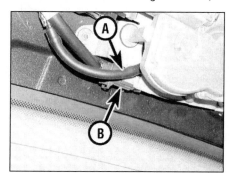

15.4 Disconnect the tailgate washer fluid hose (A) and the wiring connector (B) from the wiper motor

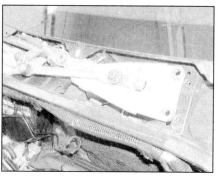

14.7b . . . and manipulate the wiper motor/linkage assembly from the scuttle

motor mounting bracket, to the tailgate **(see illustration)**.

6 Withdraw the motor assembly from the tailgate.

Refitting

7 Refitting is a reversal of removal, using new rivets to secure the motor in position.

16 Windscreen/rear window washer system components – removal and refitting

Windscreen/rear window washer fluid reservoir

Removal

1 Disconnect the battery negative terminal

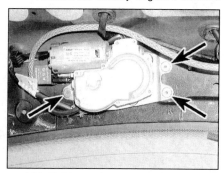

15.5 Tailgate wiper motor mounting bracket securing rivets (arrowed) – Hatchback model

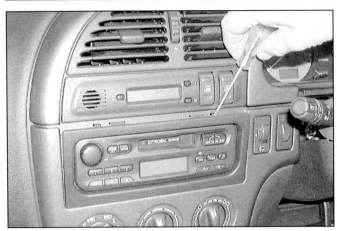

17.2 Carefully prise off the radio/cassette player trim plate

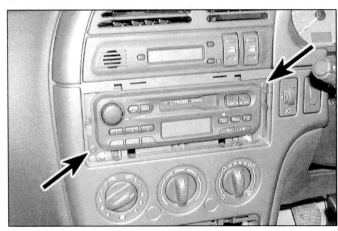

17.3 Undo the two screws (arrowed) securing the radio/cassette player to the facia

(refer to *Disconnecting the battery* in the Reference Section of this manual).

2 Working in the engine compartment, unscrew the filler neck from the reservoir.

3 Jack up the front of the vehicle, and support it securely on axle stands (see *Jacking and vehicle support*).

4 Remove the right-hand roadwheel.

5 Remove the securing screws and clips, and withdraw the splash shield and the wheelarch liner to expose the fluid reservoir.

6 Disconnect the wiring plug from the washer pump located in the reservoir.

7 Disconnect the supply pipe(s) from the washer pump. Be prepared for fluid spillage if there is still fluid in the reservoir.

8 Slacken and remove the reservoir retaining bolts, then lower the reservoir out from underneath the wheelarch.

Refitting

9 Refitting is a reversal of removal.

Washer pump

Removal

Note: *Prior to removing the pump, empty the contents of the reservoir, or be prepared for fluid spillage.*

10 Disconnect the battery negative terminal (refer to *Disconnecting the battery* in the Reference Section of this manual).

11 Jack up the front of the vehicle and support it securely on axle stands (see *Jacking and vehicle support*).

12 Remove the right-hand roadwheel.

13 Remove the securing screws and clips, and withdraw the splash shield and the wheelarch liner to expose the fluid reservoir.

14 Disconnect the wiring connector from the pump, then carefully ease the pump out of its sealing grommet.

Refitting

15 Refitting is a reversal of removal.

Windscreen washer jet

16 Open the bonnet, then unclip the washer jet from the bonnet, and disconnect it from its supply pipe.

17 On refitting, ensure that the jet is clipped securely in position. If necessary, the jet nozzles can be adjusted using a pin; aim the spray to a point slightly above the centre of the wiper swept area.

Tailgate washer jet

18 The tailgate washer jet is integral with the wiper assembly.

17 Radio/cassette player – removal and refitting

Removal

Note: *Once the battery has been disconnected, the radio/cassette unit cannot be re-activated until the appropriate security code has been entered.*

1 Disconnect the battery negative terminal (refer to *Disconnecting the battery* in the Reference Section of this manual).

2 Using a small screwdriver, carefully prise off the radio/cassette player trim plate **(see illustration)**.

3 Undo the two screws securing the radio/cassette player to the facia **(see illustration)**.

4 Withdraw the unit from its location and disconnect the aerial lead and the wiring connector at the rear **(see illustrations)**.

17.4a Withdraw the unit from its location . . .

17.4b . . . and disconnect the aerial lead and the wiring connector

18.2 Prise the loudspeaker grille from the door trim panel

18.3a Undo the retaining screws . . .

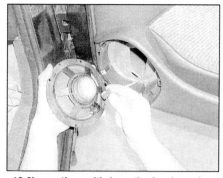

18.3b . . . then withdraw the loudspeaker and disconnect the wiring plug

Refitting

5 Reconnect the wiring connector and the aerial lead to the rear of the unit, then locate the unit in the facia.
6 Refit the two retaining screws and the trim plate.
7 Reconnect the battery negative terminal, then enter the appropriate code to activate the unit.

18 Loudspeakers – removal and refitting

Door and side panel-mounted speakers

Removal

1 Disconnect the battery negative terminal (refer to *Disconnecting the battery* in the Reference Section of this manual).
2 Prise the loudspeaker grille from the door trim panel or side trim panel **(see illustration)**.
3 Undo the screws, then withdraw the loudspeaker and disconnect the wiring plug **(see illustrations)**.

Refitting

4 Refitting is a reversal of removal.

Facia-mounted tweeters

Removal

5 Disconnect the battery negative terminal

(refer to *Disconnecting the battery* in the Reference Section of this manual).
6 Prise the tweeter from its location on the top of the facia, disconnect the wiring connector and remove the tweeter **(see illustration)**.

Refitting

7 Refitting is a reversal of removal.

19 Radio aerial – removal and refitting

Removal

1 Carefully prise the interior light and map reading light from the roof console. Disconnect the wiring connectors and remove the light units.
2 Remove the two securing screws, then lower the console from the roof, and disconnect the sunroof switch wiring plug (where fitted).
3 Slacken and remove the nut from the base of the aerial, and disengage the aerial lead collar from its stud **(see illustration)**. The aerial can then be lifted away from the outside of the vehicle, noting the rubber seal which is fitted to its base.

Refitting

4 Refitting is a reversal of removal, but check that the rubber seal is in good condition, and renew if necessary.

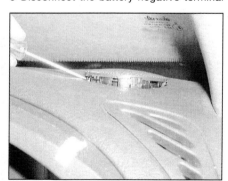

18.6 Prise the tweeter from the top of the facia, disconnect the wiring connector and remove the tweeter

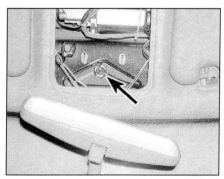

19.3 Remove the nut (arrowed) from the base of the aerial and disengage the aerial lead collar from its stud

20 Anti-theft alarm system and engine immobiliser – general information

Note: *This information is applicable only to the anti-theft alarm system fitted by Citroën as standard equipment.*

General

All models in the range are fitted with an anti-theft alarm system as standard or optional equipment. The alarm is automatically armed and disarmed using the remote central locking transmitter (where applicable). When the system is activated, the alarm indicator light, located on the facia, will flash continuously. In addition to the alarm function, the system also incorporates an engine immobiliser activated by a transponder in the ignition key.

Anti-theft alarm system

Note that if the doors are operated using the key, the alarm will not be armed or disarmed (as applicable). If for some reason the remote central locking transmitter fails whilst the alarm is armed, the alarm can be disarmed using the key. To do this, open the door with the key, then enter the vehicle, noting that the alarm will sound as the door is opened. Switch on the ignition, and once the ignition key is recognised, the alarm will be disarmed.

The alarm system has switches on the bonnet, tailgate and each of the doors. It also has ultrasonic sensing, which detects movement inside the vehicle, via sensors mounted on either side of the vehicle interior. If required, the ultrasonic sensing facility can be switched off, whilst retaining the switched side of the system. To switch off the ultrasonic sensing, with the ignition switched off, depress the alarm switch located on the facia until the alarm indicator light on the facia is continuously lit. Now, when the doors are locked using the remote central locking transmitter, and the alarm is armed, only the switched side of the alarm system is operational (and the alarm indicator light will revert to its flashing mode). This facility is useful, as it allows you to leave the windows/sunroof open, and still arm the alarm. If the windows/sunroof are left open with the ultrasonic sensing not switched off, the alarm may be falsely triggered by a gust of wind.

Should the alarm system become faulty, the vehicle should be taken to a Citroën dealer for examination.

Engine immobiliser

An electronic engine immobiliser is incorporated as part of the anti-theft system. The electronic immobiliser consists of a transponder fitted to the ignition key, and an analogue module fitted around the ignition switch. The system is controlled by the passenger compartment body computer.

When the ignition key is inserted in the switch and turned to the ignition on position, the control module sends a pre-programmed recognition code signal to the analogue module on the ignition switch. If the recognition code signal matches that of the transponder on the ignition key, an unlocking request signal is sent to the engine management ECU, or injection pump anti-theft module allowing the engine to be started. If the ignition key signal is not recognised, the engine management system remains immobilised.

When the ignition is switched off, a locking signal is sent to the ECU, or pump anti-theft module and the engine is immobilised until the unlocking request signal is again received.

The recognition code is programmed into the system during manufacture and is contained on a confidential card supplied with the vehicle. The card should be kept in a safe place – never in the vehicle. The confidential card will be required if any work is to be carried out on the system by a Citroën dealer, or if replacement keys are required.

Disconnecting the vehicle battery

Refer to *Disconnecting the battery* in the Reference Section of this manual).

21 Air bag system – general information, precautions and system de-activation

General information

A driver's air bag is fitted as standard equipment on certain models, and is an option on all other models. The air bag is fitted in the steering wheel centre pad. Additionally, a passenger's air bag located in the facia, and side air bags located in the front seats are also available.

The system is armed only when the ignition is switched on, however, a reserve power source maintains a power supply to the system in the event of a break in the main electrical supply. The steering wheel and facia

air bags are activated by a 'g' sensor (deceleration sensor), and controlled by an electronic control unit located under the centre console. The side air bags are activated by severe side impact and operate independently of the main system and of each other. A separate electrical supply and control unit is provided for each side air bag.

The air bags are inflated by a gas generator, which forces the bag out from its location in the steering wheel, facia or seat back frame.

Precautions

⚠️ **Warning: The following precautions must be observed when working on vehicles equipped with an air bag system, to prevent the possibility of personal injury.**

General precautions

The following precautions **must** be observed when carrying out work on a vehicle equipped with an air bag:

a) Do not disconnect the battery with the engine running.

b) Before carrying out any work in the vicinity of the air bag, removal of any of the air bag components, or any welding work on the vehicle, de-activate the system as described in the following sub-Section.

c) Do not attempt to test any of the air bag system circuits using test meters or any other test equipment.

d) If the air bag warning light comes on, or any fault in the system is suspected, consult a Citroën dealer without delay. **Do not** attempt to carry out fault diagnosis, or any dismantling of the components.

Precautions to be taken when handling an air bag

a) Transport the air bag by itself, bag upward.

b) Do not put your arms around the air bag.

c) Carry the air bag close to the body, bag outward.

d) Do not drop the air bag or expose it to impacts.

e) Do not attempt to dismantle the air bag unit.

f) Do not connect any form of electrical equipment to any part of the air bag circuit.

Precautions to be taken when storing an air bag unit

a) Store the unit in a cupboard with the air bag upward.

b) Do not expose the air bag to temperatures above 80°C.

c) Do not expose the air bag to flames.

d) Do not attempt to dispose of the air bag – consult a Citroën dealer.

e) Never refit an air bag which is known to be faulty or damaged.

De-activation of air bag system

The system must be de-activated before carrying out any work on the air bag components or surrounding area:

a) Switch on the ignition and check the operation of the air bag warning light on the instrument panel. The light should illuminate when the ignition is switched on, then extinguish.

b) Switch off the ignition.

c) Remove the ignition key.

d) Switch off all electrical equipment.

e) Disconnect the battery negative terminal (refer to 'Disconnecting the battery' in the Reference Section of this manual).

f) Insulate the battery negative terminal and the end of the battery negative lead to prevent any possibility of contact.

g) Wait for at least two minutes before carrying out any further work. Wait at least ten minutes if the air bag warning light did not operate correctly.

Activation of air bag system

To activate the system on completion of any work, proceed as follows:

a) Ensure that there are no occupants in the vehicle, and that there are no loose objects around the vicinity of the steering wheel. Close the vehicle doors and windows.

b) Ensure that the ignition is switched off then reconnect the battery negative terminal.

c) Open the driver's door and switch on the ignition, without reaching in front of the steering wheel. Check that the air bag warning light illuminates briefly then extinguishes.

d) Switch off the ignition.

e) If the air bag warning light does not operate as described in paragraph c), consult a Citroën dealer before driving the vehicle.

22 Air bag system components – removal and refitting

⚠️ **Warning: Refer to the precautions given in Section 21 before attempting to carry out work on any of the air bag components.**

General

1 The air bag sensors are integral with the electronic control unit.

2 Any suspected faults with the air bag system should be referred to a Citroën dealer – under no circumstances attempt to carry out any work other than removal and refitting of the front air bag unit(s) and/or the rotary connector, as described in the following paragraphs.

Air bag electronic control units

3 The main ECU is located under the front section of the centre console and is accessible after removal of the console as described in Chapter 11. Each of the side air

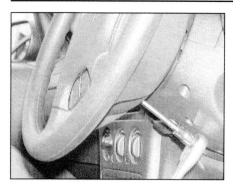

22.7 Move the steering wheel as necessary for access, and undo the two air bag securing screws

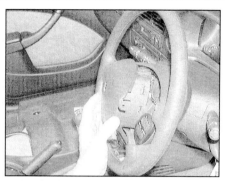

22.8 Gently pull the air bag unit from the centre of the steering wheel

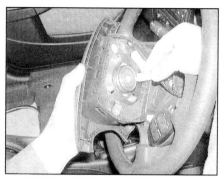

22.9 Unclip the wiring connector from the air bag unit

bags has its own ECU, fitted at the base of the centre door pillar.

Driver's air bag unit

Removal

4 The air bag unit is an integral part of the steering wheel centre boss.

5 De-activate the air bag system as described in Section 21.

6 Move the steering wheel as necessary for access to the two air bag unit securing screws. The screws are located at the rear of the steering wheel boss.

7 Remove the two air bag unit securing screws **(see illustration)**.

8 Gently pull the air bag unit from the centre of the steering wheel **(see illustration)**.

9 Carefully unclip the wiring connector from the air bag unit (use the fingers only, and pull the connector upward from the air bag unit) **(see illustration)**.

10 If the air bag unit is to be stored for any length of time, refer to the storage precautions given in Section 21.

Refitting

11 Refitting is a reversal of removal, bearing in mind the following points:

a) Do not strike the air bag unit, or expose it to impacts during refitting.
b) Tighten the air bag unit securing screws to the specified torque.
c) On completion of refitting, activate the air bag system as described in Section 21.

Air bag rotary connector

Removal

12 Remove the air bag unit, as described previously in this Section.

13 Remove the steering wheel as described in Chapter 10.

14 Remove the three securing screws, and withdraw the lower steering column shroud. Where applicable, manipulate the steering column adjuster lever as necessary to enable removal of the shroud.

15 If necessary, lower the column, then unclip the upper column shroud.

16 Trace the rotary connector wiring back to the connectors below the steering column and disconnect the wiring.

17 Unscrew the three securing screws, and withdraw the rotary connector from the steering column, feeding the wiring harness through the stalk switch bracket **(see illustrations)**. Note the routing of the wiring harness.

Refitting

18 Refitting is a reversal of removal, bearing in mind the following points:

a) Ensure that the rotary connector is centralised by aligning the marks on the rotary connector body and the rotating centre part prior to refitting. Instructions for centralising the unit are also provided on a label on the face of the unit.
b) Ensure that the roadwheels are in the straight-ahead position before refitting the rotary connector and steering wheel.
c) Before refitting the steering column shrouds, ensure that the rotary connector wiring harness is correctly routed as noted before removal.
b) Refit the steering wheel as described in Chapter 10, and refit the air bag unit as described previously in this Section.

Passenger's air bag unit

Removal

19 The passenger's air bag is fitted to the upper part of the facia, above the glovebox.

20 De-activate the air bag system as described in Section 21.

22.17a Unscrew the three rotary connector securing screws (arrowed) . . .

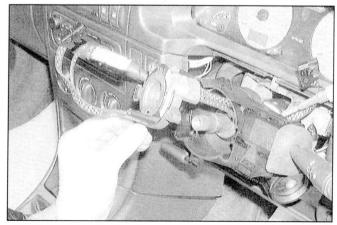

22.17b . . . and withdraw the rotary connector from the steering column

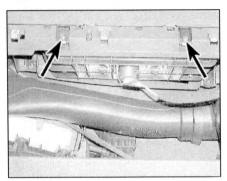

22.22a Undo the two passenger's air bag front securing screws (arrowed) . . .

22.22b . . . and rear securing screws

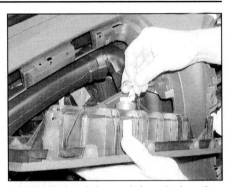

22.23 Lift the air bag unit from its location and disconnect the wiring connector

21 Remove the glovebox as described in Chapter 11, Section 28.

22 Undo the two screws securing the front edge of the air bag to the facia, and the two screws at the rear **(see illustrations)**.

23 Lift the unit up from its location on the facia and disconnect the wiring connector **(see illustration)**.

24 If the air bag unit is to be stored for any length of time, refer to the storage precautions given in Section 21.

Refitting

25 Refitting is a reversal of removal, bearing in mind the following points:

a) *Do not strike the air bag unit, or expose it to impacts during refitting.*

b) *On completion of refitting, activate the air bag system as described in Section 21.*

Side air bag units

26 The side air bags are located internally within the front seat back and no attempt should be made to remove them. Any suspected problems with the side air bag system should be referred to a Citroën dealer.

Citroen Xsara wiring diagrams

Diagram 1

Key to symbols

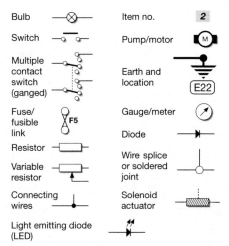

Bulb

Switch

Multiple contact switch (ganged)

Fuse/ fusible link

F5

Resistor

Variable resistor

Connecting wires

Light emitting diode (LED)

Item no.   **2**

Pump/motor

Earth and location   E22

Gauge/meter

Diode

Wire splice or soldered joint

Solenoid actuator

Wire identifier and colour (Orange) note: colours may not resemble actual vehicle due to variations in production!   CC05 (OR)

Connections to other circuits. Direction of arrow denotes current flow.

Diagram 3, Arrow A
A **High beam warning light**

Denotes alternative wiring variation (brackets)

Screened cable

Dashed outline denotes part of a larger item, containing in this case an electronic or solid state device.
C2 - connector pin identification.
2VE - 2 pin green connector.

Key to circuits

Diagram 1	Information for wiring diagrams
Diagram 2	Starting, charging and engine cooling fan
Diagram 3	Engine cooling fan and air conditioning
Diagram 4	Air conditioning
Diagram 5	Pre-heating, coolant level/seat belt warning lights
Diagram 6	Warning lights and gauges
Diagram 7	Lights on warning and key reminder, interior lighting
Diagram 8	Exterior lighting
Diagram 9	Exterior lighting continued and horn
Diagram 10	Heater blower, heated rear window and mirrors, cigar lighter, clock and external temp. sensor
Diagram 11	Clock, sunroof, headlight levelling and audio system
Diagram 12	Wash/wipe
Diagram 13	Electric windows and powered seat
Diagram 14	Central locking, electric mirrors and ABS
Diagram 15	Sagem SL96 fuel injection system
Diagram 16	Bosch MP5.2 Motronic fuel injection system
Diagram 17	MM1AP fuel injection system
Diagram 18	HDi Diesel engine management system (part 1)
Diagram 19	HDi Diesel engine management system (part 2)

Earth locations

E1	Near battery
E2	LH front of car
E3	LH front of car
E4	LH front of car
E5	LH front of car
E6	RH front inner wing
E7	RH front inner wing
E8	Front LH footwell
E9	Front LH footwell
E10	Front RH footwell
E11	Front RH footwell
E12	Centre console
E13	Centre console
E14	Centre console
E15	Centre console
E16	LH rear of car
E17	RH rear of car
E18	RH rear of car
E19	RH rear of car
E20	RH rear of car
E21	Near courtesy light
E22	On gearbox
E23	On cylinder head

Engine fuse box

Fuse	Rating	Circuit protected
F1	20A	Headlight washer timer
F2	-	Spare
F3	30A	Fan
F4	-	Spare
F5	30A	Fan
F6	20A	Front foglight relay
F7	-	Spare
F8	-	Spare
F9	15A	Fuel pump
F10	10A	Throttle housing heater resistor
F11	15A	Oxygen sensor
F12	10A	LH main beam headlight
F13	10A	RH main beam headlight
F14	10A	LH dipped beam headlight
F15	10A	RH dipped beam headlight

Passenger fuse box

Fuse	Rating	Circuit protected
F1	10A	Radio, CD player
F2	5A	A/T selector illumination, air conditioning, vehicle speed sensor, coolant level warning light, instrument cluster, central protection unit, heater blower, diagnostic socket
F3	10A	Anti-lock brakes
F4	5A	LH front sidelight, RH rear tail light
F5	5A	Spare
F6	10A	Auto. trans. information relay
F7	20A	Horn
F8	-	Shunt (**SH**) placed here on vehicle delivery
SH	-	Delivery position of shunt (replaces F8 thereafter)
F9	5A	RH front sidelight, LH rear tail light, number plate lights
F10	30A	Rear electric windows
F11	-	Spare
F12	20A	Instrument panel, stop lights, reversing lights, engine management double function relay
F13	20A	Spare
F14	-	Spare
F15	20A	Engine cooling fan, central protection unit
F16	20A	Cigar lighter, accessory socket
F17	-	Spare
F18	10A	Rear fog lights
F19	5A	Illumination rheostat
F20	-	Spare
F21	30A	Heater blower, air conditioning
F22	15A	Powered seat
F24	20A	Wash/wipe and heated rear window switch, front wiper motor, rain sensor
F25	10A	Air conditioning, instrument cluster, central protection unit, diagnostic socket, digital clock/external temp. gauge, analogue clock, radio
F26	15A	Hazard warning light
F27	30A	Electric front windows. electric sunroof
F28	15A	Rear window inhibitor switch, direction indicators, instrument cluster, glove box light
F29	30A	Heated rear window and mirrors
F30	15A	Vanity light, reading light, exterior temp. gauge, front window lift and sunroof relay, rear wiper motor, rain sensor, rear window lift relay, electric mirrors

H31990

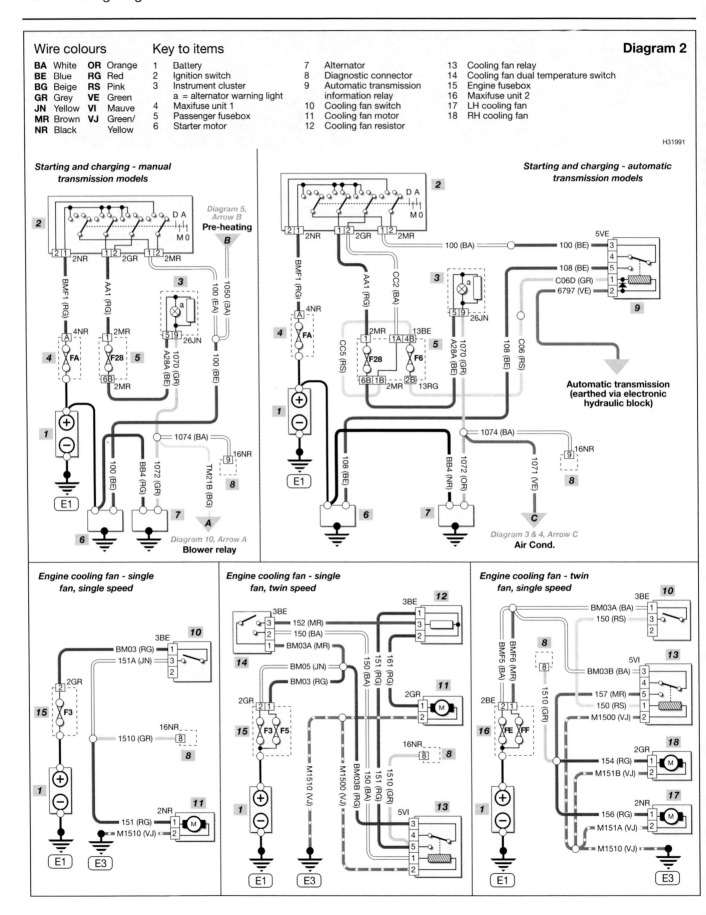

Wire colours

BA	White	OR	Orange
BE	Blue	RG	Red
BG	Beige	RS	Pink
GR	Grey	VE	Green
JN	Yellow	VI	Mauve
MR	Brown	VJ	Green/
NR	Black		Yellow

Key to items

1 Battery
2 Ignition switch
3 Instrument cluster
 a = alternator warning light
4 Maxifuse unit 1
5 Passenger fusebox
6 Starter motor

7 Alternator
8 Diagnostic connector
9 Automatic transmission
 information relay
10 Cooling fan switch
11 Cooling fan motor
12 Cooling fan resistor

13 Cooling fan relay
14 Cooling fan dual temperature switch
15 Engine fusebox
16 Maxifuse unit 2
17 LH cooling fan
18 RH cooling fan

Diagram 2

H31991

Starting and charging - manual transmission models

Starting and charging - automatic transmission models

Engine cooling fan - single fan, single speed

Engine cooling fan - single fan, twin speed

Engine cooling fan - twin fan, single speed

Wire colours

BA	White	**OR**	Orange
BE	Blue	**RG**	Red
BG	Beige	**RS**	Pink
GR	Grey	**VE**	Green
JN	Yellow	**VI**	Mauve
MR	Brown	**VJ**	Green/
NR	Black		Yellow

Key to items

1 Battery
2 Ignition switch
4 Maxifuse unit 1
5 Passenger fusebox
8 Diagnostic connector
15 Engine fusebox
17 LH cooling fan
18 RH cooling fan
20 Air conditioning engine coolant temperature unit
21 RH fan supply relay
22 LH fan supply relay
23 Air conditioning coolant temperature sensor
24 LH and RH fan series supply relay
25 A/C cut-off control unit
26 Pressostat
27 Passenger compartment temperature electronic thermostat
28 Evaporator thermistor
29 A/C compressor
30 Blower relay
31 Blower speed rheostat
32 Air inlet flap reduction motor
33 Blower motor resistor
34 Heater blower motor

Diagram 3

H31992

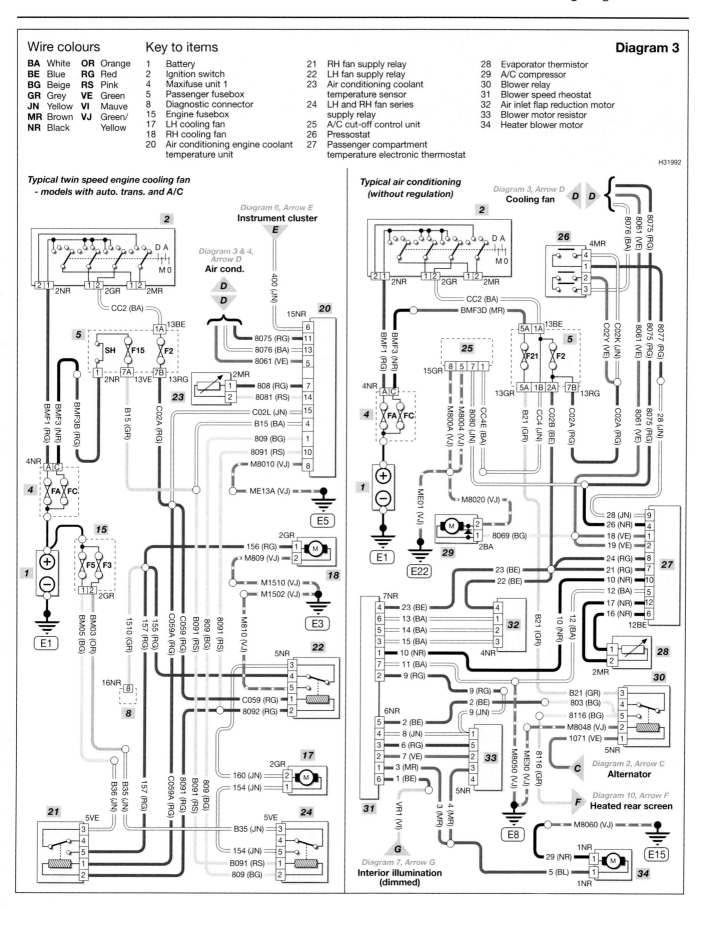

Typical twin speed engine cooling fan - models with auto. trans. and A/C

Typical air conditioning (without regulation)

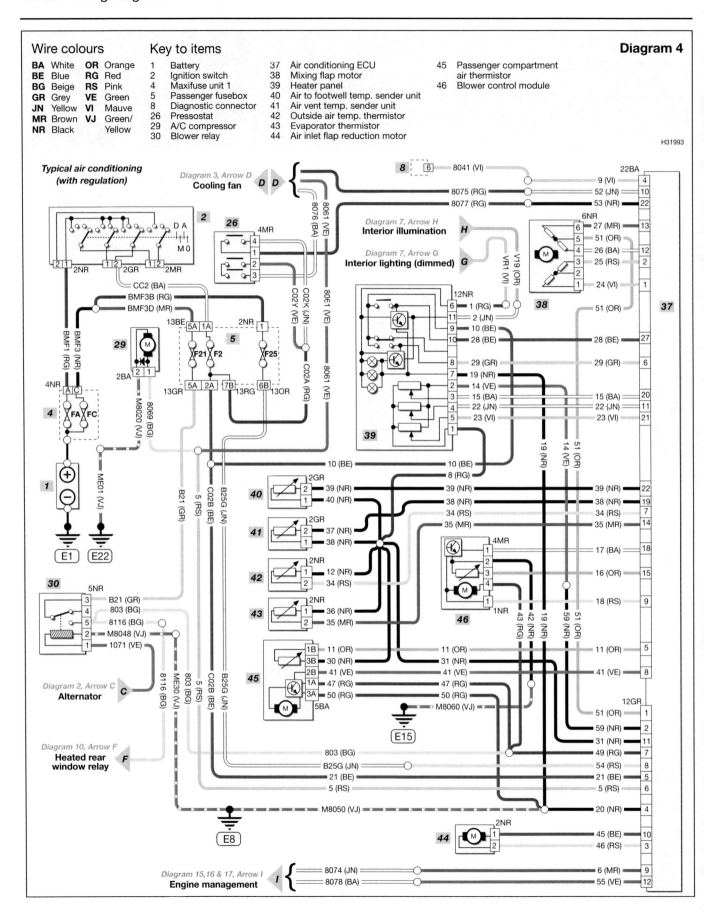

Wire colours

BA	White	OR	Orange
BE	Blue	RG	Red
BG	Beige	RS	Pink
GR	Grey	VE	Green
JN	Yellow	VI	Mauve
MR	Brown	VJ	Green/
NR	Black		Yellow

Key to items

1	Battery	37	Air conditioning ECU	45	Passenger compartment
2	Ignition switch	38	Mixing flap motor		air thermistor
4	Maxifuse unit 1	39	Heater panel	46	Blower control module
5	Passenger fusebox	40	Air to footwell temp. sender unit		
8	Diagnostic connector	41	Air vent temp. sender unit		
26	Pressostat	42	Outside air temp. thermistor		
29	A/C compressor	43	Evaporator thermistor		
30	Blower relay	44	Air inlet flap reduction motor		

Diagram 4

H31993

Typical air conditioning (with regulation)

Diagram 3, Arrow D
Cooling fan

Diagram 7, Arrow H
Interior illumination

Diagram 7, Arrow G
Interior lighting (dimmed)

Diagram 2, Arrow C
Alternator

Diagram 10, Arrow F
Heated rear window relay

Diagram 15,16 & 17, Arrow I
Engine management

Wire colours

BA	White	**OR**	Orange
BE	Blue	**RG**	Red
BG	Beige	**RS**	Pink
GR	Grey	**VE**	Green
JN	Yellow	**VI**	Mauve
MR	Brown	**VJ**	Green/
NR	Black		Yellow

Key to items

1 Battery
2 Ignition switch
4 Maxifuse unit 1
5 Passenger fusebox
8 Diagnostic connector
15 Engine fusebox
25 A/C cut-off control unit
50 Preheat control unit
51 Glow plugs
52 Post heat thermal switch

53 Anti-start relay
54 Instrument cluster
  a = glow plug warning light
  b = speedometer
  c = tachometer
  d = low coolant level warning light
  e = seat belt warning light
55 TDC sensor
56 Vehicle speed sensor

57 Diesel injection pump
  a = EGR load lever switch
  b = advance correction solenoid
  c = CAS control unit
  d = fuel cut-off solenoid
58 Post heat relay
59 EGR vacuum control solenoid
60 Coolant level switch
61 Seat belt switch

Diagram 5

H31994

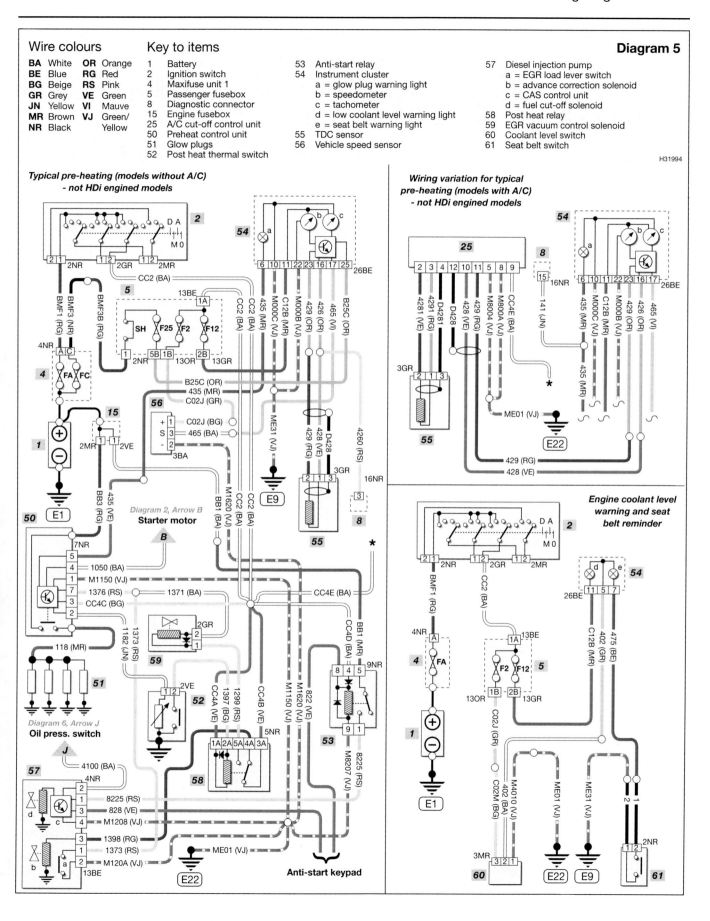

Typical pre-heating (models without A/C) - not HDi engined models

Wiring variation for typical pre-heating (models with A/C) - not HDi engined models

Engine coolant level warning and seat belt reminder

Diagram 2, Arrow B
Starter motor

Diagram 6, Arrow J
Oil press. switch

Anti-start keypad

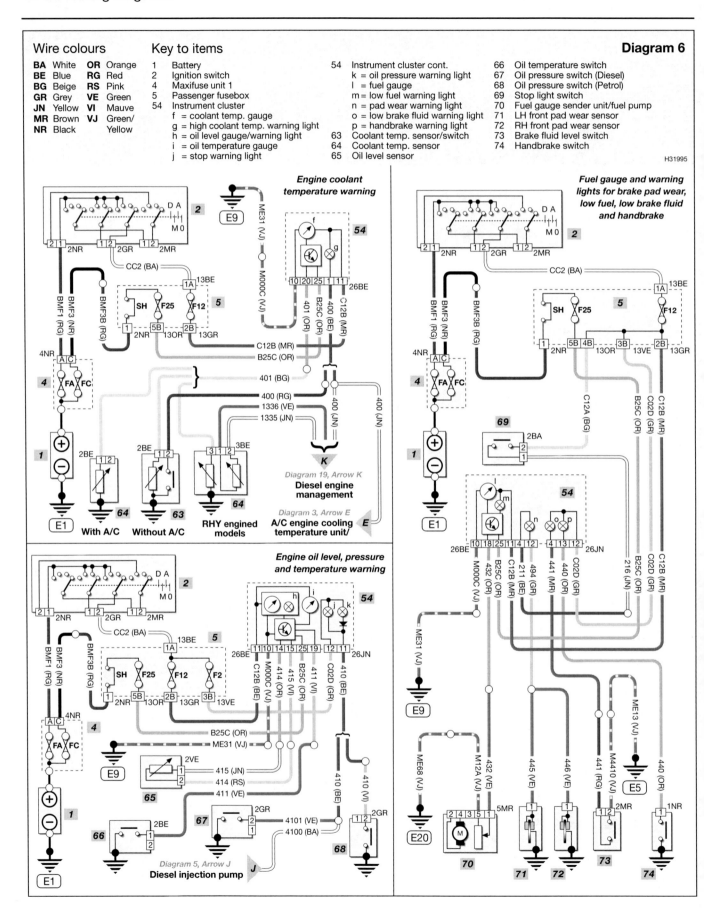

Wire colours

BA White   OR Orange
BE Blue   RG Red
BG Beige   RS Pink
GR Grey   VE Green
JN Yellow   VI Mauve
MR Brown   VJ Green/
NR Black   Yellow

Key to items

1   Battery
2   Ignition switch
4   Maxifuse unit 1
5   Passenger fusebox
54 Instrument cluster
    f = coolant temp. gauge
    g = high coolant temp. warning light
    h = oil level gauge/warning light
    i = oil temperature gauge
    j = stop warning light

54 Instrument cluster cont.
    k = oil pressure warning light
    l = fuel gauge
    m = low fuel warning light
    n = pad wear warning light
    o = low brake fluid warning light
    p = handbrake warning light
63 Coolant temp. sensor/switch
64 Coolant temp. sensor
65 Oil level sensor

66 Oil temperature switch
67 Oil pressure switch (Diesel)
68 Oil pressure switch (Petrol)
69 Stop light switch
70 Fuel gauge sender unit/fuel pump
71 LH front pad wear sensor
72 RH front pad wear sensor
73 Brake fluid level switch
74 Handbrake switch

Diagram 6

H31995

Wire colours

BA	White	**OR**	Orange
BE	Blue	**RG**	Red
BG	Beige	**RS**	Pink
GR	Grey	**VE**	Green
JN	Yellow	**VI**	Mauve
MR	Brown	**VJ**	Green/
NR	Black		Yellow

Key to items

1 Battery
2 Ignition switch
4 Maxifuse unit 1
5 Passenger fusebox
8 Diagnostic connector
54 Instrument cluster
   q = buzzer
   r = instrument illumination
78 Central protection unit

79 Front courtesy light
80 Rear courtesy light
81 Luggage compartment light
82 Luggage compartment light switch
83 Glove box light
84 Glove box light switch
85 Passenger's vanity mirror light
86 RH front reading light
87 LH front door lock assembly

88 RH front door lock assembly
89 LH rear door lock assembly
90 RH rear door lock assembly
91 Analogue module transponder
92 Illumination rheostat
93 Multifunction switch
   a = sidelight/headlight switch
94 Auto. trans. selector lever illumination

Diagram 7

H31996

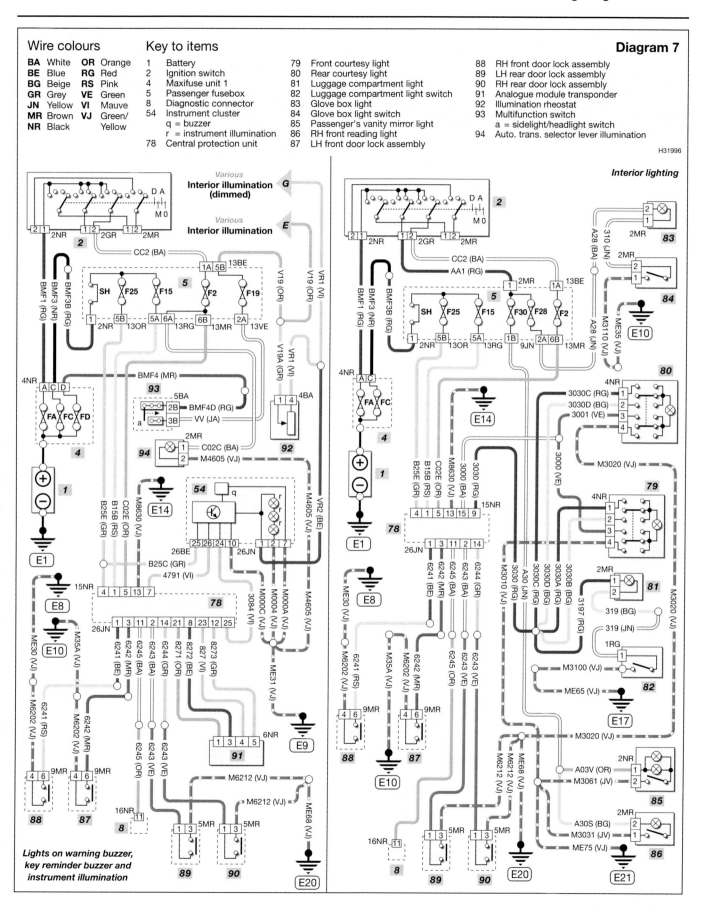

Interior lighting

Lights on warning buzzer, key reminder buzzer and instrument illumination

Diagram 8

Wire colours

BA	White	OR	Orange
BE	Blue	RG	Red
BG	Beige	RS	Pink
GR	Grey	VE	Green
JN	Yellow	VI	Mauve
MR	Brown	VJ	Green/
NR	Black		Yellow

* All other models
** Estate

Key to items

1 Battery
2 Ignition switch
4 Maxifuse unit 1
5 Passenger fusebox
15 Engine fusebox
54 Instrument cluster
   s = main beam warning light
   t = dipped beam warning light
69 Stoplight switch
93 Multifunction switch
   a = sidelight/headlight switch
   b = dipped/main beam switch
   c = headlight flasher

98 LH front sidelight (H4 headlights)
99 LH headlight (H7 headlights)
   a = sidelight
   b = main beam
   c = dipped beam
100 RH front sidelight (H4 headlights)
101 RH headlight (H7 headlights)
   (a to c as per item 99)
102 LH rear light cluster
   a = tail light
   b = stop light
   c = reversing light

103 RH rear light cluster
   (a to c as per item 102)
104 LH number plate light
105 RH number plate light
106 LH headlight (H4 headlights)
107 RH headlight (H4 headlights)
108 High level brake light
109 Reversing light switch (manual)

H31997

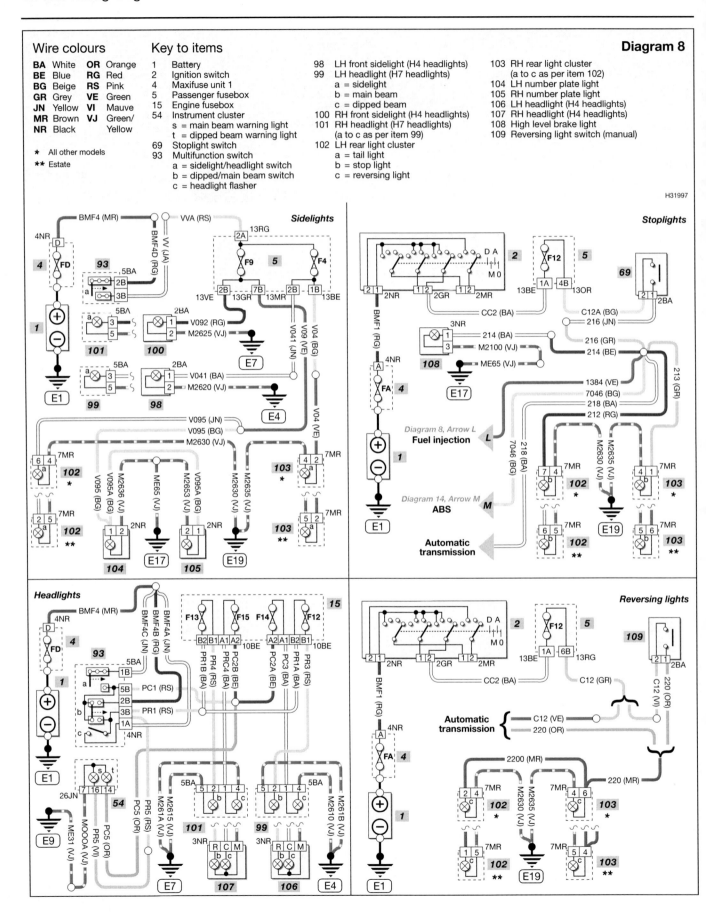

Wire colours

BA	White	OR	Orange
BE	Blue	RG	Red
BG	Beige	RS	Pink
GR	Grey	VE	Green
JN	Yellow	VI	Mauve
MR	Brown	VJ	Green/
NR	Black		Yellow

*   All other models
** Estate

Key to items

1 Battery
2 Ignition switch
4 Maxifuse unit 1
5 Passenger fusebox
15 Engine fusebox
54 Instrument cluster
  u = LH indicator warning light
  v = RH indicator warning light
  w = front foglight warning light
  x = rear foglight warning light

93 Multifunction switch
  a = sidelight/headlight switch
  d = indicator switch
  e = rear foglight switch
  f = front foglight switch
  g = horn switch
102 LH rear light cluster
  d = direction indicator
  e = foglight
103 RH rear light cluster
  (d and e as per item 102)

115 Hazard warning switch
117 Direction indicator flasher unit
118 LH front indicator
119 LH front side repeater
120 RH front indicator
121 RH front side repeater
122 Front foglight relay
123 LH front foglight
124 RH front foglight
125 Horn

Diagram 9

H31998

Direction indicators and hazard warning

Diagram 14, Arrow N
Central locking

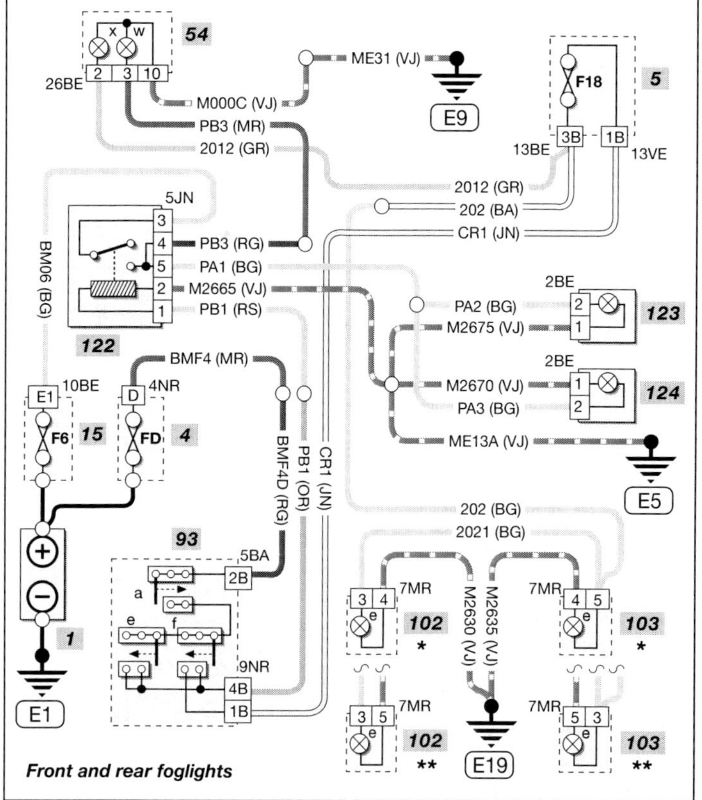

Front and rear foglights

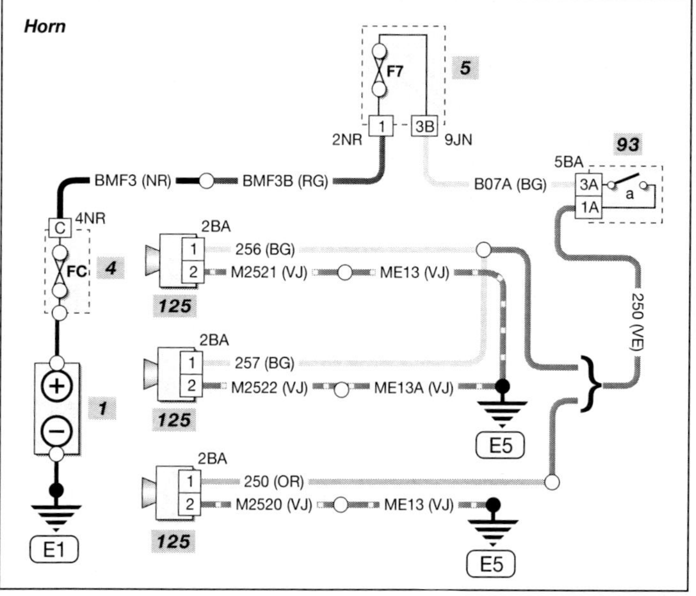

Horn

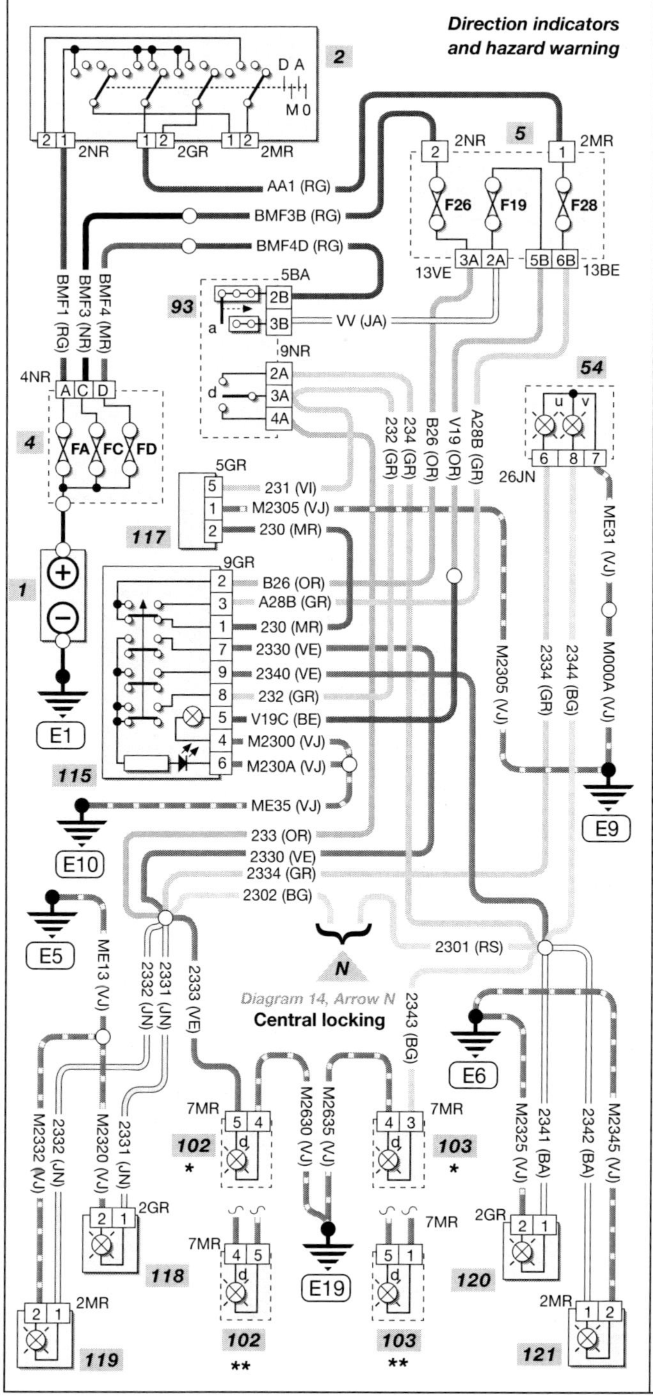

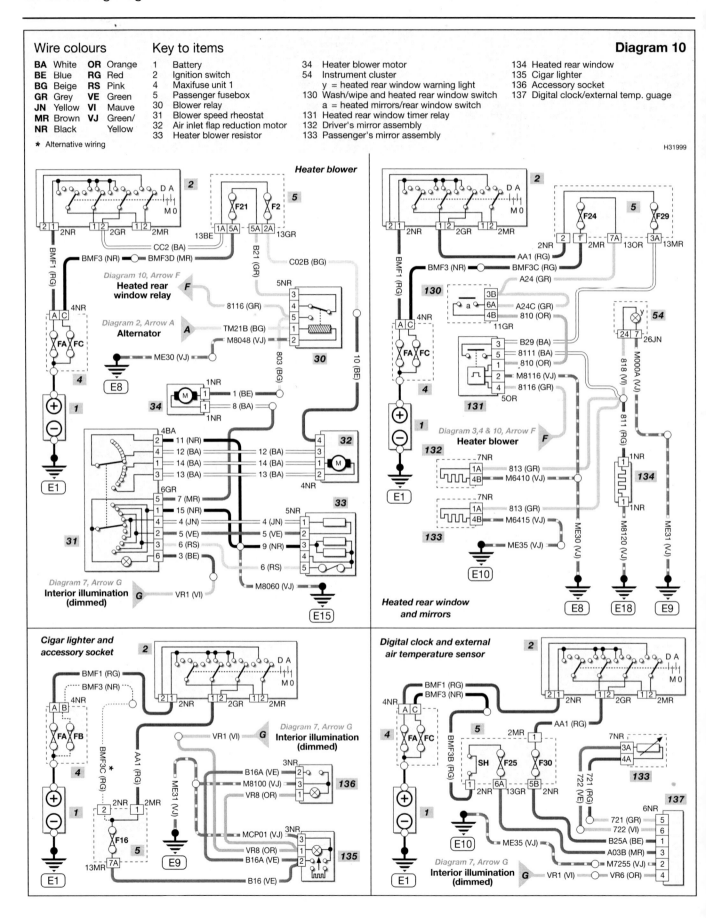

Wire colours

BA	White	**OR**	Orange
BE	Blue	**RG**	Red
BG	Beige	**RS**	Pink
GR	Grey	**VE**	Green
JN	Yellow	**VI**	Mauve
MR	Brown	**VJ**	Green/
NR	Black		Yellow

★ Alternative wiring

Key to items

1 Battery
2 Ignition switch
4 Maxifuse unit 1
5 Passenger fusebox
30 Blower relay
31 Blower speed rheostat
32 Air inlet flap reduction motor
33 Heater blower resistor
34 Heater blower motor
54 Instrument cluster
   y = heated rear window warning light
130 Wash/wipe and heated rear window switch
   a = heated mirrors/rear window switch
131 Heated rear window timer relay
132 Driver's mirror assembly
133 Passenger's mirror assembly
134 Heated rear window
135 Cigar lighter
136 Accessory socket
137 Digital clock/external temp. guage

Diagram 10

H31999

Wire colours

BA	White	**OR**	Orange
BE	Blue	**RG**	Red
BG	Beige	**RS**	Pink
GR	Grey	**VE**	Green
JN	Yellow	**VI**	Mauve
MR	Brown	**VJ**	Green/
NR	Black		Yellow

Key to items

1 Battery
2 Ignition switch
4 Maxifuse unit 1
5 Passenger fusebox
54 Instrument cluster
   z = clock
93 Multifunction switch
   a = side/headlight switch
140 Satellite control switches
141 Steering wheel rotary connector

142 Audio unit
143 LH front tweeter
144 RH front tweeter
145 Driver's front door speaker
146 Passenger's front door speaker
147 CD player
148 Front window lift and sunroof relay
149 Sunroof motor
150 Sunroof switch
151 Travel limit switch

152 Tilt limit switch
153 Sunroof relay
154 Zero point switch
155 Headlight levelling switch
156 LH headlight levelling motor
157 RH headlight levelling motor

Note:
dashed wiring denotes alternative

Diagram 11

H33000

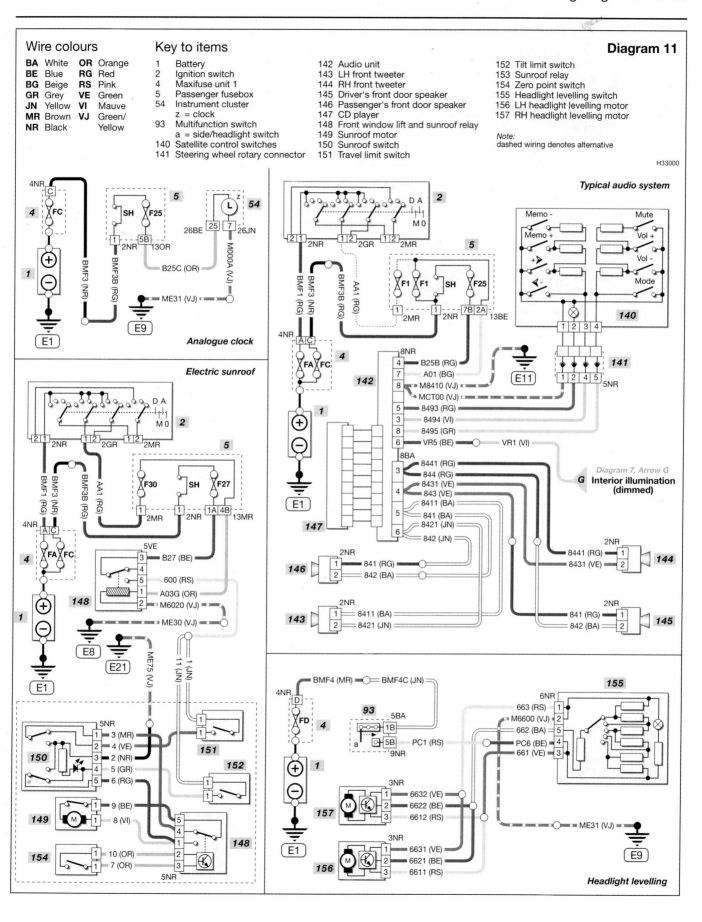

Analogue clock

Electric sunroof

Typical audio system

Diagram 7, Arrow G
Interior illumination (dimmed)

Headlight levelling

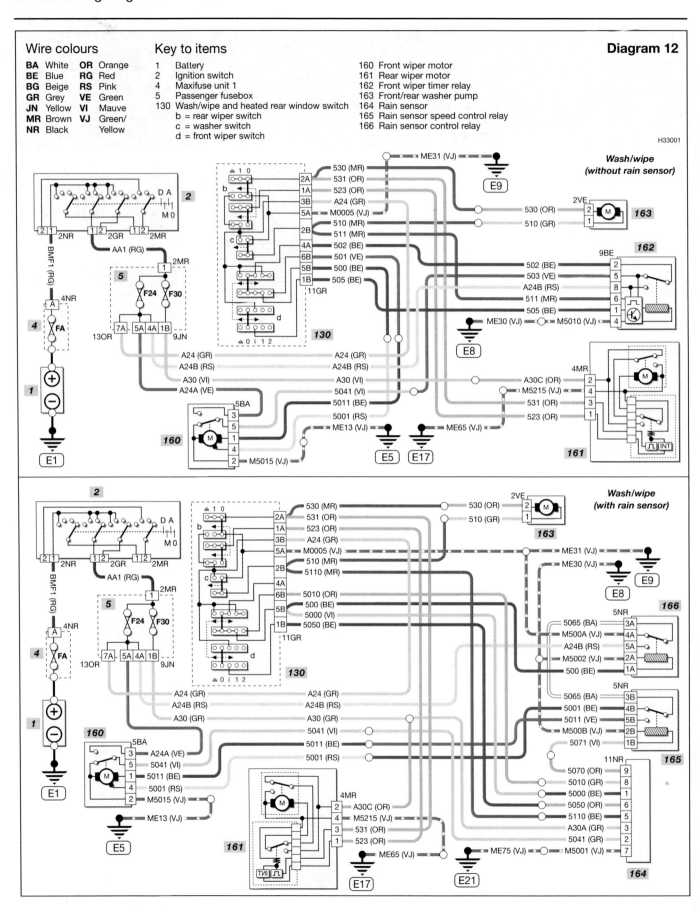

Wire colours

BA	White	OR	Orange
BE	Blue	RG	Red
BG	Beige	RS	Pink
GR	Grey	VE	Green
JN	Yellow	VI	Mauve
MR	Brown	VJ	Green/
NR	Black		Yellow

Key to items

1 Battery
2 Ignition switch
4 Maxifuse unit 1
5 Passenger fusebox
130 Wash/wipe and heated rear window switch
   b = rear wiper switch
   c = washer switch
   d = front wiper switch

160 Front wiper motor
161 Rear wiper motor
162 Front wiper timer relay
163 Front/rear washer pump
164 Rain sensor
165 Rain sensor speed control relay
166 Rain sensor control relay

Diagram 12

H33001

Wash/wipe (without rain sensor)

Wash/wipe (with rain sensor)

Wire colours

BA White   OR Orange
BE Blue   RG Red
BG Beige   RS Pink
GR Grey   VE Green
JN Yellow VI Mauve
MR Brown   VJ Green/
NR Black   Yellow

Key to items

1   Battery
2   Ignition switch
4   Maxifuse unit 1
5   Passenger fusebox
170 Front window lift relay
171 LH front window switch
172 RH front window switch

173 LH front window motor
174 RH front window motor
175 Rear window lift relay
176 Rear window lift inhibitor switch
    and alarm cut-off
177 Rear function locking relay
178 LH rear window front switch

179 LH rear window rear switch
180 LH rear window lift motor
181 RH rear window front switch
182 RH rear window rear switch
183 RH rear window lift motor
184 Driver's seat backrest switch
185 Driver's seat backrest inclination motor

Diagram 13

H33002

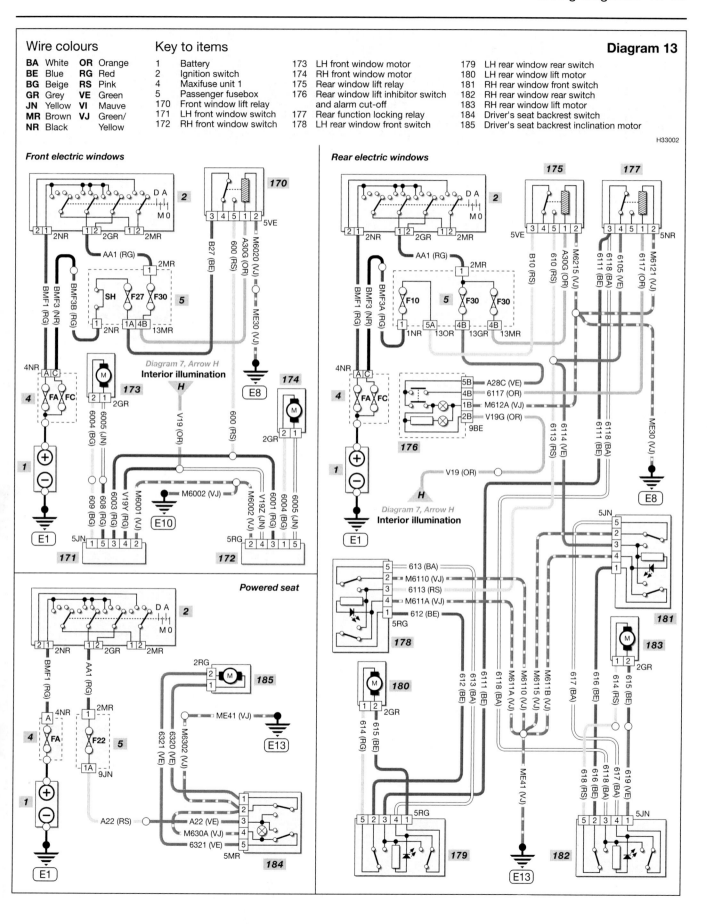

Front electric windows

Rear electric windows

Powered seat

Wire colours

BA	White	OR	Orange
BE	Blue	RG	Red
BG	Beige	RS	Pink
GR	Grey	VE	Green
JN	Yellow	VI	Mauve
MR	Brown	VJ	Green/
NR	Black		Yellow

* Models with deadlocking

Key to items

1	Battery	78	Central protection unit
2	Ignition switch	132	Driver's mirror assembly
4	Maxifuse unit 1	133	Passenger's mirror assembly
5	Passenger fusebox	190	LH front door lock assembly
8	Diagnostic connector	191	RH front door lock assembly
16	Maxifuse unit 2	192	LH rear door lock assembly
54	Instrument cluster	193	RH rear door lock assembly
a1 =	ABS warning light	194	Boot or tailgate lock motor

195	Luggage compartment switch (estate only)
196	Mirror control switch
197	ABS control unit
198	LH front wheel sensor
199	LH rear wheel sensor
200	RH front wheel sensor
201	RH rear wheel sensor

Diagram 14

H33003

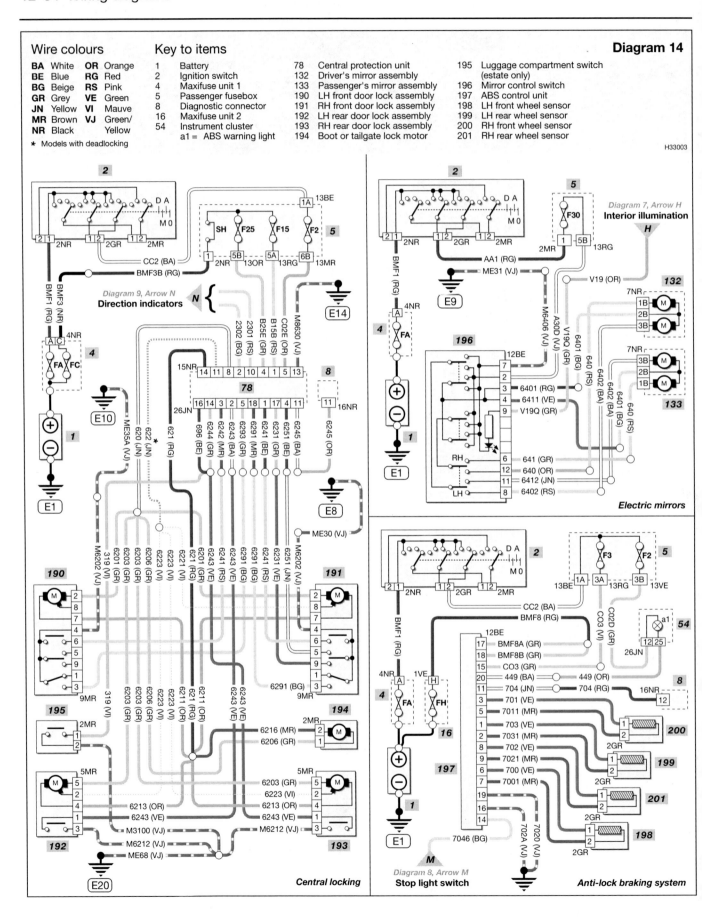

Central locking

Stop light switch

Anti-lock braking system

Electric mirrors

Wire colours

BA	White	OR	Orange
BE	Blue	RG	Red
BG	Beige	RS	Pink
GR	Grey	VE	Green
JN	Yellow	VI	Mauve
MR	Brown	VJ	Green/
NR	Black		Yellow

Key to items

1 Battery
2 Ignition switch
4 Maxifuse unit 1
5 Passenger fusebox
8 Diagnostic connector
15 Engine fusebox
54 Instrument cluster
  b = speedometer
  c = tachometer
  c1 = engine management
      warning light
56 Vehicle speed sensor
70 Fuel gauge sender unit/fuel pump
205 Engine management double function relay
206 Ignition coil
207 Engine management control unit
208 Idle speed stepper motor
209 Engine speed sensor
210 Oxygen sensor
211 Spark plug
212 Inertia switch
213 Throttle housing heater
214 Canister purge solenoid
215 Knock sensor
216 Engine coolant temp. sensor
217 Throttle position sensor
218 MAP sensor
219 Inlet air temp. sensor
220 Power steering pressure switch
221 Fuel injector

Diagram 15

H33004

Typical Sagem SL 96 fuel injection system

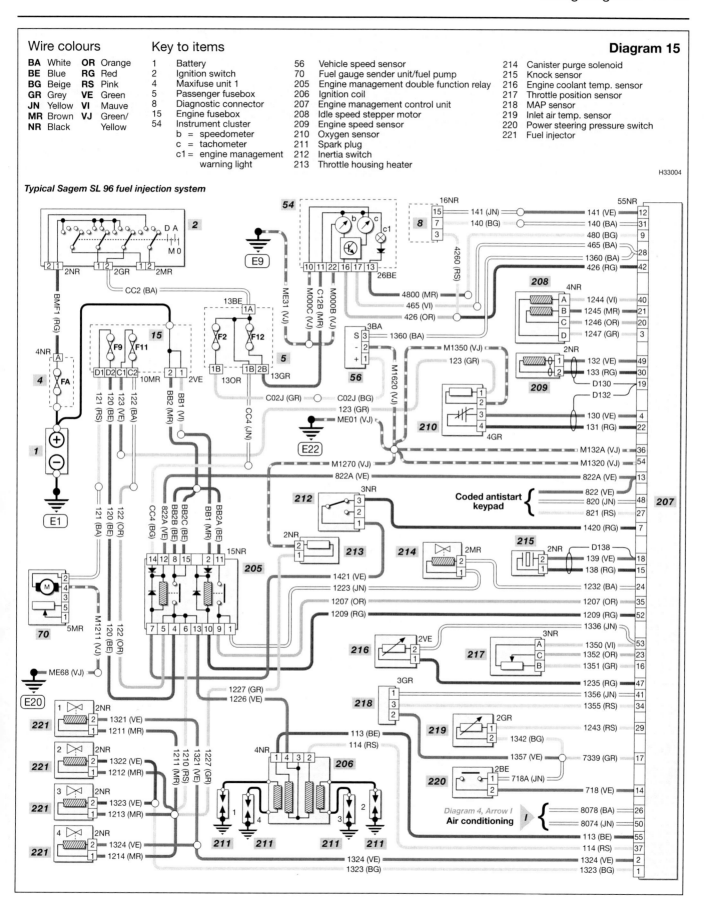

Wire colours

BA	White	**OR**	Orange
BE	Blue	**RG**	Red
BG	Beige	**RS**	Pink
GR	Grey	**VE**	Green
JN	Yellow	**VI**	Mauve
MR	Brown	**VJ**	Green/
NR	Black		Yellow

Key to items

1 Battery
2 Ignition switch
4 Maxifuse unit 1
5 Passenger fusebox
8 Diagnostic connector
15 Engine fusebox
54 Instrument cluster
  b = speedometer
  c = tachometer
  c1 = engine management
    warning light

56 Vehicle speed sensor
70 Fuel gauge sender unit/fuel pump
205 Engine management double function relay
206 Ignition coil
207 Engine management control unit
208 Idle speed stepper motor
209 Engine speed sensor
210 Oxygen sensor
211 Spark plug
212 Inertia switch
213 Throttle housing heater

214 Canister purge solenoid
215 Knock sensor
216 Engine coolant temp. sensor
217 Throttle position sensor
218 MAP sensor
219 Inlet air temp. sensor
220 Power steering pressure switch
221 Fuel injector

Diagram 16

H33005

Typical Bosch MP5.2 Motronic fuel injection system

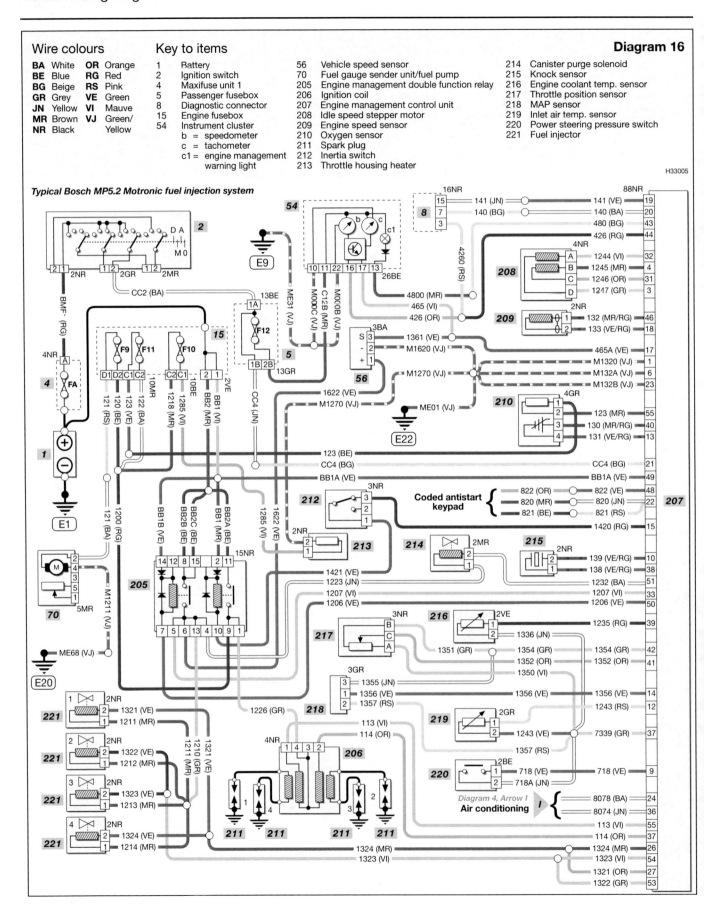

Wire colours

BA	White	OR	Orange
BE	Blue	RG	Red
BG	Beige	RS	Pink
GR	Grey	VE	Green
JN	Yellow	VI	Mauve
MR	Brown	VJ	Green/
NR	Black		Yellow

Key to items

1   Battery
2   Ignition switch
4   Maxifuse unit 1
5   Passenger fusebox
8   Diagnostic connector
15 Engine fusebox
54 Instrument cluster
   b = speedometer
   c = tachometer
   c1 = engine management
       warning light

56   Vehicle speed sensor
70   Fuel gauge sender unit/fuel pump
205 Engine management double function relay
206 Ignition coil
207 Engine management control unit
208 Idle speed stepper motor
209 Engine speed sensor
210 Oxygen sensor
211 Spark plug
212 Inertia switch
213 Throttle housing heater

214 Canister purge solenoid
215 Knock sensor
216 Engine coolant temp. sensor
217 Throttle position sensor
218 MAP sensor
219 Inlet air temp. sensor
220 Power steering pressure switch
221 Fuel injector

Diagram 17

H33006

Typical MM1AP fuel injection system

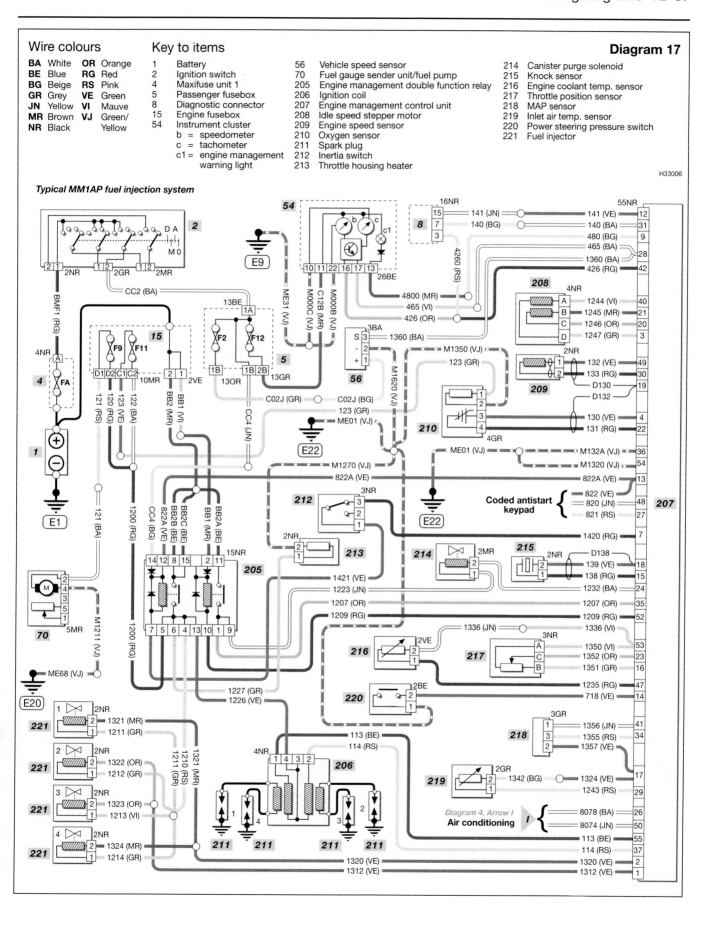

Wire colours

BA	White	OR	Orange
BE	Blue	RG	Red
BG	Beige	RS	Pink
GR	Grey	VE	Green
JN	Yellow	VI	Mauve
MR	Brown	VJ	Green/
NR	Black		Yellow

Key to items

1   Battery
2   Ignition switch
4   Maxifuse unit 1
5   Passenger fusebox
8   Diagnostic connector
15 Engine fusebox
54 Instrument cluster
   a = glow plug warning light
   b = speedometer
   c = tachometer
   c1 = engine man. warning light

56   Vehicle speed sensor
70   Fuel gauge sender unit/fuel pump
205 Engine management double function relay
207 Engine management control unit
212 Inertia switch
225 Clutch pedal info switch
233 EGR solenoid valve
234 EGR butterfly solenoid
235 3rd piston cut-out solenoid
236 Pressure regulator

Diagram 18

H33007

Typical HDi Diesel engine management system (part 1 of 2)

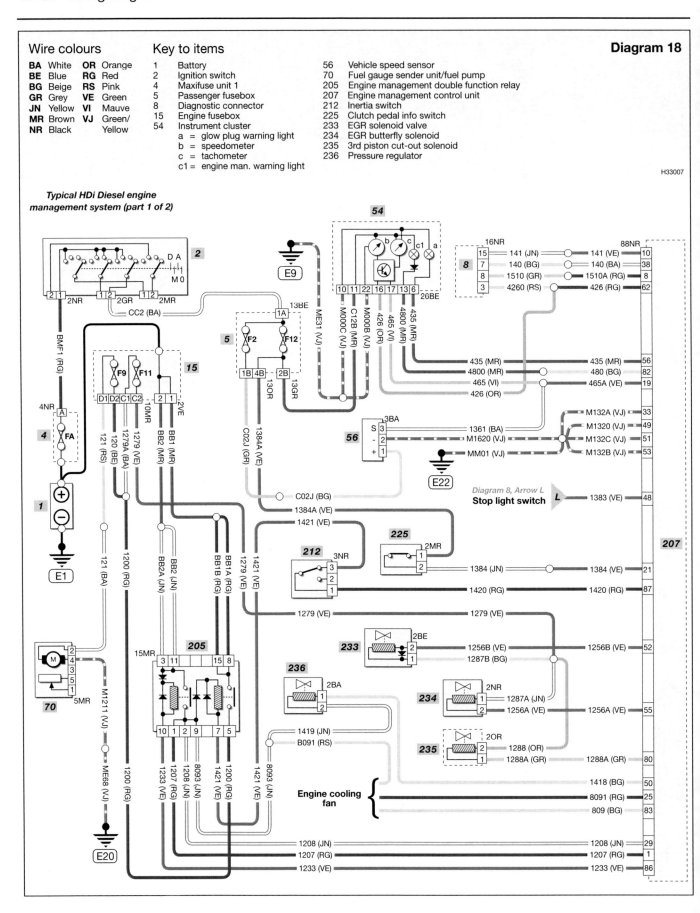

Wire colours

BA	White	**OR**	Orange
BE	Blue	**RG**	Red
BG	Beige	**RS**	Pink
GR	Grey	**VE**	Green
JN	Yellow	**VI**	Mauve
MR	Brown	**VJ**	Green/
NR	Black		Yellow

Key to items

1	Battery	221	Fuel injector
2	Ignition switch	226	3 relay protection switch unit
4	Maxifuse unit 1	227	Water circuit heater
5	Passenger fusebox	228	Accelerator pedal sensor
15	Engine fusebox	229	Pressure sensor
50	Preheat control unit	230	Diesel thermistor
51	Glow plugs	231	Air flow sensor
207	Engine management control unit	232	Cylinder reference sensor
209	Engine speed sensor		

Diagram 19

H33008

*Typical HDi Diesel engine
management system (part 2 of 2)*

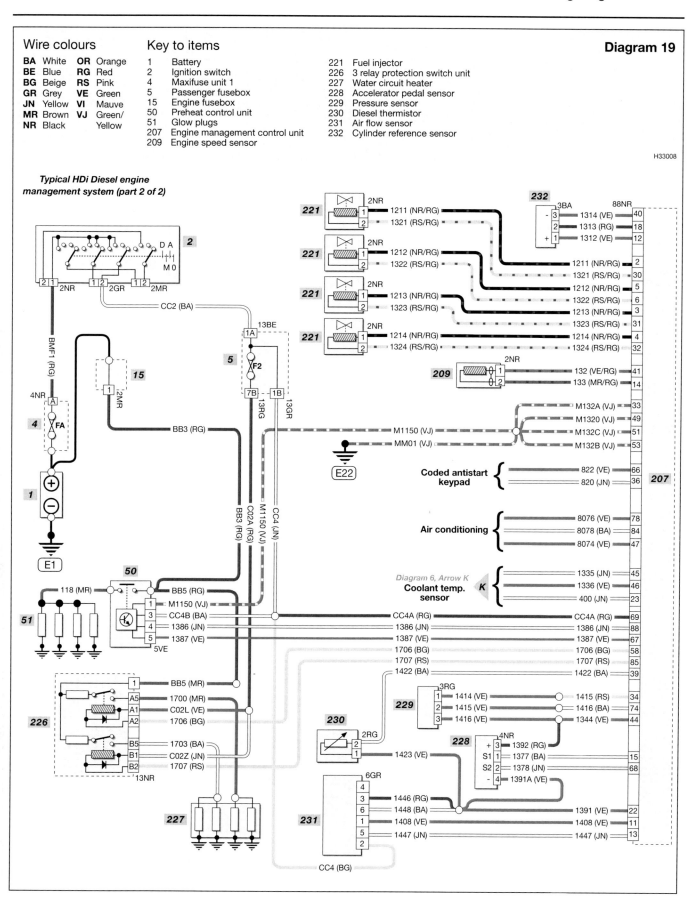

Dimensions and Weights .... **REF•1**
Conversion Factors .... **REF•2**
Buying Spare Parts .... **REF•3**
Vehicle Identification .... **REF•3**
General Repair Procedures .... **REF•4**
Jacking and Vehicle Support .... **REF•5**

Disconnecting the Battery .... **REF•6**
Tools and Working Facilities .... **REF•7**
MOT Test Checks .... **REF•9**
Fault Finding .... **REF•13**
Glossary of Technical Terms .... **REF•21**
Index .... **REF•26**

Dimensions and weights

Note: *All figures are approximate, and may vary according to model. Refer to manufacturer's data for exact figures.*

Dimensions

Overall length:
  Coupé and Hatchback models .... .4167 mm
  Estate models .... .4354 mm
Overall width (including mirrors) .... 1994 mm
Overall height (unladen):
  Coupé and Hatchback models .... .1401 mm
  Estate models .... .1426 mm
Wheelbase .... 2540 mm

Weights

Kerb weight .... 1020 to 1220 kg*
Maximum gross vehicle weight** .... 1560 to 1740 kg*
Maximum roof rack load:
  Coupé and Hatchback models .... .75 kg
  Estate models .... .100 kg
Maximum towing weight (braked trailer)** .... 900 to 1200 kg*
Maximum trailer nose weight .... 70 kg*

Depending on model and specification.
**Refer to Citroën dealer for exact recommendations.*

Conversion factors

Length (distance)

Inches (in)	x 25.4	=	Millimetres (mm)	x 0.0394	=	Inches (in)
Feet (ft)	x 0.305	=	Metres (m)	x 3.281	=	Feet (ft)
Miles	x 1.609	=	Kilometres (km)	x 0.621	=	Miles

Inches (in)	x 25.4	=	Millimetres (mm)	x 0.0394	=	Inches (in)
Feet (ft)	x 0.305	=	Metres (m)	x 3.281	=	Feet (ft)
Miles	x 1.609	=	Kilometres (km)	x 0.621	=	Miles

Volume (capacity)

Cubic inches (cu in; in^3)	x 16.387	=	Cubic centimetres (cc; cm^3)	x 0.061	=	Cubic inches (cu in; in^3)
Imperial pints (Imp pt)	x 0.568	=	Litres (l)	x 1.76	=	Imperial pints (Imp pt)
Imperial quarts (Imp qt)	x 1.137	=	Litres (l)	x 0.88	=	Imperial quarts (Imp qt)
Imperial quarts (Imp qt)	x 1.201	=	US quarts (US qt)	x 0.833	=	Imperial quarts (Imp qt)
US quarts (US qt)	x 0.946	=	Litres (l)	x 1.057	=	US quarts (US qt)
Imperial gallons (Imp gal)	x 4.546	=	Litres (l)	x 0.22	=	Imperial gallons (Imp gal)
Imperial gallons (Imp gal)	x 1.201	=	US gallons (US gal)	x 0.833	=	Imperial gallons (Imp gal)
US gallons (US gal)	x 3.785	=	Litres (l)	x 0.264	=	US gallons (US gal)

Mass (weight)

Ounces (oz)	x 28.35	=	Grams (g)	x 0.035	=	Ounces (oz)
Pounds (lb)	x 0.454	=	Kilograms (kg)	x 2.205	=	Pounds (lb)

Force

Ounces-force (ozf; oz)	x 0.278	=	Newtons (N)	x 3.6	=	Ounces-force (ozf; oz)
Pounds-force (lbf; lb)	x 4.448	=	Newtons (N)	x 0.225	=	Pounds-force (lbf; lb)
Newtons (N)	x 0.1	=	Kilograms-force (kgf; kg)	x 9.81	=	Newtons (N)

Pressure

Pounds-force per square inch (psi; lbf/in^2; lb/in^2)	x 0.070	=	Kilograms-force per square centimetre (kgf/cm^2; kg/cm^2)	x 14.223	=	Pounds-force per square inch (psi; lbf/in^2; lb/in^2)
Pounds-force per square inch (psi; lbf/in^2; lb/in^2)	x 0.068	=	Atmospheres (atm)	x 14.696	=	Pounds-force per square inch (psi; lbf/in^2; lb/in^2)
Pounds-force per square inch (psi; lbf/in^2; lb/in^2)	x 0.069	=	Bars	x 14.5	=	Pounds-force per square inch (psi; lbf/in^2; lb/in^2)
Pounds-force per square inch (psi; lbf/in^2; lb/in^2)	x 6.895	=	Kilopascals (kPa)	x 0.145	=	Pounds-force per square inch (psi; lbf/in^2; lb/in^2)
Kilopascals (kPa)	x 0.01	=	Kilograms-force per square centimetre (kgf/cm^2; kg/cm^2)	x 98.1	=	Kilopascals (kPa)
Millibar (mbar)	x 100	=	Pascals (Pa)	x 0.01	=	Millibar (mbar)
Millibar (mbar)	x 0.0145	=	Pounds-force per square inch (psi; lbf/in^2; lb/in^2)	x 68.947	=	Millibar (mbar)
Millibar (mbar)	x 0.75	=	Millimetres of mercury (mmHg)	x 1.333	=	Millibar (mbar)
Millibar (mbar)	x 0.401	=	Inches of water (inH$_2$O)	x 2.491	=	Millibar (mbar)
Millimetres of mercury (mmHg)	x 0.535	=	Inches of water (inH$_2$O)	x 1.868	=	Millimetres of mercury (mmHg)
Inches of water (inH$_2$O)	x 0.036	=	Pounds-force per square inch (psi; lbf/in^2; lb/in^2)	x 27.68	=	Inches of water (inH$_2$O)

Torque (moment of force)

Pounds-force inches (lbf in; lb in)	x 1.152	=	Kilograms-force centimetre (kgf cm; kg cm)	x 0.868	=	Pounds-force inches (lbf in; lb in)
Pounds-force inches (lbf in; lb in)	x 0.113	=	Newton metres (Nm)	x 8.85	=	Pounds-force inches (lbf in; lb in)
Pounds-force inches (lbf in; lb in)	x 0.083	=	Pounds-force feet (lbf ft; lb ft)	x 12	=	Pounds-force inches (lbf in; lb in)
Pounds-force feet (lbf ft; lb ft)	x 0.138	=	Kilograms-force metres (kgf m; kg m)	x 7.233	=	Pounds-force feet (lbf ft; lb ft)
Pounds-force feet (lbf ft; lb ft)	x 1.356	=	Newton metres (Nm)	x 0.738	=	Pounds-force feet (lbf ft; lb ft)
Newton metres (Nm)	x 0.102	=	Kilograms-force metres (kgf m; kg m)	x 9.804	=	Newton metres (Nm)

Power

Horsepower (hp)	x 745.7	=	Watts (W)	x 0.0013	=	Horsepower (hp)

Velocity (speed)

Miles per hour (miles/hr; mph)	x 1.609	=	Kilometres per hour (km/hr; kph)	x 0.621	=	Miles per hour (miles/hr; mph)

Fuel consumption*

Miles per gallon, Imperial (mpg)	x 0.354	=	Kilometres per litre (km/l)	x 2.825	=	Miles per gallon, Imperial (mpg)
Miles per gallon, US (mpg)	x 0.425	=	Kilometres per litre (km/l)	x 2.352	=	Miles per gallon, US (mpg)

Temperature

Degrees Fahrenheit = (°C x 1.8) + 32   Degrees Celsius (Degrees Centigrade; °C) = (°F - 32) x 0.56

It is common practice to convert from miles per gallon (mpg) to litres/100 kilometres (l/100km), where mpg x l/100 km = 282

Spare parts are available from many sources, including maker's appointed garages, accessory shops, and motor factors. To be sure of obtaining the correct parts, it will sometimes be necessary to quote the vehicle identification number. If possible, it can also be useful to take the old parts along for positive identification. Items such as starter motors and alternators may be available under a service exchange scheme - any parts returned should be clean.

Our advice regarding spare parts is as follows.

Officially appointed garages

This is the best source of parts which are peculiar to your car, and which are not otherwise generally available (eg, badges, interior trim, certain body panels, etc). It is also the only place at which you should buy parts if the vehicle is still under warranty.

Accessory shops

These are very good places to buy materials and components needed for the maintenance of your car (oil, air and fuel filters, light bulbs, drivebelts, greases, brake pads, tough-up paint, etc). Components of this nature sold by a reputable shop are of the same standard as those used by the car manufacturer.

Besides components, these shops also sell tools and general accessories, usually have convenient opening hours, charge lower prices, and can often be found close to home. Some accessory shops have parts counters where components needed for almost any repair job can be purchased or ordered.

Motor factors

Good factors will stock all the more important components which wear out comparatively quickly, and can sometimes supply individual components needed for the overhaul of a larger assembly (eg, brake seals and hydraulic parts, bearing shells, pistons, valves). They may also handle work such as cylinder block reboring, crankshaft regrinding, etc.

Tyre and exhaust specialists

These outlets may be independent, or members of a local or national chain. They frequently offer competitive prices when compared with a main dealer or local garage, but it will pay to obtain several quotes before making a decision. When researching prices, also ask what 'extras' may be added - for instance fitting a new valve and balancing the wheel are both commonly charged on top of the price of a new tyre.

Other sources

Beware of parts or materials obtained from market stalls, car boot sales or similar outlets. Such items are not invariably sub-standard, but there is little chance of compensation if they do prove unsatisfactory. In the case of safety-critical components such as brake pads, there is the risk not only of financial loss, but also of an accident causing injury or death.

Second-hand components or assemblies obtained from a car breaker can be a good buy in some circumstances, but his sort of purchase is best made by the experienced DIY mechanic.

Vehicle identification

Modifications are a continuing and unpublicised process in vehicle manufacture, quite apart from major model changes. Spare parts manuals and lists are compiled upon a numerical basis, the individual vehicle identification numbers being essential for correct identification of the part concerned. When ordering spare parts, always give as much information as possible. Quote the car model, year of manufacture, VIN and engine numbers as appropriate.

On Coupé and Hatchback models, the Vehicle Identification Number (VIN) plate is located inside the luggage compartment, riveted onto the rear of the body, just beneath the lock **(see illustration)**. On Estate models, the VIN plate is located in the engine compartment, on the right-hand wheelarch. Additional identification numbers for weight information, paint codes, chassis numbers, and details of the vehicle which are required by law for export to certain countries are also provided, and their locations are shown in the illustration.

The vehicle identification (chassis) number is stamped into the body, along the top edge of the right-hand wing, and can be viewed with the bonnet open. On some models, the chassis number may also be etched into the windscreen and window glass.

The engine identification numbers are situated on the front face of the cylinder block, either on a plate, or stamped directly to the centre, or side, of the block face. The engine code is located on the first line of the engine number sequence – eg, KFX.

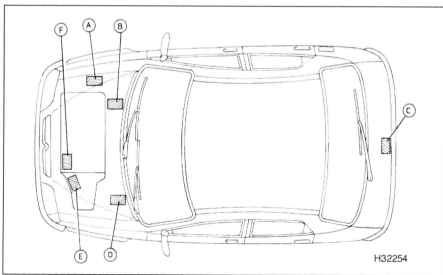

H32254

Vehicle identification details

A Chassis number
B Manufacturer's modification reference number
C VIN plate (Coupé and Hatchback models)
D Body paint colour code
E Transmission number
F Engine number

Whenever servicing, repair or overhaul work is carried out on the car or its components, observe the following procedures and instructions. This will assist in carrying out the operation efficiently and to a professional standard of workmanship.

Joint mating faces and gaskets

When separating components at their mating faces, never insert screwdrivers or similar implements into the joint between the faces in order to prise them apart. This can cause severe damage which results in oil leaks, coolant leaks, etc upon reassembly. Separation is usually achieved by tapping along the joint with a soft-faced hammer in order to break the seal. However, note that this method may not be suitable where dowels are used for component location.

Where a gasket is used between the mating faces of two components, a new one must be fitted on reassembly; fit it dry unless otherwise stated in the repair procedure. Make sure that the mating faces are clean and dry, with all traces of old gasket removed. When cleaning a joint face, use a tool which is unlikely to score or damage the face, and remove any burrs or nicks with an oilstone or fine file.

Make sure that tapped holes are cleaned with a pipe cleaner, and keep them free of jointing compound, if this is being used, unless specifically instructed otherwise.

Ensure that all orifices, channels or pipes are clear, and blow through them, preferably using compressed air.

Oil seals

Oil seals can be removed by levering them out with a wide flat-bladed screwdriver or similar implement. Alternatively, a number of self-tapping screws may be screwed into the seal, and these used as a purchase for pliers or some similar device in order to pull the seal free.

Whenever an oil seal is removed from its working location, either individually or as part of an assembly, it should be renewed.

The very fine sealing lip of the seal is easily damaged, and will not seal if the surface it contacts is not completely clean and free from scratches, nicks or grooves. If the original sealing surface of the component cannot be restored, and the manufacturer has not made provision for slight relocation of the seal relative to the sealing surface, the component should be renewed.

Protect the lips of the seal from any surface which may damage them in the course of fitting. Use tape or a conical sleeve where possible. Lubricate the seal lips with oil before fitting and, on dual-lipped seals, fill the space between the lips with grease.

Unless otherwise stated, oil seals must be fitted with their sealing lips toward the lubricant to be sealed.

Use a tubular drift or block of wood of the appropriate size to install the seal and, if the seal housing is shouldered, drive the seal down to the shoulder. If the seal housing is unshouldered, the seal should be fitted with its face flush with the housing top face (unless otherwise instructed).

Screw threads and fastenings

Seized nuts, bolts and screws are quite a common occurrence where corrosion has set in, and the use of penetrating oil or releasing fluid will often overcome this problem if the offending item is soaked for a while before attempting to release it. The use of an impact driver may also provide a means of releasing such stubborn fastening devices, when used in conjunction with the appropriate screwdriver bit or socket. If none of these methods works, it may be necessary to resort to the careful application of heat, or the use of a hacksaw or nut splitter device.

Studs are usually removed by locking two nuts together on the threaded part, and then using a spanner on the lower nut to unscrew the stud. Studs or bolts which have broken off below the surface of the component in which they are mounted can sometimes be removed using a stud extractor. Always ensure that a blind tapped hole is completely free from oil, grease, water or other fluid before installing the bolt or stud. Failure to do this could cause the housing to crack due to the hydraulic action of the bolt or stud as it is screwed in.

When tightening a castellated nut to accept a split pin, tighten the nut to the specified torque, where applicable, and then tighten further to the next split pin hole. Never slacken the nut to align the split pin hole, unless stated in the repair procedure.

When checking or retightening a nut or bolt to a specified torque setting, slacken the nut or bolt by a quarter of a turn, and then retighten to the specified setting. However, this should not be attempted where angular tightening has been used.

For some screw fastenings, notably cylinder head bolts or nuts, torque wrench settings are no longer specified for the latter stages of tightening, "angle-tightening" being called up instead. Typically, a fairly low torque wrench setting will be applied to the bolts/nuts in the correct sequence, followed by one or more stages of tightening through specified angles.

Locknuts, locktabs and washers

Any fastening which will rotate against a component or housing during tightening should always have a washer between it and the relevant component or housing.

Spring or split washers should always be renewed when they are used to lock a critical component such as a big-end bearing retaining bolt or nut. Locktabs which are folded over to retain a nut or bolt should always be renewed.

Self-locking nuts can be re-used in non-critical areas, providing resistance can be felt when the locking portion passes over the bolt or stud thread. However, it should be noted that self-locking stiffnuts tend to lose their effectiveness after long periods of use, and should then be renewed as a matter of course.

Split pins must always be replaced with new ones of the correct size for the hole.

When thread-locking compound is found on the threads of a fastener which is to be re-used, it should be cleaned off with a wire brush and solvent, and fresh compound applied on reassembly.

Special tools

Some repair procedures in this manual entail the use of special tools such as a press, two or three-legged pullers, spring compressors, etc. Wherever possible, suitable readily-available alternatives to the manufacturer's special tools are described, and are shown in use. In some instances, where no alternative is possible, it has been necessary to resort to the use of a manufacturer's tool, and this has been done for reasons of safety as well as the efficient completion of the repair operation. Unless you are highly-skilled and have a thorough understanding of the procedures described, never attempt to bypass the use of any special tool when the procedure described specifies its use. Not only is there a very great risk of personal injury, but expensive damage could be caused to the components involved.

Environmental considerations

When disposing of used engine oil, brake fluid, antifreeze, etc, give due consideration to any detrimental environmental effects. Do not, for instance, pour any of the above liquids down drains into the general sewage system, or onto the ground to soak away. Many local council refuse tips provide a facility for waste oil disposal, as do some garages. If none of these facilities are available, consult your local Environmental Health Department, or the National Rivers Authority, for further advice.

With the universal tightening-up of legislation regarding the emission of environmentally-harmful substances from motor vehicles, most vehicles have tamperproof devices fitted to the main adjustment points of the fuel system. These devices are primarily designed to prevent unqualified persons from adjusting the fuel/air mixture, with the chance of a consequent increase in toxic emissions. If such devices are found during servicing or overhaul, they should, wherever possible, be renewed or refitted in accordance with the manufacturer's requirements or current legislation.

OIL CARE
FOLLOW THE CODE

OIL BANK LINE
0800 66 33 66
www.oilbankline.org.uk

Note: It is antisocial and illegal to dump oil down the drain. To find the location of your local oil recycling bank, call this number free.

The jack supplied with the vehicle should only be used for changing the roadwheels – see *Wheel changing* at the front of this manual. When carrying out any other kind of work, raise the vehicle using a hydraulic (or 'trolley') jack, and always supplement the jack with axle stands at the vehicle jacking points.

When using a hydraulic jack or axle stands, always position the jack head or axle stand head under one of the relevant jacking points in the ridge on the underside of the sill **(see illustrations)**.

To raise the front of the vehicle, position the jack with an interposed block of wood underneath the centre of the front subframe **(see illustration)**. **Do not** jack the vehicle under the sump, or any of the steering or suspension components.

To raise the rear of the vehicle, position the jack head underneath the centre of the rear axle tubular crossmember **(see illustration)**. **Do not** attempt to raise the vehicle with the jack positioned underneath the spare wheel, as the vehicle floor will almost certainly be damaged.

The jack supplied with the vehicle locates in the jacking points in the ridge on the underside of the sill. Ensure that the jack head is correctly engaged before attempting to raise the vehicle.

Never work under, around, or near a raised vehicle, unless it is adequately supported in at least two places.

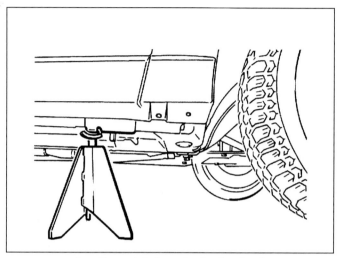

Location points for axle stands – front

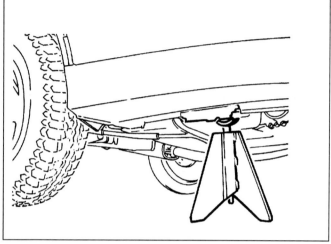

Location points for axle stands – rear

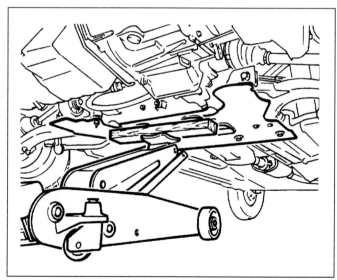

When raising the front of the vehicle, locate the jack under the centre of the front subframe

Note the use of the block of wood placed on the jack head

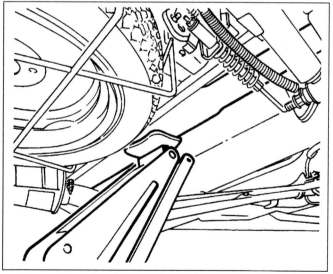

When raising the rear of the vehicle, position the jack head underneath the rear axle tubular crossmember

Numerous systems fitted to the vehicle require battery power to be available at all times, either to ensure their continued operation (such as the clock) or to maintain control unit memories which would be erased if the battery were to be disconnected. Whenever the battery is to be disconnected therefore, first note the following, to ensure that there are no unforeseen consequences of this action:

a) *First, on any vehicle with central locking, it is a wise precaution to remove the key from the ignition, and to keep it with you, so that it does not get locked in if the central locking should engage accidentally when the battery is reconnected.*

b) *The majority of models covered in this manual are equipped with a Citroën anti-theft alarm system. When reconnecting the battery after disconnection, the alarm may be automatically activated. If so, use the remote transmitter to turn off the alarm, or turn off the alarm manually by switching on the ignition. To fully reactivate the system once the battery is reconnected, lock then unlock the vehicle using the remote transmitter; the alarm will be functional again the next time the vehicle is locked with the remote transmitter.*

c) *If a security-coded audio unit is fitted, and the unit and/or the battery is disconnected, the unit will not function again on reconnection until the correct security code is entered. Details of this procedure, which varies according to the unit fitted, are given in the vehicle owner's handbook. Ensure you have the correct code before you disconnect the battery. If you do not have the code or details of the correct procedure, but can supply proof of ownership and a legitimate reason for wanting this information, a Citroën dealer may be able to help.*

d) *On all petrol engines, and 2.0 litre diesel engines, the engine management electronic control unit is of the 'self-learning' type, meaning that as it operates, it also monitors and stores the settings which give optimum engine performance under all operating conditions. When the battery is disconnected, these settings are lost and the ECU reverts to the base settings programmed into its memory at the factory. On restarting, this may lead to the engine running/idling roughly for a short while, until the ECU has re-learned the optimum settings. This process is best accomplished by taking the vehicle on a road test (for approximately 15 minutes), covering all engine speeds and loads, concentrating mainly in the 2500 to 3500 rpm region.*

e) *On all models, when reconnecting the battery after disconnection, switch on the ignition and wait 10 seconds to allow the electronic vehicle systems to stabilise and re-initialise.*

Devices known as 'memory-savers' (or 'code-savers') can be used to avoid some of the above problems. Precise details vary according to the device used. Typically, it is plugged into the cigarette lighter, and is connected by its own wires to a spare battery; the vehicle's own battery is then disconnected from the electrical system, leaving the 'memory-saver' to pass sufficient current to maintain audio unit security codes and any other memory values, and also to run permanently-live circuits such as the clock.

 Warning: Some of these devices allow a considerable amount of current to pass, which can mean that many of the vehicle's systems are still operational when the main battery is disconnected. If a 'memory saver' is used, ensure that the circuit concerned is actually 'dead' before carrying out any work on it!

Introduction

A selection of good tools is a fundamental requirement for anyone contemplating the maintenance and repair of a motor vehicle. For the owner who does not possess any, their purchase will prove a considerable expense, offsetting some of the savings made by doing-it-yourself. However, provided that the tools purchased meet the relevant national safety standards and are of good quality, they will last for many years and prove an extremely worthwhile investment.

To help the average owner to decide which tools are needed to carry out the various tasks detailed in this manual, we have compiled three lists of tools under the following headings: *Maintenance and minor repair, Repair and overhaul*, and *Special*. Newcomers to practical mechanics should start off with the *Maintenance and minor repair* tool kit, and confine themselves to the simpler jobs around the vehicle. Then, as confidence and experience grow, more difficult tasks can be undertaken, with extra tools being purchased as, and when, they are needed. In this way, a *Maintenance and minor repair* tool kit can be built up into a *Repair and overhaul* tool kit over a considerable period of time, without any major cash outlays. The experienced do-it-yourselfer will have a tool kit good enough for most repair and overhaul procedures, and will add tools from the *Special* category when it is felt that the expense is justified by the amount of use to which these tools will be put.

Maintenance and minor repair tool kit

The tools given in this list should be considered as a minimum requirement if routine maintenance, servicing and minor repair operations are to be undertaken. We recommend the purchase of combination spanners (ring one end, open-ended the other); although more expensive than open-ended ones, they do give the advantages of both types of spanner.

☐ *Combination spanners:*
Metric - 8 to 19 mm inclusive
☐ *Adjustable spanner - 35 mm jaw (approx.)*
☐ *Spark plug spanner (with rubber insert) - petrol models*
☐ *Spark plug gap adjustment tool - petrol models*
☐ *Set of feeler gauges*
☐ *Brake bleed nipple spanner*
☐ *Screwdrivers:*
Flat blade - 100 mm long x 6 mm dia
Cross blade - 100 mm long x 6 mm dia
Torx - various sizes (not all vehicles)
☐ *Combination pliers*
☐ *Hacksaw (junior)*
☐ *Tyre pump*
☐ *Tyre pressure gauge*
☐ *Oil can*
☐ *Oil filter removal tool*
☐ *Fine emery cloth*
☐ *Wire brush (small)*
☐ *Funnel (medium size)*
☐ *Sump drain plug key (not all vehicles)*

Repair and overhaul tool kit

These tools are virtually essential for anyone undertaking any major repairs to a motor vehicle, and are additional to those given in the *Maintenance and minor repair* list. Included in this list is a comprehensive set of sockets. Although these are expensive, they will be found invaluable as they are so versatile - particularly if various drives are included in the set. We recommend the half-inch square-drive type, as this can be used with most proprietary torque wrenches.

The tools in this list will sometimes need to be supplemented by tools from the *Special* list:

☐ *Sockets (or box spanners) to cover range in previous list (including Torx sockets)*
☐ *Reversible ratchet drive (for use with sockets)*
☐ *Extension piece, 250 mm (for use with sockets)*
☐ *Universal joint (for use with sockets)*
☐ *Flexible handle or sliding T "breaker bar" (for use with sockets)*
☐ *Torque wrench (for use with sockets)*
☐ *Self-locking grips*
☐ *Ball pein hammer*
☐ *Soft-faced mallet (plastic or rubber)*
☐ *Screwdrivers:*
Flat blade - long & sturdy, short (chubby), and narrow (electrician's) types
Cross blade – long & sturdy, and short (chubby) types
☐ *Pliers:*
Long-nosed
Side cutters (electrician's)
Circlip (internal and external)
☐ *Cold chisel - 25 mm*
☐ *Scriber*
☐ *Scraper*
☐ *Centre-punch*
☐ *Pin punch*
☐ *Hacksaw*
☐ *Brake hose clamp*
☐ *Brake/clutch bleeding kit*
☐ *Selection of twist drills*
☐ *Steel rule/straight-edge*
☐ *Allen keys (inc. splined/Torx type)*
☐ *Selection of files*
☐ *Wire brush*
☐ *Axle stands*
☐ *Jack (strong trolley or hydraulic type)*
☐ *Light with extension lead*
☐ *Universal electrical multi-meter*

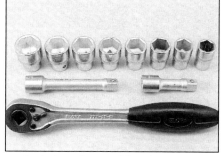

Sockets and reversible ratchet drive

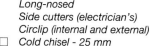

Brake bleeding kit

Torx key, socket and bit

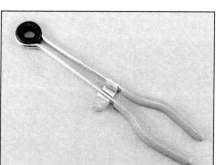

Hose clamp

Angular-tightening gauge

Special tools

The tools in this list are those which are not used regularly, are expensive to buy, or which need to be used in accordance with their manufacturers' instructions. Unless relatively difficult mechanical jobs are undertaken frequently, it will not be economic to buy many of these tools. Where this is the case, you could consider clubbing together with friends (or joining a motorists' club) to make a joint purchase, or borrowing the tools against a deposit from a local garage or tool hire specialist. It is worth noting that many of the larger DIY superstores now carry a large range of special tools for hire at modest rates.

The following list contains only those tools and instruments freely available to the public, and not those special tools produced by the vehicle manufacturer specifically for its dealer network. You will find occasional references to these manufacturers' special tools in the text of this manual. Generally, an alternative method of doing the job without the vehicle manufacturers' special tool is given. However, sometimes there is no alternative to using them. Where this is the case and the relevant tool cannot be bought or borrowed, you will have to entrust the work to a dealer.

☐ Angular-tightening gauge
☐ Valve spring compressor
☐ Valve grinding tool
☐ Piston ring compressor
☐ Piston ring removal/installation tool
☐ Cylinder bore hone
☐ Balljoint separator
☐ Coil spring compressors (where applicable)
☐ Two/three-legged hub and bearing puller
☐ Impact screwdriver
☐ Micrometer and/or vernier calipers
☐ Dial gauge
☐ Stroboscopic timing light
☐ Dwell angle meter/tachometer
☐ Fault code reader
☐ Cylinder compression gauge
☐ Hand-operated vacuum pump and gauge
☐ Clutch plate alignment set
☐ Brake shoe steady spring cup removal tool
☐ Bush and bearing removal/installation set
☐ Stud extractors
☐ Tap and die set
☐ Lifting tackle
☐ Trolley jack

Buying tools

Reputable motor accessory shops and superstores often offer excellent quality tools at discount prices, so it pays to shop around.

Remember, you don't have to buy the most expensive items on the shelf, but it is always advisable to steer clear of the very cheap tools. Beware of 'bargains' offered on market stalls or at car boot sales. There are plenty of good tools around at reasonable prices, but always aim to purchase items which meet the relevant national safety standards. If in doubt, ask the proprietor or manager of the shop for advice before making a purchase.

Care and maintenance of tools

Having purchased a reasonable tool kit, it is necessary to keep the tools in a clean and serviceable condition. After use, always wipe off any dirt, grease and metal particles using a clean, dry cloth, before putting the tools away. Never leave them lying around after they have been used. A simple tool rack on the garage or workshop wall for items such as screwdrivers and pliers is a good idea. Store all normal spanners and sockets in a metal box. Any measuring instruments, gauges, meters, etc, must be carefully stored where they cannot be damaged or become rusty.

Take a little care when tools are used. Hammer heads inevitably become marked, and screwdrivers lose the keen edge on their blades from time to time. A little timely attention with emery cloth or a file will soon restore items like this to a good finish.

Working facilities

Not to be forgotten when discussing tools is the workshop itself. If anything more than routine maintenance is to be carried out, a suitable working area becomes essential.

It is appreciated that many an owner-mechanic is forced by circumstances to remove an engine or similar item without the benefit of a garage or workshop. Having done this, any repairs should always be done under the cover of a roof.

Wherever possible, any dismantling should be done on a clean, flat workbench or table at a suitable working height.

Any workbench needs a vice; one with a jaw opening of 100 mm is suitable for most jobs. As mentioned previously, some clean dry storage space is also required for tools, as well as for any lubricants, cleaning fluids, touch-up paints etc, which become necessary.

Another item which may be required, and which has a much more general usage, is an electric drill with a chuck capacity of at least 8 mm. This, together with a good range of twist drills, is virtually essential for fitting accessories.

Last, but not least, always keep a supply of old newspapers and clean, lint-free rags available, and try to keep any working area as clean as possible.

Micrometers

Dial test indicator ("dial gauge")

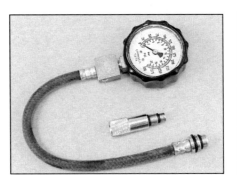

Strap wrench

Compression tester

Fault code reader

This is a guide to getting your vehicle through the MOT test. Obviously it will not be possible to examine the vehicle to the same standard as the professional MOT tester. However, working through the following checks will enable you to identify any problem areas before submitting the vehicle for the test.

Where a testable component is in borderline condition, the tester has discretion in deciding whether to pass or fail it. The basis of such discretion is whether the tester would be happy for a close relative or friend to use the vehicle with the component in that condition. If the vehicle presented is clean and evidently well cared for, the tester may be more inclined to pass a borderline component than if the vehicle is scruffy and apparently neglected.

It has only been possible to summarise the test requirements here, based on the regulations in force at the time of printing. Test standards are becoming increasingly stringent, although there are some exemptions for older vehicles.

An assistant will be needed to help carry out some of these checks.

The checks have been sub-divided into four categories, as follows:

1 Checks carried out **FROM THE DRIVER'S SEAT**

2 Checks carried out **WITH THE VEHICLE ON THE GROUND**

3 Checks carried out **WITH THE VEHICLE RAISED AND THE WHEELS FREE TO TURN**

4 Checks carried out on **YOUR VEHICLE'S EXHAUST EMISSION SYSTEM**

---

1 Checks carried out **FROM THE DRIVER'S SEAT**

Handbrake

☐ Test the operation of the handbrake. Excessive travel (too many clicks) indicates incorrect brake or cable adjustment.
☐ Check that the handbrake cannot be released by tapping the lever sideways. Check the security of the lever mountings.

Footbrake

☐ Depress the brake pedal and check that it does not creep down to the floor, indicating a master cylinder fault. Release the pedal, wait a few seconds, then depress it again. If the pedal travels nearly to the floor before firm resistance is felt, brake adjustment or repair is necessary. If the pedal feels spongy, there is air in the hydraulic system which must be removed by bleeding.

☐ Check that the brake pedal is secure and in good condition. Check also for signs of fluid leaks on the pedal, floor or carpets, which would indicate failed seals in the brake master cylinder.
☐ Check the servo unit (when applicable) by operating the brake pedal several times, then keeping the pedal depressed and starting the engine. As the engine starts, the pedal will move down slightly. If not, the vacuum hose or the servo itself may be faulty.

Steering wheel and column

☐ Examine the steering wheel for fractures or looseness of the hub, spokes or rim.
☐ Move the steering wheel from side to side and then up and down. Check that the steering wheel is not loose on the column, indicating wear or a loose retaining nut. Continue moving the steering wheel as before, but also turn it slightly from left to right.
☐ Check that the steering wheel is not loose on the column, and that there is no abnormal

movement of the steering wheel, indicating wear in the column support bearings or couplings.

Windscreen, mirrors and sunvisor

☐ The windscreen must be free of cracks or other significant damage within the driver's field of view. (Small stone chips are acceptable.) Rear view mirrors must be secure, intact, and capable of being adjusted.

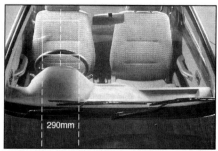

290mm

☐ The driver's sunvisor must be capable of being stored in the "up" position.

Seat belts and seats

Note: *The following checks are applicable to all seat belts, front and rear.*

☐ Examine the webbing of all the belts (including rear belts if fitted) for cuts, serious fraying or deterioration. Fasten and unfasten each belt to check the buckles. If applicable, check the retracting mechanism. Check the security of all seat belt mountings accessible from inside the vehicle.

☐ Seat belts with pre-tensioners, once activated, have a "flag" or similar showing on the seat belt stalk. This, in itself, is not a reason for test failure.

☐ The front seats themselves must be securely attached and the backrests must lock in the upright position.

Doors

☐ Both front doors must be able to be opened and closed from outside and inside, and must latch securely when closed.

2 Checks carried out WITH THE VEHICLE ON THE GROUND

Vehicle identification

☐ Number plates must be in good condition, secure and legible, with letters and numbers correctly spaced – spacing at (A) should be at least twice that at (B).

☐ The VIN plate and/or homologation plate must be legible.

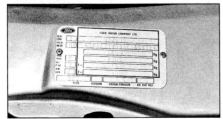

Electrical equipment

☐ Switch on the ignition and check the operation of the horn.

☐ Check the windscreen washers and wipers, examining the wiper blades; renew damaged or perished blades. Also check the operation of the stop-lights.

☐ Check the operation of the sidelights and number plate lights. The lenses and reflectors must be secure, clean and undamaged.

☐ Check the operation and alignment of the headlights. The headlight reflectors must not be tarnished and the lenses must be undamaged.

☐ Switch on the ignition and check the operation of the direction indicators (including the instrument panel tell-tale) and the hazard warning lights. Operation of the sidelights and stop-lights must not affect the indicators - if it does, the cause is usually a bad earth at the rear light cluster.

☐ Check the operation of the rear foglight(s), including the warning light on the instrument panel or in the switch.

☐ The ABS warning light must illuminate in accordance with the manufacturers' design. For most vehicles, the ABS warning light should illuminate when the ignition is switched on, and (if the system is operating properly) extinguish after a few seconds. Refer to the owner's handbook.

Footbrake

☐ Examine the master cylinder, brake pipes and servo unit for leaks, loose mountings, corrosion or other damage.

☐ The fluid reservoir must be secure and the fluid level must be between the upper (**A**) and lower (**B**) markings.

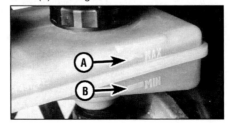

☐ Inspect both front brake flexible hoses for cracks or deterioration of the rubber. Turn the steering from lock to lock, and ensure that the hoses do not contact the wheel, tyre, or any part of the steering or suspension mechanism. With the brake pedal firmly depressed, check the hoses for bulges or leaks under pressure.

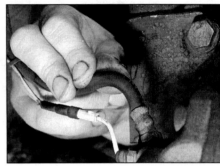

Steering and suspension

☐ Have your assistant turn the steering wheel from side to side slightly, up to the point where the steering gear just begins to transmit this movement to the roadwheels. Check for excessive free play between the steering wheel and the steering gear, indicating wear or insecurity of the steering column joints, the column-to-steering gear coupling, or the steering gear itself.

☐ Have your assistant turn the steering wheel more vigorously in each direction, so that the roadwheels just begin to turn. As this is done, examine all the steering joints, linkages, fittings and attachments. Renew any component that shows signs of wear or damage. On vehicles with power steering, check the security and condition of the steering pump, drivebelt and hoses.

☐ Check that the vehicle is standing level, and at approximately the correct ride height.

Shock absorbers

☐ Depress each corner of the vehicle in turn, then release it. The vehicle should rise and then settle in its normal position. If the vehicle continues to rise and fall, the shock absorber is defective. A shock absorber which has seized will also cause the vehicle to fail.

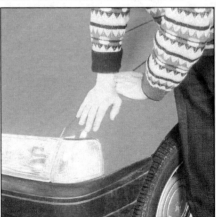

Exhaust system

☐ Start the engine. With your assistant holding a rag over the tailpipe, check the entire system for leaks. Repair or renew leaking sections.

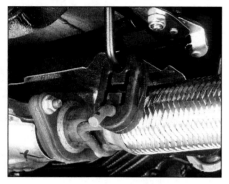

3 Checks carried out
WITH THE VEHICLE RAISED AND THE WHEELS FREE TO TURN

Jack up the front and rear of the vehicle, and securely support it on axle stands. Position the stands clear of the suspension assemblies. Ensure that the wheels are clear of the ground and that the steering can be turned from lock to lock.

Steering mechanism

☐ Have your assistant turn the steering from lock to lock. Check that the steering turns smoothly, and that no part of the steering mechanism, including a wheel or tyre, fouls any brake hose or pipe or any part of the body structure.

☐ Examine the steering rack rubber gaiters for damage or insecurity of the retaining clips. If power steering is fitted, check for signs of damage or leakage of the fluid hoses, pipes or connections. Also check for excessive stiffness or binding of the steering, a missing split pin or locking device, or severe corrosion of the body structure within 30 cm of any steering component attachment point.

Front and rear suspension and wheel bearings

☐ Starting at the front right-hand side, grasp the roadwheel at the 3 o'clock and 9 o'clock positions and rock gently but firmly. Check for free play or insecurity at the wheel bearings, suspension balljoints, or suspension mountings, pivots and attachments.

☐ Now grasp the wheel at the 12 o'clock and 6 o'clock positions and repeat the previous inspection. Spin the wheel, and check for roughness or tightness of the front wheel bearing.

☐ If excess free play is suspected at a component pivot point, this can be confirmed by using a large screwdriver or similar tool and levering between the mounting and the component attachment. This will confirm whether the wear is in the pivot bush, its retaining bolt, or in the mounting itself (the bolt holes can often become elongated).

☐ Carry out all the above checks at the other front wheel, and then at both rear wheels.

Springs and shock absorbers

☐ Examine the suspension struts (when applicable) for serious fluid leakage, corrosion, or damage to the casing. Also check the security of the mounting points.

☐ If coil springs are fitted, check that the spring ends locate in their seats, and that the spring is not corroded, cracked or broken.

☐ If leaf springs are fitted, check that all leaves are intact, that the axle is securely attached to each spring, and that there is no deterioration of the spring eye mountings, bushes, and shackles.

☐ The same general checks apply to vehicles fitted with other suspension types, such as torsion bars, hydraulic displacer units, etc. Ensure that all mountings and attachments are secure, that there are no signs of excessive wear, corrosion or damage, and (on hydraulic types) that there are no fluid leaks or damaged pipes.

☐ Inspect the shock absorbers for signs of serious fluid leakage. Check for wear of the mounting bushes or attachments, or damage to the body of the unit.

Driveshafts
(fwd vehicles only)

☐ Rotate each front wheel in turn and inspect the constant velocity joint gaiters for splits or damage. Also check that each driveshaft is straight and undamaged.

Braking system

☐ If possible without dismantling, check brake pad wear and disc condition. Ensure that the friction lining material has not worn excessively, (A) and that the discs are not fractured, pitted, scored or badly worn (B).

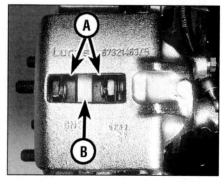

☐ Examine all the rigid brake pipes underneath the vehicle, and the flexible hose(s) at the rear. Look for corrosion, chafing or insecurity of the pipes, and for signs of bulging under pressure, chafing, splits or deterioration of the flexible hoses.

☐ Look for signs of fluid leaks at the brake calipers or on the brake backplates. Repair or renew leaking components.

☐ Slowly spin each wheel, while your assistant depresses and releases the footbrake. Ensure that each brake is operating and does not bind when the pedal is released.

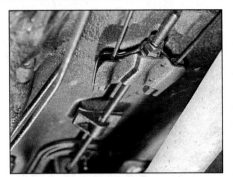

☐ Examine the handbrake mechanism, checking for frayed or broken cables, excessive corrosion, or wear or insecurity of the linkage. Check that the mechanism works on each relevant wheel, and releases fully, without binding.

☐ It is not possible to test brake efficiency without special equipment, but a road test can be carried out later to check that the vehicle pulls up in a straight line.

Fuel and exhaust systems

☐ Inspect the fuel tank (including the filler cap), fuel pipes, hoses and unions. All components must be secure and free from leaks.

☐ Examine the exhaust system over its entire length, checking for any damaged, broken or missing mountings, security of the retaining clamps and rust or corrosion.

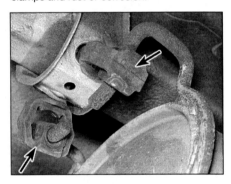

Wheels and tyres

☐ Examine the sidewalls and tread area of each tyre in turn. Check for cuts, tears, lumps, bulges, separation of the tread, and exposure of the ply or cord due to wear or damage. Check that the tyre bead is correctly seated on the wheel rim, that the valve is sound and properly seated, and that the wheel is not distorted or damaged.

☐ Check that the tyres are of the correct size for the vehicle, that they are of the same size and type on each axle, and that the pressures are correct.

☐ Check the tyre tread depth. The legal minimum at the time of writing is 1.6 mm over at least three-quarters of the tread width. Abnormal tread wear may indicate incorrect front wheel alignment.

Body corrosion

☐ Check the condition of the entire vehicle structure for signs of corrosion in load-bearing areas. (These include chassis box sections, side sills, cross-members, pillars, and all suspension, steering, braking system and seat belt mountings and anchorages.) Any corrosion which has seriously reduced the thickness of a load-bearing area is likely to cause the vehicle to fail. In this case professional repairs are likely to be needed.

☐ Damage or corrosion which causes sharp or otherwise dangerous edges to be exposed will also cause the vehicle to fail.

4 Checks carried out on **YOUR VEHICLE'S EXHAUST EMISSION SYSTEM**

Petrol models

☐ Have the engine at normal operating temperature, and make sure that it is in good tune (ignition system in good order, air filter element clean, etc).

☐ Before any measurements are carried out, raise the engine speed to around 2500 rpm, and hold it at this speed for 20 seconds. Allow the engine speed to return to idle, and watch for smoke emissions from the exhaust tailpipe. If the idle speed is obviously much too high, or if dense blue or clearly-visible black smoke comes from the tailpipe for more than 5 seconds, the vehicle will fail. As a rule of thumb, blue smoke signifies oil being burnt (engine wear) while black smoke signifies unburnt fuel (dirty air cleaner element, or other carburettor or fuel system fault).

☐ An exhaust gas analyser capable of measuring carbon monoxide (CO) and hydrocarbons (HC) is now needed. If such an instrument cannot be hired or borrowed, a local garage may agree to perform the check for a small fee.

CO emissions (mixture)

☐ At the time of writing, for vehicles first used between 1st August 1975 and 31st July 1986 (P to C registration), the CO level must not exceed 4.5% by volume. For vehicles first used between 1st August 1986 and 31st July 1992 (D to J registration), the CO level must not exceed 3.5% by volume. Vehicles first

used after 1st August 1992 (K registration) must conform to the manufacturer's specification. The MOT tester has access to a DOT database or emissions handbook, which lists the CO and HC limits for each make and model of vehicle. The CO level is measured with the engine at idle speed, and at "fast idle". The following limits are given as a general guide:

At idle speed -
CO level no more than 0.5%
At "fast idle" (2500 to 3000 rpm) -
CO level no more than 0.3%
(Minimum oil temperature 60°C)

☐ If the CO level cannot be reduced far enough to pass the test (and the fuel and ignition systems are otherwise in good condition) then the carburettor is badly worn, or there is some problem in the fuel injection system or catalytic converter (as applicable).

HC emissions

☐ With the CO within limits, HC emissions for vehicles first used between 1st August 1975 and 31st July 1992 (P to J registration) must not exceed 1200 ppm. Vehicles first used after 1st August 1992 (K registration) must conform to the manufacturer's specification. The MOT tester has access to a DOT database or emissions handbook, which lists the CO and HC limits for each make and model of vehicle. The HC level is measured with the engine at "fast idle". The following is given as a general guide:

At "fast idle" (2500 to 3000 rpm) -
HC level no more than 200 ppm
(Minimum oil temperature 60°C)

☐ Excessive HC emissions are caused by incomplete combustion, the causes of which can include oil being burnt, mechanical wear and ignition/fuel system malfunction.

Diesel models

☐ The only emission test applicable to Diesel engines is the measuring of exhaust smoke density. The test involves accelerating the engine several times to its maximum unloaded speed.

Note: *It is of the utmost importance that the engine timing belt is in good condition before the test is carried out.*

☐ The limits for Diesel engine exhaust smoke, introduced in September 1995 are:
Vehicles first used before 1st August 1979:
Exempt from metered smoke testing, but must not emit "dense blue or clearly visible black smoke for a period of more than 5 seconds at idle" or "dense blue or clearly visible black smoke during acceleration which would obscure the view of other road users".
Non-turbocharged vehicles first used after 1st August 1979: 2.5m-1
Turbocharged vehicles first used after 1st August 1979: 3.0m-1

☐ Excessive smoke can be caused by a dirty air cleaner element. Otherwise, professional advice may be needed to find the cause.

Engine
- ☐ Engine fails to rotate when attempting to start
- ☐ Engine rotates, but will not start
- ☐ Engine difficult to start when cold
- ☐ Engine difficult to start when hot
- ☐ Starter motor noisy or excessively-rough in engagement
- ☐ Engine starts, but stops immediately
- ☐ Engine idles erratically
- ☐ Engine misfires at idle speed
- ☐ Engine misfires throughout the driving speed range
- ☐ Engine hesitates on acceleration
- ☐ Engine stalls
- ☐ Engine lacks power
- ☐ Engine backfires
- ☐ Oil pressure warning light on with engine running
- ☐ Engine runs-on after switching off
- ☐ Engine noises

Cooling system
- ☐ Overheating
- ☐ Overcooling
- ☐ External coolant leakage
- ☐ Internal coolant leakage
- ☐ Corrosion

Fuel and exhaust systems
- ☐ Excessive fuel consumption
- ☐ Fuel leakage and/or fuel odour
- ☐ Excessive noise or fumes from exhaust system

Clutch
- ☐ Pedal travels to floor – no pressure or very little resistance
- ☐ Clutch fails to disengage (unable to select gears)
- ☐ Clutch slips (engine speed rises, with no increase in vehicle speed)
- ☐ Judder as clutch is engaged
- ☐ Noise when depressing or releasing clutch pedal

Manual transmission
- ☐ Noisy in neutral with engine running
- ☐ Noisy in one particular gear
- ☐ Difficulty engaging gears
- ☐ Jumps out of gear
- ☐ Vibration
- ☐ Lubricant leaks

Automatic transmission
- ☐ Fluid leakage
- ☐ Transmission fluid brown, or has burned smell
- ☐ General gear selection problems
- ☐ Transmission will not downshift (kickdown) on full throttle
- ☐ Engine won't start in any gear, or starts in gears other than P or N
- ☐ Transmission slips, shifts roughly, is noisy, or has no drive in forward or reverse gears

Driveshafts
- ☐ Clicking or knocking noise on turns (at slow speed on full-lock)
- ☐ Vibration when accelerating or decelerating

Braking system
- ☐ Vehicle pulls to one side under braking
- ☐ Noise (grinding or high-pitched squeal) when brakes applied
- ☐ Excessive brake pedal travel
- ☐ Brake pedal feels spongy when depressed
- ☐ Excessive brake pedal effort required to stop vehicle
- ☐ Judder felt through brake pedal or steering wheel when braking
- ☐ Brakes binding
- ☐ Rear wheels locking under normal braking

Suspension and steering systems
- ☐ Vehicle pulls to one side
- ☐ Wheel wobble and vibration
- ☐ Excessive pitching and/or rolling around corners, or during braking
- ☐ Wandering or general instability
- ☐ Excessively-stiff steering
- ☐ Excessive play in steering
- ☐ Lack of power assistance
- ☐ Tyre wear excessive

Electrical system
- ☐ Battery will not hold a charge for more than a few days
- ☐ Ignition/no-charge warning light stays on with engine running
- ☐ Ignition/no-charge warning light fails to come on
- ☐ Lights inoperative
- ☐ Instrument readings inaccurate or erratic
- ☐ Horn inoperative, or unsatisfactory in operation
- ☐ Windscreen/tailgate wipers failed, or unsatisfactory in operation
- ☐ Windscreen/tailgate washers failed, or unsatisfactory in operation
- ☐ Electric windows inoperative, or unsatisfactory in operation
- ☐ Central locking system inoperative, or unsatisfactory in operation

Introduction

The vehicle owner who does his or her own maintenance according to the recommended service schedules should not have to use this section of the manual very often. Modern component reliability is such that, provided those items subject to wear or deterioration are inspected or renewed at the specified intervals, sudden failure is comparatively rare. Faults do not usually just happen as a result of sudden failure, but develop over a period of time. Major mechanical failures in particular are usually preceded by characteristic symptoms over hundreds or even thousands of miles. Those components which do occasionally fail without warning are often small and easily carried in the vehicle.

With any fault-finding, the first step is to decide where to begin investigations. This may be obvious, but some detective work may be necessary. The owner who makes half a dozen haphazard adjustments or replacements may be successful in curing a fault (or its symptoms), but will be none the wiser if the fault recurs, and ultimately may have spent more time and money than was necessary. A calm and logical approach will be found to be more satisfactory in the long run. Always take into account any warning signs that may have been noticed in the period preceding the fault – power loss, high or low gauge readings, unusual smells, etc – and remember – failure of components such as fuses or spark plugs may only be pointers to some underlying fault.

The pages which follow provide an easy-reference guide to the more common problems which may occur during the operation of the vehicle. These problems and their possible causes are grouped under headings denoting various components or systems, such as Engine, Cooling system, etc. The Chapter which deals with the problem is shown in brackets, but in some instances it will be necessary to refer to the specific Chapter Part, depending on model or system, as applicable. Some problems may be more obvious, such as loose or disconnected wiring, and in these instances a Chapter reference may not be given as the problem can be simply overcome by dealing with the fault as it stands. Whatever the problem, certain basic principles apply. These are as follows:

□ *Verify the fault.* This is simply a matter of being sure that you know what the symptoms are before starting work. This is particularly important if you are investigating a fault for someone else, who may not have described it very accurately.

□ *Don't overlook the obvious.* For example, if the vehicle won't start, is there fuel in the tank? (Don't take anyone else's word on this particular point, and don't trust the fuel gauge either!) If an electrical fault is indicated, look for loose or broken wires before digging out the test gear.

□ *Cure the disease, not the symptom.* Substituting a flat battery with a fully-charged one will get you off the hard shoulder, but if the underlying cause is not attended to, the new battery will go the same way. Similarly, changing oil-fouled spark plugs for a new set will get you moving again, but remember that the reason for the fouling (if it wasn't simply an incorrect grade of plug) will have to be established and corrected.

□ *Don't take anything for granted.* Particularly, don't forget that a 'new' component may itself be defective (especially if it's been rattling around in the boot for months), and don't leave components out of a fault diagnosis sequence just because they are new or recently-fitted. When you do finally diagnose a difficult fault, you'll probably realise that all the evidence was there from the start.

Engine

Engine fails to rotate when attempting to start

□ Battery terminal connections loose or corroded (*Weekly Checks*).
□ Battery discharged or faulty (Chapter 5).
□ Broken, loose or disconnected wiring in the starting circuit (Chapter 5).
□ Defective starter solenoid (Chapter 5).
□ Defective starter motor (Chapter 5).
□ Starter pinion or flywheel ring gear teeth loose or broken (Chapters 2 and 5).
□ Engine earth strap broken or disconnected.

Engine rotates, but will not start

□ Fuel tank empty.
□ Battery discharged (engine rotates slowly) (Chapter 5).
□ Battery terminal connections loose or corroded (*Weekly Checks*).
□ Ignition components damp or damaged – petrol engine models (Chapters 1 and 5).
□ Broken, loose or disconnected wiring in the ignition circuit – petrol engine models (Chapters 1 and 5).
□ Worn, faulty or incorrectly-gapped spark plugs – petrol engine models (Chapter 1).
□ Preheating system faulty – diesel engine models (Chapter 5).
□ Fuel injection or engine management system fault – petrol engine models (Chapter 4).
□ Stop solenoid or anti-theft module faulty – diesel engine models (Chapter 4).
□ Air in fuel system – diesel models (Chapter 4).
□ Major mechanical failure (eg camshaft drive) (Chapter 2).

Engine difficult to start when cold

□ Battery discharged (Chapter 5).
□ Battery terminal connections loose or corroded (*Weekly Checks*).
□ Worn, faulty or incorrectly-gapped spark plugs – petrol engine models (Chapter 1).
□ Preheating system faulty – diesel models (Chapter 5).
□ Fuel injection or engine management system fault – petrol engine models (Chapter 4).
□ Other ignition system fault – petrol engine models (Chapters 1 and 5).
□ Fast idle valve incorrectly adjusted – diesel engine models (Chapter 4).
□ Low cylinder compressions (Chapter 2).

Engine difficult to start when hot

□ Air filter element dirty or clogged (Chapter 1).

□ Fuel injection or engine management system fault – petrol engine models (Chapter 4).
□ Low cylinder compressions (Chapter 2).

Starter motor noisy or excessively-rough in engagement

□ Starter pinion or flywheel ring gear teeth loose or broken (Chapters 2 and 5).
□ Starter motor mounting bolts loose or missing (Chapter 5).
□ Starter motor internal components worn or damaged (Chapter 5).

Engine starts, but stops immediately

□ Loose or faulty electrical connections in the ignition circuit – petrol engine models (Chapters 1 and 5).
□ Vacuum leak at the throttle housing or inlet manifold – petrol engine models (Chapter 4).
□ Blocked injector/fuel injection system fault – petrol engine models (Chapter 4).

Engine idles erratically

□ Air filter element clogged (Chapter 1).
□ Vacuum leak at the throttle housing, inlet manifold or associated hoses – petrol engine models (Chapter 4).
□ Worn, faulty or incorrectly-gapped spark plugs – petrol engine models (Chapter 1).
□ Uneven or low cylinder compressions (Chapter 2).
□ Camshaft lobes worn (Chapter 2).
□ Timing belt incorrectly fitted (Chapter 2).
□ Blocked injector/fuel injection system fault – petrol engine models (Chapter 4).
□ Faulty injector(s) – diesel models (Chapter 4).

Engine misfires at idle speed

□ Worn, faulty or incorrectly-gapped spark plugs – petrol engine models (Chapter 1).
□ Faulty spark plug HT leads – petrol engine models (Chapter 1).
□ Vacuum leak at the throttle housing, inlet manifold or associated hoses – petrol engine models (Chapter 4).
□ Blocked injector/fuel injection system fault – petrol engine models (Chapter 4).
□ Faulty injector(s) – diesel engine models (Chapter 4).
□ Uneven or low cylinder compressions (Chapter 2).
□ Disconnected, leaking, or perished crankcase ventilation hoses (Chapter 4).

Engine (continued)

Engine misfires throughout the driving speed range

- [ ] Fuel filter choked (Chapter 1).
- [ ] Fuel pump faulty, or delivery pressure low (Chapter 4).
- [ ] Fuel tank vent blocked, or fuel pipes restricted (Chapter 4).
- [ ] Vacuum leak at the throttle housing, inlet manifold or associated hoses – petrol engine models (Chapter 4).
- [ ] Worn, faulty or incorrectly-gapped spark plugs – petrol engine models (Chapter 1).
- [ ] Faulty spark plug HT leads – petrol engine models (Chapter 1).
- [ ] Faulty injector(s) – diesel engine models (Chapter 4).
- [ ] Distributor cap cracked or tracking internally – petrol models (where applicable) (Chapter 1).
- [ ] Faulty ignition coil – petrol models (Chapter 5).
- [ ] Uneven or low cylinder compressions (Chapter 2).
- [ ] Blocked carburettor jet(s) or internal passages – carburettor petrol models (Chapter 4).
- [ ] Blocked injector/fuel injection system fault – fuel-injected petrol models (Chapter 4).

Engine hesitates on acceleration

- [ ] Worn, faulty or incorrectly-gapped spark plugs – petrol engine models (Chapter 1).
- [ ] Vacuum leak at the throttle housing, inlet manifold or associated hoses (Chapter 4).
- [ ] Blocked injector/fuel injection system fault – petrol engine models (Chapter 4).
- [ ] Faulty injector(s) – diesel engine models (Chapter 4).

Engine stalls

- [ ] Vacuum leak at the throttle housing, inlet manifold or associated hoses – petrol engine models (Chapter 4).
- [ ] Fuel filter choked (Chapter 1).
- [ ] Fuel pump faulty, or delivery pressure low – petrol engine models (Chapter 4).
- [ ] Fuel tank vent blocked, or fuel pipes restricted (Chapter 4).
- [ ] Blocked injector/fuel injection system fault – petrol engine models (Chapter 4).
- [ ] Faulty injector(s) – diesel engine models (Chapter 4).

Engine lacks power

- [ ] Timing belt incorrectly fitted or adjusted (Chapter 2).
- [ ] Fuel filter choked (Chapter 1).
- [ ] Fuel pump faulty, or delivery pressure low (Chapter 4).
- [ ] Uneven or low cylinder compressions (Chapter 2).
- [ ] Worn, faulty or incorrectly-gapped spark plugs – petrol engine models (Chapter 1).
- [ ] Vacuum leak at the throttle housing, inlet manifold or associated hoses – petrol engine models (Chapter 4).
- [ ] Blocked injector/fuel injection system fault – petrol engine models (Chapter 4).
- [ ] Faulty injector(s) – diesel engine models (Chapter 4).
- [ ] Injection pump timing incorrect – 1.9 litre diesel engine models (Chapter 4).
- [ ] Brakes binding (Chapters 1 and 9).
- [ ] Clutch slipping (Chapter 6).

Engine backfires

- [ ] Timing belt incorrectly fitted or adjusted (Chapter 2).
- [ ] Vacuum leak at the throttle housing, inlet manifold or associated hoses – petrol engine models (Chapter 4).
- [ ] Blocked injector/fuel injection system fault – petrol engine models (Chapter 4).

Oil pressure warning light on with engine running

- [ ] Low oil level, or incorrect oil grade (*Weekly Checks*).
- [ ] Faulty oil pressure warning light switch (Chapter 5).
- [ ] Worn engine bearings and/or oil pump (Chapter 2).
- [ ] High engine operating temperature (Chapter 3).
- [ ] Oil pressure relief valve defective (Chapter 2).
- [ ] Oil pick-up strainer clogged (Chapter 2).

Engine runs-on after switching off

- [ ] Excessive carbon build-up in engine (Chapter 2).
- [ ] High engine operating temperature (Chapter 3).
- [ ] Fuel injection or engine management system fault – petrol engine models (Chapter 4).

Engine noises

Pre-ignition (pinking) or knocking during acceleration or under load

- [ ] Ignition or engine management system fault – petrol engine models (Chapters 1 and 5).
- [ ] Incorrect grade of spark plug – petrol engine models (Chapter 1).
- [ ] Incorrect grade of fuel (Chapter 1).
- [ ] Vacuum leak at the throttle housing, inlet manifold or associated hoses – petrol engine models (Chapter 4).
- [ ] Excessive carbon build-up in engine (Chapter 2).
- [ ] Blocked injector/fuel injection system fault – petrol engine models (Chapter 4).

Whistling or wheezing noises

- [ ] Leaking inlet manifold or throttle housing gasket – petrol engine models (Chapter 4).
- [ ] Leaking exhaust manifold gasket or pipe-to-manifold joint (Chapter 4).
- [ ] Leaking vacuum hose (Chapters 4, 5 and 9).
- [ ] Blowing cylinder head gasket (Chapter 2).

Tapping or rattling noises

- [ ] Worn valve gear or camshaft (Chapter 2).
- [ ] Ancillary component fault (coolant pump, alternator, etc) (Chapters 3, 5, etc).

Knocking or thumping noises

- [ ] Worn big-end bearings (regular heavy knocking, perhaps less under load) (Chapter 2).
- [ ] Worn main bearings (rumbling and knocking, perhaps worsening under load) (Chapter 2).
- [ ] Piston slap (most noticeable when cold) (Chapter 2).
- [ ] Ancillary component fault (coolant pump, alternator, etc) (Chapters 3, 5, etc).

Cooling system

Overheating

- ☐ Insufficient coolant in system (*Weekly Checks*).
- ☐ Thermostat faulty (Chapter 3).
- ☐ Radiator core blocked, or grille restricted (Chapter 3).
- ☐ Electric cooling fan or thermoswitch faulty (Chapter 3).
- ☐ Pressure cap faulty (Chapter 3).
- ☐ Engine management system fault – petrol engine models (Chapters 1 and 5).
- ☐ Inaccurate temperature gauge sender unit (Chapter 3).
- ☐ Airlock in cooling system (Chapter 1).

Overcooling

- ☐ Thermostat faulty (Chapter 3).
- ☐ Inaccurate temperature gauge sender unit (Chapter 3).

External coolant leakage

- ☐ Deteriorated or damaged hoses or hose clips (Chapter 1).
- ☐ Radiator core or heater matrix leaking (Chapter 3).
- ☐ Pressure cap faulty (Chapter 3).
- ☐ Coolant pump seal leaking (Chapter 3).
- ☐ Boiling due to overheating (Chapter 3).
- ☐ Core plug leaking (Chapter 2).

Internal coolant leakage

- ☐ Leaking cylinder head gasket (Chapter 2).
- ☐ Cracked cylinder head or cylinder bore (Chapter 2).

Corrosion

- ☐ Infrequent draining and flushing (Chapter 1).
- ☐ Incorrect coolant mixture or inappropriate coolant type (Chapter 1).

Fuel and exhaust systems

Excessive fuel consumption

- ☐ Air filter element dirty or clogged (Chapter 1).
- ☐ Fuel injection or engine management system fault – petrol engine models (Chapter 4).
- ☐ Faulty injector(s) – diesel engine models (Chapter 4).
- ☐ Ignition system fault – petrol engine models (Chapters 1 and 5).
- ☐ Tyres under-inflated (*Weekly Checks*).
- ☐ Brakes binding (Chapters 1 and 9).

Fuel leakage and/or fuel odour

- ☐ Damaged or corroded fuel tank, pipes or connections (Chapter 4).

Excessive noise or fumes from exhaust system

- ☐ Leaking exhaust system or manifold joints (Chapters 1 and 4).
- ☐ Leaking, corroded or damaged silencers or pipe (Chapters 1 and 4).
- ☐ Broken mountings causing body or suspension contact (Chapter 1).

Clutch

Pedal travels to floor – no pressure or very little resistance

- ☐ Broken clutch cable (Chapter 6).
- ☐ Broken clutch release bearing or fork (Chapter 6).
- ☐ Broken diaphragm spring in clutch pressure plate (Chapter 6).

Clutch fails to disengage (unable to select gears)

- ☐ Clutch disc sticking on gearbox input shaft splines (Chapter 6).
- ☐ Clutch disc sticking to flywheel or pressure plate (Chapter 6).
- ☐ Faulty pressure plate assembly (Chapter 6).
- ☐ Clutch release mechanism worn or incorrectly assembled (Chapter 6).

Clutch slips (engine speed rises, with no increase in vehicle speed)

- ☐ Clutch disc linings excessively worn (Chapter 6).
- ☐ Clutch disc linings contaminated with oil or grease (Chapter 6).
- ☐ Faulty pressure plate or weak diaphragm spring (Chapter 6).

Judder as clutch is engaged

- ☐ Clutch disc linings contaminated with oil or grease (Chapter 6).
- ☐ Clutch disc linings excessively worn (Chapter 6).
- ☐ Clutch cable sticking or frayed (Chapter 6).
- ☐ Faulty or distorted pressure plate or diaphragm spring (Chapter 6).
- ☐ Worn or loose engine/transmission mountings (Chapter 2).
- ☐ Clutch disc hub or gearbox input shaft splines worn (Chapter 6).

Noise when depressing or releasing clutch pedal

- ☐ Worn clutch release bearing (Chapter 6).
- ☐ Worn or dry clutch pedal bushes (Chapter 6).
- ☐ Faulty pressure plate assembly (Chapter 6).
- ☐ Pressure plate diaphragm spring broken (Chapter 6).
- ☐ Broken clutch disc cushioning springs (Chapter 6).

Manual transmission

Noisy in neutral with engine running

- [ ] Input shaft bearings worn (noise apparent with clutch pedal released, but not when depressed) (Chapter 7).*
- [ ] Clutch release bearing worn (noise apparent with clutch pedal depressed, possibly less when released) (Chapter 6).

Noisy in one particular gear

- [ ] Worn, damaged or chipped gear teeth (Chapter 7).*

Difficulty engaging gears

- [ ] Clutch fault (Chapter 6).
- [ ] Worn or damaged gear linkage (Chapter 7).
- [ ] Incorrectly-adjusted gear linkage (Chapter 7).
- [ ] Worn synchroniser units (Chapter 7).*

Jumps out of gear

- [ ] Worn or damaged gear linkage (Chapter 7).
- [ ] Worn synchroniser units (Chapter 7).*
- [ ] Worn selector forks (Chapter 7).*

Vibration

- [ ] Lack of oil (Chapter 1).
- [ ] Worn bearings (Chapter 7).*

Lubricant leaks

- [ ] Leaking differential output oil seal (Chapter 7).
- [ ] Leaking housing joint (Chapter 7).*
- [ ] Leaking input shaft oil seal (Chapter 7).*

Although the corrective action necessary to remedy the symptoms described is beyond the scope of the home mechanic, the above information should be helpful in isolating the cause of the condition, so that the owner can communicate clearly with a professional mechanic.

Automatic transmission

Note: *Due to the complexity of the automatic transmission, it is difficult for the home mechanic to properly diagnose and service this unit. For problems other than the following, the vehicle should be taken to a dealer service department or automatic transmission specialist. Don't be in a hurry to remove the transmission if a fault is suspected, as most testing is carried out with the unit still fitted.*

Fluid leakage

- [ ] Automatic transmission fluid is usually dark in colour. Fluid leaks should not be confused with engine oil, which can easily be blown onto the transmission by airflow.
- [ ] To determine the source of a leak, first remove all built-up dirt and grime from the transmission housing and surrounding areas using a degreasing agent. Drive the vehicle at low speed, so airflow will not blow the leak far from its source. Raise and support the vehicle, and determine where the leak is coming from. The following are common areas of leakage:
a) *Fluid pan or 'sump' (Chapter 1 and 7).*
b) *Dipstick tube (Chapter 1 and 7).*
c) *Transmission-to-fluid cooler pipes/unions (Chapter 7).*

Transmission fluid brown, or has burned smell

- [ ] Transmission fluid level low, or fluid in need of renewal (Chapter 1 and 7).

General gear selection problems

- [ ] Chapter 7 deals with checking and adjusting the selector cable on automatic transmissions. The following are common problems which may be caused by a poorly-adjusted cable:

a) *Engine starting in gears other than Park or Neutral.*
b) *Indicator panel showing a gear other than that being used.*
c) *Vehicle moves when in Park or Neutral.*
d) *Poor gear shift quality or erratic gear changes.*
    Refer to Chapter 7 for the selector cable adjustment procedure.

Transmission will not downshift (kickdown) at full throttle

- [ ] Low transmission fluid level (Chapter 1).
- [ ] Incorrect selector cable adjustment (Chapter 7).
- [ ] Transmission ECU fault (Section 7).

Engine won't start in any gear, or starts in gears other than Park or Neutral

- [ ] Incorrect starter/inhibitor switch adjustment (Chapter 7).
- [ ] Incorrect selector cable adjustment (Chapter 7).

Transmission slips, shifts roughly, is noisy, or has no drive in forward or reverse gears

- [ ] There are many probable causes for the above problems, but the home mechanic should be concerned with only two possibilities – fluid level, or a problem with the transmission ECU (where applicable). Before taking the vehicle to a dealer or transmission specialist, check the fluid level and condition of the fluid as described in Chapter 1. Correct the fluid level as necessary, or change the fluid and filter. If the problem persists, professional help will be necessary.

Driveshafts

Clicking or knocking noise on turns (at slow speed on full-lock)

- [ ] Lack of constant velocity joint lubricant, possibly due to damaged gaiter (Chapter 8).
- [ ] Worn outer constant velocity joint (Chapter 8).

Vibration when accelerating or decelerating

- [ ] Worn inner constant velocity joint (Chapter 8).
- [ ] Bent or distorted driveshaft (Chapter 8).

Braking system

Note: *Before assuming that a brake problem exists, make sure that the tyres are in good condition and correctly inflated, that the front wheel alignment is correct, and that the vehicle is not loaded with weight in an unequal manner. Apart from checking the condition of all pipe and hose connections, any faults occurring on the anti-lock braking system should be referred to a Citroën dealer for diagnosis.*

Vehicle pulls to one side under braking

☐ Worn, defective, damaged or contaminated brake pads/shoes on one side (Chapters 1 and 9).
☐ Seized or partially-seized front brake caliper/wheel cylinder piston (Chapters 1 and 9).
☐ A mixture of brake pad/shoe lining materials fitted between sides (Chapters 1 and 9).
☐ Brake caliper or backplate mounting bolts loose (Chapter 9).
☐ Worn or damaged steering or suspension components (Chapters 1 and 10).

Noise (grinding or high-pitched squeal) when brakes applied

☐ Brake pad or shoe friction lining material worn down to metal backing (Chapters 1 and 9).
☐ Excessive corrosion of brake disc or drum. May be apparent after the vehicle has been standing for some time (Chapters 1 and 9).
☐ Foreign object (stone chipping, etc) trapped between brake disc and shield (Chapters 1 and 9).

Excessive brake pedal travel

☐ Inoperative rear brake self-adjust mechanism – drum brakes (Chapters 1 and 9).
☐ Faulty master cylinder (Chapter 9).
☐ Air in hydraulic system (Chapters 1 and 9).
☐ Faulty vacuum servo unit (Chapter 9).

Brake pedal feels spongy when depressed

☐ Air in hydraulic system (Chapters 1 and 9).
☐ Deteriorated flexible rubber brake hoses (Chapters 1 and 9).
☐ Master cylinder mounting nuts loose (Chapter 9).
☐ Faulty master cylinder (Chapter 9).

Excessive brake pedal effort required to stop vehicle

☐ Faulty vacuum servo unit (Chapter 9).
☐ Disconnected, damaged or insecure brake servo vacuum hose (Chapter 9).
☐ Primary or secondary hydraulic circuit failure (Chapter 9).
☐ Seized brake caliper or wheel cylinder piston(s) (Chapter 9).
☐ Brake pads or brake shoes incorrectly fitted (Chapters 1 and 9).
☐ Incorrect grade of brake pads or brake shoes fitted (Chapters 1 and 9).
☐ Brake pads or brake shoe linings contaminated (Chapters 1 and 9).

Judder felt through brake pedal or steering wheel when braking

☐ Excessive run-out or distortion of discs/drums (Chapters 1 and 9).
☐ Brake pad or brake shoe linings worn (Chapters 1 and 9).
☐ Brake caliper or brake backplate mounting bolts loose (Chapter 9).
☐ Wear in suspension or steering components or mountings (Chapters 1 and 10).

Brakes binding

☐ Seized brake caliper or wheel cylinder piston(s) (Chapter 9).
☐ Incorrectly-adjusted handbrake mechanism (Chapter 9).
☐ Faulty master cylinder (Chapter 9).

Rear wheels locking under normal braking

☐ Rear brake shoe linings contaminated (Chapters 1 and 9).
☐ Faulty brake pressure regulator (Chapter 9).

Suspension and steering

Note: *Before diagnosing suspension or steering faults, be sure that the trouble is not due to incorrect tyre pressures, mixtures of tyre types, or binding brakes.*

Vehicle pulls to one side

☐ Defective tyre (*Weekly Checks*).
☐ Excessive wear in suspension or steering components (Chapters 1 and 10).
☐ Incorrect front wheel alignment (Chapter 10).
☐ Damage to steering or suspension components (Chapter 1).

Wheel wobble and vibration

☐ Front roadwheels out of balance (vibration felt mainly through the steering wheel) (Chapters 1 and 10).
☐ Rear roadwheels out of balance (vibration felt throughout the vehicle) (Chapters 1 and 10).
☐ Roadwheels damaged or distorted (Chapters 1 and 10).
☐ Faulty or damaged tyre (*Weekly Checks*).
☐ Worn steering or suspension joints, bushes or components (Chapters 1 and 10).
☐ Wheel bolts loose (Chapters 1 and 10).

Excessive pitching and/or rolling around corners, or during braking

☐ Defective shock absorbers (Chapters 1 and 10).
☐ Broken or weak spring and/or suspension part (Chapters 1 and 10).
☐ Worn or damaged anti-roll bar or mountings (Chapter 10).

Wandering or general instability

☐ Incorrect front wheel alignment (Chapter 10).
☐ Worn steering or suspension joints, bushes or components (Chapters 1 and 10).
☐ Roadwheels out of balance (Chapters 1 and 10).
☐ Faulty or damaged tyre (*Weekly Checks*).
☐ Wheel bolts loose (Chapters 1 and 10).
☐ Defective shock absorbers (Chapters 1 and 10).

Excessively-stiff steering

☐ Broken or incorrectly-adjusted auxiliary drivebelt (Chapter 1).
☐ Faulty power steering pump (Chapter 10).
☐ Lack of steering gear lubricant (Chapter 10).
☐ Seized track rod end balljoint or suspension balljoint (Chapters 1 and 10).
☐ Incorrect front wheel alignment (Chapter 10).
☐ Steering rack or column bent or damaged (Chapter 10).

Steering and suspension (continued)

Excessive play in steering

- [ ] Worn steering column intermediate shaft universal joint (Chapter 10).
- [ ] Worn steering track rod balljoints (Chapters 1 and 10).
- [ ] Worn rack-and-pinion steering gear (Chapter 10).
- [ ] Worn steering or suspension joints, bushes or components (Chapters 1 and 10).

Lack of power assistance

- [ ] Broken or incorrectly-adjusted auxiliary drivebelt (Chapter 1).
- [ ] Incorrect power steering fluid level (*Weekly Checks*).
- [ ] Restriction in power steering fluid hoses (Chapter 1).
- [ ] Faulty power steering pump (Chapter 10).
- [ ] Faulty rack-and-pinion steering gear (Chapter 10).

Tyre wear excessive

Tyre treads exhibit feathered edges

- [ ] Incorrect toe setting (Chapter 10).

Tyres worn in centre of tread

- [ ] Tyres over-inflated (*Weekly Checks*).

Tyres worn on inside and outside edges

- [ ] Tyres under-inflated (*Weekly Checks*).

Tyres worn on inside or outside edges

- [ ] Incorrect camber/castor angles (wear on one edge only) (Chapter 10).
- [ ] Worn steering or suspension joints, bushes or components (Chapters 1 and 10).
- [ ] Excessively-hard cornering.
- [ ] Accident damage.

Tyres worn unevenly

- [ ] Tyres/wheels out of balance (*Weekly Checks*).
- [ ] Excessive wheel or tyre run-out (Chapter 1).
- [ ] Worn shock absorbers (Chapters 1 and 10).
- [ ] Faulty tyre (*Weekly Checks*).

Electrical system

Note: *For problems associated with the starting system, refer to the faults listed under 'Engine' earlier in this Section.*

Battery won't hold a charge for more than a few days

- [ ] Battery defective internally (Chapter 5).
- [ ] Battery terminal connections loose or corroded (*Weekly Checks*).
- [ ] Auxiliary drivebelt worn or incorrectly adjusted (Chapter 1).
- [ ] Alternator not charging at correct output (Chapter 5).
- [ ] Alternator or voltage regulator faulty (Chapter 5).
- [ ] Short-circuit causing continual battery drain (Chapters 5 and 12).

Ignition/no-charge warning light stays on with engine running

- [ ] Auxiliary drivebelt broken, worn, or incorrectly adjusted (Chapter 1).
- [ ] Alternator brushes worn, sticking, or dirty (Chapter 5).
- [ ] Alternator brush springs weak or broken (Chapter 5).
- [ ] Internal fault in alternator or voltage regulator (Chapter 5).
- [ ] Broken, disconnected, or loose wiring in charging circuit (Chapter 5).

Ignition/no-charge warning light fails to come on

- [ ] Warning light bulb blown (Chapter 12).
- [ ] Broken, disconnected, or loose wiring in warning light circuit (Chapter 12).
- [ ] Alternator faulty (Chapter 5).

Lights inoperative

- [ ] Bulb blown (Chapter 12).
- [ ] Corrosion of bulb or bulbholder contacts (Chapter 12).
- [ ] Blown fuse (Chapter 12).
- [ ] Faulty relay (Chapter 12).
- [ ] Broken, loose, or disconnected wiring (Chapter 12).
- [ ] Faulty switch (Chapter 12).

Instrument readings inaccurate or erratic

Instrument readings increase with engine speed

- [ ] Faulty voltage regulator (Chapter 12).

Fuel or temperature gauges give no reading

- [ ] Faulty gauge sender unit (Chapters 3 and 4).
- [ ] Wiring open-circuit (Chapter 12).
- [ ] Faulty gauge (Chapter 12).

Fuel or temperature gauges give continuous maximum reading

- [ ] Faulty gauge sender unit (Chapters 3 and 4).
- [ ] Wiring short-circuit (Chapter 12).
- [ ] Faulty gauge (Chapter 12).

Horn inoperative, or unsatisfactory in operation

Horn operates all the time

- [ ] Horn push either earthed or stuck down (Chapter 12).
- [ ] Horn cable-to-horn push earthed (Chapter 12).

Horn fails to operate

- [ ] Blown fuse (Chapter 12).
- [ ] Cable or cable connections loose, broken or disconnected (Chapter 12).
- [ ] Faulty horn (Chapter 12).

Horn emits intermittent or unsatisfactory sound

- [ ] Cable connections loose (Chapter 12).
- [ ] Horn mountings loose (Chapter 12).
- [ ] Faulty horn (Chapter 12).

Windscreen/tailgate wipers failed, or unsatisfactory in operation

Wipers fail to operate, or operate very slowly

- [ ] Wiper blades stuck to screen, or linkage seized or binding (Chapters 1 and 12).
- [ ] Blown fuse (Chapter 12).
- [ ] Cable or cable connections loose, broken or disconnected (Chapter 12).
- [ ] Faulty relay (Chapter 12).
- [ ] Faulty wiper motor (Chapter 12).

Electrical system (continued)

Wiper blades sweep over too large or too small an area of the glass

- ☐ Wiper arms incorrectly positioned on spindles (Chapter 1).
- ☐ Excessive wear of wiper linkage (Chapter 12).
- ☐ Wiper motor or linkage mountings loose or insecure (Chapter 12).

Wiper blades fail to clean the glass effectively

- ☐ Wiper blade rubbers worn or perished (*Weekly Checks*).
- ☐ Wiper arm tension springs broken, or arm pivots seized (Chapter 12).
- ☐ Insufficient windscreen washer additive to adequately remove road film (*Weekly Checks*).

Windscreen/tailgate washers failed, or unsatisfactory in operation

One or more washer jets inoperative

- ☐ Blocked washer jet.
- ☐ Disconnected, kinked or restricted fluid hose (Chapter 12).
- ☐ Insufficient fluid in washer reservoir (*Weekly Checks*).

Washer pump fails to operate

- ☐ Broken or disconnected wiring or connections (Chapter 12).
- ☐ Blown fuse (Chapter 12).
- ☐ Faulty washer switch (Chapter 12).
- ☐ Faulty washer pump (Chapter 12).

Washer pump runs for some time before fluid is emitted from jets

- ☐ Faulty one-way valve in fluid supply hose.

Electric windows inoperative, or unsatisfactory in operation

Window glass will only move in one direction

- ☐ Faulty switch (Chapter 12).

Window glass slow to move

- ☐ Regulator seized or damaged, or in need of lubricant (Chapter 11).
- ☐ Door internal components or trim fouling regulator (Chapter 11).
- ☐ Faulty motor (Chapter 11).

Window glass fails to move

- ☐ Blown fuse (Chapter 12).
- ☐ Faulty relay (Chapter 12).
- ☐ Broken or disconnected wiring or connections (Chapter 12).
- ☐ Faulty motor (Chapter 11).

Central locking system inoperative, or unsatisfactory in operation

Complete system failure

- ☐ Blown fuse (Chapter 12).
- ☐ Faulty relay (Chapter 12).
- ☐ Broken or disconnected wiring or connections (Chapter 12).
- ☐ Faulty control unit (Chapter 11).

Latch locks but will not unlock, or unlocks but will not lock

- ☐ Faulty master switch (Chapter 12).
- ☐ Broken or disconnected latch operating rods or levers (Chapter 11).
- ☐ Faulty relay (Chapter 12).
- ☐ Faulty control unit (Chapter 11).

One solenoid/motor fails to operate

- ☐ Broken or disconnected wiring or connections (Chapter 12).
- ☐ Faulty solenoid/motor (Chapter 11).
- ☐ Broken, binding or disconnected latch operating rods or levers (Chapter 11).
- ☐ Fault in door latch (Chapter 11).

A

ABS (Anti-lock brake system) A system, usually electronically controlled, that senses incipient wheel lockup during braking and relieves hydraulic pressure at wheels that are about to skid.

Air bag An inflatable bag hidden in the steering wheel (driver's side) or the dash or glovebox (passenger side). In a head-on collision, the bags inflate, preventing the driver and front passenger from being thrown forward into the steering wheel or windscreen.

Air cleaner A metal or plastic housing, containing a filter element, which removes dust and dirt from the air being drawn into the engine.

Air filter element The actual filter in an air cleaner system, usually manufactured from pleated paper and requiring renewal at regular intervals.

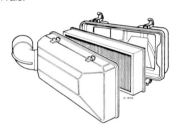

Air filter

Allen key A hexagonal wrench which fits into a recessed hexagonal hole.

Alligator clip A long-nosed spring-loaded metal clip with meshing teeth. Used to make temporary electrical connections.

Alternator A component in the electrical system which converts mechanical energy from a drivebelt into electrical energy to charge the battery and to operate the starting system, ignition system and electrical accessories.

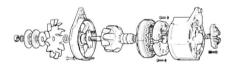

Alternator (exploded view)

Ampere (amp) A unit of measurement for the flow of electric current. One amp is the amount of current produced by one volt acting through a resistance of one ohm.

Anaerobic sealer A substance used to prevent bolts and screws from loosening. Anaerobic means that it does not require oxygen for activation. The Loctite brand is widely used.

Antifreeze A substance (usually ethylene glycol) mixed with water, and added to a vehicle's cooling system, to prevent freezing of the coolant in winter. Antifreeze also contains chemicals to inhibit corrosion and the formation of rust and other deposits that would tend to clog the radiator and coolant passages and reduce cooling efficiency.

Anti-seize compound A coating that reduces the risk of seizing on fasteners that are subjected to high temperatures, such as exhaust manifold bolts and nuts.

Anti-seize compound

Asbestos A natural fibrous mineral with great heat resistance, commonly used in the composition of brake friction materials. Asbestos is a health hazard and the dust created by brake systems should never be inhaled or ingested.

Axle A shaft on which a wheel revolves, or which revolves with a wheel. Also, a solid beam that connects the two wheels at one end of the vehicle. An axle which also transmits power to the wheels is known as a live axle.

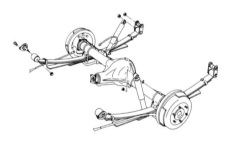

Axle assembly

Axleshaft A single rotating shaft, on either side of the differential, which delivers power from the final drive assembly to the drive wheels. Also called a driveshaft or a halfshaft.

B

Ball bearing An anti-friction bearing consisting of a hardened inner and outer race with hardened steel balls between two races.

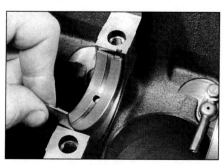

Bearing

Bearing The curved surface on a shaft or in a bore, or the part assembled into either, that permits relative motion between them with minimum wear and friction.

Big-end bearing The bearing in the end of the connecting rod that's attached to the crankshaft.

Bleed nipple A valve on a brake wheel cylinder, caliper or other hydraulic component that is opened to purge the hydraulic system of air. Also called a bleed screw.

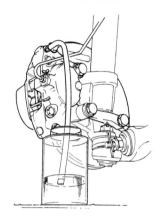

Brake bleeding

Brake bleeding Procedure for removing air from lines of a hydraulic brake system.

Brake disc The component of a disc brake that rotates with the wheels.

Brake drum The component of a drum brake that rotates with the wheels.

Brake linings The friction material which contacts the brake disc or drum to retard the vehicle's speed. The linings are bonded or riveted to the brake pads or shoes.

Brake pads The replaceable friction pads that pinch the brake disc when the brakes are applied. Brake pads consist of a friction material bonded or riveted to a rigid backing plate.

Brake shoe The crescent-shaped carrier to which the brake linings are mounted and which forces the lining against the rotating drum during braking.

Braking systems For more information on braking systems, consult the *Haynes Automotive Brake Manual*.

Breaker bar A long socket wrench handle providing greater leverage.

Bulkhead The insulated partition between the engine and the passenger compartment.

C

Caliper The non-rotating part of a disc-brake assembly that straddles the disc and carries the brake pads. The caliper also contains the hydraulic components that cause the pads to pinch the disc when the brakes are applied. A caliper is also a measuring tool that can be set to measure inside or outside dimensions of an object.

Camshaft A rotating shaft on which a series of cam lobes operate the valve mechanisms. The camshaft may be driven by gears, by sprockets and chain or by sprockets and a belt.

Canister A container in an evaporative emission control system; contains activated charcoal granules to trap vapours from the fuel system.

Canister

Carburettor A device which mixes fuel with air in the proper proportions to provide a desired power output from a spark ignition internal combustion engine.

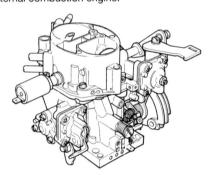

Carburettor

Castellated Resembling the parapets along the top of a castle wall. For example, a castellated balljoint stud nut.

Castellated nut

Castor In wheel alignment, the backward or forward tilt of the steering axis. Castor is positive when the steering axis is inclined rearward at the top.

Catalytic converter A silencer-like device in the exhaust system which converts certain pollutants in the exhaust gases into less harmful substances.

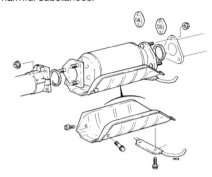

Catalytic converter

Circlip A ring-shaped clip used to prevent endwise movement of cylindrical parts and shafts. An internal circlip is installed in a groove in a housing; an external circlip fits into a groove on the outside of a cylindrical piece such as a shaft.

Clearance The amount of space between two parts. For example, between a piston and a cylinder, between a bearing and a journal, etc.

Coil spring A spiral of elastic steel found in various sizes throughout a vehicle, for example as a springing medium in the suspension and in the valve train.

Compression Reduction in volume, and increase in pressure and temperature, of a gas, caused by squeezing it into a smaller space.

Compression ratio The relationship between cylinder volume when the piston is at top dead centre and cylinder volume when the piston is at bottom dead centre.

Constant velocity (CV) joint A type of universal joint that cancels out vibrations caused by driving power being transmitted through an angle.

Core plug A disc or cup-shaped metal device inserted in a hole in a casting through which core was removed when the casting was formed. Also known as a freeze plug or expansion plug.

Crankcase The lower part of the engine block in which the crankshaft rotates.

Crankshaft The main rotating member, or shaft, running the length of the crankcase, with offset "throws" to which the connecting rods are attached.

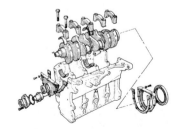

Crankshaft assembly

Crocodile clip See Alligator clip

D

Diagnostic code Code numbers obtained by accessing the diagnostic mode of an engine management computer. This code can be used to determine the area in the system where a malfunction may be located.

Disc brake A brake design incorporating a rotating disc onto which brake pads are squeezed. The resulting friction converts the energy of a moving vehicle into heat.

Double-overhead cam (DOHC) An engine that uses two overhead camshafts, usually one for the intake valves and one for the exhaust valves.

Drivebelt(s) The belt(s) used to drive accessories such as the alternator, water pump, power steering pump, air conditioning compressor, etc. off the crankshaft pulley.

Accessory drivebelts

Driveshaft Any shaft used to transmit motion. Commonly used when referring to the axleshafts on a front wheel drive vehicle.

Driveshaft

Drum brake A type of brake using a drum-shaped metal cylinder attached to the inner surface of the wheel. When the brake pedal is pressed, curved brake shoes with friction linings press against the inside of the drum to slow or stop the vehicle.

Drum brake assembly

E

EGR valve A valve used to introduce exhaust gases into the intake air stream.

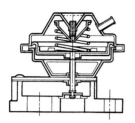

EGR valve

Electronic control unit (ECU) A computer which controls (for instance) ignition and fuel injection systems, or an anti-lock braking system. For more information refer to the *Haynes Automotive Electrical and Electronic Systems Manual.*

Electronic Fuel Injection (EFI) A computer controlled fuel system that distributes fuel through an injector located in each intake port of the engine.

Emergency brake A braking system, independent of the main hydraulic system, that can be used to slow or stop the vehicle if the primary brakes fail, or to hold the vehicle stationary even though the brake pedal isn't depressed. It usually consists of a hand lever that actuates either front or rear brakes mechanically through a series of cables and linkages. Also known as a handbrake or parking brake.

Endfloat The amount of lengthwise movement between two parts. As applied to a crankshaft, the distance that the crankshaft can move forward and back in the cylinder block.

Engine management system (EMS) A computer controlled system which manages the fuel injection and the ignition systems in an integrated fashion.

Exhaust manifold A part with several passages through which exhaust gases leave the engine combustion chambers and enter the exhaust pipe.

Exhaust manifold

F

Fan clutch A viscous (fluid) drive coupling device which permits variable engine fan speeds in relation to engine speeds.

Feeler blade A thin strip or blade of hardened steel, ground to an exact thickness, used to check or measure clearances between parts.

Feeler blade

Firing order The order in which the engine cylinders fire, or deliver their power strokes, beginning with the number one cylinder.

Flywheel A heavy spinning wheel in which energy is absorbed and stored by means of momentum. On cars, the flywheel is attached to the crankshaft to smooth out firing impulses.

Free play The amount of travel before any action takes place. The "looseness" in a linkage, or an assembly of parts, between the initial application of force and actual movement. For example, the distance the brake pedal moves before the pistons in the master cylinder are actuated.

Fuse An electrical device which protects a circuit against accidental overload. The typical fuse contains a soft piece of metal which is calibrated to melt at a predetermined current flow (expressed as amps) and break the circuit.

Fusible link A circuit protection device consisting of a conductor surrounded by heat-resistant insulation. The conductor is smaller than the wire it protects, so it acts as the weakest link in the circuit. Unlike a blown fuse, a failed fusible link must frequently be cut from the wire for replacement.

G

Gap The distance the spark must travel in jumping from the centre electrode to the side

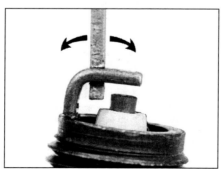

Adjusting spark plug gap

electrode in a spark plug. Also refers to the spacing between the points in a contact breaker assembly in a conventional points-type ignition, or to the distance between the reluctor or rotor and the pickup coil in an electronic ignition.

Gasket Any thin, soft material - usually cork, cardboard, asbestos or soft metal - installed between two metal surfaces to ensure a good seal. For instance, the cylinder head gasket seals the joint between the block and the cylinder head.

Gasket

Gauge An instrument panel display used to monitor engine conditions. A gauge with a movable pointer on a dial or a fixed scale is an analogue gauge. A gauge with a numerical readout is called a digital gauge.

H

Halfshaft A rotating shaft that transmits power from the final drive unit to a drive wheel, usually when referring to a live rear axle.

Harmonic balancer A device designed to reduce torsion or twisting vibration in the crankshaft. May be incorporated in the crankshaft pulley. Also known as a vibration damper.

Hone An abrasive tool for correcting small irregularities or differences in diameter in an engine cylinder, brake cylinder, etc.

Hydraulic tappet A tappet that utilises hydraulic pressure from the engine's lubrication system to maintain zero clearance (constant contact with both camshaft and valve stem). Automatically adjusts to variation in valve stem length. Hydraulic tappets also reduce valve noise.

I

Ignition timing The moment at which the spark plug fires, usually expressed in the number of crankshaft degrees before the piston reaches the top of its stroke.

Inlet manifold A tube or housing with passages through which flows the air-fuel mixture (carburettor vehicles and vehicles with throttle body injection) or air only (port fuel-injected vehicles) to the port openings in the cylinder head.

J

Jump start Starting the engine of a vehicle with a discharged or weak battery by attaching jump leads from the weak battery to a charged or helper battery.

L

Load Sensing Proportioning Valve (LSPV) A brake hydraulic system control valve that works like a proportioning valve, but also takes into consideration the amount of weight carried by the rear axle.

Locknut A nut used to lock an adjustment nut, or other threaded component, in place. For example, a locknut is employed to keep the adjusting nut on the rocker arm in position.

Lockwasher A form of washer designed to prevent an attaching nut from working loose.

M

MacPherson strut A type of front suspension system devised by Earle MacPherson at Ford of England. In its original form, a simple lateral link with the anti-roll bar creates the lower control arm. A long strut - an integral coil spring and shock absorber - is mounted between the body and the steering knuckle. Many modern so-called MacPherson strut systems use a conventional lower A-arm and don't rely on the anti-roll bar for location.

Multimeter An electrical test instrument with the capability to measure voltage, current and resistance.

N

NOx Oxides of Nitrogen. A common toxic pollutant emitted by petrol and diesel engines at higher temperatures.

O

Ohm The unit of electrical resistance. One volt applied to a resistance of one ohm will produce a current of one amp.

Ohmmeter An instrument for measuring electrical resistance.

O-ring A type of sealing ring made of a special rubber-like material; in use, the O-ring is compressed into a groove to provide the sealing action.

O-ring

Overhead cam (ohc) engine An engine with the camshaft(s) located on top of the cylinder head(s).

Overhead valve (ohv) engine An engine with the valves located in the cylinder head, but with the camshaft located in the engine block.

Oxygen sensor A device installed in the engine exhaust manifold, which senses the oxygen content in the exhaust and converts this information into an electric current. Also called a Lambda sensor.

P

Phillips screw A type of screw head having a cross instead of a slot for a corresponding type of screwdriver.

Plastigage A thin strip of plastic thread, available in different sizes, used for measuring clearances. For example, a strip of Plastigage is laid across a bearing journal. The parts are assembled and dismantled; the width of the crushed strip indicates the clearance between journal and bearing.

Plastigage

Propeller shaft The long hollow tube with universal joints at both ends that carries power from the transmission to the differential on front-engined rear wheel drive vehicles.

Proportioning valve A hydraulic control valve which limits the amount of pressure to the rear brakes during panic stops to prevent wheel lock-up.

R

Rack-and-pinion steering A steering system with a pinion gear on the end of the steering shaft that mates with a rack (think of a geared wheel opened up and laid flat). When the steering wheel is turned, the pinion turns, moving the rack to the left or right. This movement is transmitted through the track rods to the steering arms at the wheels.

Radiator A liquid-to-air heat transfer device designed to reduce the temperature of the coolant in an internal combustion engine cooling system.

Refrigerant Any substance used as a heat transfer agent in an air-conditioning system. R-12 has been the principle refrigerant for many years; recently, however, manufacturers have begun using R-134a, a non-CFC substance that is considered less harmful to the ozone in the upper atmosphere.

Rocker arm A lever arm that rocks on a shaft or pivots on a stud. In an overhead valve engine, the rocker arm converts the upward movement of the pushrod into a downward movement to open a valve.

Rotor In a distributor, the rotating device inside the cap that connects the centre electrode and the outer terminals as it turns, distributing the high voltage from the coil secondary winding to the proper spark plug. Also, that part of an alternator which rotates inside the stator. Also, the rotating assembly of a turbocharger, including the compressor wheel, shaft and turbine wheel.

Runout The amount of wobble (in-and-out movement) of a gear or wheel as it's rotated. The amount a shaft rotates "out-of-true." The out-of-round condition of a rotating part.

S

Sealant A liquid or paste used to prevent leakage at a joint. Sometimes used in conjunction with a gasket.

Sealed beam lamp An older headlight design which integrates the reflector, lens and filaments into a hermetically-sealed one-piece unit. When a filament burns out or the lens cracks, the entire unit is simply replaced.

Serpentine drivebelt A single, long, wide accessory drivebelt that's used on some newer vehicles to drive all the accessories, instead of a series of smaller, shorter belts. Serpentine drivebelts are usually tensioned by an automatic tensioner.

Serpentine drivebelt

Shim Thin spacer, commonly used to adjust the clearance or relative positions between two parts. For example, shims inserted into or under bucket tappets control valve clearances. Clearance is adjusted by changing the thickness of the shim.

Slide hammer A special puller that screws into or hooks onto a component such as a shaft or bearing; a heavy sliding handle on the shaft bottoms against the end of the shaft to knock the component free.

Sprocket A tooth or projection on the periphery of a wheel, shaped to engage with a chain or drivebelt. Commonly used to refer to the sprocket wheel itself.

Starter inhibitor switch On vehicles with an automatic transmission, a switch that prevents starting if the vehicle is not in Neutral or Park.

Strut See MacPherson strut.

T

Tappet A cylindrical component which transmits motion from the cam to the valve stem, either directly or via a pushrod and rocker arm. Also called a cam follower.

Thermostat A heat-controlled valve that regulates the flow of coolant between the cylinder block and the radiator, so maintaining optimum engine operating temperature. A thermostat is also used in some air cleaners in which the temperature is regulated.

Thrust bearing The bearing in the clutch assembly that is moved in to the release levers by clutch pedal action to disengage the clutch. Also referred to as a release bearing.

Timing belt A toothed belt which drives the camshaft. Serious engine damage may result if it breaks in service.

Timing chain A chain which drives the camshaft.

Toe-in The amount the front wheels are closer together at the front than at the rear. On rear wheel drive vehicles, a slight amount of toe-in is usually specified to keep the front wheels running parallel on the road by offsetting other forces that tend to spread the wheels apart.

Toe-out The amount the front wheels are closer together at the rear than at the front. On front wheel drive vehicles, a slight amount of toe-out is usually specified.

Tools For full information on choosing and using tools, refer to the *Haynes Automotive Tools Manual.*

Tracer A stripe of a second colour applied to a wire insulator to distinguish that wire from another one with the same colour insulator.

Tune-up A process of accurate and careful adjustments and parts replacement to obtain the best possible engine performance.

Turbocharger A centrifugal device, driven by exhaust gases, that pressurises the intake air. Normally used to increase the power output from a given engine displacement, but can also be used primarily to reduce exhaust emissions (as on VW's "Umwelt" Diesel engine).

U

Universal joint or U-joint A double-pivoted connection for transmitting power from a driving to a driven shaft through an angle. A U-joint consists of two Y-shaped yokes and a cross-shaped member called the spider.

V

Valve A device through which the flow of liquid, gas, vacuum, or loose material in bulk may be started, stopped, or regulated by a movable part that opens, shuts, or partially obstructs one or more ports or passageways. A valve is also the movable part of such a device.

Valve clearance The clearance between the valve tip (the end of the valve stem) and the rocker arm or tappet. The valve clearance is measured when the valve is closed.

Vernier caliper A precision measuring instrument that measures inside and outside dimensions. Not quite as accurate as a micrometer, but more convenient.

Viscosity The thickness of a liquid or its resistance to flow.

Volt A unit for expressing electrical "pressure" in a circuit. One volt that will produce a current of one ampere through a resistance of one ohm.

W

Welding Various processes used to join metal items by heating the areas to be joined to a molten state and fusing them together. For more information refer to the *Haynes Automotive Welding Manual.*

Wiring diagram A drawing portraying the components and wires in a vehicle's electrical system, using standardised symbols. For more information refer to the *Haynes Automotive Electrical and Electronic Systems Manual.*

Note: *References throughout this index are in the form - "Chapter number" • "Page number"*

A

Accelerator cable
diesel engines – 4B•15, 4C•5
petrol engines – 4A•3
Accelerator pedal
diesel engines – 4B•15, 4C•6
petrol engines – 4A•4
Accelerator pedal position sensor – 4C•11
Accumulator rail – 4C•8
Acknowledgements – 0•6
Aerial – 12•17
Air bags – 0•5, 2•18
renewal
diesel engine models – 1B•21
petrol engine models – 1A•20
Air cleaner assembly and inlet ducts
diesel engines – 4B•4, 4C•4
petrol engines – 4A•2
Air conditioning system – 3•12, 3•13
refrigerant leak check
diesel engine models – 1B•8
petrol engine models – 1A•9
Air filter renewal
diesel engine models – 1B•17
petrol engine models – 1A•15
Air injection – 4D•1, 4D•3
Air mass meter – 4C•12
Air pump – 4D•3
Alarm system – 12•17
Alternator – 5A•4, 5A•5
drivebelt check and renewal
diesel engine models – 1B•10
petrol engine models – 1A•9
Antifreeze mixture
diesel engine models – 1B•21
petrol engine models – 1A•20
Anti-lock braking system (ABS) – 9•18
electronic control unit – 9•18
modulator assembly – 9•18
wheel sensor – 9•18, 9•19
Anti-roll bar – 10•8
Anti-theft alarm system – 12•17
Asbestos – 0•5
ATF – 0•18, 7B•11
leak check – 1A•9
level check– 1A•13
renewal – 1A•15
Automatic transmission – 2E•6, 7B•1 *et seq*
fault finding – REF•17
fluid – 0•18, 7B•11
leak check – 1A•9
level check – 1A•13
renewal – 1A•15

Auxiliary drivebelt check and renewal
diesel engine models – 1B•10
petrol engine models – 1A•9
Axle assembly – 10•12

B

Badges – 11•19
Battery – 0•5, 0•17, 5A•2, 5A•3
disconnecting – REF•6
Big-end bearings
diesel engine – 2F•16
petrol engine – 2E•14
running clearance
diesel engine – 2F•20
petrol engine – 2E•21
Bleeding
brakes – 9•3
diesel fuel system – 4B•4, 4C•4
power steering – 10•17
Blower motor – 3•111
Body corrosion – REF•12
Body electrical systems – 12•1 *et seq*
Bodywork and fittings – 11•1 *et seq*
Bonnet – 11•5
Bosch Motronic system – 4A•8
coolant temperature
sensor – 4A•10, 4A•11
crankshaft sensor – 4A•10, 4A•11
electronic control unit
(ECU) – 4A•9, 4A•11
fuel pressure regulator – 4A•9, 4A•11
fuel rail and injectors – 4A•8, 4A•10
idle speed auxiliary air valve – 4A•9
idle speed stepper motor – 4A•9, 4A•11
inlet air temperature sensor – 4A•10, 4A•11
knock sensor – 4A•10, 4A•11
manifold pressure sensor – 4A•10, 4A•11
throttle potentiometer – 4A•9, 4A•11
vehicle speed sensor – 4A•10, 4A•11
Brake caliper
front – 9•12
rear – 9•13
Brake disc
front – 9•10
rear – 9•11
Brake drum – 9•11
Brake fluid – 0•18
leak check
diesel engine models – 1B•8
petrol engine models – 1A•9
level – 0•15, 0•18
renewal
diesel engine models – 1B•18
petrol engine models – 1A•16

Brake pads
condition check
diesel engine models – 1B•14
petrol engine models – 1A•12
front – 9•4
rear – 9•7
Brake pedal – 9•15
Brake pressure-regulating valve – 9•17
Brake shoes – 9•8
condition check
diesel engine models – 1B•17
petrol engine models – 1A•16
Braking system – 9•1 *et seq*, REF•10,
REF•11
check
diesel engine models – 1B•15, 1B•19
petrol engine models – 1A•13, 1A•18
fault finding – REF•18
Bulbs
courtesy light – 12•9
digital clock illumination bulb – 12•11
direction indicator – 12•7
foglight – 12•7
glovebox light – 12•10
headlight – 12•6
heater/ventilation control unit illumination
bulbs – 12•11
high-level stoplight – 12•8
instrument panel illumination and warning
light bulbs – 12•11
luggage compartment light – 12•10
map reading light – 12•10
number plate light – 12•9
rear light cluster – 12•8
sidelight – 12•7
Bumpers – 11•4
Burning – 0•5
Buying spare parts – REF•3

C

Cables
accelerator
diesel engines – 4B•15, 4C•5
petrol engines – 4A•3
bonnet release – 11•5
clutch – 6•2
gear selector – 7B•4
handbrake – 9•16
heater/ventilation control – 3•9
Caliper
front – 9•12
rear – 9•13

Camshaft
DW series diesel engine – 2D•14, 2D•15
TU series petrol engine – 2A•9
XU series petrol engine – 2B•14
XUD series diesel engine – 2C•9
Camshaft oil seal
DW series diesel engine – 2D•19
TU series petrol engine – 2A•9
XU series petrol engine – 2B•13
XUD series diesel engine – 2C•14
Camshaft position sensor – 4C•11
Camshaft sprocket
DW series diesel engine – 2D•12
TU series petrol engine – 2A•7, 2A•8
XU series petrol
    engine – 2B•12, 2B•13
XUD series diesel engine – 2C•6
Carpets – 11•2, 11•27
Cassette player – 12•16
Catalytic converter – 4D•5
diesel engines – 4B•19, 4D•3
petrol engines – 4A•16, 4A•17, 4D•2
Central locking
    components – 11•18
Centre console – 11•28
switches – 12•6
Centre pillar trim panels – 11•25
Charcoal canister – 4D•2
Charging system – 5A•4
Cigarette lighter – 12•14
Clock – 12•13
Clutch – 6•1 *et seq*
cable – 6•2
control mechanism check
    diesel engine models – 1B•13
    petrol engine models – 1A•11
fault finding – REF•16
pedal – 6•2
release mechanism – 6•4
Coil – 5B•2
Compression test
DW series diesel engine – 2D•4
TU series petrol engine – 2A•3
XU series petrol engine – 2B•4
XUD series diesel engine – 2C•3
Connecting rod assembly
diesel engine – 2F•12, 2F•14, 2F•19
petrol engine –
Console – 11•28
switches – 12•6
Contents – 0•2, 0•3
Conversion factors – REF•2
Coolant – 0•18
level – 0•14, 0•18
renewal
    diesel engine models – 1B•20
    petrol engine models – 1A•19
Coolant pump – 3•8
sprocket
    DW series diesel engine – 2D•13
    XUD series diesel engine – 2C•8
Coolant temperature sensor – 3•7
Bosch Motronic and Sagem Lucas
    system – 4A•10, 4A•11
diesel engines – 4B•20, 4C•11
Magneti Marelli system – 4A•12, 4A•13
Cooling fans – 3•6
switch – 3•7

Cooling, heating and ventilation
    systems – 3•1 *et seq*
fault finding – REF•16
hoses – 3•2
switches and sensors – 3•7
Courtesy light – 12•9
switches – 12•6
Crankcase
diesel engine – 2F•13
petrol engine – 2E•11
Crankcase emission control
diesel engines – 4D•2, 4D•3
petrol engines – 4D•1, 4D•2
Crankshaft
diesel engine – 2F•12, 2F•15, 2F•17
petrol engine – 2E•10, 2E•13, 2E•15
Crankshaft oil seal
DW series diesel engine – 2D•19
TU series petrol engine – 2A•14
XU series petrol engine – 2B•20
XUD series diesel engine – 2C•13
Crankshaft pulley
DW series diesel engine – 2D•6
XU series petrol engine – 2B•7
XUD series diesel engine – 2C•5
Crankshaft sensor
Bosch Motronic and Sagem Lucas
    system – 4A•10, 4A•11
diesel engines – 4B•20, 4C•11
Magneti Marelli system – 4A•12, 4A•13
Crankshaft sprocket
DW series diesel engine – 2D•12
TU series petrol engine – 2A•8, 2A•9
XU series petrol engine – 2B•13
XUD series diesel engine – 2C•7
Crushing – 0•5
Cylinder block/crankcase
diesel engine – 2F•13
petrol engine – 2E•11
Cylinder head and valves
diesel engine – 2F•10
petrol engine – 2E•8
Cylinder head
diesel engine – 2F•8, 2F•9, 2F•11
DW series diesel engine – 2D•17
petrol engine – 2E•7, 2E•9
TU series petrol engine – 2A•11
XU series petrol engine – 2B•16
XUD series diesel engine – 2C•11
Cylinder head cover
DW series diesel engine – 2D•6
TU series petrol engine – 2A•4
XU series petrol engine – 2B•5
XUD series diesel engine – 2C•4

D

Dents in bodywork – 11•2
Depressurisation (fuel system) – 4A•5
Diesel engine removal and overhaul
    procedures – 2F•1 *et seq*
Diesel injection equipment – 0•5
Digital clock illumination bulb – 12•11
Dimensions and weights – REF•1
Direction indicators – 12•7
Disc
front – 9•10
rear – 9•11

Disconnecting the battery – REF•6
Doors – 11•6, REF•10
handle and lock components – 11•8
inner trim panel – 11•6
window glass and regulator – 11•12
Drivebelt check and renewal
diesel engine models – 1B•10
petrol engine models – 1A•9
Driveplate
TU series petrol engine – 2A•14
XU series petrol engine – 2B•20
Driveshafts – 8•1 *et seq*, REF•11
fault finding – REF•17
gaiters – 8•4
gaiter check
    diesel engine models – 1B•13
    petrol engine models – 1A•12
oil seals – 7A•4
Drivetrain check
diesel engine models – 1B•15
petrol engine models – 1A•13
Drum – 9•11
DW series diesel engine in-car repair
    procedures – 2D•1 *et seq*

E

Earth fault – 12•2
EGR system coolant temperature
    switch/sensor – 3•7
EGR valves
diesel engines – 4B•20, 4C•12
Electric cooling fans – 3•6
Electric shock – 0•5
Electrical equipment – REF•10
Electrical equipment check
diesel engine models – 1B•1515
petrol engine models – 1A•13
Electrical systems – 0•17
fault finding – 12•2, REF•20, REF•21
Electronic control system
accelerator pedal position sensor – 4C•11
air mass meter – 4C•12
camshaft position sensor – 4C•11
coolant temperature sensor/
    switch – 4B•20, 4C•11
crankshaft sensor – 4B•20, 4C•11
diesel engines – 4B•20, 4C•10
EGR valves – 4B•20, 4C•12
electronic control unit
    (ECU) – 4B•20, 4C•10
fuel pressure control valve – 4C•12
fuel pressure sensor – 4C•12
fuel temperature sensor – 4C•11
injector needle lift sensor – 4B•20
preheating system control
    unit – 4B•20, 4C•12
throttle position sensor – 4B•20
throttle position switch – 4B•20
Electronic control unit (ECU)
air bag – 12•18
anti-lock braking system – 9•18
automatic transmission – 7B•8
Bosch Motronic and Sagem Lucas
    system – 4A•9, 4A•11
diesel engines – 4B•20, 4C•10
Magneti Marelli system – 4A•12, 4A•13

Emission control
  systems – 4D•1 *et seq*, REF•12
  air injection valve – 4D•3
  air pump – 4D•3
  catalytic converter – 4D•2, 4D•3, 4D•5
  charcoal canister – 4D•2
  crankcase emission
      control – 4D•1, 4D•2, 4D•2, 4D•3
  diesel engines – 4D•3
  evaporative emission control – 4D•1, 4D•2
  exhaust emission
      control – 4D•1, 4D•2, 4D•3
  exhaust gas recirculation – 4D•2, 4D•3
  lambda sensors – 4D•2
  petrol engines – 4D•2
  purge valves – 4D•2
  secondary air injection – 4D•1, 4D•3
Engine assembly/valve timing holes
  DW series diesel engine – 2D•5
  TU series petrol engine – 2A•4
  XU series petrol engine – 2B•4
  XUD series diesel engine – 2C•4
Engine fault finding – REF•14, REF•15
Engine immobiliser – 12•18
Engine management system coolant
  temperature sensor – 3•7
Engine oil – 0•18
  leak check
      diesel engine models – 1B•8
      petrol engine models – 1A•9
  level – 0•13
  renewal
      diesel engine models – 1B•7
      petrol engine models – 1A•7
Environmental considerations – REF•4
Evaporative emission control – 4D•1, 4D•2
Exhaust emission control
  diesel engines – 4D•2, 4D•3
  petrol engines – 4D•1, 4D•2
Exhaust gas emissions check – 1A•13
Exhaust gas recirculation – 4D•2, 4D•3
Exhaust manifold
  diesel engines – 4B•16, 4C•13
  petrol engines – 4A•15
Exhaust system – REF•11, REF•12
  diesel engines – 4B•19, 4C•14
  petrol engines – 4A•16
  check
      diesel engine models – 1B•14
      petrol engine models – 1A•13
Exterior light units – 12•11

F

Facia panel assembly – 11•29
  switches – 12•4
Fans – 3•6
  switch – 3•7
Fast idle thermostatic sensor– 4B•8
Fault finding – REF•13 *et seq*
  automatic transmission – REF•17
  braking system – REF•18
  clutch – REF•16
  cooling system – REF•16
  driveshafts – REF•17
  electrical system – 12•2, REF•20, REF•21
  engine – REF•14, REF•15

  fuel and exhaust systems – REF•16
  manual transmission – REF•17
  suspension and steering
      systems – REF•18, REF•19
Filling and respraying – 11•3
Filters
  air – 1A•15, 1B•17
  fuel – 1A•19, 1B•8, 1B•15
  oil – 1A•7, 1B•7
  pollen – 1A•11, 1B•13
Fire – 0•5
Fluid cooler – 7B•7
Fluid leak check – 1A•8
Fluids – 0•18
Flywheel
  DW series diesel engine – 2D•19
  TU series petrol engine – 2A•14
  XU series petrol engine – 2B•20
  XUD series diesel engine – 2C•14
Foglight – 12•7, 12•13
Footbrake – REF•9
Fuel and exhaust systems fault
  finding – REF•16
Fuel filter housing – 3•8
Fuel filter renewal
  diesel engine models – 1B•15
  petrol engine models – 1A•19
Fuel filter water draining – 1B•8
Fuel gauge sender and pick-up
  unit
  diesel engines – 4B•15, 4C•6
  petrol engines – 4A•6
Fuel injection pump
  diesel engines – 4B•8, 4B•10, 4B•12
  sprocket
      DW series diesel engine – 2D•1
      XUD series diesel engine – 2C•7
Fuel injection system – 4A•7
Fuel injectors
  Bosch Motronic and Sagem Lucas
      system – 4A•8, 4A•10
  diesel engines – 4B•11, 4B•14, 4C•9
  Magneti Marelli
      system – 4A•11, 4A•12, 4A•13
Fuel leak check
  diesel engine models – 1B•8
  petrol engine models – 1A•8
Fuel pressure control valve
  diesel engines – 4C•12
Fuel pressure regulator
  Bosch Motronic and Sagem Lucas
      system – 4A•9, 4A•11
  Magneti Marelli system – 4A•12, 4A•13
Fuel pressure sensor – 4C•12
Fuel pump
  diesel engines – 4C•6
  petrol engines – 4A•5
Fuel rail and injectors
  Bosch Motronic and Sagem Lucas
      system – 4A•8, 4A•10
  Magneti Marelli system – 4A•11, 4A•12
Fuel system – REF•12
Fuel tank
  diesel engines – 4B•15, 4C•6
  petrol engines – 4A•6
Fuel temperature sensor – 4C•11
Fuel/exhaust systems –
  1.9 *litre diesel engines* – 4B•1 *et seq*

Fuel/exhaust systems –
  2.0 *litre diesel engines* – 4C•1 *et seq*
Fuel/exhaust systems –
  petrol engines – 4A•1 *et seq*
Fume or gas intoxication – 0•5
Fuses – 12•3

G

Gaiters (driveshaft) – 8•4
  check
      diesel engine models – 1B•13
      petrol engine models – 1A•12
Gashes in bodywork – 11•2
Gaskets – REF•4
Gearchange linkage – 7A•3
General repair procedures – REF•4
Glossary of technical
  terms – REF•21 *et seq*
Glovebox – 11•31
  light – 12•10
Glow plugs – 5C•2

H

Handbrake – 9•16, REF•9
  cables – 9•16
  check and adjustment
      diesel engine models – 1B•18
      petrol engine models – 1A•16
  lever – 9•16
  'on' warning light switch – 9•18
Handle and lock components
  (doors) – 11•8
Hazard warning switch – 12•5
Headlight – 12•6, 12•11
  beam alignment – 12•13
Headlining – 11•27
Heat shield(s)
  diesel engines – 4B•19
  petrol engines – 4A•16
Heating and ventilation system – 3•9
  blower motor – 3•111
  control cables – 3•9
  control unit illumination bulbs – 12•11
  matrix – 3•9
  hoses – 3•3
High pressure fuel pump – 4C•6
  sprocket – 2D•13
High-level stoplight – 12•8
Hinge and lock operation and lubrication
  diesel engine models – 1B•15
  petrol engine models – 1A•15
Holes or gashes in bodywork – 11•2
Horn – 12•14
Hoses – 9•4
HT coil – 5B•2
Hub assembly
  front – 10•2
  rear – 10•9
Hub bearings
  front – 10•4
  rear – 10•10
Hydraulic pipes and hoses – 9•4
Hydrofluoric acid – 0•5

I

Idle speed auxiliary air valve – 4A•9
Idle speed control stepper motor
    Bosch Motronic and Sagem Lucas
        system – 4A•9, 4A•11
    Magneti Marelli system – 4A•12, 4A•13
Idler roller – 2D•14
Ignition HT coil – 5B•2
Ignition switch/steering column
    lock – 10•16
Ignition system (petrol engines) –
    5B•1 et seq
Ignition timing – 5B•4
Immobiliser – 12•18
Indicators – 12•7
Injection timing – 4B•11
Injector needle lift sensor – 4B•20
Injectors
    Bosch Motronic and Sagem Lucas
        system – 4A•8, 4A•10
    diesel engines – 4B•11, 4B•14, 4C•9
    Magneti Marelli
        system – 4A•11, 4A•12, 4A•13
Inlet air temperature sensor
    Bosch Motronic and Sagem Lucas
        system – 4A•10, 4A•11
    Magneti Marelli system – 4A•12, 4A•13
Inlet ducts – 4B•4, 4C•4
Inlet manifold
    diesel engines – 4B•16, 4C•12
    petrol engines – 4A•13
Input shaft oil seal – 7A•6
Input speed sensor – 7B•8
Instrument panel – 12•13
    check
        diesel engine models – 1B•15
        petrol engine models – 1A•13
    illumination and warning light
        bulbs – 12•11
    surround – 11•30
Intercooler – 4B•18
Intermediate bearing (driveshaft) – 8•7
Introduction – 0•6

J

Jacking and vehicle support – REF•5
Joint mating faces – REF•4
Jump starting – 0•8

K

Knock sensor – 5B•4
    Bosch Motronic and Sagem Lucas
        system – 4A•10, 4A•11
    Magneti Marelli system – 4A•12, 4A•13

L

Lambda sensors – 4D•2
Leak check – 0•10
    diesel engine models – 1B•8
    petrol engine models – 1A•8

Leakdown test
    DW series diesel engine – 2D•4
    XUD series diesel engine – 2C•3
Locks
    bonnet – 11•6
    door – 11•8
    operation and lubrication
        diesel engine models – 1B•15
        petrol engine models – 1A•15
    steering column – 10•16
    tailgate – 11•15
Locknuts, locktabs and washers – REF•4
Loudspeakers – 12•17
Lower arm – 10•5, 10•7
Lubricants and fluids – 0•18
Luggage compartment
    light – 12•10
    trim panels – 11•22, 11•24

M

Magneti Marelli system – 4A•11
    coolant temperature
        sensor – 4A•12, 4A•13
    crankshaft sensor – 4A•12, 4A•13
    electronic control unit
        (ECU) – 4A•12, 4A•13
    fuel injectors – 4A•13
    fuel pressure regulator – 4A•12, 4A•13
    fuel rail and injectors – 4A•11, 4A•12
    idle speed stepper motor – 4A•12, 4A•13
    inlet air temperature sensor – 4A•12, 4A•13
    knock sensor – 4A•12, 4A•13
    manifold pressure sensor – 4A•12, 4A•13
    throttle potentiometer – 4A•12, 4A•13
    vehicle speed sensor – 4A•12, 4A•13
Main and big-end bearings
    diesel engine – 2F•16
    petrol engine – 2E•14
    running clearance check
        diesel engine – 2F•17
        petrol engine – 2E•17
Maintenance schedule
    diesel engine models – 1B•3
    petrol engine models – 1A•6
Manifold pressure sensor
    Bosch Motronic and Sagem Lucas
        system – 4A•10, 4A•11
    Magneti Marelli system – 4A•12, 4A•13
Manual transmission – 2E•4, 7A•1 et seq
    fault finding – REF•17
    oil – 0•18, 7A•2
    level check
        diesel engine models – 1B•18
        petrol engine models – 1A•18
Map reading light – 12•10
Master cylinder – 9•14
Mirrors and mirror glass – 11•18, REF•9
Modulator assembly (anti-lock braking
    system) – 9•18
MOT test checks – REF•9 et seq
Mountings
    DW series diesel engine – 2D•19
    TU series petrol engine – 2A•14
    XU series petrol engine – 2B•21
    XUD series diesel engine – 2C•8, 2C•14
Mud shields – 11•19

N

Number plate light – 12•9

O

Oil cooler
    DW series diesel engine – 2D•21
    XU series petrol engine – 2B•19
    XUD series diesel engine – 2C•14
Oil
    engine – 0•13, 0•18, 1A•7, 1B•7, 1B•8
    manual transmission – 0•18, 1A•18,
        1B•18, 7A•2
Oil filter renewal
    diesel engine models – 1B•7
    petrol engine models – 1A•7
Oil level sensor – 5A•6
Oil pressure warning light switch – 5A•6
Oil pump
    DW series diesel engine – 2D•19
    TU series petrol engine – 2A•13
    XU series petrol engine – 2B•19
    XUD series diesel engine – 2C•13
Oil seals – 7A•4, 7B•6, REF•4
    camshaft – 2A•9
        DW series diesel engine – 2D•19
        XU series petrol engine – 2B•13
        XUD series diesel engine – 2C•14
    crankshaft
        DW series diesel engine – 2D•19
        XU series petrol engine – 2B•20
        XUD series diesel engine – 2C•13
    driveshaft – 7A•4
    input shaft – 7A•6
    selector shaft – 7A•6, 7B•6
Open-circuit – 12•2
Output speed sensor – 7B•8

P

Pads
    condition check
        diesel engine models – 1B•14
        petrol engine models – 1A•12
    renewal
        front – 9•4
        rear – 9•7
Park lock solenoid – 7B•9
Parts – REF•3
Passenger compartment trim
    panels – 11•22, 11•24
Pedal
    accelerator
        diesel engines – 4B•15, 4C•6, 4C•11
        petrol engines – 4A•4
    brake – 9•15
    clutch – 6•2
Petrol engine removal and overhaul
    procedures – 2E•1 et seq
Pipes and hoses – 9•4
Piston rings
    diesel engine – 2F•17
    petrol engine – 2E•15
Piston/connecting rod assembly
    diesel engine – 2F•12, 2F•14, 2F•19
    petrol engine – 2E•9, 2E•13, 2E•21

Plastic components – 11•3
Poisonous or irritant substances – 0•5
Pollen filter renewal
  diesel engine models – 1B•13
  petrol engine models – 1A•11
Power steering fluid – 0•18
  leak check
    diesel engine models – 1B•8
    petrol engine models – 1A•9
  level – 0•13, 0•18
Power steering pump – 10•17
Preheating system (diesel engines) –
  5C•1 et seq
  control unit – 4B•20, 4C•12
Preheating/EGR system coolant
  temperature switch/sensor – 3•7
Pressure-regulating valve (brakes) – 9•17
Priming and bleeding (diesel fuel
  system) – 4B•4, 4C•4
Puncture repair – 0•9
Purge valves – 4D•2

Q

Quarter window glass – 11•19

R

Radiator – 3•4
  diesel engine models – 1B•20
  grille – 11•19
  hoses – 3•2, 3•3
  petrol engine models – 1A•20
Radio aerial – 12•17
Radio/cassette player – 12•16
Rain sensor – 12•15
Rear axle assembly – 10•12
Rear light cluster – 12•8
Rear quarter window glass – 11•19
Refrigerant leak check
  diesel engine models – 1B•8
  petrol engine models – 1A•9
Relays – 12•3
Release mechanism (clutch) – 6•4
Remote control transmitter battery – 11•18
Repair procedures – REF•4
Respraying – 11•3
Reversing light switch – 7A•7
Ride height – 10•13
Road test
  diesel engine models – 1B•15
  petrol engine models – 1A•13
Roadside repairs – 0•7 et seq
Rocker arms
  DW series diesel engine – 2D•15
  TU series petrol engine – 2A•9
Routine maintenance
  bodywork and underframe – 11•1
  upholstery and carpets – 11•2
Routine maintenance and servicing –
  diesel engine models – 1B•1 et seq
Routine maintenance and servicing –
  petrol engine models – 1A•1 et seq

S

Safety first! – 0•5, 0•13, 0•15
Sagem Lucas system – 4A•8
  coolant temperature
    sensor – 4A•10, 4A•11
  crankshaft sensor – 4A•10, 4A•11
  electronic control unit (ECU) – 4A•9, 4A•11
  fuel pressure regulator – 4A•9, 4A•11
  fuel rail and injectors – 4A•8, 4A•10
  idle speed auxiliary air valve – 4A•9
  idle speed stepper motor – 4A•9, 4A•11
  inlet air temperature
    sensor – 4A•10, 4A•11
  knock sensor – 4A•10, 4A•11
  manifold pressure
    sensor – 4A•10, 4A•11
  throttle potentiometer – 4A•9, 4A•11
  vehicle speed sensor – 4A•10, 4A•11
Scalding – 0•5
Scratches in bodywork – 11•2
Screen washer fluid level – 0•14
Screw threads and fastenings – REF•4
Seat belt pre-tensioner renewal
  diesel engine models – 1B•21
  petrol engine models – 1A•20
Seat belts – 11•20
Seats – 11•20
Secondary air injection – 4D•1, 4D•3
Selector (automatic transmission)
  cable – 7B•4
  lever assembly – 7B•5
  lever position switch – 7B•9
Selector shaft oil seal
  automatic transmission – 7B•6
  manual transmission – 7A•6
Service interval display
  diesel engine models – 1B•7
  petrol engine models – 1A•7
Shock absorber – 10•4, 10•11, REF•10,
  REF•11
  check
    diesel engine models – 1B•14
    petrol engine models – 1A•12
Shoes – 9•8
  condition check
    diesel engine models – 1B•17
    petrol engine models – 1A•16
Short-circuit – 12•2
Sidelight – 12•7
Smoke test – 1B•14
Spare parts – REF•3
Spark plug renewal – 1A•17
Springs – REF•11
Starter inhibitor/reversing light
  switch – 7B•7
Starter motor – 5A•5, 5A•6
Starting and charging
  systems – 5A•1 et seq
Start-up after overhaul
  diesel engine – 2F•21
  petrol engine – 2E•22
Steering – REF•10, REF•11
  check
    diesel engine models – 1B•14, 1B•15
    petrol engine models – 1A•12, 1A•13
Steering angles – 10•18

Steering column – 10•14, REF•9
  combination switches – 12•4
  lock – 10•16
  shrouds – 11•30
Steering gear assembly – 10•16
Steering wheel – 10•13, REF•9
  switches – 12•3
Stoplight – 12•8
  switch – 9•18
Subframe – 10•8
Sump
  DW series diesel engine – 2D•19
  TU series petrol engine – 2A•13
  XU series petrol engine – 2B•18
  XUD series diesel engine – 2C•13
Sunroof – 11•19
  switch – 12•6
Suspension and
  steering – 10•1 et seq, REF•10, REF•11
  fault finding – REF•18, REF•19
  check
    diesel engine models – 1B•14, 1B•15
    petrol engine models – 1A•12, 1A•13
Switches – 12•3
  centre console-mounted – 12•6
  courtesy light – 12•6
  facia-mounted – 12•4
  handbrake 'on' warning light – 9•18
  hazard warning – 12•5
  ignition – 10•16
  oil pressure warning light – 05a•6
  reversing light – 07a•7
  steering column – 12•4
  steering wheel – 12•3
  stoplight – 9•18
  sunroof – 12•6
  temperature warning light – 3•7
Swivel hub assembly – 10•2

T

Tailgate – 11•15
  trim panel – 11•26
  window glass – 11•19
Tappets and rocker arms – 2D•15
Temperature sensor – 3•7
  diesel engines – 4B•20, 4C•11
  petrol engines - 4A•10, 4A•11, 4A•12, 4A•13
Tensioner pulleys
  DW series diesel engine – 2D•13
  TU series petrol engine – 2A•8, 2A•9
  XU series petrol engine – 2B•13
Thermostat – 3•5
  housing – 3•8
Throttle housing – 4A•7
Throttle position sensor – 4B•20
Throttle position switch – 4B•20
Throttle potentiometer
  Bosch Motronic and Sagem Lucas
    system – 4A•9, 4A•11
  Magneti Marelli system – 4A•12, 4A•13
Timing belt
  renewal
    diesel engine models – 1B•19
    petrol engine models – 1A•19
  DW series diesel engine – 2D•8, 2D•9
  TU series petrol engine – 2A•6
  XU series petrol engine – 2B•8, 2B•9
  XUD series diesel engine – 2C•5

Timing belt covers
DW series diesel engine – 2D•7
TU series petrol engine – 2A•5
XU series petrol engine – 2B•7
XUD series diesel engine – 2C•5
Timing belt idler roller – 2C•9
Timing belt sprockets and tensioner
DW series diesel engine – 2D•12
TU series petrol engine – 2A•7
XU series petrol engine – 2B•12
XUD series diesel engine – 2C•6, 2C•8
Timing
diesel engines – 4B•11
petrol engines – 5B•4
Timing holes
DW series diesel engine – 2D•5
TU series petrol engine – 2A•4
XU series petrol engine – 2B•4
XUD series diesel engine – 2C•4
Tools – REF•4
Tools and working facilities – REF•7 *et seq*
Towing – 0•10
Track rod balljoint – 10•18
Transmission – 2F•3, 2F•4, 2F•5
mountings
DW series diesel engine – 2D•19
TU series petrol engine – 2A•14
XU series petrol engine – 2B•21
XUD series diesel engine – 2C•8, 2C•14
**Trim panels, strips and
badges** – 11•6, 11•19, 11•22
*TU series petrol engine in-car repair
procedures* – 2A•1 *et seq*
Turbocharger
diesel engines – 4B•16, 4B•17, 4B•18,
4C•5, 4C•14

U

Tyres – 0•16, REF•12
pressures – 0•19

**Underbonnet check
points** – 0•11, 0•12
Underframe – 11•1
Unleaded petrol – 4A•4
Upholstery and carpets – 11•2

V

Vacuum hoses leak check
diesel engine models – 1B•9
petrol engine models – 1A•9
Vacuum pump (diesel models) – 9•19, 9•20
Vacuum servo unit – 9•15
check valve – 9•16
Valves
clearances
DW series diesel engine – 2D•16
TU series petrol engine – 2A•9
XU series petrol engine – 2B•15
XUD series diesel engine – 2C•10
diesel engine – 2F•10
petrol engine – 2E•8
Valve timing holes
DW series diesel engine – 2D•5
TU series petrol engine – 2A•4
XU series petrol engine – 2B•4
XUD series diesel engine – 2C•4
Vehicle identification – REF•3, REF•10
Vehicle ride height – 10•13

W

Vehicle speed sensor – 7A•7
Bosch Motronic and Sagem Lucas
system – 4A•10, 4A•11
Magneti Marelli system – 4A•12, 4A•13
Vehicle support – REF•5

Warning light bulbs – 12•11
Washer system – 12•15, 12•16
fluid level – 0•14
Weekly checks – 0•11 *et seq*
Weights – REF•1
Wheel bearings – REF•11
Wheel cylinder – 9•14
**Wheel sensor (anti-lock braking
system)** – 9•18, 9•19
Wheelarch liners and mud shields – 11•19
Wheels – REF•12
alignment and steering angles – 10•18
changing – 0•9
Window glass and regulator – 11•12
Windscreen – 11•19, REF•9
Wiper arm – 12•14
Wiper blades – 0•15
Wiper motor – 12•14, 12•15
Wiring diagrams – 12•21 *et seq*
Working facilities – REF•8

X

*XU series petrol engine in-car repair
procedures* – 2B•1 *et seq*
*XUD series diesel engine in-car repair
procedures* – 2C•1 *et seq*

Haynes Manuals – The Complete **UK Car** List

Title	Book No.
ALFA ROMEO Alfasud/Sprint (74 - 88) up to F *	0292
Alfa Romeo Alfetta (73 – 87) up to E *	0531
AUDI 80, 90 & Coupe Petrol (79 – Nov 88) up to F	0605
Audi 80, 90 & Coupe Petrol (Oct 86 – 90) D to H	1491
Audi 100 & A6 Petrol & Diesel (May 91 – May 97) H to P	3504
Audi A3 Petrol & Diesel (96 – May 03) P to 03	4253
Audi A3 Petrol & Diesel (June 03 – Mar 08) 03 to 08	4884
Audi A4 Petrol & Diesel (95 – 00) M to X	3575
Audi A4 Petrol & Diesel (01 – 04) X to 54	4609
Audi A4 Petrol & Diesel (Jan 05 – Feb 08) 54 to 57	4885
AUSTIN A35 & A40 (56 – 67) up to F *	0118
Mini (59 – 69) up to H *	0527
Mini (69 – 01) up to X	0646
Austin Healey 100/6 & 3000 (56 – 68) up to G *	0049
BEDFORD/Vauxhall Rascal & Suzuki Supercarry (86 – Oct 94) C to M	3015
BMW 1-Series 4-cyl Petrol & Diesel (04 – Aug 11) 54 to 11	4918
BMW 316, 320 & 320i (4-cyl)(75 – Feb 83) up to Y *	0276
BMW 3- & 5- Series Petrol (81 – 91) up to J	1948
BMW 3-Series Petrol (Apr 91 – 99) H to V	3210
BMW 3-Series Petrol (Sept 98 – 06) S to 56	4067
BMW 3-Series Petrol & Diesel (05 – Sept 08) 54 to 58	4782
BMW 5-Series 6-cyl Petrol (April 96 – Aug 03) N to 03	4151
BMW 5-Series Diesel (Sept 03 – 10) 53 to 10	4901
BMW 1500, 1502, 1600, 1602, 2000 & 2002 (59 – 77) up to S *	0240
CHRYSLER PT Cruiser Petrol (00-09) W to 09	4058
CITROEN 2CV, Ami & Dyane (67 – 90) up to H	0196
Citroen AX Petrol & Diesel (87- 97) D to P	3014
Citroen Berlingo & Peugeot Partner Petrol & Diesel (96 – 10) P to 60	4281
Citroen C1 Petrol (05 – 11) 05 to 11	4922
Citroen C2 Petrol & Diesel (03 – 10) 53 to 60	5635
Citroen C3 Petrol & Diesel (02 – 09) 51 to 59	4890
Citroen C4 Petrol & Diesel (04 – 10) 54 to 60	5576
Citroen C5 Petrol & Diesel (01 – 08) Y to 08	4745
Citroen C15 Van Petrol & Diesel (89 – Oct 98) F to S	3509
Citroen CX Petrol (75 – 88) up to F	0528
Citroen Saxo Petrol & Diesel (96 – 04) N to 54	3506
Citroen Xantia Petrol & Diesel (93 – 01) K to Y	3082
Citroen XM Petrol & Diesel (89 – 00) G to X	3451
Citroen Xsara Petrol & Diesel (97 – Sept 00) R to W	3751
Citroen Xsara Picasso Petrol & Diesel (00 – 02) W to 52	3944
Citroen Xsara Picasso (Mar 04 – 08) 04 to 58	4784
Citroen ZX Diesel (91 – 98) J to S	1922
Citroen ZX Petrol (91 – 98) H to S	1881
FIAT 126 (73 – 87) up to E *	0305
Fiat 500 (57 – 73) up to M *	0090
Fiat 500 & Panda (04 – 12) 53 to 61	5558
Fiat Bravo & Brava Petrol (95 – 00) N to W	3572
Fiat Cinquecento (93 – 98) K to R	3501
Fiat Grande Punto, Punto Evo & Punto Petrol (06 – 15) 55 to 15	5956
Fiat Panda (81 – 95) up to M	0793
Fiat Punto Petrol & Diesel (94 – Oct 99) L to V	3251
Fiat Punto Petrol (Oct 99 – July 03) V to 03	4066
Fiat Punto Petrol (03 – 07) 03 to 07	4746

Title	Book No.
Fiat Punto Petrol (Oct 99 – 07) V to 07	5634
Fiat X1/9 (74 – 89) up to G *	0273
FORD Anglia (59 – 68) up to G *	0001
Ford Capri II (& III) 1.6 & 2.0 (74 – 87) up to E *	0283
Ford Capri II (& III) 2.8 & 3.0 V6 (74 – 87) up to E	1309
Ford C-Max Petrol & Diesel (03 – 10) 53 to 60	4900
Ford Escort Mk I 1100 & 1300 (68 – 74) up to N *	0171
Ford Escort Mk I Mexico, RS 1600 & RS 2000 (70 – 74) up to N *	0139
Ford Escort Mk II Mexico, RS 1800 & RS 2000 (75 – 80) up to W *	0735
Ford Escort (75 – Aug 80) up to V *	0280
Ford Escort Petrol (Sept 80 – Sept 90) up to H	0686
Ford Escort & Orion Petrol (Sept 90 – 00) H to X	1737
Ford Escort & Orion Diesel (Sept 90 – 00) H to X	4081
Ford Fiesta Petrol (Feb 89 – Oct 95) F to N	1595
Ford Fiesta Petrol & Diesel (Oct 95 – Mar 02) N to 02	3397
Ford Fiesta Petrol & Diesel (Apr 02 – 08) 02 to 58	4170
Ford Fiesta Petrol & Diesel (08 – 11) 58 to 11	4907
Ford Focus Petrol & Diesel (98 – 01) S to Y	3759
Ford Focus Petrol & Diesel (Oct 01 – 05) 51 to 05	4167
Ford Focus Petrol (05 – 11) 54 to 61	4785
Ford Focus Diesel (05 – 11) 54 to 61	4807
Ford Focus Petrol & Diesel (11 – 14) 60 to 14	5632
Ford Fusion Petrol & Diesel (02 – 11) 02 to 61	5566
Ford Galaxy Petrol & Diesel (95 – Aug 00) M to W	3984
Ford Galaxy Petrol & Diesel (00 – 06) X to 06	5556
Ford Granada Petrol (Sept 77 – Feb 85) up to B *	0481
Ford Ka (96 – 08) P to 58	5567
Ford Ka Petrol (09 – 14) 58 to 14	5637
Ford Mondeo Petrol (93 – Sept 00) K to X	1923
Ford Mondeo Petrol & Diesel (Oct 00 – Jul 03) X to 03	3990
Ford Mondeo Petrol & Diesel (July 03 – 07) 03 to 56	4619
Ford Mondeo Petrol & Diesel (Apr 07 – 12) 07 to 61	5548
Ford Mondeo Diesel (93 – Sept 00) L to X	3465
Ford Transit Connect Diesel (02 – 11) 02 to 11	4903
Ford Transit Diesel (Feb 86 – 99) C to T	3019
Ford Transit Diesel (00 – Oct 06) X to 56	4775
Ford Transit Diesel (Nov 06 – 13) 56 to 63	5629
Ford 1.6 & 1.8 litre Diesel Engine (84 – 96) A to N	1172
HILLMAN Imp (63 – 76) up to R *	0022
HONDA Civic (Feb 84 – Oct 87) A to E	1226
Honda Civic (Nov 91 – 96) J to N	3199
Honda Civic Petrol (Mar 95 – 00) M to X	4050
Honda Civic Petrol & Diesel (01 – 05) X to 55	4611
Honda CR-V Petrol & Diesel (02 – 06) 51 to 56	4747
Honda Jazz (02 to 08) 51 to 58	4735
JAGUAR E-Type (61 – 72) up to L *	0140
Jaguar Mk I & II, 240 & 340 (55 – 69) up to H *	0098
Jaguar XJ6, XJ & Sovereign, Daimler Sovereign (68 – Oct 86) up to D	0242
Jaguar XJ6 & Sovereign (Oct 86 – Sept 94) D to M	3261
Jaguar XJ12, XJS & Sovereign, Daimler Double Six (72 – 88) up to F	0478
Jaguar X Type Petrol & Diesel (01 – 10) V to 60	5631
JEEP Cherokee Petrol (93 – 96) K to N	1943
LAND ROVER 90, 110 & Defender Diesel (83 – 07) up to 56	3017

Title	Book No.
Land Rover Discovery Petrol & Diesel (89 – 98) G to S	3016
Land Rover Discovery Diesel (Nov 98 – Jul 04) S to 04	4606
Land Rover Discovery Diesel (Aug 04 – Apr 09) 04 to 09	5562
Land Rover Freelander Petrol & Diesel (97 – Sept 03) R to 53	3929
Land Rover Freelander (97 – Oct 06) R to 56	5571
Land Rover Freelander Diesel (Nov 06 – 14) 56 to 64	5636
Land Rover Series II, IIA & III 4-cyl Petrol (58 – 85) up to C	0314
Land Rover Series II, IIA & III Petrol & Diesel (58 – 85) up to C	5568
MAZDA 323 (Mar 81 – Oct 89) up to G	1608
Mazda 323 (Oct 89 – 98) G to R	3455
Mazda B1600, B1800 & B2000 Pick-up Petrol (72 – 88) up to F	0267
Mazda MX-5 (89 – 05) G to 05	5565
Mazda RX-7 (79 – 85) up to C *	0460
MERCEDES-BENZ 190, 190E & 190D Petrol & Diesel (83 – 93) A to L	3450
Mercedes-Benz 200D, 240D, 240TD, 300D & 300TD 123 Series Diesel (Oct 76 – 85) up to C	1114
Mercedes-Benz 250 & 280 (68 – 72) up to L *	0346
Mercedes-Benz 250 & 280 123 Series Petrol (Oct 76 – 84) up to B *	0677
Mercedes-Benz 124 Series Petrol & Diesel (85 – Aug 93) C to K	3253
Mercedes-Benz A-Class Petrol & Diesel (98 – 04) S to 54	4748
Mercedes-Benz C-Class Petrol & Diesel (93 – Aug 00) L to W	3511
Mercedes-Benz C-Class (00 – 07) X to 07	4780
Mercedes-Benz E-Class Diesel (Jun 02 – Feb 10) 02 to 59	5710
Mercedes-Benz Sprinter Diesel (95 – Apr 06) M to 06	4902
MGA (55 – 62)	0475
MGB (62 – 80) up to W	0111
MGB 1962 to 1980 (special edition) *	4894
MG Midget & Austin-Healey Sprite (58 – 80) up to W *	0265
MINI Petrol (July 01 – 06) Y to 56	4273
MINI Petrol & Diesel (Nov 06 – 13) 56 to 13	4904
MITSUBISHI Shogun & L200 Pick-ups Petrol (83 – 94) up to M	1944
MORRIS Minor 1000 (56 – 71) up to K	0024
NISSAN Almera Petrol (95 – Feb 00) N to V	4053
Nissan Almera & Tino Petrol (Feb 00 – 07) V to 56	4612
Nissan Micra (83 – Jan 93) up to K	0931
Nissan Micra (93 – 02) K to 52	3254
Nissan Micra Petrol (03 – Oct 10) 52 to 60	4734
Nissan Primera Petrol (90 - Aug 99) H to T	1851
Nissan Qashqai Petrol & Diesel (07 – 12) 56 to 62	5610
OPEL Ascona & Manta (B-Series) (Sept 75 – 88) up to F *	0316
Opel Ascona Petrol (81 – 88)	3215
Opel Ascona Petrol (Oct 91 – Feb 98)	3156
Opel Corsa Petrol (83 – Mar 93)	3160
Opel Corsa Petrol (Mar 93 – 97)	3159
Opel Kadett Petrol (Oct 84 – Oct 91)	3196
Opel Omega & Senator Petrol (Nov 86 – 94)	3157
Opel Vectra Petrol (Oct 88 – Oct 95)	3158
PEUGEOT 106 Petrol & Diesel (91 – 04) J to 53	1882
Peugeot 107 Petrol (05 – 11) 05 to 11	4923
Peugeot 205 Petrol (83 – 97) A to P	0932

* Classic reprint

Title	Book No.
Peugeot 206 Petrol & Diesel (98 – 01) S to X	3757
Peugeot 206 Petrol & Diesel (02 – 09) 51 to 59	4613
Peugeot 207 Petrol & Diesel (06 – July 09) 06 to 09	4787
Peugeot 306 Petrol & Diesel (93 – 02) K to 02	3073
Peugeot 307 Petrol & Diesel (01 – 08) Y to 58	4147
Peugeot 308 Petrol & Diesel (07 – 12) 07 to 12	5561
Peugeot 405 Diesel (88 – 97) E to P	3198
Peugeot 406 Petrol & Diesel (96 – Mar 99) N to T	3394
Peugeot 406 Petrol & Diesel (Mar 99 – 02) T to 52	3982
Peugeot 407 Diesel (04 -11) 53 to 11	5550
PORSCHE 911 (65 – 85) up to C	0264
Porsche 924 & 924 Turbo (76 – 85) up to C	0397
RANGE ROVER V8 Petrol (70 – Oct 92) up to K	0606
RELIANT Robin & Kitten (73 – 83) up to A *	0436
RENAULT 4 (61 – 86) up to D *	0072
Renault 5 Petrol (Feb 85 – 96) B to N	1219
Renault 19 Petrol (89 – 96) F to N	1646
Renault Clio Petrol (91 – May 98) H to R	1853
Renault Clio Petrol & Diesel (May 98 – May 01) R to Y	3906
Renault Clio Petrol & Diesel (June 01 – 05) Y to 55	4168
Renault Clio Petrol & Diesel (Oct 05 – May 09) 55 to 09	4788
Renault Espace Petrol & Diesel (85 – 96) C to N	3197
Renault Laguna Petrol & Diesel (94 – 00) L to W	3252
Renault Laguna Petrol & Diesel (Feb 01 – May 07) X to 07	4283
Renault Megane & Scenic Petrol & Diesel (96 – 99) N to T	3395
Renault Megane & Scenic Petrol & Diesel (Apr 99 – 02) T to 52	3916
Renault Megane Petrol & Diesel (Oct 02 – 08) 52 to 58	4284
Renault Megane Petrol & Diesel (Oct 08 – 14) 58 to 64	5955
Renault Scenic Petrol & Diesel (Sept 03 – 06) 53 to 06	4297
Renault Trafic Diesel (01 – 11) Y to 11	5551
ROVER 216 & 416 Petrol (89 – 96) G to N	1830
Rover 211, 214, 216, 218 & 220 Petrol & Diesel (Dec 95 – 99) N to V	3399
Rover 25 & MG ZR Petrol & Diesel (Oct 99 – 06) V to 06	4145
Rover 414, 416 & 420 Petrol & Diesel (May 95 – 99) M to V	3453
Rover 45 / MG ZS Petrol & Diesel (99 – 05) V to 55	4384
Rover 618, 620 & 623 Petrol (93 – 97) K to P	3257
Rover 75 / MG ZT Petrol & Diesel (99 – 06) S to 06	4292
Rover 820, 825 & 827 Petrol (86 – 95) D to N	1380
Rover 3500 (76 – 87) up to E *	0365
SAAB 95 & 96 (66 – 76) up to R *	0198
Saab 90, 99 & 900 (79 – Oct 93) up to L	0765
Saab 900 (Oct 93 – 98) L to R	3512
Saab 9000 4-cyl (85 – 98) C to S	1686
Saab 9-3 Petrol & Diesel (98 – Aug 02) R to 02	4614
Saab 9-3 Petrol & Diesel (92 – 07) 52 to 57	4749
Saab 9-3 Petrol & Diesel (07-on) 57 on	5569
Saab 9-5 4-cyl Petrol (97 – 05) R to 55	4156
Saab 9-5 (Sep 05 – Jun 10) 55 to 10	4891
SEAT Ibiza & Cordoba Petrol & Diesel (Oct 93 – Oct 99) L to V	3571
Seat Ibiza & Malaga Petrol (85 – 92) B to K	1609
Seat Ibiza Petrol & Diesel (May 02 – Apr 08) 02 to 08	4889
SKODA Fabia Petrol & Diesel (00 – 06) W to 06	4376

Title	Book No.
Skoda Felicia Petrol & Diesel (95 – 01) M to X	3505
Skoda Octavia Petrol (98 – April 04) R to 04	4285
Skoda Octavia Diesel (May 04 – 12) 04 to 61	5549
SUBARU 1600 & 1800 (Nov 79 – 90) up to H *	0995
SUNBEAM Alpine, Rapier & H120 (68 – 74) up to N *	0051
SUZUKI SJ Series, Samurai & Vitara 4-cyl Petrol (82 – 97) up to P	1942
Suzuki Supercarry & Bedford/Vauxhall Rascal (86 – Oct 94) C to M	3015
TOYOTA Avensis Petrol (98 – Jan 03) R to 52	4264
Toyota Aygo Petrol (05 – 11) 05 to 11	4921
Toyota Carina E Petrol (May 92 – 97) J to P	3256
Toyota Corolla (Sept 83 – Sept 87) A to E	1024
Toyota Corolla (Sept 87 – Aug 92) E to K	1683
Toyota Corolla Petrol (Aug 92 – 97) K to P	3259
Toyota Corolla Petrol (July 97 0 Feb 02) P to 51	4286
Toyota Corolla Petrol & Diesel (02 – Jan 07) 51 to 56	4791
Toyota Hi-Ace & Hi-Lux Petrol (69 – Oct 83) up to A	0304
Toyota RAV4 Petrol & Diesel (94 – 06) L to 55	4750
Toyota Yaris Petrol (99 – 05) T to 05	4265
TRIUMPH GT6 & Vitesse (62 0 74) up to N *	0112
Triumph Herald (59 – 71) up to K *	0010
Triumph Spitfire (62 – 81) up to X	0113
Triumph Stag (70 – 78) up to T *	0441
Triumph TR2, TR3, TR3A, TR4 & TR4A (52 – 67) up to F *	0028
Triumph TR5 & TR6 (67 – 75) up to P *	0031
Triumph TR7 (75 – 82) up to Y *	0322
VAUXHALL Astra Petrol (Oct 91 – Feb 98) J to R	1832
Vauxhall/Opel Astra & Zafira Petrol (Feb 98 – Apr 04) R to 04	3758
Vauxhall/Opel Astra & Zafira Diesel (Feb 98 – Apr 04) R to 04	3797
Vauxhall/Opel Astra Petrol (04 – 08)	4732
Vauxhall/Opel Astra Diesel (04 – 08)	4733
Vauxhall/Opel Astra Petrol & Diesel (Dec 09 – 13) 59 to 13	5578
Vauxhall/Opel Calibra (90 – 98) G to S	3502
Vauxhall Cavalier Petrol (Oct 88 0 95) F to N	1570
Vauxhall/Opel Corsa Diesel (Mar 93 – Oct 00) K to X	4087
Vauxhall Corsa Petrol (Mar 93 – 97) K to R	1985
Vauxhall/Opel Corsa Petrol (Apr 97 – Oct 00) P to X	3921
Vauxhall/Opel Corsa Petrol & Diesel (Oct 03 – Aug 06) 53 to 06	4617
Vauxhall/Opel Corsa Petrol & Diesel (Sept 06 – 10) 56 to 10	4886
Vauxhall/Opel Corsa Petrol & Diesel (00 – Aug 06) X to 06	5577
Vauxhall/Opel Frontera Petrol & Diesel (91 – Sept 98) J to S	3454
Vauxhall/Opel Insignia Petrol & Diesel (08 – 12) 08 to 61	5563
Vauxhall/Opel Meriva Petrol & Diesel (03 – May 10) 03 to 10	4893
Vauxhall/Opel Omega Petrol (94 – 99) L to T	3510
Vauxhall/Opel Vectra Petrol & Diesel (95 – Feb 99) N to S	3396
Vauxhall/Opel Vectra Petrol & Diesel (Mar 99 – May 02) T to 02	3930
Vauxhall/Opel Vectra Petrol & Diesel (June 02 – Sept 05) 02 to 55	4618

Title	Book No.
Vauxhall/Opel Vectra Petrol & Diesel (Oct 05 – Oct 08) 55 to 58	4887
Vauxhall/Opel Vivaro Diesel (01 – 11) Y to 11	5552
Vauxhall/Opel Zafira Petrol & Diesel (05 -09) 05 to 09	4792
Vauxhall/Opel 1.5, 1.6 & 1.7 litre Diesel Engine (82 – 96) up to N	1222
VW Beetle 1200 (54 – 77) up to S	0036
VW Beetle 1300 & 1500 (65 – 75) up to P	0039
VW 1302 & 1302S (70 – 72) up to L *	0110
VW Beetle 1303, 1303S & GT (72 – 75) up to P	0159
VW Beetle Petrol & Diesel (Apr 99 – 07) T to 57	3798
VW Golf & Jetta Mk 1 Petrol 1.1 & 1.3 (74 – 84) up to A	0716
VW Golf, Jetta & Scirocco Mk 1 Petrol 1.5, 1.6 & 1.8 (74 – 84) up to A	0726
VW Golf & Jetta Mk 1 Diesel (78 – 84) up to A	0451
VW Golf & Jetta Mk 2 Petrol (Mar 84 – Feb 92) A to J	1081
VW Golf & Vento Petrol & Diesel (Feb 92 – Mar 98) J to R	3097
VW Golf & Bora Petrol & Diesel (Apr 98 – 00) R to X	3727
VW Golf & Bora 4-cyl Petrol & Diesel (01 – 03) X to 53	4169
VW Golf & Jetta Petrol & Diesel (04 – 09) 53 to 09	4610
VW Golf Petrol & Diesel (09 – 12) 58 to 62	5633
VW LT Petrol Vans & Light Trucks (76 – 87) up to E	0637
VW Passat 4-cyl Petrol & Diesel (May 88 – 96) E to P	3498
VW Passat 4-cyl Petrol & Diesel (Dec 96 – Nov 00) P to X	3917
VW Passat Petrol & Diesel (Dec 00 – May 05) X to 05	4279
VW Passat Diesel (June 05 – 10) 05 to 60	4888
VW Polo Petrol (Nov 90 – Aug 94) H to L	3245
VW Polo Hatchback Petrol & Diesel (94 – 99) M to S	3500
VW Polo Hatchback Petrol (00 – Jan 02) V to 51	4150
VW Polo Petrol & Diesel (02 – Sep 09) 51 to 59	4608
VW Polo Petrol & Diesel (Oct 09 – Jul 14 (59 to 14)	5638
VW Transporter 1600 (68 – 79) up to V	0082
VW Transporter 1700, 1800 & 2000 (72 – 79) up to V *	0226
VW Transporter (air cooled) Petrol (79 – 82) up to Y *	0638
VW Transporter (water cooled) Petrol (82 – 90) up to H	3452
VW T4 Transporter Diesel (90 – 03) H to 03	5711
VW T5 Transporter Diesel (July 03 – 14) 03 to 64	5743
VW Type 3 (63 – 73) up to M *	0084
VOLVO 120 & 130 Series (& P1800) (61 – 73) up to M *	0203
Volvo 142, 144 & 145 (66 – 74) up to N *	0129
Volvo 240 Series Petrol (74 – 93) up to K	0270
Volvo 440, 460 & 480 Petrol (87 – 97) D to P	1691
Volvo 740 & 760 Petrol (82 – 91) up to J	1258
Volvo 850 Petrol (92 – 96) J to P	3260
Volvo 940 Petrol (90 – 98) H to R	3249
Volvo S40 & V40 Petrol (96 – Mar 04) N to 04	3569
Volvo S40 & V50 Petrol & Diesel (Mar 04 – Jun 07) 04 to 07	4731
Volvo S40 & V50 Diesel (July 07 - 13) 07 to 13	5684
Volvo S60 Petrol & Diesel (01 – 08) X to 09	4793
Volvo S70, V70 & C70 Petrol (96 – 99) P to V	3573
Volvo V70 / S80 Petrol & Diesel (98 – 07) S to 07	4263
Volvo V70 Diesel (June 07 – 12) 07 to 61	5557
Volvo XC60 / 90 Diesel (03 – 12) 52 to 62	5630

* Classic reprint

CL 07.05.15

Preserving Our Motoring Heritage

< The Model J Duesenberg Derham Tourster. Only eight of these magnificent cars were ever built – this is the only example to be found outside the United States of America

Almost every car you've ever loved, loathed or desired is gathered under one roof at the Haynes Motor Museum. Over 300 immaculately presented cars and motorbikes represent every aspect of our motoring heritage, from elegant reminders of bygone days, such as the superb Model J Duesenberg to curiosities like the bug-eyed BMW Isetta. There are also many old friends and flames. Perhaps you remember the 1959 Ford Popular that you did your courting in? The magnificent 'Red Collection' is a spectacle of classic sports cars including AC, Alfa Romeo, Austin Healey, Ferrari, Lamborghini, Maserati, MG, Riley, Porsche and Triumph.

A Perfect Day Out

Each and every vehicle at the Haynes Motor Museum has played its part in the history and culture of Motoring. Today, they make a wonderful spectacle and a great day out for all the family. Bring the kids, bring Mum and Dad, but above all bring your camera to capture those golden memories for ever. You will also find an impressive array of motoring memorabilia, a comfortable 70 seat video cinema and one of the most extensive transport book shops in Britain. The Pit Stop Cafe serves everything from a cup of tea to wholesome, home-made meals or, if you prefer, you can enjoy the large picnic area nestled in the beautiful rural surroundings of Somerset.

> John Haynes O.B.E., Founder and Chairman of the museum at the wheel of a Haynes Light 12.

< Graham Hill's Lola Cosworth Formula 1 car next to a 1934 Riley Sports.

The Museum is situated on the A359 Yeovil to Frome road at Sparkford, just off the A303 in Somerset. It is about 40 miles south of Bristol, and 25 minutes drive from the M5 intersection at Taunton.
Open 9.30am - 5.30pm (10.00am - 4.00pm Winter) 7 days a week, *except Christmas Day, Boxing Day and New Years Day*
Special rates available for schools, coach parties and outings Charitable Trust No. 292048